W9-ACF-565

Advanced Calculus

An Introduction to Applied Mathematics

Volume I

Arthur E. Danese

Professor of Mathematics
State University of New York at Buffalo

Allyn and Bacon, Inc.
Boston, 1965

150 Tremont Street, Boston

Library of Congress Catalog Card Number: 65-21789

Printed in the United States of America

Preface

As a sequel to a two-year course in the elementary calculus, most colleges offer a course in "Advanced Calculus." This course is usually one of two types. In one course, certain topics of special importance in analysis are singled out for detailed study; in general, these topics are deemed too advanced or too specialized to be treated in elementary courses in the calculus. The nature of such a course varies widely not only in the specific topics that are studied but also in the degree of mathematical rigor and sophistication with which they are treated. In the other course, attention is focused on a rigorous development of real analysis—this is the so-called "ϵ-δ" course.

This textbook is for an advanced calculus course of the first type. The topics that have been selected are those which I feel should be a part of the background of every serious student of mathematics. In addition to their importance in mathematics, these topics also constitute a necessary prerequisite for study in such fields as physics, engineering, chemistry, biology, and other applied fields of mathematics. However, let me hasten to state at the outset that this is a textbook in mathematics—it is all mathematics—the purpose of which is to provide the student with the necessary background for pursuing courses in the applied fields of mathematics.

Every effort has been made in the present textbook to state results precisely and accurately and to use sound mathematical techniques. This does not mean, however, that it has been necessary to present the subject matter with absolute mathematical rigor. It does mean that precision of mathematical statement has not been neglected. Furthermore, it is my feeling that because a student is interested in engineering or other fields, this does not imply that such concepts as continuity and the law of the mean are beyond his grasp, especially when such knowledge can lead to smoother mathematical exposition.

Since it is supposed that most classes contain students with various backgrounds, it has been a fundamental guiding principle in this text to present no material that requires specialized knowledge of the applied fields. Furthermore, it has been my aim to present the topics as clearly as possible in a mathematical setting without extensive excursions into topics that best belong to courses in advanced analysis. This has meant compromise at every turn, so that the end result is a middle-of-the-road approach.

To tread the perilous line between effective pedagogical presentation and mathematical rigor has not always been easy. It is hoped that every definition, every theorem, every illustrative example, and every exercise is precisely stated. Proofs are presented when they are within the reach of the student and within the scope of the course. Straightforward proofs are left to the student, whereas, in all other cases, adequate references are given. I have made a considerable effort to motivate the introduction of new mathematical ideas, using the technique of passing from the known to the unknown. Detours are often made to present concepts that are needed at a particular instant, although they properly belong in a different mathematical setting; I claim effective pedagogy as ample justification.

Although the topics included in this textbook embrace a considerable amount of mathematics, the presentation affords a high degree of flexibility for classroom application in both subject matter and rigor of development. Hence, students with modest backgrounds as well as those with high mathematical maturity can use the book profitably and successfully.

It is my contention that a textbook stands or falls on its exercises. I have gone to great lengths to include a large number of exercises of every variety in this textbook—from those providing for the development of manipulative skills to those requiring a considerable amount of mathematical maturity and ingenuity. Many of the exercises explore new topics or significant details of topics presented in the text; many instructors may wish to incorporate these in the text. Such exercises are supplied with generous hints, which often amount to solutions in outline. The inclusion of such exercises leads to one aspect of the flexibility I hope to have achieved. A list of supplementary problems occurs at the end of each part; these are divided into categories, each category related to an applied field or to more advanced topics in mathematics. If the instructor is interested in supplementing the text with actual applications, he will find a number of them among these problems. *Exercises and problems that incorporate results used in the exposition in the text are marked by the symbol* $\diamondsuit$.

Scattered throughout the text are a large number of illustrative examples—a serious attempt has been made to include only those that are meaningful and which at the same time avoid lengthy and tedious calculations. Each part concludes with a list of references that the student may find helpful for more intensive or extensive study.

Results from elementary mathematics courses are summarized in a preliminary section, and references are made to it when infrequently used results are cited in the text. This eliminates the necessity of extensively presenting these topics anew and thereby curtailing the amount of time available for genuinely new topics. In particular, the theory of functions of several variables as presented in most elementary courses today is summarized, and this should prove adequate for the successful study of the text.

Part I is devoted to vector analysis. The purpose is to give the student a working knowledge of vectors and not just a superficial acquaintance with definitions and operations. This is done largely by considering some problems that the student has already solved by other techniques but whose solution by vector methods is more elegant and simpler, and by considering other problems that are new to the student, primarily because the application of other techniques to these problems is arduous. With this in mind, the geometry and algebra of vectors is treated completely before analytic methods are introduced. Otherwise, the student will probably seize upon the analytic methods at every instant in order to attack problems directly, thereby often ignoring the simplicity of the synthetic methods. An adequate treatment of point set theory, curves, and surfaces is given without deep topological considerations. Granted it would be ideal for the student to have a good background in topology; however, a student should not be denied access to Stokes' theorem, in a reasonably general form, because of the lack of such a background. Line and surface integrals are well motivated and treated in detail together with the significant integral theorems.

Part II treats complex analysis. Here the emphasis is on the consideration of the elementary calculus of complex-valued functions of a complex variable. The aim is for the student to emerge with a working knowledge of complex techniques, not with just a handful of celebrated theorems carefully memorized. Basic properties of the elementary functions as well as their geometric interpretation as mappings are considered before the notion of analytic function is introduced, thereby giving the student a good familiarity with them so that a good source for illustrative examples is available. The nth roots of a complex number are not treated until the general power function is introduced, thus giving precision to the results. The calculus of residues is considered before the introduction of series so that a fairly complete treatment of the complex integral calculus can be undertaken.

Part III deals with Fourier analysis. It begins with a formal treatment of Fourier series, proceeds to convergence theorems, develops the Fourier integral, and introduces various Fourier transforms. It concludes with an exposition of general orthogonal functions. I have found it convenient to introduce the notion of uniform convergence in this part, for the motivation is certainly available. Throughout the text, I have tried to justify interchange of limit processes wherever possible; in any event, every effort has been made to make the student very conscious of such interchanges.

A more complete treatment of special orthogonal functions and integral operators can be given only after the introduction of certain special functions. This is the subject matter of Part IV, where there is a detailed treatment of most of the special functions that occur in practice. This part includes the highly significant Sturm-Liouville theory.

Part V deals with the calculus of variations. Although the older textbooks in advanced calculus included a chapter on this subject, the more recent ones have not included it, primarily because its applications appeared to be limited. But now, with the advent of the direct methods of the solution of variational problems, the calculus of variations is found to have wide applicability in many fields of analysis. Beginning with a classical exposition, the book proceeds to a discussion of some of the direct methods and the relationship of Sturm-Liouville systems to variational problems.

Part VI deals with several aspects of operational analysis. The operational calculus is presented primarily via the Laplace transform. Other integral transforms are mentioned briefly. In order to present a satisfactory definition of the Dirac delta function, the Stieltjes integral is introduced. A more general treatment of singular functions is afforded, however, in the chapter on generalized functions, which is presented in an elementary setting. I feel that the increasing importance of generalized functions throughout the whole of analysis makes its study at an early date imperative. A general theory of operators with its excursions into the theory of vector spaces and matrices also occurs in this part. Most of the advanced topics in this textbook actually occur in Part VI.

Part VII deals with partial differential equations, with primary emphasis on boundary value problems. In a very real sense the preceding six parts of the text form a good background for a thorough treatment of this highly significant subject. However, the topics are so arranged that one may pass from the Fourier series and Fourier integrals of Part III to the boundary value problems in Part VII that involve them. Similarly, one can go directly from the integral transforms in Part VI to the boundary value problems involving them.

Since motivation and flexibility are the keynotes of the exposition in this book, I have presented the material at various increasing degrees of generalization. Hence, vector analysis is presented independently of the theory of vector spaces (although the latter depends heavily on the former for motivation), special Sturm-Liouville systems are treated in detail prior to an exposition of the general theory, and particular operators are considered before the general theory. In general, the first six parts of the book are independent of each other, except for isolated results.

The two volumes constituting this text can be used in a one-year course, one volume per semester, if the topics are appropriately selected according to the needs of the class. In a two-year course, most of the material can be presented in considerable detail. In general, Volume II is of a more advanced level than Volume I.

I welcome the pleasure of expressing my heartfelt thanks to Harry Davis, Frank Hahn, Ingo Maddaus, Jr., Zeev Nehari, and Peter Wilker for their valuable suggestions. I am indebted to Mrs. Lydia Woodruff and Mrs. Hilda Clohesy for typing preliminary editions and to Mrs. Mary Bell, Mrs. Lois Rix, and Mrs. Shirley Long for typing the manuscript for this book. Their expert typing, patience, and tolerance were necessary contributing factors to the completion of this book.

ARTHUR E. DANESE

Contents

Part IV *Special Functions*

Chapter 14 *The Gamma Function and Other Definite Integrals* 453

Chapter 15 *Orthogonal Polynomials* 475

Chapter 16 *Bessel Functions* 524

Chapter 17 *The Sturm-Liouville Theory* 541

Summary of Elementary Mathematics

I. THE REAL NUMBER SYSTEM

a. The **real number system** R is a set of elements $a, b, c, \cdots$, called *real numbers* such that

(A) there exist binary operations addition $(+)$ and multiplication $(\cdot)$ with the properties that for all a, b, c in R,

A_1: $a + b = b + a$ (commutative law for addition).
A_2: $a + (b + c) = (a + b) + c$ (associative law for addition).
A_3: There exists 0 (zero) in R such that $0 + a = 0$.
A_4: For every a in R there exists $-a$ (minus a) in R such that $a + (-a) = 0$.
M_1: $a \cdot b = b \cdot a$ (commutative law for multiplication).
M_2: $a \cdot (b \cdot c) = (a \cdot b) \cdot c$ (associative law for multiplication).
M_3: There exists 1 (one) in R such that $a \cdot 1 = a$.
M_4: For every $a \neq 0$ in R there exists $1/a$ (the reciprocal of a) in R such that $a \cdot 1/a = 1$.
D: $a \cdot (b + c) = a \cdot b + a \cdot c$ (distributive law).

(B) R is *ordered;* i.e., there exists a subset P of R, whose elements are called the *positive real numbers*, such that

P_1: If a and b are in P, then $a + b$ and $a \cdot b$ are in P.
P_2: If a is in R, then one and only one of the following holds: a is in P, $a = 0$, $-a$ is in P.

(We now define the relation "a is less than b," written as $a < b$ or $b > a$, to mean $b + (-a)$ is in P.)

(C) R is *complete;* i.e., if S is any subset of R that has an *upper bound* (any real number M such that y is less than or equal to M $(\leq)$ for every y in S), then S has a *least upper bound* (the smallest of all the upper bounds of S.)

b. The operations of subtraction and division are defined as $a - b = a + (-b)$ and $a/b = a \cdot 1/b$, $b \neq 0$. Division by zero is undefined.

c. Laws of inequality:

I$_1$: If $a < b$ and $b < c$, then $a < c$.
I$_2$: If $a < b$, then $a + c < b + c$, for every c in R.
I$_3$: If $a < b$ and $c > 0$, then $a \cdot c < b \cdot c$.
I$_4$: If $a < b$ and $c < 0$, then $a \cdot c > b \cdot c$.
I$_5$: If $a > 0$, then $1/a > 0$.
I$_6$: If $a < 0$, then $1/a < 0$.

d. The absolute value of a in R, denoted by $|a|$, is defined as

$$|a| = \begin{cases} a, & \text{if } a \geq 0 \\ -a, & \text{if } a < 0 \end{cases}.$$

It has the properties:

A$_1$: $|ab| = |a|\,|b|$.

A$_2$: $\left|\dfrac{1}{a}\right| = \dfrac{1}{|a|}$.

A$_3$: $|a + b| \leq |a| + |b|$ (triangle inequality).

e. The set J of positive integers $1, 2, 3, \cdots$ is a subset of R. It satisfies the **principle of mathematical induction:** If S is any subset of J such that 1 belongs to S and $k + 1$ belongs to S whenever k belongs to S, then $S = J$.

f. The set of integers $\cdots, -2, -1, 0, 1, 2, \cdots$ is a subset of R. The set of rational numbers r ($r = p/q$, p and q integers, $q \neq 0$) is a subset of R.

g. The **greatest integer** in a, denoted by $[a]$, is the greatest integer less than or equal to a. It satisfies $a - 1 < [a] \leq a$.

II. DETERMINANTS

a. The determinant of the coefficients of the system of linear equations

$$\text{(S)} \qquad \begin{array}{c} a_{11}x_1 + a_{12}x_2 + \cdots + a_{1n}x_n = b_1 \\ a_{21}x_1 + a_{22}x_2 + \cdots + a_{2n}x_n = b_2. \\ \cdots\cdots\cdots\cdots\cdots\cdots \\ a_{n1}x_1 + a_{n2}x_2 + \cdots + a_{nn}x_n = b_n \end{array}$$

is

$$D = \begin{vmatrix} a_{11} & a_{12} & \cdots & a_{1n} \\ a_{21} & a_{22} & \cdots & a_{2n} \\ \cdots & \cdots & \cdots & \cdots \\ a_{n1} & a_{n2} & \cdots & a_{nn} \end{vmatrix} = |a_{ij}|.$$

D is a determinant of order n.

b.

$$\begin{vmatrix} a & b \\ c & d \end{vmatrix} = ad - bc.$$

$$\begin{vmatrix} a_1 & a_2 & a_3 \\ b_1 & b_2 & b_3 \\ c_1 & c_2 & c_3 \end{vmatrix} = a_1b_2c_3 + a_2b_3c_1 + a_3b_1c_2 - a_3b_2c_1 - a_1b_3c_2 - a_2b_1c_3.$$

c. The minor M_{ij} of the element a_{ij} in D is the determinant of order $n - 1$ obtained from D by deleting its ith row and jth column. The cofactor A_{ij} of a_{ij} is defined as $A_{ij} = (-1)^{i+j}M_{ij}$. The expansion of D in cofactors of the elements of the ith row is

$$D = a_{i1}A_{i1} + a_{i2}A_{i2} + \cdots + a_{in}A_{in},$$

and in cofactors of the elements of the jth column is

$$D = a_{1j}A_{1j} + a_{2j}A_{2j} + \cdots + a_{nj}A_{nj}.$$

For example, the determinant of order 4 expanded in cofactors of elements of its first row:

$$\begin{vmatrix} a_{11} & a_{12} & a_{13} & a_{14} \\ a_{21} & a_{22} & a_{23} & a_{24} \\ a_{31} & a_{32} & a_{33} & a_{34} \\ a_{41} & a_{42} & a_{43} & a_{44} \end{vmatrix} = a_{11}\begin{vmatrix} a_{22} & a_{23} & a_{24} \\ a_{32} & a_{33} & a_{34} \\ a_{42} & a_{43} & a_{44} \end{vmatrix} - a_{12}\begin{vmatrix} a_{21} & a_{23} & a_{24} \\ a_{31} & a_{33} & a_{34} \\ a_{41} & a_{43} & a_{44} \end{vmatrix}$$

$$+ a_{13}\begin{vmatrix} a_{21} & a_{22} & a_{24} \\ a_{31} & a_{32} & a_{34} \\ a_{41} & a_{42} & a_{44} \end{vmatrix} - a_{14}\begin{vmatrix} a_{21} & a_{22} & a_{23} \\ a_{31} & a_{32} & a_{33} \\ a_{41} & a_{42} & a_{43} \end{vmatrix}.$$

d. Cramer's rule. If $D \neq 0$, the solution of the system of linear equations (S) is

$$x_j = \frac{D_j}{D}, \qquad j = 1, 2, \cdots, n,$$

where D_j is the determinant obtained from D by replacing its jth column by b_j, $j = 1, 2, \cdots, n$.

e. Properties of determinants

D_1: If the elements of any row or column of D are zero, then $D = 0$.

D_2: If D^* is the determinant obtained from D by interchanging two rows or two columns, then $D^* = -D$.

D_3: If the corresponding elements of two rows or two columns of D are equal, then $D = 0$.

D_4: If D^* is the determinant obtained from D by multiplying every element of a row or column of D by k, then $D^* = kD$.

D_5: If the jth column of D has elements of the form $a_{ij} + b_{ij}$, $i = 1, 2, \cdots, n$, then $D = D^* + D^{**}$, where D^* is obtained from D by replacing its jth column by a_{ij}, $i = 1, 2, \cdots, n$, and D^{**} is obtained from D by replacing its jth column by b_{ij}, $i = 1, 2, \cdots, n$ (same property for rows).

D_6: If D^* is the determinant obtained from D by adding to the elements of any row (or column) the corresponding elements of any other row (or column), each multiplied by the same constant, then $D^* = D$.

III. FUNCTIONS OF A SINGLE REAL VARIABLE

A. Functions, limits, and continuity

a. If to every real number x in an interval I there corresponds a unique real number y, then a **function of a real variable** f is defined on I, and we indicate the correspondence as $y = f(x)$. I is called the *domain* of f and the set of y such that $y = f(x)$, x in I, denoted by $f(I)$, is called the *range* of f. If the functions f and g are defined on I, we define the sum of f and g, $f + g$, such that $(f + g)(x) = f(x) + g(x)$, the product of f and g, fg, such that $(fg)(x) = f(x)g(x)$, and the quotient of f and g, f/g, $g(x) \neq 0$, such that $(f/g)(x) = f(x)/g(x)$, for all x in I. If f is defined on I and g on $f(I)$, then the function, $g(f)$, such that $g(f)(x) = g[f(x)]$, is a *composite function* or function of a function.

b. The limit of $f(x)$ as x approaches x_0 is c, a real number, written $\lim_{x \to x_0} f(x) = c$, if for every $\epsilon > 0$, there exists $\delta > 0$ such that $|x - x_0| < \delta$ implies $|f(x) - c| < \epsilon$.

c. If $\lim_{x \to x_0} f(x) = c$ and $\lim_{x \to x_0} g(x) = d$, then (1) $\lim_{x \to x_0} [f(x) + g(x)] = c + d$, (2) $\lim_{x \to x_0} f(x)g(x) = cd$, (3) $\lim_{x \to x_0} f(x)/g(x) = c/d$, $d \neq 0$.

d. We write $\lim_{x \to \infty} f(x) = c \left(\lim_{x \to -\infty} f(x) = c \right)$ if for every $\epsilon > 0$ there exists a real number M such that $x > M$ $(x < M)$ implies $|f(x) - c| < \epsilon$.

e. We write $\lim_{x \to x_0} f(x) = \begin{cases} \infty \\ -\infty \end{cases}$ if for every real number M there exists $\delta > 0$ such that $|x - x_0| < \delta$ implies $f(x) = \begin{cases} > M \\ < M \end{cases}$.

f. The function f is **continuous** at x_0 if $\lim_{x \to x_0} f(x) = f(x_0)$; f is continuous in an interval I if f is continuous at every point in I.

g. If f and g are continuous in I, then $f + g$, fg, f/g, $g \neq 0$ are continuous in I. If f is continuous in I and g is continuous in $f(I)$, then $f(g)$ is continuous in I.

h. If f is continuous in the closed interval $I: a \leq x \leq b$, then (1) f is bounded on I (i.e., there exists a constant M such that $|f(x)| \leq M$ for all x in I) and (2) f assumes its maximum and minimum values in I (i.e., there exist x_1 and x_2 in I such that $f(x_1) \leq f(x) \leq f(x_2)$ for every x in I).

i. If x_1 and x_2 are any two points in the domain I of f and $x_1 < x_2$ ($x_1 > x_2$) implies $f(x_1) < f(x_2)$, then f is **increasing** (**decreasing**) in I.

j. If f is increasing (or decreasing) in I, then the **inverse function** of f, denoted by f^{-1}, is a function whose domain is $f(I)$ and $f^{-1}(y) = x$, where x and y satisfy $y = f(x)$. It follows that $f[f^{-1}(y)] = y$, f^{-1} is increasing (or decreasing) in $f(I)$, f is the inverse function of f^{-1}, and $f^{-1}[f(x)] = x$.

k. If f is continuous and increasing or decreasing, then f^{-1} is continuous.

B. The derivative of a function

a. The **derivative** of f at x_0 is

$$f'(x_0) = \lim_{x\to x_0} \frac{f(x) - f(x_0)}{x - x_0},$$

if this limit exists. If the derivative of f exists at x_0, f is **differentiable** at x_0; f is differentiable in an interval I if f is differentiable at every point in I. If f is differentiable in I, we define the function f', called the derivative of f, such that $(f')(x) = f'(x)$ for every x in I.

b. If f and g are differentiable in I, then in I, (1) $(f+g)' = f' + g'$, (2) $(fg)' = f'g + fg'$, (3) $(f/g)' = (gf' - fg')/g^2$, $g \neq 0$.

c. If f is differentiable at x_0, then f is continuous at x_0. The converse is *not* true.

d. Law of the mean for derivatives. If f is continuous in $a \leq x \leq b$ and differentiable in $a < x < b$, then there exists x^* in $a < x < b$ such that $f(b) - f(a) = (b - a)f'(x^*)$.

e. The **differential** of $f(x)$ is $df(x) = f'(x)\,dx$, where dx is a real number called the differential of x.

f. The derivative of f' is called the **second derivative** of f and is denoted by f''; the nth derivative of f is the derivative of the $(n-1)$th derivative of f; it is denoted by $f^{(n)}$. We also write $f^{(n)}(x) = d^ny/dx^n$, where $y = f(x)$.

C. The definite integral

a. The definite integral of f over $a \leq x \leq b$ is

$$\int_a^b f(x)\,dx = \lim_{\substack{n\to\infty \\ ||\Delta x||\to 0}} \sum_{i=1}^{n} f(x_i')\,\Delta x_i,$$

if this limit exists, where $a = x_0 < x_1 < \cdots < x_n = b$ are points of subdivision of $a \leq x \leq b$, $\Delta x_i = x_i - x_{i-1}$, $||\Delta x|| = \max(\Delta x_i)$, $i = 1, 2, \cdots, n$, and $x_{i-1} \leq x_i' \leq x_i$. If $\int_a^b f(x)\,dx$ exists, we say that f is (Riemann) **integrable** over $a \leq x \leq b$.

b. If f is continuous in $a \leq x \leq b$, then f is integrable over $a \leq x \leq b$.

c. Duhamel's theorem. If f and g are continuous in $a \leq x \leq b$, then

$$\lim_{\substack{n\to\infty \\ \|\Delta x\|\to 0}} \sum_{i=1}^{n} f(x_i')g(x_i'')\,\Delta x_i = \int_a^b f(x)g(x)\,dx,$$

where $x_{i-1} \le x_i' \le x_i$ and $x_{i-1} \le x_i'' \le x_i$.

d. Properties of the definite integral. If f and g are integrable over $I: a \le x \le b$, then

I₁: $\int_a^b kf(x)\,dx = k\int_a^b f(x)\,dx$, k any constant.

I₂: $\int_a^b [f(x) + g(x)]\,dx = \int_a^b f(x)\,dx + \int_a^b g(x)\,dx.$

I₃: $\int_a^b f(x)\,dx = \int_a^c f(x)\,dx + \int_c^b f(x)\,dx.$

I₄: $\int_a^a f(x)\,dx = 0.$

I₅: $\int_b^a f(x)\,dx = -\int_a^b f(x)\,dx.$

I₆: If $f(x) \le g(x)$ in I, then $\int_a^b f(x)\,dx \le \int_a^b g(x)\,dx.$

I₇: $\left|\int_a^b f(x)\,dx\right| \le \int_a^b |f(x)|\,dx.$

I₈: If f is continuous in I, then

$$\frac{d}{dx}\int_a^x f(t)\,dt = f(x).$$

I₉: If f is continuous in I and $F'(x) = f(x)$, then $\int_a^b f(x)\,dx = F(b) - F(a)$ (**fundamental theorem of the calculus**).

I₁₀: If f is continuous in I, ϕ has a continuous derivative in $c \le t \le d$, $\phi(c) = a$, $\phi(d) = b$, $a \le \phi(t) \le b$, then

$$\int_a^b f(x)\,dx = \int_c^b f[\phi(t)]\phi'(t)\,dt \qquad \textbf{(change in variable).}$$

e. Law of the mean for integrals. If f is continuous in $a \le x \le b$, then there exists x^* in $a < x < b$ such that

$$\int_a^b f(x)\,dx = (b - a)f(x^*).$$

f. If f is continuous for $x \ge a$,

$$\int_a^\infty f(x)\,dx = \lim_{b\to\infty}\int_a^b f(x)\,dx, \quad \text{if this limit exists;}$$

if f is continuous for $x \le b$,

$$\int_{-\infty}^b f(x)\,dx = \lim_{a\to-\infty}\int_a^b f(x)\,dx, \quad \text{if this limit exists;}$$

if f is continuous for all x,

$$\int_{-\infty}^{\infty} f(x)\,dx = \int_{-\infty}^{a} f(x)\,dx + \int_{a}^{\infty} f(x)\,dx,$$

if the integrals on the right exist. These integrals are **improper integrals of the first kind.**

g. If f is continuous in $a < x \leq b$,

$$\int_a^b f(x)\,dx = \lim_{\epsilon\to 0} \int_{a+\epsilon}^b f(x)\,dx, \qquad \epsilon > 0, \text{ if this limit exists;}$$

if f is continuous in $a \leq x < b$,

$$\int_a^b f(x)\,dx = \lim_{\epsilon\to 0} \int_{a}^{b-\epsilon} f(x)\,dx, \qquad \epsilon > 0, \text{ if this limit exists;}$$

if f is continuous in $a \leq x \leq b$ except at x_0, $a < x_0 < b$,

$$\int_a^b f(x)\,dx = \int_a^{x_0} f(x)\,dx + \int_{x_0}^b f(x)\,dx,$$

if these integrals exist. These integrals are **improper integrals of the second kind.**

IV. FUNCTIONS OF SEVERAL REAL VARIABLES

A. Functions, limits, and continuity

a. If to every point (x, y) in a region R in the xy-plane there corresponds a unique real number z, then a **function of two real variables** f is defined on R, and we indicate the correspondence as $z = f(x, y)$; if to every point (x, y, z) in a region R in three-dimensional space there corresponds a unique real number w, then a **function of three variables** f is defined on R, and we indicate the correspondence as $w = f(x, y, z)$. R is called the *domain* of f and $f(\mathrm{R})$ is the *range* of f.

b. $\lim\limits_{\substack{x\to x_0\\ y\to y_0}} f(x, y) = c$, if for every $\epsilon > 0$ there exists $\delta > 0$ such that $(x - x_0)^2 + (y - y_0)^2 < \delta^2$ implies $|f(x, y) - c| < \epsilon$. The set of points (x, y) such that $(x - x_0)^2 + (y - y_0)^2 < \delta^2$ for some $\delta > 0$ is called a **neighborhood** of (x_0, y_0).

c. f is continuous at (x_0, y_0) if $\lim\limits_{\substack{x\to x_0\\ y\to y_0}} f(x, y) = f(x_0, y_0)$; f is continuous in a region R if f is continuous at every point in R.

d. If f is continuous in a closed bounded region R, then (1) f is bounded in R (i.e., there exists a constant M such that $|f(x, y)| \leq M$ for all (x, y) in R), and (2) f assumes its maximum and minimum values in R (i.e., there exist (x_1, y_1) and (x_2, y_2) in R such that

$$f(x_1, y_1) \leq f(x, y) \leq f(x_2, y_2)$$

for all (x, y) in R).

B. Partial differentiation

a. Let f be defined in some region R in the xy-plane. The **partial derivative** of $f(x, y)$ with respect to x is the derivative of $f(x, y)$ with respect to x, with y held fixed; we denote it as $\partial f/\partial x$, or f_x. We define the partial derivative of f with respect to y similarly, and denote it as $\partial f/\partial y$ or f_y. The partial derivatives of f_x and f_y are called the **second partial derivatives** of f and are denoted by

$$\frac{\partial^2 f}{\partial x^2} = f_{xx}, \qquad \frac{\partial^2 f}{\partial y\, \partial x} = f_{xy}, \qquad \frac{\partial^2 f}{\partial x\, \partial y} = f_{yx}, \qquad \frac{\partial^2 f}{\partial y^2} = f_{yy}.$$

b. If f, f_x, f_y, f_{xy}, f_{yx} are defined in some neighborhood of (x_0, y_0) and f_{xy} and f_{yx} are continuous at (x_0, y_0), then

$$f_{xy}(x_0, y_0) = f_{yx}(x_0, y_0).$$

c. If f is defined in a neighborhood of (x_0, y_0), then f is **differentiable** at (x_0, y_0) if there exist real numbers A and B such that

$$f(x_0 + h, y_0 + k) = f(x_0, y_0) + Ah + Bk + \epsilon\sqrt{h^2 + k^2},$$

where $\epsilon \to 0$ as $h \to 0$ and $k \to 0$; f is differentiable in a region R if f is differentiable at every point in R.

d. If f is differentiable at (x_0, y_0), then f_x and f_y exist at (x_0, y_0). The converse is *not* true.

e. If f is differentiable at (x_0, y_0), then f is continuous at (x_0, y_0). The converse is *not* true. If f_x and f_y exist at (x_0, y_0), it does *not* necessarily follow that f is continuous at (x_0, y_0).

f. If f_x and f_y are continuous in a region R, then f is differentiable in R.

g. The **total differential** of a differentiable function f in a region R is

$$df = f_x\, dx + f_y\, dy,$$

dx and dy real numbers, the differentials of x and y.

h. Chain rule. If $z = f(x, y)$ and $x = \phi(u, v)$, $y = \psi(u, v)$ and x_u, x_v, y_u, y_v are continuous in some region R in the uv-plane, and f_x, f_y are continuous in R*, the set of $[\phi(u, v), \psi(u, v)]$, (u, v) in R, then

$$\frac{\partial z}{\partial u} = \frac{\partial z}{\partial x}\frac{\partial x}{\partial u} + \frac{\partial z}{\partial y}\frac{\partial y}{\partial u},$$

$$\frac{\partial z}{\partial v} = \frac{\partial z}{\partial x}\frac{\partial x}{\partial v} + \frac{\partial z}{\partial y}\frac{\partial y}{\partial v}.$$

i. Implicit function theorem. If F is a function defined in some neighborhood N of (x_0, y_0, z_0), $F(x_0, y_0, z_0) = 0$, $F_z(x_0, y_0, z_0) \neq 0$, F_x, F_y, F_z continuous in N, then there exists a function f defined in some neighborhood N* of (x_0, y_0) such that $z = f(x, y)$, (x, y, z) in N and

(1) f is continuous on N*.
(2) f_x and f_y are continuous on N*.
(3) $f_x = -(F_x/F_z)$ and $f_y = -(F_y/F_z)$ on N*.

j. Inverse function theorem. If

$$\text{(S)} \qquad x = x(u, v),\ y = y(u, v);$$

x, y, x_u, y_u, x_v, y_v are continuous in some neighborhood of (u_0, v_0), and the Jacobian

$$\frac{\partial(x, y)}{\partial(u, v)} = \begin{vmatrix} x_u & y_u \\ x_v & y_v \end{vmatrix} \neq 0 \qquad \text{at } (u_0, v_0),$$

then there exists a neighborhood N of $[x(u_0, v_0), y(u_0, v_0)]$ such that (S) can be solved for u, v:

$$\text{(S*)} \qquad u = u(x, y),\ v = v(x, y),$$

and u, v, u_x, v_x, u_y, v_y are continuous in N.

C. Double and triple integrals

a. Let f be defined in a closed bounded region R in the xy-plane. Divide R into n subregions ΔR_i with areas ΔA_i, $i = 1, 2, \cdots, n$. Let (x_i', y_i') be any point in ΔR_i. The **double integral** of f over R is

$$\iint_R f(x, y)\, dA = \lim_{\substack{n \to \infty \\ \|\Delta A\| \to 0}} \sum_{i=1}^{n} f(x_i', y_i')\, \Delta A_i,$$

where $\|\Delta A\| = \max(\Delta A_i)$, $i = 1, 2, \cdots, n$, if this limit exists. If the double integral of f over R exists, then f is (Riemann) **integrable** over R.

b. If f is continuous in a closed bounded region R in the xy-plane, then f is integrable over R.

c. Let R be a closed bounded region in the xy-plane. Let P_1 and P_2 be the points in R with y-coordinates c and d such that the y-coordinate of every point in R is between c and d, $c < d$. Let any line between P_1 and P_2 parallel to the x-axis cut the boundary of R in exactly two points, so that for $c < y < d$, the boundary of R is formed by two smooth curves:

$$x = g_1(y), \qquad x = g_2(y), \qquad g_1(y) < g_2(y).$$

Then, if f is continuous in R,

$$\iint_R f(x, y)\, dA = \int_c^d dy \int_{g_1(y)}^{g_2(y)} f(x, y)\, dx;$$

i.e., a double integral can be expressed as an **iterated integral**—a succession of two definite integrals, the first with respect to x and the second with respect to y. If P_1 and P_2 are the points in R with x-coordinates a

and b such that the x-coordinate of every point in R is between a and b, $a < b$, and any line between P_1 and P_2 parallel to the y-axis cuts the boundary of R in exactly two points so that the boundary of R is formed by two smooth curves,

$$y = h_1(x), \qquad y = h_2(x), \qquad h_1(x) < h_2(x),$$

and if f is continuous in R, then

$$\iint_{\mathrm{R}} f(x, y)\, dA = \int_a^b dx \int_{h_1(x)}^{h_2(x)} f(x, y)\, dy,$$

an iterated integral—the first integral with respect to y and the second with respect to x.

d. Duhamel's theorem. If f is continuous in the closed bounded region R in the xy-plane, then

$$\lim_{\substack{n\to\infty \\ \|\Delta A\|\to 0}} \sum_{i=1}^{n} f(x_i', y_i')g(x_i'', y_i'')\, \Delta A_i = \iint_{\mathrm{R}} f(x, y)g(x, y)\, dA,$$

where (x_i', y_i') and (x_i'', y_i'') are in $\Delta \mathrm{R}_i$.

e. Let f be defined in a closed bounded region R in three-dimensional space. Divide R into n subregions $\Delta \mathrm{R}_i$ with volumes ΔV_i, $i = 1, 2, \cdots, n$. Let (x_i', y_i', z_i') be any point in $\Delta \mathrm{R}_i$. The **triple integral** of f over R is

$$\iiint_{\mathrm{R}} f(x, y, z)\, dV = \lim_{\substack{n\to\infty \\ \|\Delta V\|\to 0}} \sum_{i=1}^{n} f(x_i, y_i, z_i)\, \Delta V_i,$$

where $\|\Delta V\| = \max (\Delta V_i)$, $i = 1, 2, \cdots, n$, if this limit exists. If the triple integral of f over R exists, then f is (Riemann) **integrable** over R.

f. If f is continuous in a closed bounded region R in space, then f is integrable over R.

g. Let R be a closed bounded region in space. Suppose that $c \le y \le d$. Consider cross sections of R by planes parallel to the xz-plane; i.e., planes $y =$ constant. Assume that these cross sections have the properties of the region indicated in **c.** Let the largest and smallest values of x in the cross sections be $g_1(y)$ and $g_2(y)$ and let $h_1(x, y)$, $h_2(x, y)$ be the values of z for which a typical line parallel to the z-axis in the cross section cuts the boundary of R. Then, if f is continuous on R,

$$\iiint_{\mathrm{R}} f(x, y, z)\, dV = \int_c^d dy \int_{g_1(x)}^{g_2(x)} dx \int_{h_1(x,y)}^{h_2(x,y)} f(x, y, z)\, dz;$$

i.e., a triple integral can be expressed as an iterated integral; similarly, for other orders of integration in the iterated integral.

V. SEQUENCES AND SERIES

A. Definitions and fundamental theorems

a. If to each positive integer n there corresponds a real number a_n, then a **sequence** is defined. We denote a sequence as $a_1, a_2, \cdots, a_n, \cdots$, or $\{a_n\}$.

b. $\lim_{n\to\infty} a_n = c$ if for every $\epsilon > 0$ there exists a positive integer N such that $n > N$ implies $|a_n - c| < \epsilon$. We say $\{a_n\}$ is convergent if $\lim_{n\to\infty} a_n$ exists.

c. Cauchy convergence criterion. $\{a_n\}$ is convergent if and only if for every $\epsilon > 0$ there exists a positive integer N such that $m > N$ and $n > N$ imply $|a_m - a_n| < \epsilon$.

d. If $a_n \leq a_{n+1}$ ($a_n \geq a_{n+1}$) for all n, we say $\{a_n\}$ is nondecreasing (nonincreasing). If there exists a constant M (m) such that $a_n \leq M$ ($a_n \geq m$) for all n, then we say $\{a_n\}$ is bounded from above (below).

e. If $\{a_n\}$ is nondecreasing (nonincreasing) and bounded from above (below), then $\{a_n\}$ is convergent.

f. Given a sequence $\{a_n\}$. The sequence $\{s_n\}$, where $s_n = a_1 + a_2 + \cdots + a_n$, is called an **infinite series** and is denoted by $\sum_{n=1}^{\infty} a_n$. If $\lim_{n\to\infty} s_n$ exists, we say that $\sum_{n=1}^{\infty} a_n$ is **convergent;** otherwise, **divergent.** If $\lim_{n\to\infty} s_n = s$, then s is called the sum of $\sum_{n=1}^{\infty} a_n$ and we write $s = \sum_{n=1}^{\infty} a_n$.

g. $\sum_{n=1}^{\infty} a_n$ is **absolutely convergent** if $\sum_{n=1}^{\infty} |a_n|$ is convergent. $\sum_{n=1}^{\infty} a_n$ is **conditionally convergent** if it is convergent but not absolutely convergent.

B. Tests for convergence and divergence

a. *n*th term test. If $\lim_{n\to\infty} a_n \neq 0$, then $\sum a_n$ is divergent. If $\lim_{n\to\infty} a_n = 0$, the series may be convergent or divergent.

b. Comparison tests. Let $\sum x_n$ be a given series, $x_n \geq 0$. If $x_n \leq c_n$ for all n and $\sum c_n$ is convergent, then $\sum x_n$ is convergent. If $x_n \geq d_n \geq 0$ for all n and $\sum d_n$ is divergent, then $\sum x_n$ is divergent.

c. Ratio test. Let $\rho = \lim_{n\to\infty} |a_{n+1}/a_n|$. If

$$\rho \text{ is } \begin{cases} < 1 \\ > 1, \\ = 1 \end{cases} \qquad \sum a_n \text{ is } \begin{cases} \text{convergent} \\ \text{divergent} \\ \text{convergent or divergent} \end{cases}$$

d. Integral test. If f is continuous and decreasing in $x \geq c$, $\lim_{x \to \infty} f(x) = 0$, and $f(n) = a_n$, then $\sum a_n$ is convergent or divergent according as $\int_c^\infty f(x)\,dx$ exists or does not exist.

e. Leibniz's test for alternating series. If $a_n \geq 0$, $\lim_{n \to \infty} a_n = 0$, $a_{n+1} \leq a_n$ for all n, then $\sum_{n=1}^\infty (-1)^{n+1} a_n$ is convergent.

f. If $\sum a_n$ is absolutely convergent, then it is convergent.

C. Special series

a. Geometric series

$$\sum_{n=0}^{\infty} ar^n \begin{cases} = a/(1-r), & |r| < 1 \\ \text{is divergent}, & |r| \geq 1,\ a \neq 0 \end{cases}.$$

b. *p*-series

$$\sum_{n=1}^{\infty} \frac{1}{n^p} \text{ is } \begin{cases} \text{convergent, if } p > 1 \\ \text{divergent, if } p \leq 1 \end{cases}.$$

If $p = 1$, the series is the **harmonic series.**

D. Power series and Taylor series

a. $\sum_{n=0}^\infty a_n (x-a)^n$ is a **power series** about a, which is convergent in the interval of convergence $a - R < x < a + R$, $R = \lim_{n \to \infty} \left| \frac{a_n}{a_{n+1}} \right|$, the radius of convergence; it is divergent in $x > a + R$ and $x < a - R$.

b. $\sum_{n=0}^{\infty} \frac{f^{(n)}(a)}{n!} (x-a)^n$ is the **Taylor series** of f about a. If $a = 0$, it is the **Maclaurin series** of f.

c. Taylor's formula with the remainder. If f and its first $n + 1$ derivatives are continuous in a closed interval I containing a and if x is any point in I, then

$$f(x) = f(a) + f'(a)(x-a) + \cdots + \frac{f^{(n)}(a)}{n!} + R_{n+1},$$

where

$$R_{n+1} = \frac{f^{(n+1)}(x^*)}{(n+1)!} (x-a)^{n+1}, \qquad a < x^* < x.$$

R_{n+1} is called the *remainder* in Taylor's series.

d. Taylor's expansion theorem. If f has derivatives of all orders at a and $\lim_{n \to \infty} R_{n+1} = 0$, R_{n+1} the remainder in Taylor's series, then

$$f(x) = \sum_{n=0}^{\infty} \frac{f^{(n)}(a)}{n!} (x-a)^n,$$

for all x in the interval of convergence of the series.

VI. ORDINARY DIFFERENTIAL EQUATIONS

A. Definitions

Let f be defined and n times differentiable in $a \leq x \leq b$, and let $y = f(x)$. An **ordinary differential equation** is an equation of the form

$$\text{(A)} \qquad F(x, y, y', \cdots, y^{(n)}) = 0.$$

The **order** of the differential equation is the order of the highest derivative appearing in (A). $y = u(x)$ is a solution of (A) if it satisfies it identically.

B. First-order equations

a. $dy/dx = f(x)g(y)$ is a **variables separable equation** whose solution may be obtained from

$$\int \frac{dy}{g(y)} = \int f(x)\, dx.$$

b. $dy/dx + P(x)y = Q(x)$ is a linear equation whose solution is

$$y = \frac{1}{\mu} \int \mu Q(x)\, dx, \qquad \mu = e^{\int P(x)\, dx}.$$

C. Linear differential equations

a. $L(y) = a_0 y^{(n)} + a_1 y^{(n-1)} + \cdots + a_{n-1}y' + a_n y = R(x)$, where a_i, $i = 0, 1, \cdots, n$ are functions of x only, $a_0 \not\equiv 0$, is an nth order **linear differential equation.** If $R(x) = 0$, it is **homogeneous;** if $R(x) \not\equiv 0$, it is **nonhomogeneous.**

b. The functions $y_1, y_2, \cdots, y_n$ are **linearly independent** in $a \leq x \leq b$, if $c_1 y_1 + c_2 y_2 + \cdots + c_n y_n = 0$ implies $c_1 = c_2 = \cdots = c_n$; if the functions are not linearly independent in $a \leq x \leq b$, they are **linearly dependent** in $a \leq x \leq b$.

c. A necessary and sufficient condition† that the *solutions* $u_1, u_2, \cdots, u_n$ of $L(y) = 0$ be linearly independent in $a \leq x \leq b$ is that the **Wronskian** of $u_1, u_2, \cdots, u_n$:

$$W(u_1, u_2, \cdots, u_n) = \begin{vmatrix} u_1 & u_2 & \cdots & u_n \\ u_1' & u_2' & \cdots & u_n' \\ \cdot & \cdot & \cdot & \cdot \\ u_1^{(n-1)} & u_2^{(n-1)} & \cdots & u_n^{(n-1)} \end{vmatrix} \not\equiv 0 \text{ in } a \leq x \leq b.$$

d. The general solution of $L(y) = 0$ is $c_1 u_1 + c_2 u_2 + \cdots + c_n u_n$, where $u_1, u_2, \cdots, u_n$ are linearly independent solutions of $L(y) = 0$ and $c_1, c_2, \cdots, c_n$ are arbitrary constants. The general solution of $L(y) = R(x)$ is $y_c + y_p$, where y_c (complementary function) is the general solution of $L(y) = 0$ and y_p (particular integral) is any particular solution of $L(y) = R(x)$.

† p is a necessary condition for q if q implies p, and p is a sufficient condition for q if p implies q.

e. Let the coefficients of $L(y) = 0$ be real constants. Consider the algebraic equation

$$a_0 r^n + a_1 r^{n-1} + \cdots + a_{n-1} r + a_n = 0, \qquad a_0 \neq 0$$

(characteristic equation). The n roots of this equation determine n linearly independent solutions of $L(y) = 0$ of the following form:

(1) If r_0 is a distinct real root, then $e^{r_0 x}$ is a solution.

(2) If r_0 is a real root of multiplicity k, $e^{r_0 x}$, $xe^{r_0 x}$, $\cdots$, $x^{k-1}e^{r_0 x}$ are solutions.

(3) If $r_0 = \alpha + i\beta$ and $\bar{r}_0 = \alpha - i\beta$ are distinct conjugate roots, then $e^{\alpha x} \cos \beta x$ and $e^{\alpha x} \sin \beta x$ are solutions.

(4) If $r_0 = \alpha + i\beta$ and $\bar{r}_0 = \alpha - i\beta$ are conjugate roots of multiplicity k, then

$$\begin{matrix} e^{\alpha x} \cos \beta x, & xe^{\alpha x} \cos \beta x, & \cdots, & x^{k-1}e^{\alpha x} \cos \beta x, \\ e^{\alpha x} \sin \beta x, & xe^{\alpha x} \sin \beta x, & \cdots, & x^{k-1}e^{\alpha x} \sin \beta x \end{matrix}$$

are solutions.

f. If $L(y) = R_1(x) + R_2(x) + \cdots + R_k(x) = R(x)$ and y_i is a particular solution of $L(y) = R_i(x)$, $i = 1, 2, \cdots, k$, then $y_1 + y_2 + \cdots + y_k$ is a particular solution of $L(y) = R(x)$.

g. Differential operators. Let $D^n y = d^n y/dx^n, n = 1, 2, \cdots, D^0 y = y$. We define the following:

(1) $(aD^n + bD^m)y = aD^n y + bD^m y$, a and b constants.

(2) $f(D)y = (a_n D^n + a_{n-1}D^{n-1} + \cdots + a_1 D + a_0)y, a_i, i = 1, 2, \cdots, n,$ constants. $f(D)$ is a **linear differential operator** of order n with constant coefficients.

(3) $f(D)g(D)y = f(D)[g(D)y]$, $f(D)$ and $g(D)$ linear differential operators with constant coefficients.

(4) $D^m D^n y = D^{m+n} y$.

(5) $[1/(D - a)]R(x) = e^{ax} \int e^{-ax} R(x)\, dx$, the constant of integration suppressed. $1/(D - a)$ is an **inverse differential operator,** for if $(D - a)y = R(x)$, then $y = [1/(D - a)]R(x)$ is a particular solution of this equation.

The following are valid:

(a) $$f(D)g(D)y = g(D)f(D)y,$$

$f(D)$ and $g(D)$ linear differential operators with constant coefficients.

(b) $$f(D) = a_0(D - r_1)(D - r_2)\cdots(D - r_n),$$

where r_i, $i = 1, 2, \cdots, n$, are the roots of $a_0 r^n + \cdots + a_{n-1} r + a_n = 0$.

(c) $$\frac{1}{(D - a)(D - b)} R(x) = \frac{1}{D - a}\left[\frac{1}{D - b} R(x)\right].$$

(d) $$\frac{1}{f(D)} e^{ax} R(x) = e^{ax} \frac{1}{f(D + a)} R(x)$$

(**exponential shifting property**).

The following formulas enable us to determine particular solutions of $f(D)y = R(x)$ for specific $R(x)$:

P₁: $\frac{1}{f(D)} P_k(x) = (c_0 + c_1D + \cdots + c_kD^k)P_k(x)$. $P_k(x)$ a polynomial of degree k; c_i, $i = 1, 2, \cdots, k$, the coefficients of the polynomial of degree k obtained by dividing 1 by $f(r)$.

P₂: $\frac{1}{(D - a)^r f(D)} e^{ax} = \frac{e^{ax}x^r}{f(a)r!}, \qquad f(a) \neq 0.$

P₃: $\frac{1}{(D - a)^r f(D)} \begin{Bmatrix} \cos ax \\ \sin ax \end{Bmatrix} = \begin{matrix} \text{Re} \\ \text{Im} \end{matrix} \left\{ \frac{e^{iax}x^r}{f(ia)r!}, \right. \qquad f(ia) \neq 0.$

h. Variation of parameters. If $c_1u_1(x) + c_2u_2(x) + \cdots + c_nu_n(x)$ is the general solution of $L(y) = p_0(x)y^{(n)}(x) + \cdots + p_n(x)y = 0, p_0(x) \neq 0$, then a particular solution of $L(y) = R(x)$ is

$$y_p = c_1(x)u_1(x) + c_2(x)u_2(x) + \cdots + c_n(x)u_n(x),$$

where

$$c_j(x) = \int \frac{W_j(u_1, u_2, \cdots, u_n)}{p_0(x)W(u_1, u_2, \cdots, u_n)} dx, \qquad j = 1, 2, \cdots, n,$$

in which W is the Wronskian of $u_1, u_2, \cdots, u_n$ and W_j is the determinant obtained from W by replacing its jth column by $0, 0, \cdots, 0, R(x)$.

i. Euler's differential equation. The equation

$$a_0x^ny^{(n)} + a_1x^{n-1}y^{(n-1)} + \cdots + a_{n-1}xy + a_n = R(x) \qquad a_i, i = 0, 1, \cdots, n,$$

constants, may be transformed into an nth order linear differential equation with constant coefficients by the change in variable $x = e^t$. Under this transformation,

$$x^ky^{(k)} = D(D - 1)(D - 2)\cdots(D - k + 1)y,$$

where $D = d/dt$, $k = 1, 2, \cdots$.

D. Series solutions of linear differential equations

a. If $p_1(x), p_2(x), \cdots, p_n(x)$, and $R(x)$ in

$$\text{(A)} \qquad y^{(n)} + p_1(x)y^{(n-1)} + \cdots + p_{n-1}(x)y' + p_n(x)y = R(x)$$

can be expanded in Taylor series about $x = a$, valid in a common interval of convergence $|x - a| < r$, $r > 0$, then there exists a unique solution $y(x)$ of (A) satisfying the conditions

$$y(a) = b_0, y'(a) = b_1, \cdots, y^{(n-1)}(a) = b_{n-1},$$

where b_i, $i = 0, 1, \cdots, n - 1$, are arbitrary constants. The solution $y(x)$ has a unique Taylor series.

$$\text{(B)} \qquad y(x) = \sum_{n=0}^{\infty} a_n(x - a)^n$$

which converges in $|x - a| < r$. The coefficients a_n may be obtained by substituting (B) in (A), expanding the coefficients and $R(x)$ of (A) in Taylor series, performing the necessary series operations to obtain a single power series on the left-hand side of the equation, and finally equating the coefficients of this power series with the corresponding coefficients of the power series of $R(x)$.

b. The differential equation

$$a_0(x)y'' + a_1(x)y' + a_2(x)y = 0$$

has a **singular point** at $x = a$ if $a_0(a) = 0$. If a is a singular point of the differential equation and this equation can be written in the form

$$\text{(A)} \qquad (x - a)^2 p_0(x)y'' + (x - a)p_1(x)y' + p_2(x)y = 0,$$

where p_0, p_1, p_2 can be expanded in Taylor series about a, valid in a common interval $|x - a| < r$, $r > 0$, and $p_0(x) \neq 0$ in this interval, then a is called a **regular singular point** of the equation.

We obtain a series solution of (A) as follows (**method of Frobenius**): Assume a solution of the form

$$y = (x - a)^{\nu} P(x), \qquad P(x) = \sum_{n=0}^{\infty} a_n (x - a)^n,$$

$a_0 \neq 0$, ν and a_n, $n = 0, 1, 2, \cdots$ to be determined. Substituting in (A), we obtain

$$\text{(B)} \quad (x - a)^2 p_0 P'' + (x - a)(2\nu p_0 + p_1)P' + [p_0\nu(\nu - 1) + \nu p_1 + p_2]P = 0,$$

which must hold when $x = a$. Hence

$$p_0\nu(\nu - 1) + \nu p_1 + p_2 = 0,$$

called the **indicial equation.**

If the roots ν_1 and ν_2 of the indicial equation differ by a number that is not an integer, there exist two linearly independent solutions of (A):

$$(x - a)^{\nu_1} P_1(x), \qquad (x - a)^{\nu_2} P_2(x),$$

where P_1 and P_2 have Taylor series about $x = a$ valid in $|x - a| < r$, $P_1(a) \neq 0$, $P_2(a) \neq 0$.

If $\nu_1 - \nu_2$ is a positive integer or zero, $\nu_1 \geq \nu_2$, there exist linearly independent solutions of (A):

$$y_1(x) = (x - a)^{\nu_1} P_1(x),$$
$$y_2(x) = (x - a)^{\nu_2} P_2(x) + Cy_1(x) \log |x - a|,$$

where P_1 and P_2 have Taylor series about $x = a$ valid in $|x - a| < r$, $P_1(a) \neq 0$, $P_2(a) \neq 0$. The constant $C \neq 0$ if $\nu_1 = \nu_2$; if $\nu_1 - \nu_2$ is a positive integer, C may or may not be zero.

The coefficients of the Taylor series in P_1 and P_2 are obtained from (B) by substituting ν_1 and ν_2 for ν in turn and expressing the left-hand side as a single power series; the coefficients of this power series are then equated to zero

Part I

Vector Analysis

$\int \int \int$

In physics, we encounter such quantities as mass, volume, time, work, kinetic energy, temperature, and fluid pressure. Although these quantities have diverse properties, the one property that they have in common is that they can be measured, once an appropriate unit of measurement has been established for each of these quantities. Mathematically, this means that we represent them by real numbers. These real numbers, then, afford us some indication of the size or magnitude of these quantities. We can say, therefore, that all these quantities are characterized by the fact that they have magnitude.

On the other hand, let us consider such physical quantities as displacement, velocity, acceleration, and force. They can also be measured; i.e., they have magnitude. However, since they all involve motion, they are characterized by the fact that they all have direction. For example, let A, B, and C be three distinct points on a line l such that B is between A and C, and suppose that a particle at B is moving at the rate of k feet per second along l. The velocity of the particle is not completely described until we specify whether the particle is moving toward A or toward C; i.e., the direction in which it is moving. As another example, let A be the center of a sphere of radius r, and consider all possible displacements of a particle from the center A to the surface of the sphere. All these displacements have the same magnitude r, but all have different directions. It is clear, therefore, that velocity and displacement, as well as the other quantities involving motion, are characterized by both magnitude and direction.

It is of considerable interest and practical importance to study quantities that have both magnitude and direction, without considering any of their other physical properties. This situation is typical in modern mathematics; given a set of objects, certain significant properties of these objects are singled out, and these form the basis of an abstract study of these objects. By this approach, many seemingly diverse theories become special cases of one general theory; thereby we achieve an economy of time and effort, together with a highly satisfying mathematical elegance.

Our fundamental purpose in this part is to study extensively those quantities that are characterized by having both magnitude and direction. We call such quantities vectors. Hence, a **vector** is a quantity having magnitude *and* direction. Quantities having magnitude only are distinguished from vectors by being called **scalars.** Since scalars are represented by real numbers, we also use the term scalar to denote any real number.

Vector analysis is the study of the mathematical representation of vectors, operations on vectors, and various applications of vectors.

Chapter 1

The Geometry and Algebra of Vectors

1. Representation of vectors. The first step in the study of vectors is the introduction of mathematical representations of them. We first consider a **geometric representation** of vectors in three-dimensional space. In such a space, a vector will be represented by a directed line segment, as illustrated in Fig. 1. The length of the line segment will indicate the magnitude of the vector. We transform a line segment into a directed line segment by assigning one of two directions along the line. The vector represented in Fig. 1 has a direction from A to B; the arrow at B indicates this direction. We shall refer to A as the **initial point** and B as the **terminal point** of the vector. If the direction of the vector is from B to A, we say that it has an opposite, or reverse, direction to that

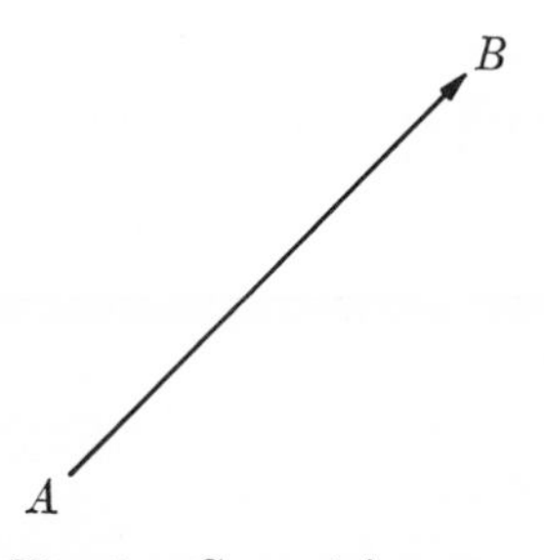

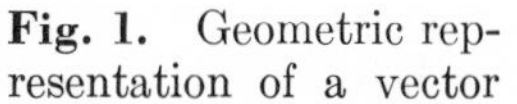
Fig. 1. Geometric representation of a vector

of the vector whose direction is from A to B. We shall refer to the directed line segment that represents a vector simply as that vector.

We have considered the simplest type of geometric representation of a vector in which its direction is one of two possible directions. We shall soon see that a large significant body of vector analysis can be developed with the representation of vectors in this simple form. However, for some purposes (e.g., the displacements from the center of the sphere cited in the introduction), it becomes necessary to widen the choice of the direction of a vector. This requires the introduction of a frame of reference such as a coordinate system; vectors can then be represented analytically with respect to such a system and their directions can be specified with reference to it. This we shall do in Chapter 2. It should be pointed out now, however, that many vector problems are more simply and elegantly treated by geometric (often called *synthetic*) methods that involve no frame of reference, rather than by analytic methods. The student will have ample opportunity to discover this for himself. Furthermore, in many applications of vectors, the results are independent of any coordinate system, and the adoption of such a system may not lead to sufficiently general results.

The geometric representation of a vector has the advantage that it exhibits both of its identifying characteristics: magnitude and direction. Frequently, however, we wish to refer to vectors just as mathematical objects. This gives rise to an **algebraic representation** of vectors. For this, we use small letters of the alphabet in boldface type, such as $\mathbf{a}$, $\mathbf{b}$, $\mathbf{c}, \cdots, \mathbf{u}, \mathbf{v}, \mathbf{x}$. On occasion, it will be more desirable to use capital letters to represent standard vectors where such representations occur commonly in practice, such as $\mathbf{F}$ for force. In some instances, if the initial point of a vector is A and its terminal point is B, then it may be convenient to represent it as $\overrightarrow{AB}$. Given a vector $\mathbf{b} = \overrightarrow{AB}$, we denote its magnitude as b or $|\mathbf{b}| = |\overrightarrow{AB}|$. Whenever $\mathbf{b}$ and b appear in the same context, b will always denote the magnitude of $\mathbf{b}$; $|\mathbf{b}|$ is sometimes used rather than b for emphasis. The magnitude of a vector will also be called the **length of the vector** or the **absolute value of the vector.** The small letters of the alphabet in lightface italic type, such as $h, k, l, \cdots, p, q, r, s, t$, will be used to denote scalars.

2. Equality of vectors. Two vectors are **equal** if they have the same magnitude and direction. We denote the equality of the vectors $\mathbf{a}$ and $\mathbf{b}$ by $\mathbf{a} = \mathbf{b}$. The following properties of the relation of equality are readily verified from the definition:

E_1: $\mathbf{a} = \mathbf{a}$ for all vectors $\mathbf{a}$.
E : $\mathbf{a} = \mathbf{b}$ implies $\mathbf{b} = \mathbf{a}$.
E_3: $\mathbf{a} = \mathbf{b}$ and $\mathbf{b} = \mathbf{c}$ imply $\mathbf{a} = \mathbf{c}$.

It should be noted that the relation of equality for real numbers has these properties.

Since we have represented a vector geometrically as a directed line segment in three-dimensional space, the question arises as to which vectors are equal to any given vector in this space. If two directed line segments have the same length, are parallel, and have the same direction, either one can represent the same vector. Hence, for a given vector represented geometrically in three-dimensional space, all parallel vectors of the same length and same direction as this vector are equal to it. Another way of stating this is to say that we do not distinguish between equal and parallel vectors having the same direction. Therefore, given any vector, we can choose any other parallel vector having the same direction and of equal length to represent the vector, as illustrated in Fig. 2. In practice, we

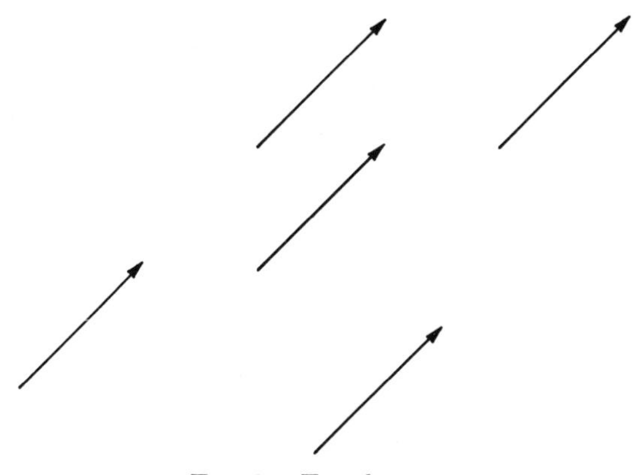

Fig. 2. Equal vectors

choose the vector that is most convenient for the purpose at hand. This vector, then, will have a fixed initial point, and is often called a **fixed vector.** It is readily seen that such a vector is uniquely determined; i.e., there is one and only one vector having a given magnitude and direction and whose initial point is a given point. On the other hand, we say that a vector with given magnitude and direction is uniquely determined up to parallelism.

3. Scalar multiplication and the zero vector. We now consider operations on vectors. The simplest of these is the "multiplication" of a vector by a scalar. We define the product of a vector $\mathbf{a}$ by a scalar h as the vector whose magnitude is $|h|\,|\mathbf{a}|$ and whose direction is that of $\mathbf{a}$ if $h > 0$ and opposite to that of $\mathbf{a}$ if $h < 0$. We denote this product by $h\mathbf{a}$ and call the operation *scalar multiplication.* We note that if $h = -1$, the product $(-1)\mathbf{a}$ is a vector whose magnitude is that of $\mathbf{a}$ but whose direction is opposite to that of **a**; we shall denote the vector $(-1)\mathbf{a}$ simply as $-\mathbf{a}$. Geometrically, the result of multiplying a vector by a scalar is a vector parallel to the given vector. If **a** is parallel to **b**, we write $\mathbf{a} \| \mathbf{b}$. Therefore, we have the

Condition for Parallelism. $\mathbf{a} \| \mathbf{b}$ if and only if there exists a scalar h such that $\mathbf{a} = h\mathbf{b}$.

We have defined the vector $h\mathbf{a}$ for $h \neq 0$, such that $|h\mathbf{a}| = |h|\,|\mathbf{a}|$. In order to define the product of a vector and the scalar zero so that this property holds, we must consider a vector whose magnitude is zero. Geometrically, such a vector can be represented as any point in space and can be considered as any directed line segment that degenerates to its initial point. The question arises as to the direction of such a vector. To say that it has no direction contradicts the definition of a vector. On the other hand, since a point cannot be assigned one of two directions, as can a line segment, it becomes a matter of convention or definition as to what direction we assign to this vector. Since it can be considered as the degenerate of any other vector, we shall find it desirable to assign any direction to this vector that will be convenient for any particular purpose. We call this vector the **zero vector**—a vector of magnitude 0 and having any direction—and denote it by **0**. In particular, the zero vector is parallel and perpendicular to every other vector. The student may find the definition of the direction of the zero vector to be strange and arbitrary, but he will soon see that this convention will eliminate the study of special cases and will enable us to state various properties of vectors quite generally.

We can now complete our definition of scalar multiplication by defining $0\mathbf{a} = \mathbf{0}$, where **a** is any vector. Scalar multiplication has the following properties:

$$
\begin{aligned}
&\mathbf{P_1}\mathbf{:}\quad |h\mathbf{a}| = |h|\,|\mathbf{a}|, \\
&\mathbf{P_2}\mathbf{:}\quad h(k\mathbf{a}) = (hk)\mathbf{a} \quad \text{(associative law)}, \\
&\mathbf{P_3}\mathbf{:}\quad k(h\mathbf{a}) = h(k\mathbf{a}) \quad \text{(commutative law)},
\end{aligned}
$$

where **a** is any vector and h and k are any scalars. P_1 and P_2 follow readily from the definition of scalar multiplication, and P_3 from P_2, using the commutative law for real numbers. In view of P_2 and P_3, $h(k\mathbf{a})$, $k(h\mathbf{a})$, or $(hk)\mathbf{a}$ will be written simply as $hk\mathbf{a}$.

The magnitude of a vector has the following properties:

$$
\begin{aligned}
&\mathbf{M_1}\mathbf{:}\quad |\mathbf{a}| \geq 0 \quad \text{for any vector } \mathbf{a}, \\
&\mathbf{M_2}\mathbf{:}\quad |\mathbf{a}| = 0 \quad \text{if and only if } \mathbf{a} = \mathbf{0},
\end{aligned}
$$

which follow immediately from the definitions.

4. Addition and subtraction of vectors. Suppose we consider the displacement of a particle from A to B and then to C, as illustrated in

Fig. 3. The effective displacement of the particle is from A to C. Hence, we can think of the displacement from A to C as the sum of the displacements from A to B and from B to C. This suggests the definition for the addition of two vectors.

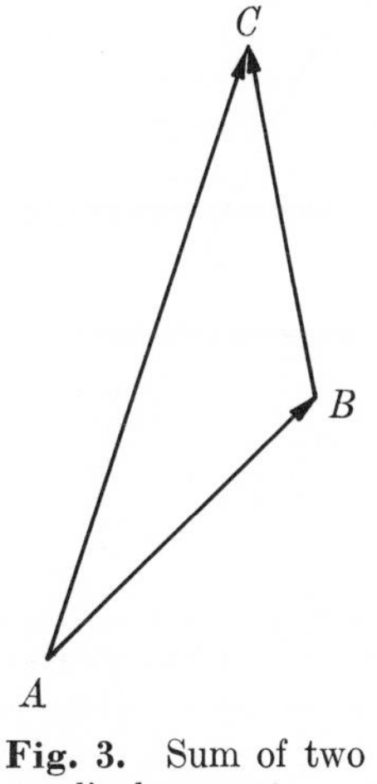

Fig. 3. Sum of two displacements

Given any two vectors, let **a** and **b** be two vectors equal to them and such that the terminal point of **a** is the initial point of **b**. We define the **sum** of the given vectors to be the vector whose initial point is the initial point of **a** and whose terminal point is the terminal point of **b**. This is illustrated in Fig. 4. We denote this sum by $\mathbf{a} + \mathbf{b}$. (Is the sum of two vectors uniquely

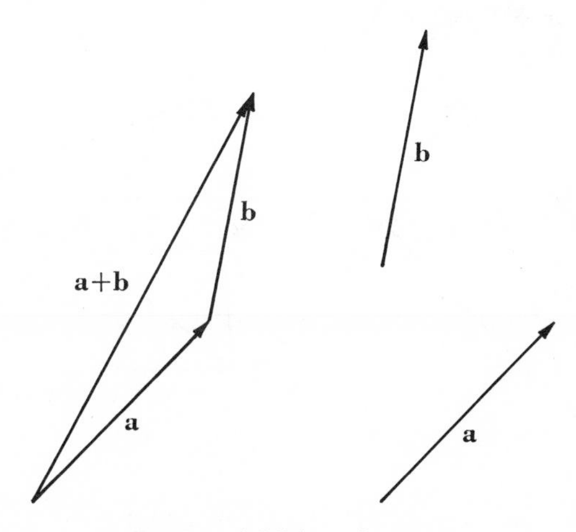

Fig. 4. Addition of vectors

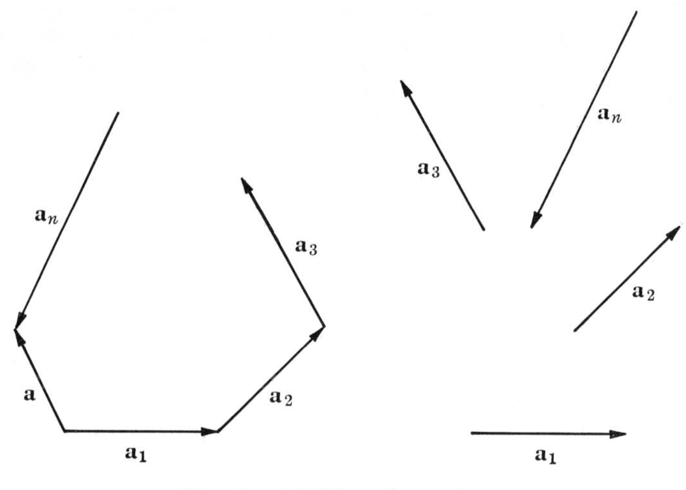

Fig. 5. Addition of n vectors

determined?) This definition of addition extends to any finite number of vectors. The vector

$$\mathbf{a} = \mathbf{a}_1 + \mathbf{a}_2 + \cdots + \mathbf{a}_n$$

is the vector illustrated in Fig. 5.

Vector addition has the following properties:

$\mathbf{A}_1$: $\mathbf{a} + \mathbf{b} = \mathbf{b} + \mathbf{a}$ (commutative law);
$\mathbf{A}_2$: $\mathbf{a} + (\mathbf{b} + \mathbf{c}) = (\mathbf{a} + \mathbf{b}) + \mathbf{c}$ (associative law);
$\mathbf{A}_3$: $h(\mathbf{a} + \mathbf{b}) = h\mathbf{a} + h\mathbf{b}$ (distributive law);
$\mathbf{A}_4$: $(h + k)\mathbf{a} = h\mathbf{a} + k\mathbf{a}$ (scalar distributive law);
$\mathbf{A}_5$: $\mathbf{a} + \mathbf{0} = \mathbf{a}$;
$\mathbf{A}_6$: $\mathbf{a} + (-\mathbf{a}) = \mathbf{0}$;

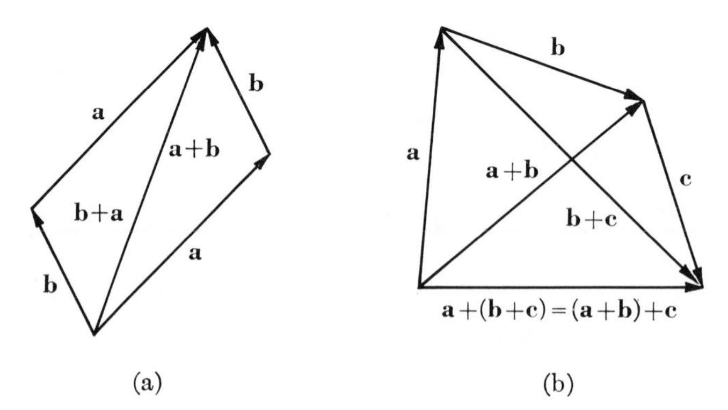

Fig. 6. Addition of vectors: (a) commutative law; (b) associative law

where **a**, **b**, **c** are any vectors and h and k are any scalars. A_1 and A_2 are illustrated in Fig. 6. The student should verify A_3, A_4, A_5, and A_6 geometrically. In establishing A_5 and A_6, note the convenience of our convention regarding the direction of the zero vector. A_3 extends to any finite number of vectors and A_4 extends to any finite number of scalars.

We define the **difference** of two vectors **a** and **b** as the vector $\mathbf{a} + (-\mathbf{b})$, and write it as $\mathbf{a} - \mathbf{b}$. This means that to subtract **b** from **a**, we find $-\mathbf{b}$ and then add it to **a**. Hence, if **a** and **b** are two vectors with a common initial point, then $\mathbf{a} - \mathbf{b}$ is the vector from the terminal point of **b** to the terminal point of **a**, and $\mathbf{b} - \mathbf{a}$ is the vector from the terminal point of **a** to the terminal point of **b**, as indicated in Fig. 7.

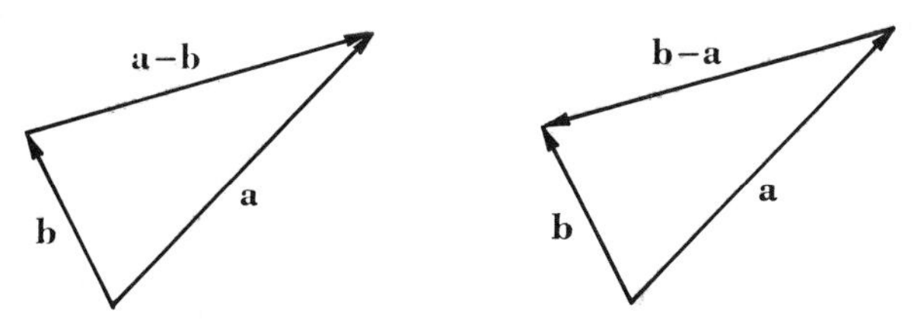

Fig. 7. Subtraction of vectors

It should be noted that the properties A_1 through A_6 hold if the vectors are replaced by real numbers. This means that any of the properties of real numbers that follow from these properties will be valid for vectors. For example, the vector equation

$$\mathbf{a} + 3\mathbf{x} = \mathbf{b}$$

with two fixed or constant vectors **a** and **b** and an "unknown" vector **x** can be solved so that

$$\mathbf{x} = \tfrac{1}{3}(\mathbf{b} - \mathbf{a}).$$

The student should verify this by noting what properties of vectors are used to obtain it.

The definition of addition of vectors enables us to state the following alternate

Condition for Parallelism. $\mathbf{a} \| \mathbf{b}$ if and only if there exist scalars h and k, not both zero, such that $h\mathbf{a} + k\mathbf{b} = \mathbf{0}$.

The proof is left to the student. A useful consequence of this condition is the following:

If **a** and **b** are nonparallel, nonzero vectors, and $h\mathbf{a} + k\mathbf{b} = \mathbf{0}$, then necessarily $h = k = 0$.

5. Representation of a vector in terms of other vectors. First we note that every nonzero vector **a** can be represented as $\mathbf{a} = a\mathbf{u}$, where **u**

is a vector such that $|\mathbf{u}| = 1$ and its direction is that of $\mathbf{a}$. We call $\mathbf{u}$ a **unit vector.**

Let us now turn to the problem of representing a given vector in terms of other given vectors. We first consider this problem in the plane (two-dimensional space). We shall have frequent occasion to impose the restriction that all vectors under discussion are in a plane, and we shall then refer to such vectors as plane vectors. We have the following:

PLANE REPRESENTATION THEOREM. If $\mathbf{a}$ and $\mathbf{b}$ are any two nonzero, nonparallel vectors and $\mathbf{c}$ is any vector in the plane of $\mathbf{a}$ and $\mathbf{b}$, then there exist two uniquely determined scalars h and k such that

$$\mathbf{c} = h\mathbf{a} + k\mathbf{b}.$$

Proof. Since $\mathbf{a}$ and $\mathbf{b}$ are not parallel, there exist $\mathbf{d}$ and $\mathbf{e}$, $\mathbf{d}||\mathbf{a}$ and $\mathbf{e}||\mathbf{b}$, such that $\mathbf{c}$, $\mathbf{d}$, $\mathbf{e}$ form the sides of a triangle. See Fig. 8. Then

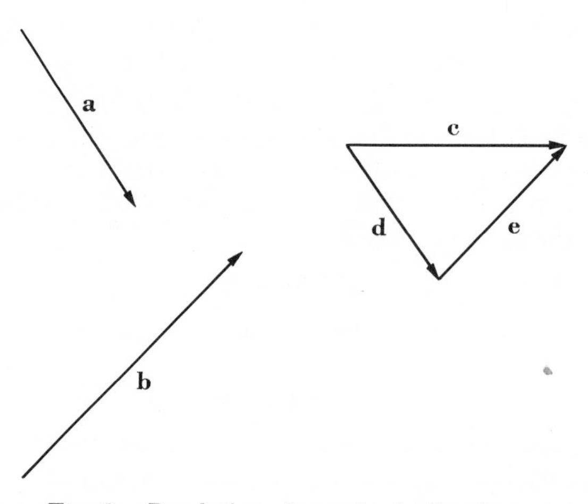

Fig. 8. Resolution of a vector in the plane

$\mathbf{c} = \mathbf{d} + \mathbf{e}$. Now $\mathbf{d}||\mathbf{a}$ implies that there exists a scalar h such that $\mathbf{d} = h\mathbf{a}$, and $\mathbf{e}||\mathbf{b}$ implies that there exists a scalar k such that $\mathbf{e} = k\mathbf{b}$. Hence, $\mathbf{c} = h\mathbf{a} + k\mathbf{b}$. To show that h and k are uniquely determined, assume that h' and k' exist so that $\mathbf{c} = h'\mathbf{a} + k'\mathbf{b}$. Then $h\mathbf{a} + k\mathbf{b} = h'\mathbf{a} + k'\mathbf{b}$ or $(h - h')\mathbf{a} + (k - k')\mathbf{b} = \mathbf{0}$. Since $\mathbf{a}$ and $\mathbf{b}$ are nonzero, nonparallel vectors, it follows that $h = h'$ and $k = k'$.

In the representation $\mathbf{c} = h\mathbf{a} + k\mathbf{b}$, we say that $\mathbf{c}$ is expressed as a linear combination of $\mathbf{a}$ and $\mathbf{b}$ or that $\mathbf{c}$ has been resolved into vectors along $\mathbf{a}$ and $\mathbf{b}$.

The student should note the following special cases:

(1) $h = k = 0$ if and only if $\mathbf{c} = \mathbf{0}$.
(2) $\mathbf{c}||\mathbf{a}$ if and only if $k = 0$.
(3) $\mathbf{c}||\mathbf{b}$ if and only if $h = 0$.

We see from (2) and (3) that a plane vector can be expressed in terms of just one other plane vector only if the vectors are parallel.

We now prove the

SPACE REPRESENTATION THEOREM. If $\mathbf{a}$, $\mathbf{b}$, $\mathbf{c}$ are three nonzero, nonparallel, noncoplanar vectors and $\mathbf{d}$ is any vector in space, then there exist three uniquely determined scalars h, k, l such that

$$\mathbf{d} = h\mathbf{a} + k\mathbf{b} + l\mathbf{c}$$

Proof. Let $\mathbf{a}$, $\mathbf{b}$, $\mathbf{c}$, $\mathbf{d}$ have a common initial point O. Construct a vector $\mathbf{f}$ whose initial point is the terminal point of $\mathbf{d}$, is parallel to $\mathbf{c}$, and has its terminal point P in the plane of the vectors $\mathbf{a}$ and $\mathbf{b}$. See Fig. 9.

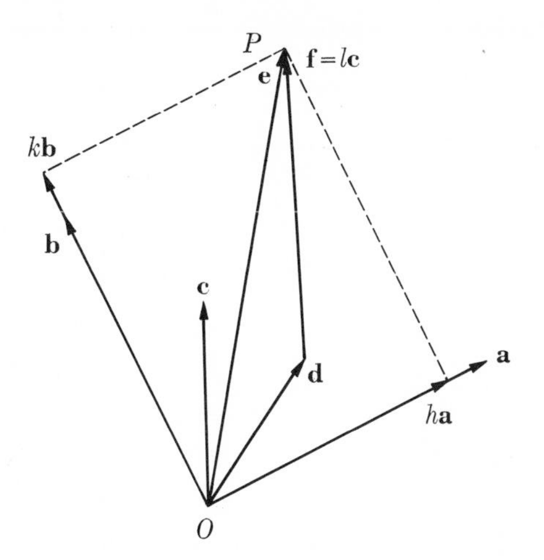

Fig. 9. Resolution of a vector in a space

Then there exists l such that $\mathbf{f} = l\mathbf{c}$. Let $\mathbf{e} = \overrightarrow{OP}$; then, by the plane representation theorem, there exist scalars h and k such that $\mathbf{e} = h\mathbf{a} + k\mathbf{b}$. Since $\mathbf{d} - \mathbf{e} = l\mathbf{c}$, we have $\mathbf{d} = h\mathbf{a} + k\mathbf{b} + l\mathbf{c}$. The student should show that h, k, l are uniquely determined.

The student should consider the following special cases and interpret each geometrically:

(1) One and only one of h, k, l is zero.
(2) Two and only two of h, k, l are zero.
(3) $h = k = l = 0$.

6. Applications to elementary geometry. Many of the theorems of elementary geometry can be proved quite easily and elegantly by using vector methods. The starting point is either to assign directions to the line segments comprising the rectilinear figures occurring in a given problem, and thus representing the sides of the figures by vectors, or by taking a reference point and forming vectors by joining this point to the vertices of the figures. We shall illustrate both methods.

EXAMPLE 1. Prove that the diagonals of a parallelogram bisect each other.

Solution. Let $ABCD$ be the parallelogram and let $\overrightarrow{AB} = \mathbf{a}$ and $\overrightarrow{AD} = \mathbf{b}$. (See figure.) Since the opposite sides of a parallelogram are equal and parallel,

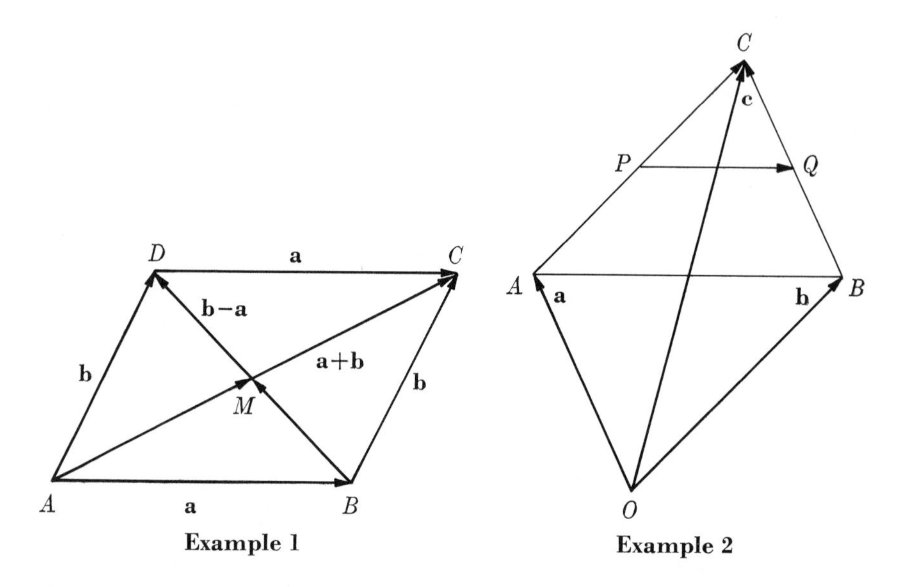

Example 1

Example 2

$\overrightarrow{DC} = \mathbf{a}$ and $\overrightarrow{BC} = \mathbf{b}$. Vector addition and subtraction yield $\overrightarrow{AC} = \mathbf{a} + \mathbf{b}$ and $\overrightarrow{BD} = \mathbf{b} - \mathbf{a}$ for the diagonals. Let M be the midpoint of BD. Then $\overrightarrow{AB} + \overrightarrow{BM} = \overrightarrow{AM}$, or

$$\mathbf{a} + \frac{1}{2}(\mathbf{b} - \mathbf{a}) = \frac{\mathbf{a} + \mathbf{b}}{2} = \overrightarrow{AM}.$$

But, since $\overrightarrow{AC} = \mathbf{a} + \mathbf{b}$, we have $\overrightarrow{AM} = \frac{1}{2}\overrightarrow{AC}$; it follows that M is the midpoint of $\overrightarrow{AC}$ as well as of $\overrightarrow{BD}$.

EXAMPLE 2. Prove that the line segment joining the midpoints of two sides of a triangle is parallel to and one-half the length of the third side.

Solution. Let the triangle be ABC and let O be a reference point (see figure).

Let $\overrightarrow{OA} = \mathbf{a}$, $\overrightarrow{OB} = \mathbf{b}$, $\overrightarrow{OC} = \mathbf{c}$. Then $\overrightarrow{AC} = \mathbf{c} - \mathbf{a}$ and $\overrightarrow{BC} = \mathbf{c} - \mathbf{b}$. (Note how the notation can be used to advantage!) Let P and Q be the midpoints of $\overrightarrow{AC}$ and $\overrightarrow{BC}$. Then $\overrightarrow{PC} = \frac{1}{2}(\mathbf{c} - \mathbf{a})$, $\overrightarrow{QC} = \frac{1}{2}(\mathbf{c} - \mathbf{b})$ and $\overrightarrow{PQ} = \frac{1}{2}(\mathbf{b} - \mathbf{a}) = \frac{1}{2}\overrightarrow{AB}$. Hence, $\overrightarrow{PQ} \| \overrightarrow{AB}$ and $|\overrightarrow{PQ}| = \frac{1}{2}|\overrightarrow{AB}|$.

EXAMPLE 3. Prove that the medians of a triangle meet in a point that divides each median in the ratio 2:1.

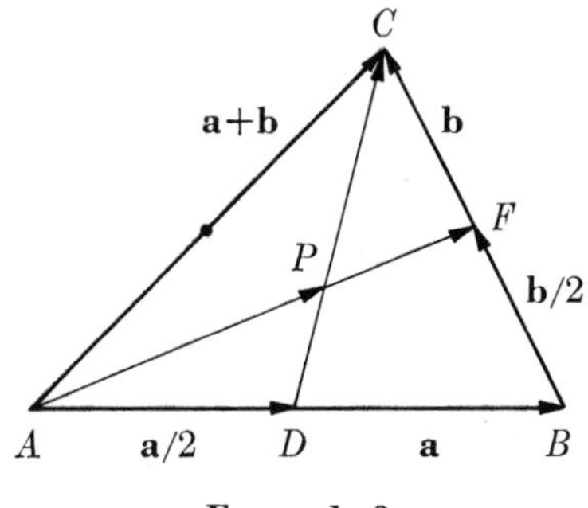

Example 3

Solution. Let the triangle be ABC, with vectors as indicated in the figure. Let the medians CD and AF intersect at P. Then $\overrightarrow{AF} = \mathbf{a} + \frac{1}{2}\mathbf{b}$. There exists a scalar h such that $\overrightarrow{AP} = h(\mathbf{a} + \frac{1}{2}\mathbf{b})$. (Why?) Now $\overrightarrow{DC} = \mathbf{a} + \mathbf{b} - \frac{1}{2}\mathbf{a} = \frac{1}{2}\mathbf{a} + \mathbf{b}$. There exists a scalar k such that $\overrightarrow{DP} = k(\frac{1}{2}\mathbf{a} + \mathbf{b})$. But $\overrightarrow{AD} + \overrightarrow{DP} = \overrightarrow{AP}$, or $\frac{1}{2}\mathbf{a} + k(\frac{1}{2}\mathbf{a} + \mathbf{b}) = h(\mathbf{a} + \frac{1}{2}\mathbf{b})$, or

$$(h - \tfrac{1}{2}k - \tfrac{1}{2})\mathbf{a} + (\tfrac{1}{2}h - k)\mathbf{b} = \mathbf{0}.$$

This can only hold if $h - \frac{1}{2}k - \frac{1}{2} = 0$ and $\frac{1}{2}h - k = 0$. (Why?) Hence $h = \frac{2}{3}$, $k = \frac{1}{3}$. The student should complete the proof.

EXERCISES

1. Let $\mathbf{a}$, $\mathbf{b}$, $\mathbf{c}$ be arbitrary nonzero, nonparallel vectors. Represent geometrically each of the following vectors:

(a) $2\mathbf{a} + \frac{1}{2}\mathbf{b}$; (b) $\mathbf{a} - 3\mathbf{c}$; (c) $\mathbf{a} + 2\mathbf{b} + 3\mathbf{c}$; (d) $3\mathbf{a} - \mathbf{b} + \mathbf{c}$; (e) $\mathbf{a}/a$; (f) $(\mathbf{a} + \mathbf{b})/(|\mathbf{a} + \mathbf{b}|)$; (g) $3(\mathbf{a} - \mathbf{c})$; (h) $\mathbf{x}$, where $2\mathbf{a} + 3\mathbf{x} = \frac{1}{2}(\mathbf{b} - \mathbf{c})$;
(i) $2(\mathbf{a} - \frac{1}{2}\mathbf{b} + \mathbf{c}) - [\mathbf{a} - \mathbf{b} - 3(\mathbf{a} + \mathbf{b} - \mathbf{c})]$;
(j) $h\mathbf{a}$ and $k\mathbf{b}$ so that $\mathbf{c} = h\mathbf{a} + k\mathbf{b}$.

2. (a) Let $\mathbf{a} = \overrightarrow{AB}$ and $\mathbf{b} = \overrightarrow{AD}$, where AB and AD are adjacent sides of the parallelogram $ABCD$. Show that $\mathbf{a} + \mathbf{b} = \overrightarrow{AC}$. This is the "parallelogram law" for the sum of two vectors and is equivalent to our "triangle law." Express $\overrightarrow{BD}$ in terms of $\mathbf{a}$ and $\mathbf{b}$.

(b) If the vectors **c** and **d** represent the diagonals of a parallelogram, represent the adjacent sides of the parallelogram in terms of **c** and **d**.

(c) Let **a**, **b**, **c** represent three sides of a parallelepiped having a common vertex. Express the remaining sides and the diagonals of the parallelepiped in terms of **a**, **b**, **c**.

3. (a) In the regular pentagon $ABCDE$, let $\overrightarrow{AB} = \mathbf{a}$, $\overrightarrow{BC} = \mathbf{b}$, $\overrightarrow{CD} = \mathbf{c}$, $\overrightarrow{DE} = \mathbf{d}$. Express $\overrightarrow{EA}$, $\overrightarrow{DA}$, $\overrightarrow{DB}$, $\overrightarrow{CA}$, $\overrightarrow{EC}$, $\overrightarrow{BE}$ in terms of **a**, **b**, **c**, **d**.

(b) If O is the center of the regular pentagon in (a), show that $\overrightarrow{OA} + \overrightarrow{OB} + \overrightarrow{OC} + \overrightarrow{OD} + \overrightarrow{OE} = \mathbf{0}$. (*Hint:* Construct a pentagon with sides equal to these vectors.)

(c) Generalize the result of (b) to a regular polygon of n sides.

4. (a) Let **a** and **b** represent adjacent sides of a regular hexagon so that the initial point of **b** is the terminal point of **a**. Represent the remaining sides of the hexagon by vectors and express them in terms of **a** and **b**.

(b) Let **a**, **b** represent two consecutive sides of a regular octagon, assigning directions arbitrarily. Represent the remaining sides of the octagon by vectors and express them in terms of **a**, **b**.

(c) Can you generalize (a) and (b) to regular polygons of $2n$ sides?

5. If **a** and **b** are nonparallel vectors such that $\mathbf{c} = (h + k - 1)\mathbf{a} + (h + k)\mathbf{b}$, $\mathbf{d} = (h - k)\mathbf{a} + (2h - k + 1)\mathbf{b}$, find h and k such that $\mathbf{c} = 2\mathbf{d}$.

Ans.: $h = -\frac{1}{2}$, $k = \frac{1}{6}$.

6. (a) Show geometrically that $|\mathbf{a} + \mathbf{b}| \leq |\mathbf{a}| + |\mathbf{b}|$ for any vectors **a** and **b**. (Triangle inequality.) When does the equality sign hold?

(b) Generalize (a) to any n vectors.

(c) Use (a) to show that $|\mathbf{a} - \mathbf{b}| \geq ||\mathbf{a}| - |\mathbf{b}||$.

7. (a) A line is drawn connecting the midpoints of the two nonparallel sides of a trapezoid. Show that the line is equal to half the sum of the parallel sides and is parallel to them.

(b) P and Q divide the sides AC and BC of the triangle ABC in the ratios $h/(1 - h)$ and $k/(1 - k)$. If $\overrightarrow{PQ} = \lambda\overrightarrow{AB}$, show that $\lambda = h = k$.

(c) Show that there exists a triangle with sides that are equal and parallel to the medians of any given triangle. (*Hint:* Show that if ABC is the given triangle with medians CD, AE, BF, then $\overrightarrow{BF} + \overrightarrow{CD} + \overrightarrow{AE} = \mathbf{0}$.)

8. If ABC is any triangle and L, M, N are the midpoints of its sides, show that for any choice of O, $\overrightarrow{OA} + \overrightarrow{OB} + \overrightarrow{OC} = \overrightarrow{OL} + \overrightarrow{OM} + \overrightarrow{ON}$.

9. (a) Show that the figure formed by joining successive midpoints of any quadrilateral (plane or skew) is a parallelogram.

(b) Show that if the diagonals of a quadrilateral bisect each other, then it is a parallelogram.

10. Show that the line that joins one vertex of a parallelogram to the midpoint of an opposite side divides the diagonal in the ratio 2:1.

11. Show that the lines joining the midpoints of the opposite edges of a tetrahedron are concurrent and bisect one another.

12. The line segment DE is drawn parallel to the base AB of the triangle ABC and is included between its sides. If the lines AE, BD meet at P, show that the line CP bisects AB.

13. (a) If **a**, **b**, **c**, **d** represent the consecutive sides of a quadrilateral, show that a necessary and sufficient condition that the quadrilateral be a parallelogram is that $\mathbf{a} + \mathbf{c} = \mathbf{0}$ and show that this implies that $\mathbf{b} + \mathbf{d} = \mathbf{0}$.

(b) Given the distinct points O, A, B, C, D. Let $\mathbf{a} = \overrightarrow{OA}$, $\mathbf{b} = \overrightarrow{OB}$, $\mathbf{c} = \overrightarrow{OC}$, $\mathbf{d} = \overrightarrow{OD}$. Show that if $\mathbf{b} - \mathbf{a} = \mathbf{c} - \mathbf{d}$, then $ABCD$ is a parallelogram.

14. (a) Show that the angle bisectors of any triangle are concurrent. (*Hint:* The sum of unit vectors along two sides lies along the bisector of the included angle.)

(b) Show that if O is a point in space and ABC is a triangle with sides of length a, b, c, then $a\overrightarrow{OA} + b\overrightarrow{OB} + c\overrightarrow{OC} = (a + b + c)\overrightarrow{OD}$, where D is the center of the inscribed circle. (The center of the inscribed circle is the point of intersection of the angle bisectors of the triangle.)

(c) Show that if $|\overrightarrow{AB}| = |\overrightarrow{AC}|$, then a point P lies on the bisector of the angle BAC if and only if for any point Q in space there exists a scalar h such that $\overrightarrow{QP} = \overrightarrow{QA} + h(\overrightarrow{AB} + \overrightarrow{AC})$.

15. (a) Let O, A, B be three distinct points and let M be the midpoint of AB. Let $\mathbf{a} = \overrightarrow{OA}$, $\mathbf{b} = \overrightarrow{OB}$, $\mathbf{m} = \overrightarrow{OM}$. Show that $\mathbf{m} = \frac{1}{2}(\mathbf{a} + \mathbf{b})$.

(b) Show that a necessary and sufficient condition that the terminal points of any three vectors **a**, **b**, **c**, with common initial point O on a straight line, is that nonzero scalars h, k, l exist such that $h + k + l = 1$ and $h\mathbf{a} + k\mathbf{b} + l\mathbf{c} = \mathbf{0}$. Show that (a) is a special case of this.

(c) Let **a** and **b** be any two fixed vectors having a common initial point O. Let L be the line passing through the terminal points of **a** and **b**. Show that the vector equation of L is $\mathbf{x} = m\mathbf{a} + n\mathbf{b}$, where **x** is any vector whose initial point is O and whose terminal point is on L and $m + n = 1$.

16. (a) If the vectors **a**, **b**, **c**, **d** have a common initial point, find a necessary and sufficient condition that their terminal points be coplanar.

(b) Show that a vector cannot be represented as a linear combination of two vectors that are not in the plane of that vector.

17. If A and B are two distinct fixed points in space, determine the set of points P that satisfies each of the following equations:

(a) $|\overrightarrow{AP}| = |\overrightarrow{BP}|$; (b) $|\overrightarrow{AP}| + |\overrightarrow{BP}| = 2|\overrightarrow{AB}|$; (c) $|\overrightarrow{AP}| - |\overrightarrow{BP}| = 2|\overrightarrow{AB}|$; (d) $|\overrightarrow{AP}| + |\overrightarrow{BP}| = |\overrightarrow{AB}|$; (e) $|\overrightarrow{AB}| + |\overrightarrow{BP}| = |\overrightarrow{AP}|$.

18. Let n particles with masses $m_1, m_2, \cdots, m_n$ be located at points $A_1, A_2, \cdots, A_n$, respectively. A centroid of the system of particles is any point P such that $m_1\overrightarrow{PA_1} + m_2\overrightarrow{PA_2} + \cdots + m_n\overrightarrow{PA_n} = \mathbf{0}$. Show that P exists and is unique; and if O is any point,

$$\overrightarrow{OP} = \frac{m_1\overrightarrow{OA_1} + m_2\overrightarrow{OA_2} + \cdots + m_n\overrightarrow{OA_n}}{m_1 + m_2 + \cdots + m_n}$$

19. Lines drawn through a point P and the vertices A, B, C, D of a tetrahedron cut the planes of the opposite faces at A', B', C', D'. Show that

$$\frac{PA'}{PA} + \frac{PB'}{PB} + \frac{PC'}{PC} + \frac{PD'}{PD} = -1.$$

20. A set of vectors $\mathbf{a}_1, \mathbf{a}_2, \cdots, \mathbf{a}_n$ is said to be **linearly independent** if, whenever $h_1\mathbf{a}_1 + h_2\mathbf{a}_2 + \cdots + h_n\mathbf{a}_n = \mathbf{0}$, it necessarily follows that $h_1 = h_2 = \cdots = h_n = 0$. A set of vectors that is not linearly independent is **linearly dependent.** Show that

(a) If n vectors are linearly independent, then any subset of these vectors is linearly independent.

(b) If a subset of n vectors is linearly dependent, then the n vectors are linearly dependent.

(c) Any set of vectors containing the zero vector is linearly dependent.

(d) If n vectors are linearly dependent, $n > 1$, then at least one of the vectors is a linear combination of the remaining vectors.

(e) If $\mathbf{a}_1, \mathbf{a}_2, \cdots, \mathbf{a}_n$ are linearly independent, but $\mathbf{a}_1, \mathbf{a}_2, \cdots, \mathbf{a}_n, \mathbf{a}_{n+1}$ are linearly dependent, then $\mathbf{a}_{n+1}$ is a linear combination of $\mathbf{a}_1, \mathbf{a}_2, \cdots, \mathbf{a}_n$.

7. Angles, components, and projections. Given two vectors, let **a** and **b** be equal to these vectors and such that they have a common initial point. Then the **angle** between the given vectors is the angle θ between **a** and **b**, where $0 \leq \theta \leq \pi$. It is often convenient to assign a direction to θ, and we shall then say it is the angle from **a** to **b**.

For the vectors **a** and **b** with common initial point, we define the **component** of **a** along **b** as the scalar $a \cos \theta$, where θ is the angle between **a** and **b**. We denote the component of **a** along **b** as $\text{comp}_b\, \mathbf{a}$. Hence,

$$\text{comp}_b\, \mathbf{a} = a \cos \theta.$$

We note that $\text{comp}_b\, \mathbf{a} > 0$, if $0 \leq \theta < \pi/2$; and $\text{comp}_b\, \mathbf{a} < 0$ if $\pi/2 < \theta \leq \pi$, as illustrated in Fig. 10.

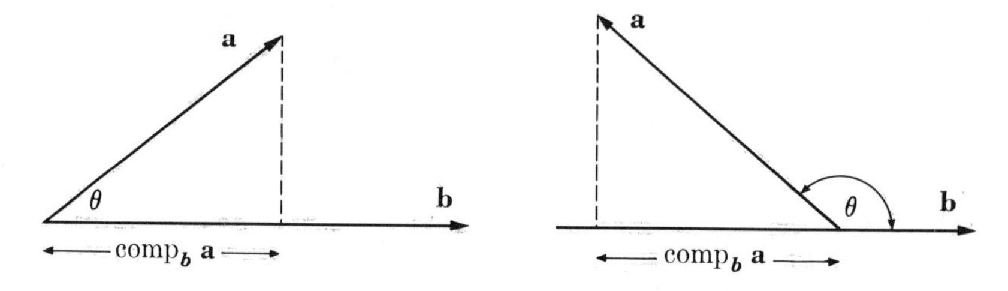

Fig. 10. Components of a vector

Of particular significance is the

Distributive law for components:

$$\text{comp}_a\, (\mathbf{b} + \mathbf{c}) = \text{comp}_a\, \mathbf{b} + \text{comp}_a\, \mathbf{c},$$

which is illustrated in Fig. 11.

Given the vectors **a** and **b** with common initial point, we define the **projection** of **a** onto **b** as the vector

$$\frac{a \cos \theta}{b}\, \mathbf{b},$$

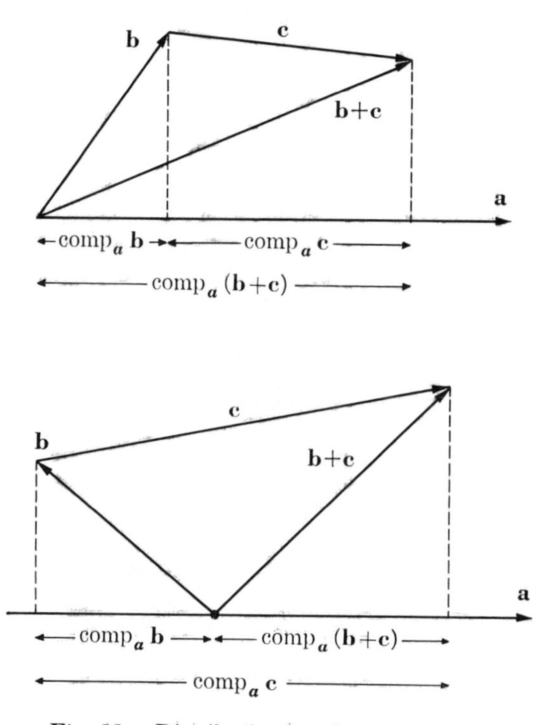

Fig. 11. Distributive law for components

where θ is the angle between **a** and **b**. This projection or projected vector is in the direction of **b** if $0 \leq \theta < \pi/2$, and in the opposite direction of **b**

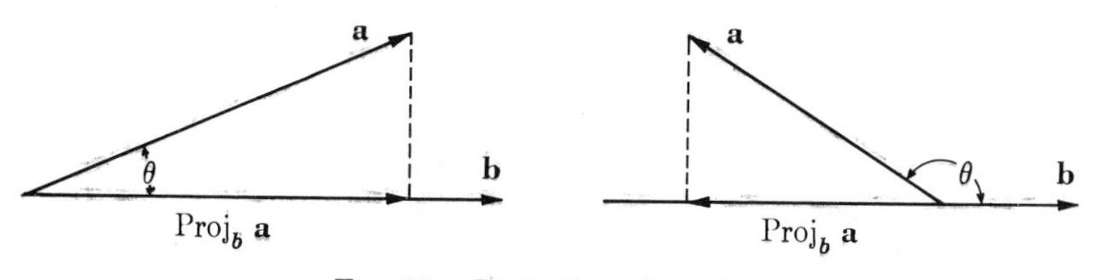

Fig. 12. Projection of a vector

if $\pi/2 < \theta \leq \pi$, as illustrated in Fig. 12. We denote the projection of **a** onto **b** as $\text{proj}_b\, \mathbf{a}$. If $\theta = \pi/2$, $\text{proj}_b\, \mathbf{a} = \mathbf{0}$. We have the

Distributive law for projections:

$$\text{proj}_a\, (\mathbf{b} + \mathbf{c}) = \text{proj}_a\, \mathbf{b} + \text{proj}_a\, \mathbf{c},$$

which the student should verify geometrically, taking into account all the possible cases.

8. The scalar or dot product. Although work is a scalar, it involves two vectors: force and displacement. If a force $\mathbf{F}$ acts on a particle in the same direction as its displacement $\mathbf{r}$, then we define the work done by the force as $W = Fr$. If $\mathbf{F}$ acts on the particle so that the angle between $\mathbf{F}$ and $\mathbf{r}$ is θ, then we define the work done by $\mathbf{F}$ as the product of r and the component of $\mathbf{F}$ along $\mathbf{r}$; i.e., $W = r \operatorname{comp}_{\mathbf{r}} \mathbf{F} = Fr \cos \theta$. This is a type of product that suggests a generalization to a product of any two vectors.

Let $\mathbf{a}$ and $\mathbf{b}$ be vectors equal to any two given vectors but having the same initial point. Let θ be the angle between $\mathbf{a}$ and $\mathbf{b}$. We define the **scalar product** of $\mathbf{a}$ and $\mathbf{b}$ to be $ab \cos \theta$. The term scalar product stems from the fact that this type of product of two vectors is a scalar. We note that since $\cos(-\theta) = \cos \theta$, it is immaterial whether θ is measured from $\mathbf{a}$ to $\mathbf{b}$ or from $\mathbf{b}$ to $\mathbf{a}$. We denote the scalar product of $\mathbf{a}$ and $\mathbf{b}$ as $\mathbf{a}\cdot\mathbf{b}$. Hence,

$$\mathbf{a}\cdot\mathbf{b} = ab \cos \theta,$$

where θ is the angle between $\mathbf{a}$ and $\mathbf{b}$. Because of this notation, the scalar product is also called the **dot product.** In obtaining the scalar product $\mathbf{a}\cdot\mathbf{b}$, we often say that "$\mathbf{a}$ is dotted with $\mathbf{b}$." The term **inner product** is also used for scalar product.

The scalar product can be interpreted in terms of components. We have

$$\mathbf{a}\cdot\mathbf{b} = a \operatorname{comp}_{\mathbf{a}} \mathbf{b} = b \operatorname{comp}_{\mathbf{b}} \mathbf{a}.$$

Note also that

$$\cos \theta = \frac{\mathbf{a}\cdot\mathbf{b}}{ab}, \qquad ab \neq 0.$$

The scalar product has the following properties:

S_1: $\mathbf{a}\cdot\mathbf{b} = \mathbf{b}\cdot\mathbf{a}$ (commutative law).
S_2: $\mathbf{a}\cdot h\mathbf{b} = h\mathbf{a}\cdot\mathbf{b} = h(\mathbf{a}\cdot\mathbf{b})$ for any scalar h.
S_3: $\mathbf{a}\cdot(\mathbf{b}+\mathbf{c}) = \mathbf{a}\cdot\mathbf{b} + \mathbf{a}\cdot\mathbf{c}$ (distributive law).

S_1 follows immediately from the definition of scalar product and the commutative law of multiplication for real numbers. S_2 follows immediately from the definition of scalar product. S_3 can be expressed in terms of components as $a \operatorname{comp}_{\mathbf{a}} (\mathbf{b}+\mathbf{c}) = a \operatorname{comp}_{\mathbf{a}} \mathbf{b} + a \operatorname{comp}_{\mathbf{a}} \mathbf{c}$, which follows immediately from the distributive law for components.

The student should prove that

$$(\mathbf{a}+\mathbf{b})\cdot(\mathbf{c}+\mathbf{d}) = \mathbf{a}\cdot\mathbf{c} + \mathbf{a}\cdot\mathbf{d} + \mathbf{b}\cdot\mathbf{c} + \mathbf{b}\cdot\mathbf{d}.$$

Generalize this to the scalar product of the sum of n vectors and the sum of m vectors.

We have seen an important physical interpretation of the scalar product as work; i.e., $W = \mathbf{F}\cdot\mathbf{r}$, where $\mathbf{F}$ is the force acting on a body whose displacement is $\mathbf{r}$. The scalar product also has a very important geometric interpretation. If the angle θ between $\mathbf{a}$ and $\mathbf{b}$ is a right angle, then $\cos \theta = 0$ and $\mathbf{a}\cdot\mathbf{b} = 0$. In this case, $\mathbf{a}$ and $\mathbf{b}$ are perpendicular, and we write $\mathbf{a} \perp \mathbf{b}$. With our convention regarding the zero vector, if $\mathbf{a}\cdot\mathbf{b} = 0$, then $\mathbf{a} \perp \mathbf{b}$, for if $\mathbf{a} = \mathbf{0}$, we choose the direction of $\mathbf{0}$ so that $\mathbf{0} \perp \mathbf{b}$; similarly, if $\mathbf{b} = \mathbf{0}$. Hence, we have the

Condition for perpendicularity. $\mathbf{a} \perp \mathbf{b}$ if and only if $\mathbf{a}\cdot\mathbf{b} = 0$.

If $\mathbf{a} \neq \mathbf{0}$, then $\mathbf{a}\cdot\mathbf{a} \neq 0$. Although $\mathbf{a}\cdot\mathbf{a} = a^2$, we often write $\mathbf{a}\cdot\mathbf{a} = \mathbf{a}^2$.

As applications of the scalar product, let us consider some examples.

EXAMPLE 1. Prove that an angle inscribed in a semicircle is a right angle.

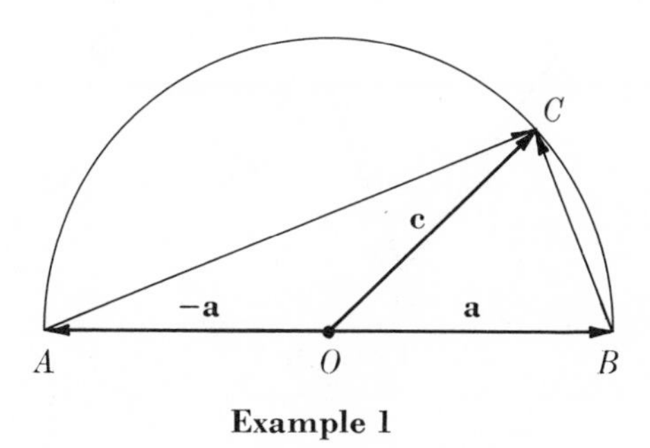

Example 1

Solution. Let ACB be any angle inscribed in a semicircle with center at O and radius r, as illustrated in the figure. Let $\overrightarrow{OB} = \mathbf{a}$. Then $\overrightarrow{OA} = -\mathbf{a}$. Let $\overrightarrow{OC} = \mathbf{c}$. Then $\overrightarrow{AC} = \mathbf{a} + \mathbf{c}$ and $\overrightarrow{BC} = \mathbf{c} - \mathbf{a}$. Now $\overrightarrow{AC}\cdot\overrightarrow{BC} = (\mathbf{a} + \mathbf{c})\cdot(\mathbf{c} - \mathbf{a}) = c^2 - a^2 = 0$, since $c^2 = a^2 = r^2$. The condition for perpendicularity is now used to complete the proof.

EXAMPLE 2. Let $\mathbf{a} = \mathbf{a}_1 + \mathbf{a}_2$, where $\mathbf{a}_1 \perp \mathbf{b}$ and $\mathbf{a}_2 \| \mathbf{b}$. Show that

$$\mathbf{a}_2 = \frac{\mathbf{a}\cdot\mathbf{b}}{b^2}\mathbf{b} \quad \text{and} \quad \mathbf{a}_1 = \mathbf{a} - \frac{\mathbf{a}\cdot\mathbf{b}}{b^2}\mathbf{b}.$$

Solution. Since $\mathbf{a}_2 \| \mathbf{b}$, there exists a scalar h such that $\mathbf{a}_2 = h\mathbf{b}$. Dotting both sides of this equation by $\mathbf{b}$ yields $h = \mathbf{a}_2\cdot\mathbf{b}/b^2$. Noting that $\mathbf{a}_1\cdot\mathbf{b} = 0$, we have that $\mathbf{a}\cdot\mathbf{b} = \mathbf{a}_2\cdot\mathbf{b}$. Hence, $h = (\mathbf{a}\cdot\mathbf{b})/b^2$ and the first required relation is established; the second follows immediately.

EXAMPLE 3. Show that the altitudes of any triangle are concurrent.

Solution. Let ABC be any triangle and O any point. Let D be the point of intersection of the altitudes CE and BG (see figure). Let $\mathbf{a} = \overrightarrow{OA}$, $\mathbf{b} = \overrightarrow{OB}$, $\mathbf{c} = \overrightarrow{OC}$, $\mathbf{d} = \overrightarrow{OD}$. The result follows from the identity

$$(\mathbf{d} - \mathbf{a})\cdot(\mathbf{b} - \mathbf{c}) + (\mathbf{d} - \mathbf{b})\cdot(\mathbf{c} - \mathbf{a}) + (\mathbf{d} - \mathbf{c})\cdot(\mathbf{a} - \mathbf{b}) = 0,$$

which is true for arbitrary vectors **a**, **b**, **c**, and which the student is invited to prove. Since CE and BG are altitudes, the last two terms on the right vanish; this means

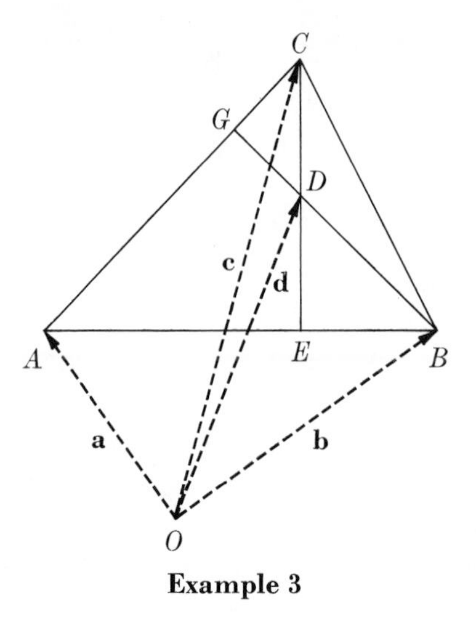

Example 3

that the first term vanishes, implying that AD is the third altitude. This example is instructive in that it indicates that a result may be obtained readily by first establishing a vector identity.

9. The vector or cross product. The scalar product of two vectors is a scalar. Now we define the product of two vectors in such a manner that this product is a vector. Let any two vectors be given; let **a** and **b** be two vectors equal to these vectors but having a common initial point. Let θ be the angle between **a** and **b**, measured from **a** to **b**. We define the **vector product** of **a** and **b** to be the vector **c** such that

(1) $|\mathbf{c}| = ab \sin \theta$.

(2) $\mathbf{c} \perp \mathbf{a}$ and $\mathbf{c} \perp \mathbf{b}$.

(3) The direction of **c** is that given by the **right-hand rule:** If the fingers of the right hand moving toward the palm of the hand indicate the rotation of **a** into **b**, then the direction of **c** is indicated by the thumb; this direction is the positive direction; the opposite direction is the negative direction. (See Fig. 13.)

We denote the vector product of **a** and **b** by $\mathbf{a} \times \mathbf{b}$. This accounts for the fact that the vector product is often called the **cross product.** We will say that the vectors **a**, **b**, **c**, in this order, constitute a **positive triple of vectors** if the direction of **c** is as indicated by the right-hand rule when **a** is rotated into **b**. We can write the definition of the vector product tersely as follows:

$$\mathbf{a} \times \mathbf{b} = ab \sin \theta \mathbf{u},$$

where θ is the angle from **a** to **b**, **u** is a unit vector such that $\mathbf{u} \perp \mathbf{a}$, $\mathbf{u} \perp \mathbf{b}$, and **a**, **b**, **u** form a positive triple of vectors.

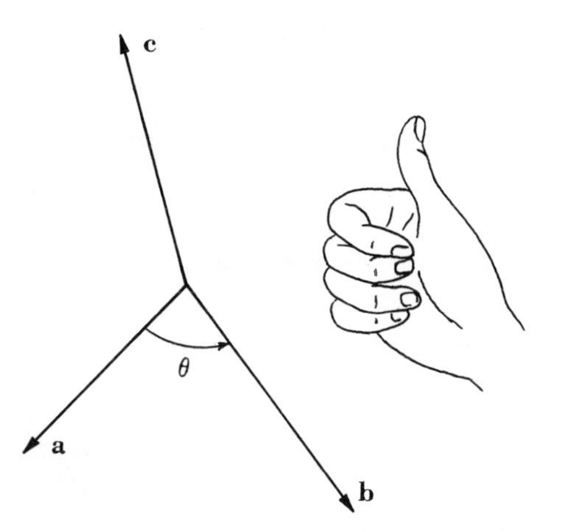

Fig. 13. The right-hand rule

We now exhibit a geometric construction for the vector product $\mathbf{a} \times \mathbf{b}$. Let M be the plane perpendicular to **a** and passing through the initial point of **a**. The construction is completed with three operations (see Fig. 14):

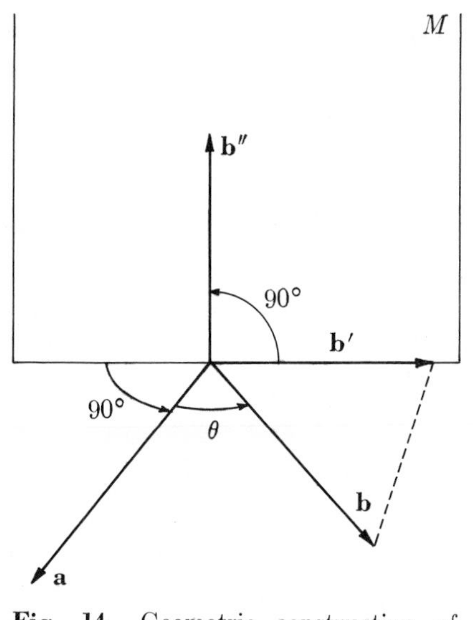

Fig. 14. Geometric construction of vector product

(1) Project $\mathbf{b}$ onto M, producing $\mathbf{b}'$.

(2) Rotate $\mathbf{b}'$ counterclockwise through a right angle in the plane M, producing $\mathbf{b}''$.

(3) Multiply $\mathbf{b}''$ by a. Note that $\mathbf{a}$, $\mathbf{b}$, $\mathbf{b}'$ are coplanar.

The student should show that this construction does indeed yield the vector product; i.e., $\mathbf{a} \times \mathbf{b} = a\mathbf{b}''$.

The vector product has the following properties:

$\mathbf{V_1}$: $\mathbf{b} \times \mathbf{a} = -(\mathbf{a} \times \mathbf{b})$ (anticommutative law).
$\mathbf{V_2}$: $h\mathbf{a} \times \mathbf{b} = \mathbf{a} \times h\mathbf{b} = h(\mathbf{a} \times \mathbf{b})$, for any scalar h.
$\mathbf{V_3}$: $\mathbf{a} \times (\mathbf{b} + \mathbf{c}) = \mathbf{a} \times \mathbf{b} + \mathbf{a} \times \mathbf{c}$ (distributive law).
$\mathbf{V_4}$: $\mathbf{a} \times \mathbf{a} = \mathbf{0}$ for any $\mathbf{a}$.
$\mathbf{V_5}$: $\mathbf{a} \times \mathbf{0} = \mathbf{0}$ for any $\mathbf{a}$.

V_1, V_2, V_4, V_5 follow immediately from the definition of vector product. To prove V_3, consider the triangle whose sides are $\mathbf{b}$, $\mathbf{c}$, $\mathbf{b} + \mathbf{c}$. Projecting this triangle onto a plane M that is perpendicular to $\mathbf{a}$ and contains its initial point (see geometric construction of the vector product) yields a triangle with sides $\mathbf{b}'$, $\mathbf{c}'$, $(\mathbf{b} + \mathbf{c})'$. Rotating this triangle about $\mathbf{a}$ as an axis, counterclockwise through an angle of 90 deg, yields another triangle with sides $\mathbf{b}''$, $\mathbf{c}''$, $(\mathbf{b} + \mathbf{c})''$. But $(\mathbf{b} + \mathbf{c})'' = \mathbf{b}'' + \mathbf{c}''$ and $a(\mathbf{b} + \mathbf{c})'' = a\mathbf{b}'' + a\mathbf{c}''$. Hence, $\mathbf{a} \times (\mathbf{b} + \mathbf{c}) = \mathbf{a} \times \mathbf{b} + \mathbf{a} \times \mathbf{c}$.

The areas of two elementary geometric figures can be expressed in terms of the vector product:

(1) Area of triangle with sides a and b and included angle θ is $\frac{1}{2}|\mathbf{a} \times \mathbf{b}|$.

(2) Area of parallelogram with adjacent sides a and b and included angle θ is $|\mathbf{a} \times \mathbf{b}|$.

(1) follows from the area formula $A = \frac{1}{2}ab \sin \theta$ and (2) follows immediately from (1).

If $\mathbf{a}||\mathbf{b}$, then $\sin \theta = 0$. Hence, $\mathbf{a} \times \mathbf{b} = \mathbf{0}$. If $\mathbf{a} \times \mathbf{b} = \mathbf{0}$, then $\mathbf{a}||\mathbf{b}$, with our convention regarding the direction of the zero vector. Therefore, we have the

Condition for parallelism. $\mathbf{a}||\mathbf{b}$ if and only if $\mathbf{a} \times \mathbf{b} = \mathbf{0}$.

The student should show that this condition for nonzero vectors is equivalent to the one we have been using; namely, for $\mathbf{a} \neq \mathbf{0}$ and $\mathbf{b} \neq \mathbf{0}$, $\mathbf{a}||\mathbf{b}$ if and only if there exists a scalar h such that $\mathbf{a} = h\mathbf{b}$.

EXERCISES

1. Prove the following identities and interpret each geometrically:
(a) $(a\mathbf{b} + b\mathbf{a})\cdot(a\mathbf{b} - b\mathbf{a}) = 0$; (b) $(\mathbf{a} - \mathbf{b}) \times (\mathbf{a} + \mathbf{b}) = 2\mathbf{a} \times \mathbf{b}$;
(c) $(\mathbf{a} + \mathbf{b})\cdot(\mathbf{a} - \mathbf{b}) = a^2 - b^2$.

2. If A, B, C, D are any four points in space, show that
(a) $\overrightarrow{AB}\cdot\overrightarrow{CD} + \overrightarrow{BC}\cdot\overrightarrow{AD} + \overrightarrow{CA}\cdot\overrightarrow{BD} = 0$.
(b) $\overrightarrow{AB} \times \overrightarrow{CD} + \overrightarrow{BC} \times \overrightarrow{AD} + \overrightarrow{CA} \times \overrightarrow{BD} = 2\overrightarrow{AB} \times \overrightarrow{CA}$.

3. (a) Let ABC be any triangle, O any point, $\mathbf{a} = \overrightarrow{OA}$, $\mathbf{b} = \overrightarrow{OB}$, $\mathbf{c} = \overrightarrow{OC}$. Show that the area of ABC is $\frac{1}{2}|\mathbf{a} \times \mathbf{b} + \mathbf{b} \times \mathbf{c} + \mathbf{c} \times \mathbf{a}|$.

(b) Prove the identity

$$(\mathbf{a} - \mathbf{d}) \times (\mathbf{b} - \mathbf{c}) + (\mathbf{b} - \mathbf{d}) \times (\mathbf{c} - \mathbf{a}) + (\mathbf{c} - \mathbf{d}) \times (\mathbf{a} - \mathbf{b}) = 2(\mathbf{a} \times \mathbf{b} + \mathbf{b} \times \mathbf{c} + \mathbf{c} \times \mathbf{a}).$$

In view of (a), what is the geometric interpretation of this identity?

4. Solve for h: $(\mathbf{a} + h\mathbf{b}) \cdot \mathbf{a} = 0$. Is there always a solution? If a solution exists, is it unique? Interpret geometrically.

5. If $a \neq 0$, are the following laws of cancellation valid for vectors?
(a) If $\mathbf{a} \cdot \mathbf{b} = \mathbf{a} \cdot \mathbf{c}$, then $\mathbf{b} = \mathbf{c}$; (b) if $\mathbf{a} \times \mathbf{b} = \mathbf{a} \times \mathbf{c}$, then $\mathbf{b} = \mathbf{c}$. Explain.

6. (a) Prove the Pythagorean theorem for the right triangle ABC:

$$(AB)^2 + (BC)^2 = (AC)^2.$$

State and prove the converse.

(b) Given any triangle ABC and any point O, let D, E, F be the midpoints of the sides of the triangle. Show that

$$(OD)^2 + (OE)^2 + (OF)^2 + (\tfrac{1}{2}BC)^2 + (\tfrac{1}{2}CA)^2 + (\tfrac{1}{2}AB)^2 = (OA)^2 + (OB)^2 + (OC)^2.$$

7. Prove that the perpendicular bisectors of the sides of any triangle are concurrent.

8. If α, β, γ are the angles of any triangle and a, b, c are the sides opposite these angles, respectively, prove

(a) The law of sines: $\dfrac{\sin \alpha}{a} = \dfrac{\sin \beta}{b} = \dfrac{\sin \gamma}{c}$.

(*Hint:* $\mathbf{a} + \mathbf{b} + \mathbf{c} = \mathbf{0}$.)

(b) The law of cosines: $c^2 = a^2 + b^2 - 2ab \cos \gamma$.

Show that the converse of the law of sines is not true. However, prove that if $\mathbf{a}$, $\mathbf{b}$, $\mathbf{c}$ are nonparallel vectors and $\mathbf{a} \times \mathbf{b} = \mathbf{b} \times \mathbf{c} = \mathbf{c} \times \mathbf{a}$, then $\mathbf{a} + \mathbf{b} + \mathbf{c} = \mathbf{0}$. Is the converse of the law of cosines true?

9. If $\mathbf{u}$ and $\mathbf{v}$ are unit vectors and θ is the angle between them, show that $\frac{1}{2}|\mathbf{u} - \mathbf{v}| = |\sin \frac{1}{2}\theta|$. [*Hint:* $|\mathbf{u} - \mathbf{v}|^2 = (\mathbf{u} - \mathbf{v}) \cdot (\mathbf{u} - \mathbf{v})$.]

10. (a) Prove: If $\mathbf{a}$, $\mathbf{b}$, $\mathbf{c}$ are mutually perpendicular vectors of equal length, then the angles between $\mathbf{a} + \mathbf{b} + \mathbf{c}$ and $\mathbf{a}$, $\mathbf{b}$, $\mathbf{c}$ are equal.

(b) Three vectors of length a, a, $a\sqrt{2}$ have the same initial point and are mutually perpendicular. Determine the length of the sum of these vectors and the angles between the vectors and their sum. *Ans.:* $2a$, $\pi/3$, $\pi/3$, $\pi/4$.

11. (a) If $\mathbf{a}$, $\mathbf{b}$, $\mathbf{c}$ are coplanar and $\mathbf{a}$ is not parallel to $\mathbf{b}$, show that

$$\mathbf{c} = \frac{\begin{vmatrix} \mathbf{c}\cdot\mathbf{a} & \mathbf{a}\cdot\mathbf{b} \\ \mathbf{c}\cdot\mathbf{b} & \mathbf{b}\cdot\mathbf{b} \end{vmatrix} \mathbf{a} + \begin{vmatrix} \mathbf{a}\cdot\mathbf{a} & \mathbf{c}\cdot\mathbf{a} \\ \mathbf{a}\cdot\mathbf{b} & \mathbf{c}\cdot\mathbf{b} \end{vmatrix} \mathbf{b}}{\begin{vmatrix} \mathbf{a}\cdot\mathbf{a} & \mathbf{a}\cdot\mathbf{b} \\ \mathbf{a}\cdot\mathbf{b} & \mathbf{b}\cdot\mathbf{b} \end{vmatrix}}.$$

Why doesn't the determinant in the denominator vanish?

(b) If $\mathbf{a}$, $\mathbf{b}$, $\mathbf{c}$ are nonparallel, noncoplanar vectors and $\mathbf{d}$ is any vector in space, express $\mathbf{d}$ as a linear combination of $\mathbf{a}$, $\mathbf{b}$, $\mathbf{c}$, analogous to the expression in (a).

12. Prove that the median to the base of an isosceles triangle is perpendicular to the base.

13. (a) Let $ABCD$ be a parallelogram. Prove that

$$(AB)^2 + (BC)^2 + (CD)^2 + (DA)^2 = (AC)^2 + (BD)^2.$$

(b) Show that the difference of the squares of the diagonals of the parallelogram in (a), $(AC)^2 - (BD)^2$, equals $4\overrightarrow{AB}\cdot\overrightarrow{BC}$.

(c) Generalize (a) to a quadrilateral by showing that

$$(AB)^2 + (BC)^2 + (CD)^2 + (DA)^2 = (AC)^2 + (BD)^2 + 4(PQ)^2,$$

where P and Q are the midpoints of its diagonals.

14. Show that parallelograms having the same base and lying between the same parallel lines are equal in area.

15. Given AB and CD as the parallel sides of a trapezoid. Show that the area of triangle MDB is one-half the area of the trapezoid, where M is the midpoint of AC.

16. Show that the area of a plane convex polygon whose vertices are the terminal points of the vectors $\mathbf{a}_1, \mathbf{a}_2, \cdots, \mathbf{a}_n$, having a common initial point, is

$$A = \frac{1}{2}\left|\sum_{i=1}^{n} \mathbf{a}_i \times \mathbf{a}_{i+1}\right|, \qquad \mathbf{a}_{n+1} = \mathbf{a}_1.$$

[*Hint:* Divide the polygon into triangles and use Exercise 3(a).]

17. (a) Show that the vector equation of a circle is $\mathbf{r}\cdot(\mathbf{r} - \mathbf{a}) = 0$, where a is the diameter and $\mathbf{r}$ is the vector (called the position vector) from one end of the diameter to any point on the circle.

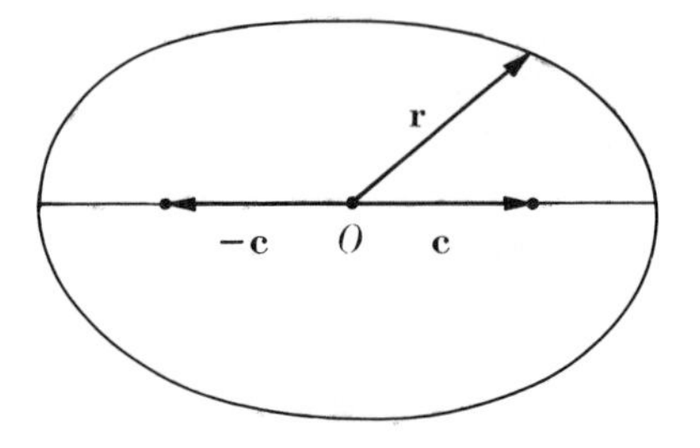

Exercise 17(b)

(b) Given an ellipse with center at O and length of major axis $2a$. The position vectors of the foci, $\mathbf{c}$ and $-\mathbf{c}$ and the position vector $\mathbf{r}$ of any point on the ellipse are indicated in the figure. Show that the equation of the ellipse is

$$a^4 - a^2(r^2 + c^2) + (\mathbf{c}\cdot\mathbf{r})^2 = 0.$$

(c) Find the vector equation of the hyperbola, the length of whose transverse axis is $2a$ and whose foci have position vectors $\mathbf{c}$ and $-\mathbf{c}$ from the center O of the hyperbola.

(d) Show that if two circles intersect, the line joining the centers is the perpendicular bisector of the line segment joining the points of intersection.

18. If O is a fixed point, AB is a given straight line, and a point Q is taken on the line OP drawn to a point P on AB, such that $\overrightarrow{OP} \cdot \overrightarrow{OQ} = h^2$, a constant, find the locus of Q.

19. (a) Show that $|\mathbf{a} \times \mathbf{b}|^2 + (\mathbf{a} \cdot \mathbf{b})^2 = a^2 b^2$.

(b) Use (a) to establish Cauchy's inequality: $|\mathbf{a} \cdot \mathbf{b}| \leq ab$. When does the equality sign hold?

(c) With the use of $|\mathbf{a} + \mathbf{b}|^2 = (\mathbf{a} + \mathbf{b}) \cdot (\mathbf{a} + \mathbf{b})$, and (b), establish the triangle inequality: $|\mathbf{a} + \mathbf{b}| \leq a + b$. When does the equality sign hold?

20. Show that

$$\text{(a)} \quad \mathbf{a} \cdot \mathbf{b} = \tfrac{1}{2}(|\mathbf{a} + \mathbf{b}|^2 - a^2 - b^2).$$
$$\text{(b)} \quad \mathbf{a} \cdot \mathbf{b} = \tfrac{1}{4}(|\mathbf{a} + \mathbf{b}|^2 - |\mathbf{a} - \mathbf{b}|^2).$$

When $\mathbf{a} \cdot \mathbf{b} = 0$, what geometric theorems do these identities establish?

21. If $(\mathbf{c} - \tfrac{1}{2}\mathbf{a}) \cdot \mathbf{a} = (\mathbf{c} - \tfrac{1}{2}\mathbf{b}) \cdot \mathbf{b} = 0$, prove that $\mathbf{a} - \mathbf{b}$ is perpendicular to $\mathbf{c} - \tfrac{1}{2}(\mathbf{a} + \mathbf{b})$, and interpret the result geometrically.

22. The vertices of a regular tetrahedron are O, A, B, C. Prove that the vector $\overrightarrow{OA} + \overrightarrow{OB} + \overrightarrow{OC}$ is perpendicular to the plane ABC.

23. In triangle ABC, $AB = AC$, D is the midpoint of BC, E is the foot of the perpendicular from D on AC, and F is the midpoint of DE. Prove that $\overrightarrow{AF} \perp \overrightarrow{BE}$.

24. (a) Prove the generalized distributive law:

$$\mathbf{a} \cdot (\mathbf{b}_1 + \mathbf{b}_2 + \cdots + \mathbf{b}_n) = \mathbf{a} \cdot \mathbf{b}_1 + \mathbf{a} \cdot \mathbf{b}_2 + \cdots + \mathbf{a} \cdot \mathbf{b}_n.$$

(b) Show that the work done by a constant force acting on a particle moving from A to B is the same for all broken lines joining A to B.

25. (a) If P is the centroid of a system of particles located at $A_1, A_2, \cdots, A_n$ with masses $m_1, m_2, \cdots, m_n$ (see p. 15, Exercise 18), prove the theorems of Lagrange:

$$(1) \qquad \sum_{i=1}^{n} m_i (OA_i)^2 = m(OP)^2 + \sum_{i=1}^{n} m_i (PA_i)^2$$

$$(2) \qquad \sum_{i=1}^{n} \sum_{j=1}^{n} m_i m_j (A_i A_j)^2 = m \sum_{i=1}^{n} m_i (PA_i)^2,$$

where

$$m = \sum_{i=1}^{n} m_i$$

and O is any point.

(b) If $ABCD$ is a square, show that $(OA)^2 + (OC)^2 = (OB)^2 + (CD)^2$ for any O. Generalize.

(c) If r is the radius of a sphere circumscribed about a regular tetrahedron of side a, show that $r^2 = 3a^2/8$.

10. The scalar triple product. Given any three vectors, let $\mathbf{a}$, $\mathbf{b}$, $\mathbf{c}$ be equal to them and such that they have a common initial point. We define the **scalar triple product** of the three given vectors as the scalar $\mathbf{a} \cdot \mathbf{b} \times \mathbf{c}$. There is no ambiguity in writing the scalar triple product as $\mathbf{a} \cdot \mathbf{b} \times \mathbf{c}$

rather than $\mathbf{a}\cdot(\mathbf{b}\times\mathbf{c})$, for $(\mathbf{a}\cdot\mathbf{b})\times\mathbf{c}$ is undefined, since it indicates the vector product of a scalar and a vector that is undefined.

We now give a geometric interpretation of the scalar triple product. Let $\mathbf{a}$, $\mathbf{b}$, $\mathbf{c}$ represent three edges of a parallelepiped P having a common vertex with base determined by $\mathbf{b}$ and $\mathbf{c}$. We can write

$$\mathbf{a}\cdot\mathbf{b}\times\mathbf{c} = |\mathbf{b}\times\mathbf{c}|\ \text{comp}_{\mathbf{b}\times\mathbf{c}}\ \mathbf{a}. \tag{1}$$

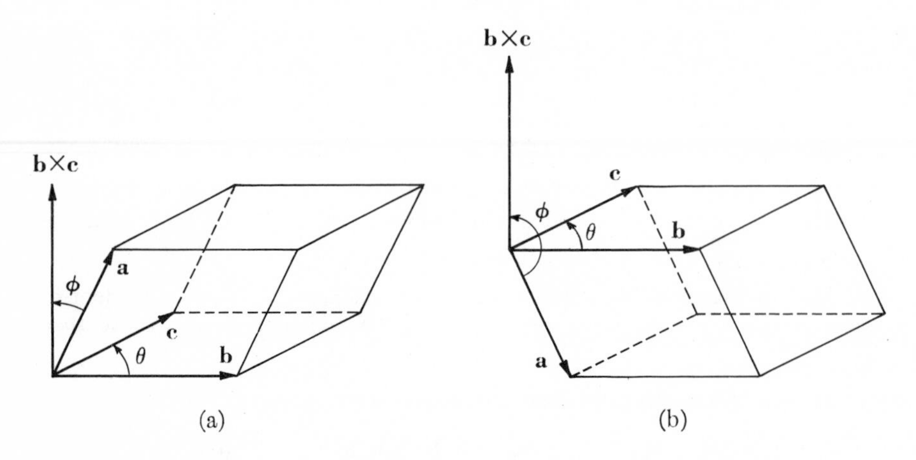

Fig. 15. Volume of a parallepiped: (a) $0 < \phi \leq \pi/2$; (b) $\pi/2 < \phi < \pi$

Let ϕ be the angle between $\mathbf{a}$ and $\mathbf{b}\times\mathbf{c}$ (see Fig. 15). If h is the length of the altitude of P, then

$$h = \begin{cases} \text{comp}_{\mathbf{b}\times\mathbf{c}}\ \mathbf{a}, & \text{if } 0 < \phi \leq \pi/2 \\ -\text{comp}_{\mathbf{b}\times\mathbf{c}}\ \mathbf{a}, & \text{if } \pi/2 < \phi < \pi, \end{cases}$$

or

$$h = |\text{comp}_{\mathbf{b}\times\mathbf{c}}\ \mathbf{a}|. \tag{2}$$

Let V be the volume of P. Then $V = Bh$, where B is the area of the base of P. But $B = |\mathbf{b}\times\mathbf{c}|$. Hence (1) and (2) yield

$$V = |\mathbf{a}\cdot\mathbf{b}\times\mathbf{c}|.$$

(Determine the parallelepiped of maximum volume with edges $\mathbf{a}$, $\mathbf{b}$, $\mathbf{c}$ having a common vertex.)

It is readily seen that when $0 < \phi < \pi/2$, $\mathbf{a}$, $\mathbf{b}$, $\mathbf{c}$ form a positive triple. Hence, we have the

Criterion for a positive triple. $\mathbf{a}$, $\mathbf{b}$, $\mathbf{c}$ form a positive triple if and only if $\mathbf{a}\cdot\mathbf{b}\times\mathbf{c} > 0$.

If $\mathbf{a}$, $\mathbf{b}$, $\mathbf{c}$ are coplanar, the altitude of the parallelepiped is zero, and conversely. Hence, we have the

Condition for coplanarity. $\mathbf{a}$, $\mathbf{b}$, $\mathbf{c}$ are coplanar if and only if $\mathbf{a} \cdot \mathbf{b} \times \mathbf{c} = 0$.

An immediate result is that *if any two vectors in a scalar triple product are equal, then that product is zero;* i.e.,

$$\mathbf{a} \cdot \mathbf{a} \times \mathbf{c} = 0, \quad \mathbf{a} \cdot \mathbf{b} \times \mathbf{b} = 0, \quad \mathbf{c} \cdot \mathbf{b} \times \mathbf{c} = 0.$$

We now prove the

Fundamental identity for the scalar triple product.

$\mathbf{a} \cdot \mathbf{b} \times \mathbf{c} = \mathbf{a} \times \mathbf{b} \cdot \mathbf{c}$, for any vectors $\mathbf{a}$, $\mathbf{b}$, $\mathbf{c}$.

Proof. Starting with the identity $(\mathbf{a} + \mathbf{c}) \cdot (\mathbf{a} + \mathbf{c}) \times \mathbf{b} = 0$, we have

$$(\mathbf{a} + \mathbf{c}) \cdot [(\mathbf{a} \times \mathbf{b}) + (\mathbf{c} \times \mathbf{b})] = \mathbf{a} \cdot \mathbf{a} \times \mathbf{b} + \mathbf{c} \cdot \mathbf{a} \times \mathbf{b} + \mathbf{a} \cdot \mathbf{c} \times \mathbf{b} + \mathbf{c} \cdot \mathbf{c} \times \mathbf{b} = 0.$$

Hence,

$$\mathbf{c} \cdot \mathbf{a} \times \mathbf{b} + \mathbf{a} \cdot \mathbf{c} \times \mathbf{b} = 0$$

or

$$\mathbf{c} \cdot \mathbf{a} \times \mathbf{b} = -\mathbf{a} \cdot \mathbf{c} \times \mathbf{b} = \mathbf{a} \cdot \mathbf{b} \times \mathbf{c}.$$

But $\mathbf{c} \cdot \mathbf{a} \times \mathbf{b} = \mathbf{a} \times \mathbf{b} \cdot \mathbf{c}$, and we have the result. The student should justify every step in this proof.

This fundamental identity is commonly expressed by saying that *in a scalar triple product, we can interchange dot and cross without changing its value.* Since the position of the dot and cross in the scalar triple product is immaterial, we often write

$$\mathbf{a} \cdot \mathbf{b} \times \mathbf{c} = (\mathbf{a}\,\mathbf{b}\,\mathbf{c}).$$

The question arises as to how the scalar triple product is affected if we rearrange the order of the vectors $\mathbf{a}$, $\mathbf{b}$, $\mathbf{c}$. We have the following results:

$$(\mathbf{a}\,\mathbf{b}\,\mathbf{c}) = (\mathbf{b}\,\mathbf{c}\,\mathbf{a}) = (\mathbf{c}\,\mathbf{a}\,\mathbf{b}) \tag{1}$$

$$(\mathbf{a}\,\mathbf{b}\,\mathbf{c}) = -(\mathbf{a}\,\mathbf{c}\,\mathbf{b}) = -(\mathbf{b}\,\mathbf{a}\,\mathbf{c}) = -(\mathbf{c}\,\mathbf{b}\,\mathbf{a}). \tag{2}$$

The first equation in (1) follows, since

$$(\mathbf{a}\,\mathbf{b}\,\mathbf{c}) = \mathbf{a} \cdot \mathbf{b} \times \mathbf{c} = \mathbf{b} \times \mathbf{c} \cdot \mathbf{a} = (\mathbf{b}\,\mathbf{c}\,\mathbf{a}),$$

using the commutative law for the scalar product. The second equation in (1) is proved similarly. The first equation in (2) follows, since

$$(\mathbf{a}\,\mathbf{b}\,\mathbf{c}) = \mathbf{a} \cdot \mathbf{b} \times \mathbf{c} = -\mathbf{a} \cdot \mathbf{c} \times \mathbf{b} = -(\mathbf{a}\,\mathbf{c}\,\mathbf{b}),$$

using the anticommutative law for the vector product. The other equations in (2) are proved similarly.

We now consider a scheme for readily remembering (1) and (2). Note in (2) that $(\mathbf{a}\,\mathbf{c}\,\mathbf{b})$, $(\mathbf{b}\,\mathbf{a}\,\mathbf{c})$, $(\mathbf{c}\,\mathbf{b}\,\mathbf{a})$ differ from $(\mathbf{a}\,\mathbf{b}\,\mathbf{c})$ in that $\mathbf{b}$ and $\mathbf{c}$, $\mathbf{a}$ and $\mathbf{b}$, and $\mathbf{a}$ and $\mathbf{c}$ are interchanged, respectively; (2) then indicates that if we interchange two vectors in $(\mathbf{a}\,\mathbf{b}\,\mathbf{c})$ we merely change its sign. Also note in (1) that $(\mathbf{b}\,\mathbf{c}\,\mathbf{a})$ is obtained from $(\mathbf{a}\,\mathbf{b}\,\mathbf{c})$ by interchanging $\mathbf{a}$ and $\mathbf{b}$ and then interchanging $\mathbf{c}$ and $\mathbf{a}$—two interchanges; $(\mathbf{c}\ \mathbf{a}\ \mathbf{b})$ can be obtained similarly from $(\mathbf{a}\ \mathbf{b}\ \mathbf{c})$. Therefore, we have the following statement, which is equivalent to (1) and (2):

If in a scalar triple product we perform an odd number of interchanges of vectors, its sign is changed; if we perform an even number of interchanges of vectors, it remains the same.

11. The vector triple product. Given any three vectors, let $\mathbf{a}$, $\mathbf{b}$, $\mathbf{c}$ be equal to them and such that they all have a common initial point. We define the vector triple product of the three given vectors as the vector

$$\mathbf{a} \times (\mathbf{b} \times \mathbf{c}).$$

Here, the parentheses are required; it will be shown later that, in general, $\mathbf{a} \times (\mathbf{b} \times \mathbf{c}) \neq (\mathbf{a} \times \mathbf{b}) \times \mathbf{c}$; i.e., the associative law is not valid for the vector product.

We now prove the

Fundamental identity for the vector triple product.

$$\mathbf{a} \times (\mathbf{b} \times \mathbf{c}) = (\mathbf{a}\cdot\mathbf{c})\mathbf{b} - (\mathbf{a}\cdot\mathbf{b})\mathbf{c}.$$

Proof. If any one of the vectors $\mathbf{a}$, $\mathbf{b}$, $\mathbf{c}$ is $\mathbf{0}$, then the identity is trivially true. If $\mathbf{b} \| \mathbf{c}$, then it is readily seen that both sides of the identity are $\mathbf{0}$. Therefore, let us assume that $\mathbf{a}$, $\mathbf{b}$, $\mathbf{c}$ are nonzero vectors and $\mathbf{b}$ and $\mathbf{c}$ are nonparallel. The vectors $\mathbf{b}$, $\mathbf{c}$, $\mathbf{a} \times (\mathbf{b} \times \mathbf{c})$ are coplanar, since their scalar triple product is zero. (Can you supply a geometric proof of this fact?) Hence, there exist scalars h and k such that

$$\mathbf{a} \times (\mathbf{b} \times \mathbf{c}) = h\mathbf{b} - k\mathbf{c}.$$

We dot both sides with $\mathbf{a}$ to obtain

$$h(\mathbf{a}\cdot\mathbf{b}) - k(\mathbf{a}\cdot\mathbf{c}) = \mathbf{a}\cdot[\mathbf{a} \times (\mathbf{b} \times \mathbf{c})] = 0.$$

Now, if $\mathbf{a}\cdot\mathbf{b} = 0$, $\mathbf{a} \perp \mathbf{b}$. But $\mathbf{a} \perp \mathbf{a} \times (\mathbf{b} \times \mathbf{c})$, and hence $\mathbf{a}$ is perpendicular to the plane of $\mathbf{b}$ and $\mathbf{c}$; hence, $\mathbf{a} \| \mathbf{b} \times \mathbf{c}$ or $\mathbf{a} \times (\mathbf{b} \times \mathbf{c}) = \mathbf{0}$ and $\mathbf{a}\cdot\mathbf{c} = 0$ and the identity is trivially true. Hence, we can assume $\mathbf{a}\cdot\mathbf{b} \neq 0$ and $\mathbf{a}\cdot\mathbf{c} \neq 0$. Then

$$\frac{h}{\mathbf{a}\cdot\mathbf{c}} = \frac{k}{\mathbf{a}\cdot\mathbf{b}} = \lambda$$

and we have

$$\mathbf{a} \times (\mathbf{b} \times \mathbf{c}) = \lambda[(\mathbf{a}\cdot\mathbf{c})\mathbf{b} - (\mathbf{a}\cdot\mathbf{b})\mathbf{c}].$$

To determine λ, we dot both sides with a vector $\mathbf{d}$ such that $\mathbf{b}$, $\mathbf{c}$, $\mathbf{d}$ are coplanar, $\mathbf{d} \perp \mathbf{c}$, and $\mathbf{d}$, $\mathbf{c}$, $\mathbf{b} \times \mathbf{c}$ form a positive triple (see figure). Since $\mathbf{c}\cdot\mathbf{d} = 0$,

$$\lambda(\mathbf{a}\cdot\mathbf{c})(\mathbf{b}\cdot\mathbf{d}) = [\mathbf{a} \times (\mathbf{b} \times \mathbf{c})]\cdot\mathbf{d} = \mathbf{a}\cdot[(\mathbf{b} \times \mathbf{c}) \times \mathbf{d}]. \tag{1}$$

Now $(\mathbf{b} \times \mathbf{c}) \times \mathbf{d}$ is coplanar with $\mathbf{b}$ and $\mathbf{c}$ and perpendicular to $\mathbf{d}$; hence,

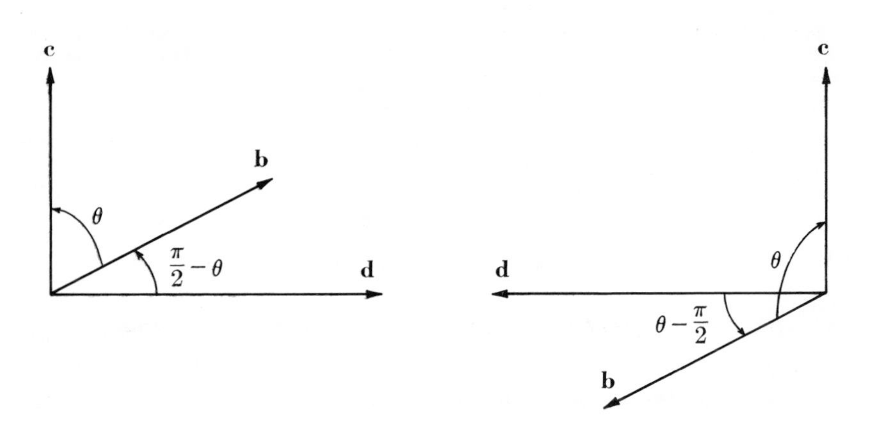

it is parallel to $\mathbf{c}$ because $\mathbf{d} \perp \mathbf{c}$ and is in the same direction as $\mathbf{c}$, since $\mathbf{d}, \mathbf{c}, \mathbf{b} \times \mathbf{c}$ form a positive triple. Therefore, there exists a scalar $r > 0$ such that

$$(\mathbf{b} \times \mathbf{c}) \times \mathbf{d} = r\mathbf{c}.$$

Then, if θ is the angle between $\mathbf{b}$ and $\mathbf{c}$,

$$rc = |(\mathbf{b} \times \mathbf{c}) \times \mathbf{d}| = bcd \sin \theta,$$

or

$$r = bd \sin \theta = bd \cos \left(\frac{\pi}{2} - \theta\right) = \mathbf{b} \cdot \mathbf{d},$$

and

$$(\mathbf{b} \times \mathbf{c}) \times \mathbf{d} = (\mathbf{b} \cdot \mathbf{d})\mathbf{c}. \tag{2}$$

Now (1) and (2) immediately yield $\lambda = 1$.

The fundamental identity indicates that the vector triple product $\mathbf{a} \times (\mathbf{b} \times \mathbf{c})$ can be expressed as a linear combination of $\mathbf{b}$ and $\mathbf{c}$, thus reducing it to the sum of two vectors. The student should prove that

$$(\mathbf{a} \times \mathbf{b}) \times \mathbf{c} = (\mathbf{a} \cdot \mathbf{c})\mathbf{b} - (\mathbf{b} \cdot \mathbf{c})\mathbf{a}.$$

Then it is clear that $(\mathbf{a} \times \mathbf{b}) \times \mathbf{c} \neq \mathbf{a} \times (\mathbf{b} \times \mathbf{c})$. The identities

$$\mathbf{a} \times (\mathbf{b} \times \mathbf{c}) = (\mathbf{a} \cdot \mathbf{c})\mathbf{b} - (\mathbf{a} \cdot \mathbf{b})\mathbf{c}$$
$$(\mathbf{a} \times \mathbf{b}) \times \mathbf{c} = (\mathbf{a} \cdot \mathbf{c})\mathbf{b} - (\mathbf{b} \cdot \mathbf{c})\mathbf{a}$$

are easily remembered if we note the rule: *The vector triple product is equal to the middle vector times the scalar product of the remaining vectors minus the other vector in the parentheses times the scalar product of the remaining vectors.*

EXAMPLE. Show that if $\mathbf{a} \neq \mathbf{0}$ and both conditions (1) $\mathbf{a} \cdot \mathbf{b} = \mathbf{a} \cdot \mathbf{c}$ and (2) $\mathbf{a} \times \mathbf{b} = \mathbf{a} \times \mathbf{c}$ hold simultaneously, then $\mathbf{b} = \mathbf{c}$, but if only one of these conditions holds, then $\mathbf{b} \neq \mathbf{c}$ necessarily.

Solution. We cross both sides of (2) by $\mathbf{a}$ so that $\mathbf{a} \times (\mathbf{a} \times \mathbf{b}) = \mathbf{a} \times (\mathbf{a} \times \mathbf{c})$ or $(\mathbf{a} \cdot \mathbf{b})\mathbf{a} - (\mathbf{a} \cdot \mathbf{a})\mathbf{b} = (\mathbf{a} \cdot \mathbf{c})\mathbf{a} - (\mathbf{a} \cdot \mathbf{a})\mathbf{c}$. Using (1), $(\mathbf{a} \cdot \mathbf{a})\mathbf{b} = (\mathbf{a} \cdot \mathbf{a})\mathbf{c}$ or $\mathbf{b} = \mathbf{c}$.

If (1) holds and (2) does not hold, assume $\mathbf{b} = \mathbf{c}$, and cross both sides by $\mathbf{a}$, thus arriving at a contradiction. The proof is similar if (1) does not hold and (2) holds.

Once the scalar triple product and the vector triple product have been defined, more complex products can be simplified by the use of them. Two of frequent occurrence are

(1) $$(\mathbf{a} \times \mathbf{b}) \times (\mathbf{c} \times \mathbf{d}) = (\mathbf{a}\,\mathbf{b}\,\mathbf{d})\mathbf{c} - (\mathbf{a}\,\mathbf{b}\,\mathbf{c})\mathbf{d}.$$

(2) $$(\mathbf{a} \times \mathbf{b}) \cdot (\mathbf{c} \times \mathbf{d}) = (\mathbf{a} \cdot \mathbf{c})(\mathbf{b} \cdot \mathbf{d}) - (\mathbf{b} \cdot \mathbf{c})(\mathbf{a} \cdot \mathbf{d}).$$

(Lagrange's identity.)

(1) is established by considering the vector triple product of $\mathbf{a} \times \mathbf{b}$, $\mathbf{c}$, $\mathbf{d}$; (2) is found by noting that $(\mathbf{a} \times \mathbf{b}) \cdot (\mathbf{c} \times \mathbf{d}) = \mathbf{a} \cdot [\mathbf{b} \times (\mathbf{c} \times \mathbf{d})]$. Can you devise schemes for readily remembering these identities?

EXERCISES

1. Show that

(a) $(\mathbf{a} + \mathbf{b}) \cdot (\mathbf{a} \times \mathbf{c}) \times (\mathbf{a} + \mathbf{b}) = 0$.

(b) $\mathbf{a} \times [\mathbf{a} \times (\mathbf{a} \times \mathbf{b})] = (\mathbf{a} \cdot \mathbf{a})(\mathbf{b} \times \mathbf{a})$.

(c) $(\mathbf{a} + \mathbf{b}) \cdot (\mathbf{b} + \mathbf{c}) \times (\mathbf{c} + \mathbf{a}) = 2(\mathbf{a}\,\mathbf{b}\,\mathbf{c})$.

(d) $\mathbf{a} \times (\mathbf{b} \times \mathbf{c}) + \mathbf{b} \times (\mathbf{c} \times \mathbf{a}) + \mathbf{c} \times (\mathbf{a} \times \mathbf{b}) = \mathbf{0}$.

(e) $\mathbf{d} \times (\mathbf{a} \times \mathbf{b}) \cdot (\mathbf{a} \times \mathbf{c}) = (\mathbf{a} \cdot \mathbf{d})(\mathbf{a}\,\mathbf{b}\,\mathbf{c})$.

(f) $|\mathbf{a} \times \mathbf{b}|^2 = \begin{vmatrix} \mathbf{a} \cdot \mathbf{a} & \mathbf{a} \cdot \mathbf{b} \\ \mathbf{a} \cdot \mathbf{b} & \mathbf{b} \cdot \mathbf{b} \end{vmatrix}$.

(g) $(\mathbf{a} \times \mathbf{b}) \cdot (\mathbf{c} \times \mathbf{d}) + (\mathbf{b} \times \mathbf{c}) \cdot (\mathbf{a} \times \mathbf{d}) + (\mathbf{c} \times \mathbf{a}) \cdot (\mathbf{b} \times \mathbf{d}) = 0$.

(h) $$\begin{aligned}(\mathbf{a} \times \mathbf{b})(\mathbf{c} \times \mathbf{d})(\mathbf{e} \times \mathbf{f}) &= (\mathbf{a}\,\mathbf{b}\,\mathbf{d})(\mathbf{c}\,\mathbf{e}\,\mathbf{f}) - (\mathbf{a}\,\mathbf{b}\,\mathbf{c})(\mathbf{d}\,\mathbf{e}\,\mathbf{f}) \\ &= (\mathbf{a}\,\mathbf{b}\,\mathbf{e})(\mathbf{f}\,\mathbf{c}\,\mathbf{d}) - (\mathbf{a}\,\mathbf{b}\,\mathbf{f})(\mathbf{e}\,\mathbf{c}\,\mathbf{d}) \\ &= (\mathbf{c}\,\mathbf{d}\,\mathbf{a})(\mathbf{b}\,\mathbf{e}\,\mathbf{f}) - (\mathbf{c}\,\mathbf{d}\,\mathbf{b})(\mathbf{a}\,\mathbf{e}\,\mathbf{f}).\end{aligned}$$

(i) $$\begin{aligned}(\mathbf{a} \times \mathbf{b} \quad \mathbf{c} \times \mathbf{d} \quad \mathbf{e} \times \mathbf{f}) &+ (\mathbf{a} \times \mathbf{d} \quad \mathbf{c} \times \mathbf{f} \quad \mathbf{e} \times \mathbf{b}) \\ &+ (\mathbf{a} \times \mathbf{f} \quad \mathbf{c} \times \mathbf{b} \quad \mathbf{e} \times \mathbf{d}) = 0.\end{aligned}$$

(j) $(\mathbf{b}\,\mathbf{c}\,\mathbf{d})\mathbf{a} - (\mathbf{c}\,\mathbf{d}\,\mathbf{a})\mathbf{b} + (\mathbf{d}\,\mathbf{a}\,\mathbf{b})\mathbf{c} - (\mathbf{a}\,\mathbf{b}\,\mathbf{c})\mathbf{d} = \mathbf{0}$.

(k) $(\mathbf{b} \times \mathbf{c}) \times (\mathbf{a} \times \mathbf{d}) + (\mathbf{c} \times \mathbf{a}) \times (\mathbf{b} \times \mathbf{d}) + (\mathbf{a} \times \mathbf{b}) \times (\mathbf{c} \times \mathbf{d}) = -2(\mathbf{a}\,\mathbf{b}\,\mathbf{c})\mathbf{d}$.

2. Show that for any vector $\mathbf{d}$,

$$\mathbf{d} = \frac{(\mathbf{d}\,\mathbf{b}\,\mathbf{c})}{(\mathbf{a}\,\mathbf{b}\,\mathbf{c})}\mathbf{a} + \frac{(\mathbf{d}\,\mathbf{c}\,\mathbf{a})}{(\mathbf{a}\,\mathbf{b}\,\mathbf{c})}\mathbf{b} + \frac{(\mathbf{d}\,\mathbf{a}\,\mathbf{b})}{(\mathbf{a}\,\mathbf{b}\,\mathbf{c})}\mathbf{c},$$

where $\mathbf{a}$, $\mathbf{b}$, $\mathbf{c}$ are any three noncoplanar vectors.

3. (a) Show that $(\mathbf{a} \times \mathbf{b}) \cdot (\mathbf{b} \times \mathbf{c}) \times (\mathbf{c} \times \mathbf{a}) = (\mathbf{a}\,\mathbf{b}\,\mathbf{c})^2$.

(b) Prove $\mathbf{a} \times \mathbf{b}$, $\mathbf{b} \times \mathbf{c}$, $\mathbf{c} \times \mathbf{a}$ are coplanar if and only if $\mathbf{a}$, $\mathbf{b}$, $\mathbf{c}$ are coplanar.

(c) If $\mathbf{a}$, $\mathbf{b}$, $\mathbf{c}$ are not coplanar, show that

$$\mathbf{d} = \frac{(\mathbf{c} \cdot \mathbf{d})}{(\mathbf{a}\,\mathbf{b}\,\mathbf{c})}\mathbf{a} \times \mathbf{b} + \frac{(\mathbf{a} \cdot \mathbf{d})}{(\mathbf{a}\,\mathbf{b}\,\mathbf{c})}\mathbf{b} \times \mathbf{c} + \frac{(\mathbf{b} \cdot \mathbf{d})}{(\mathbf{a}\,\mathbf{b}\,\mathbf{c})}\mathbf{c} \times \mathbf{a}.$$

4. (a) Show that $(\mathbf{a} \times \mathbf{b}) \times (\mathbf{c} \times \mathbf{d}) = (\mathbf{a}\,\mathbf{c}\,\mathbf{d})\mathbf{b} - (\mathbf{b}\,\mathbf{c}\,\mathbf{d})\mathbf{a}$.

(b) Show that the vector $(\mathbf{a} \times \mathbf{b}) \times (\mathbf{c} \times \mathbf{d})$ lies along the line of intersection of the plane determined by $\mathbf{a}$ and $\mathbf{b}$ and the plane determined by $\mathbf{c}$ and $\mathbf{d}$.

(c) If $\mathbf{a}$, $\mathbf{b}$, $\mathbf{c}$, $\mathbf{d}$ are coplanar, show that $(\mathbf{a} \times \mathbf{b}) \times (\mathbf{c} \times \mathbf{d}) = \mathbf{0}$. Is the converse true?

5. If $\mathbf{a} \neq \mathbf{0}$, show that for any $\mathbf{b}$,

$$\mathbf{b} = \frac{\mathbf{a} \times (\mathbf{b} \times \mathbf{a}) + (\mathbf{a} \cdot \mathbf{b})\mathbf{a}}{a^2}.$$

6. If $\mathbf{a}$ and $\mathbf{b}$ lie in a plane perpendicular to a plane containing $\mathbf{c}$ and $\mathbf{d}$, show that $(\mathbf{a} \times \mathbf{b}) \cdot (\mathbf{c} \times \mathbf{d}) = 0$.

7. Prove or disprove:

$$\mathbf{a} \times [\mathbf{a} \times (\mathbf{a} \times \mathbf{b})] \cdot \mathbf{c} = -a^2(\mathbf{a}\ \mathbf{b}\ \mathbf{c}).$$

8. Prove that a necessary and sufficient condition that $\mathbf{a} \times (\mathbf{b} \times \mathbf{c}) = (\mathbf{a} \times \mathbf{b}) \times \mathbf{c}$ is $(\mathbf{a} \times \mathbf{c}) \times \mathbf{b} = 0$. Discuss the cases $\mathbf{a} \cdot \mathbf{b} = 0$ and $\mathbf{b} \cdot \mathbf{c} = 0$.

9. (a) Prove that if $\mathbf{a} \| \mathbf{b}$ then $\mathbf{a} \times (\mathbf{b} \times \mathbf{c}) = \mathbf{b} \times (\mathbf{a} \times \mathbf{c})$. (*Hint:* One form of the condition for parallelism is more feasible.) Is the converse true?

(b) Prove that if $\mathbf{a}, \mathbf{b}, \mathbf{c}$ are noncoplanar and $(\mathbf{a} \times \mathbf{b}) \times \mathbf{c} = \mathbf{a} \times (\mathbf{b} \times \mathbf{c}) = \mathbf{0}$, then $\mathbf{a}, \mathbf{b}, \mathbf{c}$ are mutually perpendicular.

10. If $\mathbf{a}$ and $\mathbf{b}$ are given vectors and h is a given scalar, solve for $\mathbf{x}$: (a) $\mathbf{x} \times \mathbf{a} + h\mathbf{x} = \mathbf{b}$; (b) $\mathbf{a} \times \mathbf{x} = \mathbf{b}$ and $\mathbf{a} \cdot \mathbf{x} = h$, $\mathbf{a} \neq \mathbf{0}$.

11. Show that the vectors $\mathbf{a} - \mathbf{b} + \mathbf{c}$, $2\mathbf{a} - 3\mathbf{b}$, $\mathbf{a} + 3\mathbf{c}$ are parallel to the same plane.

12. Show that

(a) $(h\mathbf{a}\ \mathbf{b}\ \mathbf{c}) = (\mathbf{a}\ h\mathbf{b}\ \mathbf{c}) = (\mathbf{a}\ \mathbf{b}\ h\mathbf{c}) = h(\mathbf{a}\ \mathbf{b}\ \mathbf{c})$ for any scalar h.

(b) $(\mathbf{a} + \mathbf{d}\ \mathbf{b}\ \mathbf{c}) = (\mathbf{a}\ \mathbf{b}\ \mathbf{c}) + (\mathbf{d}\ \mathbf{b}\ \mathbf{c})$.

(c) $(\mathbf{a} + h\mathbf{b} + k\mathbf{c}\ \mathbf{b}\ \mathbf{c}) = (\mathbf{a}\ \mathbf{b}\ \mathbf{c})$ for any scalars h and k.

13. If $\mathbf{a} = h_1\mathbf{d} + k_1\mathbf{e} + l_1\mathbf{f}$, $\mathbf{b} = h_2\mathbf{d} + k_2\mathbf{e} + l_2\mathbf{f}$, $\mathbf{c} = h_3\mathbf{d} + k_3\mathbf{e} + l_3\mathbf{f}$, show that

$$(\mathbf{a}\ \mathbf{b}\ \mathbf{c}) = \begin{vmatrix} h_1 & k_1 & l_1 \\ h_2 & k_2 & l_2 \\ h_3 & k_3 & l_3 \end{vmatrix} (\mathbf{d}\ \mathbf{e}\ \mathbf{f}).$$

14. Let PQR be a spherical triangle whose sides p, q, r are arcs of great circles. Prove the law of cosines for spherical triangles: $\cos p = \cos q \cos r - \sin q \sin r \cos p$. (*Hint:* Interpret appropriately both sides of Lagrange's identity.)

15. (a) Show that for constant vectors $\mathbf{a}$ and $\mathbf{b}$, $\mathbf{r} = \mathbf{a} + h\mathbf{b}$ is the vector equation of a line with position vector $\mathbf{r}$.

(b) Show that the lines $\mathbf{r} = \mathbf{a} + h\mathbf{b}$ and $\mathbf{r} = \mathbf{c} + k\mathbf{d}$ intersect if $(\mathbf{d}\ \mathbf{c}\ \mathbf{b}) = (\mathbf{d}\ \mathbf{a}\ \mathbf{b})$ and that the point of intersection is the terminal point of

$$\mathbf{a} + \frac{(\mathbf{a}\ \mathbf{c}\ \mathbf{d})}{(\mathbf{d}\ \mathbf{a}\ \mathbf{b})}\mathbf{d} \quad \text{or of} \quad \mathbf{c} + \frac{(\mathbf{a}\ \mathbf{c}\ \mathbf{b})}{(\mathbf{d}\ \mathbf{c}\ \mathbf{b})}\mathbf{b}.$$

16. (a) Let $\mathbf{r}_1$, $\mathbf{r}_2$, $\mathbf{r}_3$ be three distinct vectors with a common initial point. Show that the equation of the plane through the terminal points of these vectors and with $\mathbf{r}$ as position vector is

$$(\mathbf{r}\ \mathbf{r}_2\ \mathbf{r}_3) + (\mathbf{r}\ \mathbf{r}_3\ \mathbf{r}_1) + (\mathbf{r}\ \mathbf{r}_1\ \mathbf{r}_2) = (\mathbf{r}_1\ \mathbf{r}_2\ \mathbf{r}_3).$$

(b) Prove that a necessary and sufficient condition that four points, A, B, C, D, be coplanar is that

$$(\mathbf{d}\ \mathbf{b}\ \mathbf{c}) + (\mathbf{a}\ \mathbf{d}\ \mathbf{c}) + (\mathbf{a}\ \mathbf{b}\ \mathbf{d}) = (\mathbf{a}\ \mathbf{b}\ \mathbf{c}),$$

where $\mathbf{a} = \overrightarrow{OA}$, $\mathbf{b} = \overrightarrow{OB}$, $\mathbf{c} = \overrightarrow{OC}$, $\mathbf{d} = \overrightarrow{OD}$, O any point in space.

17. Show that the equation of a cone with axis parallel to the vector $\mathbf{b}$, vertex at O, and semivertical angle θ is $(\mathbf{r}\cdot\mathbf{b})^2 = \cot^2\theta[\mathbf{b}\times(\mathbf{r}\times\mathbf{b})]^2$, where $\mathbf{r}$ is the position vector from O to any point on the cone.

18. Prove that $\mathbf{a}$, $\mathbf{b}$, $\mathbf{c}$ are linearly dependent (see p. 16, Exercise 20) if and only if $(\mathbf{a}\,\mathbf{b}\,\mathbf{c}) = 0$. Interpret linear dependence and independence geometrically.

19. Given a cube and any one of its diagonals, there exist six edges of the cube that do not meet this diagonal. Show that the midpoints of these edges are coplanar.

20. (a) If

$$\mathbf{a}' = \frac{\mathbf{b}\times\mathbf{c}}{(\mathbf{a}\,\mathbf{b}\,\mathbf{c})}, \qquad \mathbf{b}' = \frac{\mathbf{c}\times\mathbf{a}}{(\mathbf{a}\,\mathbf{b}\,\mathbf{c})}, \qquad \mathbf{c}' = \frac{\mathbf{a}\times\mathbf{b}}{(\mathbf{a}\,\mathbf{b}\,\mathbf{c})},$$

show that

$$\mathbf{a} = \frac{\mathbf{b}'\times\mathbf{c}'}{(\mathbf{a}'\,\mathbf{b}'\,\mathbf{c}')}, \qquad \mathbf{b} = \frac{\mathbf{c}'\times\mathbf{a}'}{(\mathbf{a}'\,\mathbf{b}'\,\mathbf{c}')}, \qquad \mathbf{c} = \frac{\mathbf{a}'\times\mathbf{b}'}{(\mathbf{a}'\,\mathbf{b}'\,\mathbf{c}')}.$$

(b) If $\mathbf{a}$, $\mathbf{b}$, $\mathbf{c}$ and $\mathbf{a}'$, $\mathbf{b}'$, $\mathbf{c}'$ are such that $\mathbf{a}\cdot\mathbf{a}' = \mathbf{b}\cdot\mathbf{b}' = \mathbf{c}\cdot\mathbf{c}' = 1$ and $\mathbf{a}'\cdot\mathbf{b} = \mathbf{a}'\cdot\mathbf{c} = \mathbf{b}'\cdot\mathbf{a} = \mathbf{b}'\cdot\mathbf{c} = \mathbf{c}'\cdot\mathbf{a} = \mathbf{c}'\cdot\mathbf{b} = 0$, prove that

$$\mathbf{a}' = \frac{\mathbf{b}\times\mathbf{c}}{(\mathbf{a}\,\mathbf{b}\,\mathbf{c})}, \quad \mathbf{b}' = \frac{\mathbf{c}\times\mathbf{a}}{(\mathbf{a}\,\mathbf{b}\,\mathbf{c})}, \quad \mathbf{c}' = \frac{\mathbf{a}\times\mathbf{b}}{(\mathbf{a}\,\mathbf{b}\,\mathbf{c})}, \qquad (\mathbf{a}\,\mathbf{b}\,\mathbf{c}) \neq 0.$$

($\mathbf{a}$, $\mathbf{b}$, $\mathbf{c}$ and $\mathbf{a}'$, $\mathbf{b}'$, $\mathbf{c}'$ are called **reciprocal sets** of vectors.)

(c) Show that for two reciprocal sets of vectors $\mathbf{a}$, $\mathbf{b}$, $\mathbf{c}$ and $\mathbf{a}'$, $\mathbf{b}'$, $\mathbf{c}'$, $(\mathbf{a}\,\mathbf{b}\,\mathbf{c})(\mathbf{a}'\,\mathbf{b}'\,\mathbf{c}') = 1$. (This accounts for the term *reciprocal.*)

(d) If $\mathbf{a}$, $\mathbf{b}$, $\mathbf{c}$ are nonzero, nonparallel vectors, show that any vector $\mathbf{d}$ can be represented as

$$\mathbf{d} = (\mathbf{d}\cdot\mathbf{a}')\mathbf{a} + (\mathbf{d}\cdot\mathbf{b}')\mathbf{b} + (\mathbf{d}\cdot\mathbf{c}')\mathbf{c},$$

where $\mathbf{a}$, $\mathbf{b}$, $\mathbf{c}$ and $\mathbf{a}'$, $\mathbf{b}'$, $\mathbf{c}'$ are reciprocal sets of vectors.

(e) Show that

$$(\mathbf{a}\,\mathbf{b}\,\mathbf{c})(\mathbf{d}\,\mathbf{e}\,\mathbf{f}) = \begin{vmatrix} \mathbf{a}\cdot\mathbf{d} & \mathbf{a}\cdot\mathbf{e} & \mathbf{a}\cdot\mathbf{f} \\ \mathbf{b}\cdot\mathbf{d} & \mathbf{b}\cdot\mathbf{e} & \mathbf{b}\cdot\mathbf{f} \\ \mathbf{c}\cdot\mathbf{d} & \mathbf{c}\cdot\mathbf{e} & \mathbf{c}\cdot\mathbf{f} \end{vmatrix}.$$

[*Hint:* Express $\mathbf{a}$, $\mathbf{b}$, $\mathbf{c}$ in terms of the reciprocal set of $\mathbf{d}$, $\mathbf{e}$, $\mathbf{f}$ and compute $(\mathbf{a}\,\mathbf{b}\,\mathbf{c})$.]

(f) If $\mathbf{a}$, $\mathbf{b}$, $\mathbf{c}$ and $\mathbf{a}'$, $\mathbf{b}'$, $\mathbf{c}'$ are reciprocal sets, show that $\mathbf{b}\times\mathbf{c}$, $\mathbf{c}\times\mathbf{a}$, $\mathbf{a}\times\mathbf{b}$ and $\mathbf{b}'\times\mathbf{c}'$, $\mathbf{c}'\times\mathbf{a}'$, $\mathbf{a}'\times\mathbf{b}'$ are also reciprocal sets.

(g) Prove: If $\mathbf{a} = \overrightarrow{OA}$, $\mathbf{b} = \overrightarrow{OB}$, $\mathbf{c} = \overrightarrow{OC}$, $(\mathbf{a}\,\mathbf{b}\,\mathbf{c}) \neq 0$, then the reciprocal set of vectors $\mathbf{a}'$, $\mathbf{b}'$, $\mathbf{c}'$ are vectors perpendicular to the planes OBC, OCA, OAB and having lengths equal to the reciprocals of the distances of A, B, C from these planes.

(h) Solve for $\mathbf{x}$: $\mathbf{x}\cdot\mathbf{a} = h$; $\mathbf{x}\cdot\mathbf{b} = k$; $\mathbf{x}\cdot\mathbf{c} = l$; $\mathbf{a}$, $\mathbf{b}$, $\mathbf{c}$ noncoplanar vectors.

Chapter 2

Vectors in a Coordinate System

Up to this point, we have been able to develop a large and significant body of vector analysis without the introduction of a coordinate system. However, there are some problems that can be solved more expediently when the vectors involved are referred to a convenient coordinate system. Furthermore, if numerical results are required or if the range of the direction of a vector is extended, then a coordinate system becomes mandatory. In any particular situation, if a choice of geometric versus analytic methods is possible, the student must decide which approach is more feasible.

1. Base vectors in a rectangular coordinate system. In three-dimensional space, we introduce a right-handed rectangular coordinate system, as illustrated in Fig. 1. The term *right-handed* implies that if $\mathbf{a}$, $\mathbf{b}$, $\mathbf{c}$ are vectors lying along the positive x, y, z axes, with initial points at the origin of the coordinate system, then $\mathbf{a}$, $\mathbf{b}$, $\mathbf{c}$ form a positive triple of vectors. We now consider three unit vectors, all of whose initial points are at the origin O: $(0, 0, 0)$ and whose terminal points are at $(1, 0, 0)$, $(0, 1, 0)$, $(0, 0, 1)$; these will be denoted by $\mathbf{i}$, $\mathbf{j}$, $\mathbf{k}$, respectively, and are indicated in Fig. 1. It is clear that $\mathbf{i}$, $\mathbf{j}$, $\mathbf{k}$ are mutually perpendicular. We have the following relations:

$$\mathbf{B}_1: \quad \mathbf{i}\cdot\mathbf{i} = \mathbf{j}\cdot\mathbf{j} = \mathbf{k}\cdot\mathbf{k} = 1,$$
$$\mathbf{B}_2: \quad \mathbf{i}\cdot\mathbf{j} = \mathbf{j}\cdot\mathbf{k} = \mathbf{k}\cdot\mathbf{i} = 0,$$
$$\mathbf{B}_3: \quad \mathbf{i}\times\mathbf{i} = \mathbf{j}\times\mathbf{j} = \mathbf{k}\times\mathbf{k} = \mathbf{0},$$
$$\mathbf{B}_4: \quad \mathbf{i}\times\mathbf{j} = \mathbf{k}, \quad \mathbf{j}\times\mathbf{k} = \mathbf{i}, \quad \mathbf{k}\times\mathbf{i} = \mathbf{j},$$
$$\mathbf{B}_5: \quad \mathbf{j}\times\mathbf{i} = -\mathbf{k}, \quad \mathbf{k}\times\mathbf{j} = -\mathbf{i}, \quad \mathbf{i}\times\mathbf{k} = -\mathbf{j},$$

which the student can verify readily.

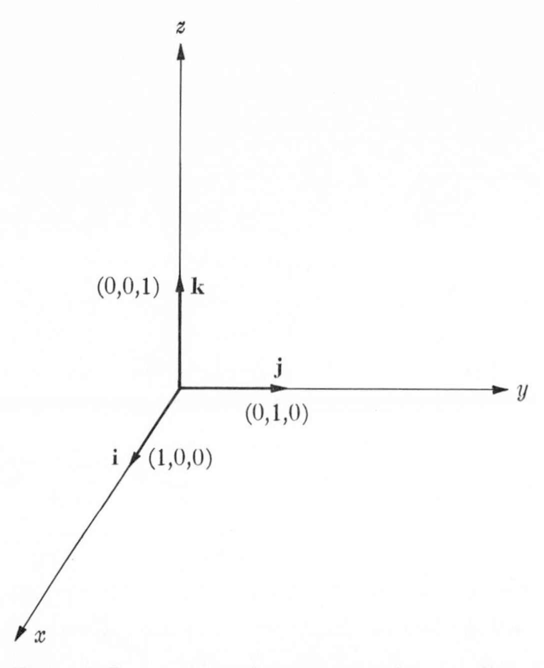

Fig. 1. Base vectors in a rectangular coordinate system

Now let any vector in three-dimensional space be given. Let $\mathbf{a}$ be the vector equal to this vector, with its initial point at the origin of our coordinate system. Then there exist unique scalars a_1, a_2, a_3 such that

$$\mathbf{a} = a_1\mathbf{i} + a_2\mathbf{j} + a_3\mathbf{k}$$

(p. 11, space representation theorem); this is illustrated in Fig. 2. Therefore, every vector in space can be expressed as a linear combination of $\mathbf{i}$, $\mathbf{j}$, $\mathbf{k}$, and for this reason we call these vectors the **base vectors** of our coordinate system. The symbols $\mathbf{i}$, $\mathbf{j}$, $\mathbf{k}$ will be reserved exclusively for denoting these base vectors. It is readily seen that if $\mathbf{a} = a_1\mathbf{i} + a_2\mathbf{j} + a_3\mathbf{k}$, then $a_1 = \text{comp}_i\, \mathbf{a}$, $a_2 = \text{comp}_j\, \mathbf{a}$, $a_3 = \text{comp}_k\, \mathbf{a}$; hence, we shall call a_1, a_2, a_3 the components of $\mathbf{a}$—more specifically, a_1 is the x component of $\mathbf{a}$, a_2 is the y component of $\mathbf{a}$, and a_3 is the z component of $\mathbf{a}$. A vector $\mathbf{a}$ is uniquely determined by its components a_1, a_2, a_3; we can write, therefore, $\mathbf{a} = a_1\mathbf{i} + a_2\mathbf{j} + a_3\mathbf{k}$ as $\mathbf{a} = [a_1, a_2, a_3]$. This means that there is a one-to-one correspondence between the set of triples of numbers (or points in space) and the set of vectors whose initial points are at the origin. For any such vector, its components are equal to the coordinates of its terminal point. On the other hand, a point in space with coordinates (a_1, a_2, a_3) determines a vector $a_1\mathbf{i} + a_2\mathbf{j} + a_3\mathbf{k}$, which is called the **position vector** of the point

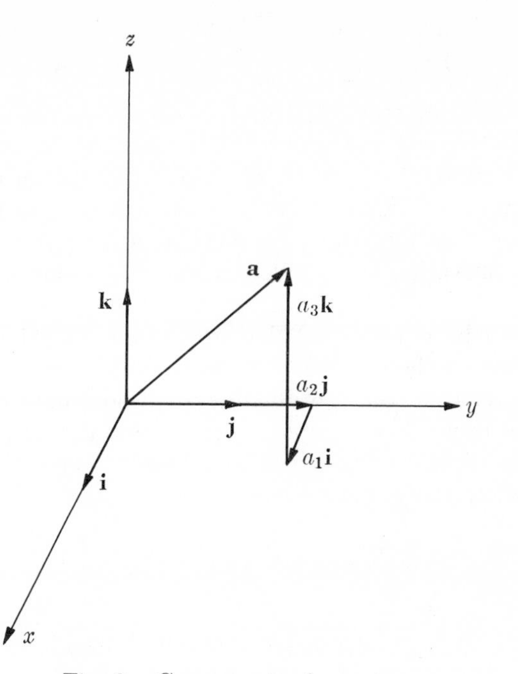

Fig. 2. Components of a vector

(a_1, a_2, a_3). The representations $a_1\mathbf{i} + a_2\mathbf{j} + a_3\mathbf{k}$ and $[a_1, a_2, a_3]$ are called **analytic representations** of **a**. The analytic representation of the zero vector is $[0, 0, 0]$. Furthermore, $\mathbf{i} = [1, 0, 0]$, $\mathbf{j} = [0, 1, 0]$, $\mathbf{k} = [0, 0, 1]$.

2. Analytic expressions of the fundamental relations and operations. Let $\mathbf{a} = a_1\mathbf{i} + a_2\mathbf{j} + a_3\mathbf{k}$, $\mathbf{b} = b_1\mathbf{i} + b_2\mathbf{j} + b_3\mathbf{k}$, $\mathbf{c} = c_1\mathbf{i} + c_2\mathbf{j} + c_3\mathbf{k}$. Then, we have the following:

A_1: Equality of Vectors. $\mathbf{a} = \mathbf{b}$ if and only if $a_1 = b_1$, $a_2 = b_2$, $a_3 = b_3$.
A_2: Scalar Multiplication. $h\mathbf{a} = ha_1\mathbf{i} + ha_2\mathbf{j} + ha_3\mathbf{k}$, for any scalar h.
A_3: Addition of Vectors. $\mathbf{a} + \mathbf{b} = (a_1 + b_1)\mathbf{i} + (a_2 + b_2)\mathbf{j} + (a_3 + b_3)\mathbf{k}$.
A_4: Scalar Product. $\mathbf{a}\cdot\mathbf{b} = a_1b_1 + a_2b_2 + a_3b_3$.
A_5: Vector Product.

$$\mathbf{a} \times \mathbf{b} = (a_2b_3 - a_3b_2)\mathbf{i} - (a_1b_3 - a_3b_1)\mathbf{j} + (a_1b_2 - a_2b_1)\mathbf{k}$$
$$= \begin{vmatrix} \mathbf{i} & \mathbf{j} & \mathbf{k} \\ a_1 & a_2 & a_3 \\ b_1 & b_2 & b_3 \end{vmatrix}.$$

A_6: Scalar Triple Product.

$$(\mathbf{a}\,\mathbf{b}\,\mathbf{c}) = \begin{vmatrix} a_1 & a_2 & a_3 \\ b_1 & b_2 & b_3 \\ c_1 & c_2 & c_3 \end{vmatrix}.$$

Proofs. A_1 follows immediately from the fact that $\mathbf{a} = \mathbf{b}$ implies

$$(a_1 - b_1)\mathbf{i} + (a_2 - b_2)\mathbf{j} + (a_3 - b_3)\mathbf{k} = \mathbf{0} = [0, 0, 0].$$

A_2 follows from the scalar distributive law for addition. A_3 follows from the commutative law and scalar distributive law for addition. A_4 and A_5 can be established by the use of the distributive law for the scalar product and vector product, respectively. Note the determinant form of the vector product—a simple form to remember! A_6 follows from A_4 and A_5, with suitable simplification and rearrangement. The student should supply all the details.

It should be remembered that any result involving vectors that we have obtained by the use of geometric methods is still available when the vectors are referred to a coordinate system, and need only be translated into analytic terms. For example, we found that the volume V of a parallelepiped with edges having a common vertex represented by $\mathbf{a}$, $\mathbf{b}$, $\mathbf{c}$ is $|(\mathbf{a}\,\mathbf{b}\,\mathbf{c})|$. Analytically, this becomes

$$V = \text{absolute value of} \begin{vmatrix} a_1 & a_2 & a_3 \\ b_1 & b_2 & b_3 \\ c_1 & c_2 & c_3 \end{vmatrix}.$$

Furthermore, $\mathbf{a}$, $\mathbf{b}$, $\mathbf{c}$ form a positive triple if and only if the foregoing determinant is positive. The student will have ample opportunity to make use of many of these results translated into analytic form.

Now let us consider any vector whose initial point is not at the origin but at (x_1, x_2, x_3) and whose terminal point is at (y_1, y_2, y_3). It is not con-

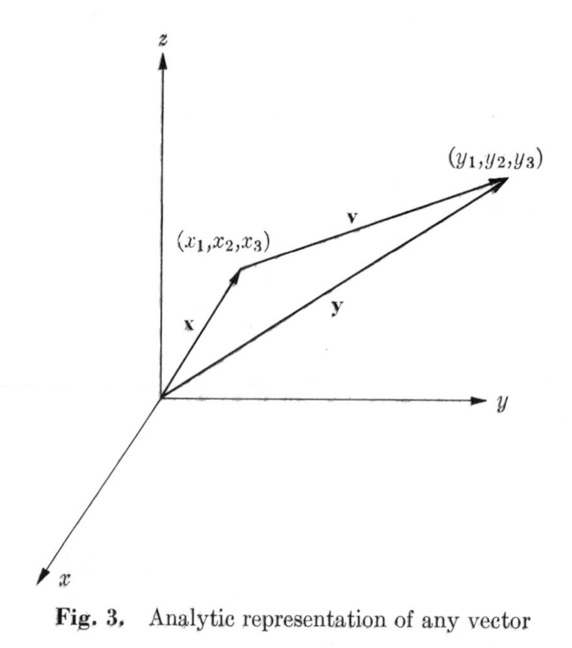

Fig. 3. Analytic representation of any vector

venient to determine the components of such a vector by considering the vector that is equal to it but having its initial point at the origin. However, since the initial and terminal points of a vector uniquely determine it, we should expect that the components of a vector can be expressed in terms of the coordinates of its initial and terminal points. This is indeed the case. Let $\mathbf{v}$ be the vector whose initial point is at (x_1, x_2, x_3) and whose terminal point is at (y_1, y_2, y_3). Then (x_1, x_2, x_3) determines the position vector $\mathbf{x} = x_1\mathbf{i} + x_2\mathbf{j} + x_3\mathbf{k}$, and (y_1, y_2, y_3) determines the position vector $\mathbf{y} = y_1\mathbf{i} + y_2\mathbf{j} + y_3\mathbf{k}$. Then $\mathbf{v} = \mathbf{y} - \mathbf{x}$ (see Fig. 3) so that

$$\mathbf{v} = (y_1 - x_1)\mathbf{i} + (y_2 - x_2)\mathbf{j} + (y_3 - x_3)\mathbf{k}.$$

Hence, *the components of a vector with initial point at* (x_1, x_2, x_3) *and terminal point at* (y_1, y_2, y_3) are $[y_1 - x_1, y_2 - x_2, y_3 - x_3]$.

3. Analytic characterization of vectors. We have seen that a vector $\mathbf{a}$ can be completely characterized by its components $[a_1, a_2, a_3]$. We have defined a vector to be a quantity that has both magnitude and direction; now that we have introduced a coordinate system, it remains to give analytic representations of these properties, i.e., the magnitude and direction of a vector should be expressible in terms of its components.

The magnitude or length of the vector $\mathbf{a}$ is $a = \sqrt{\mathbf{a}\cdot\mathbf{a}}$, since $\mathbf{a}\cdot\mathbf{a} = a^2$. Therefore, if $\mathbf{a} = a_1\mathbf{i} + a_2\mathbf{j} + a_3\mathbf{k}$,

$$|\mathbf{a}| = \text{length of } \mathbf{a} = \sqrt{a_1^2 + a_2^2 + a_3^2}.$$

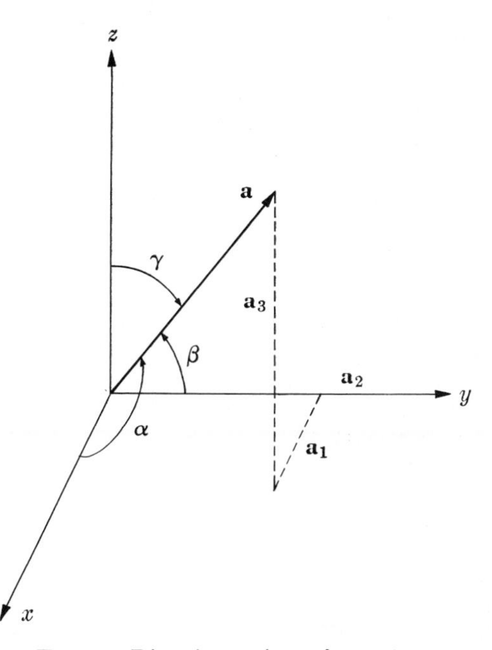

Fig. 4. Direction cosines of a vector

Note the inequalities involving the length of a vector and its components:

$$|a_r| \leq a \leq |a_1| + |a_2| + |a_3|, \qquad r = 1, 2, 3.$$

When do the equality signs hold?

In the absence of a coordinate system, one of two directions is assigned to a vector. Now that we have introduced a coordinate system, we can extend the range of the direction of a vector. Let α, β, γ be the angles between the nonzero vector $\mathbf{a} = a_1\mathbf{i} + a_2\mathbf{j} + a_3\mathbf{k}$ and the positive x, y, z axes, respectively, where $0 \leq \alpha, \beta, \gamma \leq \pi$. Then it is readily seen that

$$\cos\alpha = \frac{a_1}{a}, \quad \cos\beta = \frac{a_2}{a}, \quad \cos\gamma = \frac{a_3}{a}, \qquad a \neq 0,$$

as illustrated in Fig. 4. These are the **direction cosines** of the vector $\mathbf{a}$ and are an analytic characterization of its direction. The direction cosines of the zero vector are undefined; we maintain our convention of assigning any direction to it.

Given the vectors $\mathbf{a} = a_1\mathbf{i} + a_2\mathbf{j} + a_3\mathbf{k}$ and $\mathbf{b} = b_1\mathbf{i} + b_2\mathbf{j} + b_3\mathbf{k}$ with θ the angle between them, $ab \neq 0$, the definition of the scalar product yields

$$\cos\theta = \frac{\mathbf{a}\cdot\mathbf{b}}{ab} = \frac{a_1 b_1 + a_2 b_2 + a_3 b_3}{\sqrt{a_1^2\, a_2^2\, a_3^2}\sqrt{b_1^2\, b_2^2\, b_3^2}}.$$

We now consider some examples illustrating analytic methods.

EXAMPLE 1. Find a unit vector parallel to the sum of the vectors $\mathbf{a} = 2\mathbf{i} + 4\mathbf{j} - 5\mathbf{k}$ and $\mathbf{b} = \mathbf{i} + 2\mathbf{j} + 3\mathbf{k}$.

Solution. $\mathbf{a} + \mathbf{b} = 3\mathbf{i} + 6\mathbf{j} - 2\mathbf{k}$. All vectors parallel to $\mathbf{a} + \mathbf{b}$ are of the form $h(3\mathbf{i} + 6\mathbf{j} - 2\mathbf{k})$, where h is any scalar. The length of these vectors is $7h$ if $h > 0$; $-7h$, if $h < 0$. Hence, the required unit vector is

$$\tfrac{3}{7}\mathbf{i} + \tfrac{6}{7}\mathbf{j} - \tfrac{2}{7}\mathbf{k} \quad \text{or} \quad -\tfrac{3}{7}\mathbf{i} - \tfrac{6}{7}\mathbf{j} + \tfrac{2}{7}\mathbf{k}.$$

EXAMPLE 2. Find all unit vectors parallel to the xy-plane and perpendicular to the vector $4\mathbf{i} - 3\mathbf{j} - \mathbf{k}$.

Solution. We first determine all vectors having the indicated properties. Denote them by $x\mathbf{i} + y\mathbf{j} + z\mathbf{k}$. Since they must be parallel to the xy-plane, $z = 0$. The perpendicularity condition yields $4x - 3y = 0$. Hence, the vectors $x(\mathbf{i} + \frac{4}{3}\mathbf{j})$ for any choice of x are parallel to the xy-plane and perpendicular to $4\mathbf{i} - 3\mathbf{j} - \mathbf{k}$. The unit vectors with these properties are $\pm\frac{1}{5}(3\mathbf{i} + 4\mathbf{j})$.

EXAMPLE 3. Find the volume V of the tetrahedron whose vertices are at $(0, 1, 1)$, $(1, 2, 0)$, $(1, 1, 1)$, $(0, -1, 0)$.

Solution. For a tetrahedron, $V = \frac{1}{3}Bh$, where B is the area of its base and h its altitude. If $\mathbf{a}$, $\mathbf{b}$, $\mathbf{c}$ are three sides of the tetrahedron, having a common vertex, then $V = \frac{1}{6}|(\mathbf{a}\;\mathbf{b}\;\mathbf{c})|$. (*Proof?*) Let the initial points of $\mathbf{a}$, $\mathbf{b}$, $\mathbf{c}$ be at $(1, 1, 1)$ and

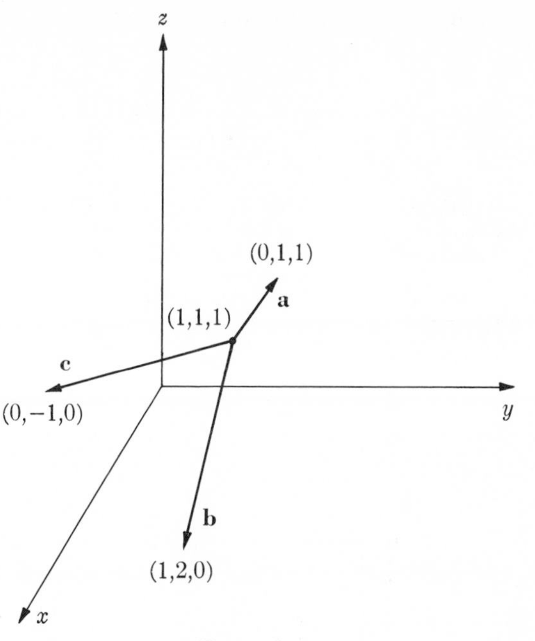

Example 3

their terminal points at (0, 1, 1), (1, 2, 0), (0, −1, 0), respectively. (See figure.) Then $\mathbf{a} = -\mathbf{i}$, $\mathbf{b} = \mathbf{j} - \mathbf{k}$, $\mathbf{c} = -\mathbf{i} - 2\mathbf{j} - \mathbf{k}$ and

$$V = \frac{1}{6}\begin{vmatrix} -1 & 0 & 0 \\ 0 & 1 & -1 \\ -1 & -2 & -1 \end{vmatrix} = \frac{1}{2}.$$

EXAMPLE 4. Given the points $A: (1, 0, 1)$, $B: (2, 1, -1)$, $C: (-1, 1, 2)$, $D: (1, 2, 2)$. (a) Find the area of triangle ABC. (b) Determine whether $\overrightarrow{AC} \perp \overrightarrow{BD}$.

Solution. $\overrightarrow{AB} = [1, 1, -2]$, $\overrightarrow{AC} = [-2, 1, 1]$, $\overrightarrow{BD} = [-1, 1, 3]$.

(a)
$$\overrightarrow{AB} \times \overrightarrow{AC} = \begin{vmatrix} \mathbf{i} & \mathbf{j} & \mathbf{k} \\ 1 & 1 & -2 \\ -2 & 1 & 1 \end{vmatrix} = [3, 3, 3] = 3[1, 1, 1].$$

Hence, area of triangle $ABC = \frac{1}{2}|\overrightarrow{AB} \times \overrightarrow{AC}| = \frac{3}{2}\sqrt{3}$.

(b) $\overrightarrow{AC} \cdot \overrightarrow{BD} = 2 + 1 + 3 = 6 \neq 0$. Hence, $\overrightarrow{AC}$ is not perpendicular to $\overrightarrow{BD}$.

Problems in analytic geometry can be more expediently solved by the use of analytic vector methods in many instances. However, it is not our purpose to develop the subject systematically. The interested student may find such a treatment in Randolph, *Calculus and Analytic Geometry*, Agnew, *Calculus*, or Apostol, *Calculus*.

Our next examples will supply illustrations; others will be found in the exercises.

EXAMPLE 5. Find the shortest distance d between two lines AB and CD determined by the points A: $(1, -2, -1)$, B: $(4, 0, -3)$, C: $(1, 2, -1)$, D: $(2, -4, -5)$.

Solution. Problems of this type are best solved by first determining a general expression for the required quantity using geometric methods and evaluating this expression in the specific case by analytic methods.

$\overrightarrow{AB} \times \overrightarrow{CD}$ is perpendicular to both $\overrightarrow{AB}$ and $\overrightarrow{CD}$. Let $\mathbf{u}$ be the unit vector $(\overrightarrow{AB} \times \overrightarrow{CD})/(|\overrightarrow{AB} \times \overrightarrow{CD}|)$. Then $d = |\text{comp}_{\mathbf{u}}\, \overrightarrow{AC}|$. (see figure).

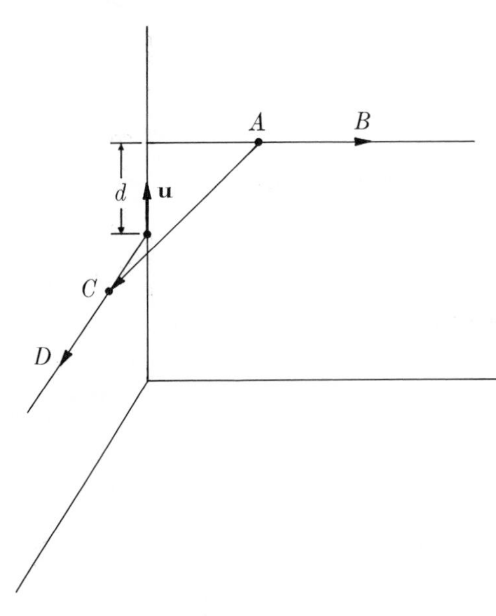

Example 5

Hence,

$$d = \frac{|\overrightarrow{AC} \cdot \overrightarrow{AB} \times \overrightarrow{CD}|}{|\overrightarrow{AB} \times \overrightarrow{CD}|} = \frac{|(\overrightarrow{AC}\ \overrightarrow{AB}\ \overrightarrow{AD})|}{|\overrightarrow{AB} \times \overrightarrow{CD}|},$$

and for the given points,

$$d = \frac{\begin{vmatrix} 0 & 4 & 0 \\ 3 & 2 & -2 \\ 1 & -6 & -4 \end{vmatrix}}{30} = \frac{4}{3}.$$

EXAMPLE 6. Find the equation of the line through P: (3, −2, 1) perpendicular to the line

$$l: \frac{x-2}{2} = \frac{y+1}{-2} = \frac{z}{1}.$$

Solution. We first transform the three equations of l into a single vector equation. Let $\mathbf{r} = x\mathbf{i} + y\mathbf{j} + z\mathbf{k}$, (x, y, z) any point on l, $\mathbf{a} = 2\mathbf{i} - \mathbf{j}$, $\mathbf{b} = 2\mathbf{i} - 2\mathbf{j} + \mathbf{k}$. The vector equation of l is $(\mathbf{r} - \mathbf{a}) \times \mathbf{b} = \mathbf{0}$. (Draw a figure.) The position vector of P is $\mathbf{c} = 3\mathbf{i} - 2\mathbf{j} + \mathbf{k}$. Let $\mathbf{v} = \mathbf{a} - \mathbf{c}$. We wish to find a vector $\mathbf{w}$ such that $\mathbf{w} \perp \mathbf{b}$ and $\mathbf{w} \perp \mathbf{b} \times \mathbf{v}$. Hence,

$$\begin{aligned}\mathbf{w} &= \mathbf{b} \times (\mathbf{b} \times \mathbf{v}) = (\mathbf{b}\cdot\mathbf{v})\mathbf{b} - (\mathbf{b}\cdot\mathbf{b})\mathbf{v} \\ &= -5(2\mathbf{i} - 2\mathbf{j} + \mathbf{k}) - 9(-\mathbf{i} + \mathbf{j} - \mathbf{k}) = -\mathbf{i} + \mathbf{j} + 4\mathbf{k}.\end{aligned}$$

The equation of the required line is $(\mathbf{s} - \mathbf{c}) \times \mathbf{w} = \mathbf{0}$, where $\mathbf{s}$ is the position vector of any point on the line, and it can be written as

$$\frac{x-3}{-1} = \frac{y+2}{1} = \frac{z-1}{4}.$$

EXERCISES

1. Evaluate:
(a) $(3\mathbf{i} + 2\mathbf{k}) + (7\mathbf{i} - \mathbf{j} - 2\mathbf{k}) - (\mathbf{i} + 2\mathbf{j} - 3\mathbf{k})$;
(b) $(2\mathbf{j} - \mathbf{k})\cdot(4\mathbf{i} - 2\mathbf{j} - \mathbf{k})$;
(c) $(2\mathbf{i} - 4\mathbf{k}) \times (\mathbf{i} + 2\mathbf{j})$;
(d) $(2\mathbf{i} - 3\mathbf{j})\cdot(\mathbf{i} + \mathbf{j} - \mathbf{k}) \times (3\mathbf{i} - \mathbf{k})$;
(e) $\mathbf{k} \times [(3\mathbf{i} - \mathbf{j}) \times (2\mathbf{i} - \mathbf{j} - \mathbf{k})]$;
(f) $|\mathbf{i} + \mathbf{j} + \mathbf{k}|$;
(g) $(\mathbf{i}\ \mathbf{j}\ \mathbf{k})$;
(h) $(2\mathbf{i}\ 3\mathbf{j}\ -\mathbf{k})$;
(i) $\text{comp}_{\mathbf{i}}\,(\mathbf{i} + \mathbf{j} + \mathbf{k})$;
(j) $\text{proj}_{\mathbf{a}}\,(8\mathbf{i} + \mathbf{j} + 4\mathbf{k})$; $\mathbf{a} = \mathbf{i} + 2\mathbf{j} + 2\mathbf{k}$.

Ans.: (a) $9\mathbf{i} - 3\mathbf{j} + 3\mathbf{k}$; (b) -3; (c) $8\mathbf{i} - 4\mathbf{j} + 4\mathbf{k}$; (d) 4; (e) $-3\mathbf{i} + \mathbf{j}$; (f) $\sqrt{3}$; (g) 1; (h) -6; (i) 1; (j) $2(\mathbf{i} + 2\mathbf{j} + 2\mathbf{k})$.

2. Let $\mathbf{a} = 2\mathbf{i} - 3\mathbf{j} + 6\mathbf{k}$, $\mathbf{b} = \mathbf{i} + 8\mathbf{j} - 4\mathbf{k}$, $\mathbf{c} = 10\mathbf{i} + 10\mathbf{j} + 5\mathbf{k}$. Find (a) $|\mathbf{a}|$, $|\mathbf{b}|$, $|\mathbf{c}|$, $|\mathbf{a} - \mathbf{b}|$; (b) $\mathbf{a}\cdot\mathbf{b}$; (c) $\text{comp}_{\mathbf{a}}\,\mathbf{b}$; (d) direction cosines of $\mathbf{a}$ and $2\mathbf{a} - \mathbf{c}$; (e) angle between $\mathbf{a}$ and $\mathbf{b}$; (f) $(\mathbf{a}\ \mathbf{b}\ \mathbf{c})$. Do $\mathbf{a}$, $\mathbf{b}$, $\mathbf{c}$ form a positive triple?

Ans.: (a) 7, 9, 15, $\sqrt{222}$, (b) -46, (c) $-46/7$, (d) $2/7$, $-3/7$, $6/7$; $-6/\sqrt{341}$, $16/\sqrt{341}$, $7/\sqrt{341}$, (e) $\cos^{-1} -46/63$, (f) -125.

3. Let $\mathbf{a} = \mathbf{i} + 2\mathbf{j} + \mathbf{k}$, $\mathbf{b} = 2\mathbf{i} - \mathbf{k}$, $\mathbf{c} = -\mathbf{j} + 2\mathbf{k}$. Find (a) $\mathbf{a} \times (\mathbf{b} \times \mathbf{c})$; (b) the volume of the parallelepiped having $\mathbf{a} + \mathbf{b}$, $\mathbf{a} + 2\mathbf{c}$, $\mathbf{b}$ as concurrent edges; (c) the area of the triangle whose vertices are the terminal points of $\mathbf{a}$, $\mathbf{b}$, $\mathbf{c}$; (d) $|2\mathbf{a} - \mathbf{b} + 3\mathbf{c}|$; (e) a unit vector parallel to $\mathbf{c}$; (f) $(\mathbf{a} \times \mathbf{b}) \times (\mathbf{b} \times \mathbf{c})$, (g) $(\mathbf{b}\cdot\mathbf{c})(\mathbf{a} \times \mathbf{b})$; (h) scalars h, k, l such that $h\mathbf{a} + k\mathbf{b} + l\mathbf{c} = 2\mathbf{i} - 7\mathbf{j} + 2\mathbf{k}$.

Ans.: (a) $\mathbf{j} - 2\mathbf{k}$; (b) 22; (c) $3\sqrt{10}/2$; (d) $\sqrt{82}$; (e) $-\mathbf{j} + (2\mathbf{k}/\sqrt{5})$; (f) $-11(2\mathbf{i} - \mathbf{k})$; (g) $-2(-2\mathbf{i} + 3\mathbf{j} - 4\mathbf{k})$; (h) -2, 2, 3.

4. Given the points O: (0, 0, 0), A: (−2, 3, 1), B: (−3, 3, 5), C: (−5, 9, −5), D: (2, −1, 5). Find (a) $\overrightarrow{OA} - \overrightarrow{OD}$; (b) $\overrightarrow{OA} \times \overrightarrow{OB}$; (c) $(\overrightarrow{OA}\ \overrightarrow{OB}\ \overrightarrow{CD})$; (d) $|\overrightarrow{AB} - \overrightarrow{CD}|$;

(e) $(\overrightarrow{AD} - \overrightarrow{BC})\cdot(\overrightarrow{AC} - \overrightarrow{BD})$; (f) the area of the triangle ABC; (g) the volume of the tetrahedron $OABC$; (h) the angle CAB; (i) the vectors perpendicular to the plane BCD; (j) the shortest distance between the lines AC and BD.

Ans.: (a) $4\sqrt{3}$; (b) $12\mathbf{i} - 7\mathbf{j} - 3\mathbf{k}$; (c) 102; (d) $10\sqrt{2}$; (e) -232; (f)$3\sqrt{26}$; (g) 2; (h) $\cos^{-1} -9/\sqrt{238}$; (i) $-40\mathbf{i} - 50\mathbf{j} - 22\mathbf{k}$; (j) $4\sqrt{2}/5$.

5. If a is any vector show that
(a) $\mathbf{a} = (\mathbf{a}\cdot\mathbf{i})\mathbf{i} + (\mathbf{a}\cdot\mathbf{j})\mathbf{j} + (\mathbf{a}\cdot\mathbf{k})\mathbf{k}$.
(b) $\mathbf{a} = (\mathbf{a}\ \mathbf{j}\ \mathbf{k})\mathbf{i} + (\mathbf{a}\ \mathbf{k}\ \mathbf{i})\mathbf{j} + (\mathbf{a}\ \mathbf{i}\ \mathbf{j})\mathbf{k}$.

6. Find the work done in moving an object in the direction of $\mathbf{r} = 3\mathbf{i} + 2\mathbf{j} - 5\mathbf{k}$ with an applied force $\mathbf{F} = 2\mathbf{i} - \mathbf{j} - \mathbf{k}$. *Ans.:* 9.

7. The diagonals of a parallelogram are represented by $3\mathbf{i} - 4\mathbf{j} - \mathbf{k}$ and $2\mathbf{i} + 3\mathbf{j} - 6\mathbf{k}$. Show that the parallelogram is a rhombus and determine the length of its sides and its angles. *Ans.:* $5\sqrt{3}/2$, $\cos^{-1} 23/75$, $\cos^{-1} -23/75$.

8. Show that the vectors $3\mathbf{i} + \mathbf{j} - 2\mathbf{k}$, $-\mathbf{i} + 3\mathbf{j} + 4\mathbf{k}$, $4\mathbf{i} - 2\mathbf{j} - 6\mathbf{k}$ can represent the sides of a triangle; find the lengths of the medians of the triangle.
Ans.: $\sqrt{6}$, $\sqrt{57/2}$, $\sqrt{75/2}$.

9. For what values of h are $\mathbf{a} = h\mathbf{i} - 2\mathbf{j} + \mathbf{k}$ and $\mathbf{b} = 2h\mathbf{i} + h\mathbf{j} - 4\mathbf{k}$ perpendicular? Are there values h such that $\mathbf{a}\|\mathbf{b}$? *Ans.:* $h = 2, 1$.

10. Find the unit vectors perpendicular to both

$$2\mathbf{i} + \mathbf{j} - 4\mathbf{k} \quad \text{and} \quad 4\mathbf{i} + 3\mathbf{j} + 2\mathbf{k}.$$

Ans.: $\pm(7\mathbf{i} - 10\mathbf{j} + \mathbf{k})/5\sqrt{6}$.

11. Find the unit vectors parallel to the plane of $\mathbf{i} + 2\mathbf{j} - 2\mathbf{k}$ and $\mathbf{i} - 2\mathbf{j} + \mathbf{k}$ and perpendicular to $2\mathbf{i} + 2\mathbf{j} - \mathbf{k}$. *Ans.:* $\pm(11\mathbf{i} - 10\mathbf{j} + 2\mathbf{k})/15$.

12. Let $\mathbf{a} = \mathbf{i} + \mathbf{j} + \mathbf{k}$, $\mathbf{b} = \mathbf{i}$, $\mathbf{c} = c_1\mathbf{i} + c_2\mathbf{j} + c_3\mathbf{k}$.
(a) If $c_1 = 1$, $c_2 = 2$, find c_3 so that $\mathbf{a}$, $\mathbf{b}$, $\mathbf{c}$ are coplanar.
(b) If $c_2 = -1$ and $c_3 = 1$, show that no value of c_1 can be determined so as to make $\mathbf{a}$, $\mathbf{b}$, $\mathbf{c}$ coplanar. What is the geometric reason for this?

13. Three vectors of lengths a, $2a$, $3a$ meet in a point and are directed along the diagonals of the three faces of a cube, meeting at the point. Find the sum of the three vectors. *Ans.:* $a(4\mathbf{i} + 3\mathbf{j} + 5\mathbf{k})/\sqrt{2}$.

14. If $\mathbf{a} = \mathbf{i} + 2\mathbf{j} + \mathbf{k}$, $\mathbf{b} = 2\mathbf{i} + \mathbf{j}$, $\mathbf{c} = 3\mathbf{i} - 4\mathbf{j} - 5\mathbf{k}$, express $\mathbf{i} + 2\mathbf{j} + 3\mathbf{k}$ as a linear combination of $\mathbf{a}$, $\mathbf{b}$, $\mathbf{c}$. (See p. 30, Exercise 2.)

15. If $\mathbf{a} = a_1\mathbf{i} + a_2\mathbf{j} + a_3\mathbf{k}$, $\mathbf{b} = b_1\mathbf{i} + b_2\mathbf{j} + b_3\mathbf{k}$, $\mathbf{c} = c_1\mathbf{i} + c_2\mathbf{j} + c_3\mathbf{k}$, $\mathbf{d} = d_1\mathbf{i} + d_2\mathbf{j} + d_3\mathbf{k}$, show that the system of equations

$$(\mathbf{S}): \qquad a_ix + b_iy + c_iz = d_i, \qquad i = 1, 2, 3$$

is equivalent to the single vector equation

$$(\mathbf{V}): \qquad x\mathbf{a} + y\mathbf{b} + z\mathbf{c} = \mathbf{d}.$$

Assuming that $(\mathbf{a}\ \mathbf{b}\ \mathbf{c}) \neq 0$, solve (V) for x, y, z and show that the result is equivalent to that obtained by solving (S) by Cramer's rule.

16. An object P is acted upon by three coplanar forces, as shown in the figure. Determine the force needed to prevent P from moving.
Ans.: P at the origin, $-50[5\mathbf{i} + 2(\sqrt{3} - 1)\mathbf{j}]$.

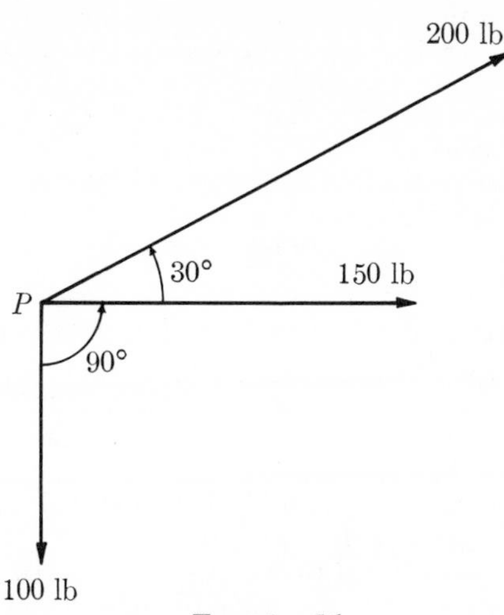

Exercise 16

17. *ABCDEF* is a regular hexagon. Find the sum of the forces represented by (a) $\overrightarrow{AB}$, $\overrightarrow{AC}$, $\overrightarrow{AD}$, $\overrightarrow{AE}$, $\overrightarrow{AF}$; (b) $\overrightarrow{AB}$, $2\overrightarrow{AC}$, $3\overrightarrow{AD}$, $4\overrightarrow{AE}$, $5\overrightarrow{AF}$.

Ans.: A at the origin, D on the positive x axis, side a; (a) $6a\mathbf{i}$; (b) $3a(6\mathbf{i} - \sqrt{3}\mathbf{j})$.

18. Let $\mathbf{u}_1$ and $\mathbf{u}_2$ be unit vectors in the xy-plane making angles α and β with the positive x-axis.

(a) Prove that $\mathbf{u}_1 = \cos\alpha\mathbf{i} + \sin\alpha\mathbf{j}$, $\mathbf{u}_2 = \cos\beta\mathbf{i} + \sin\beta\mathbf{j}$.

(b) By considering $\mathbf{u}_1 \cdot \mathbf{u}_2$, establish the formula $\cos(\alpha - \beta) = \cos\cos\beta + \sin\alpha\sin\beta$. How would you prove that $\sin(\alpha + \beta) = \sin\alpha\cos\beta + \cos\alpha\sin\beta$?

19. Let $\mathbf{a}$ be the position vector of a given point (a_1, a_2, a_3) and $\mathbf{r}$ the position vector of any point (x, y, z). Describe the locus of the terminal point of $\mathbf{r}$ if (a) $|\mathbf{r} - \mathbf{a}| = 3$; (b) $(\mathbf{r} - \mathbf{a}) \cdot \mathbf{a} = 0$; (c) $(\mathbf{r} - \mathbf{a}) \cdot \mathbf{r} = 0$; (d) $(\mathbf{r} - \mathbf{a})^2 = b^2$, b any scalar; (e) $|\mathbf{r} \times \mathbf{a}| = 1$.

20. For a given plane, let $\mathbf{a}$ be the position vector of a fixed point in the plane, $\mathbf{r}$ the position vector of any point in the plane, and $\mathbf{b}$ a vector perpendicular to the plane. Show that the equation of the plane is $(\mathbf{r} - \mathbf{a}) \cdot \mathbf{b} = 0$.

21. (a) Show that the distance D from a point P to a plane through a given point A and perpendicular to a given vector is

$$D = \frac{|(\mathbf{d} - \mathbf{a}) \cdot \mathbf{b}|}{b},$$

where $\mathbf{d}$ is the position vector of P, $\mathbf{a}$ is the position vector of A, and $\mathbf{b}$ is the given vector. (*Hint:* Let P be the position vector of the foot of the perpendicular from P to the plane. Then show that $\mathbf{p} = \mathbf{d} + k\mathbf{b}$, $(\mathbf{a} - \mathbf{p}) \cdot \mathbf{b} = 0$, $D = |\mathbf{d} - \mathbf{p}| = kb$, and eliminate k.)

(b) Given P: (3, 1, 2) and Q: (1, −2, −4), determine the distance from (−1, 1, 1) to the plane passing through Q and perpendicular to the line PQ.

Ans.: 5.

22. Let $\mathbf{a}$, $\mathbf{b}$, $\mathbf{c}$ be the position vectors of any three points in a plane.

(a) Show that $\mathbf{v} = \mathbf{a} \times \mathbf{b} + \mathbf{b} \times \mathbf{c} + \mathbf{c} \times \mathbf{a}$ is perpendicular to the plane. What is the direction of $\mathbf{v}$?

(b) Show that the vector equation of the plane is $\mathbf{r}\cdot\mathbf{v} = (\mathbf{a}\,\mathbf{b}\,\mathbf{c})$, where $\mathbf{r}$ is the position vector of any point in the plane.

(c) Show that the perpendicular distance D from a point, whose position vector is $\mathbf{d}$, to the plane is

$$D = \frac{|(\mathbf{a}\,\mathbf{b}\,\mathbf{c}) - \mathbf{d}\cdot\mathbf{v}|}{v}.$$

(d) Find the perpendicular distance from $(1, -2, 1)$ to the plane determined by $(2, 4, 1)$, $(-1, 0, 1)$, $(-1, 4, 2)$. *Ans.:* $14/13$.

23. Let $\mathbf{r}$ be the position vector of any point on a line.

(a) Show that the equation of the line through a point with position vector $\mathbf{a}$ and parallel to $\mathbf{b}$ is $(\mathbf{r} - \mathbf{a}) \times \mathbf{b} = \mathbf{0}$.

(b) Show that the equation of the line through two points whose position vectors are $\mathbf{a}$ and $\mathbf{b}$ is $(\mathbf{r} - \mathbf{a}) \times (\mathbf{b} - \mathbf{a}) = \mathbf{0}$.

(c) Show that the equation of the line through a given point whose position vector is $\mathbf{a}$ and is perpendicular to the plane through three points whose position vectors are $\mathbf{b}$, $\mathbf{c}$, $\mathbf{d}$ is $(\mathbf{r} - \mathbf{a}) \times \mathbf{v} = 0$, where $\mathbf{v} = \mathbf{b} \times \mathbf{c} + \mathbf{c} \times \mathbf{d} + \mathbf{d} \times \mathbf{b}$.

(d) Show that the distance D from any point with position vector $\mathbf{d}$ to the line in (a) is

$$D = \frac{|(\mathbf{d} - \mathbf{a}) \times \mathbf{b}|}{b}.$$

What is D for the lines in (b) and (c)?

(e) Find the distance from $(1, 3, 0)$ to the line (1) passing through $(1, -2, 1)$ and parallel to $3\mathbf{i} - \mathbf{j} + 4\mathbf{k}$; (2) passing through $(2, 1, -3)$ and $(1, 0, 1)$; (3) passing through $(1, -1, 1)$ and perpendicular to the plane determined by $(-1, -1, 0)$, $(2, 3, 5)$, $(1, 6, -1)$. *Ans.:* (e) (1) $\sqrt{595/26}$; (2) $\sqrt{139/18}$.

24. Given $A\colon (-2, -3, 4)$, $B\colon (2, 3, 0)$, $C\colon (-2, 3, 2)$, $D\colon (2, 0, 1)$. Show that the lines AB, CD are coplanar and find the point in which they meet. (*Hint:* $\overrightarrow{CD} \| \overrightarrow{CP} = \overrightarrow{AP} - \overrightarrow{AC} = \lambda\overrightarrow{AB} - \overrightarrow{AC}$; find λ and then P from $\overrightarrow{OP} = \overrightarrow{PA} + \lambda\overrightarrow{AB}$.)
Ans.: $(2/3, 1, 4/3)$.

25. Find the point P where the line AB pierces the plane CDE if $A\colon (1, 2, 0)$, $B\colon (2, 3, 1)$, $C\colon (2, 0, 3)$, $D\colon (0, 4, 2)$, $E\colon (-1, 2, -2)$. (*Hint:*

$$\overrightarrow{AP} = \lambda\overrightarrow{AB}, \quad (\overrightarrow{CP}\,\overrightarrow{CD}\,\overrightarrow{CE}) = (\overrightarrow{CA} + \lambda\overrightarrow{AB}\,\overrightarrow{CD}\,\overrightarrow{CE}) = 0.)$$

Ans.: $(-3/17, 14/17, -20/17)$.

26. Line L passes through a point A with position vector $\mathbf{a}$ and is parallel to $\mathbf{b}$. Line L' passes through a point A' with position vector $\mathbf{a}'$ and is parallel to $\mathbf{b}'$. The vector $\mathbf{d}$ has its initial point on L and its terminal point on L' and lies along the common perpendicular of these lines. Show that if $\mathbf{v} = \mathbf{b} \times \mathbf{b}'$,

$$\mathbf{d} = \frac{(\mathbf{a}' - \mathbf{a})\cdot\mathbf{v}}{v^2}.$$

27. Show that the equation of the tangent plane to a sphere of radius a, with center having position vector $\mathbf{c}$, at a point on the sphere whose position vector is $\mathbf{b}$, is

$$(\mathbf{r} - \mathbf{c})\cdot(\mathbf{b} - \mathbf{c}) = a^2,$$

where $\mathbf{r}$ is the position vector of any point on the plane.

28. The vertices of a regular tetrahedron are $A: (1, -1, -1)$, $B: (-1, 1, -1)$, $C: (-1, -1, 1)$, $D: (1, 1, 1)$.

(a) Show that $\overrightarrow{AB}$, $\overrightarrow{AC}$, $\overrightarrow{AD}$ are linearly independent (see p. 16, Exercise 20).

(b) Express $\overrightarrow{BC}$ as a linear combination of $\overrightarrow{AB}$ and $\overrightarrow{AC}$ (see p. 32, Exercise 20).

(c) If unit masses are placed at the vertices of the tetrahedron, show that the centroid G is such that $\overrightarrow{OG} = \frac{1}{4}(\overrightarrow{OA} + \overrightarrow{OB} + \overrightarrow{OC} + \overrightarrow{OD})$ (see p. 15, Exercise 18) and find the coordinates of G. *Ans.:* $(0, 0, 0)$.

29. Define a sequence of vectors $\{\mathbf{a}_n\}$ by $\mathbf{a}_1 = \mathbf{a}$, $\mathbf{a}_2 = \mathbf{i}$, $\mathbf{a}_3 = \mathbf{a} \times \mathbf{i}$, $\mathbf{a}_4 = \mathbf{a} \times \mathbf{a}_3, \cdots, \mathbf{a}_n = \mathbf{a} \times \mathbf{a}_{n-1}$, where $\mathbf{a}$ is an arbitrary vector. What is the limit of this sequence if $a < 1$, $a = 1$, $a > 1$?

30. Define the length of a vector $\mathbf{a} = a_1\mathbf{i} + a_2\mathbf{j} + a_3\mathbf{k}$ as

$$|\mathbf{a}| = \max(|\mathbf{a}_1|, |\mathbf{a}_2|, |\mathbf{a}_3|).$$

Prove or disprove:

(a) $|\mathbf{a}| > 0$.
(b) $|\mathbf{a}| = 0$ if and only if $\mathbf{a} = \mathbf{0}$.
(c) $|\mathbf{a} + \mathbf{b}| \leq |\mathbf{a}| + |\mathbf{b}|$.
(d) $|\mathbf{a} \cdot \mathbf{b}| \leq |\mathbf{a}|\,|\mathbf{b}|$.

Are there any properties of length of vector as defined here that do not hold for length as previously defined?

Chapter 3

The Vector Differential Calculus

1. Vector functions. Let E be the set of real numbers in any one of the intervals:

$$\alpha \leq t \leq \beta, \quad \alpha \leq t < \infty, \quad -\infty < t \leq \beta, \quad -\infty < t < \infty,$$

where α and β are finite. If to every t in E we assign a unique vector $\boldsymbol{\phi}(t)$, we say that a vector-valued function or, more simply, a **vector function** is defined in E. The vector function is designated by $\boldsymbol{\phi}$ and the vector functional value at t by $\boldsymbol{\phi}(t)$.

Most vector functions that occur in practice can be defined in the following manner: Let f be any real-valued function of the real variable t, defined in E; for any t in E, $f(t)$ is a scalar, and therefore f will be called a **scalar function.** All functions that the student encountered in the elementary calculus are scalar functions. Now let $\mathbf{a}$ be any vector; then for every t in E, $f(t)\mathbf{a}$ yields another vector by scalar multiplication. Hence, to every t in E, we have assigned a vector, namely, $f(t)\mathbf{a}$; therefore, the vector function $\boldsymbol{\phi} = f\mathbf{a}$ has been defined in E so that $\boldsymbol{\phi}(t) = f(t)\mathbf{a}$ for t in E. The sum of two vector functions $\boldsymbol{\phi}$ and $\boldsymbol{\psi}$ defined in E, denoted by $\boldsymbol{\phi} + \boldsymbol{\psi}$, is defined as the vector function such that $(\boldsymbol{\phi} + \boldsymbol{\psi})(t) = \boldsymbol{\phi}(t) + \boldsymbol{\psi}(t)$ for every t in E. Now the sum of any finite number of vector functions can be defined. Other vector functions can be defined with the use of vector operations that yield vectors; e.g., if $\boldsymbol{\phi}$ and $\boldsymbol{\psi}$ are any two vector functions defined in E, then the vector product of $\boldsymbol{\phi}$ and $\boldsymbol{\psi}$, denoted by $\boldsymbol{\phi} \times \boldsymbol{\psi}$, is defined as the vector function such that $(\boldsymbol{\phi} \times \boldsymbol{\psi})(t) = \boldsymbol{\phi}(t) \times \boldsymbol{\psi}(t)$ for every t in E. In some instances, vector functions are combined so as to yield scalar functions; if $\boldsymbol{\phi}$, $\boldsymbol{\psi}$, $\boldsymbol{\chi}$ are vector functions defined in E, then $\boldsymbol{\phi} \cdot \boldsymbol{\psi}$ and

$(\boldsymbol{\phi}\,\boldsymbol{\psi}\,\boldsymbol{\chi})$ are scalar functions such that $(\boldsymbol{\phi}\cdot\boldsymbol{\psi})(t) = \boldsymbol{\phi}(t)\cdot\boldsymbol{\psi}(t)$ and $(\boldsymbol{\phi}\,\boldsymbol{\psi}\,\boldsymbol{\chi})(t) = (\boldsymbol{\phi}(t)\,\boldsymbol{\psi}(t)\,\boldsymbol{\chi}(t))$ for every t in E.

Now, given any vector function $\boldsymbol{\phi}$ defined in E, for any t in E, we refer the vector $\boldsymbol{\phi}(t)$ to a rectangular coordinate system. We have, then, that

$$\boldsymbol{\phi}(t) = \phi_1(t)\mathbf{i} + \phi_2(t)\mathbf{j} + \phi_3(t)\mathbf{k},$$

where $\phi_1(t)$, $\phi_2(t)$, $\phi_3(t)$ are the components of $\boldsymbol{\phi}(t)$. This means that the vector function $\boldsymbol{\phi}$ can be expressed as

$$\boldsymbol{\phi} = \phi_1\mathbf{i} + \phi_2\mathbf{j} + \phi_3\mathbf{k},$$

where the scalar functions ϕ_1, ϕ_2, ϕ_3 can be thought of as the component functions or, more simply, as the components of $\boldsymbol{\phi}$. This is an analytic representation of $\boldsymbol{\phi}$. We shall develop the theory of vector functions by using their analytic representations.

2. Limits, continuity, and differentiability. We now define what we mean when we say that the limit of the vector function $\boldsymbol{\phi}$ is the constant vector $\mathbf{a}$ when t approaches t_0, written as

$$\lim_{t\to t_0} \boldsymbol{\phi}(t) = \mathbf{a}.$$

Intuitively, this means that we can make the length of the vector $\boldsymbol{\phi}(t) - \mathbf{a}$ (i.e., $|\boldsymbol{\phi}(t) - \mathbf{a}|$) as small as we please merely by letting t become sufficiently close to t_0. More precisely, $\lim_{t\to t_0} \boldsymbol{\phi}(t) = \mathbf{a}$ if for every scalar $\epsilon > 0$ there exists a scalar $\delta > 0$ such that for $0 < |t - t_0| < \delta$, we have $|\boldsymbol{\phi}(t) - \mathbf{a}| < \epsilon$. Note that this becomes the definition for the limit of a scalar function if $\boldsymbol{\phi}$ is replaced by a scalar function and $\mathbf{a}$ by a scalar. We have the following important

THEOREM. If $\boldsymbol{\phi} = \phi_1\mathbf{i} + \phi_2\mathbf{j} + \phi_3\mathbf{k}$ and $\mathbf{a} = a_1\mathbf{i} + a_2\mathbf{j} + a_3\mathbf{k}$, then $\lim_{t\to t_0} \boldsymbol{\phi}(t) = \mathbf{a}$ if and only if $\lim_{t\to t_0} \phi_i(t) = a_i$, $i = 1, 2, 3$.

Proof. If $\lim_{t\to t_0} \boldsymbol{\phi} = \mathbf{a}$, then, by definition, for $\epsilon > 0$ there exists $\delta > 0$ such that for $0 < |t - t_0| < \delta$, $|\boldsymbol{\phi}(t) - \mathbf{a}| < \epsilon$. But for $0 < |t - t_0| < \delta$, $|\phi_i(t) - a_i| \leq |\boldsymbol{\phi}(t) - \mathbf{a}| < \epsilon$, $i = 1, 2, 3$. Hence, $\lim_{t\to t_0} \phi_i(t) = a_i$.

If $\lim_{t\to t_0} \phi_i(t) = a_i$, $i = 1, 2, 3$, for every $\epsilon > 0$, there exists $\delta > 0$ such that for $0 < |t - t_0| < \delta$, $|\phi_i(t) - a_i| < \epsilon/3$. Then

$$\begin{aligned} |\boldsymbol{\phi}(t) - \mathbf{a}| &= |(\phi_1(t) - a_1)\mathbf{i} + (\phi_2(t) - a_2)\mathbf{j} + (\phi_3(t) - a_3)\mathbf{k}| \\ &\leq |\phi_1(t) - a_1| + |\phi_2(t) - a_2| + |\phi_3(t) - a_3| < \epsilon. \end{aligned}$$

Hence, $\lim_{t\to t_0} \boldsymbol{\phi}(t) = \mathbf{a}$.

With this theorem and the corresponding theorem on limits for scalar functions, we can establish the

THEOREM ON LIMITS. If $\lim_{t \to t_0} \boldsymbol{\phi}(t) = \mathbf{a}$, $\lim_{t \to t_0} \boldsymbol{\psi}(t) = \mathbf{b}$, and $\lim_{t \to t_0} f(t) = h$, then

$$\mathbf{L_1}: \quad \lim_{t \to t_0} f(t)\boldsymbol{\phi}(t) = h\mathbf{a}.$$

$$\mathbf{L_2}: \quad \lim_{t \to t_0} [\boldsymbol{\phi}(t) + \boldsymbol{\psi}(t)] = \mathbf{a} + \mathbf{b}.$$

$$\mathbf{L_3}: \quad \lim_{t \to t_0} \boldsymbol{\phi}(t) \cdot \boldsymbol{\psi}(t) = \mathbf{a} \cdot \mathbf{b}.$$

$$\mathbf{L_4}: \quad \lim_{t \to t_0} \boldsymbol{\phi}(t) \times \boldsymbol{\psi}(t) = \mathbf{a} \times \mathbf{b}.$$

Note the special cases $f(t) = h$ and $\boldsymbol{\phi}(t) = \mathbf{a}$ in L_1. L_2 extends to any finite number of vector functions.

A vector function $\boldsymbol{\phi}$ is said to be **continuous** at t_0 if $\lim_{t \to t_0} \boldsymbol{\phi}(t) = \boldsymbol{\phi}(t_0)$. $\boldsymbol{\phi}$ is continuous in E if it is continuous at every t in E. The foregoing theorems enable us to establish the following

THEOREM. $\boldsymbol{\phi} = \phi_1\mathbf{i} + \phi_2\mathbf{j} + \phi_3\mathbf{k}$ is continuous in E if and only if ϕ_1, ϕ_2, ϕ_3 are continuous in E.

THEOREM. If $\boldsymbol{\phi}$, $\boldsymbol{\psi}$, and f are continuous in E and $\boldsymbol{\phi}$ is continuous in the range of f, then $f\boldsymbol{\phi}$, $\boldsymbol{\phi} + \boldsymbol{\psi}$, $\boldsymbol{\phi} \cdot \boldsymbol{\psi}$, $\boldsymbol{\phi} \times \boldsymbol{\psi}$, $\boldsymbol{\phi}(f)$ are continuous in E.

Now in E, let t_0 be a fixed point and t any point; for the vector function $\boldsymbol{\phi}$ defined on E, we consider the

$$\lim_{t \to t_0} \frac{\boldsymbol{\phi}(t) - \boldsymbol{\phi}(t_0)}{t - t_0}.$$

If this limit exists, we call it the **derivative** of $\boldsymbol{\phi}$ at t_0 and denote it by $\boldsymbol{\phi}'(t_0)$. If the limit exists at every point t in E, we denote the derivative of $\boldsymbol{\phi}$ at t as $\boldsymbol{\phi}'(t)$ or $[d\boldsymbol{\phi}(t)]/dt$ and say that $\boldsymbol{\phi}$ is **differentiable** in E. We have the following important

THEOREM. $\boldsymbol{\phi} = \phi_1\mathbf{i} + \phi_2\mathbf{j} + \phi_3\mathbf{k}$ is differentiable in E if and only if ϕ_i, $i = 1, 2, 3$, are differentiable in E; furthermore,

$$\boldsymbol{\phi}'(t) = \phi_1'(t)\mathbf{i} + \phi_2'(t)\mathbf{j} + \phi_3'(t)\mathbf{k},$$

which follows readily from L_1 and L_2 in the theorem on limits, and the definition of the derivative of a scalar function.

With the preceding theorem and the rules for the differentiation of scalar functions, we can establish the following **rules for the differentiation of vector functions:**

If $\boldsymbol{\phi}$, $\boldsymbol{\psi}$, $\boldsymbol{\chi}$, f are differentiable in E, then for every t in E:

$$\mathbf{D_1}: \quad \frac{d}{dt}[f(t)\boldsymbol{\phi}(t)] = f(t)\boldsymbol{\phi}'(t) + \boldsymbol{\phi}(t)f'(t).$$

$$\mathbf{D_2:}\quad \frac{d}{dt}[\boldsymbol{\phi}(t) + \boldsymbol{\psi}(t)] = \boldsymbol{\phi}'(t) + \boldsymbol{\psi}'(t).$$

$$\mathbf{D_3:}\quad \frac{d}{dt}[\boldsymbol{\phi}(t)\cdot\boldsymbol{\psi}(t)] = \boldsymbol{\phi}(t)\cdot\boldsymbol{\psi}'(t) + \boldsymbol{\psi}(t)\cdot\boldsymbol{\phi}'(t).$$

$$\mathbf{D_4:}\quad \frac{d}{dt}[\boldsymbol{\phi}(t)\times\boldsymbol{\psi}(t)] = \boldsymbol{\phi}(t)\times\boldsymbol{\psi}'(t) + \boldsymbol{\phi}'(t)\times\boldsymbol{\psi}(t).$$

$$\mathbf{D_5:}\quad \frac{d}{dt}(\boldsymbol{\phi}(t)\;\boldsymbol{\psi}(t)\;\boldsymbol{\chi}(t)) = (\boldsymbol{\phi}(t)\;\boldsymbol{\psi}(t)\;\boldsymbol{\chi}'(t)) + (\boldsymbol{\phi}(t)\;\boldsymbol{\psi}'(t)\;\boldsymbol{\chi}(t)) + (\boldsymbol{\phi}'(t)\;\boldsymbol{\psi}(t)\;\boldsymbol{\chi}(t)).$$

Note the special cases of D_1: $f(t) = h$, constant, $(d/dt)h\boldsymbol{\phi}(t) = h\boldsymbol{\phi}'(t)$; $\boldsymbol{\phi}(t) = \mathbf{a}$, constant, $(d/dt)f(t)\mathbf{a} = \mathbf{a}f'(t)$, this being $\mathbf{0}$ if f is constant. D_2 extends to the sum of any finite number of differentiable vector functions. *The given order of the terms in the vector product must be observed in* D_3. What is the rule for differentiating a vector triple product? The student should prove D_1 to D_5, using the definition of the derivative and the theorem on limits.

D_6 (Chain Rule): If $t = f(s)$ is differentiable in E and $\boldsymbol{\phi}$ is differentiable in E^*, where t is in E^* whenever s is in E, then

$$\frac{d\boldsymbol{\phi}(t)}{ds} = \frac{d\boldsymbol{\phi}(t)}{dt}\cdot\frac{df(s)}{ds}.$$

Proof. Let s_0 be any point in E; then $t_0 = f(s_0)$ is in E^*. Define the vector function $\boldsymbol{\psi}$ such that

$$\boldsymbol{\psi}(t) = \frac{\boldsymbol{\phi}(t) - \boldsymbol{\phi}(t_0)}{t - t_0} - \boldsymbol{\phi}'(t_0), \qquad t \neq t_0,\ \boldsymbol{\psi}(t_0) = \mathbf{0}.$$

Then, since $\boldsymbol{\phi}$ is differentiable at t_0, $\lim_{t\to t_0}\boldsymbol{\psi}(t) = \mathbf{0}$; hence, $\boldsymbol{\psi}$ is continuous at t_0. Since f is differentiable at s_0, it is continuous at s_0, and hence $\boldsymbol{\psi}[f]$ is continuous at s_0, so that

$$\lim_{s\to s_0}\boldsymbol{\psi}[f(s)] = \boldsymbol{\psi}[f(s_0)] = \boldsymbol{\psi}[t_0] = \mathbf{0}.$$

Now

$$\boldsymbol{\psi}[f(s)] = \frac{\boldsymbol{\phi}[f(s)] - \boldsymbol{\phi}(t_0)}{f(s) - t_0} - \boldsymbol{\phi}'(t_0), \qquad f(s) \neq t_0,$$

or

$$\boldsymbol{\phi}[f(s)] - \boldsymbol{\phi}(t_0) = [\boldsymbol{\psi}[f(s)] + \boldsymbol{\phi}'(t_0)][f(s) - t_0],$$

which is also valid if $f(s) = t_0$. Dividing both sides by $s - s_0$, $s \neq s_0$, we obtain

$$\frac{\boldsymbol{\phi}[f(s)] - \boldsymbol{\phi}[f(s_0)]}{s - s_0} = [\boldsymbol{\psi}[f(s)] + \boldsymbol{\phi}'(t_0)]\left[\frac{f(s) - f(s_0)}{s - s_0}\right]$$

and upon letting $s \to s_0$,

$$\frac{d\boldsymbol{\phi}[f(s_0)]}{ds} = \boldsymbol{\phi}'(t_0)f'(s_0).$$

But s_0 is any point in E.

3. Geometric representation of vector functions. Let the vector function $\boldsymbol{\phi} = \phi_1\mathbf{i} + \phi_2\mathbf{j} + \phi_3\mathbf{k}$ be defined in E. Let $x = \phi_1(t)$, $y = \phi_2(t)$, $z = \phi_3(t)$; for a fixed t in E, (x, y, z) determines a point in space and $\boldsymbol{\phi}(t) = x\mathbf{i} + y\mathbf{j} + z\mathbf{k}$ is the position vector of that point. The totality of these points as t ranges through E can serve as a geometric representation of $\boldsymbol{\phi}$; this set of points is called the **graph** of $\boldsymbol{\phi}$. Now let $\boldsymbol{\phi}$ be a vector function, continuous in E (in what follows, vector function will always imply continuous vector function, unless the contrary is noted explicitly). As t ranges from one end of the interval E to the other end, $\boldsymbol{\phi}$ determines a succession of points in space, which we call the **curve** of $\boldsymbol{\phi}$. More precisely, the points (x, y, z) determined by t in E are ordered in the sense that if t_1 and t_2 in E are such that $t_1 < t_2$, t_1, and t_2, determining (x_1, y_1, z_1) and (x_2, y_2, z_2), respectively, then $(x_1, y_1, z_1) \prec (x_2, y_2, z_2)$, where the symbol $\prec$ may be read "precedes." The graph of $\boldsymbol{\phi}$ and the curve of $\boldsymbol{\phi}$ are conceptually different: The graph of $\boldsymbol{\phi}$ is merely a set of points that are distinct and for which the relationship among pairs of points is immaterial, whereas in the succession of points that defines a curve, a point may occur several times.

The curve of a vector function $\boldsymbol{\phi} = \phi_1\mathbf{i} + \phi_2\mathbf{j} + \phi_3\mathbf{k}$ defined in E can be given a physical interpretation as follows: Let (x, y, z) [where $x = \phi_1(t)$, $y = \phi_2(t)$, $z = \phi_3(t)$ and t in E denotes time] be the position of a particle; then, as t increases in E, the particle traces out a **path.** Such a path is the same succession of points that constitutes the curve of $\boldsymbol{\phi}$; we use the terms *curve* and *path* interchangeably. The motion of the particle indicates that the path has a direction—the direction in which the particle moves as t increases in E. Since a path is just another way of describing the curve of a vector function, such a curve has a direction—the direction in which a particle moves along the curve as t increases in E. We now have a fundamental difference between the graph of $\boldsymbol{\phi}$, a set of points for which direction is meaningless, and the curve of $\boldsymbol{\phi}$ for which direction is an identifying characteristic that stems from the ordering relationship that $\boldsymbol{\phi}$ determines.

In considering the curve of the vector function $\boldsymbol{\phi} = \phi_1\mathbf{i} + \phi_2\mathbf{j} + \phi_3\mathbf{k}$, we let $x = \phi_1(t)$, $y = \phi_2(t)$, $z = \phi_3(t)$. These three equations are called **parametric equations** of the curve of $\boldsymbol{\phi}$ with t as **parameter** or a parametric representation of the curve. We also say these equations are a **parametrization** of the curve or that the curve is parametrized by these equations. The curve of a vector function, or equivalently the curve with a given parametrization, is uniquely determined; i.e., there is only one curve of a given vector function. However, many vector functions may have the same curve. Therefore, we speak of *the* curve of a vector function or *the* curve with a given parametric representation, but we say *a* vector function of the curve or *a* parametric representation of the curve (for a more precise formulation, see p. 69, Exercise 26). Generally speaking, our point of departure is a given vector function that we wish to represent geometrically as a curve. However, in some instances we are interested in a given curve, and this can be the curve of any number of vector functions. The phrase "can be" was judiciously chosen, for there do exist curves that are not the curves of any vector functions; they are called *nonparametrizable curves* and our association with them will be practically nonexistent, so that we shall use the term *curve* to mean parametrizable curve. We shall denote the curve of the vector function $\boldsymbol{\phi}$ by C: $\boldsymbol{\phi}$, E or C: $x = \phi_1(t)$, $y = \phi_2(t)$, $z = \phi_3(t)$, E. If we are considering a curve without any particular interest to any vector function that it represents, then we shall denote it simply as C.

A curve C may have properties that do not depend on the specific vector function that it may represent. However, the direction of C does depend on its parametrization. The direction of the curve of a given vector function is automatically determined, but for a given curve, we can choose the parametrization that will give it one of two directions. For example, if the vector function $\boldsymbol{\phi}$, $\alpha \leq t \leq \beta$, yields one direction for the curve, then the vector function $\boldsymbol{\psi}$ with $\boldsymbol{\psi}(t) = \boldsymbol{\phi}(-t)$, $-\beta \leq t \leq -\alpha$, yields the opposite direction for the curve. The graphs of $\boldsymbol{\phi}$ and $\boldsymbol{\psi}$ are the same.

We have noted that a curve may have many parametric representations. Let $x = \phi_1(t)$, $y = \phi_2(t)$, $z = \phi_3(t)$, t in E, be a given parametric representation of C. If ϕ_1 is an increasing or a decreasing function in E and is continuous there, then it has a unique inverse, and we can write $t = \phi_1^{-1}(x)$, where x belongs to the interval E', which may be $\phi_1(\alpha) \leq x \leq \phi_1(\beta)$, $-\infty < x < \phi_1(\beta)$, or $\phi_1(\alpha) \leq x < \infty$, if ϕ_1 is increasing; $\phi_1(\beta) \leq x \leq \phi_1(\alpha)$, $-\infty < x \leq \phi_1(\alpha)$, or $\phi_1(\beta) \leq x < \infty$, if ϕ_1 is decreasing; or $-\infty < x < \infty$ if ϕ_1 is increasing or decreasing. Then

$$y = \phi_2[\phi_1^{-1}(x)] = f_1(x) \quad \text{and} \quad z = \phi_3[\phi_1^{-1}(x)] = f_2(x).$$

Hence, we have the parametric representation $x = x$, $y = f_1(x)$, $z = f_2(x)$, x in E'. If the curve is in the xy-plane, we speak of its equation $y = f_1(x)$, x in E', and if it is in space, of its equations $y = f_1(x)$ and $z = f_2(x)$, x in E'. Similarly, we have the parametric representations of C: $y = y$, $x = g_1(y)$, $z = g_2(y)$ and $z = z$, $x = h_1(z)$, $y = h_2(z)$, defined in the appropriate intervals. These parametrizations of C, where x, y, or z is the parameter, are called **standard parametrizations.** If we start with the parametric representation of a curve C: $x = \phi_1(t)$, $y = \phi_2(t)$, $z = \phi_3(t)$, t in E, and obtain one of the standard parametrizations, we say that we have obtained such parametrizations by eliminating the parameter t. The standard parametrizations are uniquely determined. (Why?) This fact enables us very often to determine whether two different parametric representations are indeed parametric representations of the same curve; we eliminate the parameter in each of the given parametric representations and note whether the resulting standard parametrization is the same in both cases.

We now consider certain points of curves of vector functions that are particularly significant. Given C: $\boldsymbol{\phi}$, $\alpha \leq t \leq \beta$; the terminal point of the vector $\boldsymbol{\phi}(\alpha)$ is called the **initial point** of C and is denoted by I and the terminal point of the vector $\boldsymbol{\phi}(\beta)$ is called the **terminal point** of C and is denoted by T. If I = T, then C is a **closed curve;** i.e., a curve is closed if its initial and terminal points coincide. Now, given C: $\boldsymbol{\phi}$, E; a point (x_0, y_0, z_0) on C is called a **multiple point** if there exist t^* and t^{**} in E, $t^* \neq t^{**}$, such that $x_0 = \phi_1(t^*) = \phi_1(t^{**})$, $y_0 = \phi_2(t^*) = \phi_2(t^{**})$, $z_0 = \phi_3(t^*) = \phi_3(t^{**})$. In other words, a multiple point of C is a point that occurs more than once in the succession of points that determine C. Geometrically, a multiple point occurs where C crosses itself or is tangent to itself. Here we have a further difference between the curve of $\boldsymbol{\phi}$ and the graph of $\boldsymbol{\phi}$—the same point may occur several times on the curve of $\boldsymbol{\phi}$ but only once on the graph of $\boldsymbol{\phi}$. Every closed curve has at least one multiple point: I = T. We call this point a **nonordinary multiple point;** all other multiple points are called **ordinary multiple points.** C is called a **simple curve** or **arc** if it has no ordinary multiple points; in particular, we call a curve that is both simple and closed a **simple closed curve.** A multiple point is an **isolated multiple point** if there exist no other multiple points in its vicinity on C. More precisely, if $\boldsymbol{\phi}(t_0)$ is the position vector of a multiple point P_0 on C: $\boldsymbol{\phi}$, E, and if there exist t_1 and t_2 in E such that $t_1 < t_0 < t_2$, and if for any t, $t_1 < t < t_2$, $\boldsymbol{\phi}(t)$ is *not* the position vector of a multiple point of C, then P_0 is an isolated multiple point.

Although the graph of a vector function $\boldsymbol{\phi}$ is not the same as the curve of $\boldsymbol{\phi}$, it is often very useful in providing a geometric representation of the curve. If the curve of a vector function $\boldsymbol{\phi}$ has only isolated multiple points, then we can represent it geometrically by first plotting the points of the graph of $\boldsymbol{\phi}$ and then indicating the direction of the curve by an arrow. If the multiple points of a curve are not isolated, then it is best to describe the curve rather than to represent it geometrically.

EXAMPLE 1. $\boldsymbol{\phi}(t) = t\mathbf{i} + t^2\mathbf{j}$, $\boldsymbol{\psi}(t) = t^2\mathbf{i} + t^4\mathbf{j}$, $0 \leq t \leq 1$.

Eliminating t in $\boldsymbol{\phi}(t)$ and $\boldsymbol{\psi}(t)$, we obtain the parametric representation $x = x$, $y = x^2$, $0 \leq x \leq 1$. Hence, two different vector functions have the same curve. The curve is a parabolic arc—a simple curve. (See figure.)

EXAMPLE 2. $\boldsymbol{\phi}(t) = \cos t\mathbf{i} + \sin t\mathbf{j}$, $0 \leq t \leq 2\pi$.

Since I = T = (1, 0), the curve is closed. Since $\cos t$ is decreasing for $0 \leq t \leq \pi$ and increasing for $\pi \leq t \leq 2\pi$, eliminating t yields $x = x$, $y = \sqrt{1 - x^2}$, $-1 \leq x \leq 1$, and $x = x$, $y = -\sqrt{1 - x^2}$, $-1 \leq x \leq 1$. Each of these is a semicircle of the same circle. Hence, the curve is a circle—a simple closed curve. (See figure.)

EXAMPLE 3. $\boldsymbol{\phi}(t) = \cos 2t\mathbf{i} + \sin 2t\mathbf{j}$, $0 \leq t \leq 3\pi/2$.

The graph of this vector function is the set of points (x, y) such that $x^2 + y^2 = 1$ —identical to the graph of the vector function in Example 2. However, this vector

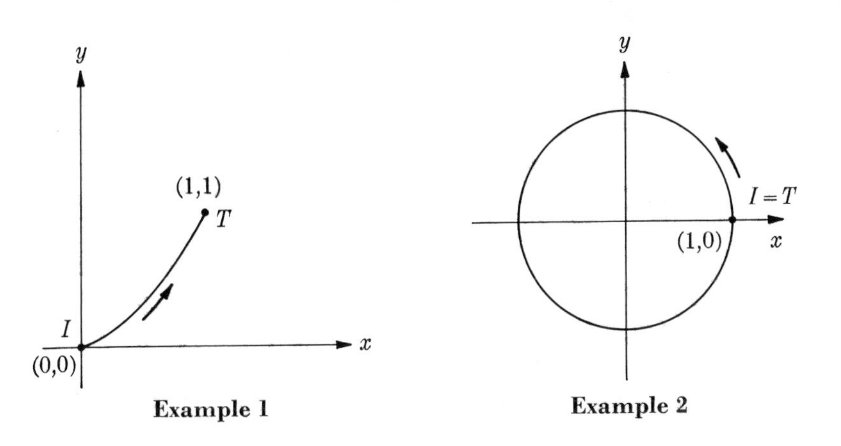

Example 1 **Example 2**

function has a different curve, which is more easily described than drawn because of the presence of nonisolated multiple points. The initial point of the curve is $(1, 0)$ and its terminal point $(-1, 0)$; hence, the curve is not closed. In terms of a particle moving along the curve, it starts at $(1, 0)$, goes around the circle $x^2 + y^2 = 1$, once in a counterclockwise direction, and then proceeds in a counterclockwise direction along the circle until it comes to $(-1, 0)$, where it stops. All points (x, y), $y = \sqrt{1 - x^2}$, $-1 \leq x \leq 1$ are nonisolated multiple points; obviously, this curve is not a simple curve.

EXAMPLE 4. $\boldsymbol{\phi}(t) = \cos t\mathbf{i} + \sin t\mathbf{j} + \sin t\mathbf{k}$, $0 \leq t \leq 2\pi$.

Since $\mathrm{I} = \mathrm{T} = (1, 0, 0)$, the curve is closed. Eliminating t, we obtain $y = y$, $x = \sqrt{1 - y^2}$, $z = y$, $0 \leq y \leq 1$ and $y = y$, $x = -\sqrt{1 - y^2}$, $z = y$, $0 \leq y \leq 1$; the curve is an ellipse—a simple closed curve. (See figure.)

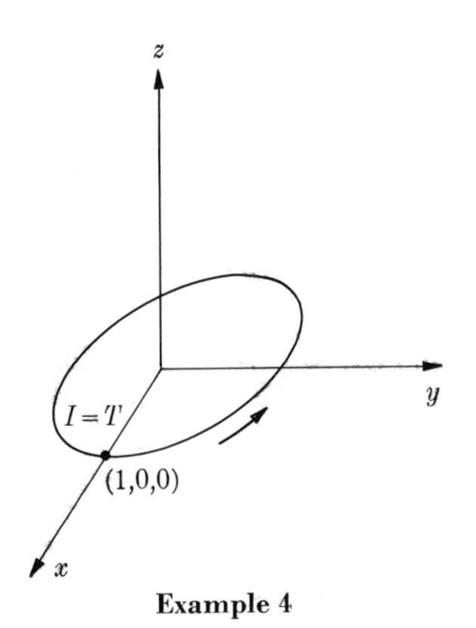

Example 4

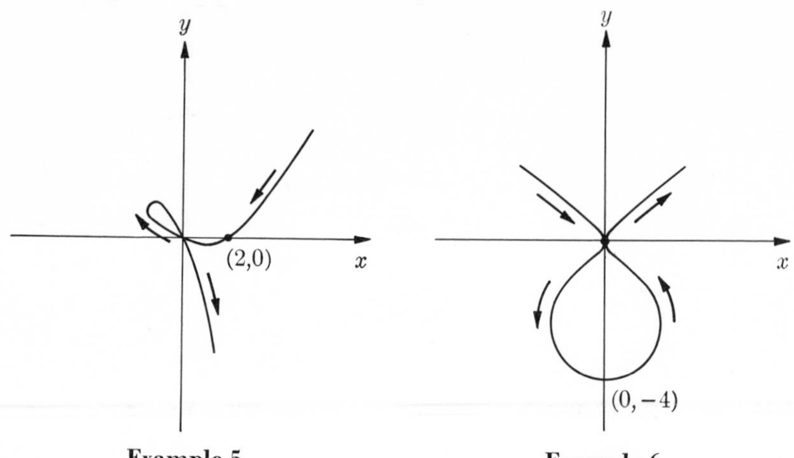

Example 5 **Example 6**

EXAMPLE 5. $\boldsymbol{\phi}(t) = (t^2 - t)\mathbf{i} + (t - t^3)\mathbf{j}, -\infty < t < \infty$.

The point (0, 0) is a multiple point; there are no others. The simplest way to represent this curve geometrically is by noting how $x = t^2 - t$, $y = t - t^3$ vary as t goes from $-\infty$ to $+\infty$. Note that the curve crosses itself at the multiple point. This is not a simple curve. (See figure.)

EXAMPLE 6. $\boldsymbol{\phi}(t) = t(t^2 - 4)^2\mathbf{i} + (t^2 - 4)\mathbf{j}, -\infty < t < \infty$.

The point (0, 0) is a multiple point; there are no others. Note that the curve is tangent to itself at this point. (See figure.)

EXAMPLE 7. $\boldsymbol{\phi}(t) = \cos t\mathbf{i} + \sin 2t\mathbf{j}, 0 \leq t \leq 2\pi$.

Since I = T = (1, 0), the curve is closed. But it is not a simple closed curve, since there is an ordinary multiple point at (0, 0). (See figure.)

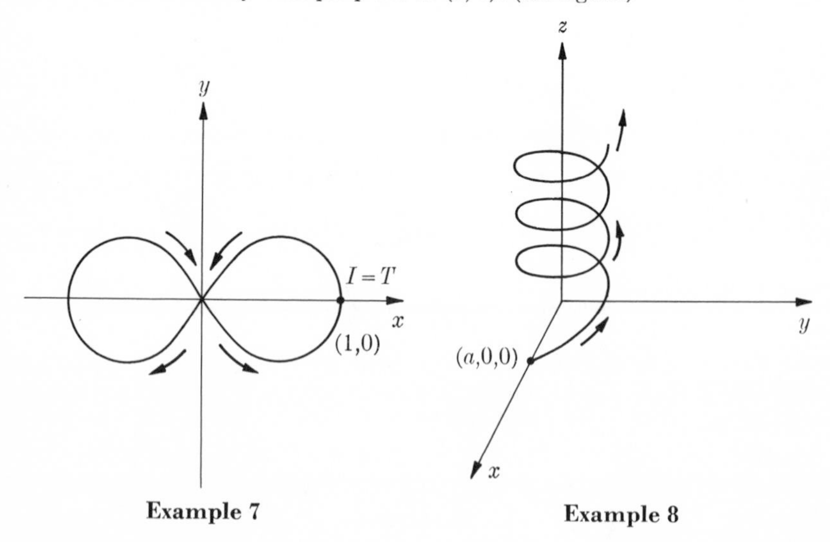

Example 7 **Example 8**

EXAMPLE 8. $\boldsymbol{\phi}(t) = a\cos t\mathbf{i} + b\sin t\mathbf{j} + ct\mathbf{k}$, $c > 0$, $0 \leq t < \infty$. The curve is a cylindrical helix—a simple curve. (See figure.)

We now consider a geometric interpretation of the derivative of a vector function at a point. Let C be the curve of the vector function $\boldsymbol{\phi} = \phi_1\mathbf{i} + \phi_2\mathbf{j} + \phi_3\mathbf{k}$, differentiable in E, and let t_0 be a fixed point and t any point in E. Then $\boldsymbol{\phi}(t_0)$ and $\boldsymbol{\phi}(t)$ will be the position vectors of the two

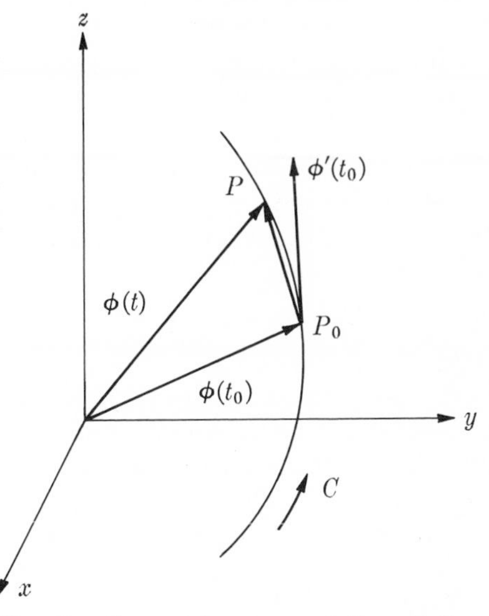

Fig. 1. Geometric representation of the derivative

points P_0 and P, as illustrated in Fig. 1. Then $\overrightarrow{P_0P}$ is the vector $\boldsymbol{\phi}(t) - \boldsymbol{\phi}(t_0)$. As $t \to t_0$,

$$\frac{\boldsymbol{\phi}(t) - \boldsymbol{\phi}(t_0)}{t - t_0} \to \boldsymbol{\phi}'(t_0),$$

a vector that is tangent to C at P_0. We call this vector the **tangent vector** to C at P_0. Its magnitude is $|\boldsymbol{\phi}'(t_0)|$ and its direction cosines are

$$\frac{\phi_i'(t_0)}{|\boldsymbol{\phi}'(t_0)|}, \qquad i = 1, 2, 3,$$

provided $|\boldsymbol{\phi}'(t_0)| \neq 0$. Hence, this tangent vector can serve as a geometric representation of the derivative of a vector function at a point. If $|\boldsymbol{\phi}'(t_0)| = 0$, then $\boldsymbol{\phi}'(t_0)$ is the zero vector whose geometric representation is the point (x_0, y_0, z_0), where $x_0 = \phi_1(t_0)$, $y_0 = \phi_2(t_0)$, $z_0 = \phi_3(t_0)$, and whose direction cosines are undefined. A point on C such that $|\boldsymbol{\phi}'(t_0)| = 0$ is called a **singular point** of C. Such a point is also called a singular point of $\boldsymbol{\phi}$.

We now define the *direction of the curve of a vector function at a non-singular point* to be the direction of the tangent vector to the curve at that point. The student should show that the tangent vectors along C turn in the direction of C, as previously defined; i.e., the direction in which a particle moves along C as t increases in E.

In the elementary calculus a curve is called smooth if there is no abrupt change of direction at any point of the curve, or stated otherwise, if the curve has a continuously turning tangent at every point of the curve. Our concern is with the curve of a vector function; we wish to determine what properties a vector function must have to ensure that its curve be smooth. First, we define a **smooth vector function** in E to be a vector function that has a continuous derivative and no singular points in E. If the vector function $\boldsymbol{\phi} = \phi_1\mathbf{i} + \phi_2\mathbf{j} + \phi_3\mathbf{k}$ is smooth in E, then its curve C is smooth in E in the sense that it will have no abrupt change in direction at any point. This follows from the fact that this direction is specified by the direction cosines

$$\frac{\phi_i'(t)}{|\boldsymbol{\phi}'(t)|}, \qquad i = 1, 2, 3,$$

which are continuous in E. However, *a vector function which is not smooth may have a smooth curve.* It can be shown (the proof is beyond the scope of this course) that if a parametrizable curve is smooth, then it is the curve of some smooth vector function. The vector functions in Examples 1 to 8 are smooth (proof?); hence, their curves are smooth.

EXAMPLE 9. $\boldsymbol{\phi}(t) = t^3\mathbf{i} + |t^3|\mathbf{j}, \ -\infty < t < \infty.$

Although the derivative of $\boldsymbol{\phi}$ is continuous, $\boldsymbol{\phi}$ is not smooth, since 0 is a singular point. The curve C of $\boldsymbol{\phi}$ is not smooth; furthermore, there exists no smooth vector function having C as its curve. (See figure.)

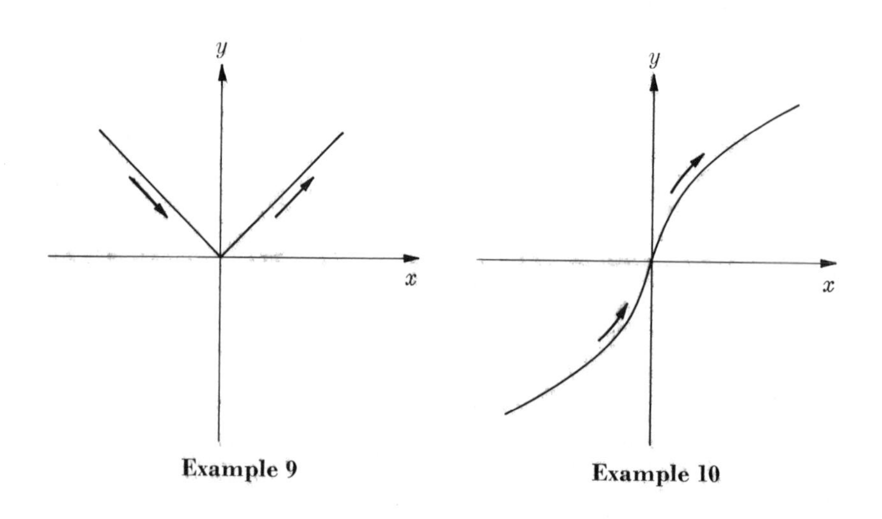

Example 9 **Example 10**

EXAMPLE 10. $\boldsymbol{\phi}(t) = t\mathbf{i} + t^{1/3}\mathbf{j}, -\infty < t < \infty.$

$\boldsymbol{\phi}$ is *not* a smooth function since the derivative of $\boldsymbol{\phi}$ is not continuous at $t = 0$. However, a glance at the geometric representation of the curve of $\boldsymbol{\phi}$ (see figure) suggests strongly that the curve is smooth. Hence, we suspect there exists a smooth vector function such that this is its curve. Such a function is $\boldsymbol{\psi}$, where $\boldsymbol{\psi}(t) = t^3\mathbf{i} + t\mathbf{j}, -\infty < t < \infty.$

Given any number of smooth vector functions $\boldsymbol{\phi}_n$, $n = 1, 2, 3, \cdots$, defined in E_n, whose curves have initial points I_n and terminal points T_n such that $I_{n+1} = T_n$. The curve formed by joining these smooth curves in succession is called a **piecewise smooth curve.** It is clear, then, that the direction of such a curve is well defined. Note in particular that every smooth curve is a piecewise smooth curve, but not conversely. A **closed piecewise smooth curve** consists of a finite number of smooth curves $(C_1, \cdots, C_n)$ forming a piecewise smooth curve and such that the initial point of C_1 is the terminal point of C_n. If $C_1, C_2, \cdots$ are the smooth curves that constitute the piecewise smooth curve C, we shall write $C = C_1 + C_2 + \cdots$.

EXAMPLE 11. C_1: $\boldsymbol{\phi}(t) = \cos t\mathbf{i} - \sin t\mathbf{j}, -\pi \le t \le -\pi/2;$

C_2: $\boldsymbol{\psi}(t) = t\mathbf{i} + (1 - t)\mathbf{j}, 0 \le t \le 1.$

$C = C_1 + C_2$ is a piecewise smooth curve consisting of a quarter-circle joined to a line segment (see figure). It is not closed.

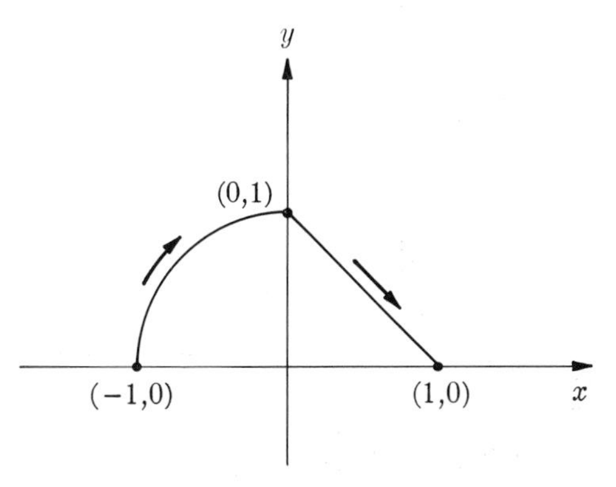

Example 11

EXAMPLE 12. C_n: $\boldsymbol{\phi}_n(t) = t\mathbf{i} + (t - n)\mathbf{j}, \quad 2n \le t \le 2n + 1,$
$n = 0, 1, 2, \cdots$

$\boldsymbol{\phi}_n(t) = t\mathbf{i} + n\mathbf{j}, \quad 2n - 1 \le t \le 2n, n = 1, 2, 3, \cdots.$

$C = C_1 + C_2 + \cdots$ is a piecewise smooth curve (see figure) that can also be considered as the curve of a vector function that is smooth in $0 \le t < \infty$ except at a finite number of points in every finite interval.

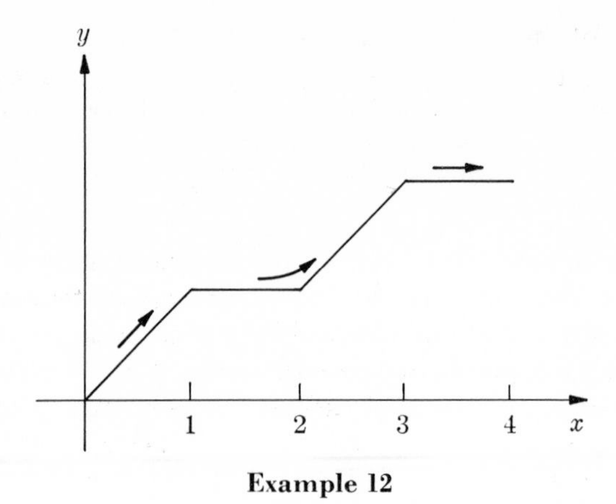

Example 12

EXAMPLE 13. C_1: $\boldsymbol{\phi}_1(t) = \mathbf{i} + \mathbf{j} + t\mathbf{k},\ 0 \le t \le 1;$
C_2: $\boldsymbol{\phi}_2(t) = (1-t)\mathbf{i} + (1-t)\mathbf{j} + (1-t)\mathbf{k},\ 0 \le t \le 1;$
C_3: $\boldsymbol{\phi}_3(t) = t\mathbf{i} + 2(1-t)\mathbf{k},\ 0 \le t \le 1;$
C_4: $\boldsymbol{\phi}_4(t) = \mathbf{i} + t\mathbf{j},\ 0 \le t \le 1.$

$C = C_1 + C_2 + C_3 + C_4$ is a skew quadrilateral—a closed piecewise smooth curve (see figure).

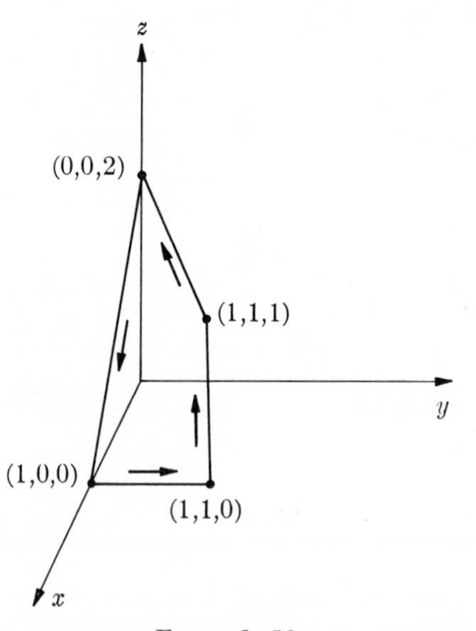

Example 13

A piecewise smooth curve such that all smooth curves constituting it are simple curves that do not cross each other will be called a **regular**

curve. Which are the regular curves in Examples 1 to 13? Our primary concern will be with regular curves.

4. Arc length, unit tangent and normal vectors, and curvature. Let $\boldsymbol{\phi} = \phi_1\mathbf{i} + \phi_2\mathbf{j} + \phi_3\mathbf{k}$ be a smooth vector function defined in $\alpha \le t \le \beta$ and whose curve is C. Since $\boldsymbol{\phi}$ is a smooth vector function in $\alpha \le t \le \beta$, $\boldsymbol{\phi}'(t)$ is continuous there, and hence so is $|\boldsymbol{\phi}'(t)|$. This implies the existence of the integral

$$\int_\alpha^\beta |\boldsymbol{\phi}'(t)|\,dt$$

which is the vector form of

$$\int_\alpha^\beta \sqrt{[\phi_1'(t)]^2 + [\phi_2'(t)]^2 + [\phi_3'(t)]^2}\,dt.$$

The student will recognize this as the expression for the length of C, which we denote as L_C. Hence,

$$L_C = \int_\alpha^\beta |\boldsymbol{\phi}'(t)|\,dt.$$

We have the following significant

THEOREM. If $\boldsymbol{\phi}$ is a smooth vector function in $\alpha \le t \le \beta$ and $\boldsymbol{\psi}$ is a smooth vector function in $\gamma \le t \le \delta$, and both $\boldsymbol{\phi}$ and $\boldsymbol{\psi}$ have the same curve C, then

$$L_C = \int_\alpha^\beta |\boldsymbol{\phi}'(t)|\,dt = \int_\gamma^\delta |\boldsymbol{\psi}'(t)|\,dt.$$

Proof. Since $\boldsymbol{\phi}$ and $\boldsymbol{\psi}$ have the same curve, for every t in $[\gamma, \delta]$, there exists u in $[\alpha, \beta]$ such that $\boldsymbol{\phi}(u) = \boldsymbol{\psi}(t)$. Since $\boldsymbol{\phi}$ and $\boldsymbol{\psi}$ are smooth, $d\boldsymbol{\phi}/dt$ and $d\boldsymbol{\psi}/dt$ are continuous and never zero in $[\alpha, \beta]$ and $[\gamma, \delta]$, respectively. Then

$$\frac{\boldsymbol{\phi}'(u)\,du}{dt} = \boldsymbol{\psi}'(t)$$

so that $du/dt \ne 0$ and is continuous in $[\gamma, \delta]$; hence du/dt is of one sign.

Now

$$\begin{aligned}\int_\gamma^\delta |\boldsymbol{\psi}'(t)|\,dt &= \int_\alpha^\beta |\boldsymbol{\phi}'(u)|\,\frac{du}{dt}\,dt \\ &= \int_\alpha^\beta |\boldsymbol{\phi}'(u)|\,du \\ &= \int_\alpha^\beta |\boldsymbol{\phi}'(t)|\,dt.\end{aligned}$$

This theorem indicates that the length of a curve C remains the same if we represent C by any other vector function, provided that vector function is smooth. This fact has a very important practical application: If

$$L_C = \int_\alpha^\beta |\boldsymbol{\phi}'(t)|\,dt$$

is difficult to evaluate, replace $\boldsymbol{\phi}$ by another smooth vector function whose curve is C and such that the corresponding integral is easier to evaluate.

If C is a piecewise smooth curve, we define L_C as the sum of the lengths of the smooth curves constituting C.

If for any $\alpha \leq t \leq \beta$, where $\boldsymbol{\phi}$ is smooth, we consider the integral $\int_\alpha^t |\boldsymbol{\phi}'(u)|\, du$, we obtain a function of t known as **arc length** and denoted by $s(t)$. Hence,

$$\text{Arc length} = s(t) = \int_\alpha^t |\boldsymbol{\phi}'(u)|\, du.$$

Now $ds/dt = |\boldsymbol{\phi}'(t)| > 0$ in $\alpha \leq t \leq \beta$. (Why?) Hence, s is an increasing function there; furthermore, it is continuous there. This implies that s has a unique inverse $t = g(s)$, $0 \leq s \leq L_C$. [IIIAj]† Hence, starting with the smooth vector function $\boldsymbol{\phi}$ with parameter t, a smooth vector function $\boldsymbol{\psi}$ with parameter s such that $\boldsymbol{\psi}(s) = \boldsymbol{\phi}[g(s)]$ can always be determined.

We have seen that for the smooth vector function $\boldsymbol{\phi} = \phi_1\mathbf{i} + \phi_2\mathbf{j} + \phi_3\mathbf{k}$ defined in E, the tangent vector to the curve C of $\boldsymbol{\phi}$ at any point is the vector $\boldsymbol{\phi}'(t)$. Now, if $|\boldsymbol{\phi}'(t)| \neq 0$, $\boldsymbol{\phi}'(t)/|\boldsymbol{\phi}'(t)|$ is a unit vector; we shall call it the **unit tangent vector** to C, and shall always denote it by **T**. Hence,

$$\mathbf{T} = \frac{\boldsymbol{\phi}'(t)}{|\boldsymbol{\phi}'(t)|}, \qquad |\mathbf{T}| = 1.$$

The unit tangent vector assumes a simpler form when C is the curve of a vector function whose parameter is s, arc length. Let $t = g(s)$ in $\boldsymbol{\phi}'(t)$, where

$$s(t) = \int_\alpha^t |\boldsymbol{\phi}'(u)|\, du,$$

and let $\boldsymbol{\psi}(s) = \boldsymbol{\phi}[g(s)]$. Then

$$\boldsymbol{\psi}'(s) = \boldsymbol{\phi}'(t)\,\frac{dt}{ds}$$

and

$$|\boldsymbol{\psi}'(s)| = \frac{|\boldsymbol{\phi}'(t)|}{ds/dt} = 1.$$

Hence

$$\mathbf{T} = \boldsymbol{\psi}'(s).$$

EXAMPLE 1. $\boldsymbol{\phi}(t) = \cos t\,\mathbf{i} + \sin t\,\mathbf{j} + t\,\mathbf{k}$, $t \geq 0$.

$$s = \int_0^t \sqrt{2}\, du = \sqrt{2}t.$$

Hence $t = s/\sqrt{2}$ and

$$\boldsymbol{\psi}(s) = \cos\frac{s}{\sqrt{2}}\,\mathbf{i} + \sin\frac{s}{\sqrt{2}}\,\mathbf{j} + \frac{s}{\sqrt{2}}\,\mathbf{k}, \qquad s \geq 0.$$

† Notation in brackets refers to the Summary of Elementary Mathematics.

Here we have started with the vector function $\boldsymbol{\phi}$ with parameter t and have effected a change in parameter so as to obtain a vector function $\boldsymbol{\psi}$ with parameter s. $\boldsymbol{\phi}$ and $\boldsymbol{\psi}$ have the same curve. Furthermore,

$$\mathbf{T} = \boldsymbol{\psi}'(s) = \frac{1}{\sqrt{2}}\left(-\sin\frac{s}{\sqrt{2}}\,\mathbf{i} + \cos\frac{s}{\sqrt{2}}\,\mathbf{j} + \mathbf{k}\right).$$

EXAMPLE 2. $\boldsymbol{\phi}(t) = \sin\frac{t}{\sqrt{2}}\,\mathbf{i} + \sin\frac{t}{\sqrt{2}}\,\mathbf{j} + \cos t\,\mathbf{k},\ t \geq 0.$

Here,

$$s = \int_0^t du = t;$$

i.e., the parameter t *is* the arc length.

$$\mathbf{T} = \cos\frac{t}{\sqrt{2}}\,\mathbf{i} + \cos\frac{t}{\sqrt{2}}\,\mathbf{j} - \sin t\,\mathbf{k}.$$

Once we have defined the derivative of a vector function $\boldsymbol{\phi}$ at a point t in E, we can consider higher derivatives at that point:

$$\frac{d^2\boldsymbol{\phi}(t)}{dt^2},\quad \frac{d^3\boldsymbol{\phi}(t)}{dt^3},\quad \ldots,\quad \frac{d^n\boldsymbol{\phi}(t)}{dt^n},$$

defined as

$$\frac{d^k\boldsymbol{\phi}(t)}{dt^k} = \frac{d}{dt}\left[\frac{d^{k-1}\boldsymbol{\phi}(t)}{dt^{k-1}}\right], \qquad k = 2, 3, \cdots, n.$$

If $d^k\boldsymbol{\phi}(t)/dt^k$ exists in E, we say that $\boldsymbol{\phi}$ is k times differentiable in E.

Let $\boldsymbol{\phi}$ be twice differentiable in E, with $\mathbf{T}$ the unit tangent vector at any point of C, the curve of $\boldsymbol{\phi}$. Differentiating both sides of $\mathbf{T}\cdot\mathbf{T} = 1$ with respect to s yields $(d\mathbf{T}/ds)\cdot\mathbf{T} = 0$, so that $d\mathbf{T}/ds \perp \mathbf{T}$. Let $\mathbf{N}$ be the unit vector in the direction of $d\mathbf{T}/ds$; then $d\mathbf{T}/ds \| \mathbf{N}$; $\mathbf{N}$ is called the **unit principal normal** at any point of C. (The student will readily convince himself that there exist other normals.) We have that $d\mathbf{T}/ds = |d\mathbf{T}/ds|\mathbf{N}$.

We now show that $|d\mathbf{T}/ds| = K$, the curvature of C at any point. Let us first define the curvature of C at any point. Let $\mathbf{T}$ and $\mathbf{T} + \Delta\mathbf{T}$ be unit tangent vectors at points P_1 and P_2 of C and let θ be the angle between these vectors, as illustrated in Fig. 2(a). Let Δs be the length of that part of C from P_1 to P_2. We define the **curvature** of C at P_1 as

$$K = \lim_{\Delta s\to 0}\frac{\theta}{\Delta s}.$$

The curvature of a curve at a point is a measure of the rate at which the curve is turning away from its tangent line at that point. Since $\mathbf{T}$ and $\mathbf{T} + \Delta\mathbf{T}$ are unit vectors, we can represent them with a common initial point at the center of a circle, of radius one and terminal points on the circle, as illustrated in Fig. 2(b). Then $|\Delta\mathbf{T}| = 2\sin\theta/2$, and for small θ, $|\Delta\mathbf{T}| = \theta$. Hence,

$$K = \lim_{\Delta s\to 0}\frac{\theta}{\Delta s} = \lim_{\Delta s\to 0}\left|\frac{\Delta\mathbf{T}}{\Delta s}\right| = \left|\frac{d\mathbf{T}}{ds}\right|$$

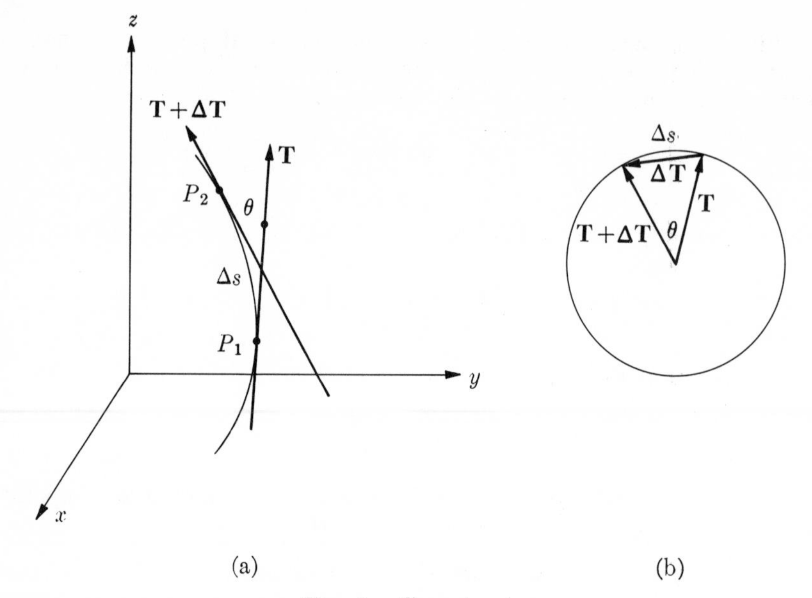

Fig. 2. Curvature

and $d\mathbf{T}/ds = K\mathbf{N}$. If $K \neq 0$, we define the **radius of curvature** at a point of C to be $\rho = 1/K$.

EXAMPLE. Show that the curvature K at any point of the curve of $\boldsymbol{\phi}(t) = a \cos t\,\mathbf{i} + a \sin t\,\mathbf{j} + bt\,\mathbf{k}$ is a constant.

Solution

$$\mathbf{T} = \frac{-a \sin t\,\mathbf{i} + a \cos t\,\mathbf{j} + b\,\mathbf{k}}{\sqrt{a^2 + b^2}} \cdot \frac{ds}{dt}$$

$$= |\boldsymbol{\phi}'(t)| = \sqrt{a^2 + b^2} \cdot \frac{d\mathbf{T}}{ds} = \frac{d\mathbf{T}/dt}{ds/dt}$$

$$= \frac{-a \cos t\,\mathbf{i} - a \sin t\,\mathbf{j}}{a^2 + b^2} \cdot K$$

$$= \left|\frac{d\mathbf{T}}{ds}\right| = \frac{a}{a^2 + b^2}.$$

5. Displacement, velocity, and acceleration vectors. If a particle moves along the curve C of a given vector function, the motion of the particle can be completely described by specifying the displacement, velocity, and acceleration of the particle at any time t. Since these quantities are vectors, we now consider their analytic representations.

Let $\mathbf{r} = r_1\mathbf{i} + r_2\mathbf{j} + r_3\mathbf{k}$ be a vector function defined on E, with the parameter t denoting time, and let C be its curve. Then for any t in E,

$\mathbf{r}(t)$ is the **position vector** of a particle moving along C. Suppose that the starting point of the particle has a position vector $\mathbf{r}(t_0)$; then, for any t, the **displacement vector** of the particle is $\mathbf{r}(t) - \mathbf{r}(t_0)$. We define the **velocity vector** of the particle at a given time t in E as the time rate of change of the position vector at that time; i.e., if $\mathbf{v}(t)$ is this velocity vector, then $\mathbf{v}(t) = \mathbf{r}'(t)$. Hence, the velocity vector will be tangent to C at the terminal point of $\mathbf{r}(t)$. Furthermore, $\mathbf{v}(t) = v(t)\mathbf{T}$, in which $v(t) = |\mathbf{v}(t)|$ is called the **speed** of the particle at time t. We define the **acceleration vector** of the particle $\mathbf{a}(t)$ as the time rate of change of the velocity vector; i.e., $\mathbf{a}(t) = \mathbf{v}'(t) = \mathbf{r}''(t)$. Hence, if

$$\mathbf{r}(t) = r_1(t)\mathbf{i} + r_2(t)\mathbf{j} + r_3(t)\mathbf{k},$$

then

$$\mathbf{v}(t) = r_1'(t)\mathbf{i} + r_2'(t)\mathbf{j} + r_3'(t)\mathbf{k},$$

and

$$\mathbf{a}(t) = r_1''(t)\mathbf{i} + r_2''(t)\mathbf{j} + r_3''(t)\mathbf{k}.$$

We have seen that the velocity vector will be tangent to the curve of the position vector of the particle. The acceleration vector can be constructed from its components. However, since at any point on C the acceleration vector $\mathbf{a}$, the unit tangent vector $\mathbf{T}$, and the unit principal normal vector $\mathbf{N}$ are coplanar (proof?), it is more convenient to resolve $\mathbf{a}$ into the sum of two vectors, one in the direction of $\mathbf{T}$ and the other in the direction of $\mathbf{N}$. We write

$$\mathbf{a} = a_t\mathbf{T} + a_n\mathbf{N} \tag{1}$$

and call a_t and a_n the tangential component and normal component of $\mathbf{a}$. We now determine a_t and a_n. If we dot both sides of (1) by $\mathbf{v}$, the velocity vector, we obtain $a_t = \mathbf{a}\cdot\mathbf{v}/v$, since $\mathbf{v}\cdot\mathbf{T} = v$ and $\mathbf{v}\cdot\mathbf{N} = 0$; if we cross both sides of (1) by $\mathbf{v}$ and then take the absolute value of both sides, we obtain

$$a_n = \frac{|\mathbf{a} \times \mathbf{v}|}{v},$$

since $\mathbf{v} \times \mathbf{T} = \mathbf{0}$ and $|\mathbf{v} \times \mathbf{N}| = v$. Hence,

$$\mathbf{a} = \frac{\mathbf{a}\cdot\mathbf{v}}{v}\mathbf{T} + \frac{|\mathbf{a} \times \mathbf{v}|}{v}\mathbf{N}. \tag{2}$$

The student should show that we also have $a_t = dv/dt$ and $a_n = v^2/\rho$, where v is the speed and ρ is the radius of curvature, so that

$$\mathbf{a} = \frac{dv}{dt}\mathbf{T} + \frac{v^2}{\rho}\mathbf{N}. \tag{3}$$

The representation (3) is illustrated in Fig. 3. The vector $\mathbf{a}$ is so directed that it is on the other side of the curve from $\mathbf{v}$. This representation has an important physical interpretation. Let a particle move along the curve C, acted on by a force $\mathbf{F} = \mathbf{F}_t + \mathbf{F}_n$, where $\mathbf{F}_t$ is a force acting in the direction

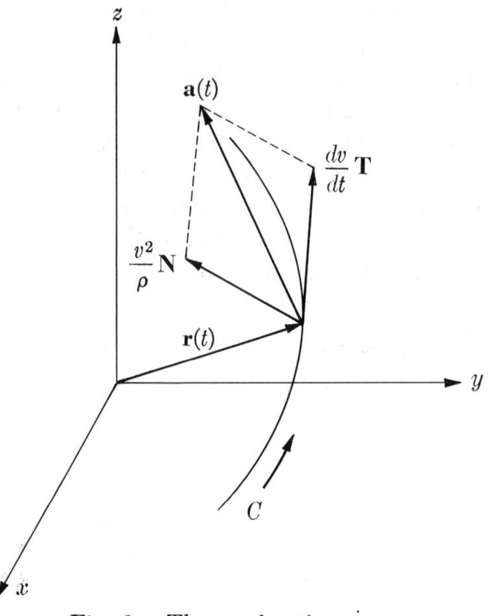

Fig. 3. The acceleration vector

of $\mathbf{T}$ and $\mathbf{F}_n$ a force acting in the direction of $\mathbf{N}$. Then, by Newton's law, $\mathbf{F}_t = m(dv/dt)\mathbf{T}$, so that this force controls the speed of the particle while $\mathbf{F}_n = (mv^2/\rho)\mathbf{N}$ is the force that constrains the particle to move along the curve (the centripetal force). If the position vector $\mathbf{r}$ of the particle is given, the tangential and normal components of $\mathbf{a}$ are more readily determined from the representation of $\mathbf{a}$ in (2) rather than that in (3).

EXAMPLE. The position vector of a particle is $\mathbf{r}(t) = t\mathbf{i} + t^2\mathbf{j} + \frac{2}{3}\mathbf{k}$, $t \geq 0$. Determine its displacement, velocity, and acceleration vectors. Determine the tangential and normal components of the acceleration vector. What are $\mathbf{T}$ and $\mathbf{N}$?

Solution

$$\begin{aligned} \mathbf{r}(t) - \mathbf{r}(0) &= t\mathbf{i} + t^2\mathbf{j} + \tfrac{2}{3}t^3\mathbf{k}, \\ \mathbf{v}(t) &= \mathbf{i} + 2t\mathbf{j} + 2t^2\mathbf{k}, \\ \mathbf{a}(t) &= 2(\mathbf{j} + 2t\mathbf{k}). \end{aligned}$$

$$a_t = \frac{\mathbf{a}\cdot\mathbf{v}}{v} = \frac{4(t + 2t^3)}{\sqrt{1 + 4t^2 + 4t^4}} = 4t,$$

$$a_n = \frac{|\mathbf{a}\times\mathbf{v}|}{v} = 2.$$

Hence $\mathbf{a} = 4t\mathbf{T} + 2\mathbf{N}$, where

$$\mathbf{T} = \frac{\mathbf{v}}{v} = \frac{\mathbf{i} + 2t\mathbf{j} + 2t^2\mathbf{k}}{1 + 2t^2}$$

and

$$\mathbf{N} = \frac{d\mathbf{T}/ds}{|d\mathbf{T}/ds|} = \frac{d\mathbf{T}/dt}{|d\mathbf{T}/dt|}$$

$$= -2t\mathbf{i} + (1 - 2t^2)\mathbf{j} + \frac{2t\mathbf{k}}{1 + 2t^2}.$$

EXERCISES

1. Let $\boldsymbol{\phi}(t) = t\mathbf{i} - 2t^2\mathbf{j} + 4t^3\mathbf{k}$, $\boldsymbol{\psi}(t) = \mathbf{i} + t\mathbf{j} + (1 - t)\mathbf{k}$. Evaluate at $t = 1$:
(a) $\boldsymbol{\phi}'(t)$; (b) $|\boldsymbol{\psi}'(t)|$; (c) $(d/dt)[\boldsymbol{\phi}(t)\cdot\boldsymbol{\psi}(t)]$; (d) $(d/dt)[\boldsymbol{\phi}(t) \times \boldsymbol{\psi}(t)]$; (e) $d\boldsymbol{\psi}/ds$.

Ans.: (a) $\mathbf{i} - 4\mathbf{j} + 12\mathbf{k}$; (b) $\sqrt{2}/2$; (c) -6; (d) $-11\mathbf{i} + 13\mathbf{j} + 6\mathbf{k}$; (e) $\mathbf{j} - \mathbf{k}/\sqrt{2}$.

2. Let $\boldsymbol{\phi}(t) = \sin t\mathbf{i} + \cos t\mathbf{j} + \sin t\,\mathbf{k}$, $\boldsymbol{\psi}(t) = e^t\mathbf{i} + t\mathbf{j} + \mathbf{k}$, $\boldsymbol{\chi}(t) = \cos t\,\mathbf{i} + \sin t\,\mathbf{j} + t\,\mathbf{k}$. Evaluate at $t = 0$:
(a) $(d/dt)[\boldsymbol{\phi}(t)\;\boldsymbol{\psi}(t)\;\boldsymbol{\chi}(t)]$; (b) $(d/dt)[\boldsymbol{\phi}(t) \times [\boldsymbol{\psi}(t) \times \boldsymbol{\chi}(t)]]$.

Ans.: (a) 1; (b) $2(-\mathbf{i} + \mathbf{k})$.

3. Show that if $\boldsymbol{\phi}$ is any twice differentiable vector function, then
(a) $d/dt[\boldsymbol{\phi}(t)\cdot\boldsymbol{\phi}'(t)] = [\boldsymbol{\phi}'(t)]^2 + \boldsymbol{\phi}(t)\cdot\boldsymbol{\phi}''(t)$.
(b) $d/dt[\boldsymbol{\phi}(t) \times \boldsymbol{\phi}'(t)] = \boldsymbol{\phi}(t) \times \boldsymbol{\phi}''(t)$.

4. Show that if $\boldsymbol{\phi}$ is any thrice differentiable vector function, then

$$d/dt[\boldsymbol{\phi}(t)\;\boldsymbol{\phi}'(t)\;\boldsymbol{\phi}''(t)] = [\boldsymbol{\phi}(t)\;\boldsymbol{\phi}'(t)\;\boldsymbol{\phi}'''(t)].$$

5. Show that $\boldsymbol{\phi}(t) = e^{-t}(\mathbf{a}\cos 2t + \mathbf{b}\sin 2t)$, where $\mathbf{a}$ and $\mathbf{b}$ are arbitrary constant vectors, is a solution of the vector differential equation

$$\boldsymbol{\phi}''(t) + 2\boldsymbol{\phi}'(t) + 5\boldsymbol{\phi}(t) = \mathbf{0}.$$

6. If $\mathbf{a}$ and $\mathbf{b}$ are constant vectors, f is twice differentiable, and $\boldsymbol{\phi}(t) = \mathbf{a} + f(t)\mathbf{b}$, show that $\boldsymbol{\phi}'(t) \times \boldsymbol{\phi}''(t) = \mathbf{0}$.

7. If $\boldsymbol{\phi}(t) \times \boldsymbol{\phi}'(t) = \mathbf{0}$, show that $\boldsymbol{\phi}(t)$ has a constant direction.

8. (a) Show that $\boldsymbol{\phi}(t)\cdot\boldsymbol{\phi}'(t) = \phi(t)\phi'(t)$.
(b) If $\boldsymbol{\phi}(t)$ has constant magnitude, show that $\boldsymbol{\phi}(t) \perp \boldsymbol{\phi}'(t)$. [*Hint:* Differentiate both sides of $|\boldsymbol{\phi}(t)|^2 = \boldsymbol{\phi}(t)\cdot\boldsymbol{\phi}(t)$.]
(c) Show that $|(d/dt)|\boldsymbol{\phi}(t)|| \le |(d/dt)\boldsymbol{\phi}(t)|$. When does equality hold?

9. Let $\boldsymbol{\phi}(t) = \sin t\,\mathbf{i} + \cos t\,\mathbf{j} + \mathbf{k}$.
(a) Show that $\boldsymbol{\phi}'(t)$ is parallel to the xy-plane for all t.
(b) Determine the values of t for which $\boldsymbol{\phi}'(t)$ is parallel to the xz-plane.
(c) Show that $\boldsymbol{\phi}(t)$ and $\boldsymbol{\phi}'(t)$ have constant magnitude.

Ans.: (b) $t = (2k + 1)(\pi/2)$, $k = 0, \pm 1, \pm 2, \cdots$.

10. Sketch the curves of each of the following vector functions. Determine all multiple points and singular points. Indicate which curves are (1) simple, (2) closed, (3) simple closed curves, (4) smooth, (5) piecewise smooth, (6) regular.
(a) $(t + 1)\mathbf{i} + (t + 2)\mathbf{j} + (t + 3)\mathbf{k}$, $-\infty < t < \infty$.
(b) $t\mathbf{i} + t^4\mathbf{j}$, $|t| \le 1$.
(c) $\sin t\,\mathbf{i} + \cos t\,\mathbf{j}$, $0 \le t \le 2\pi$.
(d) $t\mathbf{i} + t^2\mathbf{j} + t^3\mathbf{k}$, $t \ge 0$.
(e) $a\cos t\,\mathbf{i} + b\sin t\,\mathbf{j}$, $0 \le t \le 2\pi$.

(f) $\frac{1}{2}(1 + t^{1/3})\mathbf{i} + \frac{1}{4}(1 + 2t^{1/3} + t^{2/3})\mathbf{j}$, $|t| \leq 1$.
(g) $\cosh t\,\mathbf{i} + \sinh t\,\mathbf{j}$, $t \geq 0$.
(h) $\sin 2\pi t\,\mathbf{i} + \cos 2\pi t\,\mathbf{j} + (2t - t^2)\mathbf{k}$, $0 \leq t \leq 2$.
(i) $t^2\mathbf{i} + (t^3 - 4t)\mathbf{j}$, $-\infty < t < \infty$.
(j) $(t^2 - 2t)\mathbf{i} + 3t\mathbf{j} - t^2\mathbf{k}$, $-\infty < t < \infty$.

(k) $\dfrac{3t\,\mathbf{i}}{1 + t^3} + \dfrac{3t^2\mathbf{j}}{1 + t^3}$, $-\infty < t < \infty$.

(l) $t\,\mathbf{i} + |t|\mathbf{j}$, $|t| \leq 1$.
(m) $\cos^3 t\,\mathbf{i} + \sin^3 t\,\mathbf{j}$, $0 \leq t \leq 2\pi$.
(n) $(t - \sin t)\mathbf{i} + (1 - \cos t)\mathbf{j}$, $t \geq 0$.
(o) $2\sin^2 t\,\mathbf{i} + \sin 2t\,\mathbf{j} + 2\cos t\,\mathbf{k}$, $0 \leq t \leq 2\pi$.

(p) $\dfrac{(1 - t^2)\mathbf{i}}{1 - 4t^2} + \dfrac{t(1 - t^2)\mathbf{j}}{1 - 4t^2}$, $|t| < \dfrac{1}{2}$.

(q) $(1 + t^3)\mathbf{i} + t(1 - t^3)\mathbf{j}$, $-\infty < t < \infty$.
(r) $(3t - t^3)\mathbf{i} + 3t^2\mathbf{j} + (3t + t^3)\mathbf{k}$, $-\infty < t < \infty$.
(s) $(1 + \sin t)\mathbf{i} + (1 - \sin t)\mathbf{j} + 2\sin t\,\mathbf{k}$, $0 \leq t \leq 2\pi$.

(t) $\dfrac{2t(24 - 5t^2)\mathbf{i}}{3t^4 - 24t^2 + 64} - \dfrac{2(t^2 - 4)(t^2 - 16)\mathbf{j}}{3t^4 - 24t^2 + 64}$, $-\infty < t < \infty$.

(*Note:* $t = \pm\infty$ both determine the point $(0, -\frac{2}{3})$ on the curve. Conclusion?)
(u) $t\,\mathbf{i} + (|t + 2| - |t - 2|)\mathbf{j}$, $-\infty < t < \infty$.
(v) $f(t)\mathbf{i} + f(-t)\mathbf{j}$, $f(t) = t^4$, $t > 0$, $f(t) = 0$, $t \leq 0$.
(w) $x\mathbf{i} + y\mathbf{j}$, $y^2(y + 1)^3 = x^2(x + 1)^4$.
(x) $t\,\mathbf{i} + f(t)\mathbf{j}$, $f(t) = \sin t$, $0 \leq t \leq 2\pi$, $f(t + 2\pi) = f(t)$, $t \geq 2\pi$.
(y) $x\mathbf{i} + y\mathbf{j}$, $5|y| + |3x + 4y| = 15$.

11. Describe the curves of each of the following vector functions:
(a) $(t^3 - 3t + 1)\mathbf{i}$, $-\infty < t < \infty$.
(b) $\cos t\,\mathbf{i} + \sin t\,\mathbf{j}$, $(3\pi/2) \leq t \leq 5\pi$.
(c) $\cos t\,\mathbf{i} + \sin t\,\mathbf{j} + \sin t\,\mathbf{k}$, $0 \leq t \leq 3\pi$.
(d) $f(t)\mathbf{i} + g(t)\mathbf{j}$, $f(t) = \cos t$, $g(t) = \sin t$, $0 \leq t \leq \pi/2$; $f(t) = \sin t$, $g(t) = -\cos t$, $(\pi/2) \leq t \leq (3/2)\pi$; $f(t) = \cos t$, $g(t) = \sin t$, $(3\pi/2) \leq t \leq (7\pi/2)$.

12. (a) Sketch the curve of the vector function $\boldsymbol{\phi}$, $t \geq 0$, where

$$\boldsymbol{\phi}(t) = \begin{cases} t\,\mathbf{i} + t\,\mathbf{j}, & 0 \leq t \leq 1 \\ t\,\mathbf{i} + (2 - t)\mathbf{j}, & 1 \leq t \leq 3 \\ t\,\mathbf{i} + (t - 4)\mathbf{j}, & 3 \leq t \leq 4 \end{cases}$$

and $\boldsymbol{\phi}(t + 4) = \boldsymbol{\phi}(t)$, $t \geq 4$. Is it piecewise smooth? Regular?

(b) Construct a piecewise smooth curve that comprises the curves of the following vector functions, joined in succession, changing the parametrization of any curve if necessary:

(1) $\boldsymbol{\phi}(t) = -\cos t\,\mathbf{i} + \sin t\,\mathbf{j}$, $0 \leq t \leq \dfrac{\pi}{2}$.

(2) $\boldsymbol{\psi}(t) = \mathbf{j}$, $0 \leq t \leq 2$.
(3) $\boldsymbol{\chi}(t) = t\,\mathbf{i} + (t - 1)\mathbf{j}$, $0 \leq t \leq 2$.

(c) Given the points $(1, 1, 1)$, $(2, 0, 1)$, $(1, 2, 3)$, $(-1, 2, 1)$; join them in order to form a skew quadrilateral. Determine vector functions of the form $t\mathbf{i} + f(t)\mathbf{j} + g(t)\mathbf{k}$ so that their curves form the piecewise smooth curve that is this quadrilateral.

13. Find the length of the curves of each of the following vector functions:

(a) $5t\,\mathbf{i} + 3t^2\mathbf{j} + \sqrt{11}t\,\mathbf{k}$, $0 \le t \le 1$; (b) $t\,\mathbf{i} + \sin 2\pi t\,\mathbf{j} + \cos 2\pi t\,\mathbf{k}$, $0 \le t \le 1$; (c) $(\sin t - t\cos t)\mathbf{i} + (\cos t + t\sin t)\mathbf{j} + t^2\mathbf{k}$, $0 \le t \le 2\pi$; (d) $e^t\cos t\,\mathbf{i} + e^t\sin t\,\mathbf{j}$, $0 \le t \le 2\pi$; (e) $\cos 3t\,\mathbf{i} + \sin 3t\,\mathbf{j}$, $0 \le t \le 2\pi$; (f) $\log\cos t\,\mathbf{i} + \log\sin t\,\mathbf{j} + \sqrt{2}\mathbf{k}$, $(\pi/4) \le t \le (\pi/3)$; (g) $C_1 + C_2 + C_3$, where C_1: $t\,\mathbf{i} + (1 - t^2)\mathbf{j}$, $0 \le t \le 1$; C_2: $\cos t\,\mathbf{i} + \sin t\,\mathbf{j}$, $\pi \le t \le (3\pi/2)$; C_3: $(t-1)\mathbf{i} + t\,\mathbf{j}$, $-1 \le t \le 0$; (h) $t^{3/2}\mathbf{i} + t^3\mathbf{j}$, $0 \le t \le 1$. (*Hint:* Find a parametrization of the curve that will give a simpler integral.)

Ans.: (a) $3[\sqrt{2} + \log(1 + \sqrt{2})]$; (b) $\sqrt{1 + 4\pi^2}$; (c) $2\sqrt{5}\pi^2$; (d) $\sqrt{2}(e - 1)$; (e) 6π; (f) $\log\left[\dfrac{\sqrt{3}(2 + \sqrt{2})}{2(2 + \sqrt{3})}\right]$; (g) $\dfrac{\sqrt{5}}{2} + \dfrac{1}{4}\log(2 + \sqrt{5}) + \pi + \sqrt{2}$; (h) $\frac{1}{8}[\sqrt{5} - \frac{1}{2}\log(\sqrt{5} + 2)]$.

14. Find the unit tangent vector $\mathbf{T}$ to the curves of the following vector functions at the points specified:

(a) $(t^2 + 1)\mathbf{i} + (4t - 3)\mathbf{j} + (2t^2 - 6t)\mathbf{k}$, $t = 2$;
(b) $a\cos t\,\mathbf{i} + b\sin t\,\mathbf{j}$, $t = 3\pi/2$;
(c) $(\sin t - t\cos t)\mathbf{i} + (\cos t + t\sin t)\mathbf{j} + t^2\mathbf{k}$, $t = \pi$;
(d) $a\sin 2t\,\mathbf{i} + a(1 + \cos 2t)\mathbf{j} + 2a\sin t\,\mathbf{k}$, $t = 0$;
(e) $a\cos\omega t\,\mathbf{i} + a\sin\omega t\,\mathbf{j} + bt\,\mathbf{k}$, t any point.

Ans.: (a) $2\mathbf{i} + 2\mathbf{j} + (\mathbf{k}/3)$; (b) $\mathbf{i}$; (c) $(\sqrt{5}/5)(-\mathbf{j} + 2\mathbf{k})$; (d) $\mathbf{i} + \mathbf{k}/\sqrt{2}$.

15. (a) Prove: If $\boldsymbol{\phi}$ is a smooth vector function in E, then the parameter t is the arc length of the curve of $\boldsymbol{\phi}$ if and only if $|\boldsymbol{\phi}'(t)| = 1$ for all t in E.

(b) Is the parameter t the arc length of the curve whose vector function is

$$\frac{\sqrt{t^2 + t + 4}}{2}\mathbf{i} + \frac{\sqrt{t^2 - t + 4}}{2}\mathbf{j} + \sqrt{2}\log\frac{\sqrt{t^2 + t + 4}}{2}\mathbf{k}?$$

(c) Determine the parametrization of the curve, one of whose vector functions is $e^t\mathbf{i} + e^{-t}\mathbf{j} + \sqrt{2}t\,\mathbf{k}$, so that the parameter is arc length.

16. (a) Show that the curvature at any point of the curve of the twice differentiable vector function $\boldsymbol{\phi}$ is

$$K = \frac{|\boldsymbol{\phi}'(t) \times \boldsymbol{\phi}''(t)|}{|\boldsymbol{\phi}'(t)|^3},$$

which becomes

$$K = \frac{|\mathbf{v}(t) \times \mathbf{a}(t)|}{[v(t)]^3},$$

if $\boldsymbol{\phi}(t)$ is the position vector of a particle.

(b) Show that if $\mathbf{r}(t) = a(t - \sin t)\mathbf{i} + a(1 - \cos t)\mathbf{j}$,

$$\mathbf{T} = \sin\frac{t}{2}\mathbf{i} + \cos\frac{t}{2}\mathbf{j},$$

$$\mathbf{v}(t) = 2a\sin\frac{t}{2},$$

$$\rho = 4a\sin\frac{t}{2}.$$

(c) Show that if a particle moves along a curve so that its velocity and acceleration vectors always have unit length, then $K = 1$ for all points on the curve.

17. Determine the tangential and normal components of the acceleration vector of a particle whose position vector is

(a) $t^2\mathbf{i} - t^3\mathbf{j} + t^4\mathbf{k}$ at $t = 1$.

(b) $(t^3 - 4t)\mathbf{i} + (t^2 + 4t)\mathbf{j} + (8t^2 - 3t^3)\mathbf{k}$ at $t = 2$.

Ans.: (a) $70/\sqrt{29}$, $4\sqrt{109/29}$; (b) 16, $2\sqrt{73}$.

18. Show that if a particle moves along a circle of radius a with constant angular speed $\omega = d\theta/dt$, then $\mathbf{r}(t) = a\cos\theta\,\mathbf{i} + a\sin\theta\,\mathbf{j}$ and $a(t) = -\omega^2\mathbf{r}(t)$.

19. Show that the curve of the vector function $a\sin^2 t\,\mathbf{i} + a\sin t\cos t\,\mathbf{j} + a\cos t\,\mathbf{k}$ lies on a sphere. Show that $(a, 0, 0)$ is a multiple point of the curve and that the tangent vectors to the curve at this point are perpendicular.

20. Prove that the tangent to a hyperbola at any point bisects the angle between the focal radii to the point.

21. Let $\mathbf{r}_0$ be the position vector of a fixed point P in space and let $\mathbf{r}(s)$ be the position vector of a variable point Q where $\mathbf{r}$ is twice differentiable. Show that if the distance PQ is a minimum, then $\mathbf{r} - \mathbf{r}_0$ is perpendicular to the tangent at Q. Show also that

$$\mathbf{r}\cdot\frac{d^2\mathbf{r}}{ds^2} + \left(\frac{d\mathbf{r}}{ds}\right)^2 > \mathbf{r}_0\cdot\frac{d^2\mathbf{r}}{ds^2}.$$

22. Let C be the curve of a thrice differentiable vector function $\boldsymbol{\phi}$. If $\mathbf{T}$ and $\mathbf{N}$ are the unit tangent vector and unit principal normal vector to C at any point, then the vector $\mathbf{B} = \mathbf{T}\times\mathbf{N}$ is called the **binormal vector** to C at that point. Show

(a) $|\mathbf{B}| = 1$; (b) $\mathbf{B} \perp d\mathbf{B}/ds$; (c) $d\mathbf{B}/ds = -\tau\mathbf{N}$, where at any point on C, $\tau \geq 0$ is a constant, called the *torsion* of C at that point.

(d) $$\tau = \frac{|\boldsymbol{\phi}'(t)\ \boldsymbol{\phi}''(t)\ \boldsymbol{\phi}'''(t)|}{|\boldsymbol{\phi}'(t)\times\boldsymbol{\phi}''(t)|^2}.$$

(e) $$\mathbf{B} = \frac{\boldsymbol{\phi}'(t)\times\boldsymbol{\phi}''(t)}{|\boldsymbol{\phi}'(t)\times\boldsymbol{\phi}''(t)|}.$$

(f) $$\mathbf{N} = \frac{[\boldsymbol{\phi}'(t)\times\boldsymbol{\phi}''(t)]\times\boldsymbol{\phi}'(t)}{|[\boldsymbol{\phi}'(t)\times\boldsymbol{\phi}''(t)]\times\boldsymbol{\phi}'(t)|}.$$

(g) $d\mathbf{N}/ds = \tau\mathbf{B} - K\mathbf{T}$.

23. Referring to Exercise 22, for the curve of

(a) $(3t - t^3)\mathbf{i} + 3t^2\mathbf{j} + (3t + t^3)\mathbf{k}$, show that $K = \tau = \frac{1}{3}(1 + t^2)^2$.

(b) $3t\cos t\,\mathbf{i} + 3t\sin t\,\mathbf{j} + 4t\,\mathbf{k}$; find $\mathbf{T}$, $\mathbf{N}$, $\mathbf{B}$, K and τ at $t = 0$.

Ans.: (a) $\mathbf{T} = 3\mathbf{i} + 4\mathbf{k}/5$, $\mathbf{B} = -4\mathbf{i} + 3\mathbf{k}/5$;
(b) $\mathbf{N} = \mathbf{j}$, $K = \tau = 6/25$.

24. The formulas

$$(1)\ d\mathbf{T}/ds = K\mathbf{N},\quad (2)\ d\mathbf{B}/ds = -\tau\mathbf{N},\quad (3)\ d\mathbf{N}/ds = \tau\mathbf{B} - K\mathbf{T}$$

(see Exercise 22) are known as the **Frenet-Serret formulas.** With the use of these formulas, show that for the curve whose vector function is $\boldsymbol{\phi} = \boldsymbol{\phi}(s)$, s arc length,

(a) $d\mathbf{T}/ds\cdot d\mathbf{B}/ds = -K\tau$; (b) $\mathbf{B}\cdot d\mathbf{N}/ds = -K$; (c) $\boldsymbol{\phi}'(s)\cdot\boldsymbol{\phi}'''(s) = -K^2$; (d) $\mathbf{B}\cdot d\mathbf{N}/ds = \tau$; (e) $\boldsymbol{\phi}'(s)\cdot\boldsymbol{\phi}^{(\text{iv})}(s) = -3K(dK/ds)$; (f) if $\mathbf{R} = \tau\mathbf{T} + K\mathbf{B}$, $d\mathbf{T}/ds = \mathbf{R}\times\mathbf{T}$, $d\mathbf{N}/ds = \mathbf{R}\times\mathbf{N}$, $d\mathbf{B}/ds = \mathbf{R}\times\mathbf{B}$.

25. (a) Show that for motion in a plane, the acceleration vector $\mathbf{a}$ can be expressed as $\mathbf{a} = [(d^2r/dt^2) - r(d\theta/dt)^2]\mathbf{R} + [d/dt(r^2\,d\theta/dt)(\mathbf{P}/r)]$, where the position vector $\mathbf{r} = r\mathbf{R}$, $\mathbf{R}$ a unit vector, $\mathbf{P}$ is a unit vector such that $\mathbf{P} \perp \mathbf{R}$, and θ is the angle between $\mathbf{i}$ and $\mathbf{R}$.

[*Hint:* $\mathbf{v} = [(dr/dt)\mathbf{R}] + (r\, d\mathbf{R}/dt)$, $(d\mathbf{R}/dt) \perp \mathbf{R}$, $\mathbf{R} = \cos\theta\mathbf{i} + \sin\theta\mathbf{j}$,

$$|d\mathbf{R}/dt| = d\theta/dt, \quad d\mathbf{P}/dt = -(d\theta/dt)\mathbf{R}.]$$

(b) If the acceleration of a particle moving in a plane is directed toward the origin, show that $\frac{1}{2}r^2\, d\theta/dt =$ constant. Show that the particle moves so that it sweeps out equal areas in equal time **(Kepler's law).** (*Hint:* If A is the area swept out at any time t, then $dA/d\theta = r^2/2$ and $dA/dt =$ constant.)

26. (a) The vector functions $\boldsymbol{\phi}$, $a \leq t \leq b$ and $\boldsymbol{\psi}$, $\alpha \leq t \leq \beta$ are said to be **parametrically equivalent** if there exists a continuous scalar function f in $[\alpha, \beta]$ such that there is a one-to-one correspondence between the points in $[a, b]$ and the functional values of f in $[\alpha, \beta]$, with $f(\alpha) = a$, $f(\beta) = b$, and $\boldsymbol{\psi}(t) = \boldsymbol{\phi}[f(t)]$ for every t in $[\alpha, \beta]$.

(1) Show that $\boldsymbol{\phi}(t) = t\,\mathbf{i} + t^2\mathbf{j}$, $0 \leq t \leq 1$ and

$$\boldsymbol{\phi}(t) = \tfrac{1}{2}(1 + t^{1/3})\mathbf{i} + \tfrac{1}{4}(1 + 2t^{1/3} + t^{2/3})\mathbf{j}, \quad -1 \leq t \leq 1$$

are parametrically equivalent.

(2) Show that if $\boldsymbol{\phi}(t)$ and $\boldsymbol{\psi}(t)$ are parametrically equivalent, then they have the same graph.

(b) The vector functions $\boldsymbol{\phi}$, $a \leq t \leq b$ and $\boldsymbol{\psi}$, $\alpha \leq t \leq \beta$, are said to be **smoothly equivalent** if they are smooth and parametrically equivalent with the scalar function f continuously differentiable and $f'(t) > 0$ in $[\alpha, \beta]$.

(1) Show that the vector functions in (a)(1) are not smoothly equivalent.

(2) Show that if $\boldsymbol{\phi}$ and $\boldsymbol{\psi}$ are smoothly equivalent and P is any nonsingular point on their graph, then the unit tangent vectors of the curves of $\boldsymbol{\phi}$ and $\boldsymbol{\psi}$ at P are equal. Hence the curves of smoothly equivalent vector functions are the same.

6. Regions. We have found it convenient to define vector functions on intervals along the real line. In order to study vector functions of two or three variables in a similar fashion, we must consider the analog of such intervals in two-dimensional space E^2 (the plane) and three-dimensional space E^3. This leads to the concept of region, for which we shall presently give a precise definition. We need some preliminary definitions.

Given the points $A_1, A_2, \cdots, A_n$, the set of line segments A_1A_2, A_2A_3, $\cdots$, $A_{n-1}A_n$ is called a **polygonal line.** A set of points S in E^2 or E^3 is called a **polygonally connected set,** if for every pair of points in S there exists a polygonal line L joining this pair of points such that every point in L is in S. The set of points (x, y) in E^2 such that $x^2 + y^2 < 1$ and the set of points (x, y, z) in E^3 such that $x^2 + y^2 \geq z^2$ are polygonally connected sets, whereas the set of points (x, y) in E^2 such that $xy \geq 1$ and the set of points (x, y, z) in E^3 such that $x^2 - y^2 + z^2 + 1 < 0$ are not polygonally connected sets. These sets are illustrated in Fig. 4.

Let $\mathbf{r}_0$ be the position vector of a point P_0. If $\mathbf{r}$ is the position vector of any point P such that $|\mathbf{r} - \mathbf{r}_0| < \epsilon$, $\epsilon > 0$, then the set of these points P is called an **ϵ-neighborhood** of P_0. In E^2 an ϵ-neighborhood of P_0 is the inside of a circle, and in E^3 it is the inside of a sphere—centered at P_0 and with radius ϵ. We shall have occasion to refer to ϵ-neighborhoods of points in sets, without specifying whether these sets are in E^2 or E^3; in such cases, it will always be tacitly assumed that if the set is in E^2, any ϵ-neighborhood is the inside of a circle, whereas in E^3 it is the inside of a sphere.

A point P is said to be an **interior point** of a set S if there exists an ϵ-neighborhood of P wholly contained in S. The collection of interior points of a set is called the **interior** of the set. In Fig. 4, every point in the sets illustrated in (a) and (d) is an interior point; the interior of the set in (b) is the set of points (x, y, z) such that $x^2 + y^2 > z^2$; and the interior of the set in (c) is the set of points (x, y) such that $xy > 1$.

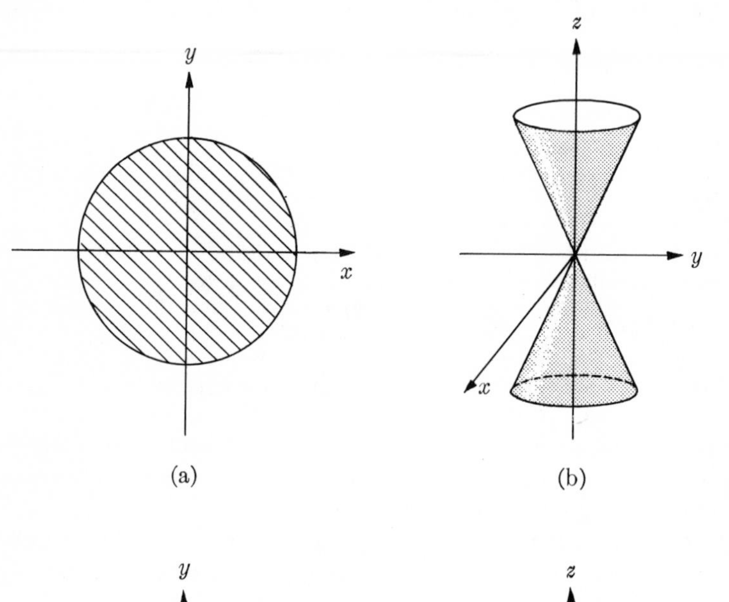

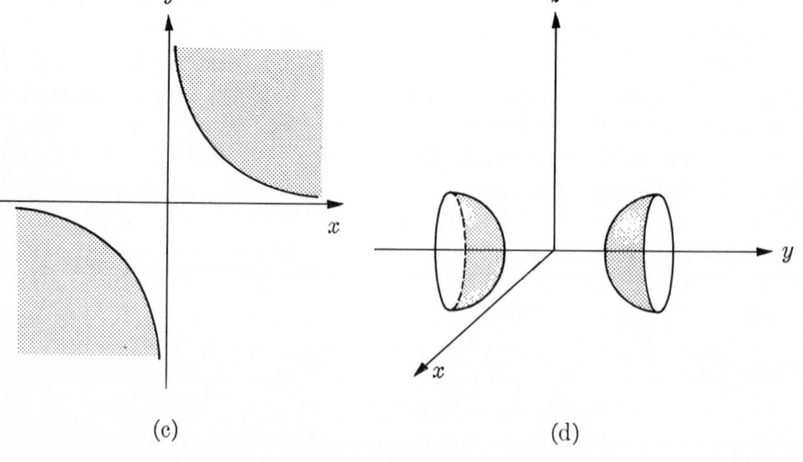

Fig. 4. Polygonally connected and nonconnected sets

The **complement of a set S in E^2** is the set of points in E^2 that are not in S and the **complement of a set S in E^3** is the set of points in E^3 that are not in S. The complement of a set S will be denoted by S'. A point P is said to be a **boundary point** of a set S if every ϵ-neighborhood of P contains at least one point in S and at least one point in S'. The collection of boundary points of a set is called the **boundary** of the set. The boundary of a set may or may not belong to the set, or only part of it may belong to the set. In the examples in Fig. 4, the boundary of the set in (a) is the set of points (x, y) such that $x^2 + y^2 = 1$—no part of the boundary belongs to the set; the boundary of the set in (b) is the set of points (x, y, z) such that $x^2 + y^2 = z^2$—all of the boundary belongs to the set. What are the boundaries of the sets in (c) and (d)? For the set of points (x, y) in E^2 such that $-\sqrt{1 - x^2} \leq y < \sqrt{1 - x^2}$, the boundary consists of the points on the circle $x^2 + y^2 = 1$, but only those points (x, y) such that $y = -\sqrt{1 - x^2}$ belong to the set; i.e., the points on the lower semicircle.

We define a **region** to be a polygonally connected set of points that may contain all its boundary, none of its boundary, or part of its boundary. If it contains all of its boundary, it is called a **closed region;** if it contains none of its boundary, it is called an **open region** or **domain;** if it contains part of its boundary, the region is neither open nor closed.

EXAMPLES

(1) The set of points (x, y) in E^2 such that $x^2 + y^2 < 1$ is an open region.

(2) The set of points (x, y, z) in E^3 such that $x^2 + y^2 + z^2 \leq 1$ is a closed region.

(3) The set of points (x, y) in E^2 such that $x^2 - y^2 > 1$ is not a region. (Why?)

(4) The set of points (x, y, z) in E^3 such that $x \geq 0, y \geq 0, z \geq 0, x + y + z \leq 1$ is a closed region. Indicate this region graphically.

(5) E^2 and E^3 are *both* open and closed. (Why?)

(6) The set of points (x, y) in E^2 such that $1 \leq x^2 + y^2 < 2$ is a region; it is neither open nor closed. Its boundary consists of two concentric circles centered at the origin, with radii 1 and 2.

(7) The set of points (x, y) in E^2 such that $x > 1$ (a half-plane) is an open region.

(8) The set of points (x, y, z) in E^3, where x, y, and z are rational numbers, is not a region. (Why?)

We shall denote a region in general by R, an open region by D, and a region in the xy-plane by R_{xy}.

A region R is bounded if there exists a constant M such that for any point in R with position vector $\mathbf{r}$, $|\mathbf{r}| < M$. In the preceding examples, we see that the regions in (1), (2), (4), (6) are bounded, whereas those in (5) and (7) are unbounded.

A region R in E^2 is a **simply connected region** if *every* regular closed curve in R is the boundary of a bounded region wholly contained in R. We shall postpone the definition of a simply connected region in E^3. Examples (1), (5), (7) indicate simply connected regions, whereas the region in (6) is not simply connected. Pictorially, a region that is not simply connected is one that has one or more "holes" in it. Such regions are called **multiply connected regions** (more precisely, doubly connected if it has one hole, triply connected if it has two holes, $\cdots$, n-tuply connected if it has $n - 1$ holes). See Fig. 5.

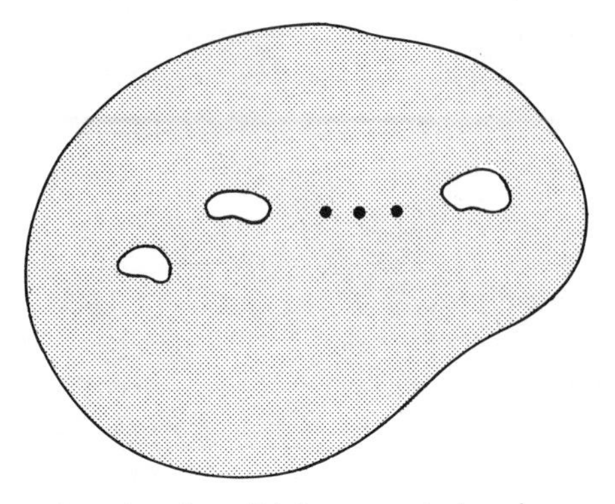

Fig. 5. A multiply connected region

7. Vector functions of two or three variables. If to every point (u, v) in some region in E^2, or to every point (u, v, w) in some region in E^3, a unique vector is assigned, we obtain vector functions of two and three variables, respectively. The functional value of the vector function $\boldsymbol{\phi}$ at (u, v, w) will be represented analytically as

$$\boldsymbol{\phi}(u, v, w) = \phi_1(u, v, w)\mathbf{i} + \phi_2(u, v, w)\mathbf{j} + \phi_3(u, v, w)\mathbf{k},$$

where ϕ_1, ϕ_2, ϕ_3 are scalar functions of the three variables u, v, w. If $w = 0$, this becomes the functional value of a vector function of the two variables u and v.

If ϕ_1, ϕ_2, ϕ_3 are continuous in some region, we shall say that $\boldsymbol{\phi}$ is **continuous** in that region. If ϕ_1, ϕ_2, ϕ_3 are differentiable in some region, we shall say that $\boldsymbol{\phi}$ is **differentiable** in that region and that

$$\frac{\partial \boldsymbol{\phi}}{\partial u} = \frac{\partial \phi_1}{\partial u}\mathbf{i} + \frac{\partial \phi_2}{\partial u}\mathbf{j} + \frac{\partial \phi_3}{\partial u}\mathbf{k}$$

is the partial derivative of $\boldsymbol{\phi}$ with respect to u, with similar expressions for $\partial \boldsymbol{\phi}/\partial v$ and $\partial \boldsymbol{\phi}/\partial w$ as the partial derivatives of $\boldsymbol{\phi}$ with respect to v and w. We shall also write $\boldsymbol{\phi}_u$ for $\partial \boldsymbol{\phi}/\partial u$, $\boldsymbol{\phi}_v$ for $\partial \boldsymbol{\phi}/\partial v$ and $\boldsymbol{\phi}_w$ for $\partial \boldsymbol{\phi}/\partial w$. Higher partial derivatives of $\boldsymbol{\phi}$ are defined in the obvious manner. All properties of vector functions of two or three variables that are analogous to properties of scalar functions of two or three variables will be tacitly assumed; where necessary, the student should establish their validity.

A simple geometric representation for vector functions of three variables does not exist. However, for vector functions of two variables, a convenient geometric representation is available. We shall consider only vector functions that are continuous in some region in E^2. For the vector function $\boldsymbol{\phi} = \phi_1\mathbf{i} + \phi_2\mathbf{j} + \phi_3\mathbf{k}$, continuous in some region R_{uv} in the uv-plane, let $x = \phi_1(u, v)$, $y = \phi_2(u, v)$, $z = \phi_3(u, v)$; then the totality of points (x, y, z) can serve as a geometric representation of $\boldsymbol{\phi}$. We call such a representation the **graph** of $\boldsymbol{\phi}$. Since the graph of $\boldsymbol{\phi}$ is merely a set of points, it will give no indication as to how many points (u, v) in R_{uv} determine the same point (x, y, z) in space. We shall have a better idea of the nature of the vector function $\boldsymbol{\phi}$ if we think of it as a **transformation** or **mapping** of a region in the uv-plane into a set of points in E^3. For example, a curve in R_{uv} will be mapped into a space curve in E^3 under the transformation $\boldsymbol{\phi}$. The resulting configuration of a transformation or mapping is called a **map.** However, for "map," we shall use the term most commonly employed and familiar to the student; namely, **surface.** We shall say that the point (x_0, y_0, z_0) on the surface is the image of (u_0, v_0) in R_{uv} under the transformation or mapping $\boldsymbol{\phi}$ if $x_0 = \phi_1(u_0, v_0)$, $y_0 = \phi_2(u_0, v_0)$, $z_0 = \phi_3(u_0, v_0)$. Hence, the surface of a vector function $\boldsymbol{\phi}$ is the map of $\boldsymbol{\phi}$ when we think of $\boldsymbol{\phi}$ as a transformation of a region in the uv-plane to a set of points in space. The student is familiar with such surfaces as planes, spheres, cones, cylinders, and the quadric surfaces. However, for our purposes, it is necessary to study surfaces in general; we now turn to a detailed study of surfaces.

8. Surfaces. We have seen that a given vector function of two variables can be represented by a surface. This surface is uniquely determined; i.e., a given vector function has one and only one surface. Hence, we shall speak of *the* surface of a vector function. However, many vector functions may have the same surface; hence, we shall speak of the surface represented by *a* vector function. We shall denote the surface of a vector function $\boldsymbol{\phi}$ defined in R_{uv} as $S\colon \boldsymbol{\phi}, R_{uv}$, or $S\colon \phi_1(u, v)\mathbf{i} + \phi_2(u, v)\mathbf{j} + \phi_3(u, v)\mathbf{k}, R_{uv}$, or $S\colon x = \phi_1(u, v),\ y = \phi_2(u, v),\ z = \phi_3(u, v),\ R_{uv}$. In some cases, especially when the specific function representing the surface is immaterial, we shall denote the surface simply as S. We say that $x = \phi_1(u, v)$, $y = \phi_2(u, v)$, $z = \phi_3(u, v)$ are **parametric equations** of S or that they are a **parametric representation** of S with u and v as parameters. The parametric representation of S with which the student is familiar is

$$S\colon \quad x = x, \quad y = y, \quad z = f(x, y), \quad R_{xy},$$

with x and y as parameters. The parametric representations

$$S\colon \quad x = x, \quad z = z, \quad y = g(x, z), \quad R_{xz},$$
$$S\colon \quad y = y, \quad z = z, \quad x = h(y, z), \quad R_{yz}$$

also occur frequently. We shall call the foregoing parametric representations of S, with two of the three variables x, y, z as parameters, the **standard parametric representations**—they are uniquely determined. We shall be primarily concerned with the standard parametric representations of S and will write

$$S: \quad z = f(x, y), \quad R_{xy}, \qquad \text{or} \qquad S: \quad y = g(x, z), \quad R_{xz},$$

or

$$S: \quad x = h(y, z), \quad R_{yz}.$$

The student is also familiar with the implicit representation of a surface S: $f(x, y, z) = 0$; we shall have frequent occasion to use this representation and shall write

$$S: \quad f(x, y, z) = 0, \quad R_{xy}, \qquad \text{or} \qquad S: \quad f(x, y, z) = 0, \quad R_{yz},$$

or

$$S: \quad f(x, y, z) = 0, \quad R_{xz}.$$

A point (x_0, y_0, z_0) on S: $\phi_1(u, v)\mathbf{i} + \phi_2(u, v)\mathbf{j} + \phi_3(u, v)\mathbf{k}$, R_{uv}, will be called a **multiple point** of S if there exist points (u^*, v^*) and (u^{**}, v^{**}) in R_{uv} such that $x_0 = \phi_1(u^*, v^*) = \phi_1(u^{**}, v^{**})$, $y_0 = \phi_2(u^*, v^*) = \phi_2(u^{**}, v^{**})$, $z_0 = \phi_3(u^*, v^*) = \phi_3(u^{**}, v^{**})$. Given S: $\boldsymbol{\phi}$, R_{uv}, such that R_{uv} is a bounded region whose boundary is a regular closed curve C; then, the image of C under the transformation $\boldsymbol{\phi}$ is called the **boundary** of S. We shall denote the boundary of S by Γ or, more explicitly, as $\Gamma(S)$. It is readily seen that Γ is a closed curve. If R_{uv} is not bounded or its boundary is not a regular closed curve, we shall say that the boundary of S does not exist or is undefined. Now suppose that C, a regular closed curve, is the boundary of R_{uv} and S: $\boldsymbol{\phi}$, R_{uv}; if under the transformation $\boldsymbol{\phi}$, as a point moves along

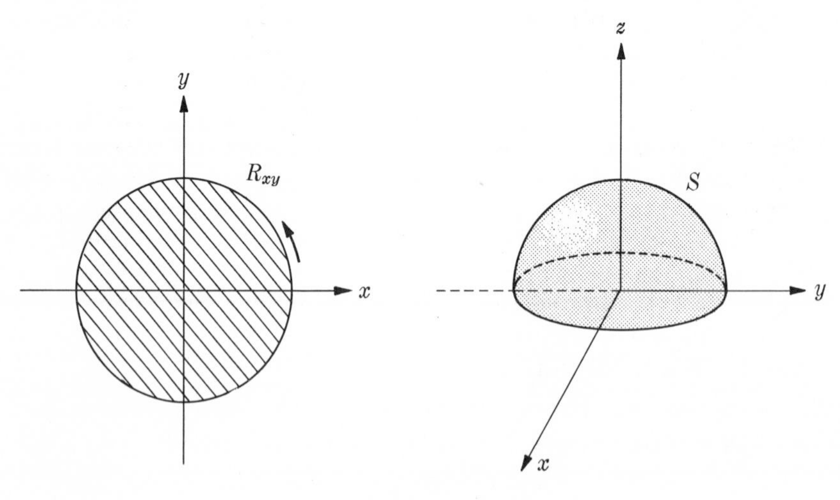

Example 1

C once, its image moves along $\Gamma(S)$ twice in opposite directions, we shall say that S is a **closed surface.** Hence, every point on the boundary of a closed surface is a multiple point—these points are called **nonordinary multiple points;** all other multiple points are called **ordinary multiple points.** A surface S is called a **simple surface** if it has no ordinary multiple points. In particular, we have that S is a **simple closed surface** if it is both simple and closed.

EXAMPLES

(1) S: $z = \sqrt{1 - x^2 - y^2}$, $0 \leq x^2 + y^2 \leq 1$.
S is a hemisphere, a simple surface. $\Gamma(S)$: $x^2 + y^2 = 1, z = 0$; i.e., the boundary of R_{xy} is mapped into itself. S is not closed.

(2) S: $x = \cos u \sin v$, $y = \sin u \sin v$, $z = \cos v$, $0 \leq u \leq 2\pi$, $0 \leq v \leq \pi$.
We note that $x^2 + y^2 + z^2 = 1$, $-1 \leq x, y, z \leq 1$, which we recognize as the implicit representation of a sphere.

$\Gamma(S)$: the semicircle $x = \sqrt{1 - z^2}$, $y = 0$, traversed twice in opposite directions. There are no ordinary multiple points. S is a simple closed surface. (See figure.)

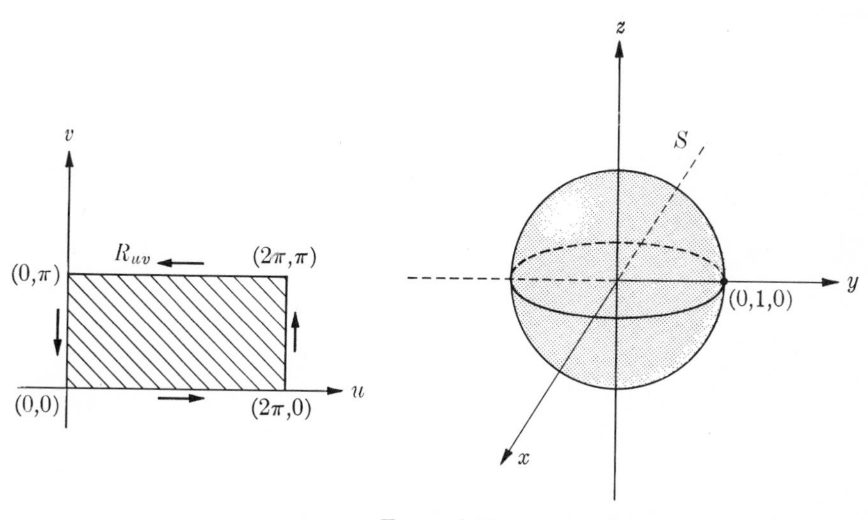

Example 2

In a standard parametric representation, the sphere can be obtained only as two surfaces: two hemispheres S_1 and S_2; e.g., S_1: $z = \sqrt{1 - x^2 - y^2}$ and S_2: $z = -\sqrt{1 - x^2 - y^2}$, $0 \leq x^2 + y^2 \leq 1$. The parametric representation of the sphere in (2), although unfamiliar to the student, has the advantage that it yields the sphere as a single surface.

Let us consider the following parametric representation of the above sphere:

$$S: \quad x = \cos u \cos v, \quad y = \cos u \sin v, \quad z = \sin u, \quad 0 \leq u \leq 2\pi, \quad 0 \leq v \leq \pi.$$

$\Gamma(S)$ consists of the circle $x^2 + z^2 = 1$, $y = 0$, and the semicircle $y = \sqrt{1 - x^2}$, $z = 0$, each traversed twice in opposite directions. It is clear from this example that $\Gamma(S)$ depends on the parametrization of S.

(3) S: $x = \cos u$, $y = \sin u$, $z = v$, $0 \leq u \leq 2\pi$, $0 \leq v \leq 1$. Since $x^2 + y^2 = 1$, $0 \leq z \leq 1$, we recognize the surface as a right circular cylinder. $\Gamma(S)$: $x^2 + y^2 = 1$, $z = 0$, in a counterclockwise direction; $x = 1$, $y = 0$, $0 \leq z \leq 1$, directed upward; $x^2 + y^2 = 1$, $z = 1$, in a counterclockwise direction; $x = 1$, $y = 0$, $0 \leq z \leq 1$, directed downward. This is *not* a closed surface and it is *not* simple. (See figure.)

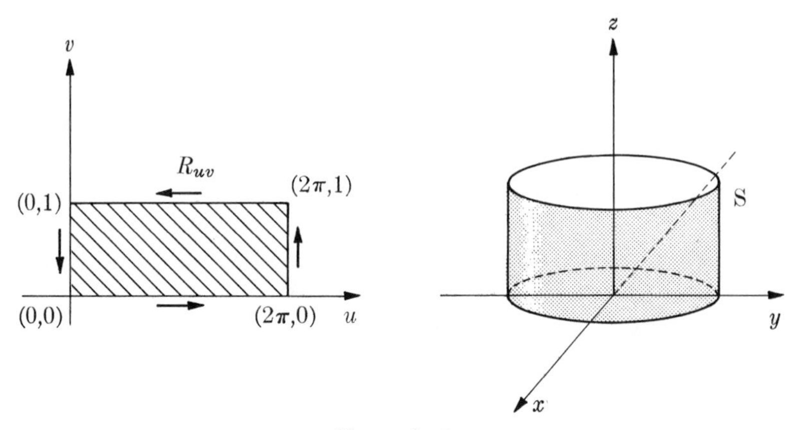

Example 3

The student should consider a standard parametric representation of this right circular cylinder.

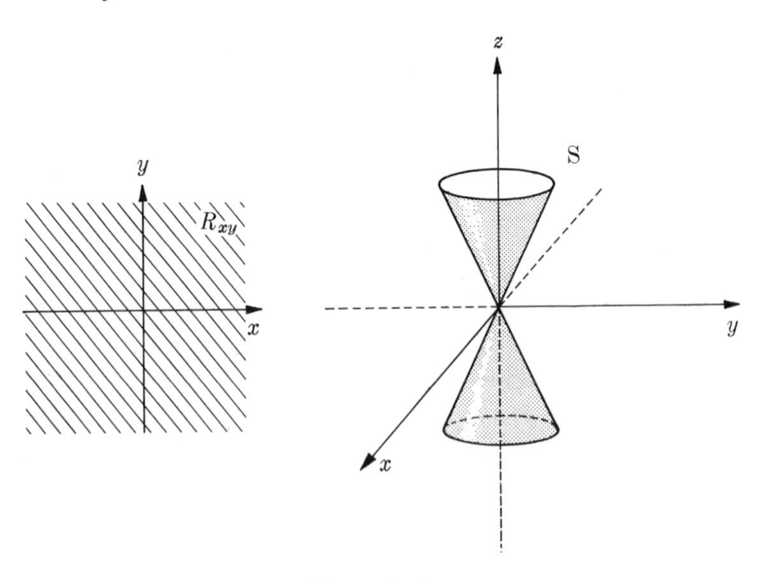

Example 4

(4) S_1: $z = \sqrt{x^2 + y^2}$, all x and y; S_2: $z = -\sqrt{x^2 + y^2}$, all x and y. S_1 and S_2 constitute the two nappes of a cone.

With the parametric representation S: $x = u \cos v$, $y = u \sin v$, $z = u$, $0 \leq v \leq 2\pi$, u arbitrary, we have a representation for the entire cone. $\Gamma(S)$ does not exist, since R_{uv} is not a bounded region. (See figure.)

(5) S: $x = (a + b \cos u) \sin v$, $y = (a + b \cos u) \cos v$, $z = b \sin u$, $-\pi \leq u \leq \pi$, $-\pi \leq v \leq \pi$, $b < a$.

S is a torus. $\Gamma(S)$: $x^2 + y^2 = (a - b)^2$, $z = 0$, and $(y + a)^2 + z^2 = b^2$, $x = 0$—each traversed twice in opposite directions. The torus is a simple closed surface. (See figure.)

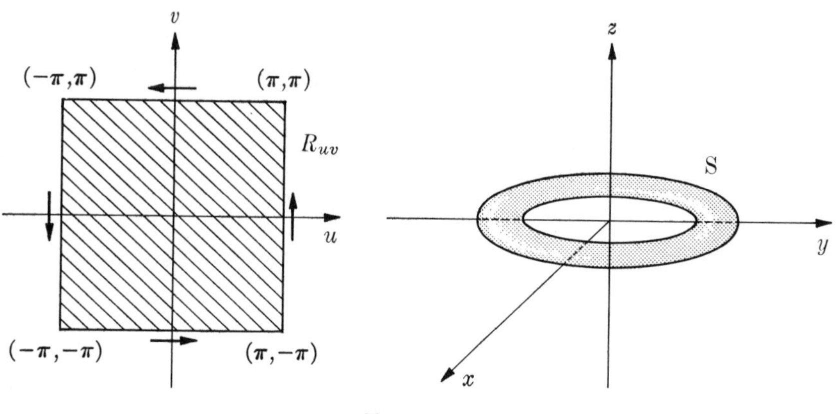

Example 5

In our study of the curves of vector functions, we noted that the parametric representation of a curve determined its direction. Actually, there are two possible directions of a curve and we can always choose a parametrization of a curve that will yield a desired direction. If we think of ourselves as moving along the curve, we decide in what direction we want to go and then choose the parametrization of the curve so that this will be the direction. Once this decision has been made, we can think of ourselves as being "oriented." Now, direction as such is meaningless for a surface. But where there is a choice of two directions on a curve, if we restrict our surfaces appropriately, there will be a choice of one of two sides on the surface in which to move. Once we have chosen a side of the surface on which to move, we can be said to be "oriented." We recall that for curves of vector functions, the direction of the unit tangent vector to the curve was conveniently used to determine analytically the direction of the curve. Serving an analogous purpose for surfaces is the unit normal vector to a surface at a point, which has one of two directions, each corresponding to one of the two sides of the surface.

Let us now make the foregoing ideas precise. Given S: $\boldsymbol{\phi}(u, v) = \phi_1(u, v)\mathbf{i} + \phi_2(u, v)\mathbf{j} + \phi_3(u, v)\mathbf{k}$, continuous and differentiable in R_{uv}. Let

P be any point on S; P is the image of some point (u_0, v_0) in R_{uv}. (See Fig. 6.) If $u = u_0$, $\boldsymbol{\phi}(u_0, v) = \phi_1(u_0, v)\mathbf{i} + \phi_2(u_0, v)\mathbf{j} + \phi_3(u_0, v)\mathbf{k}$ represents a curve C_1 on S passing through P. Similarly, if $v = v_0$, $\boldsymbol{\phi}(u, v_0) = \phi_1(u, v_0)\mathbf{i} + \phi_2(u, v_0)\mathbf{j} + \phi_3(u, v_0)\mathbf{k}$ represents a curve C_2 on S passing through P. The tangent vector to C_1 at P is $\boldsymbol{\phi}_u(u_0, v_0)$, and the tangent

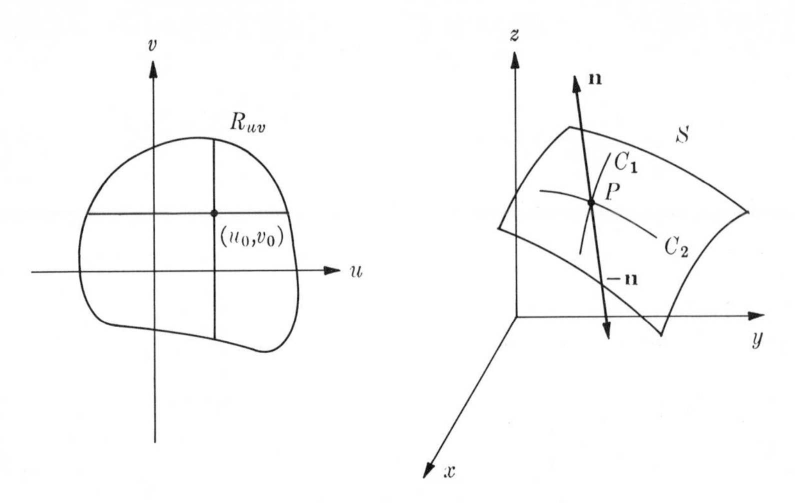

Fig. 6. Normal vectors to a surface

vector to C_2 at P is $\boldsymbol{\phi}_v(u_0, v_0)$. These tangent vectors determine a plane tangent to S at P. A normal vector to S at P is a vector perpendicular to the tangent plane at P; i.e., a vector perpendicular to both tangent vectors. There are two such normal vectors to S at P, oppositely directed. Now the unit normal vectors to S at P, denoted by **n**, are

$$\mathbf{n} = \pm \frac{\boldsymbol{\phi}_u(u_0, v_0) \times \boldsymbol{\phi}_v(u_0, v_0)}{|\boldsymbol{\phi}_u(u_0, v_0) \times \boldsymbol{\phi}_v(u_0, v_0)|}, \quad |\boldsymbol{\phi}_u(u_0, v_0) \times \boldsymbol{\phi}_v(u_0, v_0)| \neq 0.$$

A point on S that is the image of (u_0, v_0) in R_{uv} such that

$$|\boldsymbol{\phi}_u(u_0, v_0) \times \boldsymbol{\phi}_v(u_0, v_0)| = 0$$

is called a **singular point** of S or a singular point of $\boldsymbol{\phi}$.

A vector function $\boldsymbol{\phi}$, continuous and differentiable in R_{uv} and having no singular points, will be called a **smooth vector function.** A surface S will be called a **smooth surface** if there is no abrupt change in the direction of the unit normal vector at any point on S. If a vector function is smooth, then its surface is smooth (why?); however, a surface may be smooth and represent a vector function that is not smooth. Nevertheless, if S is smooth and parametrizable, then there exists a smooth vector function whose surface is S. Which vector functions and which surfaces in Examples 1 to 5, p. 75, are smooth?

Suppose that we vary the point P along the smooth surface S: $\boldsymbol{\phi}$, R_{uv}; then the unit normal vector will depend on the two variables u and v, and therefore it is a vector function of two variables: $\mathbf{n}(u, v)$. Now, if $\mathbf{n}$ is continuous in R_{uv}, then we say that S is an **orientable surface.** Geometrically, this implies that if S is an orientable surface and if we start at any point P_0 on S with unit normal vector $\mathbf{n}_0$ and move continuously along the surface, then when we return to P_0, the direction of $\mathbf{n}_0$ will be unaltered. Intuitively, this means that an orientable surface is a two-sided surface. The student may be surprised to learn that there do exist one-sided or nonorientable surfaces. Such a surface is the **Möbius strip,** which may be formed by taking a long rectangular strip of paper, giving it one twist, and pasting its ends together. This is illustrated in Fig. 7. [The curious

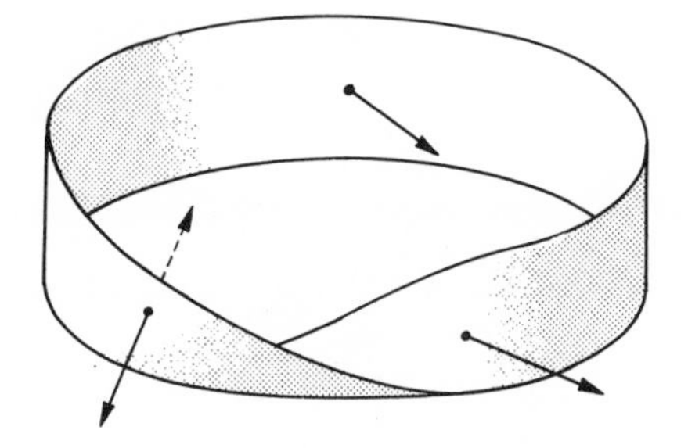

Fig. 7. The Möbius strip

student may be interested in the following parametric representation of the **Möbius strip** $S = S_1 + S_2$: $x = [2 - v \sin(u/2)] \cos y$, $y = [2 - v \sin(u/2)] \sin u$, $z = v \cos(u/2)$; S_1: $-1 < v < 1$, $0 < u < 2\pi$; S_2: $-1 < v < 1$, $-(\pi/2) < u < (\pi/2)$.] The student should note that a unit normal vector to any point on the Möbius strip can be moved continuously around the strip and returned to the original point, but with its direction reversed.

It is clear, then, that for an orientable surface S, we can select one of the two unit normal vectors that exist at each point of S. This corresponds to choosing a side of the surface, and hence accounts for the term *orientable*. For many purposes it is immaterial which of the two unit normal vectors we choose; however, in some instances, one of these two unit normal vectors is specified. This can be done in several ways. One way is to choose the sign of $\mathbf{n}$ so that $\boldsymbol{\phi}_u(u_0, v_0)$, $\boldsymbol{\phi}_v(u_0, v_0)$, $\mathbf{n}$ form a positive triple; the choice will then depend on the parametrization of S. However, the geometric nature of S often suggests a choice of sign; for example, for concave surfaces, $\mathbf{n}$ is often directed so that the planes tangent to S at P and $\mathbf{n}$ are on the same side of S. For closed surfaces, $\mathbf{n}$ is often directed outward from the surface and is then called the **outer unit normal vector.** Some examples will be considered in the next section.

Given any number of smooth surfaces S_1, S_2, $\cdots$ with boundaries Γ_1, Γ_2, $\cdots$, then the surface S obtained by joining these surfaces along curves C_1, C_2, $\cdots$, such that the points on C_1 belong to both Γ_1 and Γ_2, and the points on C_2 belong to both Γ_2 and Γ_3, $\cdots$, is called a **piecewise smooth surface.** We write $S = S_1 + S_2 + \cdots$. The boundary of S is $\Gamma_1 + \Gamma_2 + \cdots$. In order to orient a piecewise smooth surface, we must adopt some convention regarding the directions of the curves C_1, C_2, $\cdots$. We proceed as follows: Choose a unit normal vector $\mathbf{n}$ on S_1; now choose the direction of C_1 relative to S_1 in such a way that $\mathbf{n}$, $\mathbf{T}$, and $\mathbf{N}$ form a positive triple, $\mathbf{T}$ the unit tangent vector to C_1, and $\mathbf{N}$ the normal to C_1, directed toward S_1 (called the *inner normal* vector). (See Fig. 8.) In other

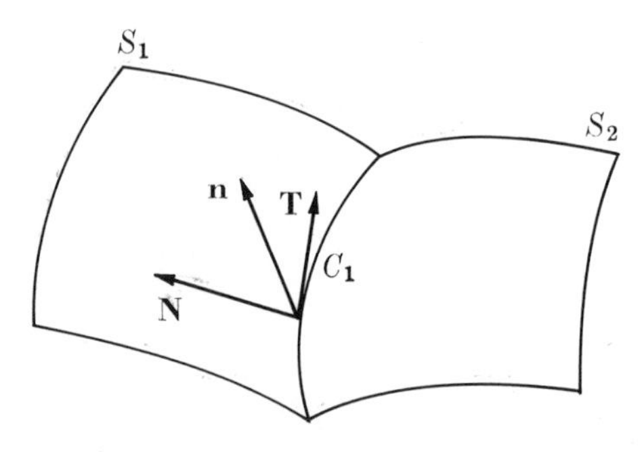

Fig. 8. Orienting a piecewise smooth surface

words, for S_1, $\mathbf{N}$ is automatically determined, $\mathbf{n}$ is chosen, and then $\mathbf{T}$ is chosen so that $\mathbf{n}$, $\mathbf{T}$, $\mathbf{N}$ form a positive triple. Now choose the direction of C_1 relative to S_2 opposite to the direction of C_1 relative to S_1. Continuing in this fashion, we can orient $S = S_1 + S_2 + \cdots$ and thus obtain an **oriented piecewise smooth surface.** An oriented piecewise smooth surface $S = S_1 + S_2 + \cdots + S_n$, S_i: $\boldsymbol{\phi}_i$, R^i_{uv}, $i = 1, 2, \cdots, n$, is **closed** if $\Gamma(S_1) + \Gamma(S_2) + \cdots + \Gamma(S_n)$ is traversed twice in opposite directions as the boundaries of R^i_{uv}, $i = 1, 2, \cdots, n$ are traversed once.

A surface that is an oriented piecewise smooth surface comprising simple surfaces such that the constituent smooth surfaces intersect only at the boundaries of these surfaces is called a **regular surface.** We shall be primarily concerned with regular surfaces.

We now are in a position to define a **simply connected region** in E^3 as that region R in which every closed regular surface is the boundary of a bounded region wholly contained in R.

EXAMPLE

S_1: $x = \cos u$, $y = \sin u$, $z = v$, $0 \leq u \leq 2\pi$, $0 \leq v \leq 1$; S_2: $x = \cos u$, $y = \sin u$, $z = 0$, $0 \leq u \leq 2\pi$; S_3: $x = \cos u$, $y = \sin u$, $z = 1$, $0 \leq u \leq 2\pi$.

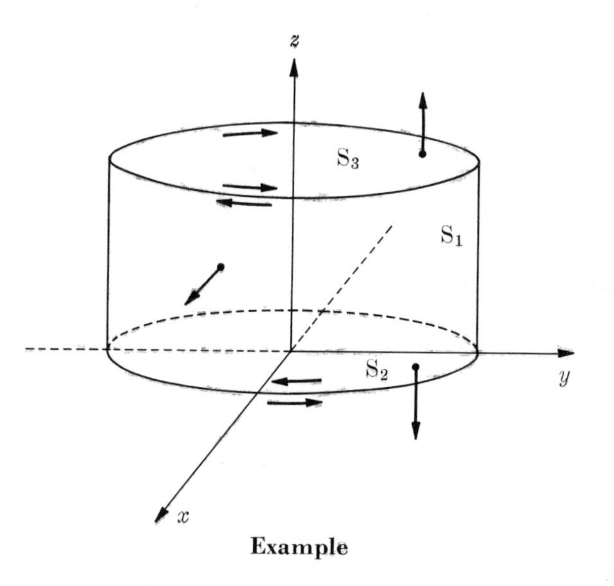

Example

$S = S_1 + S_2 + S_3$ is a right circular cylinder of radius 1 and height 1, bounded above and below by two circular discs. It is shown in the figure with the directions of the boundaries and the unit normal vectors as indicated. The boundary of S consists of $x^2 + y^2 = 1$, $z = 0$; $x^2 + y^2 = 1$, $z = 2$; $x = 1$, $y = 0$, $0 \leq z \leq 1$, each traversed twice; hence, S is closed. S is a regular surface.

EXERCISES

1. Represent geometrically the following sets of points and determine which sets are regions. Indicate whether these regions are closed, open, bounded, simply connected, and determine their boundaries.

In E^2, the set of points (x, y) such that (a) $xy \neq 0$; (b) $x^2 \geq y^2$ and $x^2 + y^2 \geq 1$; (c) $3x - 2y + 1 > 0$; (d) $-5 \leq x^2 - 2x + y^2 - 4y < -4$; (e) $x^2 + y^2 \leq 4$, $1 \leq x \leq 2$; (f) $x^2 + y^2 < 1$ and $x^2 - y^2 > 1$; (g) $x^2 + y^2 < 4$ and $y > 0$, with the points $x = 1/n$, $n = 1, 2, \cdots$, $0 < y \leq 1$ removed. Same problem with $y \geq 0$; (h) $(x^2 + y^2 + x)^2 \geq x^2 + y^2$; (i) $|x + y| \leq 1$; (j) $y^2 - x^2 \leq 1$, $-1 \leq x \leq 1$; (k) $y \leq f(x)$, $x \geq 0$, $y \geq 0$, where $f(x) = x$, $0 \leq x \leq 1$, $f(x) = 2 - x$, $1 \leq x \leq 2$, $f(x + 2) = f(x)$, $x \geq 2$. Same problem with $y > 0$; (l) (x, y) is in the interior of the polygon formed by joining in succession $(0, 3)$, $(1, 1)$, $(3, 0)$, $(2, -1)$, $(3, -4)$, $(0, -3)$, $(-3, -4)$, $(-2, -1)$, $(-3, 0)$, $(-1, 1)$; (m) $x^2 + y^2 \leq 4$ with the points $x^2 + y^2 < 1/(n - 1)^2$, $n = 1, 2, 3, \cdots$ removed.

In E^3, the set of points (x, y, z) such that (n) $z > 0$; (o) $x^2 + y^2 > 0$; (p) $x^2 + y^2 + z^2 > 4$; (q) $xy \neq 0$; (r) $1 < x < 2$; (s) $1 \leq x^2 + y^2 < 4$; (t) $1 \leq y^2 - 4x < 2$.

2. Sketch the following surfaces. Determine all singular points of these surfaces. Indicate which surfaces are smooth and which are regular. Determine the boundaries of the surfaces if they exist and indicate whether these surfaces are closed. Determine the unit normal vectors at each point of these surfaces.

(a) Ellipsoid: $a \sin u \cos v\,\mathbf{i} + b \sin u \sin v\,\mathbf{j} + c \cos u\,\mathbf{k}$, $0 \le u \le 2\pi$, $0 \le v \le \pi$.

(b) Cone: $(\sin \alpha)u \cos v\,\mathbf{i} + (\sin \alpha)u \sin v\,\mathbf{j} + (\cos \alpha)u\,\mathbf{k}$, $-\infty < u < \infty$, $0 \le v \le 2\pi$.

(c) Cone: $a \sinh u \sinh v\,\mathbf{i} + b \sinh u \cosh v\,\mathbf{j} + c \sinh u\,\mathbf{k}$, $-\infty < u < \infty$, $0 \le v \le 1$.

(d) Elliptic paraboloid: $x = a\,u \cos v$, $y = b\,u \sin v$, $c = u^2$, $0 \le u < \infty$, $0 \le v \le 2\pi$.

(e) Hyperboloid of one sheet: $x = a \sin u \cosh v$, $y = b \cos u \cosh v$, $z = c \sinh v$, $0 \le u \le 2\pi$, $-\infty < v < \infty$.

(f) Hyperboloid of two sheets: $x = a \sinh u \cos v$, $y = b \sinh u \sin v$, $z = \cosh u$, $-\infty < u < \infty$, $0 \le v \le \pi$.

(g) Hyperbolic paraboloid: $x = a\,u \cosh v$, $y = b\,u \sinh v$, $z = u^2$, $-\infty < u < \infty$, $0 \le v \le 1$.

(h) Hyperbolic paraboloid: $x = a(u + v)$, $y = b(u - v)$, $z = uv$, $0 \le u \le \infty$, $0 \le v < \infty$.

(i) Surface of revolution: Rotate $z = f(x)$ about the z-axis, $x = u \cos v$, $y = u \sin v$, $z = f(u)$, $-\infty < u < \infty$, $0 \le v \le 2\pi$.

(j) Helicoid: $x = a(\cos u - v \sin u)$, $y = a(\sin u + v \cos u)$, $z = b(u - v)$, $0 \le u \le \pi$, $0 \le v < \infty$.

3. Construct the following piecewise smooth surfaces by determining vector functions of the smooth surfaces comprising them in such a way as to obtain orientable piecewise smooth surfaces. Determine the boundaries and indicate the directions of all significant curves and the unit normal vectors on these surfaces. Which surfaces are closed?

(a) Cube with unit edge; (b) cube without the top face; (c) regular tetrahedron; (d) hemisphere and a circular disc having the same diameter; (e) right circular cone surmounted by a hemisphere; (f) rectangular parallelepiped; (g) circular cone and the circular discs determined by two parallel planes equidistant from the vertex and cutting the cone; (h) cube with the top face replaced by a surmounted pyramid; (i) right circular cylinder joined by a circular disc at one end and a surmounted hemisphere at the other end; (j) elliptic paraboloid and that part of a plane perpendicular to its axis and cutting it.

4. (a) Show that the equation of the tangent plane to S: $\boldsymbol{\phi}$, R_{uv}, at the point P is

$$[\mathbf{r} - \boldsymbol{\phi}(u_0, v_0)] \cdot \mathbf{n} = 0,$$

where $\mathbf{r}$ is the position vector of any point in the plane, $\boldsymbol{\phi}(u_0, v_0)$ is the position vector of P, and $\mathbf{n}$ is the unit normal vector to S at P.

(b) Determine the equation of the tangent plane at any point of

$$\text{S:}\quad \boldsymbol{\phi} = (u + v)\mathbf{i} + (u - v)\mathbf{j} + 4v^2\mathbf{k}, \qquad -\infty < u < \infty,\ -\infty < v < \infty.$$

(c) Determine the equation of the tangent plane to S: $x = u^2 - v^2$, $y = u - v$, $z = u^2 + 4v$, $-1 \le u \le 1$, $0 \le v \le 1$, at the point $(-\frac{1}{4}, \frac{1}{2}, 2)$.

5. A point p is a **limit point** of a set of points S if every ϵ-neighborhood of p contains a point $q \neq p$ such that q belongs to S. S is a **closed set** if every limit point of S is a point of S. S is an **open set** if every point of S is an interior point of S.

(a) Show that a set is open if and only if its complement is closed, and that it is closed if and only if its complement is open.

(b) Let S^D (called the **derived set** of S) be the set of limit points of S. Show that S^D is closed. Let $\bar{S}$ be the set of points in S and S^D. $\bar{S}$ is called the **closure** of S. Show that $\bar{S}$ is closed, that the interior of S is equal to the complement of the closure of the complement of S, and that the boundary of S is the set of points belonging to both $\bar{S}$ and $\bar{S}'$.

(c) Show that an open region is an open polygonally connected set of points and that a closed region is a closed polygonally connected set of points.

(d) Indicate which sets in Exercise 1 are open and which are closed. Determine the derived set and the closure of each of these sets.

6. A set S is **connected** if it cannot be divided into two open sets S_1 and S_2, each having at least one point, and such that there is no point belonging to both S_1 and S_2.

(a) Which sets in Exercise 1 are connected?

(b) Show that if a set is polygonally connected, then it is connected.

(c) A set S is **arcwise connected** if every pair of points in S can be joined by a regular curve in S. Show that if S is polygonally connected, then it is arcwise connected, and if it is arcwise connected, it is connected.

7. A region R in E^2 is a **star-shaped region** if there exists a point P in R such that for any other point Q in R, the line segment joining P and Q is in R. A region R in E^2 is a **convex region** if for every pair of points P and Q in R, the line segment joining P and Q is in R.

(a) Show that if R is convex, then it is star-shaped. Is a convex region simply connected? Is a star-shaped region simply connected?

(b) Determine which sets in E^2 of Exercise 1 are star-shaped and which are convex. Extend the definition of star-shaped and convex regions to regions in E^3 and determine which sets in E^3 of Exercise 1 are star-shaped and which are convex.

9. The gradient vector. We have seen that the unit normal vectors to any point of the surface of a smooth vector function S: $\boldsymbol{\phi}$, R_{uv}, are

$$\mathbf{n} = \frac{\pm\, \boldsymbol{\phi}_u \times \boldsymbol{\phi}_v}{|\boldsymbol{\phi}_u \times \boldsymbol{\phi}_v|}.$$

We shall reserve the notation **n** for these unit normal vectors, and unless explicit specification is made to the contrary, the sign of **n** will be chosen so that for a point (u_0, v_0) in R_{uv}, $\boldsymbol{\phi}_u(u_0, v_0)$, $\boldsymbol{\phi}_v(u_0, v_0)$, $\mathbf{n}(u_0, v_0)$ form a positive triple. We shall refer to this choice of sign as the standard choice. We now derive expressions for **n** for various parametrizations of S. For the standard parametric representation

$$\text{S:}\ \ z = f(x, y), \quad R_{xy},$$

$$\boldsymbol{\phi}_x = \mathbf{i} + \frac{\partial z}{\partial x}\mathbf{k} \quad \text{and} \quad \boldsymbol{\phi}_y = \mathbf{j} + \frac{\partial z}{\partial y}\mathbf{k},$$

so that

$$\mathbf{n} = \frac{\pm\left(-\dfrac{\partial z}{\partial x}\mathbf{i} - \dfrac{\partial z}{\partial y}\mathbf{j} + \mathbf{k}\right)}{\sqrt{1 + \left(\dfrac{\partial z}{\partial x}\right)^2 + \left(\dfrac{\partial z}{\partial y}\right)^2}}.$$

The student should determine $\mathbf{n}$ for the other standard parametric representations of S. Furthermore, the student should show that if

$$\mathrm{S}\colon\ \boldsymbol{\phi},\quad R_{uv},$$

then

$$\mathbf{n} = \frac{\pm \boldsymbol{\phi}_u \times \boldsymbol{\phi}_v}{\sqrt{EG - F^2}},$$

where $E = \boldsymbol{\phi}_u^2$, $F = \boldsymbol{\phi}_u \cdot \boldsymbol{\phi}_v$, $G = \boldsymbol{\phi}_v^2$.

Now let us determine $\mathbf{n}$ for

$$\mathrm{S}\colon\ f(x, y, z) = 0,\quad R_{xy}.$$

We have that

$$\boldsymbol{\phi}_x = \mathbf{i} + \frac{\partial z}{\partial x}\mathbf{k} = \mathbf{i} - \frac{\partial f/\partial x}{\partial f/\partial z}\mathbf{k}$$

and

$$\boldsymbol{\phi}_y = \mathbf{j} + \frac{\partial z}{\partial y}\mathbf{k} = \mathbf{j} - \frac{\partial f/\partial y}{\partial f/\partial z}\mathbf{k}. \quad \text{[IVBi]}$$

Hence,

$$\mathbf{n} = \frac{\pm(\partial f/\partial x)\mathbf{i} + (\partial f/\partial y)\mathbf{j} + (\partial f/\partial z)\mathbf{k}}{\sqrt{(\partial f/\partial x)^2 + (\partial f/\partial y)^2 + (\partial f/\partial z)^2}}.$$

This can be expressed more compactly if we introduce some new notation. Let

$$\boldsymbol{\nabla} = \frac{\partial}{\partial x}\mathbf{i} + \frac{\partial}{\partial y}\mathbf{j} + \frac{\partial}{\partial z}\mathbf{k}.$$

The symbol $\boldsymbol{\nabla}$ (an inverted delta), called *del*, is an operator which, when applied to a differentiable scalar function of three variables f, produces the vector function

$$\boldsymbol{\nabla} f = \frac{\partial f}{\partial x}\mathbf{i} + \frac{\partial f}{\partial y}\mathbf{j} + \frac{\partial f}{\partial z}\mathbf{k}.$$

This vector function is called the **gradient vector,** or simply **gradient,** of $f(x, y, z)$. The gradient of $f(x, y, z)$, in addition to being denoted as $\boldsymbol{\nabla} f$, is also often denoted as $\operatorname{grad} f$ so that

$$\boldsymbol{\nabla} f = \operatorname{grad} f = \frac{\partial f}{\partial x}\mathbf{i} + \frac{\partial f}{\partial y}\mathbf{j} + \frac{\partial f}{\partial z}\mathbf{k}.$$

We have introduced the gradient at this point in order to simplify the expression $\mathbf{n}$ for $\mathrm{S}\colon f(x, y, z) = 0$, R_{xy}; indeed, we have

$$\mathbf{n} = \pm\frac{\boldsymbol{\nabla} f}{|\boldsymbol{\nabla} f|}.$$

However, we shall find other uses and interpretations for the gradient.

The gradient has the following properties, f and g being differentiable scalar functions in some region in space:

$\mathbf{G}_1$: $\nabla cf = c\nabla f$, c any constant.
$\mathbf{G}_2$: $\nabla(f + g) = \nabla f + \nabla g$.
$\mathbf{G}_3$: $\nabla(fg) = f\nabla g + g\nabla f$.

$$\mathbf{G}_4\text{:} \quad \nabla\left(\frac{f}{g}\right) = \frac{g\nabla f - f\nabla g}{g^2}, \qquad g \neq 0.$$

These properties are readily verified, using the definition of the gradient.

EXAMPLE 1. Determine the unit normal vector to S: $x^2y + 2xz = 4$ at $(2, -2, 3)$.

Solution. $\nabla(x^2y + 2xz - 4) = (2xy + 2z)\mathbf{i} + x^2\mathbf{j} + 2x\,\mathbf{k} = -2\mathbf{i} + 4\mathbf{j} + 4\mathbf{k}$ at $(2, -2, 3)$. Then $\mathbf{n} = \pm\frac{1}{3}(\mathbf{i} - 2\mathbf{j} - 2\mathbf{k})$. Since $\mathbf{a} = \mathbf{i} + \frac{1}{2}\mathbf{k}$ and $\mathbf{b} = \mathbf{j} + \mathbf{k}$ are the tangent vectors to the curve determined by S and $x = 2$ and $y = -2$ at $(2, -2, 3)$, respectively, $\mathbf{a}$, $\mathbf{b}$, $\mathbf{n}$ form a positive triple only if

$$\mathbf{n} = -\tfrac{1}{3}(\mathbf{i} - 2\mathbf{j} - 2\mathbf{k}).$$

EXAMPLE 2. Determine the outer unit normal vectors to S: $z = 3x^2 + 4y^2$ at $(0, 0, 0)$ and $(1, 0, 3)$.

Solution. $\nabla(z - 3x^2 - 4y^2) = -6x\,\mathbf{i} - 8y\,\mathbf{j} + \mathbf{k} = \mathbf{k}$ at $(0, 0, 0)$, $\mathbf{n} = \pm\mathbf{k}$, and the outer unit normal vector to S at $(0, 0, 0)$ is $-\mathbf{k}$, since S is an elliptic paraboloid lying completely above the xy-plane. At $(1, 0, 3)$, $\mathbf{n} = \pm(1/\sqrt{37})(6\mathbf{i} + \mathbf{k})$. Now the vector $(1/\sqrt{37})(6\mathbf{i} + \mathbf{k})$, with initial point at the origin and terminal point at $(6/\sqrt{37}, 0, 1/\sqrt{37})$ when translated so that its initial point is $(1, 0, 3)$, is the required outer unit normal vector to S at $(1, 0, 3)$.

EXAMPLE 3. Let P be any point on an ellipse whose foci are at F_1 and F_2. Prove that the lines F_1P and F_2P make equal angles with the tangent to the ellipse at P.

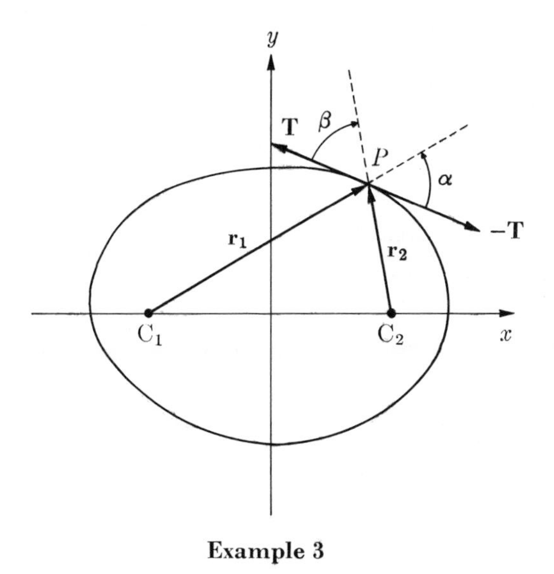

Example 3

Solution. Let $\mathbf{r}_1 = \overrightarrow{F_1P}$, $\mathbf{r}_2 = \overrightarrow{F_2P}$, and $\mathbf{T}$ the unit tangent vector to the ellipse at P. The equation of the ellipse is $r_1 + r_2 = k$, where k is a constant, since an ellipse is the set of points the sum of whose distances from two fixed points is a constant. $\nabla(r_1 + r_2)$ is a normal vector to the ellipse (why?). Hence,

$$\nabla(r_1 + r_2)\cdot\mathbf{T} = 0 \quad \text{or} \quad \nabla r_1\cdot\mathbf{T} = -\nabla r_2\cdot\mathbf{T}.$$

But $\nabla r_1 = \mathbf{r}_1/r_1$ and $\nabla r_2 = \mathbf{r}_2/r_2$ (prove these relations), so that

$$\nabla r_1\cdot\mathbf{T} = |\nabla r_1|\,|\mathbf{T}|\cos\alpha = \cos\alpha,$$

where α is the angle between $\mathbf{r}_1$ and $\mathbf{T}$, $0 \le \alpha \le (\pi/2)$, and

$$-\nabla r_2\cdot\mathbf{T} = \nabla r_2\cdot(-\mathbf{T}) = |\nabla r_2|\,|\mathbf{T}|\cos\beta = \cos\beta,$$

where β is the angle between $\mathbf{r}_2$ and $-\mathbf{T}$, $0 \le \beta \le (\pi/2)$. Hence, $\cos\alpha = \cos\beta$ and $\alpha = \beta$.

10. Surface area. Let $\boldsymbol{\phi} = \phi_1\mathbf{i} + \phi_2\mathbf{j} + \phi_3\mathbf{k}$ be a smooth vector function defined in a bounded region R_{uv}. We now define the surface area of S: $\boldsymbol{\phi}$, R_{uv}, and then formulate an integral expression for this surface area. Projecting R_{uv} onto the u-axis determines an interval $a \le u \le b$; projecting R_{uv} onto the v-axis determines an interval $c \le v \le d$. Divide the interval $a \le u \le b$ into n parts by the points u_i, $i = 1, 2, \cdots, n$ and the interval $c \le v \le d$ into m parts by the points v_j, $j = 1, 2, \cdots, m$. Then (u_i, v_j), $(u_i + \Delta u_i, v_j)$, $(u_i, v_j + \Delta v_j)$, $(u_i + \Delta u_i, v_j + \Delta v_j)$, where $\Delta u_i = u_{i+1} - u_i$ and $\Delta v_i = v_{j+1} - v_j$, are the vertices of a rectangle in R_{uv}. $\boldsymbol{\phi}$ maps this rectangle into a subsurface S_{ij} of S bounded by the curves whose vector functions are $\boldsymbol{\phi}(u_i, v)$, $\boldsymbol{\phi}(u_i + \Delta u_i, v)$, $\boldsymbol{\phi}(u, v_j)$, $\boldsymbol{\phi}(u, v_j + \Delta v_j)$. (See Fig. 9.)

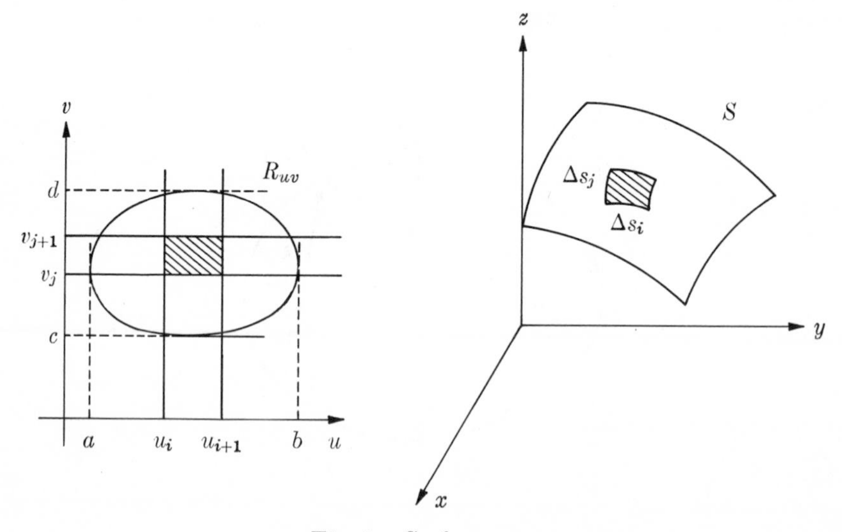

Fig. 9. Surface area

We determine the lengths of two adjacent "sides" of S_{ij}:

$$\Delta s_i = \int_{u_i}^{u_i+\Delta u_i} |\boldsymbol{\phi}_u|\, du \quad\text{and}\quad \Delta s_j = \int_{v_j}^{v_j+\Delta v} |\boldsymbol{\phi}_v|\, dv,$$

which by the law of the mean for integrals [IIICe] become

$$\Delta s_i = |\boldsymbol{\phi}_u(u_i', v)|\, \Delta u_i \quad\text{and}\quad \Delta s_j = |\boldsymbol{\phi}_v(u, v_j')|\, \Delta v_j,$$

where $u_i \leq u_i' \leq u_i + \Delta u_i$ and $v_j \leq v_j' \leq v_j + \Delta v_j$. The area of S_{ij} is then approximately

$$\Delta s_i\, \Delta s_j = |\boldsymbol{\phi}_u(u_i', v)|\, |\boldsymbol{\phi}_v(u, v_j')|\, \Delta u_i\, \Delta v_j,$$

which is approximately equal to

$$|\boldsymbol{\phi}_u(u_i', v)|\, |\boldsymbol{\phi}_v(u, v_j')| \sin\theta_{ij}\, \Delta u_i\, \Delta v_j = |\boldsymbol{\phi}_u(u_i', v) \times \boldsymbol{\phi}_v(u, v_j')|\, \Delta u_i\, \Delta v_j,$$

where θ_{ij} is the angle between the curves whose vector functions are $\boldsymbol{\phi}(u_i', v)$ and $\boldsymbol{\phi}(u, v_j')$. We now define the **surface area** of S to be

$$\lim_{\substack{n,m\to\infty\\ ||\Delta u||,||\Delta v||\to 0}} \sum_{j=1}^{m}\sum_{i=1}^{n} |\boldsymbol{\phi}_u(u_i', v) \times \boldsymbol{\phi}_v(u, v_j')|\, \Delta u_i\, \Delta v_j,$$

where $||\Delta u||$ is the largest of the Δu_i, $i = 1, 2, \cdots, n$, and $||\Delta v||$ is the largest of the Δv_j, $j = 1, 2, \cdots, m$. This limit does exist, since we have assumed that $\boldsymbol{\phi}$ is a smooth vector function, and it can be shown that this condition is sufficient for the existence of the limit. Since this limit is a double integral, denoting the surface area of S by σ, we have that

$$\sigma = \iint_{R_{uv}} |\boldsymbol{\phi}_u \times \boldsymbol{\phi}_v|\, du\, dv.$$

The surface area of a piecewise smooth surface is defined as the sum of the surface areas of the smooth surfaces constituting this surface.

The expression

$$d\sigma = |\boldsymbol{\phi}_u \times \boldsymbol{\phi}_v|\, du\, dv$$

is known as the **element of surface area.** For the commonly employed parametrizations of S, we have the following expressions for $d\sigma$:

(1) S: $z = f(x, y)$, R_{xy}, $\quad d\sigma = \sqrt{1 + f_x^2 + f_y^2}\, dx\, dy.$

(2) S: $x = g(y, z)$, R_{yz}, $\quad d\sigma = \sqrt{1 + g_y^2 + g_z^2}\, dy\, dz,$

(3) S: $y = h(x, z)$, R_{xz}, $\quad d\sigma = \sqrt{1 + h_x^2 + h_z^2}\, dx\, dz,$

(4) S: $f(x, y, z) = 0$, R_{xy}, $\quad d\sigma = \dfrac{\sqrt{f_x^2 + f_y^2 + f_z^2}\, dx\, dy}{|f_z|} = \dfrac{|\nabla f|}{|\nabla f \cdot \mathbf{k}|}\, dx\, dy, \quad f_z \neq 0.$

The proofs are left to the student.

11. The directional derivative. If f is differentiable in some region R in E^3, we know that $\dfrac{\partial f}{\partial x}, \dfrac{\partial f}{\partial y}, \dfrac{\partial f}{\partial z}$, evaluated at some point P_0: (x_0, y_0, z_0)

in R, can be interpreted physically as the instantaneous rates of change of $f(x, y, z)$ at P_0 in the positive directions of the x-axis, y-axis, z-axis, respectively; i.e., in the directions of $\mathbf{i}$, $\mathbf{j}$, $\mathbf{k}$. It is now natural to ask what the instantaneous rate of change of $f(x, y, z)$ is at P_0 in any other direction, say in the direction of the vector $\overrightarrow{P_0P}$ where P: (x, y, z) is any point in R. This leads to the notion of directional derivative which we now define. Given the point P_0: (x_0, y_0, z_0) in R and the vector $\overrightarrow{P_0P}$, where P: $(x_0 + \Delta x,$

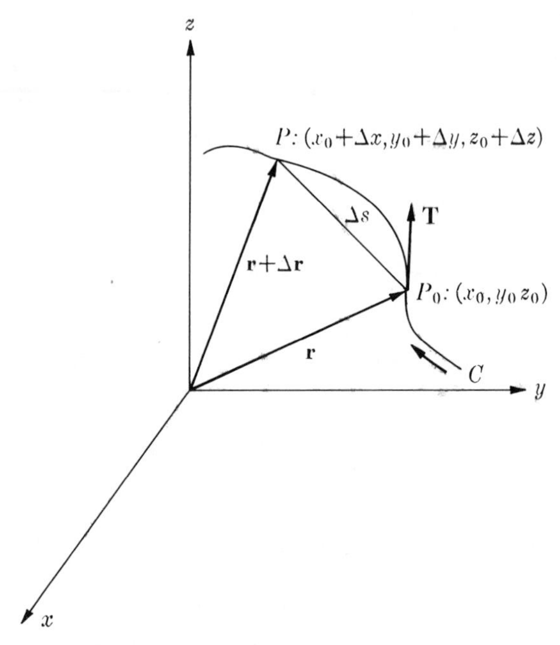

Fig. 10. The directional derivative

$y_0 + \Delta y,\ z_0 + \Delta z)$ is a point in R. (See Fig. 10.) The position vector of P_0 is $\mathbf{r}_0 = x_0\mathbf{i} + y_0\mathbf{j}$ and $z_0\mathbf{k}$ and the position vector of P is

$$\mathbf{r} + \Delta\mathbf{r} = (x + \Delta x)\mathbf{i} + (y + \Delta y)\mathbf{j} + (z + \Delta z)\mathbf{k}.$$

Let f be continuous and differentiable in R. We define the **directional derivative** of $f(x, y, z)$ at P_0 in the direction of $\overrightarrow{P_0P}$ as

$$\lim_{\Delta s \to 0} \frac{f(x_0 + \Delta x,\ y_0 + \Delta y,\ z_0 + \Delta z) - f(x_0,\ y_0,\ z_0)}{\Delta s},$$

where $\Delta s = |\Delta\mathbf{r}|$. It can be shown that the properties prescribed for f are sufficient for the existence of this limit. Let $\overrightarrow{P_0P} = \mathbf{u}$; then we denote the directional derivative of $f(x, y, z)$ at P_0 in the direction of $\mathbf{u}$ as

$$\frac{\partial f(x_0, y_0, z_0)}{\partial \mathbf{u}} \quad \text{or} \quad f_{\mathbf{u}}(x_0, y_0, z_0).$$

We can think of the directional derivative of $f(x, y, z)$ at P_0 in the direction of $\overrightarrow{P_0P}$ as a directional derivative along the line determined by P_0 and P in the given direction. This suggests that we generalize the definition of directional derivative. Let P_0: (x_0, y_0, z_0) be a nonsingular point on a regular curve C and let P: $(x_0 + \Delta x, y_0 + \Delta y, z_0 + \Delta z)$ be any other point on C. If f is continuous and differentiable in some region R which contains the arc of C from P_0 to P, we define the **directional derivative of f(x, y, z) at P_0 in the direction of C** as

$$\lim_{\Delta s \to 0} \frac{f(x_0 + \Delta x, y_0 + \Delta y, z_0 + \Delta z) - f(x_0, y_0, z_0)}{\Delta s},$$

where Δs is the length of C from P_0 to P. The conditions prescribed for f insure the existence of this limit.

In practice, to find a specific directional derivative from the definition leads to the analogous difficulties in finding the derivative of a function from its definition. Fortunately, we have a simple expression for the directional derivative. In order to establish it, we make use of the

LAW OF THE MEAN FOR FUNCTIONS OF THREE VARIABLES. If f is continuous and differentiable in some regular region R in E^3 and the points on the line joining (x, y, z) and $(x + \Delta x, y + \Delta y, z + \Delta z)$ are in R, then

$$f(x + \Delta x, y + \Delta y, z + \Delta z) - f(x, y, z) = \left.\frac{\partial f}{\partial x}\right]_{P^*} \Delta x + \left.\frac{\partial f}{\partial y}\right]_{P^*} \Delta y + \left.\frac{\partial f}{\partial z}\right]_{P^*} \Delta z,$$

where P^* is the point $(x + \theta\,\Delta x, y + \theta\,\Delta y, z + \theta\,\Delta z)$, $0 < \theta < 1$.

Proof. Let the function g of the single real variable t be defined on $0 \le t \le 1$ as

$$g(t) \equiv f(x + t\,\Delta x, y + t\,\Delta y, z + t\,\Delta z).$$

Since g is continuous in $0 \le t \le 1$ and differentiable in $0 < t < 1$ (why?), the law of the mean for functions of a single variable can be applied [IIIBd]; i.e., $g(1) - g(0) = g'(0)$. This is equivalent to the result.

We are now ready to prove the

FUNDAMENTAL THEOREM FOR DIRECTIONAL DERIVATIVES. If f is continuous and differentiable in a region R and P_0: (x_0, y_0, z_0) is a nonsingular point on a regular curve C which in some neighborhood of P_0 is contained in R, then the directional derivative of $f(x, y, z)$ at P_0 in the direction of C is

$$\frac{\partial f(x_0, y_0, z_0)}{\partial \mathbf{T}} = \nabla f(x_0, y_0, z_0) \cdot \mathbf{T},$$

where $\mathbf{T}$ is the unit tangent vector to C at P_0.

Proof. Let P: $(x_0 + \Delta x, y_0 + \Delta y, z_0 + \Delta z)$ be a point on C near P_0. Then, by definition, the directional derivative of $f(x, y, z)$ at P_0 in the direction of C is

$$\lim_{\Delta s \to 0} \frac{f(x_0 + \Delta x, y_0 + \Delta y, z_0 + \Delta z) - f(x_0, y_0, z_0)}{\Delta s}$$

which is the

$$\lim_{\Delta s \to 0} \left\{ \frac{\partial f}{\partial x}\bigg]_{P^*} \frac{\Delta x}{\Delta s} + \frac{\partial f}{\partial y}\bigg]_{P^*} \frac{\Delta y}{\Delta s} + \frac{\partial f}{\partial z}\bigg]_{P^*} \frac{\Delta z}{\Delta s} \right\},$$

by the law of the mean, or

$$\frac{\partial f}{\partial x}\frac{dx}{ds} + \frac{\partial f}{\partial y}\frac{dy}{ds} + \frac{\partial f}{\partial z}\frac{dz}{ds}, \text{ evaluated at } P_0.$$

Now, since $\mathbf{T} = \frac{dx}{ds}\mathbf{i} + \frac{dy}{ds}\mathbf{j} + \frac{dz}{ds}\mathbf{k}$, and $\nabla f = \frac{\partial f}{\partial x}\mathbf{i} + \frac{\partial f}{\partial y}\mathbf{j} + \frac{\partial f}{\partial z}\mathbf{k}$, the result is immediate.

The above theorem indicates, as we would suspect, that the directional derivative of $f(x, y, z)$ at P_0 on C in the direction of C is equal to the directional derivative of $f(x, y, z)$ at P_0 in the direction of the unit tangent vector to C at P_0.

Since we can also write

$$\frac{\partial f}{\partial \mathbf{T}} = |\nabla f|\,|\mathbf{T}| \cos\theta = |\nabla f| \cos\theta,$$

where θ is the angle between ∇f and $\mathbf{T}$, it is clear that $\frac{\partial f}{\partial \mathbf{T}}$ is a maximum when $\theta = 0$; i.e., when the direction of $\mathbf{T}$ is the direction of ∇f. Simply stated this means that the direction for which the directional derivative of $f(x, y, z)$ at a point is a maximum is the direction of ∇f at that point and this maximum value is $|\nabla f|$. On the other hand, the direction for which the directional derivative at a point is a minimum is the direction of $-\nabla f$ at that point and this minimum value is $-|\nabla f|$.

EXAMPLE 1. Find the directional derivative of $f(x, y, z) = x^2 + y^2 + z^2$ at $(1, 0, 1)$ in the direction from this point to $(2, 1, 2)$. Determine the direction in which the directional derivative of $f(x, y, z)$ at $(1, 0, 1)$ is a maximum and the value of this maximum.

Solution. Let $\mathbf{T}$ be the unit vector in the direction from $(1, 0, 1)$ to $(2, 1, 2)$; i.e.,

$$\mathbf{T} = \frac{\mathbf{i} + \mathbf{j} + \mathbf{k}}{\sqrt{3}}.$$

At (1, 0, 1), $\nabla f = 2\mathbf{i} + \mathbf{j} + 2\mathbf{k}$. Hence

$$\frac{\partial f}{\partial \mathbf{T}} = \nabla f \cdot \mathbf{T} = \frac{5}{\sqrt{3}}.$$

The maximum directional derivative occurs in the direction of ∇f and this maximum value is $|\nabla f| = 3$.

EXAMPLE 2. Find the directional derivative of $f(x, y, z) = x^2y + y^2z + z^2x$ at (1, 1, 1) in the direction of C: $t\mathbf{i} + t^2\mathbf{j} + t^3\mathbf{k}$.

Solution. At (1, 1, 1), $\mathbf{T} = \dfrac{\mathbf{i} + 2\mathbf{j} + 3\mathbf{k}}{\sqrt{14}}$, $\nabla f = 3(\mathbf{i} + \mathbf{j} + \mathbf{k})$, so that

$$\frac{\partial f}{\partial \mathbf{T}} = \nabla f \cdot \mathbf{T} = \frac{18}{\sqrt{14}}.$$

12. The divergence of a vector function.

The operator

$$\nabla = \frac{\partial}{\partial x}\mathbf{i} + \frac{\partial}{\partial y}\mathbf{j} + \frac{\partial}{\partial z}\mathbf{k}$$

is not a vector and by itself is actually quite meaningless. However, as we have seen, when this operator is applied to a differentiable scalar function, we obtain a very important vector function, the gradient. Nevertheless, if we think of ∇ as a symbolic vector, then ∇f can be formally considered as the vector resulting from scalar "multiplication," where "multiplication" here means taking certain partial derivatives. Now, still thinking of ∇ as a symbolic vector, suppose we consider another type of "product"—the scalar product of ∇ and a differentiable vector function $\boldsymbol{\phi}$. Then, formally, we obtain

$$\begin{aligned}\nabla \cdot \boldsymbol{\phi} &= \left(\frac{\partial}{\partial x}\mathbf{i} + \frac{\partial}{\partial y}\mathbf{j} + \frac{\partial}{\partial z}\mathbf{k}\right) \cdot (\phi_1\mathbf{i} + \phi_2\mathbf{j} + \phi_3\mathbf{k}) \\ &= \frac{\partial \phi_1}{\partial x} + \frac{\partial \phi_2}{\partial y} + \frac{\partial \phi_3}{\partial z}.\end{aligned}$$

Hence, a vector function is transformed into a scalar function, which turns out to be very useful in practice. We call the scalar function

$$\nabla \cdot \boldsymbol{\phi} = \frac{\partial \phi_1}{\partial x} + \frac{\partial \phi_2}{\partial y} + \frac{\partial \phi_3}{\partial z}$$

the **divergence** of the differentiable function $\boldsymbol{\phi} = \phi_1\mathbf{i} + \phi_2\mathbf{j} + \phi_3\mathbf{k}$; it is also denoted as div $\boldsymbol{\phi}$. For a physical interpretation of the divergence of a vector function, which also indicates the reason for this terminology, see Supplementary Problem 14.

If $\boldsymbol{\phi}$ and $\boldsymbol{\psi}$ are differentiable vector functions and f is a differentiable scalar function in some region, the following properties of divergence are readily established from the definitions:

$$\mathbf{D}_1\text{:}\quad \nabla\cdot(\boldsymbol{\phi}+\boldsymbol{\psi}) = \nabla\cdot\boldsymbol{\phi}+\nabla\cdot\boldsymbol{\psi}.$$
$$\mathbf{D}_2\text{:}\quad \nabla\cdot(f\boldsymbol{\phi}) = \nabla f\cdot\boldsymbol{\phi}+f\nabla\cdot\boldsymbol{\phi}.$$
$$\mathbf{D}_3\text{:}\quad \nabla\cdot\nabla f = \frac{\partial^2 f}{\partial x^2}+\frac{\partial^2 f}{\partial y^2}+\frac{\partial^2 f}{\partial z^2}.$$

In D_3 we require that the second partial derivatives of f exist. $\nabla\cdot\nabla f$ is ordinarily written as $\nabla^2 f$ so that ∇^2 is the operator

$$\frac{\partial^2}{\partial x^2}+\frac{\partial^2}{\partial y^2}+\frac{\partial^2}{\partial z^2}.$$

∇^2 is called the **Laplacian.** $\nabla^2 f = 0$ is called **Laplace's equation.** A function f that has continuous second partial derivatives and satisfies Laplace's equation is called a **harmonic function.** Harmonic functions play a central role in many of the applications of mathematical physics and we shall have occasion to encounter them frequently.†

EXAMPLE 1. Find $\nabla\cdot(f\boldsymbol{\phi})$ at the point $(1, -1, 1)$ if $\boldsymbol{\phi} = 3xyz^2\mathbf{i} + 2xy^3\mathbf{j} - x^2yz\mathbf{k}$, and $f = 3x^2 - yz$.

Solution. By D_2, $\nabla\cdot(f\boldsymbol{\phi}) = \nabla\cdot f\boldsymbol{\phi} + f\nabla\cdot\boldsymbol{\phi}$. At $(1, -1, 1)$, $\nabla f = 6\mathbf{i} - \mathbf{j} + \mathbf{k}$, $\boldsymbol{\phi} = -3\mathbf{i} - 2\mathbf{j} + \mathbf{k}$, $\nabla\cdot\boldsymbol{\phi} = 4$, $\nabla f\cdot\boldsymbol{\phi} = -15$, $f\nabla\cdot\boldsymbol{\phi} = 16$. Hence, $\nabla\cdot(f\boldsymbol{\phi}) = 1$ at $(1, -1, 1)$.

EXAMPLE 2. Show that $\nabla\cdot(f\nabla g - g\nabla f) = f\nabla^2 g - g\nabla^2 f$.

Solution. (1) $\nabla\cdot(f\nabla g) = \nabla f\cdot\nabla g + f(\nabla\cdot\nabla g) = \nabla f\cdot\nabla g + f\nabla^2 g$. (2) Interchanging f and g in (1) yields (2) $\nabla\cdot(g\,\nabla f) = \nabla g\cdot\nabla f + g\,\nabla^2 f$. Now subtracting (2) from (1) yields the result.

13. The curl of a vector function. Just as the divergence of a vector function $\boldsymbol{\phi}$ can be defined formally as the scalar product of the operator ∇ and the differentiable vector function $\boldsymbol{\phi}$, by defining the operation

$$\nabla\times\boldsymbol{\phi} = \left(\frac{\partial}{\partial x}\mathbf{i}+\frac{\partial}{\partial y}\mathbf{j}+\frac{\partial}{\partial z}\mathbf{k}\right)\times(\phi_1\mathbf{i}+\phi_2\mathbf{j}+\phi_3\mathbf{k})$$
$$= \begin{vmatrix} \mathbf{i} & \mathbf{j} & \mathbf{k} \\ \dfrac{\partial}{\partial x} & \dfrac{\partial}{\partial y} & \dfrac{\partial}{\partial z} \\ \phi_1 & \phi_2 & \phi_3 \end{vmatrix}$$
$$= \left(\frac{\partial\phi_3}{\partial y}-\frac{\partial\phi_2}{\partial z}\right)\mathbf{i}+\left(\frac{\partial\phi_1}{\partial z}-\frac{\partial\phi_3}{\partial x}\right)\mathbf{j}+\left(\frac{\partial\phi_2}{\partial x}-\frac{\partial\phi_1}{\partial y}\right)\mathbf{k},$$

we obtain a vector function known as the **curl** of $\boldsymbol{\phi}$. We also write $\nabla\times\boldsymbol{\phi} =$ curl $\boldsymbol{\phi}$. Hence, formally, the curl of a vector function $\boldsymbol{\phi}$ is the vector prod-

† Examples of harmonic functions are: gravitational, electric, and magnetic potentials in a region free of sources; temperature in source-free regions under steady-state conditions; velocity potential in irrotational hydrodynamic flow.

uct of ∇ and $\boldsymbol{\phi}$. For a physical interpretation of the curl of a vector, see Supplementary Problem 14.

The curl of a vector function has the following properties, which can be established by the use of the definitions, the required differentiability conditions being assumed:

C_1: $\nabla \times (\boldsymbol{\phi} + \boldsymbol{\psi}) = \nabla \times \boldsymbol{\phi} + \nabla \times \boldsymbol{\psi}$.
C_2: $\nabla \times (f\boldsymbol{\phi}) = \nabla f \times \boldsymbol{\phi} + f(\nabla \times \boldsymbol{\phi})$.
C_3: $\nabla \cdot (\boldsymbol{\phi} \times \boldsymbol{\psi}) = \boldsymbol{\psi} \cdot (\nabla \times \boldsymbol{\phi}) - \boldsymbol{\phi} \cdot (\nabla \times \boldsymbol{\psi})$.
C_4: $\nabla \times (\boldsymbol{\phi} \times \boldsymbol{\psi}) = (\boldsymbol{\psi} \cdot \nabla)\boldsymbol{\phi} - \boldsymbol{\psi}(\nabla \cdot \boldsymbol{\phi}) - (\boldsymbol{\phi} \cdot \nabla)\boldsymbol{\psi} + \boldsymbol{\phi}(\nabla \cdot \boldsymbol{\psi})$.
C_5: $\nabla(\boldsymbol{\phi} \cdot \boldsymbol{\psi}) = (\boldsymbol{\psi} \cdot \nabla)\boldsymbol{\phi} + (\boldsymbol{\phi} \cdot \nabla)\boldsymbol{\psi} + \boldsymbol{\psi} \times (\nabla \times \boldsymbol{\phi}) + \boldsymbol{\phi} \times (\nabla \times \boldsymbol{\psi})$.
C_6: $\nabla \times (\nabla f) = \mathbf{0}$; i.e., curl grad $f = \mathbf{0}$.
C_7: $\nabla \cdot (\nabla \times \boldsymbol{\phi}) = 0$; i.e., div curl $\boldsymbol{\phi} = 0$.
C_8: $\nabla \times (\nabla \times \boldsymbol{\phi}) = \nabla(\nabla \cdot \boldsymbol{\phi}) - \nabla^2 \boldsymbol{\phi}$.

In C_4 and C_5, $\boldsymbol{\phi} \cdot \nabla$ is the vector operator $\phi_1(\partial/\partial x) + \phi_2(\partial/\partial y) + \phi_3(\partial/\partial z)$ so that

$$(\boldsymbol{\phi} \cdot \nabla)\boldsymbol{\psi} = \phi_1 \frac{\partial \boldsymbol{\psi}}{\partial x} + \phi_2 \frac{\partial \boldsymbol{\psi}}{\partial y} + \phi_3 \frac{\partial \boldsymbol{\psi}}{\partial z}.$$

Note that $\boldsymbol{\phi} \cdot \nabla \neq \nabla \cdot \boldsymbol{\phi}$. In C_8,

$$\nabla^2 \boldsymbol{\phi} = \frac{\partial^2 \boldsymbol{\phi}}{\partial x^2} + \frac{\partial^2 \boldsymbol{\phi}}{\partial y^2} + \frac{\partial^2 \boldsymbol{\phi}}{\partial z^2}.$$

The converse of C_6: If curl $\boldsymbol{\phi} = \mathbf{0}$, there exists f such that $\boldsymbol{\phi} =$ grad f; and the converse of C_7: if div $\boldsymbol{\psi} = 0$, then there exists $\boldsymbol{\phi}$ such that curl $\boldsymbol{\phi} = \boldsymbol{\psi}$ are true under appropriate restrictions. We shall consider the first of these later; a complete discussion of the second occurs in Kaplan, *Advanced Calculus*, Chapter V.

EXAMPLE 1. Show that the curl of $\boldsymbol{\phi} = (xyz)^b(x^a\mathbf{i} + y^a\mathbf{j} + z^a\mathbf{k}) = \mathbf{0}$ if and only if either $b = 0$ or $a = -1$.

Solution. By C_2,

$$\begin{aligned} \text{curl } \boldsymbol{\phi} &= \nabla(xyz)^b \times (x^a\mathbf{i} + y^a\mathbf{j} + z^a\mathbf{k}) + (xyz)^b \text{ curl } (x^a\mathbf{i} + y^a\mathbf{j} + z^a\mathbf{k}) \\ &= \nabla(xyz)^b \times (x^a\mathbf{i} + y^a\mathbf{j} + z^a\mathbf{k}), \end{aligned}$$

$$\left(\text{since curl } (x^a\mathbf{i} + y^a\mathbf{j} + z^a\mathbf{k}) = \begin{vmatrix} \mathbf{i} & \mathbf{j} & \mathbf{k} \\ \dfrac{\partial}{\partial x} & \dfrac{\partial}{\partial y} & \dfrac{\partial}{\partial z} \\ x^a & y^a & z^a \end{vmatrix} = \mathbf{0}\right)$$

$$= b(xyz)^{b-1}[x(z^{a+1} - y^{a+1})\mathbf{i} + y(x^{a+1} - y^{a+1})\mathbf{j} + z(y^{a+1} - x^{a+1})\mathbf{k}],$$

from which the conclusion is immediate.

EXAMPLE 2. Prove curl $(f \text{ grad } f) = \mathbf{0}$ for any twice differentiable scalar function f.

Solution. By C_2, curl $(f \text{ grad } f) = \nabla f \times \nabla f + f\nabla \times (\nabla f) = \mathbf{0}$, with C_6.

EXERCISES

1. Find the surface area of each of the following:

(a) S: $z = x^2 + y^2$, $x^2 + y^2 \leq 1$.

(b) S: $z = \sqrt{x^2 + y^2}$, $x^2 + y^2 \leq 1$.

(c) S: $z = xy$, $x^2 + y^2 \leq 1$.

(d) S: $x^2 + y^2 + 2z = 4$, $1 \leq x^2 + y^2 \leq 2$.

(e) The surface cut off the paraboloid $x = y^2 + z^2$ by the plane $x = 1$.

(f) The part of the cylinder $z = x^2$ whose projection on the xy-plane is the triangle bounded by $y = 0$, $y = x$, $x = 1$.

(g) The part of the sphere $x^2 + y^2 + z^2 = 1$ about the xy-plane cut out by the cylinder $x^2 + y^2 = x$. (*Hint:* Use polar coordinates.)

(h) S: $a\,v \cos u\,\mathbf{i} + b\,v \sin u\,\mathbf{j} + v\,\mathbf{k}$, $0 \leq u \leq 1$, $0 \leq v \leq 1$.

Ans.: (a) $\pi/4(\sqrt{125} - 1)$; (b) $2\pi\sqrt{2}$; (c) $2\pi/3\,(2\sqrt{2} - 1)$; (d) $\frac{4\pi}{3}(5^{3/2} - 2^{3/2})$; (e) $\frac{\pi}{6}(5^{3/2} - 1)$; (f) $(5^{3/2} - 1)/12$; (g) $\pi - 2$.

2. Find $d\sigma$ for each of the following surfaces:

(a) S: $\dfrac{x^2}{a^2} + \dfrac{y^2}{b^2} + \dfrac{z^2}{c^2} = 1$, $\dfrac{x^2}{a^2} + \dfrac{y^2}{b^2} \leq 1$.

(b) S: $a \cos u \cosh v\,\mathbf{i} + b \sin u \cosh v\,\mathbf{j} + c \sinh v\,\mathbf{k}$, $0 \leq u \leq 2\pi$, $-\infty < v < \infty$.

(c) S: $z = \dfrac{x^2}{a^2} + \dfrac{y^2}{b^2} = 1$, all x and y.

(d) S: $u \cos v\,\mathbf{i} + u \sin v\,\mathbf{j} + f(u)\mathbf{k}$, where $z = f(x)$ is rotated about the z-axis, $-\infty < u < \infty$, $0 \leq v \leq 2\pi$.

3. If $\boldsymbol{\phi} = 3xyz^2\mathbf{i} + 2xy^3\mathbf{j} - x^2yz\,\mathbf{k}$ and $f = 3x^2 - yz$, find at $(1, -1, 1)$:
(a) $\nabla \cdot \boldsymbol{\phi}$; (b) $\boldsymbol{\phi} \cdot \nabla f$; (c) $\nabla \cdot (f\boldsymbol{\phi})$; (d) $\nabla \times \boldsymbol{\phi}$; (e) $\nabla \times (f\boldsymbol{\phi})$; (f) $\nabla^2 f$.

Ans.: (a) 4; (b) -15; (c) 1; (d) $-\mathbf{i} - 8\mathbf{j} - 5\mathbf{k}$; (e) $-3\mathbf{i} - 41\mathbf{j} - 35\mathbf{k}$; (f) 6.

4. Let $\mathbf{r} = x\mathbf{i} + y\mathbf{j} + z\mathbf{k}$ be the position vector of any point in space. Establish each of the following:

(a) $\nabla f(r) = f'(r)\mathbf{r}/r$, f any differentiable function. In particular,

$$\nabla r^n = nr^{n-2} \quad \text{and} \quad \nabla \log r = \frac{\mathbf{r}}{r^2}.$$

(b) $\nabla \times \mathbf{r} = \mathbf{0}$. Use this to prove generally that $\nabla \times f(r)\mathbf{r} = 0$, f any differentiable function.

(c) $\nabla \cdot \mathbf{r} = 3$.

(d) $\nabla \cdot \mathbf{r}/r^3 = 0$.

(e) For $\mathbf{a}$, an arbitrary constant vector, grad $\mathbf{a} \cdot \mathbf{r} = \mathbf{a}$, div $(\mathbf{a} \times \mathbf{r}) = 0$, curl $(\mathbf{a} \times \mathbf{r}) = 2\mathbf{a}$, grad $(\mathbf{a} \cdot \mathbf{r}/r^3)$ + curl $(\mathbf{a} \times \mathbf{r})/r^3 = \mathbf{0}$,

$$\nabla\left(\mathbf{a} \cdot \nabla \frac{1}{r}\right) + \nabla \times \left(\mathbf{a} \times \nabla \frac{1}{r}\right) = \mathbf{0}.$$

(f) $(\boldsymbol{\phi} \cdot \nabla)\mathbf{r} = \boldsymbol{\phi}$ and $\nabla \cdot (\boldsymbol{\phi} \times \mathbf{r}) = \mathbf{r} \cdot (\nabla \times \boldsymbol{\phi})$, $\boldsymbol{\phi}$ any differentiable vector function.

(g) $\nabla^2(1/r) = 0$.

(h) $\nabla^2 \log r = 1/r^2$.

5. If the position vectors of two points P_1 and P_2 in space are $\mathbf{r}_1$ and $\mathbf{r}_2$ and $\boldsymbol{\phi} = (\mathbf{r} - \mathbf{r}_1) \times (\mathbf{r} - \mathbf{r}_2)$, where $\mathbf{r}$ is the position vector of any point P in space, show that

(a) $\operatorname{div} \boldsymbol{\phi} = 0$; (b) $\operatorname{curl} \boldsymbol{\phi} = 2(\mathbf{r}_2 - \mathbf{r}_1)$, (c) $\boldsymbol{\nabla}(\mathbf{r} - \mathbf{r}_1)\cdot(\mathbf{r} - \mathbf{r}_2) = 2\mathbf{r} - \mathbf{r}_1 - \mathbf{r}_2$.

6. Determine the unit normal vectors $\mathbf{n}$ to $z = x^2 + y^2$ at $(1, 2, 3)$.

(a) What is the standard choice of sign for $\mathbf{n}$?

(b) What is the outer unit normal vector? *Ans.:* $\pm(2\mathbf{i} - 4\mathbf{j} - \mathbf{k})/\sqrt{21}$.

7. (a) What is the angle between the normals to the surface $S\colon xy = z^2$ at the points $(1, 1, 1)$ and $(-1, -2, 2)$?

(b) Find the angle between the surfaces $S_1\colon x^2 + y^2 + z^2 = 9$ and $S_2\colon z = x^2 + y^2 - 3$ at the point $(2, -1, 2)$. *Ans.:* (a) $\cos^{-1} \frac{5}{3}\sqrt{14}$; (b) $\cos^{-1} \frac{8}{3}\sqrt{21}$.

8. If $\boldsymbol{\phi}$ and $\boldsymbol{\psi}$ are the vectors that join the fixed points $P_1\colon (x_1, y_1, z_1)$ and $P_2\colon (x_2, y_2, z_2)$ to the variable point $P\colon (x, y, z)$, prove that $\operatorname{grad}(\boldsymbol{\phi}\cdot\boldsymbol{\psi}) = \boldsymbol{\phi} + \boldsymbol{\psi}$. Find $\operatorname{div}(\boldsymbol{\phi} \times \boldsymbol{\psi})$ and $\operatorname{curl}(\boldsymbol{\phi} \times \boldsymbol{\psi})$.

9. If $f = 3x^2y$, $g = xz^2 - 2y$, find $\operatorname{grad}(\operatorname{grad} f\cdot\operatorname{grad} g)$.

Ans.: $(6yz^2 - 12x)\mathbf{i} + 6xz^2\mathbf{j} + 12xyz\mathbf{k}$.

10. Determine the constant m so that $\operatorname{curl} \boldsymbol{\phi} = \mathbf{0}$, where $(mxy - z^3)\mathbf{i} + (m - 2)x^2\mathbf{j} + (1 - m)xz^2\mathbf{k}$. *Ans.:* $m = 4$.

11. If $f = (\mathbf{r} \times \mathbf{a})\cdot(\mathbf{r} \times \mathbf{b})$, show that $\boldsymbol{\nabla} f = \mathbf{b} \times (\mathbf{r} \times \mathbf{a}) + \mathbf{a} \times (\mathbf{r} \times \mathbf{b})$, where $\mathbf{a}$ and $\mathbf{b}$ are constant vectors and $\mathbf{r}$ is the position vector of an arbitrary point.

12. Find the directional derivative of

(a) $f = 4e^{2x-y+z}$ at the point $(1, 1, -1)$ in the direction toward the point $(-1, -3, -5)$.

(b) $f = x^2 + xy + y^2$ at $(1, 1)$ in the direction of the vector making an angle of 60 deg with the positive x-axis.

(c) $f = x^2 + y^2 - 3xy$ at $(1, 1)$ in the direction of the tangent to the curve of $y = x^2$ at $(1, 1)$.

(d) $f = x^3 + 3xy - 3yz + z^3$ at $(1, 2, 1)$ in the direction of the curve of $x = t$, $y = 2t^2$, $z = t^3$, $t \geq 0$.

(e) $f = x^2 - 5xy + z^2$ at $(1, 1, 2)$ in the direction of the outer unit normal to $S\colon x^2 + y^2 + z = 4$ at $(1, 1, 2)$. *Ans.:* (a) $-8/3$; (b) $\frac{3}{2}(1 + \sqrt{3})$; (c) -2; (d) 12; (e) $5\sqrt{2}$.

13. In what direction from the point $(1, 2, 3)$ is the directional derivative of $xyz - y^2$ a maximum? A minimum? What are the maximum and minimum directional derivatives of this function at $(1, 2, 3)$?

Ans.: $6\mathbf{i} - \mathbf{j} + 2\mathbf{k}$; $-6\mathbf{i} + \mathbf{j} - 2\mathbf{k}$; $\sqrt{41}$; $-\sqrt{41}$.

14. The temperature at any point (x, y, z) in space is $T = x^2 + y^2 - z$. A mosquito located at $(1, 1, 2)$ desires to fly in such a direction so that he will get warm as soon as possible. In what direction should he move?

Ans.: $2\mathbf{i} + 2\mathbf{j} - \mathbf{k}$.

15. Show that $\partial f/\partial \mathbf{T} = (\mathbf{T}\cdot\boldsymbol{\nabla})f$ for every unit vector $\mathbf{T}$ at any point of a differentiable vector function f.

16. Show that if u and v are differentiable functions in some region of the xy-plane such that $\partial u/\partial x = \partial v/\partial y$, $\partial u/\partial y = -\partial v/\partial x$ in that region, then $\partial u/\partial \mathbf{a} = \partial v/\partial \mathbf{b}$, where $\mathbf{a}$ and $\mathbf{b}$ are vectors making angles θ and $\theta + (\pi/2)$ with $\mathbf{i}$.

17. (a) Show that the curl of any vector whose direction is constant is perpendicular to a vector in that direction.

(b) Is there a differentiable vector function $\boldsymbol{\phi}$ such that curl $\boldsymbol{\phi} = \mathbf{r}$, the position vector of any point? curl $\boldsymbol{\phi} = 2\mathbf{i} + \mathbf{j} + 3\mathbf{k}$? If so, find $\boldsymbol{\phi}$.

(c) In general, if curl $\boldsymbol{\phi} = \mathbf{a}$, what is $\boldsymbol{\phi}$?

18. If $\mathbf{u}$ is a constant unit vector, show that

$$\mathbf{u}\cdot[\nabla(\boldsymbol{\phi}\cdot\mathbf{u}) - \nabla \times (\boldsymbol{\phi} \times \mathbf{u})] = \nabla\cdot\boldsymbol{\phi},$$

where $\boldsymbol{\phi}$ is any differentiable vector function.

19. Show that $(\boldsymbol{\phi}\cdot\nabla) = \frac{1}{2}\nabla\phi^2 - (\boldsymbol{\phi} \times \nabla) \times \boldsymbol{\phi}$ for any differentiable vector function $\boldsymbol{\phi}$.

20. What meaning can be assigned to $(\boldsymbol{\phi} \times \nabla)f$? Determine this vector if $\boldsymbol{\phi} = 2z\mathbf{i} - x^2\mathbf{j} + x\mathbf{k}$ and $f = 2x^2y^2z^2$ at $(1, -1, 1)$. *Ans.:* $-8\mathbf{i} - 4\mathbf{j} + 4\mathbf{k}$.

21. If to each point (x, y, z) of a region R in space, a vector $\boldsymbol{\phi}(x, y, z)$ is assigned, then the totality of these vectors is said to constitute a **vector field** in R. We refer to it as the vector field $\boldsymbol{\phi}$. The vector field $\boldsymbol{\phi}$ is called **solenoidal** if $\boldsymbol{\phi}$ is differentiable and div $\boldsymbol{\phi} = 0$, and **irrotational** if $\boldsymbol{\phi}$ is differentiable and curl $\boldsymbol{\phi} = \mathbf{0}$. Show that

(a) If $\boldsymbol{\phi}$ and $\boldsymbol{\psi}$ are irrotational, then $\boldsymbol{\phi} \times \boldsymbol{\psi}$ is solenoidal.

(b) If f and g are scalar functions having continuous second partial derivatives, then $\nabla f \times \nabla g$ is solenoidal.

(c) If f is harmonic, then ∇f is both solenoidal and irrotational.

22. (a) Show that if f and g are harmonic in R, then $f + g$, cf, c arbitrary constant, are harmonic in R.

(b) Show that $\nabla^2(fg) = f\nabla^2 g + 2\nabla f\cdot\nabla g + g\nabla^2 f$, for any twice differentiable functions f and g.

(c) Determine which of the following functions are harmonic: $e^x \cos y$, $x^3 - 3xy^2 + z^3$, $\log\sqrt{x^2 + y^2 + z^2}$, $xe^x \cos y$, $e^x \cos y - z$.

(d) Show that $\nabla^2 f(r) = d^2f/dr^2 + (2/r)df/dr$, for any twice differentiable function f; $r = |\mathbf{r}|$, $\mathbf{r}$ the position vector of any point.

(e) Find $f(r)$ such that $\nabla^2 f(r) = 0$.

Ans.: (e) $f(r) = c_1 + c_2/r$, c_1 and c_2 arbitrary constants.

23. (a) Show that the ellipse $r_1 + r_2 = c_1$ and the hyperbola $r_1 - r_2 = c_1$ intersect at right angles when they have the same foci. Formulate and prove this statement for the hyperboloid of one or two sheets and the ellipsoid.

(b) Given a parabola with focus at the origin and directrix $x = -p$. If $\mathbf{r}$ is the position vector of any point on the parabola, then $r = p + x$. Show that $(\mathbf{R} - \mathbf{i})\cdot\mathbf{T} = 0$, where $\mathbf{T}$ is the unit tangent vector to the parabola and $\mathbf{R} = \mathbf{r}/r$; interpret this equation geometrically.

24. Let f be continuous on a closed regular surface S and its interior, and let f assume its maximum value on S at a point P. Show that $\partial f/\partial\mathbf{n} \leq 0$ at P, where $\mathbf{n}$ is the unit normal vector directed toward the interior of S.

25. (a) Show that

$$(\nabla f \quad \nabla g \quad \nabla h) = \begin{vmatrix} \dfrac{\partial f}{\partial x} & \dfrac{\partial f}{\partial y} & \dfrac{\partial f}{\partial z} \\[2ex] \dfrac{\partial g}{\partial x} & \dfrac{\partial g}{\partial y} & \dfrac{\partial g}{\partial z} \\[2ex] \dfrac{\partial h}{\partial x} & \dfrac{\partial h}{\partial y} & \dfrac{\partial h}{\partial z} \end{vmatrix}$$

for any differentiable scalar functions f, g, h. A necessary and sufficient condition that f, g, h be **functionally dependent** (i.e., for which there exists a function F such that $F(f, g, h) = 0$) is the vanishing of the above determinant, called the **Jacobian** of f, g, h and denoted by $\partial(f, g, h)/\partial(x, y, z)$.

(b) Determine whether $x + y + z$, $x^2 + y^2 + z^2$, $xy + yz + zx$ are functionally dependent. If so, find the relationship between them.

Chapter 4

The Vector Integral Calculus

1. Line integrals. In defining the definite integral in elementary calculus, we begin by considering a function defined in a given interval. This interval is then divided into subintervals, and an arbitrary point is selected from each subinterval. For each subinterval, the value of the function at this arbitrary point is multiplied by the length of the subinterval. The sum of these products for all subintervals is formed and the limit of this sum, as the number of subdivisions becomes larger and larger in such a manner that the length of the largest subinterval approaches zero, is considered. If this limit exists, it is called the **definite integral** of the function in the given interval. A sufficient condition for the existence of this limit is the continuity of the function in the given interval. There are various ways in which this procedure can be generalized. One way is to replace the given interval by any regular curve and to define a function on this curve; i.e., to assign a real number to every point on the curve. This leads to the definition of a line integral, which we now examine in some detail.

Let C be the curve of the smooth vector function $\boldsymbol{\phi} = \phi_1\mathbf{i} + \phi_2\mathbf{j} + \phi_3\mathbf{k}$, $\alpha \leq t \leq \beta$. To every point (x, y, z) on C, we assign a real number denoted by $f(x, y, z)$. We say that a function f of three variables has been defined on C. Now divide the interval $\alpha \leq t \leq \beta$ into n parts in any arbitrary manner, with $\alpha = t_0 < t_1 < \cdots < t_{i-1} < t_i < \cdots < t_n = \beta$ being the division points. (See Fig. 1.) Let t_i' be any point such that $t_{i-1} \leq t_i' \leq t_i$. Corresponding to t_i and t_i' are the points (x_i, y_i, z_i) and (x_i', y_i', z_i') on C. Consider the sum

$$\sum_{i=1}^{n} f(x_i', y_i', z_i')\,\Delta s_i,$$

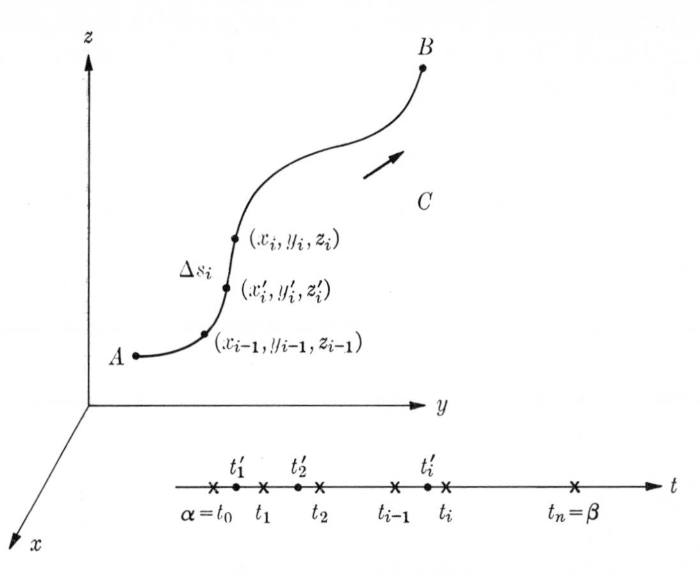

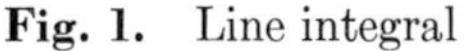

Fig. 1. Line integral

where Δs_i is the length of C from $(x_{i-1}, y_{i-1}, z_{i-1})$ to (x_i, y_i, z_i). Denote by $||\Delta s||$ the largest of the Δs_i $(i = 1, 2, \cdots, n)$. If

$$\lim_{\substack{n \to \infty \\ ||\Delta s|| \to 0}} \sum_{i=1}^{n} f(x_i', y_i', z_i') \, \Delta s_i$$

exists (the limit is taken as $n \to \infty$ in such a manner that $||\Delta s|| \to 0$), we call it the **line integral** of f on C and denote it as

$$\int_C f(x, y, z) \, ds, \quad \int_A^B f(x, y, z) \, dx,$$

or

$$\int_{(a,b,c)}^{(d,e,f)} f(x, y, z) \, ds,$$

where (a, b, c) and (d, e, f) are the coordinates of the initial and terminal points A and B of the curve C.

Now let C be any regular curve consisting of the smooth curves $C_1, C_2, \cdots, C_n$. Let f be defined on C. Then we define the line integral of f on C as the sum of the line integrals of f on $C_1, C_2, \cdots, C_n$ and denote it as

$$\int_C f(x, y, z) \, ds.$$

The generalization of the definite integral to a line integral would be fruitless if the line integral did not have geometric or physical interpretations. But it does, indeed. For example, if we consider C physically as a wire, then $\int_C f(x, y, z) \, ds$ denotes (1) the length of the wire if $f(x, y, z) = 1$;

(2) the mass of the wire M if $f(x, y, z) = \rho(x, y, z)$, the density function; (3) $M\bar{x}$, $M\bar{y}$, or $M\bar{z}$, if $f(x, y, z) = x\rho(x, y, z)$, $y\rho(x, y, z)$, or $z\rho(x, y, z)$, where $(\bar{x}, \bar{y}, \bar{z})$ is the center of gravity of the wire; (4) the moments of inertia of the wire I_x, I_y, or I_z about the x, y, z axes if

$$f(x, y, z) = (y^2 + z^2)\rho(x, y, z), \ (x^2 + z^2)\rho(x, y, z), \quad \text{or} \quad (x^2 + y^2)\rho(x, y, z).$$

The student should convince himself of the reasonableness of these interpretations, starting with basic physical principles.

Let $\mathbf{F} = P(x, y, z)\mathbf{i} + Q(x, y, z)\mathbf{j} + R(x, y, z)\mathbf{k}$ be a force acting on a particle moving along the curve C of the smooth vector function $\boldsymbol{\phi}$. We now express the work W done on the particle by $\mathbf{F}$ as a line integral. Let the curve C be divided into n parts. Let $\mathbf{r}_i$ be the position vector of the point of division (x_i, y_i, z_i). Let $\Delta\mathbf{r}_i = \mathbf{r}_{i+1} - \mathbf{r}_i$. (See Fig. 2.) Now the

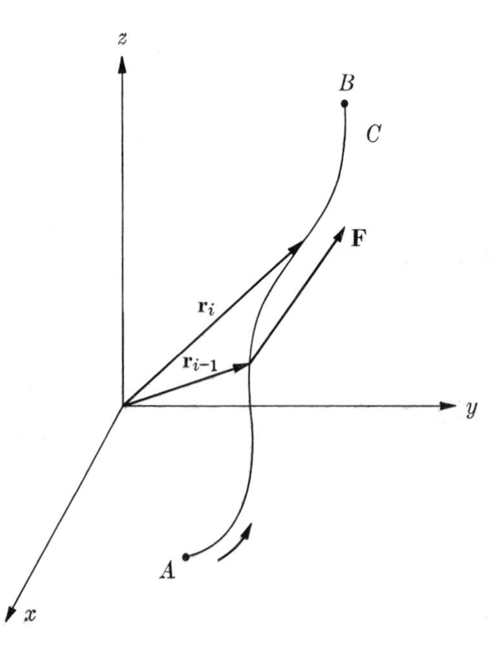

Fig. 2. Work

work done by the force $\mathbf{F}$ on the particle as it moves from (x_i, y_i, z_i) to $(x_{i+1}, y_{i+1}, z_{i+1})$ along C is approximately

$$\mathbf{F}(x_i, y_i, z_i) \cdot \Delta\mathbf{r}_i = \mathbf{F}(x_i, y_i, z_i) \cdot \frac{\Delta\mathbf{r}_i}{\Delta s_i} \Delta s_i,$$

where Δs_i is the length of C from (x_i, y_i, z_i) to $(x_{i+1}, y_{i+1}, z_{i+1})$. Furthermore, since

$$\lim_{\Delta s_i \to 0} \frac{\Delta\mathbf{r}_i}{\Delta s_i} = \mathbf{T}(x_i, y_i, z_i),$$

the unit tangent vector at (x_i, y_i, z_i), the work done is approximately $\mathbf{F}(x_i, y_i, z_i) \cdot \mathbf{T}(x_i, y_i, z_i)\, \Delta s_i$, and it is reasonable to define

$$W = \lim_{\substack{n\to\infty \\ ||\Delta s||\to 0}} \sum_{i=1}^{n} \mathbf{F}(x_i, y_i, z_i) \cdot \mathbf{T}(x_i, y_i, z_i)\, \Delta s_i.$$

But this limit is the line integral

$$\int_C \mathbf{F} \cdot \mathbf{T}\, ds.$$

Note that this can be expressed as the special case of a line integral with $f(x, y, z) = \mathbf{F} \cdot \mathbf{T}$. We have

$$W = \int_C \mathbf{F} \cdot \mathbf{T}\, ds = \int_C \mathbf{F} \cdot d\mathbf{r},$$

since $\mathbf{T} = d\mathbf{r}/ds$, $\mathbf{r} = x\mathbf{i} + y\mathbf{j} + z\mathbf{k}$, and we define $d\mathbf{r} = dx\,\mathbf{i} + dy\,\mathbf{j} + dz\,\mathbf{k}$. Therefore, we can also write

$$W = \int_C \mathbf{F} \cdot d\mathbf{r} = \int_C P\, dx + Q\, dy + R\, dz,$$

since $\mathbf{F} = P\mathbf{i} + Q\mathbf{j} + R\mathbf{k}$. This line integral represents work, but may represent other quantities, depending on the interpretation of the vector function $\mathbf{F}$.

In the equation

$$\int_C P\, dx + Q\, dy + R\, dz = \int_C \mathbf{F} \cdot d\mathbf{r},$$

we shall say that the left-hand side is the **cartesian form** of the line integral and the right-hand side is the **vector form.** The vector form is distinguished by its compact form.

Incidentally, the preceding procedure indicates how we can define the line integral of a vector function.

Just as in the case of the definite integral, the definition of the line integral leads to significant geometric and physical interpretations, as we have seen (and many others which the student may encounter in his future studies). However, the definition is highly impractical for the determination of the value of a given line integral. For this we turn to the

FUNDAMENTAL THEOREM FOR LINE INTEGRALS. If (1) C: $x = \phi_1(t)$, $y = \phi_2(t)$, $z = \phi_3(t)$, $\alpha \leq t \leq \beta$ is smooth, and (2) f, P, Q, R are continuous on C, then $\int_C f(x, y, z)\, ds$ and $\int_C P\, dx + Q\, dy + R\, dz$ exist and

(a) $$\int_C f(x, y, z)\, ds = \int_\alpha^\beta f[\phi_1(t), \phi_2(t), \phi_3(t)] \times \sqrt{[\phi_1'(t)]^2 + [\phi_2'(t)]^2 + [\phi_3'(t)]^2}\, dt$$

(b) $\int_C P\,dx + Q\,dy + R\,dz = \int_\alpha^\beta \{P[\phi_1(t), \phi_2(t), \phi_3(t)]\phi_1'(t)$
$+ Q[\phi_1(t), \phi_2(t), \phi_3(t)]\phi_2'(t)$
$+ R[\phi_1(t), \phi_2(t), \phi_3(t)]\phi_3'(t)\}\,dt.$

Proof. By definition,

$$\int_C f(x, y, z)\,ds = \lim_{\substack{n\to\infty \\ ||\Delta s||\to 0}} \sum_{i=1}^n f(x_i, y_i, z_i)\,\Delta s_i$$

$$= \lim_{\substack{n\to\infty \\ ||\Delta t||\to 0}} \sum_{i=1}^n f(x_i, y_i, z_i)\frac{\Delta s_i}{\Delta t_i}\,\Delta t_i,$$

since $||\Delta t|| \to 0$ as $||\Delta s|| \to 0$. Since

$$s = \int_0^t \sqrt{[\phi_1'(u)]^2 + [\phi_2'(u)]^2 + [\phi_3'(u)]^2}\,du,$$

by the law of the mean for derivatives (why is it applicable?), there exists $t_{i-1} < t_i^* < t_i$ such that

$$\Delta s_i = \sqrt{[\phi_1'(t_i^*)]^2 + [\phi_2'(t_i^*)]^2 + [\phi_3'(t_i^*)]^2}\,\Delta t_i.$$

Hence, the above limit becomes

$$\lim_{\substack{n\to\infty \\ ||\Delta t||\to 0}} \sum_{i=1}^n f(x_i, y_i, z_i)\sqrt{[\phi_1'(t_i^*)]^2 + [\phi_2'(t_i^*)]^2 + [\phi_3'(t_i^*)]^2}\,\Delta t_i,$$

with

$$x_i = \phi_1(t_i'),\ y_i = \phi_2(t_i'),\ z_i = \phi_3(t_i'),\ t_{i-1} < t_i' < t_i.$$

Since f is continuous on C and ϕ_1, ϕ_2, ϕ_3, ϕ_1', ϕ_2', ϕ_3' are continuous on $\alpha \le t \le \beta$, C being smooth, the above limit exists by Duhamel's theorem [IIICc], and this limit is the definite integral in (a).

To obtain (b), we write

$$\int_C P\,dx + Q\,dy + R\,dz = \int_C \mathbf{F}\cdot d\mathbf{r},$$

where $\mathbf{F} = P\mathbf{i} + Q\mathbf{j} + R\mathbf{k}$. This integral can be written as

$$\int_C \mathbf{F}\cdot\frac{d\mathbf{r}}{ds}\,ds = \int_C \left(P\frac{dx}{ds} + Q\frac{dy}{ds} + R\frac{dz}{ds}\right)ds,$$

which yields (b) when we apply (a).

If C is piecewise smooth, the preceding theorem is applied to each smooth curve constituting C and the resulting integrals are added.

The fundamental theorem for line integrals indicates that a line integral is evaluated by evaluating a certain definite integral, for which we have available the methods of the elementary integral calculus. In fact, given the line integral of f on C: $x = \phi_1(t)$, $y = \phi_2(t)$, $z = \phi_3(t)$, $\alpha \le t \le \beta$, we formally obtain this definite integral by replacing x by

$\phi_1(t)$, y by $\phi_2(t)$, z by $\phi_3(t)$, dx by $\phi_1'(t)\,dt$, dy by $\phi_2'(t)\,dt$, dz by $\phi_3'(t)\,dt$, and ds by $\sqrt{[\phi_1'(t)]^2 + [\phi_2'(t)]^2 + [\phi_3'(t)]^2}\,dt$, and letting α and β become the limits of integration.

If the curve C has the standard parametric representation $x = x$, $y = g(x)$, $z = h(x)$, $a \leq x \leq b$, then

$$(1) \qquad \int_C f(x, y, z)\,ds = \int_a^b f[x, g(x), h(x)]\sqrt{1 + \left(\frac{dy}{dx}\right)^2 + \left(\frac{dz}{dx}\right)^2}\,dx,$$

$$(2) \quad \int_C P\,dx + Q\,dy + R\,dz = \int_a^b \{P[x, g(x), h(x)] + Q[x, g(x), h(x)]g'(x) + R[x, g(x), h(x)]h'(x)\}\,dx,$$

with similar identities for the other standard parametric representations of C. (The student should determine them for future reference. What do they become if C is in the xy-plane? yz-plane? xz-plane?)

If the space curve C consists of the points of intersection of the surfaces of $F(x, y, z) = 0$ and $G(x, y, z) = 0$, and if these equations can be solved for y and z in terms of x, then we have the parametric representation of C: $x = x$, $y = g(x)$, $z = h(x)$, $a \leq x \leq b$; similarly, if the equations are solved for x and y in terms of z or x and z in terms of y. In such cases we can use the fundamental theorem for line integrals in the preceding form.

Since line integrals can be expressed as definite integrals, as indicated in the fundamental theorem for line integrals, various properties of definite integrals will lead directly to the corresponding properties of line integrals. Hence,

L₁: $\int_C kf(x, y, z)\,ds = k\int_C f(x, y, z)\,ds$, $\quad k$ any constant.

L₂: $\int_C [f(x, y, z) + g(x, y, z)]\,ds = \int_C f(x, y, z)\,ds + \int_C g(x, y, z)\,ds$.

L₃: $\int_A^B f(x, y, z)\,ds = \int_A^P f(x, y, z)\,ds + \int_P^B f(x, y, z)\,ds$,

where P is any point on C.

L₄: $\int_A^B f(x, y, z)\,ds = -\int_B^A f(x, y, z)\,ds$.

L₅: $\int_A^A f(x, y, z)\,ds = 0$.

We can write L_3 alternately as

L₃′: $\int_{C_1+C_2} f(x, y, z)\,ds = \int_{C_1} f(x, y, z)\,ds + \int_{C_2} f(x, y, z)\,ds$,

where C_1 is the path from A to P and C_2 is the path from P to B.

We have seen that L_C = length of C $= \int_C ds$. It follows that if $|f(x, y, z)| \leq M$, a constant, on C (we say that f is **bounded** on C), then

L₆: $\left|\int_C f(x, y, z)\, ds\right| \leq \int_C |f(x, y, z)|\, ds \leq ML_C.$

All integrals in L_1 to L_6 are assumed to exist.

EXAMPLE 1. Evaluate

$$\int_C (x + \sqrt{y})\, dx, \quad \int_C (x + \sqrt{y})\, dy \quad \text{and} \quad \int_C (x + \sqrt{y})\, ds,$$

where (0, 0) and (1, 1) are the initial and terminal points of the following plane curves C: (a) the straight line joining (0, 0) and (1, 1); (b) the parabola $y = x^2$; (c) the polygonal line (0, 0) to (1, 0) to (1, 1); (d) the polygonal line (0, 0) to (0, 1) to (1, 1).

Solution. (a) Since $y = x$, we have simply that

$$\int_C (x + \sqrt{y})\, dx = \int_0^1 (x + \sqrt{x})\, dx = \tfrac{7}{6},$$

$$\int_C (x + \sqrt{y})\, dy = \int_C (y + \sqrt{y})\, dy = \tfrac{7}{6},$$

$$\int_C (x + \sqrt{y})\, ds = \int_0^1 (x + \sqrt{x})\sqrt{2}\, dx = 7\sqrt{\tfrac{2}{6}}.$$

(b)

$$\int_C (x + \sqrt{y})\, dx = 2\int_0^1 x\, dx = 1,$$

$$\int_C (x + \sqrt{y})\, dy = 2\int_0^1 \sqrt{y}\, dy = \tfrac{4}{3},$$

$$\int_C (x + \sqrt{y})\, ds = 2\int_0^1 x\sqrt{1 + 4x^2}\, dx = \frac{(5^{3/2} - 1)}{6}.$$

(c) Each line integral is the sum of the line integrals along the line segments from (0, 0) to (1, 0) and from (1, 0) to (1, 1). Along (0, 0) to (1, 0), $y = 0$, $dy = 0$; along (1, 0) to (1, 1), $x = 1$, $dx = 0$. Hence,

$$\int_C (x + \sqrt{y})\, dx = \int_0^1 x\, dx = \tfrac{1}{2},$$

$$\int_C (x + \sqrt{y})\, dy = \int_0^1 (1 + \sqrt{y})\, dy = \tfrac{5}{3},$$

$$\int_C (x + \sqrt{y})\, ds = \int_0^1 x\, dx + \int_0^1 (1 + \sqrt{y})\, dy = \tfrac{13}{6}.$$

(d)

$$\int_C (x + \sqrt{y})\, dx = \int_0^1 (x + 1)\, dx = \tfrac{3}{2},$$

$$\int_C (x + \sqrt{y})\, dy = \int_0^1 \sqrt{y}\, dy = \tfrac{2}{3},$$

$$\int_C (x + \sqrt{y})\, ds = \int_0^1 \sqrt{y}\, dy + \int_0^1 (x + 1)\, dx = \tfrac{13}{6}.$$

We note in this example that the values of the line integrals depend not only on the initial and the terminal points of the curve but on the paths as well.

EXAMPLE 2. Evaluate

$$\mathrm{I} = \int_{(1,0,0)}^{(1,0,2\pi)} z\,dx + x\,dy + yz\,dz$$

along the curve of $x = \cos t$, $y = \sin t$, $z = t$, $0 \le t \le 2\pi$.

Solution

$$\mathrm{I} = \int_0^{2\pi} (-t \sin t + \cos^2 t + t \sin t)\,dt = \pi.$$

EXAMPLE 3. Evaluate

$$\mathrm{I} = \int_{\mathrm{C}} x^2 y\,dx + xy^2\,dy$$

where C is the curve of $x = t^2$, $y = t$, $0 \le t \le 1$.

Solution. We shall evaluate I in three different ways:

(a)
$$\mathrm{I} = \int_0^1 (2t^6 + t^4)\,dt = \tfrac{17}{35}.$$

(b) Since $y^2 = x$, $0 \le y \le 1$,

$$\mathrm{I} = \int_0^1 (2y^6 + y^4)\,dy = \tfrac{17}{35},$$

(c)
$$\mathrm{I} = \int_0^1 (x^{5/2} + x^{3/2})\,dx = \tfrac{17}{35}.$$

Which is the simplest of the three ways?

EXAMPLE 4. Evaluate

$$\mathrm{I} = \int_{\mathrm{C}} (x^2 - y^2)\,dx, \quad \mathrm{C}\colon\ x^2 + y^2 = 1, \quad |x| \le 1.$$

Solution. We express C in the parametric form: $x = \cos t$, $y = \sin t$, $0 \le t \le 2\pi$. Then

$$\mathrm{I} = -\int_0^{2\pi} (\cos^2 t - \sin^2 t) \sin t\,dt = \int_0^{2\pi} (2\cos^2 t - 1)d \cos t = 0.$$

The student should evaluate I with C represented as $x = x$, $y = \pm\sqrt{1 - x^2}$, $|x| \le 1$ and as $y = y$, $x = \pm\sqrt{1 - y^2}$, $|y| \le 1$, and compare with the foregoing solution with regard to simplicity.

For line integrals on closed curves in E^2, it is convenient to choose a parametrization of the curve so that its direction will be *the direction in which an observer moves along the curve so as to keep the region enclosed by the curve always to his left.* This enables us to determine the direction of such curves at a glance. We shall call this direction the *positive* direction for plane closed curves. It is convenient for the symbol of the line integral along such curves to exhibit this positive direction. We shall write

$\ointctrclockwise_C f(x, y)\, ds$ to indicate the line integral of f along the closed curve C in the positive direction, and $\ointclockwise_C f(x, y)\, ds$ the line integral of f along C in the opposite, or negative, direction. Note that

$$\ointctrclockwise_C f(x, y)\, ds = -\ointclockwise_C f(x, y)\, ds.$$

Hence, in evaluating $\ointctrclockwise_C f(x, y)\, ds$, we choose either a parametrization of C so that C has a positive direction, or a parametrization of C so that C has a negative direction and then evaluate $-\ointclockwise_C f(x, y)\, ds$.

EXAMPLE 5. Evaluate $\mathrm{I} = \ointctrclockwise_C y^2\, dx + x^2\, dy$, C: the triangle with vertices (1, 0), (1, 1), (0, 0).

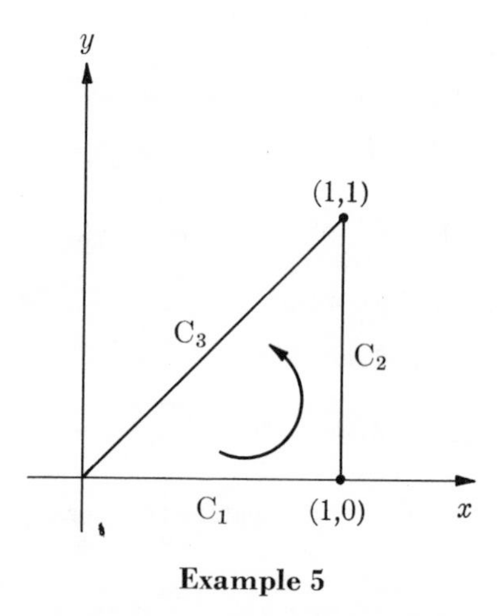

Example 5

Solution. Here we determine the value of I along C_1, C_2, and C_3, as indicated in the figure and add. Note that the standard parametrizations that are chosen yield a positive direction for the closed curve C.

$$\begin{aligned} \mathrm{I} &= \int_{C_1} y^2\, dx + x^2\, dy + \int_{C_2} y^2\, dx + x^2\, dy + \int_{C_3} y^2\, dx + x^2\, dy \\ &= 0 + \int_0^1 dy + 2\int_0^1 x^2\, dx = \tfrac{1}{3}. \end{aligned}$$

EXAMPLE 6. Find the work done in moving a particle acted on by the force $\mathbf{F} = 3x\mathbf{i} + (2xz - y)\mathbf{j} + z\mathbf{k}$ along (a) the straight line from (0, 0, 0) to (2, 1, 3); (b) the curve of $x = 2t^2$, $y = t$, $z = 4t^2 - t$, $0 \le t \le 1$; (c) the curve defined by $x^2 = 4y$, $3x^3 = 8z$, $0 \le x \le 2$.

Solution. (a) A parametric form for the line segment is $x = 2t$, $y = t$, $z = 3t$, $0 \leq t \leq 1$. Then,

$$W = \int_C \mathbf{F} \cdot d\mathbf{r} = \int_C [3x^2\mathbf{i} + (2xz - y)\mathbf{j} + z\mathbf{k}] \cdot d\mathbf{r}$$

$$= \int_0^1 (24t^2 + 12t^2 - t + 9t)\, dt = 16.$$

(b) $W = \int_0^1 [48t^5 + (16t^4 - 4t^3 - t) + (8t - 1)(4t^2 - t)]\, dt = \frac{71}{5}.$

(c) Let $x = x$, $y = x^2/4$, $z = 3x^3/8$, $0 \leq x \leq 2$; then

$$W = \int_0^2 \left(3x^2 + \frac{3}{8}x^5 - \frac{x^3}{8} + \frac{27x^5}{64}\right) dx = 16.$$

EXAMPLE 7. Evaluate

$$I = \int_C 2xy^3\, dx + 3x^2y^2\, dy$$

if C goes from (a) (0, 0) to (1, 1) along $y = x^2$; (b) (0, 0) to (1, 1) along $y^2 = x$; (c) (1, 1) to (2, 2) along the straight line joining these points; (d) (1, 1) to (2, 2) along the polygonal line (1, 1) to (2, 1) to (2, 2).

Solution

(a) $$I = \int_0^1 (2x^7 + 6x^7)\, dx = 1.$$

(b) $$I = \int_0^1 (4y^6 + 3y^6)\, dy = 1.$$

(c) $$I = 5\int_1^2 x^4\, dx = 31,$$

(d) $$I = \int_1^2 2x\, dx + 12\int_1^2 y^2\, dy = 31.$$

Note that in (a) and (b) we obtain the same result for the same end points of C, but along different paths, and similarly in (c) and (d). We shall show later that under certain conditions, some line integrals depend only on the initial and terminal points of C and not on the paths joining them.

On occasion we wish to evaluate a line integral along the boundary of a given region in E^2, which consists of several curves that have no points in common, say, $C_1, C_2, \cdots, C_n$. If we denote the total boundary by B, we shall write $B = C_1 + C_2 + \cdots + C_n$ and

$$\int_B f(x, y, z)\, ds = \int_{C_1} f(x, y, z)\, ds + \cdots + \int_{C_n} f(x, y, z)\, ds.$$

In practice, we are interested in evaluating line integrals on the boundaries of plane regions that consist of closed curves. By the line integral $\oint_B f(x, y)\, ds$, where B is the boundary of a region R_{xy} consisting of the closed curves $C_1, C_2, \cdots, C_n$, we mean

$$\int_{C_1} f(x, y)\, ds + \cdots + \int_{C_n} f(x, y)\, ds,$$

with each of these integrals evaluated on its indicated curve in such a direction that R_{xy} always remains to the left of an observer as he moves along this curve in this direction. This is illustrated in

EXAMPLE 8. Let R_{xy} be the set of points $1 \leq x^2 + y^2 \leq 4$. Evaluate

$$\mathrm{I} = \oint_B xy\, dx + x^2\, dy$$

where B is the boundary of R_{xy}.

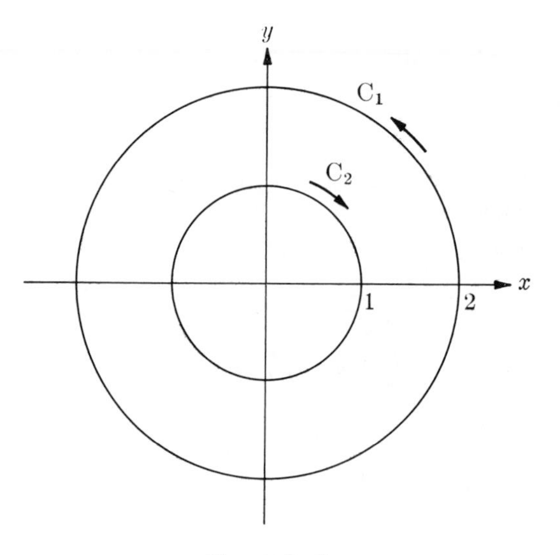

Example 8

Solution. $B = C_1 + C_2$ where $C_1: x^2 + y^2 = 4$, $|x| \leq 4$, and $C_2: x^2 + y^2 = 1$, $|x| \leq 1$, the required directions indicated in the figure. Note that the direction of C_1 is positive and that of C_2 is negative, according to our definition. However, it is these directions that will give us the required directions. Then,

$$\begin{aligned} \mathrm{I} &= \oint_{C_1} xy\, dx + x^2\, dy - \oint_{C_2} xy\, dx + x^2\, dy \\ &= \int_0^{2\pi} [-8 \sin^2 t \cos t + 8 \cos^3 t + \sin^2 t \cos t - \cos^3 t]\, dt \\ &= 0. \end{aligned}$$

EXERCISES

1. Evaluate $\int_C y\, dx + 2x\, dy$, where C goes from (0, 1) to (1, 0) along
(a) The straight line joining these points.

(b) The first quadrant arc of the circle centered at the origin.
(c) The polygonal line (0, 1) to (0, 0) to (1, 0).
(d) $C_1 + C_2$, C_1: the line segment joining (0, 1) and (−1, 0),

$$C_2: \quad y = -\sqrt{1 - x^2}, \qquad |x| \leq 1.$$

Ans.: (a) −1/2; (b) $-\pi/4$; (c) 0; (d) $(\pi + 1)/2$.

2. Evaluate $\int_{(1,0,1)}^{(2,3,2)} x^2\,dx - xz\,dy + y^2\,dz$ along

(a) The straight line joining (1, 0, 1) and (2, 3, 2).
(b) The polygonal line (1, 0, 1) to (0, 0, 3) to (2, 3, 2).

Ans.: (a) $-\frac{5}{3}$; (b) −8.

3. If $\mathbf{F} = (x^2 + y^2)\mathbf{i} + 2xy\mathbf{j}$, evaluate $\int_C \mathbf{F}\cdot d\mathbf{r}$, where C goes from (0, 0) to (1, 1) along
(a) The line $y = x$.
(b) The parabola $y = x^2$.
(c) The polygonal line with corner at (1, 0).
(d) The circle passing through (0, 0) and (1, 1) and tangent to the x-axis.
(e) The polygonal line (0, 0) to (h, k) to (1, 1) where h and k are arbitrary constants.

Ans.: (a) $\frac{4}{3}$; (b) $\frac{4}{3}$; (c) $\frac{4}{3}$; (d) $\frac{4}{3}$; (e) $\frac{4}{3}$.

4. Evaluate

$$\int_C z\,dx + x^2\,dy + y\,dz, \qquad C: \quad x = t,\ y = t^2,\ z = t^3.$$

(a) $0 \leq t \leq 1$.
(b) $-1 \leq t \leq 1$.

Ans.: (a) 27/20; (b) 13/10.

5. Evaluate

$$\int_{(0,-1)}^{(0,1)} y^2\,dx + x^2\,dy$$

along the semicircles
(a) $x = \sqrt{1 - y^2}$,
(b) $x = -\sqrt{1 - y^2}$.

Ans.: (a) $\frac{4}{3}$; (b) $-\frac{4}{3}$.

6. Evaluate $\oint_C z\,dx + x^2\,dy + y\,dz$, C: the quadrilateral whose successive vertices are (0, 0, 0), (2, 0, 0), (2, 3, 0), (0, 0, 1).

Ans.: 31/2.

7. Evaluate $\oint_C (x^2 - y^2)\,ds$, where C is
(a) $x^2 + y^2 = 4$,
(b) $a \cos t\,\mathbf{i} + b \sin t\,\mathbf{j}$, $0 \leq t \leq 2\pi$,
(c) the intersection of $x^2 + y^2 = 4z$ and $2x + 2y + 4z = 1$.

Ans.: (a) 0; (b) 0; (c) 0.

8. Evaluate $\oint_C \mathbf{F}\cdot d\mathbf{r}$, $\mathbf{F} = 2xy^2z\mathbf{i} + 2x^2yz\mathbf{j} + x^2y^2\mathbf{k}$, C: the circle

$$x^2 + y^2 = 1, \qquad z = 2.$$

Ans.: 0.

9. Evaluate $\oint_C y^2\,dx + xy\,dy$, C: the square with vertices (1, 1), (−1, 1), (−1, −1), (1, −1).

Ans.: 0.

10. Evaluate $\oint_C \mathbf{F}\cdot d\mathbf{r}$, $\mathbf{F} = (4xy - 3x^2z^2)\mathbf{i} + 2x^2\mathbf{j} - 2x^3z\mathbf{k}$, $C: x = \cos t$, $y = \cos 2t$, $z = \cos 3t$, $0 \leq t \leq 2$. *Ans.:* 0.

11. Evaluate:

(a)
$$\int_{(-1,0)}^{(1,0)} y(1 + x)\, dy$$

along the x-axis and then along $y = 1 - x^2$;

(b) The same problem with dy replaced by dx and then by ds.

Ans.: (a) 8/15.

12. Evaluate $\int_{(0,0,0)}^{(1,1,1)} \mathbf{F}\cdot d\mathbf{r}$, $\mathbf{F} = 3xy\mathbf{i} + 4yz\mathbf{j} + \frac{5}{2}xz\mathbf{k}$, $C: x^2 + y^2 = 2z$, $x = y$.

Ans.: 3.

13. Evaluate each of the following line integrals along the boundaries of the given regions:

(a) $\oint_B \dfrac{dx + dy}{\sqrt{x^2 + y^2}}$, R_{xy}: $2 \leq x^2 + y^2 \leq 4$.

(b) $\oint_B xy\, dx + (x^2 + y^2)\, dy$, R_{xy}: $0 \leq x^2 + y^2 \leq 20$, with the circular discs with centers at (2, 0), (−2, 0), (0, 2), (0, −2) and unit radius removed.

(c) $\oint_B e^y\, dx + xy\, dy$, R_{xy}: the region between the triangles with vertices at (0, 0), (5, 0), (0, 10) and (1, 2), (3, 2), (1, 4).

(d) $\oint_B x^2y\, dx + yx^2\, dy$, R_{xy}: the region between $x^2 + y^2 = 10$ and the square with vertices at (1, 0), (0, 1), (−1, 0), (0, −1).

(e) $\int_B \sin x\, dy + \cos x\, dx$, R_{xy}: the region between the rectangles with vertices at (4, 2), (−4, 2), (−4, −2), (4, −2) and (2, 1), (−2, 1), (−2, −1), (2, −1).

Ans.: (a) 0; (b) $-121\pi/4$;

(c) $\dfrac{39}{2} - \dfrac{e^{10}}{2} - e^{-2} - 2e^2$; (d) $-\dfrac{71}{3}$;

(e) 0.

14. (a) Determine the centroid of the wire whose shape is $C: x = a\cos^3\phi$, $y = a\sin^3\phi$, $0 \leq \phi \leq \pi/2$.

(b) Determine I_x for C: $x = (y^2/2) - \log(y/4)$, $2 \leq y \leq 4$.

(c) Determine I_y for C: $6xy = x^4 + 3$, $1 \leq x \leq 2$.

(d) Determine I_z for C: $\mathbf{i} + t\mathbf{j} + t^2\mathbf{k}$, $0 \leq t \leq 1$.

Ans.: (a) $\bar{x} = \bar{y} = 48a^2/5\pi$; (b) 123/2; (c) $18\rho/5$.

15. (a) Determine the value of λ for which the integral

$$\int_{(0,0)}^{(1,0)} -y^2\, dx + x^2\, dy,$$

along the path $y = \lambda x(1 - x)$ attains its largest value.

(b) For

$$\int_{(0,0)}^{(1,1)} xy\, dx + (x^2 + y)\, dy,$$

determine whether integration along a parabolic arc, a straight-line segment, or the polygonal line (0, 0) to (1, 0) to (1, 1) will yield the maximum value for the integral.

Ans.: (a) 5/2.

16. Evaluate $\int_A^B \mathbf{F}\cdot d\mathbf{r}$ over any regular curve for
(a) $\mathbf{F} = a_1\mathbf{i} + a_2\mathbf{j} + a_3\mathbf{k}$, a_1, a_2, a_3 constants;
(b) $\mathbf{F} = \mathbf{r}$;
(c) $\mathbf{F} = -\mathbf{r}/r^3$,
where $\mathbf{r} = x\mathbf{i} + y\mathbf{j} + z\mathbf{k}$.

Ans.: For A: (a, b, c), B: (d, e, f),
(a) $a_1(d - a) + a_2(e - b) + a_3(f - c)$;
(b) $\frac{1}{2}(d^2 + e^2 + f^2 - a^2 - b^2 - c^2)$;
(c) $(d^2 + e^2 + f^2)^{-1} - (a^2 + b^2 + c^2)^{-1}$.

17. Evaluate

(a) $\oint_C \mathbf{T}\cdot d\mathbf{r}$,

(b) $\oint_C \mathbf{n}\cdot d\mathbf{r}$,

C: $x^2 + y^2 = 1$.

Ans: (a) 2π; (b) 0.

18. (a) Find the work done in moving a particle under the action of a force $\mathbf{F} = 3x^2\mathbf{i} + (2xz - y)\mathbf{j} + z\mathbf{k}$ along
(1) The straight line from (0, 0, 0) to (2, 1, 3).
(2) C: $2t^2\mathbf{i} + t\mathbf{j} + (4t^2 - t)\mathbf{k}$, $0 \le t \le 1$.
(3) C: $x^2 = 4y$, $3x^3 = 8z$, $0 \le x \le 2$.

(b) The gravitational force near a particle of mass m on the earth's surface is approximately $\mathbf{F} = -mg\mathbf{j}$. Find the work done by $\mathbf{F}$ on the particle as it moves in a vertical plane from height h_1 to height h_2 along any path.

Ans.: (a) (1) 16, (2) 71/50, (3) 16;
(b) $mg(h_1 - h_2)$.

19. Show that if $f(x, y) > 0$ on C, the line integral $\int_C f(x, y)\, ds$ can be interpreted as the area of the cylindrical surface $0 \le z \le f(x, y)$, (x, y) on C. What is the corresponding interpretation if ds is replaced by dx or dy?

20. Given C: $\boldsymbol{\phi}(t)$, $\alpha \le t \le \beta$. Divide the interval into n subintervals by points $\alpha = t_0 < t_1 < \cdots < t_{i-1} < t_i < \cdots < t_n = \beta$. Let $\mathbf{r}_i = \boldsymbol{\phi}(t_i)$ and $\Delta\mathbf{r}_i = \mathbf{r}_i - \mathbf{r}_{i-1}$. Define

$$\int_C \mathbf{F}\times d\mathbf{r} = \lim_{\substack{n\to\infty \\ \|\Delta r_i\|\to 0}} \sum_{i=1}^{n} \mathbf{F}_i \times \Delta\mathbf{r}_i,$$

if this limit exists.

(a) Show that

$$\int_C \mathbf{F}\times d\mathbf{r} = \mathbf{i}\int_C F_2\,dz - F_3\,dy + \mathbf{j}\int_C F_3\,dx - F_1\,dz + \mathbf{k}\int_C F_1\,dy - F_2\,dx,$$

where $\mathbf{F} = F_1\mathbf{i} + F_2\mathbf{j} + F_3\mathbf{k}$.

(b) Define $\int_C f(x, y, z)\, d\mathbf{r}$ and express it in component form.

2. Green's theorem. We now come to a theorem of far-reaching importance, known as Green's theorem (also called Gauss's theorem, but since Gauss has so many theorems to his credit, he will pardon us if we attribute this one to Green). This theorem is concerned with certain bounded regions in E^2; in order to state it in a form whose proof is readily accessible, it becomes necessary to impose further restrictions on plane regions. A bounded region R_{xy} whose boundary C is a closed curve and which can be represented as $C_1 + C_2$, where $C_1: y = f_1(x)$, $C_2: y = f_2(x)$, $a \leq x \leq b$ *and* as $C_1^* + C_2^*$, $C_1^*: x = g_1(y)$, $C_2^*: x = g_2(y)$, $c \leq y \leq d$, so that if (x, y) is in R_{xy},

$$f_1(x) \leq y \leq f_2(x), \qquad a \leq x \leq b$$

and

$$g_1(y) \leq x \leq g_2(y), \qquad c \leq y \leq d$$

will be called a **standard region.** A **regular region** is a standard region or a region that can be decomposed into a finite number of standard regions by introducing regular curves. For example, the set of points (x, y) in E^2 such that $(x^2/a^2) + (y^2/b^2) \leq 1$ is a standard region, for

$$-(b/a)\sqrt{a^2 - x^2} \leq y \leq (b/a)\sqrt{a^2 - x^2}, \; -a \leq x \leq a$$

and

$$-(a/b)\sqrt{b^2 - y^2} \leq x \leq (a/b)\sqrt{b^2 - y^2}, \; -b \leq y \leq b.$$

On the other hand, the triangular region with vertices at $(0, 0)$, $(0, 1)$, $(\frac{1}{2}, 5)$ is a regular region, since it is decomposable into two standard regions, as the student can readily verify.

We are now ready to prove

GREEN'S THEOREM FOR REGULAR REGIONS. If
(1) D is an open region in the xy-plane,
(2) R is a bounded closed regular region in D whose boundary is a closed regular curve C, and
(3) P, Q, $\partial P/\partial y$, $\partial Q/\partial x$ are continuous in D, then

$$\oint_C P\,dx + Q\,dy = \iint_R \left(\frac{\partial Q}{\partial x} - \frac{\partial P}{\partial y}\right) dx\,dy.$$

Proof. First let R be a standard region. Then there exist $C_1: f_1(x)$, $C_2: f_2(x)$, $a \leq x \leq b$; $C_1^*: g_1(y)$, $C_2^*: g_2(y)$, $c \leq y \leq d$ such that $C = C_1 + C_2 = C_1^* + C_2^*$, and if (x, y) is in R,

$$f_1(x) \leq y \leq f_2(x), \qquad a \leq x \leq b$$

and

$$g_1(y) \leq x \leq g_2(y), \qquad c \leq y \leq d.$$

(See Fig. 3.) We first show that

$$\text{(A)} \qquad \iint_R \frac{\partial P}{\partial y}\,dx\,dy = -\oint_C P\,dx.$$

Since $\partial P/\partial y$ is continuous in D, this double integral can be written as an iterated integral:

$$\iint_R \frac{\partial P}{\partial y}\,dx\,dy = \int_a^b \int_{f_1(x)}^{f_2(x)} \frac{\partial P}{\partial y}\,dy\,dx.$$

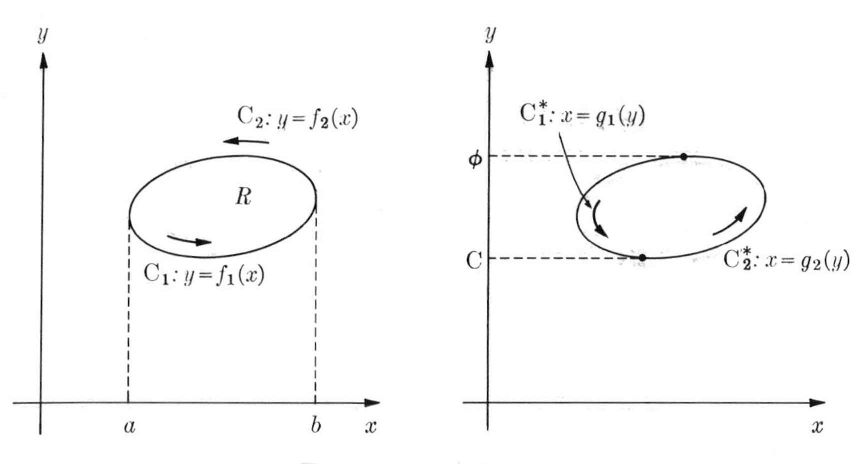

Fig. 3. Green's theorem

Evaluating the integral with respect to y yields

$$\int_a^b \{P[x, f_2(x)] - P[x, f_1(x)]\}\, dx,$$

which can be written as

$$-\int_b^a P[x, f_2(x)]\, dx - \int_a^b P[x, f_1(x)]\, dx,$$

or

$$-\left[\int_{C_2} P(x, y)\, dx + \int_{C_1} P(x, y)\, dx\right].$$

But this is just $-\oint_C P(x, y)\, dx$. Be sure that you see the significance of the positive direction of C (see p. 105 for definition of positive direction). Hence (A) is established. Similarly, the student can now show that

(B) $$\iint_R \frac{\partial Q}{\partial x}\, dx\, dy = \oint_C Q(x, y)\, dy.$$

The proof of the theorem for standard regions is completed by adding (A) and (B).

Now suppose that R is not a standard region. Since it is a regular region, it is decomposable into a finite number of standard regions, $R_1, R_2, \cdots, R_n$, by regular curves $\gamma_1, \gamma_2, \cdots, \gamma_k$ (see Fig. 4), so that the boundaries of the subregions are $C_1, C_2, \cdots, C_n$. Now we apply the foregoing result to each of these subregions and add so as to obtain

$$\sum_{i=1}^{n} \oint_{C_i} P\, dx + Q\, dy = \sum_{i=1}^{n} \iint_{R_i} \left(\frac{\partial Q}{\partial x} - \frac{\partial P}{\partial y}\right) dx\, dy.$$

But in forming the line integrals, $\gamma_1, \gamma_2, \cdots, \gamma_{n-1}$ are traversed twice in opposite directions, and hence the line integrals over these paths cancel

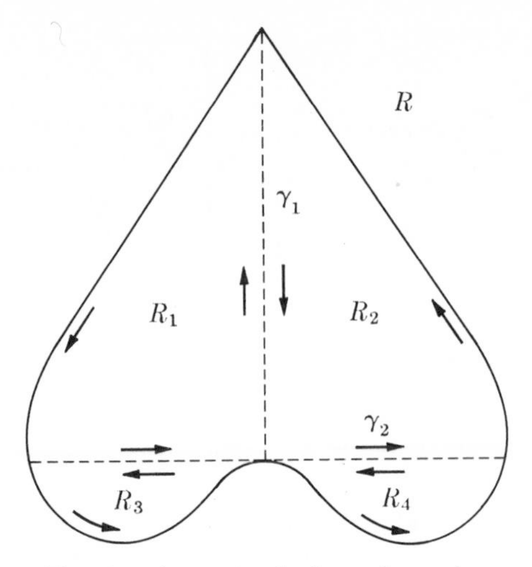

Fig. 4. A nonstandard regular region

out, leaving a sum of line integrals equal to $\oint_C P\,dx + Q\,dy$. Furthermore, the sum of the double integrals over $R_1, R_2, \cdots, R_n$ is equal to the double integral over R. Hence, we have proved the theorem for regular regions.

Green's theorem is valid for more general regions than regular regions. However, the proof in such cases is more difficult and would take us too far afield. Let us state without proof

GREEN'S THEOREM FOR SIMPLY CONNECTED REGIONS. If

(1) D is an open region in the xy-plane,

(2) R is a bounded, closed, simply connected region in D whose boundary is a closed regular curve C, and

(3) P, Q, $\partial P/\partial y$, $\partial Q/\partial y$ are continuous in D, then

$$\oint_C P\,dx + Q\,dy = \iint_R \left(\frac{\partial Q}{\partial x} - \frac{\partial P}{\partial y}\right).$$

We shall not hesitate to use Green's theorem in this more general form, especially when we wish to achieve wide generality in some of our future results. However, the regions that occur most frequently in practice are regular regions. As a matter of fact, to exhibit a region that is simply connected but not regular, we must turn to some highly contrived regions. Such a region is the one that is bounded by $y = x^3 \sin 1/x$, $y = -5$, $x = 0$, and $x = 10$, as illustrated in Fig. 5; the student should have no difficulty in observing that $x^3 \sin 1/x$ oscillates infinitely often in any interval that includes the origin; hence this region cannot be decomposed into a *finite* number of standard regions.

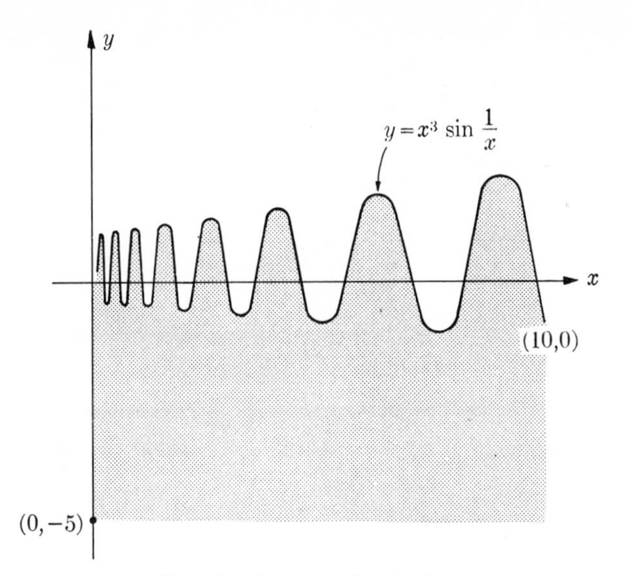

Fig. 5. A nonregular region

EXAMPLE 1. Evaluate $I = \oint_C (3x + 4y)\,dx + (2x - 3y)\,dy$, C: $x^2 + y^2 = 4$.

Solution. Using Green's theorem (why is it applicable?),

$$I = \iint_R (2 - 4)\,dx\,dy = -2 \iint_R dx\,dy$$

$$= -2\ (\text{area of } R) = -8\pi,$$

since R is a circular disc of radius 2.

Now let us evaluate I, using the fundamental theorem for line integrals. Let $x = 2\cos t$, $y = 2\sin t$, $0 \le t \le 2\pi$. Then

$$I = \int_0^{2\pi} (8\cos^2 t - 16\sin^2 t - 24 \sin t \cos t)\,dt = -8\pi.$$

Note the simplicity of the first method.

EXAMPLE 2. Evaluate $I = \oint_C (x^2 + 2y^2)\,dx$, C: square with vertices at $(\pm 1, \pm 1)$.

Solution

$$I = -\iint_R 4y\,dx\,dy$$

$$= -(\text{area of square})(y \text{ coordinate of centroid of square})$$
$$= 0,$$

since the centroid of the square is at (0, 0).

EXAMPLE 3. Evaluate

$$\mathrm{I} = \oint_{\mathrm{C}} \frac{y\,dx - x\,dy}{x^2 + y^2}, \quad \mathrm{C}: \; x^2 + y^2 = 1.$$

Solution. $P = y/(x^2 + y^2)$, $Q = -x/(x^2 + y^2)$ are not defined at $(0, 0)$, which is in the interior of C. Hence, Green's theorem is not applicable. Letting $x = \cos t$, $y = \sin t$, $0 \leq t \leq 2\pi$,

$$\mathrm{I} = -\int_0^{2\pi} dt = -2\pi.$$

A careless application of Green's theorem would have yielded

$$\iint_R \left(\frac{\partial Q}{\partial x} - \frac{\partial P}{\partial y} \right) dx\,dy = 0,$$

if we neglected to note that $\partial Q/\partial x = \partial P/\partial y$ *only* if $(x, y) \neq (0, 0)$.

EXAMPLE 4. Evaluate

$$\mathrm{I} = \oint_{\mathrm{C}} (3x^2 - 8y^2)\,dx + (4y - 6xy)\,dy,$$

C: boundary of region bounded by $y = \sqrt{x}$ and $y = x^2$.

Solution. By Green's theorem,

$$\mathrm{I} = 10 \iint_R y\,dx\,dy = \int_0^1 \int_{x^2}^{\sqrt{x}} y\,dy\,dx = 5 \int_0^1 (x - x^4)\,dx = \tfrac{3}{2}.$$

EXAMPLE 5. Let A be the area and $(\bar{x}, \bar{y})$ the coordinates of the centroid of a regular region bounded by a regular closed curve C, C and R included in an open region. Express $\bar{x}$ and $\bar{y}$ as line integrals.

Solution

$$\mathrm{A}\bar{x} = \iint_R x\,dx\,dy = \tfrac{1}{2} \oint_{\mathrm{C}} x^2\,dy = -\oint_{\mathrm{C}} xy\,dx.$$

$$\mathrm{A}\bar{y} = \iint_R y\,dx\,dy = -\tfrac{1}{2} \oint_{\mathrm{C}} y^2\,dx = \oint_{\mathrm{C}} xy\,dy.$$

EXAMPLE 6. Evaluate

$$\mathrm{I} = \iint_R xy(x + y)\,dx\,dy,$$

where C: $x^2 + y^2 = 1$ is the boundary of R.

Solution. Let $\partial Q/\partial x = xy^2$ and $\partial P/\partial y = -x^2 y$; then we can take $Q = x^2y^2/2$ and $P = -(x^2y^2/2)$. Hence,

$$\mathrm{I} = \tfrac{1}{2} \oint_{\mathrm{C}} x^2y^2\,dy - x^2y^2\,dx$$
$$= \tfrac{1}{2} \int_0^{2\pi} (\cos^3\theta \sin^2\theta + \cos^2\theta \sin^3\theta)\,d\theta = 0.$$

We now prove

GREEN'S THEOREM FOR MULTIPLY CONNECTED REGIONS. If

(1) D is an open region in the xy-plane,
(2) R is a bounded closed n-tuply connected region with boundary consisting of a closed regular curve C and nonintersecting closed regular curves $\mathrm{C}_1, \mathrm{C}_2, \cdots, \mathrm{C}_n$ in the interior of C, and
(3) $P, Q, \partial P/\partial y, \partial Q/\partial x$ are continuous in D, then

$$\oint_{\mathrm{C}} P\,dx + Q\,dy = \sum_{i=1}^{n-1} \oint_{\mathrm{C}_i} P\,dx + Q\,dy + \iint_R \left(\frac{\partial Q}{\partial x} - \frac{\partial P}{\partial y}\right) dx\,dy.$$

Proof. From C to C_i we draw two arcs d_i and d_i' ($i = 1, 2, \cdots, n-1$), as illustrated in Fig. 6. These arcs decompose R into the simply connected

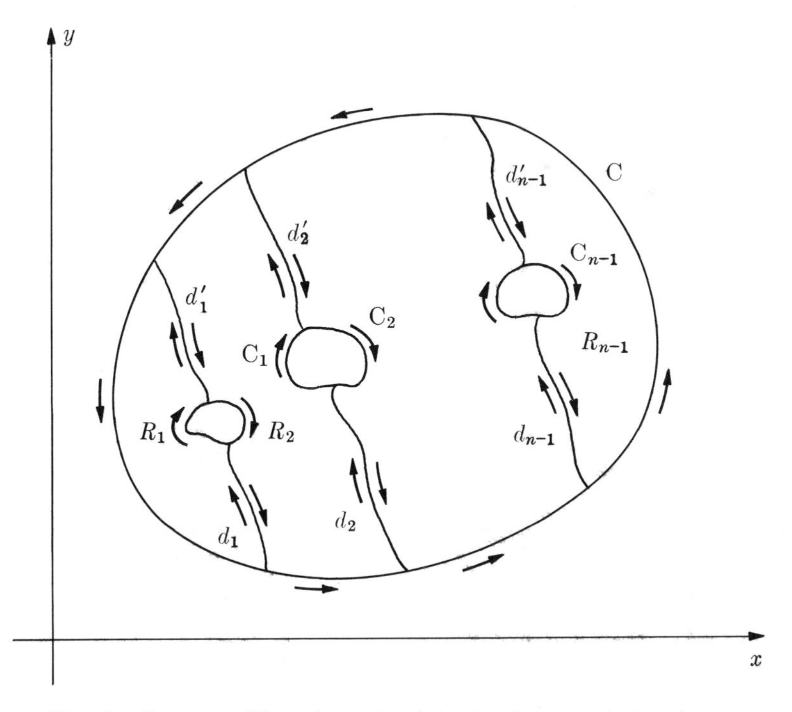

Fig. 6. Decomposition of a region into simply connected regions

regions $R_1, R_2, \cdots, R_n$, to each of which Green's theorem for simply connected regions is applicable. We now consider $\oint P\,dx + Q\,dy$ along the curves that are the boundaries of these regions—bearing in mind that the positive direction of a curve is that direction for which the region remains to our left as we move along the curve—and then add these integrals. Since the paths d_i and d_i', $i = 1, 2, \cdots, n-1$, are each traversed twice in opposite directions, the line integrals over these paths add up to zero. Hence, the line integral becomes

$$\oint_C P\,dx + Q\,dy + \sum_{i=1}^{n-1} \oint_{C_i} P\,dx + Q\,dy.$$

(Note the directions of the curves in these line integrals.) But this is equal to

$$\sum_{i=1}^{n} \iint_{R_i} \left(\frac{\partial Q}{\partial x} - \frac{\partial P}{\partial y}\right) dx\,dy$$

which equals

$$\iint_R \left(\frac{\partial Q}{\partial x} - \frac{\partial P}{\partial y}\right) dx\,dy,$$

and the result is immediate.

EXAMPLE. Evaluate

$$\mathrm{I} = \oint_B (2x - y^3)\,dx - xy\,dy,$$

B: the boundary of the region R, the set of points (x, y) such that $1 \le x^2 + y^2 \le 9$.

Solution. $B = C_1 + C_2$, C_1: $x^2 + y^2 = 1$, C_2: $x^2 + y^2 = 9$. Hence,

$$\begin{aligned} \mathrm{I} &= \oint_{C_2} (2x - y^3)\,dx - xy\,dy + \oint_{C_1} (2x - y^3)\,dx - xy\,dy \\ &= \iint_R (-y + 3y^2)\,dx\,dy \\ &= \int_0^{2\pi} \int_1^3 (-r\sin\theta + 3r^2\sin^2\theta) r\,dr\,d\theta = 60\pi. \end{aligned}$$

An immediate consequence of Green's theorem for simply connected regions is that if $\partial Q/\partial x = \partial P/\partial y$ in R, and all other conditions of the theorem are satisfied, then $\oint_C P\,dx + Q\,dy = 0$. For multiply connected regions, $\partial Q/\partial x = \partial P/\partial y$ in R implies that

$$\oint_C P\,dx + Q\,dy = \sum_{i=1}^{n-1} \oint_{C_i} P\,dx + Q\,dy.$$

In practice, the situation is as follows: Given $\oint_C P\,dx + Q\,dy$ to evaluate, where C is the boundary of a region where P, Q, $\partial P/\partial y$, or $\partial Q/\partial x$ fails to be continuous. The points of discontinuity are enclosed by one or more nonoverlapping curves, lying entirely within C, these being as simple as possible; now, if $\partial Q/\partial x = \partial P/\partial y$, the original line integrals, which may very well have a complicated C, can be reduced to line integrals that are simpler to evaluate.

EXAMPLE. Evaluate

$$\mathrm{I} = \oint_C \frac{y\,dx - x\,dy}{x^2 + y^2}, \quad \mathrm{C}\colon \frac{x^2}{9} + \frac{y^2}{16} = 1.$$

Solution. $P = y/(x^2 + y^2)$ and $Q = -[x/(x^2 + y^2)]$ are not continuous at the origin. Let us enclose the origin by the curve $C_1\colon x^2 + y^2 = 1$, which is in the interior of C. Then $\partial Q/\partial x = \partial P/\partial y$ in the region whose boundary is $C + C_1$. Hence,

$$\mathrm{I} = \int_{C_1} \frac{y\,dx - x\,dy}{x^2 + y^2} = \int_{C_1} y\,dx - x\,dy = -2\pi,$$

this integral being much simpler to evaluate.

Green's theorem enables us to express the area A of a simply connected region R in the xy-plane in terms of a line integral taken over the boundary of that region. For if $Q(x, y) = x$ and $P(x, y) = 0$, or $Q(x, y) = 0$ and $P(x, y) = -y$, we have

$$\mathrm{A} = \iint_R dx\,dy = \oint_C x\,dy - \oint_C y\,dx,$$

or

$$\mathrm{A} = \tfrac{1}{2} \oint_C x\,dy - y\,dx.$$

EXAMPLE. Determine the area of the region enclosed by the ellipse whose major axis is $2a$ and whose minor axis is $2b$.

Solution. Let C: $x = a\cos t$, $y = b\sin t$, $0 \le t \le 2\pi$. Let R be the region with C as boundary. Then the area of R is

$$\mathrm{A} = \tfrac{1}{2} \oint_C x\,dy - y\,dx = \tfrac{1}{2} \int_0^{2\pi} ab\,dt = \pi ab.$$

We now express in vector form the equation in Green's theorem for simply connected regions. Let

$$\boldsymbol{\phi} = P\mathbf{i} + Q\mathbf{j} \quad \text{and} \quad \mathbf{r} = x\mathbf{i} + y\mathbf{j}.$$

Then

$$\oint_C P\,dx + Q\,dy = \oint_C \boldsymbol{\phi} \cdot d\mathbf{r}.$$

Since

$$\operatorname{curl} \boldsymbol{\phi} = \begin{vmatrix} \mathbf{i} & \mathbf{j} & \mathbf{k} \\ \dfrac{\partial}{\partial x} & \dfrac{\partial}{\partial y} & \dfrac{\partial}{\partial z} \\ P & Q & 0 \end{vmatrix} = \left(\frac{\partial Q}{\partial x} - \frac{\partial P}{\partial y}\right)\mathbf{k},$$

we see that

$$\frac{\partial Q}{\partial x} - \frac{\partial P}{\partial y} = \operatorname{curl} \boldsymbol{\phi} \cdot \mathbf{k} = \nabla \times \boldsymbol{\phi} \cdot \mathbf{k}.$$

Hence, we have

$$\oint_C \boldsymbol{\phi} \cdot d\mathbf{r} = \iint_R \nabla \times \boldsymbol{\phi} \cdot \mathbf{k}\, dx\, dy.$$

This equation can be expressed in another vector form. For if $\mathbf{T}$ is

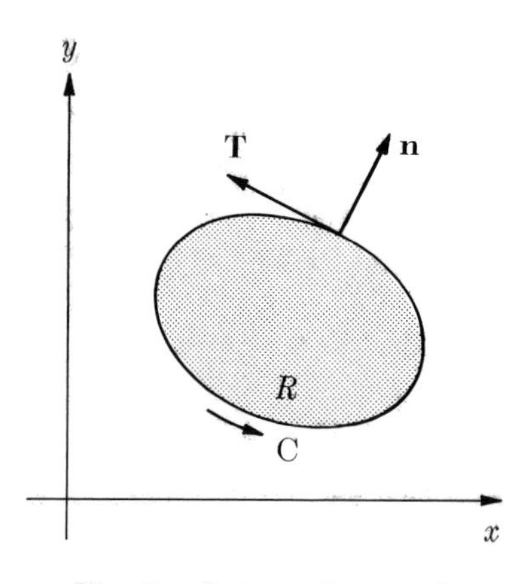

Fig. 7. Outer unit normal

the unit tangent vector to C (see Fig. 7) and $\mathbf{n}$ is the unit normal vector to C in the direction away from R (outer unit normal), then

$$\boldsymbol{\phi} \cdot d\mathbf{r} = \left(\boldsymbol{\phi} \cdot \frac{d\mathbf{r}}{ds}\right) ds = (\boldsymbol{\phi} \cdot \mathbf{T})\, ds = (\boldsymbol{\phi} \times \mathbf{k} \cdot \mathbf{n})\, ds = \boldsymbol{\psi} \cdot \mathbf{n}\, ds,$$

where $\boldsymbol{\psi} = \boldsymbol{\phi} \times \mathbf{k} = Q\mathbf{i} - P\mathbf{j}$ and $\operatorname{div} \boldsymbol{\psi} = \nabla \cdot \boldsymbol{\psi} = \dfrac{\partial Q}{\partial x} - \dfrac{\partial P}{\partial y}.$

Hence,

$$\oint_C \boldsymbol{\psi} \cdot \mathbf{n}\, ds = \iint_R \nabla \cdot \boldsymbol{\phi}\, dx\, dy.$$

EXAMPLE 1. Show that $\oint_C \nabla f \cdot d\mathbf{r} = 0$, where f and its partial derivatives are continuous and the conditions of Green's theorem are satisfied.

Solution. $\oint_C \nabla f \cdot d\mathbf{r} = \iint_R \nabla \times \nabla f \cdot \mathbf{k}\, dx\, dy = 0$, since $\nabla \times \nabla f = \mathbf{0}$.

EXAMPLE 2. Show that if f is harmonic in a simply connected region whose boundary is the closed regular curve C, then $\oint_C \nabla f \cdot \mathbf{n}\, ds = 0$.

Solution

$$\oint_C \nabla f \cdot \mathbf{n}\, ds = \iint_R \nabla^2 f\, dx\, dy = 0,$$

since $\nabla^2 f = 0$, f being harmonic.

EXERCISES

1. Evaluate, using Green's theorem:

(a) $\oint_C (3x^2 - 8y^2)\, dx + (4y - 6xy)\, dy$, C: boundary of R: set of (x, y) such that $x \geq 0$, $y \geq 0$, $x + y \leq 1$.

(b) $\oint_C e^x \sin y\, dx + e^x \cos y\, dy$, C: rectangle with vertices $(0, 0), (1, 0), (1, \pi/2)$, $(0, \pi/2)$.

(c) $\oint_C (3x^2 + 2y)\, dx - (x + 3\cos y)\, dy$, C: parallelogram with vertices $(0, 0)$, $(2, 0)$, $(3, 1)$, $(1, 1)$.

(d) $\oint_C (x^2 + y^2)\, dx + 3xy^2\, dy$, C: $x^2 + y^2 = 4$.

(e) $\oint_C ay\, dx + bx\, dy$, a and b arbitrary constants, C: arbitrary closed regular curve.

(f) $\oint_C \nabla(x^2 y) \cdot d\mathbf{r}$, C: $x^2 + y^2 = 1$.

(g) $\oint_C \boldsymbol{\phi} \cdot \mathbf{n}\, ds$, $\boldsymbol{\phi} = (x^2 + y^2)\mathbf{i} - 2xy\mathbf{j}$, $\mathbf{n}$ = outer unit normal, C: $x^2 + y^2 = 1$.

(h) $\oint_C f(x)\, dx + g(y)\, dy$, f and g arbitrary continuously differentiable functions, C: arbitrary closed regular curve.

Ans.: (a) $5/3$; (b) 0; (c) -6; (d) 12π; (e) $(b - a)$A, A area of region; (f) 0; (g) 0; (h) 0.

2. Evaluate:

(a) $\oint_C (x^2 + 2y)\, dx + (y - x)\, dy$, C: the boundary of R: set of (x, y) such that $x \geq 0$, $y \leq (x/2) + 1$, $y \leq \frac{1}{2}(x - 4)^2$.

(b) $\oint_C (x^2 + 3y)\, dx + (y - 2x)\, dy$, C: boundary of R: set of (x, y) such that $y \leq x$, $y \leq 2$, $y \leq 8 - 2x$, $y \geq 0$.

(c) $\oint_C (x^3 + 6x^2y + y^2 - 3y)\,dx + (2x^3 - 4xy^2 - 2xy + 3y)\,dy,$

$$C:\quad (x-2)^2 + (y-2)^2 = 4.$$

(d) $\oint_C \dfrac{(ax - by)\,dx + (bx + ay)\,dy}{x^2 + y^2}$, C: any closed regular curve having 0 in its interior, a and b constants. *Ans.:* (a) -13; (b) -25; (c) -100π; (d) $2\pi b$.

3. Evaluate:

(a) $\oint_C \dfrac{-y\,dx + x\,dy}{x^2 + y^2}$; (1) C: trapezoid with vertices at $(1, 0)$, $(2, 0)$, $(2, 3)$, $(1, 5)$; (2) C: pentagon with vertices at $(0, 5)$, $(-3, 2)$, $(-2, -2)$, $(2, -2)$, $(3, 2)$.

(b) $\oint_C \dfrac{(x^2 - y^2 - x)\,dx - y(2x - 1)\,dx}{(x^2 + y^2)(x^2 + y^2 - 2x + 1)}$; (1) C: boundary of R: set of (x, y) such that $y \geq x^2 + 1$ and $y \leq 9 - x^2$; (2) C: square with center at the origin, vertex $(\frac{1}{2}, 0)$, and diagonal along the x-axis; (3) C: $4(x-1)^2 + 9y^2 = 1$; (4) C: quadrilateral with vertices $(2, 0)$, $(1, 7)$, $(-13, 21)$, $(-7, -19)$.

Ans.: (a) $0, 2\pi$; (b) $0, 2\pi, -2\pi, 0$.

4. Find the area of the region

(a) bounded by one arch of the cycloid $x = a(t - \sin t)$, $y = a(1 - \cos t)$, $a > 0$, and the x-axis;

(b) bounded by the hypocycloid $x = a\cos^3 t$, $y = a\sin^3 t$, $a > 0$;

(c) of the loop of the folium of Descartes, $x = 3at/(1 + t^3)$, $y = 3at^2/(1 + t^3)$;

(d) whose boundary is on $x^2 = 16y$, $y = 20$, $x^2 + 2(y - 10)^2 = 1$.

Ans.: (a) $3\pi a^2$; (b) $3\pi a^2/8$; (c) $3a^2/2$; (d) $\frac{16}{3}(20)^{3/2} - \pi/2$.

5. (a) Show that in polar coordinates (r, θ), the area of a region bounded by a closed regular curve C is $A = \frac{1}{2}\oint_C r^2\,d\theta$.

(b) Find the area of one leaf of the four-leaf rose $r = 3\sin 2\theta$.

(c) Find the area of both loops of the lemniscate $r^2 = a^2\cos 2\theta$.

Ans.: (b) $9\pi/8$; (c) a^2.

6. Show that

(a) $\oint_C \mathbf{r}\cdot d\mathbf{r} = 0,$

(b) $\oint_C \mathbf{a}\cdot d\mathbf{r} = 0,$

$\mathbf{a}$ constant, $\mathbf{r} = x\mathbf{i} + y\mathbf{j} + z\mathbf{k}$, and C any arbitrary closed regular curve.

7. (a) Show that $I_z = \frac{1}{3}\oint_C x^3\,dy - y^3\,dx$, where I_z is the moment of inertia about the z-axis of the region bounded by the closed regular curve C.

(b) Find I_z of the region whose boundary is on $y = e^x$, $y = e$, $x = 0$.

8. Let P, Q, $\partial P/\partial y$, $\partial Q/\partial x$ be continuous with $\partial P/\partial y = \partial Q/\partial x$, except at $(6, 0)$, $(0, 0)$, $(-6, 0)$; C_1: $(x-3)^2 + y^2 = 16$; C_2: $(x+3)^2 + y^2 = 16$; C_3: $x^2 + y^2 = 64$; C_4: $x^2 + y^2 = 1$. Denote $\oint_C P\,dx + Q\,dy$ by $I(C)$.

(a) If $I(C_1) = 4$, $I(C_2) = 5$, $I(C_3) = -1$, find $I(C_4)$.

(b) If $I(C_2) = 1$, $I(C_3) = 7$, $I(C_4) = 2$, find $I(C_1)$.

(c) If $I(C_1) = 6$, $I(C_2) = 2$, $I(C_4) = 3$, find $I(C_3)$.

9. By changing variables from (x, y) to (u, v) according to the transformation $x = x(u, v)$, $y = (u, v)$, show that the area of a simply connected region R bounded by a closed regular curve C is

$$A = \iint_R \frac{\partial(x, y)}{\partial(u, v)}\, du\, dv,$$

where

$$\frac{\partial(x, y)}{\partial(u, v)} = \begin{vmatrix} \frac{\partial x}{\partial u} & \frac{\partial y}{\partial u} \\ \frac{\partial x}{\partial v} & \frac{\partial y}{\partial v} \end{vmatrix}$$

is the Jacobian of the transformation. (*Hint:* Show that the line integral formula for area transformed to u, v coordinates is $\oint_C (xy_u - yx_u)\, du + (xy_v - yx_v)\, dv$, and now use Green's theorem.) Illustrate with polar coordinates.

10. Let f and g be continuous with continuous derivatives in an open region D in the xy-plane. Let R be a closed simply connected region in D with boundary C, a closed regular curve. Let $\mathbf{n}$ be the outer unit normal vector to C. Show that

(a) $$\oint_C f\nabla g\cdot\mathbf{n}\, ds = \iint_R f\nabla^2 g\, dx\, dy + \iint_R \nabla f\cdot\nabla g\, dx\, dy.$$

(b) $$\oint_C (f\nabla g\cdot\mathbf{n} - g\nabla f\cdot\mathbf{n})\, ds = \iint_R (f\nabla^2 g - g\nabla^2 f)\, dx\, dy.$$

3. Independence of path. Let the functions P, Q, R be continuous in an open region D. We say that the line integral

$$I = \int_A^B P\, dx + Q\, dy + R\, dz$$

is **independent of path** in D if, for every pair of points A and B in D, the value of I is the same for all paths in D from A to B. It is of practical importance to have available criteria for determining independence of path; for, given a line integral on a complicated path in an open region D, if we can establish independence of path in D, this path can be replaced by any one we may choose in D, and naturally we choose the simplest possible one. There are several criteria for determining independence of path; let us investigate them.

Criterion I. If $\oint_C P\, dx + Q\, dy + R\, dz = 0$ for every closed regular curve in an open region D, then $\int_A^B P\, dx + Q\, dy + R\, dz$ is independent of path in D.

Proof. Let A and B be any two points in D and let C_1 and C_2 be any two paths from A to B. First let us assume that C_1 and C_2 do not

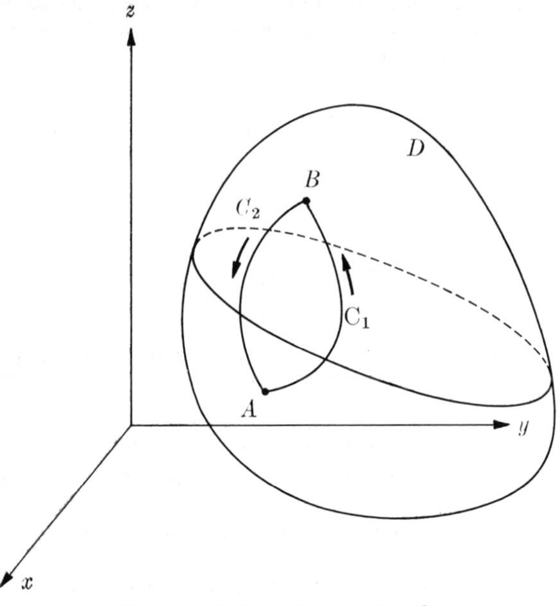

Fig. 8. Independence of path

cross. Then the path from A to B along C_1 and then from B to A along C_2 is a closed regular curve. (See Fig. 8.) By hypothesis,

$$\int_{C_1} P\,dx + Q\,dy + R\,dz - \int_{C_2} P\,dx + Q\,dy + R\,dz = 0,$$

or

$$\int_{C_1} P\,dx + Q\,dy + R\,dz = \int_{C_2} P\,dx + Q\,dy + R\,dz,$$

and we have independence of path in this case.

If C_1 and C_2 cross a finite number of times, the foregoing argument applied a finite number of times will yield the result. The student should supply the details. However, if C_1 and C_2 cross an infinite number of times (can you give an example?), then the proof requires more delicate analysis and cannot be treated here.

Converse of Criterion I. If $\int_A^B P\,dx + Q\,dy + R\,dz$ is independent of path in an open region D, then

$$\int_C P\,dx + Q\,dy + R\,dz = 0$$

for every closed regular curve in D.

The proof is left to the student.

Criterion I is not very valuable in practice, for it is not a simple matter to establish that a given line integral vanishes on *every* closed regular curve in some open region. However, if we can establish a criterion for independence of path that is readily applicable, then it will be the converse of Criterion I which will be useful because it would enable us to conclude immediately that line integrals about closed regular curves vanish. Let us turn to

Criterion II. If there exists a function F such that

$$\frac{\partial F}{\partial x} = P(x, y, z), \quad \frac{\partial F}{\partial y} = Q(x, y, z), \quad \frac{\partial F}{\partial z} = R(x, y, z)$$

in an open region D, then $\int_A^B P dx + Q\,dy + R\,dz$ is independent of path in D.

Proof. Let $x = \phi_1(t)$, $y = \phi_2(t)$, $z = \phi_3(t)$, $\alpha \leq t \leq \beta$, so that $A = [\phi_1(\alpha), \phi_2(\alpha), \phi_3(\alpha)]$ and $B = [\phi_1(\beta), \phi_2(\beta), \phi_3(\beta)]$. Then

$$\begin{aligned}\int_A^B P\,dx + Q\,dy + R\,dz &= \int_\alpha^\beta \left(\frac{\partial F}{\partial x}\frac{dx}{dt} + \frac{\partial F}{\partial y}\frac{dy}{dt} + \frac{\partial F}{\partial z}\frac{dz}{dt}\right) dt \\ &= \int_\alpha^\beta \frac{dF[\phi_1(t), \phi_2(t), \phi_3(t)]}{dt}\,dt \\ &= F[\phi_1(\beta), \phi_2(\beta), \phi_3(\beta)] - F[\phi_1(\alpha), \phi_2(\alpha), \phi_3(\alpha)] \\ &= F(B) - F(A).\end{aligned}$$

Hence,

$$\int_A^B P\,dx + Q\,dy + R\,dz = F(B) - F(A),$$

which indicates that the line integral depends on A and B but not on the path joining them.

The proof of Criterion II indicates that if we can determine a function F such that

$$dF = \frac{\partial F}{\partial x}dx + \frac{\partial F}{\partial y}dy + \frac{\partial F}{\partial z}dz,$$

then

$$\int_A^B P\,dx + Q\,dy + R\,dz = F(B) - F(A).$$

The existence of such a function means, therefore, that $P\,dx + Q\,dy + R\,dz$ is an *exact differential*. Hence, Criterion II can be stated:

If $P\,dx + Q\,dy + R\,dz$ is an exact differential in an open region D, then $\int_A^B P\,dx + Q\,dy + R\,dz$ is independent of path in D.

Note the analogy between

$$\int_A^B P\,dx + Q\,dy + R\,dz = F(B) - F(A)$$

and the evaluation of the definite integral by the fundamental theorem of the calculus.

EXAMPLE 1. Evaluate

$$\text{I} = \int_{(0,0)}^{(2,1)} (10x^4 - 2xy^3)\,dx - 3x^2y^2\,dy$$

along the path $x^4 - 6xy^3 = 4y^2$.

Solution. This path is fairly complicated and only independence of path will preserve sanity. We write

$$\begin{aligned}(10x^4 - 2xy^3)\,dx - 3x^2y^2\,dy &= 10x^4\,dx - (2xy^3\,dx + 3x^2y^2\,dy)\\ &= d(2x^5) - d(x^2y^3) = d(2x^5 - x^2y^3).\end{aligned}$$

Hence, $F(x, y) = 2x^5 - x^2y^3$ and

$$\text{I} = \int_{(0,0)}^{(2,1)} dF(x, y) = (2x^5 - x^2y^3)\Big]_{(0,0)}^{(2,1)} = 60.$$

EXAMPLE 2. Evaluate $\text{I} = \int_C \mathbf{F}\cdot d\mathbf{r}$, $\mathbf{F} = (4xy - 3x^2z^2)\mathbf{i} + 2x^2\mathbf{j} - 2x^3z\mathbf{k}$, C: $x = \cos t$, $y = \cos 2t$, $z = \cos 3t$:

(a) $0 \le t \le \pi$,
(b) $0 \le t \le 2\pi$.

Solution

$$\begin{aligned}(4xy - 3x^2z^2)\,dx + 2x^2\,dy - 2x^3z\,dz &= (4xy\,dx + 2x^2\,dy) - (3x^2z^2\,dx + 2x^3z\,dz)\\ &= d(2x^2y - x^3z^2).\end{aligned}$$

Hence,

(a) $$\text{I} = \int_{(1,1,1)}^{(-1,1,-1)} d(x^2y - x^3z^2) = 2.$$

(b) $$\text{I} = 0,$$

by the converse of Criterion I, since C is closed.

Criterion II can be expressed in vector form. If there exists F such that $\nabla F = \boldsymbol{\phi}$ in an open region D, then $\int_A^B \boldsymbol{\phi}\cdot d\mathbf{r}$ is independent of path in D. Hence,

$$\int_A^B \nabla F\cdot d\mathbf{r} = F(B) - F(A).$$

Converse of Criterion II. If $\int_A^B P\,dx + Q\,dy + R\,dz$ is independent of path in an open region D, then there exists F defined in D such that

$$\frac{\partial F}{\partial x} = P, \quad \frac{\partial F}{\partial y} = Q, \quad \frac{\partial F}{\partial z} = R.$$

Proof. If (x_0, y_0, z_0) is a fixed point and (x, y, z) any point in D, then (since the given line integral is independent of path)

$$\int_{(x_0,y_0,z_0)}^{(x,y,z)} P\,dx + Q\,dy + R\,dz = F(x, y, z),$$

for some function F. It remains to show that F has the properties indicated.

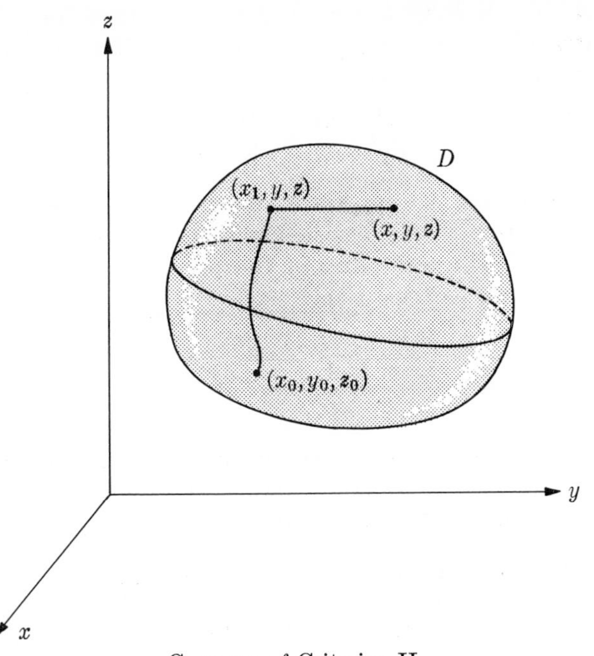

Converse of Criterion II

Let (x_1, y, z) be any point in D, $x_1 \neq x_0$. Consider the line segment from (x_1, y, z) to (x, y, z); if we now fix (x, y, z), the points on this line segment depend only on x (see figure). Since we have independence of path,

$$F(x, y, z) = \int_{(x_0,y_0,z_0)}^{(x_1,y,z)} P\,dx + Q\,dy + R\,dz = \int_{(x_1,y,z)}^{(x,y,z)} P\,dx + Q\,dy + R\,dz$$
$$= \text{constant} + \int_{x_1}^{x} P(t, y, z)dt,$$

since y and z are now fixed. Then $\partial F/\partial x = P$. Similarly, $\partial F/\partial y = Q$ and $\partial F/\partial z = R$.

We have seen that Criterion II is more useful than Criterion I for the determination of independence of path for a specific line integral. However, in the examples following Criterion II, we have established the existence of F such that

$$\int_A^B dF = \int_A^B P\,dx + Q\,dy + R\,dz = F(B) - F(A)$$

by actually discovering F by writing $P\,dx + Q\,dy + R\,dz$ in appropriate integrable combinations. Now, if we had available a criterion (in a form simple to apply) for establishing the existence of this function, then we should face the task of finding such a function with complete confidence. Let us first prove the

THEOREM. If P, Q, R are continuous and have continuous partial derivatives in an open region D and $\int_A^B P\,dx + Q\,dy + R\,dz$ is independent of path in D, then

$$\frac{\partial Q}{\partial x} = \frac{\partial P}{\partial y}, \quad \frac{\partial R}{\partial y} = \frac{\partial Q}{\partial z}, \quad \frac{\partial P}{\partial z} = \frac{\partial R}{\partial x}.$$

Proof. Since the line integral is independent of path in D, by the converse of Criterion II, there exists F such that $\partial F/\partial x = P$, $\partial F/\partial y = Q$, $\partial F/\partial z = R$ in D. The continuity of the partial derivatives ensures the equality of the cross partials. Hence,

$$\frac{\partial^2 F}{\partial y\,\partial x} = \frac{\partial P}{\partial y} = \frac{\partial^2 F}{\partial x\,\partial y} = \frac{\partial Q}{\partial x}.$$

Similarly, $\partial R/\partial y = \partial Q/\partial z$ and $\partial P/\partial z = \partial R/\partial x$.

If we could establish the converse of the foregoing theorem, we should have the criterion we are seeking. However, the converse of this theorem is not true, as is illustrated by the following

EXAMPLE. Let D be the set of points (x, y) such that $x^2 + y^2 > \frac{1}{4}$. $P = -[y/(x^2 + y^2)]$ and $Q = x/(x^2 + y^2)$ are continuous and have continuous partial derivatives in D. Moreover, $\partial Q/\partial x = \partial P/\partial y$ in D. Let us consider

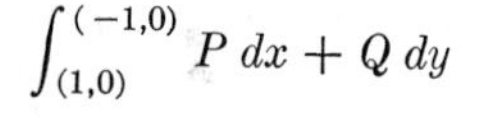

$$\int_{(1,0)}^{(-1,0)} P\,dx + Q\,dy$$

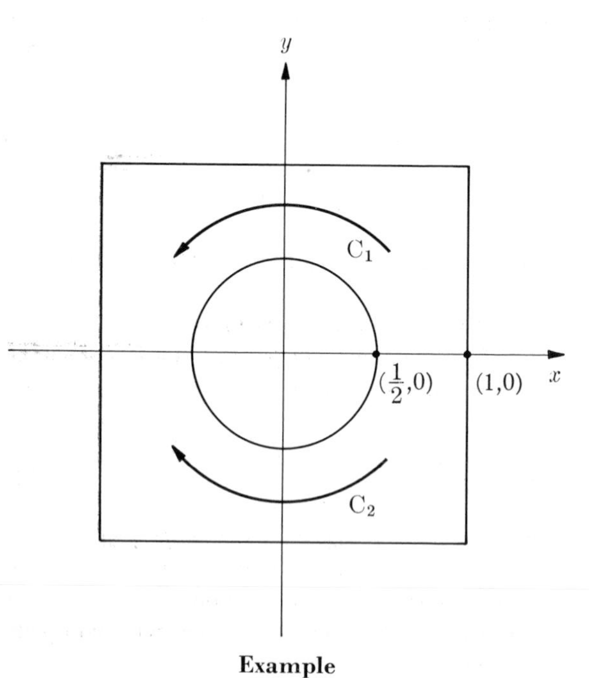

Example

first along C_1: the polygonal line (1, 0) to (1, 1) to (−1, 1) to (−1, 0), and then along C_2: the polygonal line (1, 0) to (1, −1) to (−1, −1) to (−1, 0), as indicated in the figure. It is readily seen that the value of the integral along C_1 is π and along C_2 it is $-\pi$. Hence, the line integral is not independent of path.

In the preceding example, D is not a simply connected region. The criterion for independence of path that we have been seeking is

Criterion III. If (1) P, Q, R are continuous and have continuous partial derivatives in an open *simply connected* region D, and (2)

$$\frac{\partial Q}{\partial x} = \frac{\partial P}{\partial y}, \quad \frac{\partial R}{\partial y} = \frac{\partial Q}{\partial z}, \quad \frac{\partial P}{\partial z} = \frac{\partial R}{\partial x}$$

in D, then $\int_A^B P\,dx + Q\,dy + R\,dz$ is independent of path in D.

With the use of Green's theorem for simply connected regions, Criterion III follows readily if D is in the xy-plane, for (2) implies that $\int_C P\,dx + Q\,dy = 0$ for every closed regular curve C in D, and Criterion I enables us to establish independence of path. To prove the theorem in general by the same method necessitates considering the analog of Green's theorem in space; we shall turn to this problem presently, and we shall then prove Criterion III.

EXAMPLE. Evaluate

$$I = \int_{(0,0,0)}^{(1,\pi/2,1)} (\sin y + z)\,dx + (x\cos y - z)\,dy + (x - y)\,dz$$

along the line joining (0, 0, 0) to (0, $\pi/2$, 1).

Solution

$$\frac{\partial Q}{\partial x} = \cos y = \frac{\partial P}{\partial y}, \quad \frac{\partial R}{\partial y} = -1 = \frac{\partial Q}{\partial z}, \quad \frac{\partial P}{\partial z} = 1 = \frac{\partial R}{\partial x}$$

in space, and P, Q, R satisfy the other conditions in Criterion III, we have independence of path everywhere, and we conclude that there exists F such that $dF = P\,dx + Q\,dy + R\,dz$. We determine it by rewriting

$$\begin{aligned}(\sin y + z)\,dx + (x\cos y - z)\,dy + (x - y)\,dz &= (\sin y\,dx + x\cos y\,dy) \\ &\quad + (z\,dx + x\,dz) - (z\,dy + y\,dz) \\ &= d(x\sin y + xz - yz) = dF.\end{aligned}$$

Hence,

$$I = x\sin y + xz - yz\Big]_{(0,0,0)}^{(1,\pi/2,1)} = 2 - \frac{\pi}{2}.$$

Criterion III can be expressed in vector form. Let $\boldsymbol{\phi} = P\mathbf{i} + Q\mathbf{j} + R\mathbf{k}$. Then

$$\text{curl}\,\boldsymbol{\phi} = \left(\frac{\partial R}{\partial y} - \frac{\partial Q}{\partial z}\right)\mathbf{i} + \left(\frac{\partial P}{\partial z} - \frac{\partial R}{\partial x}\right)\mathbf{j} + \left(\frac{\partial Q}{\partial x} - \frac{\partial P}{\partial y}\right)\mathbf{k}.$$

Hence, if $\boldsymbol{\phi}$ is continuously differentiable in an open simply connected region D, and curl $\boldsymbol{\phi} = \mathbf{0}$, $\int_A^B \boldsymbol{\phi} \cdot d\mathbf{r}$ is independent of path in D. (This form of Criterion III is readily remembered!) As we have seen, independence of path for this line integral implies the existence of F such that $\boldsymbol{\phi} = \text{grad } F$. We know that if $\boldsymbol{\phi}$ is twice differentiable and $\boldsymbol{\phi} = \text{grad } f$, then curl $\boldsymbol{\phi} = \text{curl grad } F = \mathbf{0}$ (C_6, p. 93). The converse is not true; however, if curl $\boldsymbol{\phi} = \mathbf{0}$ in an open *simply connected* region D, then there exists F such that grad $F = \boldsymbol{\phi}$.

EXERCISES

1. Establish independence of path and evaluate:

(a) $\displaystyle\int_{(1,-2)}^{(3,4)} \frac{y\,dx - x\,dy}{x^2}.$

(b) $\displaystyle\int_{(0,0)}^{(\pi,0)} e^{xy}(y\,dx + x\,dy).$

(c) $\displaystyle\int_{(0,0,0)}^{(1,1,1)} (12xy + yz)\,dx + (6x^2 + xz)\,dy + xy\,dz.$

(d) $\displaystyle\int_C \mathbf{F}\cdot d\mathbf{r}, \quad \mathbf{F} = e^{xz}(z\mathbf{i} + x\mathbf{k}), \quad C\colon\; x^2 + y^2 = 1, \quad x = z.$

(e) $\displaystyle\int_{(0,1,0)}^{(\pi,0,1)} \sin x\,dx + y^2\,dy + e^z\,dz.$

(f) $\displaystyle\int_{(1,1,1)}^{(2,2,2)} \frac{2(x\,dx + y\,dy)}{x^2 + y^2} + 2z\,dz.$

Ans.: (a) $-10/3$; (b) 0; (c) 7; (d) 0; (e) e $+ \frac{2}{3}$; (f) $\log 4 + 3$.

2. Evaluate as simply as possible:

(a) $\displaystyle\oint_C (x^2 + xy)\,dx + (x^2 + y^2)\,dy$, C: rectangle with vertices at $(\pm a, \pm b)$.

(b) $\displaystyle\oint_C \frac{x\,dy - y\,dx}{x^2 + y^2}, \quad C\colon\; x = 1 + 2\cos t, \quad y = 2\sin t, \quad 0 \le t \le 2\pi.$

(c) $\displaystyle\int_{(1,0)}^{(e^{2\pi},0)} \frac{x\,dx + y\,dy}{(x^2 + y^2)^{3/2}}, \quad C\colon\; x = e^t\cos t, \quad y = e^t\sin t, \quad 0 \le t \le 2\pi.$

(d) $\displaystyle\oint_C y^3\,dx - x^3\,dy, \quad C\colon\; |x| + |y| = 1.$

(e) $\displaystyle\oint_C xy^6\,dx + (3x^2y^5 + 6x)\,dy, \quad C\colon\; x^2 + y^2 = 4.$

(f) $\displaystyle\oint_C \frac{dx}{y} + \frac{dy}{x}$, C: triangle with sides on $y = 1$, $x = 4$, $y = x$.

(g) $\displaystyle\oint_C \mathbf{F}\cdot d\mathbf{r}$, $\mathbf{F} = (x - y)\mathbf{i} + (x - y)\mathbf{j}$, C: $(0, 0)$ to $(1, 1)$ along $y = x^2$ and $(1, 1)$ to $(0, 0)$ along $y^2 = x$.

(h) $\oint_C \frac{y\,dx - (x-1)\,dy}{(x-1)^2 + y^2}$, C: $x^2 + y^2 = 4$.

(i) $\oint_B \frac{(y-2)\,dx - x\,dy}{(y-2)^2 + x^2}$, $B = C_1 + C_2$, C_1: $x^2 + (y-2)^2 = 1$, C_2: $x^2 + (y-2)^2 = 4$.

(j) $\oint_C \frac{(y-2)\,dx - x\,dy}{(y-2)^2 + x^2} + \frac{(y-3)\,dx - x\,dy}{(y-3)^2 + x^2}$, C: $x^2 + y^2 = 16$.

(k) $\int_{(1,2,3)}^{(2,3,5)} \mathbf{F}\cdot d\mathbf{r}$, $\mathbf{F} = \frac{x\mathbf{i} + y\mathbf{j} + z\mathbf{k}}{x^2 + y^2 + z^2}$.

(l) $\int_{(0,0,0)}^{(1,1,1)} 3x^2yz^2\,dx + x^3z^2\,dy + 2x^3yz\,dz$, C: any regular curve passing through (0, 0, 0) and (1, 1, 1).

(m) $\oint_C 2xy\,dx + (x^2 + 1)\,dy + 6z^2\,dz$, C: quadrilateral with vertices at (1, 1, 1), (0, 1, 0), (0, 0, 1), (1, 0, 1).

(n) $\oint_C \mathbf{F}\cdot d\mathbf{r}$, $\mathbf{F} = y\mathbf{i} + x\mathbf{j} + z^2\mathbf{k}$, C: $x^2 - 2x + y^2 = 2$, $z = 1$.

(o) $\int_{(1,2,2)}^{(3,6,6)} \mathbf{r}\cdot d\mathbf{r}$ along the line joining (1, 2, 2) and (3, 6, 6). (*Hint:* $\mathbf{r}\cdot d\mathbf{r} = s\,ds$.)

Ans.: (a) 0; (b) 2π; (c) $1 - e^{-2\pi}$; (d) -2; (e) 12π; (f) $\frac{15}{4} - 2\log 4$; (g) 2; (h) -2π; (i) 0; (j) -4π; (k) $1/\sqrt{38} - 1/\sqrt{14}$; (l) 1; (m) 4; (n) 0; (o) 18.

3. Evaluate:

(a) $\oint_C \nabla f\cdot d\mathbf{r}$, $f = \log(x^2 + y^2)$, C: $x^2 + y^2 = 1$.

(b) $\oint_C \operatorname{curl} \boldsymbol{\phi}\cdot d\mathbf{r}$, $\boldsymbol{\phi} = x^2\mathbf{i} + y^2\mathbf{j} + z^2\mathbf{k}$, C: $x^2 + 2y^2 = 1$. *Ans.:* (a) 0.

4. Show that the angle subtended by any plane curve C at the origin is $\int_C \mathbf{n}\cdot\log \mathbf{r}\,ds$, $\mathbf{n}$ = outer unit normal vector to C, and $\mathbf{r}$ is the position vector of any point on C.

5. Show that if

$$\boldsymbol{\phi} = \frac{-y}{x^2 + y^2}\mathbf{i} + \frac{x}{x^2 + y^2}\mathbf{j} + \mathbf{k} \quad \text{and} \quad f = \tan^{-1}\frac{y}{x} + z,$$

then $\nabla f = \boldsymbol{\phi}$ at points of the region between the cylinders $x^2 + y^2 = \frac{1}{4}$ and $x^2 + y^2 = 4$. Evaluate $\int_{(-1,0,0)}^{(1,0,0)} \boldsymbol{\phi}\cdot d\mathbf{r}$ along the upper and lower arcs of the circle $x^2 + y^2 = 1$, $z = 0$. What conclusions do you arrive at?

6. Given a force field $\mathbf{F}$ such that the work done on a particle by $\mathbf{F}$, $W = \int_C \mathbf{F}\cdot d\mathbf{r}$, C arbitrary, is independent of path; such a field is called a **conservative field.** We know that for a conservative field, there exists a scalar function f such that $\mathbf{F} = \nabla f$; $U = -f$ is called the **potential** or **potential energy** of F.

(a) Show that U is not uniquely determined, but if $\mathbf{F} = -\operatorname{grad} U_1$ and $\mathbf{F} = -\operatorname{grad} U_2$, then $U_1 = U_2 + \text{constant}$.

(b) Determine whether the following fields are conservative: (1) $e^{xz}(\mathbf{i} + x\mathbf{k})$;

(2) $3x^2yz^2\mathbf{i} + x^3z^2\mathbf{j} + x^3yz\mathbf{k}$; (3) $(12xy + yz)\mathbf{i} + (6x^2 + xz)\mathbf{j} + xy\mathbf{k}$; (4) $\dfrac{2x\mathbf{i}}{x^2 + y^2} + \dfrac{2y\mathbf{j}}{x^2 + y^2} + 2z\mathbf{k}$.

(c) Determine the potentials of the conservative fields in (b).

(d) Determine the potential for a central force field in which the force of attraction on a particle varies directly as the square of the distance from the origin and also when it varies inversely as this distance.

7. (a) In a conservative field (see Exercise 6), show that work

$$W = \int_A^B \mathbf{F}\cdot d\mathbf{r} = U(A) - U(B),$$

where U is the potential of $\mathbf{F}$; i.e., work equals the loss in potential energy.

(b) If $\mathbf{F} = m(d\mathbf{v}/dt)$ (Newton's law), show that

$$W = \int_A^B \mathbf{F}\cdot d\mathbf{r} = \tfrac{1}{2}m[v^2(t_2) - v^2(t_1)],$$

where a particle of mass m is at A at time t_1 and at B at time t_2. Hence, the work done equals the gain in kinetic energy.

(c) Use (a) and (b) to show that the total energy (potential energy + kinetic energy) is $E = (mv^2/2) + U =$ constant. This is the **law of the conservation of energy** and accounts for the term *conservative field*.

(d) A particle of mass m moves in the xy-plane subject to a force $\mathbf{F} = -a^2x\mathbf{i} - b^2y\mathbf{j}$. Determine the potential energy, the kinetic energy, and the law of conservation of energy for this motion.

8. (a) Show that $U = -(1/r)$ is the potential of $\mathbf{r}/r^3$, $\mathbf{r} = x\mathbf{i} + y\mathbf{j} + z\mathbf{k}$. (See Exercise 6.)

(b) A particle is moved along the line segment from (1, 1, 1) to (2, 3, 4) by the force

$$\mathbf{F} = \frac{x\mathbf{i} + y\mathbf{j} + z\mathbf{k}}{(x^2 + y^2 + z^2)^{3/2}}.$$

What is the work done on the particle by $\mathbf{F}$?

4. Surface integrals. Just as the definite integral can be generalized to a line integral by replacing the interval of integration by a regular curve, the double integral can be generalized by replacing the region of integration in the plane by a regular surface. The result is a surface integral, and our attention will now be directed to such an integral.

Let $S: x = \phi_1(u, v),\ y = \phi_2(u, v),\ z = \phi_3(u, v),\ R_{uv}$, be an orientable smooth surface, where R_{uv} is bounded and closed. Let the function G be defined on S; i.e., to every point (x, y, z) on S, we assign the functional value $G(x, y, z)$. Divide the region R_{uv} into n parts or subregions ΔR_i, $i = 1, 2, \cdots, n$, in any manner whatsoever. (See Fig. 9.) Denote the area of ΔR_i by ΔA_i, $i = 1, 2, \cdots, n$. Choose a point arbitrarily in ΔR_i, $i = 1, 2, \cdots, n$, and denote this point by (u_i', v_i'), $i = 1, 2, \cdots, n$. The point (u_i', v_i') in ΔR_i will determine the point (x_i', y_i', z_i') on S, where $x_i' = \phi_1(u_i', v_i')$, $y_i' = \phi_2(u_i', v_i')$, $z_i' = \phi_3(u_i', v_i')$. Now ΔR_i with area ΔA_i will determine a

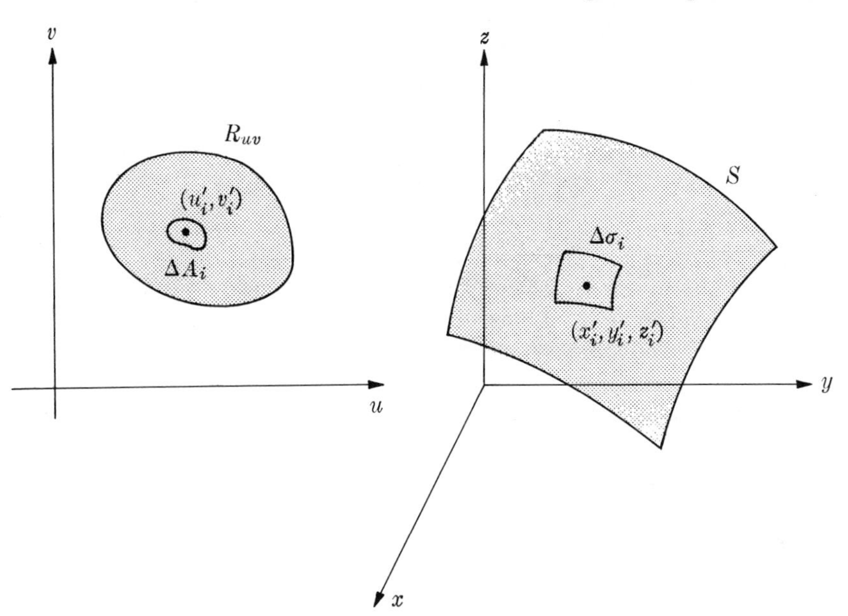

Fig. 9. The surface integral

part or subsurface of S, ΔS_i, with surface area $\Delta\sigma_i$; S_i includes the point (x_i', y_i', z_i'). We form the products $G(x_i', y_i', z_i')\Delta\sigma_i$, $i = 1, 2, \cdots, n$, sum, and take the limit:

$$\lim_{\substack{n\to\infty \\ \|\Delta\sigma\|\to 0}} \sum_{i=1}^{n} G(x_i', y_i', z_i')\Delta\sigma_i,$$

where $\|\Delta\sigma\|$ denotes the largest of the $\Delta\sigma_i$, $i = 1, 2, \cdots, n$. If this limit exists, we call it the **surface integral** of G over S and denote it by

$$\iint_S G(x, y, z)\, d\sigma.$$

We define the surface integral of G over a regular surface S, consisting of the smooth surfaces $S_1, S_2, \cdots, S_n$ as

$$\iint_S G(x, y, z)\, d\sigma = \iint_{S_1} G(x, y, z)\, d\sigma + \iint_{S_2} G(x, y, z)\, d\sigma + \cdots + \iint_{S_n} G(x, y, z)\, d\sigma.$$

Some interpretations of $I = \iint_S G(x, y, z)\, d\sigma$ are

(1) If $G(x, y, z) = 1$, I = surface area of S.
(2) If $G(x, y, z) = \rho(x, y, z)$, the density function, $I = M$, mass of S.

(3) If $G(x, y, z) = x\rho(x, y, z)$, $y\rho(x, y, z)$, or $z\rho(x, y, z)$, $I = M\bar{x}$, $M\bar{y}$, or $M\bar{z}$, where $(\bar{x}, \bar{y}, \bar{z})$ is the center of gravity of S.

(4) If $G(x, y, z) = (y^2 + z^2)\rho(x, y, z)$, $(x^2 + z^2)\rho(x, y, z)$, or $(x^2 + y^2)\rho(x, y, z)$, $I = I_x$, I_y, or I_z, the moments of inertia of S about the x, y, z axes.

The student should indicate why these interpretations are reasonable, starting from basic physical principles.

To evaluate surface integrals by resorting to the definition would generally be a formidable, if not impossible, task. Fortunately, this is not necessary, for we have the

FIRST FUNDAMENTAL THEOREM FOR SURFACE INTEGRALS. If (1) $S: x = \phi_1(u, v)$, $y = \phi_2(u, v)$, $z = \phi_3(u, v)$, R_{uv} is an orientable smooth surface, R_{uv} is bounded and closed, and (2) G is continuous on S, then

$\iint_S G(x, y, z)\, d\sigma$ exists, and

$$\iint_S G(x, y, z)\, d\sigma = \iint_{R_{uv}} G(\phi_1, \phi_2, \phi_3)|\phi_u \times \phi_v|\, du\, dv.$$

Proof. By definition,

$$\iint_S G(x, y, z)\, d\sigma = \lim_{\substack{n\to\infty \\ \|\Delta\sigma\|\to 0}} \sum_{i=1}^{n} G(x_i', y_i', z_i')\, \Delta\sigma_i.$$

But

$$\Delta\sigma_i = \iint_{\Delta R_i} |\phi_u \times \phi_v|\, dA_i,$$

by our expression for surface area. By the law of the mean for double integrals (which the student should formulate precisely and make a valiant effort to prove),

$$\Delta\sigma_i = |\phi_u \times \phi_v|\, \Delta A_i,$$

where the partial derivatives are evaluated at some point (u_i^*, v_i^*) in ΔR_i. Then

$$\iint_S G(x, y, z)\, d\sigma = \lim_{\substack{n\to\infty \\ \|\Delta\sigma\|\to 0}} \sum_{i=1}^{n} G[\phi_1(u_i', v_i'), \phi_2(u_i', v_i'), \phi_3(u_i', v_i')]|\phi_u \times \phi_v|\, \Delta A_i$$

$$= \iint_{R_{uv}} G(\phi_1, \phi_2, \phi_3)|\phi_u \times \phi_v|\, dA,$$

with the use of Duhamel's theorem for double integrals [IVCc]. We can now take as the element of area $dA = du\, dv$.

The preceding theorem indicates that evaluating a surfcae integral is equivalent to evaluating a certain double integral. As a matter of fact, to evaluate $\iint_S G(x, y, z)\, d\sigma$, $S: x = \phi_1(u, v),\ y = \phi_2(u, v),\ z = \phi_3(u, v),\ R_{uv}$, we formally replace x, y, z by $\phi_1(u, v), \phi_2(u, v), \phi_3(u, v)$ and $d\sigma$ by $|\phi_u \times \phi_v|\, du\, dv$, converting the surface integral into a double integral over R_{uv}.

From the corresponding properties for double integrals, we obtain:

I₁: $\displaystyle\iint_S kG(x, y, z)\, d\sigma = k \iint_S G(x, y, z)\, d\sigma,\qquad k$ any constant.

I₂: $\displaystyle\iint_S [G(x, y, z) + H(x, y, z)]\, d\sigma = \iint_S G(x, y, z)\, d\sigma + \iint_S H(x, y, z)\, d\sigma.$

I₃: $\displaystyle\iint_S G(x, y, z)\, d\sigma = \iint_{S_1} G(x, y, z)\, d\sigma + \cdots + \iint_{S_n} G(x, y, z)\, d\sigma,$

where $S = S_1 + \cdots + S_n$,

all surface integrals are assumed to exist.

Since it is the standard parametric representations of surfaces that we will encounter most frequently, let us express the conclusions in the fundamental theorem for surface integrals for these representations:

(1) S: $z = f(x, y),\ R_{xy}$,

$$\iint_S G(x, y, z)\, d\sigma = \iint_{R_{xy}} G[x, y, f(x, y)] \sqrt{1 + \left(\frac{\partial f}{\partial x}\right)^2 + \left(\frac{\partial f}{\partial y}\right)^2}\, dx\, dy$$

(2) S: $y = g(x, z),\ R_{xz}$,

$$\iint_S G(x, y, z)\, d\sigma = \iint_{R_{xz}} G[x, g(x, z), z] \sqrt{1 + \left(\frac{\partial g}{\partial x}\right)^2 + \left(\frac{\partial g}{\partial z}\right)^2}\, dx\, dz.$$

(3) S: $x = h(y, z),\ R_{yz}$,

$$\iint_S G(x, y, z)\, d = \iint_{R_{yz}} G[h(y, z), y, z] \sqrt{1 + \left(\frac{\partial h}{\partial y}\right)^2 + \left(\frac{\partial h}{\partial z}\right)^2}\, dy\, dz.$$

EXAMPLE 1. Evaluate

$$I = \iint_S x^2 z\, d\sigma,$$

(a) S: $z = \sqrt{1 - x^2 - y^2},\ R_{xy}: 0 \le x^2 + y^2 \le 1$,
(b) S: $x^2 + y^2 + z^2 = 1,\ R_{xy}$.

Solution. (a) By the fundamental theorem for surface integrals,

$$I = \iint_{R_{xy}} x^2\sqrt{1 - x^2 - y^2}\sqrt{1 + \left(\frac{x^2}{1 - x^2 - y^2}\right) + \left(\frac{y^2}{1 - x^2 - y^2}\right)}\, dx\, dy$$

$$= \iint_{R_{xy}} x^2\, dx\, dy,$$

which can be readily evaluated by using polar coordinates. Hence,

$$\mathrm{I} = \int_0^{2\pi}\int_0^1 r^3 \cos^2\theta\, d\theta = \frac{\pi}{4}.$$

(b) We can let $S = S_1 + S_2$, where S_1: $z = \sqrt{1 - x^2 - y^2}$, R_{xy}, S_2: $z = -\sqrt{1 - x^2 - y^2}$, R_{xy}. Then

$$\iint_{S_2} x^2 z\, d\sigma = -\iint_{R_{xy}} x^2\, dx\, dy = -\frac{\pi}{4}$$

and with the result in (a), we have $I = 0$.

Now suppose we consider the representation S: $x = \cos u \sin v$, $y = \sin u \sin v$, $z = \cos v$, $0 \leq u \leq 2\pi$, $0 \leq v \leq \pi$. Then

$$I = \int_0^{\pi}\int_0^{2\pi} \cos^2 u \sin^3 v \cos v\, du\, dv = 0.$$

Note that if we use standard parametric representations for S, it must be divided into two surfaces, whereas the preceding parametric representation gives a representation for all of S.

We now consider another physical interpretation of a surface integral. Let S be a closed surface such that the temperature of the interior of S is higher than it is on the outside of S. Our experience shows that heat will flow from points at a higher temperature to points at a lower temperature in a direction that will yield the maximum rate of change. Hence, if we denote the velocity vector of this heat flow by $\mathbf{v}$, the direction of $\mathbf{v}$ will be the same as that of $\mathbf{n}$, the outer unit normal vector to S. (Why?) Now let S be divided into n subsurfaces ΔS_i whose areas are $\Delta\sigma_i$, $i = 1, 2, \cdots, n$. Then the amount of heat per unit time that will flow through ΔS_i is approximately $\mathbf{v}\cdot\mathbf{n}\,\Delta\sigma_i$, $\mathbf{v}$ and $\mathbf{n}$ evaluated at any point of ΔS_i. We then define the total amount of heat that flows through S as

$$\lim_{\substack{n\to\infty \\ \|\Delta\sigma\|\to 0}} \sum_{i=1}^{n} \mathbf{v}\cdot\mathbf{n}\,\Delta\sigma_i.$$

But this is the surface integral $\iint_S \mathbf{v}\cdot\mathbf{n}\, d\sigma$. Heat flow is just one physical quantity that can be expressed as a surface integral; there are other physical quantities that yield analogous surface integrals. Therefore, we shall consider in general those surface integrals of the form $\iint_S \boldsymbol{\phi}\cdot\mathbf{n}\,d\sigma$, where $\boldsymbol{\phi}$ is any vector function and S is any regular surface. Note that this surface integral is a special case of $\iint_S G(x, y, z)\,d\sigma$ with $G(x, y, z) = \boldsymbol{\phi}\cdot\mathbf{n}$. Hence, we have

VECTOR FORM OF THE FIRST FUNDAMENTAL THEOREM FOR SURFACE INTEGRALS. If (1) S is a regular surface defined in a plane closed and bounded region and if (2) $\boldsymbol{\phi}$ is continuous on S, then if

(1) S: $x = \psi_1(u, v),\ y = \psi_2(u, v),\ z = \psi_3(u, v)$,

$$\iint_S \boldsymbol{\phi}\cdot\mathbf{n}\,d\sigma = \pm\iint_{R_{uv}} (\boldsymbol{\phi}\boldsymbol{\psi}_u\boldsymbol{\psi}_v)\,du\,dv.$$

(2) S: $z = f(x, y),\ R_{xy}$,

$$\iint_S \boldsymbol{\phi}\cdot\mathbf{n}\,d\sigma = \pm\iint_{R_{xy}} \boldsymbol{\phi}\cdot\frac{\mathbf{n}}{|\mathbf{n}\cdot\mathbf{k}|}\,dx\,dy$$

(3) S: $y = g(x, z),\ R_{xz}$,

$$\iint_S \boldsymbol{\phi}\cdot\mathbf{n}\,d\sigma = \pm\iint_{R_{xz}} \boldsymbol{\phi}\cdot\frac{\mathbf{n}}{|\mathbf{n}\cdot\mathbf{j}|}\,dx\,dz.$$

(4) S: $x = h(y, z),\ R_{yz}$,

$$\iint_S \boldsymbol{\phi}\cdot\mathbf{n}\,d\sigma = \pm\iint_{R_{yz}} \boldsymbol{\phi}\cdot\frac{\mathbf{n}}{|\mathbf{n}\cdot\mathbf{i}|}\,dy\,dz.$$

The sign is chosen to correspond to the choice of $\mathbf{n}$.

Note that in the preceding equations, we have $\boldsymbol{\phi} = \boldsymbol{\phi}(x, y, z)$ in the surface integrals, and in the double integrals (1) $\boldsymbol{\phi} = \boldsymbol{\phi}(\psi_1, \psi_2, \psi_3)$; (2) $\boldsymbol{\phi} = \boldsymbol{\phi}[x, y, f(x, y)]$; (3) $\boldsymbol{\phi} = \boldsymbol{\phi}[x, g(x, z), z]$; (4) $\boldsymbol{\phi} = \boldsymbol{\phi}[h(y, z), y, z]$.

EXAMPLE 2. Evaluate $I = \iint_S \boldsymbol{\phi}\cdot\mathbf{n}\,d\sigma$, S: the cylindrical surface $\boldsymbol{\psi} = \cos u\mathbf{i} + \sin u\mathbf{j} + v\mathbf{k},\ 0 \le u \le 2\pi,\ 0 \le v \le 1$; $\boldsymbol{\phi} = x\mathbf{i} + y\mathbf{j} + z\mathbf{k}$; $\mathbf{n}$ = outer unit normal vector.

Solution. $\mathbf{n} = \cos u\mathbf{i} + \sin u\mathbf{j}$ is the outer unit normal vector. $\boldsymbol{\phi}$ evaluated at $x = \cos u,\ y = \sin u,\ z = v$ is $\cos u\mathbf{i} + \sin u\mathbf{j} + v\mathbf{k}$. Now

$$(\boldsymbol{\phi}\boldsymbol{\psi}_u\boldsymbol{\psi}_v) = \begin{vmatrix} \cos u & \sin u & v \\ -\sin u & \cos u & 0 \\ 0 & 0 & 1 \end{vmatrix}$$

$$= \cos^2 u + \sin^2 u = 1.$$

Hence,

$$I = \iint_{R_{uv}} du\, dv = 2\pi.$$

If S is a region R_{xy}, then

$$\iint_S \boldsymbol{\phi}\cdot\mathbf{n}\, d\sigma = \iint_{R_{xy}} \boldsymbol{\phi}\cdot\mathbf{n}\, dx\, dy = \pm\iint_{R_{xy}} \boldsymbol{\phi}\cdot\mathbf{k}\, dx\, dy,$$

depending on whether we choose $\mathbf{n}$ to be $\mathbf{k}$ (above the xy-plane) or $-\mathbf{k}$ (below the xy-plane). In other words, a surface integral over a plane region may differ in sign from the corresponding double integral over that region. The reason for this is that in our definition of the double integral we tacitly assume that we are integrating over a region on the side of the plane determined by $\mathbf{k}$. We can generalize the definition of the double integral by removing this restriction; we let $dx\, dy$ or $-dx\, dy$ be the element of area, depending on whether we are integrating over the side of the plane determined by $\mathbf{k}$ or over the other side. Now, if we let $n = \pm\mathbf{k}$, this means that we can write $dx\, dy = \mathbf{n}\cdot\mathbf{k}\, d\sigma$, which indicates that we have $dx\, dy$ or $-dx\, dy$, according to whether $\mathbf{n} = \mathbf{k}$ or $\mathbf{n} = -\mathbf{k}$.

In general, then, for any surface S, we can write

$$\begin{aligned} dy\, dz &= \mathbf{n}\cdot\mathbf{i}\, d\sigma \\ dx\, dz &= \mathbf{n}\cdot\mathbf{j}\, d\sigma \\ dx\, dy &= \mathbf{n}\cdot\mathbf{k}\, d\sigma \end{aligned}$$

which means that in the yz-plane, the element of area is positive or negative, depending on whether $\mathbf{n}\cdot\mathbf{i} > 0$ ($\mathbf{n}$ is in front of the yz-plane) or $\mathbf{n}\cdot\mathbf{i} < 0$ ($\mathbf{n}$ is behind the yz-plane); and similarly for the elements of area in the xz and xy planes.

Now we are ready to express $\iint_S \boldsymbol{\phi}\cdot\mathbf{n}\, d\sigma$ in a cartesian form that is analogous to the cartesian form $\int_C P\, dx + Q\, dy + R\, dz$ of the line integral $\int_C \boldsymbol{\phi}\cdot d\mathbf{r}$, $\boldsymbol{\phi} = P\mathbf{i} + Q\mathbf{j} + R\mathbf{k}$. Now, with this vector function $\boldsymbol{\phi}$, we have

$$\begin{aligned} \iint_S \boldsymbol{\phi}\cdot\mathbf{n}\, d\sigma &= \iint_S (P\mathbf{i} + Q\mathbf{j} + R\mathbf{k})\cdot\mathbf{n}\, d\sigma \\ &= \iint_S (P\mathbf{i}\cdot\mathbf{n} + Q\mathbf{j}\cdot\mathbf{n} + R\mathbf{k}\cdot\mathbf{n})\, d\sigma \\ &= \iint_S P\, dy\, dz + Q\, dx\, dz + R\, dx\, dy. \end{aligned}$$

Now suppose that we begin with a surface integral in the form $\iint_S P\, dy\, dz + Q\, dx\, dz + R\, dx\, dy$. This can be converted into vector form and then, according to the nature of the representation of S, this can be evaluated by using the vector form of the first fundamental theorem for surface integrals. Assuming the conditions of that theorem and introducing the symbol

$$\epsilon(\mathbf{a}\cdot\mathbf{b}) = \begin{cases} 1, & \mathbf{a}\cdot\mathbf{b} > 0 \\ 0, & \mathbf{a}\cdot\mathbf{b} = 0, \\ -1, & \mathbf{a}\cdot\mathbf{b} < 0 \end{cases}$$

we obtain the following equations:

(I) S: $z = f(x, y)$, R_{xy},

$$\iint_{S} P\,dy\,dz + Q\,dx\,dz + R\,dx\,dy = \epsilon(\mathbf{n}\cdot\mathbf{k}) \iint_{R_{xy}} \left(-P\frac{\partial f}{\partial x} - Q\frac{\partial f}{\partial y} + R\right) dx\,dy.$$

(II) S: $y = g(x, z)$, R_{xz},

$$\iint_{S} P\,dy\,dz + Q\,dx\,dz + R\,dx\,dy = \epsilon(\mathbf{n}\cdot\mathbf{j}) \iint_{R_{xz}} \left(-P\frac{\partial g}{\partial x} + Q - R\frac{\partial g}{\partial z}\right) dx\,dz.$$

(III) S: $x = h(y, z)$, R_{yz},

$$\iint_{S} P\,dy\,dz + Q\,dx\,dz + R\,dx\,dy = \epsilon(\mathbf{n}\cdot\mathbf{i}) \iint_{R_{yz}} \left(P - Q\frac{\partial h}{\partial y} - R\frac{\partial h}{\partial z}\right) dy\,dz.$$

The functions P, Q, R occurring in the double integrals are to be evaluated at $z = f(x, y)$ in (I), at $y = g(x, z)$ in (II), and at $x = h(y, z)$ in (III). We now prove the

SECOND FUNDAMENTAL THEOREM FOR SURFACE INTEGRALS. If S is a regular surface that has the following representations: (1) $S = S_{xy} + S^*_{xy}$; $S_{xy}: z = f(x, y)$, $\mathbf{n}\cdot\mathbf{k} > 0$, R_{xy}; $S^*_{xy}: z = f^*(x, y)$, $\mathbf{n}\cdot\mathbf{k} < 0$, R^*_{xy}; (2) $S = S_{xz} + S^*_{xz}$; $S_{xz}: y = g(x, z)$, $\mathbf{n}\cdot\mathbf{j} > 0$, R_{xz}; $S^*_{xz}: y = g^*(x, z)$, $\mathbf{n}\cdot\mathbf{j} < 0$, R^*_{xz}; (3) $S = S_{yz} + S^*_{yz}$; $S_{yz}: x = h(y, z)$, $\mathbf{n}\cdot\mathbf{i} > 0$, R_{yz}; S^*_{yz}: $x = h^*(y, z)$, $\mathbf{n}\cdot\mathbf{i} < 0$, R^*_{yz}; with all plane regions closed and bounded, and if P, Q, R are continuous on S, then

$$\iint_{S} P\,dy\,dz + Q\,dx\,dz + R\,dx\,dy$$

$$= \iint_{R_{yz}} P\,[h(y, z), y, z]\,dy\,dz - \iint_{R^*_{yz}} P\,[h^*(y, z), y, z]\,dy\,dz$$

$$+ \iint_{R_{xz}} Q[x, g(x, z), z]\,dx\,dz - \iint_{R^*_{xz}} Q[x, g^*(x, z), z]\,dx\,dz$$

$$+ \iint_{R_{xy}} R[x, y, f(x, y)]\,dx\,dy - \iint_{R^*_{xy}} R[x, y, f^*(x, y)]\,dx\,dy.$$

Proof

$$\iint_S P\,dy\,dz + Q\,dx\,dz + R\,dx\,dy = \iint_S P\,dy\,dz + \iint_S Q\,dx\,dz + \iint_S R\,dx\,dy.$$

Now

$$\iint_S P\,dy\,dz = \iint_{S_{yz}} P\,dy\,dz + \iint_{S^*_{yz}} P\,dy\,dz$$

$$= \iint_{R_{yz}} P[h(y, z), y, z]\,dy\,dz - \iint_{R^*_{yz}} P[h^*(y, z), y, z]\,dy\,dz,$$

since we can let $Q = R = 0$ in (III), p. 139. We evaluate $\iint_S Q\,dx\,dz$ and $\iint_S R\,dx\,dy$ similarly.

Although this theorem appears to be complicated, its application is quite simple. In effect, to evaluate $I = \iint_S P\,dy\,dz + Q\,dx\,dz + R\,dx\,dy$, we project that part of S such that **n** on S is directed above the xy-plane onto the xy-plane and evaluate the double integral $\iint_{R_{xy}} R\,dx\,dy$, where R_{xy} is the projection of S. We now project that part of S such that **n** on S is directed below the xy-plane onto the xy-plane and evaluate the double integral $-\iint_{R^*_{xy}} R\,dx\,dy$, where R^*_{xy} is the projection of S. Next we project S onto the xz-plane in similar fashion and evaluate $\iint_{R_{xz}} Q\,dx\,dz - \iint_{R^*_{xz}} Q\,dx\,dz$. Finally, projecting S onto the yz-plane, we evaluate

$$\iint_{R_{yz}} P\,dy\,dz - \iint_{R^*_{yz}} P\,dy\,dz.$$

We add up all values of the double integrals to obtain I. This is made clear in

EXAMPLE 3. Evaluate $I = \iint_S x^2\,dy\,dz + y^2\,dx\,dz + z\,dx\,dy$,

S: $x^2 + y^2 = 1 - z$, $z \geq 0$, $x^2 + y^2 \leq 1$, $\mathbf{n}$ = outer unit normal vector.

Solution. The outer unit normal vector is above the xy-plane for every point on S: $z = 1 - x^2 - y^2$, R_{xy}: $x^2 + y^2 \leq 1$. (See figure.) Hence,

$$\iint_S z\,dx\,dy = \iint_{R_{xy}} (1 - x^2 - y^2)\,dx\,dy = \int_0^{2\pi} \int_0^1 (r - r^3)\,dr\,d\theta = \frac{\pi}{2}.$$

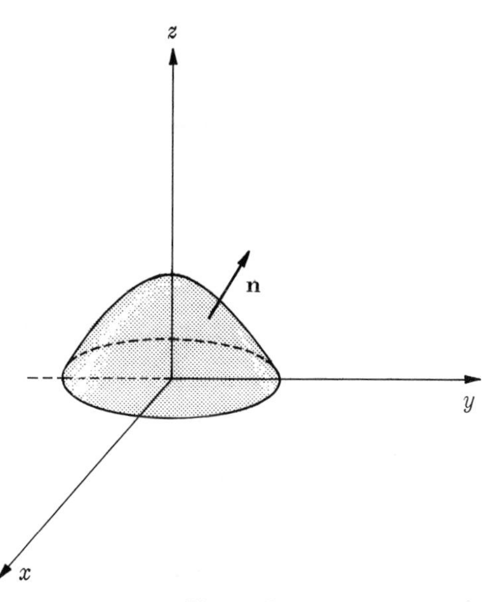

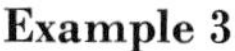
Example 3

Now

$$\iint_S y^2\,dx\,dz = \iint_{R_{xz}} (1 - x^2 - z^2)\,dx\,dz - \iint_{R^*_{xz}} (1 - x^2 - z^2)\,dx\,dz = 0,$$

since $R_{xz} = R^*_{xz}$: $-\sqrt{1-z} \le x \le \sqrt{1-z}$. Similarly, $\iint_S x^2\,dy\,dz = 0$. Hence, $I = \pi/2$.

Let us evaluate I, using (I), p. 139.

$$\begin{aligned} I &= \iint_{R_{xy}} 2x^3 + 2y^3 + 1 - x^2 - y^2\,dx\,dy \\ &= \int_0^{2\pi}\int_0^1 (2r^4\cos^3\theta + 2r^4\sin^3\theta + r - r^3\cos^2\theta - r^3\sin^2\theta)\,dr\,d\theta \\ &= \frac{\pi}{2}. \end{aligned}$$

Any preference between the two methods?

EXAMPLE 4. Evaluate $I_S = \iint_S 4xz\,dy\,dz - y^2\,dx\,dz + yz\,dx\,dy$,

S: surface of open cube bounded by $x = 0$, $x = 1$, $y = 0$, $z = 0$, $\mathbf{n}$ = outer unit normal vector.

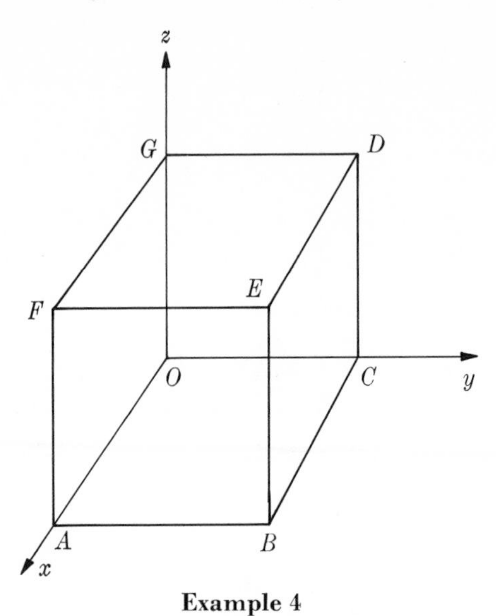

Example 4

Solution. We calculate the surface integrals I_{S_i}, $i = 1, 2, \cdots, 5$, over each of the faces S_i as indicated in the figure.

S_1: $ABCO$, $z = 0$, $\mathbf{n} = -\mathbf{k}$, $I_{S_1} = 0$;
S_2: $OAFG$, $y = 0$, $\mathbf{n} = -\mathbf{j}$, $I_{S_2} = 0$;
S_3: $OCDG$, $x = 0$, $\mathbf{n} = -\mathbf{i}$, $I_{S_3} = 0$;

$$S_4: \quad ABEF,\ x = 1,\ \mathbf{n} = \mathbf{i},\ I_{S_4} = \int_0^1 \int_0^1 4z\, dy\, dz = 2;$$

$$S_5: \quad BCDE,\ y = 1,\ \mathbf{n} = \mathbf{j},\ I_{S_5} = -\int_0^1 \int_0^1 dx\, dz = -1.$$

Hence, $I_S = I_{S_1} + I_{S_2} + I_{S_3} + I_{S_4} + I_{S_5} = 1$.

EXAMPLE 5. Show that $\iint_S R\, dx\, dy = 0$, where S is any cylindrical surface with elements parallel to the z-axis.

Solution

$$\iint_S R\, dx\, dy = \iint_S R(\mathbf{k}\cdot\mathbf{n})\, d\sigma = 0, \quad \text{since} \quad \mathbf{k}\cdot\mathbf{n} = 0.$$

EXERCISES

1. Evaluate $\iint_S x^2 z\ d\sigma$, S: $x^2 + y^2 = 1$, $0 \le z \le 1$. Determine another parametric representation of S and evaluate. *Ans.:* $\pi/2$.

2. Evaluate $\iint\limits_S x\,dy\,dz + y\,dz\,dx + 2dx\,dy$, S: the triangle with vertices at (1, 0, 0), (0, 1, 0), (0, 0, 1); direction of unit normal is from (0, 0, 0) to the surface. Show that S can be expressed parametrically as $x = u + v$, $y = u - v$, $z = 1 - 2u$, $0 \leq u \leq \frac{1}{2}$, $0 \leq v \leq \frac{1}{2}$, and evaluate the surface integral.

Ans.: $\frac{1}{2}$.

3. Evaluate $\iint\limits_S \boldsymbol{\phi}\cdot\mathbf{n}\,d\sigma$ for each of the following:

(a) $\boldsymbol{\phi} = y\mathbf{i} + 2x\mathbf{j} - z\mathbf{k}$, S: plane $2x + y = 6$ in first octant cut off by plane $z = 4$; unit normal directed from origin to surface.

(b) $\boldsymbol{\phi} = (x + y^2)\mathbf{i} - 2x\mathbf{j} + 2yz\mathbf{k}$, S: $2x + y + 2z = 6$ in first octant; unit normal directed from origin to surface.

(c) $\boldsymbol{\phi} = 6z\mathbf{i} + (2x + y)\mathbf{j} - x\mathbf{k}$, S: $x^2 + z^2 = 9$, $x = 0$, $y = 0$, $z = 0$, $y = 8$; outer unit normal.

(d) $\boldsymbol{\phi} = 2y\mathbf{i} - z\mathbf{j} + x^2\mathbf{k}$, S: $y^2 = 8x$ in first octant bounded by $y = 4$ and $z = 6$; outer unit normal.

(e) $\boldsymbol{\phi} = 4xz\mathbf{i} + xyz^2\mathbf{j} + 3z\mathbf{k}$, S: surface bounded by $z^2 = x^2 + y^2$, $z = 0$, $z = 4$; outer unit normal.

Ans.: (a) 108; (b) 81; (c) 18; (d) 132; (e) 320.

4. Evaluate $\iint\limits_S \sqrt{x^2 + y^2 + z^2}\,dx\,dy$, S: $x^2 + y^2 = z^2$, $0 \leq z \leq 1$.

Ans.: $\pi\sqrt{2}$.

5. Evaluate $\iint\limits_S G(x, y, z)\,d\sigma$, where

(a) $G(x, y, z) = (x + y)z$, S: cube with vertices at (a, b, c), where a, b, c are 0 or 1.

(b) $G(x, y, z) = x + y + z$, S: $x^2 + y^2 + z^2 = a^2$, $x, y, z > 0$.

Ans.: (a) 3; (b) $a^4(\pi + 1)/2$.

6. Find the surface area of the region common to the intersecting cylinders $x^2 + y^2 = a^2$ and $x^2 + z^2 = a^2$.

Ans.: $16a^2$.

7. Find the moment of inertia of a spherical shell of constant density about a diameter.

Ans.: $2Ma^2/3$, M the mass and a the radius of the shell.

8. Evaluate

$$\iint\limits_S (\nabla \times \boldsymbol{\phi})\cdot\mathbf{n}\,d\sigma \quad \text{and} \quad \iint\limits_S f(x, y, z)\boldsymbol{\phi}\cdot\mathbf{n}\,d\sigma$$

if $\boldsymbol{\phi} = (x + 2y)\mathbf{i} - 3z\mathbf{j} + x\mathbf{k}$, $f(x, y, z) = 4x + 3y - 2z$, S: $2x + y + 2z = 6$, $x = 0$, $x = 1$, $y = 0$, $y = 2$, $z = 0$.

Ans.: 9/2.

9. Show that $\iint\limits_S x\,d\sigma = 0$ for any regular surface that is symmetric about the origin.

10. Show that if S: $z = f(x, y)$, R_{xy}, then

$$\iint\limits_S P\,dy\,dz + Q\,dx\,dz + R\,dx\,dy$$

$$= \pm\iint\limits_{R_{xy}} \left\{-P[x, y, f(x, y)]\frac{\partial f}{\partial x} - Q[x, y, f(x, y)]\frac{\partial f}{\partial y} + 1\right\} dx\,dy.$$

11. Show that

$$\iint_S P\,dy\,dz + Q\,dz\,dx + R\,dx\,dy = \pm \iint_{R_{uv}} \left[P\frac{\partial(y, z)}{\partial(u, v)} + Q\frac{\partial(z, x)}{\partial(u, v)} + R\frac{\partial(x, y)}{\partial(u, v)} \right] du\,dv.$$

(See Exercise 9, p. 123.)

12. Let S be any bounded plane surface in space. With S we can associate the vector $\mathbf{S}$, which has the direction of the unit normal vector chosen on S and length equal to the area of S.

(a) Show that if S_1, S_2, S_3, S_4 are the faces of a tetrahedron, then $\mathbf{S}_1 + \mathbf{S}_2 + \mathbf{S}_3 + \mathbf{S}_4 = \mathbf{0}$. (*Hint:* Express $\mathbf{S}_1$, $\mathbf{S}_2$, $\mathbf{S}_3$, $\mathbf{S}_4$ in terms of a, b, c, three concurrent edges of the tetrahedron.) Extend this result to any arbitrary convex polyhedron of n faces.

(b) Show that $\iint_S \boldsymbol{\phi}\cdot d\boldsymbol{\sigma} = 0$ for any convex closed surface, $\boldsymbol{\phi}$ constant. [*Hint:* Use the generalization in (a).]

(c) Prove the distributive law for the vector product: $\mathbf{a} \times (\mathbf{b} \times \mathbf{c}) = \mathbf{a} \times \mathbf{b} + \mathbf{a} \times \mathbf{c}$, by letting $\mathbf{a}$, $\mathbf{b}$, $\mathbf{c}$, $\mathbf{b} + \mathbf{c}$ be the edges of a triangular prism.

(d) The points P, Q, R divide the sides BC, CA, AB of the triangle ABC in the ratio 1:2. The pairs of lines (AP, BQ), (BQ, CR), (CR, AP) intersect at X, Y, Z, respectively. Show that the area of triangle XYZ is $\frac{1}{7}$ the area of triangle ABC.

5. The divergence theorem and its applications.

One of the vector forms of the equation in Green's theorem (see p. 120) is

$$\oint_C \boldsymbol{\phi}\cdot\mathbf{n}\,ds = \iint_R \nabla\cdot\boldsymbol{\phi}\,dx\,dy.$$

If we replace the plane region R by a region T in space, the line integral by a surface integral of a function over a closed surface, and the double integral by a triple integral, then formally we obtain

$$\iint_S \boldsymbol{\phi}\cdot\mathbf{n}\,d\sigma = \iiint_T \operatorname{div}\boldsymbol{\phi}\,dV,$$

where $dV = dx\,dy\,dz$ is the element of volume. We are now ready to state precisely and prove this generalization of Green's theorem—it is known (for obvious reasons) as

THE DIVERGENCE THEOREM. If (1) $\boldsymbol{\phi} = P\mathbf{i} + Q\mathbf{j} + R\mathbf{k}$ and its partial derivatives are continuous in an open region D in space; (2) S is a regular surface in D, forming the boundary of a bounded closed region T in D; and (3) $\mathbf{n}$ is the outer unit normal vector to S; then

$$\iint_S \boldsymbol{\phi}\cdot\mathbf{n}\,d\sigma = \iiint_T \operatorname{div}\boldsymbol{\phi}\,dV.$$

Proof. The preceding equation in cartesian form is

$$\iint_S P\,dy\,dz + Q\,dz\,dx + R\,dx\,dy = \iiint_T \left(\frac{\partial P}{\partial x} + \frac{\partial Q}{\partial y} + \frac{\partial R}{\partial z}\right) dV.$$

Let us assume that T can be represented in the form

$$f_1(x, y) \leq z \leq f_2(x, y),$$

with (x, y) in R_{xy}, the projection of S onto the xy-plane. Let $z_1 = f_1(x, y)$ represent S_1 and $z_2 = f_2(x, y)$ represent S_2. In general, there may be a

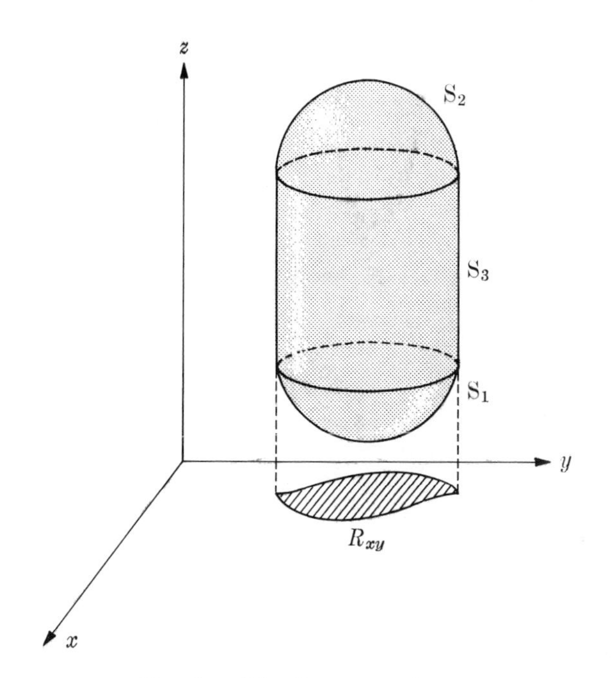

Fig. 10. The divergence theorem

cylindrical surface S_3, defined on the boundary of R_{xy}, which is surmounted by S_1 and S_2. (See Fig. 10.) Now

$$\iint_S R\,dx\,dy = \iint_{S_1} R\,dx\,dy + \iint_{S_2} R\,dx\,dy + \iint_{S_3} R\,dx\,dy.$$

The last surface integral is zero (Example 5, p. 142). Hence,

$$\iint_S R\,dx\,dy = \iint_{R_{xy}} R[x, y, f_2(x, y)]\,dx\,dy - \iint_{R_{xy}} R[x, y, f_1(x, y)]\,dx\,dy$$

(the direction of the unit normal vector to S_2 being opposite to that of S_1) and therefore

$$\iint_S R\,dx\,dy = \iint_{R_{xy}} \left[\int_{f_1(x,y)}^{f_2(x,y)} \frac{\partial R}{\partial z}\,dz\right] dx\,dy = \iiint_T \frac{\partial R}{\partial z}\,dV.$$

Similarly, it can be shown that

$$\iint_S P\,dy\,dz = \iiint_T \frac{\partial P}{\partial x}\,dV$$

and

$$\iint_S Q\,dx\,dz = \iiint_T \frac{\partial Q}{\partial y}\,dV;$$

the result is now immediate in this case.

If T is not representable in the preceding form, but can be decomposed into a finite number of subregions, each of which can be expressed in this form, then the foregoing result can be applied to each of these subregions. The student should supply the details. If, however, T does not satisfy these conditions, then a deeper investigation is necessary. The courageous student may well consult O. D. Kellogg, *Foundations of Potential Theory*, where a complete treatment appears.

EXAMPLE 1. Evaluate $I = \iint_S \boldsymbol{\phi}\cdot\mathbf{n}\,d\sigma$, $\boldsymbol{\phi} = x\mathbf{i} + y\mathbf{j} + z\mathbf{k}$, S: $x^2 + y^2 + z^2 = 1$, $-1 \le x \le 1$, $-1 \le y \le 1$.

Solution. By the divergence theorem,

$$I = 3\iiint_T dx\,dy\,dz = 3\text{ (volume of sphere)} = 4\pi.$$

The student should generalize this to the case $\boldsymbol{\phi} = ax\mathbf{i} + by\mathbf{j} + cz\mathbf{k}$, S: any closed regular surface.

EXAMPLE 2. Show that if $\boldsymbol{\phi} = \nabla f$ and $\operatorname{div}\boldsymbol{\phi} = 0$, then for a closed regular surface S that is the boundary of the region T,

$$\iiint_T \boldsymbol{\phi}^2\,dV = \iint_S f\boldsymbol{\phi}\cdot\mathbf{n}\,d\sigma.$$

Solution. $\operatorname{div} f\boldsymbol{\phi} = \nabla f\cdot\boldsymbol{\phi} + f\operatorname{div}\boldsymbol{\phi} = \boldsymbol{\phi}\cdot\boldsymbol{\phi} + 0 = \boldsymbol{\phi}^2$ (D_2, p. 92). Hence, the result follows by the divergence theorem.

EXAMPLE 3. Evaluate

$$I(S) = \iint_S x^3\,dy\,dz + x^2y\,dz\,dx + x^2z\,dx\,dy.$$

(a) S: closed surface consisting of right circular cylinder $x^2 + y^2 = 1$, $0 \le z \le 1$ and the circular discs $x^2 + y^2 = 1$, $z = 0$ and $x^2 + y^2 = 1$, $z = 1$.

(b) S*: surface in (a) with top circular disc removed; $\mathbf{n}$ = outer unit normal.

Solution. (a) By the divergence theorem,

$$\mathrm{I(S)} = \iiint_T \operatorname{div}(x^3\mathbf{i} + x^2y\mathbf{j} + x^2z\mathbf{k})\,dV = 5\iiint_T x^2\,dV$$

$$= 4.5\int_0^1\int_0^1\int_0^{\sqrt{1-y^2}} x^2\,dx\,dy\,dz = 20\int_0^1\int_0^{\pi/2}\int_0^1 r^3\cos^2\theta\,dr\,d\theta\,dz$$

$$= \frac{5\pi}{4}.$$

(b) S* is not closed and the divergence theorem is not applicable, so that we may either (1) use the result of (a) and subtract the surface integral over the top circular disc, or (2) use the second fundamental theorem. We shall do it by both methods. Let S_1 be the cylindrical surface, S_2 the bottom circular disc, and S_3 the top circular disc.

(1) $$\mathrm{I(S_3)} = \iint_{R_{xy}} x^2\,dx\,dy, \quad R_{xy}: 0 \le x^2 + y^2 \le 1$$

$$= 4\int_0^{\pi/2}\int_0^1 r^3\cos^2\theta\,dr\,d\theta = \frac{\pi}{4}.$$

Hence $\mathrm{I(S^*)} = \pi$.

(2) It is readily seen that $\mathrm{I(S_2)} = 0$. We now determine $\mathrm{I(S_1)}$. The projection of the cylinder onto the xz-plane is a square R_{xz}: $-1 \le x \le 1$, $-1 \le z \le 1$ and onto the yz-plane is a square R_{yz}: $-1 \le y \le 1$, $-1 \le z \le 1$; we have that

$$\mathrm{I(S^*)} = \int_0^1\int_0^1 (1-y^2)^{3/2}\,dy\,dz - \int_0^1\int_0^1 -(1-y^2)^{3/2}\,dy\,dz$$
$$+ \int_0^1\int_0^1 x^2\sqrt{1-x^2}\,dx\,dz - \int_0^1\int_0^1 -x^2\sqrt{1-x^2}\,dx\,dz$$

(Justify the signs!)

$$= 2\left[\int_0^1\int_0^1 (1-y^2)^{3/2}\,dy\,dz + \int_0^1\int_0^1 x^2\sqrt{1-x^2}\,dx\,dz\right] = \pi.$$

There is no question that (1) is the simpler method.

6. Stokes' theorem and its applications. The equation in Green's theorem in the vector form

$$\oint_C \boldsymbol{\phi}\cdot d\mathbf{r} = \iint_R \boldsymbol{\nabla}\times\boldsymbol{\phi}\cdot\mathbf{k}\,dx\,dy$$

(see p. 119) indicates that the double integral of the z-component of the curl of a plane vector over a region R in the xy-plane whose boundary is a simple closed curve is equal to the line integral of the tangential component of the vector on C. In generalizing this theorem to a theorem in space, we might expect to replace the double integral of the z-component of the curl of a plane vector by the surface integral of the normal component of the curl of a space vector over an orientable smooth surface, and to take the line integral of the tangential component of the vector on a simple closed curve that is the boundary of the surface. With appropriate restrictions, this is the substance of Stokes' theorem, which we now state precisely.

STOKES' THEOREM. If (1) S is a regular surface, (2) $\Gamma(S)$ is a regular closed curve that is the boundary of S, and (3) $\boldsymbol{\phi}$ and its partial derivatives are continuous in some open region that contains S, then

$$\int_\Gamma \boldsymbol{\phi}\cdot d\mathbf{r} = \iint_S \operatorname{curl}\boldsymbol{\phi}\cdot\mathbf{n}\,d\sigma,$$

where $\mathbf{r}$ is the position vector of any point on Γ, $\mathbf{n}$ is the unit normal vector to S, and the direction of Γ is that determined by the orientation of S.

Before we proceed to the proof of this theorem, let us be sure that we fully understand the phrase "the direction of Γ is that determined by the orientation of S." Since S is a regular surface, we know that it is oriented. Let S_1 be a smooth surface in S (it may be S itself) with boundary Γ_1. Choose $\mathbf{n}$ for S_1. Now the direction of Γ_1 is to be chosen so that $\mathbf{n}$, $\mathbf{T}$, $\mathbf{N}$ form a positive triple, $\mathbf{T}$ the unit tangent vector to Γ_1, $\mathbf{N}$ the inner normal vector to Γ_1. Let Γ_2 be the boundary of the smooth surface S_2 belonging to S and such that Γ_2 and Γ_1 have the same points; choose the direction of Γ_2 opposite to that of Γ_1. Continuing in this fashion, we shall have established a direction for $\Gamma(S)$.

Now let us turn to the proof of Stokes' theorem. First, we consider the case where the projections of S onto the coordinate planes are regions bounded by closed regular curves and S has the representations $z = f(x, y)$, R_{xy}; $y = g(x, z)$, R_{xz}; $x = h(y, z)$, R_{yz}. Let $\boldsymbol{\phi} = P\,dx + Q\,dy + R\,dz$. We must show that

$$\begin{aligned}\int_\Gamma \boldsymbol{\phi}\cdot d\mathbf{r} &= \int_\Gamma P\,dx + \int_\Gamma Q\,dy + \int_\Gamma R\,dz\\ &= \iint_S \nabla\times P\mathbf{i}\cdot\mathbf{n}\,d\sigma + \iint_S \nabla\times Q\mathbf{j}\cdot\mathbf{n}\,d\sigma + \iint_S \nabla\times R\mathbf{k}\cdot\mathbf{n}\,d\sigma\\ &= \iint_S \operatorname{curl}\boldsymbol{\phi}\cdot\mathbf{n}\,d\sigma.\end{aligned}$$

We show that

$$\int_\Gamma P\,dx = \iint_S \nabla\times P\mathbf{i}\cdot\mathbf{n}\,d\sigma.$$

The corresponding equations with Q and R are similarly proved; the three equations are then added to give the desired result.

Expanding,

$$\nabla\times P\mathbf{i}\cdot\mathbf{n} = \frac{\partial P}{\partial z}\mathbf{n}\cdot\mathbf{j} - \frac{\partial P}{\partial y}\mathbf{n}\cdot\mathbf{k}. \tag{1}$$

Since $\mathbf{r} = x\mathbf{i} + y\mathbf{j} + z\mathbf{k} = x\mathbf{i} + y\mathbf{j} + f(x, y)\mathbf{k}$, $\partial\mathbf{r}/\partial y = \mathbf{j} + (\partial z/\partial y)\mathbf{k}$; $\partial\mathbf{r}/\partial y$ is a vector in the tangent plane to S (why?) and hence perpendicular to $\mathbf{n}$; i.e.,

$$\mathbf{n} \cdot \frac{\partial \mathbf{r}}{\partial y} = \mathbf{n}\cdot\mathbf{j} + \frac{\partial z}{\partial y}\mathbf{n}\cdot\mathbf{k} = 0,$$

or

$$\mathbf{n}\cdot\mathbf{j} = -\left(\frac{\partial z}{\partial y}\right)\mathbf{n}\cdot\mathbf{k}.$$

Substituting in (1), we obtain

$$\nabla \times P\mathbf{i}\cdot\mathbf{n} = -\left(\frac{\partial P}{\partial y} + \frac{\partial P}{\partial z}\frac{\partial z}{\partial y}\right)\mathbf{n}\cdot\mathbf{k}.$$

By the second fundamental theorem for surface integrals, we have

$$\iint_{\mathrm{S}} \nabla \times P\mathbf{i}\cdot\mathbf{n}\, d\sigma = \pm\iint_{R_{xy}} \left(\frac{\partial P}{\partial y} + \frac{\partial P}{\partial z}\frac{\partial z}{\partial y}\right) dx\, dy.$$

By Green's theorem, the right-hand side equals $\pm\oint_{\mathrm{C}} P[x, y, f(x, y)]\, dx$ where C is the boundary of R_{xy}. But

$$\pm\oint_{\mathrm{C}} P[x, y, f(x, y)]\, dx = \pm\int_{\Gamma} P(x, y, z)\, dx.$$

(Why?) Now we choose the unit normal vector and the direction of Γ as prescribed and we have the result.

If S can be subdivided into surfaces $\mathrm{S}_1, \mathrm{S}_2, \cdots, \mathrm{S}_k$, with boundaries $\Gamma_1, \Gamma_2, \cdots, \Gamma_k$, such that each of these surfaces and boundaries is of the type considered above, then since the theorem holds for each of these surfaces, we add the surface integrals over $\mathrm{S}_1, \mathrm{S}_2, \cdots, \mathrm{S}_k$ to obtain the surface integral over S and add the line integrals on $\Gamma_1, \Gamma_2, \cdots, \Gamma_k$ to obtain the line integral on Γ. The general case is treated in Kellogg, *Foundations of Potential Theory*.

Note that Criterion III for independence of path of line integrals (p. 129) can now be completely proved:

If curl $\boldsymbol{\phi} = \mathbf{0}$ in an open region D where $\boldsymbol{\phi}$ and its partial derivatives are continuous, then $\int_{\mathrm{C}} \boldsymbol{\phi}\cdot d\mathbf{r}$ is independent of path in D.

EXAMPLE 1. Evaluate $\mathrm{I} = \iint_{\mathrm{S}} \nabla \times \boldsymbol{\phi}\cdot\mathbf{n}\, d\sigma$, $\mathrm{S}: x^2 + y^2 + z^2 = 1,\ z \geq 0$, $\boldsymbol{\phi} = (x^2 + y - 4)\mathbf{i} + 3xy\mathbf{j} + (2xz + z^2)\mathbf{k}$; $\mathbf{n}$ the outer unit normal vector. (See figure.)

Solution. I is in the form of the surface integral in Stokes' theorem. (In evaluating a surface integral, this is one of the first things to check; every surface integral is *not* of this form.) The conditions in the theorem are satisfied. Hence,

$$\mathrm{I} = \int_{\Gamma} (x^2 + y^2)\, dx + 3xy\, dy + (2xz + z^2)\, dz$$

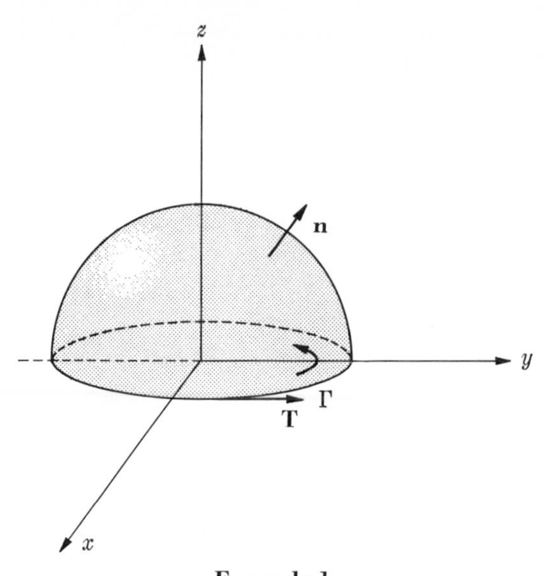

Example 1

where $\Gamma: x^2 + y^2 = 1$, $z = 0$, directed as indicated in the figure. We may choose the parametrization $\Gamma: x = \cos\theta$, $y = \sin\theta$, $z = 0$, so that

$$I = \int_0^{2\pi} (-\sin\theta + 3\cos^2\theta \sin\theta)\, d\theta = 0.$$

EXAMPLE 2. Evaluate $I = \int_C \boldsymbol{\phi} \cdot d\mathbf{r}$, $\boldsymbol{\phi} = 2y\mathbf{i} + z\mathbf{j} + 3y\mathbf{k}$, C: the intersection of $x^2 + y^2 + z^2 = 4z$ and $z = x + 2$, in a clockwise direction to an observer at the origin.

Solution. Since C is a great circle of the sphere $x^2 + y^2 + z^2 = 4z$, there is a possibility that we may use Stokes' theorem. Now $\operatorname{curl} \boldsymbol{\phi} = 2(\mathbf{i} - \mathbf{k})$, so that the integral is not independent of path. In order to use Stokes' theorem, we must find a surface S having C as its boundary and such that S has the properties indicated in the theorem. The sphere and two of its hemispheres can be parametrized so that C is the boundary of each of these surfaces. However, C is also the boundary of the circular disc, center (0, 0, 2), radius 2, and lying on the plane $z = x + 2$, and this is the simplest surface to use. For this surface $\mathbf{n} = -(\sqrt{2}/2)(\mathbf{i} - \mathbf{k})$, chosen so that $\mathbf{n}$, $\mathbf{T}$, $\mathbf{N}$ form a positive triple. Note in this case that the direction of $\mathbf{T}$ has been specified, so that we are constrained to make a specific choice for $\mathbf{n}$. Then

$$I = \iint_S \operatorname{curl} \boldsymbol{\phi} \cdot \mathbf{n}\, d\sigma = -2\sqrt{2} \iint_S d\sigma = -8\sqrt{2}\pi,$$

since the area of the circular disc is 4π.

EXERCISES

Note: Assume the conditions of the divergence theorem and Stokes' theorem to be satisfied in those cases where surfaces, regions, and functions are not explicitly specified. In all cases, $\mathbf{r} = x\mathbf{i} + y\mathbf{j} + z\mathbf{k}$.

1. Evaluate each of the following, using the divergence theorem:

(a) $\iint_S \boldsymbol{\phi}\cdot\mathbf{n}\,d\sigma$, $\boldsymbol{\phi} = 2x^2y\mathbf{i} - y\mathbf{j} + 4xz^2\mathbf{k}$, S: boundary of region bounded by $y^2 + z^2 = 9$, $x = 2$, $z = 0$, $x = 0$.

(b) $\iint_S x^2\,dy\,dz + y^2\,dz\,dx + z^2\,dx\,dy$, S: boundary of cube $0 \leq x, y, z \leq 1$.

(c) $\iint_S 2xz\,dy\,dz + y\,dz\,dx + z^2\,dx\,dy$, S: $x^2 + y^2 + z^2 = a^2$, $z \geq 0$.

(d) $\iint_S (y\mathbf{i} + x\mathbf{j} + z^2\mathbf{k})\cdot\mathbf{n}\,d\sigma$, S: cylindrical surface $x^2 + y^2 = a^2$, $z = 0$, $z = a$.

(e) $\iint_S \boldsymbol{\phi}\cdot\mathbf{n}\,d\sigma$, $\boldsymbol{\phi} = 2xy\mathbf{i} + yx^2\mathbf{j} + xz\mathbf{k}$, S: boundary of region bounded by $x = 0$, $y = 0$, $y = 3$, $z = 0$, and $x + 2z = 6$.

(f) $\iint_S \mathbf{r}\cdot\mathbf{n}\,d\sigma$, S: $z = 4 - (x^2 + y^2)$, $z \geq 0$.

(g) $\iint_S \mathbf{r}\cdot\mathbf{n}\,d\sigma$, S: $x^2 + y^2 - (1 - z)^2 = 0$, $z \geq 0$.

(h) $\iiint_T \operatorname{div}\boldsymbol{\phi}\,dV$, $\boldsymbol{\phi} = y\mathbf{i} + x\mathbf{j} + z^2\mathbf{k}$, T: region bounded by

$$z = \sqrt{1 - x^2 - y^2}, \qquad z = 0.$$

(i) $\iint_S \nabla\times\boldsymbol{\phi}\cdot\mathbf{n}\,d\sigma$, S and $\boldsymbol{\phi}$ arbitrary.

(j) $\iint_S \boldsymbol{\phi}\cdot\mathbf{n}\,d\sigma$, $\boldsymbol{\phi} = y^2\mathbf{i} + x^2\mathbf{j} + e^z\mathbf{k}$, S: $x^2 + y^2 + z^2 = 1$, $z \geq 0$.

Ans.: (a) 180; (b) 3; (c) $5\pi a^4$; (d) $\pi a^4/2$; (e) $351/2$; (f) 24π; (g) π; (h) 0; (i) 0; (j) -3π.

2. If S is closed and $\iint_S \boldsymbol{\phi}\cdot\mathbf{n}\,d\sigma = 0$, does it follow that $\boldsymbol{\phi} = 0$? Does it follow if S is not closed?

3. Let S be the boundary of a closed region T in space whose volume is V and whose centroid is $(\bar{x}, \bar{y}, \bar{z})$. Show that

(a) $V = \iint_S x\,dy\,dz = \iint_S y\,dz\,dx = \iint_S z\,dx\,dy.$

(b) $\iint_S \mathbf{r}\cdot\mathbf{n}\,d\sigma = 3V.$

(c) $\bar{x} = \dfrac{1}{6V}\iint_S x^2\,dy\,dz + 2xy\,dz\,dx + 2xz\,dx\,dy.$

Find analogous expressions for $\bar{y}$ and $\bar{z}$.

(d) $\iiint_T \operatorname{div}\mathbf{n}\,dV = \text{surface area of S}.$

(e) $\iiint_T \dfrac{dV}{r^2} = \iint_S \dfrac{\mathbf{r}\cdot\mathbf{n}}{r^2}\,d\sigma.$

4. Show that

(a) $\iiint_T \boldsymbol{\phi}\cdot\nabla f\,dV = \iint_S f\boldsymbol{\phi}\cdot\mathbf{n}\,d\sigma - \iiint_T f\nabla\cdot\boldsymbol{\phi}\,dV.$

(b) $\iiint_T f\nabla g\cdot\nabla h\,dV = \iint_S gf\nabla h\cdot\mathbf{n}\,d\sigma - \iiint_T g\nabla\cdot(f\nabla h)\,dV.$

5. If $\mathbf{x} = \frac{1}{2}\nabla\times\boldsymbol{\phi}$, $\boldsymbol{\phi} = \nabla\times\boldsymbol{\psi}$, show that

$$\iiint_T \phi^2\,dV = \iint_S (\boldsymbol{\psi}\;\boldsymbol{\phi}\;\mathbf{n})\,d\sigma + 2\iiint_T \boldsymbol{\psi}\cdot\mathbf{x}\,dV.$$

6. Show that $\iint_S r^2\mathbf{r}\cdot\mathbf{n}\,d\sigma = 5\iiint_T r^2\,dV.$

7. (a) Prove **Green's first identity:**

$$\iint_S f\nabla g\cdot\mathbf{n}\,d\sigma = \iiint_T (f\nabla^2 g + \nabla f\cdot\nabla g)\,dV.$$

(*Hint:* Use $\nabla\cdot f\boldsymbol{\phi} = \nabla f\cdot\boldsymbol{\phi} + f\nabla\cdot\boldsymbol{\phi}$.)

(b) Prove that a vector field $\boldsymbol{\phi}$ in a region T bounded by a closed regular surface S is uniquely determined if div $\boldsymbol{\phi}$ and curl $\boldsymbol{\phi}$ are given in T and $\mathbf{n}$ is given on S. (*Hint:* Assume there exist $\boldsymbol{\phi}_1 \neq \boldsymbol{\phi}_2$. Let $\boldsymbol{\psi} = \boldsymbol{\phi}_1 - \boldsymbol{\phi}_2$. Show that div $\boldsymbol{\psi} = 0$, curl $\boldsymbol{\psi} = \mathbf{0}$, $\boldsymbol{\psi} = \operatorname{grad} f$, $\nabla f\cdot\mathbf{n} = 0$, and use (a) with $f = g$ to prove $\boldsymbol{\psi} = \mathbf{0}$.)

(c) Prove **Green's second identity:**

$$\iint_S (f\nabla g - g\nabla f)\cdot\mathbf{n}\,d\sigma = \iiint_T (f\nabla^2 g - g\nabla^2 f)\,dV.$$

(d) Prove that if f and g are harmonic in T (see p. 92), then

$$\iint_S (f\nabla g - g\nabla f)\cdot\mathbf{n}\,d\sigma = 0.$$

(e) Prove that if there exists $h(x, y, z)$ such that $\nabla^2 f = hf$, $\nabla^2 g = hg$ in T, then

$$\iint_S (f\nabla g - g\nabla f)\cdot\mathbf{n}\,d\sigma = 0.$$

(f) $\nabla^2 f = -4\pi h$, $h = h(x, y, z)$, is Poisson's equation. If f and g satisfy the same Poisson equation in T and $f = g$ on S, show that $f = g$ in T.

8. With the use of Green's first and second identities (see Exercise 7), establish the following **properties of harmonic functions:**

(a) If g is harmonic in T, then $\iint_S \nabla g\cdot\mathbf{n}\,d\sigma = 0$.

(b) If f is harmonic in T, then

$$\iint_S f\nabla f\cdot\mathbf{n}\,d\sigma = \iiint_T |\nabla f|^2\,dV.$$

(c) If f is harmonic in T and $f \equiv 0$ on S, then $f \equiv 0$ in T.

(d) If f and g are harmonic in T and $f \equiv g$ on S, then $f \equiv g$ in T. Hence, if f is harmonic in T and $f = g$ on S, then there exists only one harmonic function in T (**uniqueness theorem**).

(e) If f is harmonic in T and $\nabla f\cdot\mathbf{n} = 0$ on S, then f is constant in T.

(f) If f and g are harmonic in T and $\nabla f\cdot\mathbf{n} = \nabla g\cdot\mathbf{n}$ on S, then $f = g +$ constant in T.

(g) If f and g are harmonic in T and there exists $h(x, y, z)$ such that $\nabla f\cdot\mathbf{n} = -f + h$, $\nabla g\cdot\mathbf{n} = -g + h$ on S, then $f \equiv g$ in T.

◇ **9.** Prove:

(a) If f is harmonic in a closed sphere S of radius a with center at (x_0, y_0, z_0), then

$$f(x_0, y_0, z_0) = \frac{1}{4\pi r^2}\iint_S f\,d\sigma = \frac{3}{4\pi r^2}\iiint_T f\,dV.$$

(b) If f is harmonic and not constant in a closed region T with boundary S, then f cannot have a maximum or minimum inside S.

10. Let f, ϕ_1, ϕ_2, ϕ_3 be continuous in some open region D which includes T and its boundary S. Define

$$\iint_S f\boldsymbol{\phi}\,d\sigma = \left(\iint_S f\phi_1\,d\sigma\right)\mathbf{i} + \left(\iint_S f\phi_2\,d\sigma\right)\mathbf{j} + \left(\iint_S f\phi_3\,d\sigma\right)\mathbf{k}.$$

Give a definition for $\iiint_T f\boldsymbol{\phi}\,dV$. Prove:

(a) $$\iint_S r^5\mathbf{n}\,d\sigma = 5\iiint_T r^4\mathbf{r}\,dV.$$

(b) $\iint_S \mathbf{n}\, d\sigma = \mathbf{0}.$

(c) $\iint_S (\mathbf{n} \times \boldsymbol{\phi})\, d\sigma = \iiint_T (\nabla \times \boldsymbol{\phi})\, dV.$

(d) $\iint_S \mathbf{n} \times (\mathbf{a} \times \mathbf{r})\, d\sigma = 2V\mathbf{a}$; $\mathbf{a}$, arbitrary constant vector, V = volume of T.

(e) $\iiint_T (\nabla \times \mathbf{n})\, dV = \mathbf{0}.$

(f) $\iint_S (\mathbf{r} \times \mathbf{n})\, d\sigma = \mathbf{0}.$

11. Prove that

$$\iint_S \left[\frac{1}{r}\nabla f - f\nabla\left(\frac{1}{r}\right)\right] \cdot \mathbf{n}\, d\sigma = \iiint_T \frac{\nabla^2 f}{r}\, dV + h,$$

where $h = 0$ if $(0, 0, 0)$ is outside S, $h = 4\pi f(0, 0, 0)$ if $(0, 0, 0)$ is inside S.

12. Let $\mathbf{r}_1$ and $\mathbf{r}_2$ be the position vectors of the points P_1 and P_2 on a closed surface S. Find the value of

$$\iint_S \left[\frac{1}{r_1}\nabla\left(\frac{1}{r_2}\right) - \frac{1}{r_2}\nabla\left(\frac{1}{r_1}\right)\right] \cdot \mathbf{n}\, d\sigma$$

when

(a) P_1 and P_2 are both inside S.
(b) P_1 inside S and P_2 outside S.
(c) P_1 and P_2 are both outside S.

13. Evaluate by Stokes' theorem:

(a) $\int_C \boldsymbol{\phi}\cdot d\mathbf{r}$, $\boldsymbol{\phi} = -3y\mathbf{i} + 3x\mathbf{j} + \mathbf{k}$, C: $x^2 + y^2 = 1$, $z = 2$, directed counterclockwise by an observer at the origin.

(b) $\iint_S \nabla \times \boldsymbol{\phi}\cdot\mathbf{n}\, d\sigma$, $\boldsymbol{\phi} = (x^2 + y^2 - 4)\mathbf{i} + 3xy\mathbf{j} + (2xz + z^2)\mathbf{k}$, S: $z = 4 - (x^2 + y^2)$, $\mathbf{n}$ = outer unit normal vector.

(c) $\iint_S \nabla \times \boldsymbol{\phi}\cdot\mathbf{n}\, d\sigma$, $\boldsymbol{\phi} = z^2\mathbf{i} + x^2\mathbf{j} + y^2\mathbf{k}$, S: square with vertices at $(0, 0, 1)$, $(1, 0, 1)$, $(1, 1, 1)$, $(0, 1, 1)$, $\mathbf{n} = \mathbf{k}$.

(d) $\iint_S \nabla \times \boldsymbol{\phi}\cdot\mathbf{n}\, d\sigma$, S: any closed regular surface; $\boldsymbol{\phi}$ any continuous function with continuous partial derivatives.

(e) $\int_C \boldsymbol{\phi}\cdot d\mathbf{r}$, $\boldsymbol{\phi} = x\mathbf{i} + (x + y)\mathbf{j} + (x + y + z)\mathbf{k}$, C: $x^2 + y^2 = 1$, $z = y$, directed clockwise by an observer at the origin.

(f) $\iint_S \nabla \times \boldsymbol{\phi} \cdot \mathbf{n}\, d\sigma$, $\boldsymbol{\phi}$: $(x + y)\mathbf{i} + (y - x)\mathbf{j} + x^2\mathbf{k}$, S: $x^2 + y^2 + z^2 = 1$, $z \geq 0$, $\mathbf{n}$ = outer unit normal vector.

(g) $\int_C xy\, dx + x\, dy$, C: unit circle, directed counterclockwise.

(h) $\iint_S \nabla \times \boldsymbol{\phi} \cdot \mathbf{n}\, d\sigma$, $\boldsymbol{\phi} = (z^2 - 2)\mathbf{k}$, S: $x^2 + 4(y^2 + z^2) = 4$, $z > 0$, $\mathbf{n}$ = outer unit normal vector.

Ans.: (a) 6π; (b) -4π; (c) 2; (d) 0; (e) 2π; (f) -2π; (g) π; (h) 0.

14. Verify Stokes' theorem for $\boldsymbol{\phi} = xz\mathbf{i} - y\mathbf{j} + x^2y\mathbf{k}$ where S is the boundary of the region bounded by $x = 0$, $y = 0$, $z = 0$, $2x + y + 2z = 8$, which is not included in the xz-plane.

15. If at each point of a regular surface S the vector $\boldsymbol{\phi}(x, y, z)$ is perpendicular to S, prove that either curl $\boldsymbol{\phi} = \mathbf{0}$ or $\boldsymbol{\phi}$ is everywhere tangent to S.

16. Let

$$\boldsymbol{\phi} = \frac{-y}{x^2 + y^2}\mathbf{i} + \frac{x}{x^2 + y^2}\mathbf{j} + z\mathbf{k}$$

and let D be the interior of the torus obtained by rotating the circle $(x - 2)^2 + z^2 = 1$, $y = 0$, about the z-axis. Show that curl $\boldsymbol{\phi} = \mathbf{0}$ in D, but that $\int_C \boldsymbol{\phi} \cdot d\mathbf{r} \neq 0$ when C is the circle $x^2 + y^2 = 4$, $z = 0$. Determine the possible values of the integral $\int_{(2,0,0)}^{(0,2,1)} \boldsymbol{\phi} \cdot d\mathbf{r}$ on a path in D. Explain.

Ans.: $\pi/2 \pm 2k$, $k = 0, 1, 2, \cdots$.

17. Evaluate $\int_{(1,0,0)}^{(1,0,2)} \sin yz\, dx + xz \cos yz\, dy + xy \cos yz\, dz$ on the helix $x = \cos t$, $y = \sin t$, $z = t$. *Ans.:* 0.

18. Prove Stokes' theorem when S is represented as $x = \phi_1(u, v)$, $y = \phi_2(u, v)$, $z = \phi_3(u, v)$, stipulating the necessary conditions.

19. Let S be the surface of the sphere $x^2 + y^2 + z^2 = 4$ in the first octant that is inside the cylinder $x^2 + y^2 = 2x$, having boundary Γ. Determine the values of

(a) $\int_\Gamma z\, dx - x\, dz$.

(b) $\int_\Gamma x\, dy - y\, dx$.

(c) $\int_\Gamma y\, dz - z\, dx$.

Choose the outer unit normal vector on S.

Ans.: (a) $2(3\pi - a)/3$; (b) π; (c) $8/3$.

20. Evaluate the following integrals as simply as possible, making appropriate use of the fundamental theorems for line and surface integrals, Green's theorem, the divergence theorem, Stokes' theorem, and the criteria for independence of path.

(a) $\int_{(1,-1)}^{(1,1)} (x + 2y)\, dx + yx\, dy$; along $y = -x^2$ from $(1, -1)$ to $(0, 0)$ and along $y^2 = x^3$ from $(0, 0)$ to $(1, 1)$.

(b) $\int_C \frac{x^2 - y^2}{x^2y}\,dx + \frac{y^2 - x^2}{xy^2}\,dy$ along each of the following paths: (1) (1, 1) to $(\frac{1}{2}, 2)$ along $xy = 1$; (2) the circle $(x-1)^2 + (y-1)^2 = \frac{1}{4}$ in a counterclockwise direction.

(c) $\iint_S (x^2y^2 + y^2z^2 + z^2x^2)\,d\sigma$, S: the portion of the cone $x^2 + y^2 - z^2 = 0$, cut out by the cylinder $x^2 + y^2 - 2x = 0$.

(d) $\iiint_T (xy + yz + zx)\,dV$, T: region bounded by $x = 0, y = 0, z = 0, z = 1$, $x^2 + y^2 = 1$.

(e) $\int_{(0,\pi,0)}^{(0,\pi/2,0)} \frac{\cos r}{r}(x\,dx + y\,dy + z\,dz)$, along the straight line joining $(0, \pi, 0)$ to $(0, \pi/2, 0)$.

(f) $\oint_C (x^3 + y^2)\,dx + (x^2 + y^3)\,dy$, C: pentagon with vertices at (0, 0), (1, 0), (2, 1), (1, 2), (0, 1).

(g) $\oint_C \frac{(ax - by)\,dx + (bx + ay)\,dy}{x^2 + y^2}$ along the following paths: (1) the regular hexagon with center at (0, 0) and length of side 12; (2) the rectangle with vertices at (−1, 1), (1, 1), (1, 5), (−1, 5).

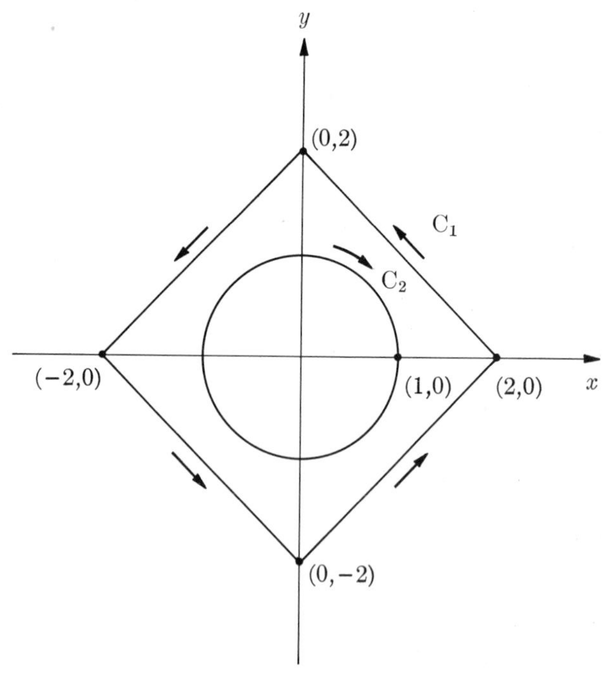

Exercise 20(i)

(h) $\int_C \boldsymbol{\phi} \cdot d\mathbf{r}$, C: $x = a \cos t, y = b \sin t, z = ct, 0 \leq t \leq 2\pi$; $\boldsymbol{\phi} = (4xy - z^3)\mathbf{i} + 2x^2\mathbf{j} - 3xz^2\mathbf{k}$.

(i) $\oint_C x^2\, dx + xy^2\, dy$, C: $C_1 + C_2$ in the accompanying figure.

(j) $\iiint_T \nabla \cdot \boldsymbol{\phi}\, dV$, S: cube with center at origin and length of side a, $\boldsymbol{\phi} = (x^2 - y^2)\mathbf{i} + 2xy\mathbf{j} + (y^2 - xy)\mathbf{k}$.

(k) $\iint_S \boldsymbol{\phi} \cdot \mathbf{n}\, d\sigma$, S: parabolic cylinder $x^2 + y = 4$, $z = 1$ in the first octant, $\boldsymbol{\phi} = (xy + y^2)\mathbf{i} + x^2y\mathbf{j}$, $\mathbf{n}$ = outer unit normal vector.

(l) $\oint_C \dfrac{(x^2 - y^2 - 1)\, dy - 2xy\, dx}{(x^2 + y^2 - 1)^2 + 4y^2}$.

(1) C: $x^2 + y^2 = \frac{1}{2}$; (2) C: $(x - 1)^2 + y^2 = 1$; (3) C: $x^2 + y^2 = 4$; (4) C = $C_1 + C_2 + C_3$, C_1: $x^2 + y^2 = 4$, C_2: $(x - 1)^2 + y^2 = \frac{1}{2}$, C_3: $(x + 1)^2 + y^2 = \frac{1}{2}$.

(m) $\oint_C xy^6\, dx + (3x^2y^5 + 6x^2)\, dy$, C: any simple closed curve.

(n) $\iint_S \nabla \times \boldsymbol{\phi} \cdot \mathbf{n}\, d\sigma$, S: $z = 1 + \sqrt{1 - x^2 - y^2}$,

$$\boldsymbol{\phi} = \frac{y^2 + z^2}{z}\mathbf{i} + \frac{z}{y^2 + z^2}\mathbf{j} + yz^2\mathbf{k},$$

$\mathbf{n}$ = outer unit normal vector.

(o) $\int_C \boldsymbol{\phi} \cdot d\mathbf{r}$, C: straight line joining $(0, 0, 0)$ and $(1, \pi/2, \pi)$, $\boldsymbol{\phi} = \sin y\mathbf{i} + (x \cos y + \cos z)\mathbf{j} - y \sin z\mathbf{k}$.

Ans.: (a) 173/120; (b) 9/4, 0; (c) $29\pi\sqrt{2}/4$; (d) 5/3; (e) 1; (f) 0; (g) 2πb, 0; (h) $8ac\pi^3$; (i) $\pi/4$; (j) 0; (k) 352/15; (l) 0, $\pi/2$, π, 0; (m) $12A\bar{x}$; (n) 0; (o) $1 - \frac{\pi}{2}$.

SUPPLEMENTARY PROBLEMS

HIGHER GEOMETRY

1. Prove: If the lines joining the corresponding vertices of two triangles are concurrent, the three pairs of corresponding sides intersect in collinear points, and conversely. **(Desargues' theorem.)**

2. Prove: If a line intersects the sides of a triangle A_1A_2, A_2A_3, A_3A_1 in B_3, B_2, B_1, then

$$A_1B_3\, A_2B_1\, A_3B_2 = A_2B_2\, A_3B_1\, A_1B_2,$$

and conversely. **(Menelaus' theorem.)**

3. Prove: If the points B_1, B_2, B_3 lie on the sides A_2A_3, A_3A_1, A_1A_2 of a triangle, and A_1B_1, A_2B_2, A_3B_3 are concurrent, then

$$A_1B_3\, A_2B_1\, A_3B_2 = -A_2B_3\, A_3B_1\, A_1B_2,$$

and conversely. **(Ceva's theorem.)**

4. Three points A_1, A_2, and A_3 lie on a line l and three points B_1, B_2, B_3 lie on another line m. Let A_1B_2 and A_2B_1 meet in P; A_1B_3 and A_3B_1 in Q; A_2B_3 and A_3B_2 in R. Prove that P, Q, R are collinear. **(Pappus' theorem.)**

5. Prove: The opposite sides of a hexagon inscribed in a conic meet in three collinear points. **(Pascal's theorem.)**

DIFFERENTIAL GEOMETRY

6. Given the curve C: $\boldsymbol{\phi}(t)$. The plane determined by the unit tangent vector $\mathbf{T}$ and the unit principal normal $\mathbf{N}$ at a point P on C is called the **osculating plane** of C at P; the plane perpendicular to $\mathbf{T}$ at P is called the **normal plane** of C at P; the plane perpendicular to $\mathbf{N}$ at P is called the **rectifying plane** of C at P.

(a) Show that the equation of the osculating plane of C at P is $(\mathbf{r} - \mathbf{r}_0)\cdot\mathbf{B} = 0$, where $\mathbf{r}$ is the position vector of any point in the plane, $\mathbf{r}_0 = \boldsymbol{\phi}(t_0)$, and $\mathbf{B}$ is the unit binormal vector to C at P. Show that the equations of the normal plane and rectifying plane of C at P are $(\mathbf{r} - \mathbf{r}_0)\cdot\mathbf{T} = 0$ and $(\mathbf{r} - \mathbf{r}_0)\cdot\mathbf{N} = 0$, where $\mathbf{r}$ is the position vector of any point in these planes.

(b) Show that if C is in a plane p and is not a straight line, then p is the osculating plane of C at every point of C. The osculating plane of a straight line is indeterminate.

(c) Show that C is a plane curve if and only if the torsion $\tau = 0$.

(d) Show that $\tau = 0$ for

$$\text{C:}\quad \frac{2t+1}{t-1}\,\mathbf{i} + \frac{t^2}{t-1}\,\mathbf{j} + (t+2)\mathbf{k}, \qquad -\infty < t < \infty,$$

and show that C lies in the plane $x - 3y + 3z = 5$.

(e) Show that C: $a \sin^2 t\,\mathbf{i} + \sin t \cos t\,\mathbf{j} + a \cos t\,\mathbf{k}$ lies on a sphere and that all its normal planes pass through the origin.

(f) Show that a curve, all of whose osculating planes are parallel to a fixed plane, is a plane curve.

7. A (cylindrical) helix is a curve defined by the property that the tangent vector at every point of the curve forms a constant angle with a fixed vector. If $\mathbf{a}$ is the fixed vector and α the constant angle, we have $\mathbf{T}\cdot\mathbf{a} = \cos\alpha = \text{constant}$.

(a) Use the Frenet-Serret formulas to show that $\mathbf{a}\cdot\mathbf{N} = 0$, and hence that $\mathbf{a}$ is parallel to the rectifying plane of the curve. Then $\mathbf{a} = \mathbf{T}\cos\alpha + \mathbf{B}\sin\alpha$. Differentiate this expression to show that $K/\tau = \tan\alpha = \text{constant}$; i.e., for a helix, the ratio of curvature to torsion is constant. Prove the converse. Study the cases $K/\tau = 0$, $K/\tau = \infty$.

(b) Show that if $\mathbf{a}$ is along the z-axis, the equation of a helix can be written in the form

$$x = \phi_1(s), \quad y = \phi_2(s), \quad z = s\cos\alpha.$$

(c) Prove: The projection of a helix on a plane perpendicular to $\mathbf{a}$ has its principal normal parallel to the corresponding principal normal of the helix, and its corresponding curvature is $K\csc^2\alpha$.

(d) Show that a necessary and sufficient condition that a curve C: $\boldsymbol{\phi}$ be a helix is that

$$(\boldsymbol{\phi}^{(\mathrm{iv})}\boldsymbol{\phi}'''\boldsymbol{\phi}'') = 0.$$

8. Given the surface S: $\boldsymbol{\phi} = \phi_1(u, v)\mathbf{i} + \phi_2(u, v)\mathbf{j} + \phi_3(u, v)\mathbf{k}$, R_{uv}. The curves $u =$ constant and $v =$ constant on S are called **parametric curves** or **coordinate curves.** These are special cases of any curve on S that can be represented as $f(u, v) = 0$.

(a) If s denotes length of arc along a curve on S, show that

$$ds^2 = d\boldsymbol{\phi}\cdot d\boldsymbol{\phi} = \left(\frac{\partial \boldsymbol{\phi}}{\partial u}\,du + \frac{\partial \boldsymbol{\phi}}{\partial v}\,dv\right)^2$$

$$= E\,du^2 + 2F\,du\,dv + G\,dv^2,$$

where

$$E = \frac{\partial \boldsymbol{\phi}}{\partial u}\cdot\frac{\partial \boldsymbol{\phi}}{\partial u}, \quad F = \frac{\partial \boldsymbol{\phi}}{\partial u}\cdot\frac{\partial \boldsymbol{\phi}}{\partial v}, \quad G = \frac{\partial \boldsymbol{\phi}}{\partial v}\cdot\frac{\partial \boldsymbol{\phi}}{\partial v}.$$

This is called the **first fundamental form for surfaces.**

(b) If the curve on S is expressed as $u = g(t)$, $v = h(t)$, then the length of the curve between two prints can be expressed as

$$\int_{t_1}^{t_2} \sqrt{E\left(\frac{du}{dt}\right)^2 + 2F\frac{du}{dt}\frac{dv}{dt} + G\left(\frac{dv}{dt}\right)^2}\,dt.$$

Show that the length of the curve $v = u$ on the sphere $x = \cos v \cos u$, $y = \cos v \sin u$, $z = \sin v$, $0 \le u \le 2\pi$, $0 \le v \le \pi$, from $u = 0$ to $u = \pi$ is $3\pi/2$.

(c) Show that the angle θ between the curves on S: $f(u, v) = 0$ and $g(u, v) = 0$ (θ is the angle between the tangent vectors at the point of intersection) is given by

$$\cos\theta = \frac{\dfrac{\partial f}{\partial v}\dfrac{\partial g}{\partial v}E + \left(\dfrac{\partial f}{\partial u}\dfrac{\partial g}{\partial v} + \dfrac{\partial f}{\partial v}\dfrac{\partial g}{\partial u}\right)F + \dfrac{\partial f}{\partial u}\dfrac{\partial g}{\partial u}G}{\sqrt{\left(\dfrac{\partial f}{\partial v}\right)^2 E - 2\dfrac{\partial f}{\partial u}\dfrac{\partial f}{\partial v}F + \left(\dfrac{\partial f}{\partial u}\right)^2 G}\sqrt{\left(\dfrac{\partial g}{\partial v}\right)^2 E - 2\dfrac{\partial g}{\partial u}\dfrac{\partial g}{\partial v}F + \left(\dfrac{\partial g}{\partial v}\right)^2 G}}.$$

Show that the angle between the curve $v = u$ and the curve $v = 0$ on the sphere in (b) is $\pi/4$.

(d) Show that two curves on S are perpendicular (orthogonal) if and only if

$$\frac{\partial f}{\partial v}\frac{\partial g}{\partial v}E + \left(\frac{\partial f}{\partial u}\frac{\partial g}{\partial v} + \frac{\partial f}{\partial v}\frac{\partial g}{\partial u}\right)F + \frac{\partial f}{\partial u}\frac{\partial g}{\partial u}G = 0.$$

(e) Show that the angle θ between the parametric curves $u =$ constant and $v =$ constant is given by

$$\cos\theta = \frac{F}{\sqrt{EG}},$$

and hence show that the condition that the parametric curves be orthogonal is $F = 0$.

(f) Show that the curves $u = ce^v \sin\alpha \cos\beta$ on the cone $x = (\sin\alpha)u \cos v$, $y = (\sin\alpha)u \sin v$, $z = (\cos\alpha)u$, where c, α, β are constants, cut the elements of the cone at a constant angle β.

9. Let $\mathbf{n}$ be the unit normal vector to S: $\boldsymbol{\phi}$, R_{uv}.

(a) Show that $-d\boldsymbol{\phi}\cdot d\mathbf{n} = e\,du^2 + 2f\,du\,dv + g\,dv^2$, where

$$e = -\frac{\partial \boldsymbol{\phi}}{\partial u}\cdot\frac{\partial \mathbf{n}}{\partial u}, \quad f = -\frac{\partial \boldsymbol{\phi}}{\partial u}\cdot\frac{\partial \mathbf{n}}{\partial v} = -\frac{\partial \boldsymbol{\phi}}{\partial v}\cdot\frac{\partial \mathbf{n}}{\partial u}, \quad g = -\frac{\partial \boldsymbol{\phi}}{\partial v}\cdot\frac{\partial \mathbf{n}}{\partial v}.$$

This is known as the **second fundamental form for surfaces.**

(b) Show that

$$e = \frac{(\partial^2\boldsymbol{\phi}/\partial u^2 \;\; \partial\boldsymbol{\phi}/\partial u \;\; \partial\boldsymbol{\phi}/\partial v)}{D},$$

$$f = \frac{(\partial^2\boldsymbol{\phi}/\partial u\,\partial v \;\; \partial\boldsymbol{\phi}/\partial u \;\; \partial\boldsymbol{\phi}/\partial v)}{D},$$

$$g = \frac{(\partial^2\boldsymbol{\phi}/\partial v^2 \;\; \partial\boldsymbol{\phi}/\partial u \;\; \partial\boldsymbol{\phi}/\partial v)}{D},$$

where $D = \sqrt{EG - F^2}$.

(c) Let C be any curve on S, passing through a point P. Define the curvature vector $\mathbf{K} = d\mathbf{T}/ds$, where s is arc length along C and $\mathbf{T}$ is the unit tangent vector. Then $|\mathbf{K}| = K$, the curvature of C at P. Express $\mathbf{K} = K_n\mathbf{N} + K_t\mathbf{T}$, where $\mathbf{N}$ is the unit principal normal at P. The coefficient K_n is called the **normal curvature** of S at P. Show that

$$K_n = \frac{e\,du^2 + 2f\,du\,dv + g\,dv^2}{E\,du^2 + 2F\,du\,dv + G\,dv^2}.$$

(d) It is clear that K_n depends on C. Let C: $f(u, v) = 0$, R_{uv}. Show that

$$K_n = \frac{e + 2f\lambda + g\lambda^2}{E + 2F\lambda + G\lambda^2}, \qquad \lambda = \frac{-(\partial f/\partial u)}{\partial f/\partial v}.$$

The sum and product of the maximum and minimum values of K_n are called the **mean curvature** and the **Gaussian curvature,** respectively. Determine these curvatures for the paraboloid of revolution $x = u\cos v$, $y = u\sin v$, $z = 1 - u^2$ at the point $u = \pi/4$, $v = 1$.

(e) Show that the normal curvature of a sphere is constant.

(f) Show that the surface S is a sphere or a plane if and only if the second fundamental form is a multiple of the first.

(g) Show that the sum of the normal curvatures at a point of a surface on two orthogonal curves is constant.

MECHANICS

10. Let A and B be two particles moving along the curves C_1 and C_2. Let $\mathbf{r}_1$ and $\mathbf{r}_2$ be the position vectors of these particles. Let $\mathbf{r} = \mathbf{r}_2 - \mathbf{r}_1$. We call $d\mathbf{r}/dt$ the **relative velocity** of B with respect to A and denote it as $v_A(B)$. Hence, $v_A(B) = v_O(A)$, where O is the origin.

(a) A man walks eastward at 3 miles per hour, and the wind appears to come from the north. He then decreases his speed to 1 mile per hour and notices that the wind comes from the northwest. What is the velocity of the wind?

Ans.: $3\mathbf{i} - 2\mathbf{j}$.

(b) Show that the relative velocity of two particles moving with the same speed v, one of which describes a circle of radius a while the other moves along the diameter, is $v(1 - \sin\theta)\mathbf{i} + v\cos\theta\,\mathbf{j}$.

11. Assume that a particle is rotating about a fixed line l with angular speed ω so that its distance from l remains constant. Define the angular velocity of the particle as the vector $\boldsymbol{\omega}$, whose length is ω and which lies along l in the direction of the thumb if the fingers move toward the palm in the direction of the rotation of the particle.

(a) Show that the velocity vector $\mathbf{v}$ of the particle is $\mathbf{v} = \boldsymbol{\omega} \times \mathbf{r}$, where $\mathbf{r}$ is the position vector of the particle with the origin on l.

(b) Show that the acceleration vector of the particle is $\mathbf{a} = \boldsymbol{\omega} \times \mathbf{v} + \boldsymbol{\alpha} \times \mathbf{r}$, where $\boldsymbol{\alpha} = d\boldsymbol{\omega}/dt$, the angular acceleration, and show that

$$\mathbf{a} = -\omega^2\mathbf{r} + \boldsymbol{\alpha} \times \mathbf{r}.$$

(c) A cube with diagonal OA, A being $(4, 4, 4)$, is rotating about this diagonal with an angular speed of 3 radians per second. Find the velocity and acceleration vectors of the point of the cube at $(1, 3, 2)$.

12. The **torque** or **moment of a force** $\mathbf{F}$ acting on a particle of mass m about a point O is defined as $\mathbf{M} = \mathbf{r} \times \mathbf{F}$, where $\mathbf{r}$ is the position vector of the particle relative to O. The **angular momentum** of the particle is defined as $\mathbf{H} = \mathbf{r} \times m\mathbf{v}$, where $\mathbf{v}$ is the velocity of the particle. Show that $\mathbf{M} = d\mathbf{H}/dt$; i.e., the torque is equal to the time rate of change of angular momentum. Does m have to be constant for this result to hold? Extend this result to a system of n particles.

13. The force acting on a planet due to the sun is $F = -(GmM\mathbf{r}/r^3)$, where G is the gravitational constant, m and M are the masses of the planet and sun, and $\mathbf{r}$ is the position vector of any point on the planet, the sun being at the origin.

(a) Using Newton's law, $\mathbf{F} = m\, d\mathbf{v}/dt$, show that

$$\frac{d}{dt}(\mathbf{r} \times \mathbf{v}) = \mathbf{r} \times \left(-\frac{GM\mathbf{r}}{r^3}\right) = \mathbf{0}$$

and hence $\mathbf{r} \times d\mathbf{r}/dt = \mathbf{h}$, a constant vector. Now show that $2dA/dt = h$, where A is the area swept out by $\mathbf{r}$, and thus prove that equal areas are swept out in equal intervals of time **(Kepler's first law of planetary motion).**

(b) Show that $(d/dt)(\mathbf{v} \times \mathbf{h}) = -(GM/r^3)\mathbf{r} \times (\mathbf{r} \times \mathbf{v})$. Writing $\mathbf{v} = d\mathbf{r}/dt = r(d\mathbf{R}/dt) + (dr/dt)\mathbf{R}$, where $\mathbf{r} = r\mathbf{R}$, $\mathbf{R}$ a unit vector, show that

$$\frac{d}{dt}(\mathbf{v} \times \mathbf{h}) = GM\,\frac{d\mathbf{R}}{dt}.$$

Integrating and dotting both sides by $\mathbf{r}$, prove that $h^2 = GMr + rw\cos\theta$, where $\mathbf{w}$ is the vector constant of integration and θ is the angle between $\mathbf{R}$ and $\mathbf{w}$. Choose the direction of the constant vector $\mathbf{w}$ along the polar axis so that (r, θ) are polar coordinates and establish the equation

$$r = \frac{h^2/GM}{1 + (w/GM)\cos\theta},$$

which is the polar equation of a conic.

(c) Show that the conic in (b) is the ellipse

$$r = \frac{ep}{1 + e\cos\theta}, \qquad e = k/GM,\ p = h^2/w,$$

the length of whose major axis is

$$2a = \frac{2h^2}{GM(1 - e^2)}$$

and the length of the minor axis is

$$2b = 2a\sqrt{1 - e^2}.$$

This is **Kepler's second law of planetary motion** (the orbits of the planets are ellipses with the sun at one of the foci).

(d) Since the area of the ellipse is $A = \pi ab$ and $dA/dt = h/2$, show that the period for one complete revolution is

$$T = 2\pi a \sqrt{\frac{a}{GM}}$$

and thus

$$T^2 = \frac{4\pi^2}{GM} a^3;$$

i.e., the square of the periods of revolution of the planets are proportional to the cubes of the mean distances from the sun **(Kepler's third law of planetary motion).**

HYDRODYNAMICS

14. (a) Let $\boldsymbol{\phi}$ be defined in an open region R in space. Let P be any point in R and let S_r denote the surface of a sphere of radius r with center at P and enclosing volume V_r. Show that at P,

$$\text{div}\,\boldsymbol{\phi} = \lim_{r \to 0} \frac{1}{V_r} \iint_{S_r} \boldsymbol{\phi} \cdot \mathbf{n}\, d\sigma.$$

(*Hint:* Show that $\iiint_{R_r} \text{div}\,\boldsymbol{\phi}\, dx\, dy\, dz = \text{div}\,\boldsymbol{\phi}(x', y', z')V_r$, for some x', y', z' in R_r, the region enclosed by S_r, by the law of the mean for integrals, and then use the divergence theorem to complete the proof.) This expression for the divergence of a vector function is often taken as its definition; it has the advantage that it is independent of a coordinate system and furthermore, as we shall see, that it is subjected to a simple physical interpretation. If this is taken as the definition, then all properties of divergence, including our definition, and the divergence theorem, must stem from it. This approach is used for example in Sokolnikoff and Redheffer, *Mathematics of Physics and Modern Engineering*, McGraw-Hill Book Company, Inc., New York, 1958, p. 384.

(b) Let $\boldsymbol{\phi} = \rho\mathbf{u}$, where $\mathbf{u}$ is the velocity vector of a fluid motion and ρ is the density of the fluid. Then $\mathbf{u} \cdot \mathbf{n}\, d\sigma$ measures the volume of fluid crossing a surface element per unit of time and $\rho\mathbf{u} \cdot \mathbf{n}\, d\sigma$ measures its mass; hence,

$$\iint_{S_r} \rho\mathbf{u} \cdot \mathbf{n}\, d\sigma$$

is a measure of the rate at which the fluid mass is leaving R_r through S_r. But at a point P, this is the rate at which the density is decreasing.

Establish the **continuity equation of hydrodynamics:**

$$\frac{\partial \rho}{\partial t} + \text{div}\,(\rho u) = 0.$$

(c) A fluid is **incompressible** if its density is a constant. Show that the velocity vector of an incompressible fluid is solenoidal.

(d) Show that at a point P,

$$\text{curl}\,\boldsymbol{\phi}\cdot\mathbf{n} = \lim_{r\to 0}\frac{1}{A_r}\int_{C_r}\boldsymbol{\phi}\cdot\mathbf{T}\,ds,$$

where P is the center of a circle C_r of radius r enclosing a region of area A_r. If $\mathbf{n}$ is taken as $\mathbf{i}$, $\mathbf{j}$, $\mathbf{k}$ successively, then the three components of curl $\boldsymbol{\phi}$ are obtained. This is often taken as the definition of curl $\boldsymbol{\phi}$.

(e) Let $\boldsymbol{\phi} = \mathbf{u}$ be the velocity vector of a fluid. $\int_{C_r}\mathbf{u}\cdot\mathbf{T}\,ds$ is a measure of the extent to which the corresponding fluid motion is a rotation around the circle C_r in the positive direction; it is called the **circulation** around C_r. Show that at a point, curl $\mathbf{u}$ is the circulation per unit area. What is the physical interpretation of curl $\mathbf{u} = \mathbf{0}$? This explains the use of the term **irrotational.**

HEAT CONDUCTION

15. Let $T(x, y, z)$ be the temperature at the point (x, y, z) of a body in which heat is conducted. Let $\mathbf{u}$ denote the velocity vector of heat flow. Then $\iint_S \mathbf{u}\cdot\mathbf{n}\,d\sigma$ indicates the number of calories crossing S in the direction of $\mathbf{n}$ per unit time. A fundamental law of heat conduction states that $\mathbf{u} = -k\nabla T$; k is called the **thermal conductivity,** which we shall assume to be constant and positive. Heat is not created (no sources) nor destroyed (no sinks).

The rate at which heat is absorbed per unit mass is measured by $c\,(\partial T/\partial t)$, where c is the specific heat, which we shall assume to be constant.

Let S be a closed surface that bounds a region R in the body.

(a) Show that $\iiint_R k\,\text{div}\,\nabla T\,dV = -\iint_S \mathbf{u}\cdot\mathbf{n}\,d\sigma.$

(b) Show that the rate at which R is receiving heat is $\iiint_R c\rho(\partial T/\partial t)dV$, where ρ is the density of the body.

(c) Establish the fundamental **heat equation:**

$$\nabla^2 T = a\frac{\partial T}{\partial t},$$

where $a = c(\rho/k)$.

(d) Show that T is harmonic if T is independent of time; i.e., the temperature distribution of the body is in a steady-state condition.

ELECTRICITY AND MAGNETISM

16. Maxwell's equations, which are the fundamental equations of electricity and magnetism, are

$$\gamma\,\text{curl}\,\mathbf{E} = -\frac{\partial \mathbf{B}}{\partial t} \quad\text{and}\quad \gamma\,\text{curl}\,\mathbf{H} = \frac{\partial \mathbf{D}}{\partial t} + \beta\mathbf{J},$$

where $\mathbf{E}$ = electric field intensity, $\mathbf{D}$ = electric flux density, $\mathbf{H}$ = magnetic field intensity, $\mathbf{B}$ = magnetic flux density, $\mathbf{J}$ = current density, and γ and β are constants. The following relations hold: $\mathbf{D} = \epsilon\mathbf{E}$, $B = \mu\mathbf{H}$, $\mathbf{J} = \sigma\mathbf{E}$, where ϵ, μ, σ are constants.

(a) Establish the equation of continuity for charge flow:

$$\nabla\cdot\mathbf{J} + \frac{\partial\rho}{\partial t} = 0,$$

where ρ is the charge density. [See Problem 14(b).]

(b) Use the second Maxwell equation to establish **Kirchoff's second law:**

$$\nabla\cdot\left[\mathbf{J} + \frac{1}{\beta}\frac{\partial\mathbf{D}}{\partial t}\right] = 0.$$

(c) Show that $\nabla\cdot\mathbf{B}$ = constant. (*Hint:* Take the divergence of both sides of the first Maxwell equation.) It can be shown experimentally that this constant is zero. Hence, $\mathbf{B}$ is solenoidal; i.e., there are no true magnetic charges.

(d) Show that

$$\nabla^2\mathbf{E} - \frac{\beta\mu\sigma}{\gamma}\frac{\partial\mathbf{E}}{\partial t} - \frac{\mu\epsilon}{\sigma^2}\frac{\partial^2 E}{\partial t^2} = \nabla(\nabla\cdot\mathbf{E}) = -\frac{\beta}{\sigma}\nabla\rho.$$

(*Hint:* Take the curl of both sides of the first Maxwell equation, express $\mathbf{B}$ in terms of $\mathbf{H}$, and finally express $\mathbf{D}$ in terms of $\mathbf{E}$ and $\mathbf{J}$ in terms of $\mathbf{E}$, and use the continuity equation.) If $\mathbf{E}$ is solenoidal, the equation becomes the **wave equation.** Derive the analogous equation for $\mathbf{H}$.

ADVANCED VECTOR ANALYSIS

17. If we rotate the coordinate axes about the origin, we obtain a new set of coordinate axes. Let (x, y, z) be the coordinates of a point P with reference to the original coordinate axes and (x', y', z') the coordinates of P with reference to the new coordinate axes.

(a) Show that

$$\begin{aligned} x' &= a_{11}x + a_{12}y + a_{13}z, \\ y' &= a_{21}x + a_{22}y + a_{23}z, \\ z' &= a_{31}x + a_{32}y + a_{33}z, \end{aligned}$$

where

$$\begin{aligned} a_{11} &= \mathbf{i}\cdot\mathbf{i}', & a_{12} &= \mathbf{i}\cdot\mathbf{j}', & a_{13} &= \mathbf{i}\cdot\mathbf{k}', \\ a_{21} &= \mathbf{j}\cdot\mathbf{i}', & a_{22} &= \mathbf{j}\cdot\mathbf{j}', & a_{23} &= \mathbf{j}\cdot\mathbf{k}', \\ a_{31} &= \mathbf{k}\cdot\mathbf{i}', & a_{32} &= \mathbf{k}\cdot\mathbf{j}', & a_{33} &= \mathbf{k}\cdot\mathbf{k}', \end{aligned}$$

$\mathbf{i}'$, $\mathbf{j}'$, $\mathbf{k}'$ being the unit vectors along the new coordinate axes.

(b) Show that

$$\sum_{p=1}^{3} a_{pm}a_{pn} = \delta_{mn},$$

where

$$\delta_{mn} = \begin{cases} 0, & m \neq n \\ 1, & m = n \end{cases}.$$

δ_{mn} is called the **Kronecker delta.**

(c) Show that if $f(x, y, z)$ is a scalar, invariant with respect to a rotation of axes; i.e., $f(x, y, z)$ remains the same, show that ∇f is invariant under this rotation.

(d) If $\boldsymbol{\phi}$ is invariant with respect to a rotation of axes, show that div $\boldsymbol{\phi}$ and curl $\boldsymbol{\phi}$ are invariant under this rotation.

(e) If **a**, **b**, **c** are invariant under a rotation, show that $\mathbf{a} + \mathbf{b}$, $\mathbf{a}\cdot\mathbf{b}$, $\mathbf{a} \times \mathbf{b}$, $(\mathbf{a}\,\mathbf{b}\,\mathbf{c})$, and $\mathbf{a} \times (\mathbf{b} \times \mathbf{c})$ are invariant under this rotation.

(f) Show that ∇ and the Laplacian ∇^2 are invariant operators under a rotation.

◇ **18.** Let the rectangular coordinates x, y, z be expressed in terms of new coordinates u, v, w by the equations

$$x = \psi_1(u, v, w), \quad y = \psi_2(u, v, w), \quad z = \psi_3(u, v, w),$$

and let us assume that these equations can be solved to express u, v, w in terms of x, y, z. Hence, any point with coordinates (x, y, z) has corresponding coordinates (u, v, w); let us assume that this correspondence is unique. If v and w are constant, the preceding equations represent a curve, the u-curve; similarly, we have v-curves and w-curves. These curves are referred to as **coordinate curves.** Given any point P in space; through P pass a u-curve, a v-curve, and a w-curve. We shall choose the coordinates u, v, w so that these curves are mutually perpendicular; these coordinates are then called **orthogonal curvilinear coordinates.**

(a) Show that if $\mathbf{r} = x\mathbf{i} + y\mathbf{j} + z\mathbf{k}$, then if s_u represents arc length along the u-curve, a tangent vector to the u-curve is

$$\mathbf{U} = \frac{\partial \mathbf{r}}{\partial s_u}\frac{ds_u}{du}.$$

Similarly, we have the tangent vectors

$$\mathbf{V} = \frac{\partial \mathbf{r}}{\partial s_v}\frac{ds_v}{dv} \quad \text{and} \quad \mathbf{W} = \frac{\partial \mathbf{r}}{\partial s_w}\frac{ds_w}{dw}$$

along the v-curve and w-curve.

Let

$$\mathbf{e}_u = \frac{\partial \mathbf{r}}{\partial s_u}, \quad \mathbf{e}_v = \frac{\partial \mathbf{r}}{\partial s_v}, \quad \mathbf{e}_w = \frac{\partial \mathbf{r}}{\partial s_w};$$

these are unit tangent vectors to the coordinate curves. Choose their direction so that $\mathbf{e}_u$, $\mathbf{e}_v$, $\mathbf{e}_w$ form a positive triple. We now have $\mathbf{U} = h_u\mathbf{e}_u$, $h_u = ds_u/du$; $\mathbf{V} = h_v\mathbf{e}_v$, $h_v = ds_v/dv$; $\mathbf{W} = h_w\mathbf{e}_w$, $h_w = ds_w/dw$.

(b) Show that

(1) $ds^2 = h_u^2\,du^2 + h_v^2\,dv^2 + h_w^2\,dw^2$.

(2) $dV = h_u h_v h_w\,du\,dv\,dw$.

(3) $$\nabla f = \frac{1}{h_u}\frac{\partial f}{\partial u}\mathbf{e}_u + \frac{1}{h_v}\frac{\partial f}{\partial v}\mathbf{e}_v + \frac{1}{h_w}\frac{\partial f}{\partial w}\mathbf{e}_w.$$

(4) $$\nabla\cdot\boldsymbol{\phi} = \frac{1}{h_u h_v h_w}\left[\frac{\partial}{\partial u}(h_v\,h_w\,\phi_u) + \frac{\partial}{\partial v}(h_u\,h_w\,\phi_v) + \frac{\partial}{\partial w}(h_u\,h_v\,\phi_w)\right];$$

$$\boldsymbol{\phi} = \phi_u\mathbf{e}_u + \phi_v\mathbf{e}_v + \phi_w\mathbf{e}_w.$$

(5) $$\nabla \times \boldsymbol{\phi} = \frac{1}{h_u h_v h_w}\begin{vmatrix} h_u\mathbf{e}_u & h_v\mathbf{e}_v & h_w\mathbf{e}_w \\ \dfrac{\partial}{\partial u} & \dfrac{\partial}{\partial v} & \dfrac{\partial}{\partial w} \\ h_u\phi_u & h_v\phi_v & h_w\phi_w \end{vmatrix}.$$

Note that if $h_u = h_v = h_w$ and $\mathbf{e}_u = \mathbf{i}$, $\mathbf{e}_v = \mathbf{j}$, $\mathbf{e}_w = \mathbf{k}$, and $u = x$, $v = y$, $w = z$, these expressions become the familiar ones in rectangular coordinates.

(c) For cylindrical coordinates (r, θ, z), $x = r\cos\theta$, $y = r\sin\theta$, $z = z$, $r \geq 0$, $0 \leq \theta \leq 2\pi$, $-\infty < z < \infty$, show that

(1) (r, θ, z) are orthogonal curvilinear coordinates.

(2) $h_r = 1$, $h_\theta = r$, $h_z = 1$.

(3) $ds^2 = dr^2 + r^2\,d\theta^2 + dz^2$.

(4) $dV = r\,dr\,d\theta\,dz$.

(5) $$\nabla f = \frac{\partial f}{\partial r}\mathbf{e}_r + \frac{1}{r}\frac{\partial f}{\partial \theta}\mathbf{e}_\theta + \frac{\partial f}{\partial z}\mathbf{e}_z.$$

(6) $$\nabla\cdot\boldsymbol{\phi} = \frac{1}{r}\left[\frac{\partial}{\partial r}(r\phi_r) + \frac{\partial \phi_\theta}{\partial \theta} + \frac{\partial}{\partial z}(r\phi_z)\right];\ \boldsymbol{\phi} = \phi_r\mathbf{e}_r + \phi_\theta\mathbf{e}_\theta + \phi_z\mathbf{e}_z.$$

(7) $$\nabla\times\boldsymbol{\phi} = \frac{1}{r}\begin{vmatrix} \mathbf{e}_r & r\mathbf{e}_\theta & \mathbf{e}_z \\ \dfrac{\partial}{\partial r} & \dfrac{\partial}{\partial \theta} & \dfrac{\partial}{\partial z} \\ \phi_r & \phi_\theta & \phi_z \end{vmatrix}.$$

(8) $$\nabla^2 f = \frac{1}{r}\frac{\partial}{\partial r}\left(r\frac{\partial f}{\partial r}\right) + \frac{1}{r^2}\frac{\partial^2 f}{\partial \theta^2} + \frac{\partial f}{\partial z^2}.$$

(d) For spherical coordinates (r, ϕ, θ), $x = r\sin\phi\cos\theta$, $y = r\sin\phi\sin\theta$, $z = r\cos\phi$, $r \geq 0$, $0 \leq \phi \leq \pi$, $0 \leq \theta \leq 2\pi$, show that

(1) (r, ϕ, θ) are orthogonal curvilinear coordinates.

(2) $h_r = 1$, $h_\phi = r$, $h_\theta = r\sin\phi$.

(3) $ds^2 = dr^2 + r^2\,d\phi^2 + r^2\sin^2\phi\,d\theta^2$.

(4) $dV = r^2\sin\phi\,dr\,d\phi\,d\theta$.

(5) $$\nabla f = \frac{\partial f}{\partial r}\mathbf{e}_r + \frac{1}{r}\frac{\partial f}{\partial \phi}\mathbf{e}_\phi + \frac{1}{r\sin\phi}\frac{\partial f}{\partial \theta}\mathbf{e}_\theta.$$

(6) $$\nabla\cdot\boldsymbol{\psi} = \frac{1}{r^2}\frac{\partial}{\partial r}(r^2\psi_r) + \frac{1}{r\sin\phi}\frac{\partial \psi_\phi}{\partial \phi}(\sin\phi\,\psi_\phi) + \frac{1}{r\sin\phi}\frac{\partial \psi_\theta}{\partial \theta},$$

$$\boldsymbol{\psi} = \psi_r\mathbf{e}_r + \psi_\phi\mathbf{e}_\phi + \psi_\theta\mathbf{e}_\theta.$$

(7) $$\nabla\times\boldsymbol{\psi} = \frac{1}{r^2\sin\phi}\begin{vmatrix} \mathbf{e}_r & r\mathbf{e}_\phi & r\sin\phi\,\mathbf{e}_\theta \\ \dfrac{\partial}{\partial r} & \dfrac{\partial}{\partial \phi} & \dfrac{\partial}{\partial \theta} \\ \psi_r & r\psi_\phi & (r\sin\phi)\psi_\theta \end{vmatrix}.$$

(8) $$\nabla^2 f = \frac{1}{r^2}\frac{\partial}{\partial r}\left(r^2\frac{\partial f}{\partial r}\right) + \frac{1}{r^2\sin\phi}\frac{\partial}{\partial \phi}\left(\sin\phi\frac{\partial f}{\partial \phi}\right) + \frac{1}{r^2\sin^2\phi}\frac{\partial^2 f}{\partial \theta^2}.$$

(e) Find the quantities in (b) for

(1) parabolic cylindrical coordinates (u, v, z), $x = \frac{1}{2}(u^2 - v^2)$, $y = uv$, $z = z$, $v \geq 0$, $-\infty < u, z < \infty$.

(2) paraboloidal coordinates (u, v, ϕ), $x = uv\cos\phi$, $y = uv\sin\phi$, $z = \frac{1}{2}(u^2 - v^2)$, $u \geq 0$, $v \geq 0$, $0 \leq \phi \leq 2\pi$.

(3) elliptic cylindrical coordinates (u, v, z), $x = a\cosh u\cos v$, $y = a\sinh u\sin v$, $z = z$, $u \geq 0$, $0 \leq v \leq 2\pi$, $-\infty < z < \infty$.

(4) prolate spheroidal coordinates (ξ, η, ϕ), $x = a\sinh\xi\sin\eta\cos\phi$, $y = a\sinh\xi\sin\eta\sin\phi$, $z = a\cosh\xi\cos\eta$, $\xi \geq 0$, $0 \leq \eta \leq \pi$, $0 \leq \phi \leq 2\pi$.

(f) Express the heat equation $\nabla^2 T = a(\partial T/\partial t)$ in spherical coordinates if T is independent of (1) θ, (2) θ and ϕ, (3) r and t, (4) θ, ϕ, and t.

Ans.: (1) $\dfrac{\partial T}{\partial t} = a\left[\dfrac{1}{r^2}\dfrac{\partial}{\partial r}\left(r^2 \dfrac{\partial T}{\partial r}\right) + \dfrac{1}{r^2 \sin\phi}\dfrac{\partial}{\partial \phi}\left(\sin\phi \dfrac{\partial T}{\partial \phi}\right)\right]$;

(2) $\dfrac{\partial T}{\partial t} = \dfrac{a}{r^2}\dfrac{\partial}{\partial r}\left(r^2 \dfrac{\partial T}{\partial r}\right)$; (3) $\sin\phi \dfrac{\partial}{\partial \phi}\left(\sin\phi \dfrac{\partial T}{\partial \phi}\right) + \dfrac{\partial^2 T}{\partial \theta^2} = 0$; (4) $\dfrac{d}{dr}\left(r^2 \dfrac{dT}{dr}\right) = 0$.

(g) Express the velocity $\mathbf{v}$ and acceleration $\mathbf{a}$ of a particle in spherical coordinates.

Ans.: $\mathbf{v} = v_r\mathbf{e}_r + v_\phi\mathbf{e}_\phi + v_\theta\mathbf{e}_\theta$, $v_r = dr/dt$, $v_\phi = r(d\phi/dt)$, $v_\theta = r \sin\phi(d\theta/dt)$; $\mathbf{a} = a_r\mathbf{e}_r + a_\phi\mathbf{e}_\phi + a_\theta\mathbf{e}_\theta$, $a_r = (d^2r/dt^2) + r(d\phi/dt)^2 + r\sin^2\phi(d\theta/dt)^2$, $a_\phi = (1/r)(d/dt)[r^2(d\phi/dt)] + r\sin\phi\cos\phi(d\theta/dt)^2$, $a_\theta = \dfrac{1}{r\sin\phi}\dfrac{d}{dt}\left(r^2\sin^2\phi\dfrac{d\theta}{dt}\right)$.

(h) Prove that in any orthogonal curvilinear system, $\operatorname{div}\operatorname{curl}\boldsymbol{\phi} = 0$ and $\operatorname{curl}\operatorname{grad} f = \mathbf{0}$, specifying the necessary restrictions on $\boldsymbol{\phi}$ and f.

19. We have considered vectors in a three-dimensional space. A great portion of the vector analysis that we have developed can be extended to a space of n dimensions, E^n. We denote the coordinates of a point P in E^n as $(x_1, x_2, \cdots, x_n)$ and define the distance between P_1: $(x_1, x_2, \cdots, x_n)$ and P_2: $(y_1, y_2, \cdots, y_n)$ as $\sqrt{(x_1 - y_1)^2 + (x_2 - y_2)^2 + \cdots + (x_n - y_n)^2}$. Note that we continue to use the same geometric language that we use for E^3, such as point, space, distance, even though in E^n they are devoid of intuitive meaning. A vector $\mathbf{a}$ in E^n is defined to be an ordered set of n numbers, called an n-tuple, and denoted by $[a_1, a_2, \cdots, a_n]$. The zero vector $\mathbf{0}$ is the n-tuple $[0, 0, \cdots, 0]$. We define the following: If $\mathbf{a} = [a_1, a_2, \cdots, a_n]$ and $\mathbf{b} = [b_1, b_2, \cdots, b_n]$, then

(1) $h\mathbf{a} = [ha_1, ha_2, \cdots, ha_n]$, h any scalar.

(2) $\mathbf{a} + \mathbf{b} = [a_1 + b_1, a_2 + b_2, \cdots, a_n + b_n]$.

(3) $\mathbf{a}\cdot\mathbf{b} = a_1b_1 + a_2b_2 + \cdots + a_nb_n$.

(4) $|\mathbf{a}| = a = \sqrt{a_1^2 + a_2^2 + \cdots + a_n^2}$.

(a) Prove:

(1) $\mathbf{a} + \mathbf{b} = \mathbf{b} + \mathbf{a}$;
(2) $\mathbf{a} + (\mathbf{b} + \mathbf{c}) = (\mathbf{a} + \mathbf{b}) + \mathbf{c}$;
(3) $h(\mathbf{a} + \mathbf{b}) = h\mathbf{a} + h\mathbf{b}$, h any scalar;
(4) $(h + k)\mathbf{a} = h\mathbf{a} + k\mathbf{a}$, h and k any scalars;
(5) $(hk)\mathbf{a} = h(k\mathbf{a}) = k(h\mathbf{a})$, h and k any scalars;
(6) $0\mathbf{a} = \mathbf{0}$;
(7) $\mathbf{a}\cdot\mathbf{b} = \mathbf{b}\cdot\mathbf{a}$;
(8) $(\mathbf{a} + \mathbf{b})\cdot\mathbf{c} = \mathbf{a}\cdot\mathbf{c} + \mathbf{b}\cdot\mathbf{c}$;
(9) $(h\mathbf{a})\cdot\mathbf{b} = h(\mathbf{a}\cdot\mathbf{b})$, h any scalar;
(10) $\mathbf{a}\cdot\mathbf{a} \geq 0$;
(11) $\mathbf{a}\cdot\mathbf{a} = 0$ if and only if $\mathbf{a} = \mathbf{0}$.

(b) A set of vectors $\mathbf{a}_1, \mathbf{a}_2, \cdots, \mathbf{a}_n$ is said to be linearly independent if the equation

$$c_1\mathbf{a}_1 + c_2\mathbf{a}_2 + \cdots + c_n\mathbf{a}_n = \mathbf{0}$$

implies $c_1 = c_2 = \cdots = c_n = 0$. Show that the vectors $\mathbf{e}_1 = [1, 0, \cdots, 0]$, $\mathbf{e}_2 = [0, 1, 0, \cdots, 0]$, $\cdots$, $\mathbf{e}_n = [0, 0, \cdots, 0, 1]$ are linearly independent. They form a **basis** for vectors in E^n and are a generalization of the basis $\mathbf{i}, \mathbf{j}, \mathbf{k}$ in E^3. It can be shown that $n + 1$ linearly independent vectors do not exist in E^n (see Kaplan, *Advanced Calculus*, p. 162). Hence, show that, given any vector $\mathbf{a}$ in E^n, we have the representation

$$\mathbf{a} = a_1\mathbf{e}_1 + a_2\mathbf{e}_2 + \cdots + a_n\mathbf{e}_n.$$

(c) Show that for any two vectors $\mathbf{a}$, $\mathbf{b}$, $|\mathbf{a}\cdot\mathbf{b}| \le |\mathbf{a}|\,|\mathbf{b}|$ with equality only when $\mathbf{a}$ and $\mathbf{b}$ are linearly dependent. **(Cauchy-Schwarz inequality.)** Define the angle θ between $\mathbf{a}$ and $\mathbf{b}$ by the equation

$$\cos\theta = \frac{\mathbf{a}\cdot\mathbf{b}}{|\mathbf{a}|\,|\mathbf{b}|}, \quad 0 \le \theta \le \pi.$$

Why is the Cauchy-Schwarz inequality necessary in order to define θ in this manner?

(d) $\mathbf{a}$ and $\mathbf{b}$ are **orthogonal** if $\mathbf{a}\cdot\mathbf{b} = 0$. The set of nonzero vectors $\mathbf{a}_1, \mathbf{a}_2, \cdots, \mathbf{a}_n$ is an orthogonal set if every pair of vectors in the set is orthogonal. Show that an orthogonal set of vectors is linearly independent. Show that the basis for vectors in E^n is an orthogonal set.

(e) We define an m-tuple vector function of n variables $\boldsymbol{\phi}$ so that

$$\boldsymbol{\phi}(x_1, x_2, \cdots, x_n) = \phi_1(x_1, x_2, \cdots, x_n)\mathbf{e}_1 + \phi_2(x_1, x_2, \cdots, x_n)\mathbf{e}_2 + \cdots + \phi_m(x_1, x_2, \cdots, x_n)\mathbf{e}_m,$$

in some part of E^n, where $\phi_1, \phi_2, \cdots, \phi_m$ are scalar functions of n variables. If these scalar functions are differentiable at a point, then we define

$$\frac{\partial\boldsymbol{\phi}}{\partial x_i} = \frac{\partial\phi_1}{\partial x_i}\mathbf{e}_1 + \frac{\partial\phi_2}{\partial x_i}\mathbf{e}_2 + \cdots + \frac{\partial\phi_m}{\partial x_i}\mathbf{e}_m, \qquad i = 1, 2, \cdots, n,$$

and say that $\boldsymbol{\phi}$ is differentiable at the point. Given the differentiable scalar function f, we define the gradient of f as

$$\text{grad}\, f = \nabla f = \frac{\partial f}{\partial x_1}\mathbf{e}_1 + \frac{\partial f}{\partial x_2}\mathbf{e}_2 + \cdots + \frac{\partial f}{\partial x_n}\mathbf{e}_n,$$

and given a differentiable vector function $\boldsymbol{\phi} = \phi_1\mathbf{e}_1 + \phi_2\mathbf{e}_2 + \cdots + \phi_n\mathbf{e}_n$, we define the divergence of $\boldsymbol{\phi}$ as

$$\text{div}\,\boldsymbol{\phi} = \nabla\cdot\boldsymbol{\phi} = \frac{\partial\phi_1}{\partial x_1} + \frac{\partial\phi_2}{\partial x_2} + \cdots + \frac{\partial\phi_n}{\partial x_n}.$$

The generalization of the curl of a vector function to E^n requires the use of tensors and will not be considered here.

Let H be a scalar function of the variables $x_1, x_2, \cdots, x_{2n}$. Define the vector function $\boldsymbol{\phi} = \phi_1\mathbf{e}_1 + \phi_2\mathbf{e}_2 + \cdots + \phi_{2n}\mathbf{e}_{2n}$ so that

$$\phi_i = \frac{\partial H}{\partial x_{i+n}}, \qquad i = (1, 2, \cdots, n),$$

$$\phi_i = \frac{\partial H}{\partial x_{i-n}}, \qquad i = (n + 1, \cdots, 2n).$$

Show that $\text{div}\,\boldsymbol{\phi} = 0$.

20. We define a **vector space** (linear space) X to be a set of elements x, y, z, $\cdots$ such that every pair of elements x and y in X can be combined by an operation called **addition** to yield another element $z = x + y$ in X and such that every element x in X and every number (real or complex, or to the algebraically wise, element in a field) α can be combined by a process called **multiplication** to yield the element αx in X, these operations being defined so that the following properties are satisfied:

(1) $x + y = y + x$.
(2) $x + (y + z) = (x + y) + z$.
(3) There exists a unique element, denoted by e, in X such that $x + e = x$ for every x in X.
(4) There exists for every x in X a unique element, denoted by $-x$, such that $x + (-x) = e$.
(5) $\alpha(x + y) = \alpha x + \alpha y$, for any number α.
(6) $(\alpha + \beta)x = \alpha x + \beta x$, for any numbers α and β.
(7) $\alpha(\beta x) = (\alpha\beta)x$, for any numbers α, β.
(8) $1x = x$ for every x in X.
(9) $0x = 0$ for every x in X.

Problem 19 indicates that the set of n-tuples with the given definitions of addition and scalar multiplication form a vector space.

(a) Let $[a, b]$ be a finite closed interval on the real axis and let x denote a continuous real-valued function whose value at the point t in $[a, b]$ is $x(t)$. Let $C[a, b]$ denote the set of all such functions. Define $z = x_1 + x_2$ so that $z(t) = x_1(t) + x_2(t)$ and $y = \alpha x$ so that $y(t) = \alpha x(t)$ for any t in $[a, b]$. Show that $C[a, b]$ is a vector space.

(b) A **normed vector space** X is a vector space such that for every x in X there exists a real number, denoted by $||x||$, called the **norm** of x, with the properties

(1) $||x_1 + x_2|| \leq ||x_1|| + ||x_2||$,
(2) $||\alpha x|| = |\alpha|\, ||x||$,
(3) $||x|| \geq 0$,
(4) $||x|| = 0$ if and only if $x = e$.

Show that the set of n-tuples in E^n with $||\mathbf{a}|| = \sqrt{a_1^2 + \cdots + a_n^2}$ is a normed vector space. Show that $C[a, b]$ with $||x|| = \max\limits_{a \leq t \leq b} |x(t)|$ is a normed vector space.

The definition of a vector space enables us to give a sophisticated treatment of three-dimensional vectors as directed line segments. Two directed line segments l_1 and l_2 are equivalent if l_1 can be made to coincide with l_2 in the same direction by a parallel displacement; we write $l_1 \equiv l_2$. The set of all directed line segments can be divided into classes such that every directed line segment belongs to some class and l_1 and l_2 belong to the same class if and only if $l_1 \equiv l_2$. Let us denote these classes as A, B, C, $\cdots$. It is clear that no two of these classes contain the same directed line segment. We now define operations on these classes. We define the sum $A + B$ as the class of all directed line segments of the form $l_1 + l_2$ where l_1 is in A and l_2 is in B, $l_1 + l_2$ being the sum of two directed line segments, defined on p. 7. We define the product aA, where a is any scalar, as the class of all directed line segments of the form al where l is in A and al is the product of a directed line segment and a scalar, defined on p. 5. We now let O be the set of points in three-dimensional space and define $O + A = A$. It is now readily seen that O, A, B, $\cdots$ with the indicated operations of addition and scalar multiplication form a vector space. We call each of these classes a vector. The student may find it difficult to conceive of a class of directed line segments as being a vector. But such a definition is a precise formulation of the notion of vector from which the whole of three-dimensional vector analysis can be deduced rigorously. In practice, one merely chooses a convenient representative of the class for the particular purpose at hand; a survey of our previous treatment of the subject will reveal that this is essentially what we have done.

SUGGESTED REFERENCES

Books on Vector Analysis

Brand, Louis. *Vector and Tensor Analysis.* New York: John Wiley & Sons, Inc., 1947. A complete treatise on vector analysis with substantial chapters on all applications.

Coburn, Nathaniel. *Vector and Tensor Analysis.* New York: The Macmillan Company, 1955. Although the format makes it difficult to spot the essentials of vector analysis, the material is carefully presented with good illustrative examples.

Coffin, Joseph. *Vector Analysis.* New York: John Wiley & Sons, Inc., 1911. This is an older work but still serviceable for its many exercises, applications to mechanics, hydrodynamics, and electrical theory, and a collection of the pertinent formulas of vector analysis.

Davis, Harry F. *Introduction to Vector Analysis.* Boston, Mass.: Allyn and Bacon, Inc., 1961. An elementary treatment of the basic ideas of vector analysis peppered by many witty remarks. A full chapter is devoted to generalizations—sighting new horizons and opening up extensive avenues so that the student is afforded a forward glance into modern vector analysis.

Hay, G. E. *Vector and Tensor Analysis.* New York: Dover Publications, Inc., 1953. Good chapters on solid analytic geometry of vectors and applications of vectors to mechanics.

Lass, Harry. *Vector and Tensor Analysis.* New York: McGraw-Hill Book Co., Inc., 1950. The essentials of vector analysis in a pleasing format, a high degree of mathematical rigor, and substantial chapters on mechanics, hydrodynamics and elasticity, and static and dynamic electricity.

Newell, Homer E., Jr. *Vector Analysis.* New York: McGraw-Hill Book Co., Inc., 1955. The basic elements of vector analysis together with a good chapter on curvilinear coordinates. Applications to mechanics and especially to electromagnetic theory.

Phillips, H. B. *Vector Analysis.* New York: John Wiley & Sons, Inc., 1933. The standard material on vector analysis with emphasis on the physical approach to vectors. Electrostatic fields, harmonic functions, and potential theory occupy a large portion of the applications.

Schwartz, Green, and Rutledge. *Vector Analysis with Applications to Geometry and Physics,* New York: Harper & Bros., 1960. A good presentation of all the aspects of vector analysis with many illustrative examples and detailed chapters on differential geometry, harmonic functions, electrostatics, magnetism and electrodynamics, statics, kinematics, and dynamics.

Spiegel, Murray R. *Theory and Problems of Vector Analysis.* New York: Schaum Publishing Company, 1959. The emphasis is on the presentation of vector analysis via worked-out examples and a large number of supplementary exercises complete with answers.

Wills, A. P. *Vector Analysis with an Introduction to Tensor Analysis.* New York: Dover Publications, 1958. This is a reprint of a classical work which still has many points of interest—a historical introduction, the basic elements of vector analysis, and many applications.

Other Books of Interest

APOSTOL, TOM M. *Mathematical Analysis, A Modern Approach to Advanced Calculus.* Reading, Mass.: Addison-Wesley Publishing Company, Inc., 1957. A completely rigorous treatment of vector analysis, including a mathematically acceptable proof of Green's theorem and a careful treatment of surfaces and surface integrals.

BUCK, R. CREIGHTON. *Advanced Calculus,* 2nd ed. New York: McGraw-Hill Book Co., Inc., 1965. An excellent treatment of curves and surfaces; this is real sophisticated vector analysis—very rewarding for the reader who allows himself to offer no resistance.

GOLDSTEIN, HERBERT. *Classical Mechanics.* Reading, Mass.: Addison-Wesley Publishing Company, Inc., 1950. The present-day standard work on mechanics, using vector analysis.

KAPLAN, WILFRED. *Advanced Calculus.* Reading, Mass.: Addison-Wesley Publishing Company, Inc., 1952. A good mathematical treatment of the elements of vector analysis.

KELLOGG, O. D. *Foundations of Potential Theory.* New York: Frederick Ungar Publishing Co. A rigorous treatment of Green's theorem, the divergence theorem, and Stokes' theorem is one of the many topics presented—all with careful mathematical techniques.

MILNE-THOMAS, L. M. *Theoretical Hydrodynamics,* 4th ed. New York: The Macmillan Company, Inc., 1960. An exhaustive treatise on hydrodynamics, using vector analysis.

STRATTON, J. A. *Electromagnetic Theory.* New York: McGraw-Hill Book Co., Inc., 1941. Electrical theory, using vector methods.

STRUIK, DIRK J. *Lectures on Classical Differential Geometry.* Reading, Mass.: Addison-Wesley Publishing Company, Inc., 1950. An excellent elementary account of differential geometry employing vector methods.

TAYLOR, ANGUS E. *Introduction to Functional Analysis.* New York: John Wiley & Sons, Inc., 1958. An introduction to the abstract approach of vector spaces and its applications to other branches of mathematics.

WIDDER, DAVID V. *Advanced Calculus,* 2nd ed. Englewood Cliffs, N. J.: Prentice-Hall, Inc., 1961. The new edition employs the dot-cross notation in a sound mathematical setting with principal applications to differential geometry.

Part II

Complex Analysis

∫ ∫ ∫

In the real number system, equations such as

$$x^2 + 1 = 0 \tag{1}$$

$$2x^2 + 2x + 1 = 0 \tag{2}$$

$$x^4 + 64 = 0 \tag{3}$$

do not have solutions; i.e., there do not exist real numbers that, when substituted for x, yield zero for the left-hand sides of these equations. In order that we can solve these equations, we must define new numbers and also define fundamental operations on these numbers, such as addition, subtraction, multiplication, and division. Now, in order that we may be able to solve (1), one of these new numbers must be such that when it is multiplied by itself the result is -1; we call it i and actually can define i as that number with the property $i^2 = -1$. The student has solved many quadratic equations such as (2) and should have no difficulty in determining that $-1 + i$ and $-1 - i$ are its solutions; he might have some difficulty in determining $2 + 2i$, $2 - 2i$, $-2 + 2i$, $-2 - 2i$ as the solutions of (3), although he should be able to verify readily that these are indeed solutions. Working with such equations, the student has discovered that all these new numbers, called *complex numbers*, can be put in the form $a + ib$, where a and b are real numbers; furthermore, he can perform all the operations involving these numbers, just as though they were real numbers, except that he replaces i^2 by -1 whenever it occurs. In this manner, the student has discovered some important properties of complex numbers, and in so doing, he has repeated the historical development of these numbers. However, this is not a mathematically sound approach—it is too haphazard and leaves too many fundamental questions open. Let us see how the modern mathematician (with just your knowledge of complex numbers) might look at this situation.

First of all, the equations (1), (2), and (3) are special cases of the general algebraic equation (4) $a_nx^n + a_{n-1}x^{n-1} + \cdots + a_1x + a_0 = 0$, $n \geq 1$, where $a_0, a_1, \cdots, a_n$ are constant real numbers, called the *coefficients* of the equation. We know that for certain choices of these coefficients, the equation has solutions in the real number system, whereas for other choices it does not. The mathematician is quite unhappy about this state of affairs; he asks whether it is possible to extend the real number system to a system in which equation (4) will always have a solution. The starting point is to define the numbers in this new system, which we shall call *complex numbers*. To define a complex number as a number of the form $a + ib$, where a and b are real numbers, is not good, for this definition is in terms of the complex number i and uses operations that have not been defined. However, the form $a + ib$ suggests that the essential parts of a complex number are two real numbers, a and b, in a certain order. Why not, then, define a complex number as an ordered pair of real numbers? This definition has the advantage that it makes use only of the notion of real numbers, of which we presumably know a great deal. Now that a complex number has been defined, the fundamental operations on these complex numbers can be defined, and then it can actually be shown that every complex number can be written in the form $a + ib$. The set of complex numbers together with the fundamental operations on these numbers constitute the complex number system. It then remains to prove that equation (4) always has a solution in the complex number system; as a matter of fact, this will be true if the coefficients are complex numbers.

The preceding outline indicates one aspect of our program in this part. Actually, it turns out to be a small, albeit vital, aspect. We have introduced complex numbers in order to be able to always solve a general algebraic equation; however, we shall find that these complex numbers admit of many other applications. One of our problems is to determine which properties of the real numbers extend to complex numbers and which do not. Furthermore, it will be of interest to determine those properties of nonreal complex numbers that are not shared by real numbers.

Let us define a complex variable to be any complex number in a given set E of complex numbers. Now, if we assign a complex number to every complex number in E, we say that a function of a complex variable is defined. Our primary purpose in this part is to study such functions of a complex variable—their properties, their representation, and operations on them such as differentiation and integration. We shall study these functions by paralleling the development of functions of a real variable.

However, we shall discover that they enjoy many properties not shared by the corresponding functions of a real variable. Furthermore, it will become apparent that the theory of functions can achieve completeness and unity of expression only if we define these functions as functions of a complex variable.

Chapter 5

The Algebra and Geometry of Complex Numbers

1. Algebraic representation and operations. We define a **complex number** to be an ordered pair of real numbers where the word "ordered" implies that it makes a difference which real number comes first in the pair. Given two real numbers x and y in that order, we can denote the complex number that they determine by (x, y). However, we shall soon see that it is more convenient to denote this complex number by $x + iy$ (and the student will do so until the end of his days), and since later it will be convenient to refer to definitions and results in this notation, for the moment let us agree that this notation merely indicates the order of the pair of real numbers x and y and that i is merely a symbol serving to specify this order.

In the event that we want to consider a complex number as an algebraic entity without specifying the pair of real numbers that constitute it, we shall denote it by a single letter such as z, so that we have $z = x + iy$. The real number x is called the **real part** of z and is denoted by $x = \text{Re } z$, and the real number y is called the **imaginary part** of z and is denoted by $y = \text{Im } z$.† The complex number whose real and imaginary parts are zero will be denoted by 0; i.e., $0 + i \cdot 0 = 0$.

We now define the relation of equality between two complex numbers and the fundamental operations of addition, subtraction, multiplication,

† The terms *real* and *imaginary* have been bequeathed to us by the early pioneers who did not fully understand the nature of complex numbers, and evidently we are saddled with this dubious bequest. The student should consider them merely as mathematical terms and ignore their connotations in common parlance.

and division of complex numbers, denoting these by the same symbols that we use for real numbers. Let $x_1 + iy_1$ and $x_2 + iy_2$ be any two complex numbers.

E: $x_1 + iy_1 = x_2 + iy_2$ if and only if $x_1 = x_2$ *and* $y_1 = y_2$.
In particular, $x_1 + iy_1 = 0$ if and only if $x_1 = y_1 = 0$.
A: $(x_1 + iy_1) + (x_2 + iy_2) = x_1 + x_2 + i(y_1 + y_2)$.
S: $(x_1 + iy_1) - (x_2 + iy_2) = x_1 + x_2 - i(y_1 + y_2)$.
M: $(x_1 + iy_1)(x_2 + iy_2) = (x_1x_2 - y_1y_2) + i(x_2y_1 + x_1y_2)$.

D: $$\frac{x_1 + iy_1}{x_2 + iy_2} = \frac{x_1x_2 + y_1y_2}{x_2^2 + y_2^2} + i\frac{x_2y_1 - x_1y_2}{x_2^2 + y_2^2}, \qquad x_2 + iy_2 \neq 0.$$

Addition and multiplication of complex numbers have the following properties, which can readily be verified by the use of the definitions and the corresponding properties for real numbers. If z_1, z_2, z_3 are any complex numbers, then

A₁: $z_1 + z_2$ is uniquely determined.
A₂: $z_1 + z_2 = z_2 + z_1$ (commutative law for addition).
A₃: $z_1 + (z_2 + z_3) = (z_1 + z_2) + z_3$ (associative law for addition).
A₄: $z + 0 = z$ for every complex number z.
A₅: There exists a unique complex number z such that $z_1 + z = z_2$.
M₁: z_1z_2 is uniquely determined.
M₂: $z_1z_2 = z_2z_1$ (commutative law for multiplication).
M₃: $z_1(z_2z_3) = (z_1z_2)z_3$ (associative law for multiplication).
M₄: $z_1(z_2 + z_3) = z_1z_2 + z_1z_3$ (distributive law).
M₅: There exists a unique complex number $z \neq 0$ such that $z_1z = z_2$.
M₆: $z_1z_2 = 0$ if and only if either $z_1 = 0$ or $z_2 = 0$.

Now let us consider the subset $C^\#$ of the set of complex numbers with the property that if z is in $C^\#$ then $\operatorname{Im} z = 0$; i.e., the complex numbers in $C^\#$ are of the form $(a, 0)$. If R denotes the set of real numbers a, then there is a one-to-one correspondence between $C^\#$ and R. Furthermore, as the student can readily verify from the definitions of the fundamental operations:

$$(a, 0) + (b, 0) = (a + b, 0), \quad (a, 0) - (b, 0) = (a - b, 0),$$

$$(a, 0)(b, 0) = (ab, 0), \quad \frac{(a, 0)}{(b, 0)} = \left(\frac{a}{b}, 0\right), \qquad b \neq 0.$$

This means that the system consisting of $C^\#$ and the operations in $C^\#$ are essentially the same as the real number system, and we can think of the set of real numbers as being a subset of the set of complex numbers; hence, we can use the notation $(a, 0)$ and a interchangeably.

We have seen that if $\operatorname{Im} z = 0$, we obtain a real number; on the other hand, if $\operatorname{Re} z = 0$, we shall say that z is a **pure imaginary number.** What complex number is the only one that is both real and pure imaginary?

In the definition of the fundamental operations, all that we really have done is to specify the real and imaginary parts of the sum, difference, product, and quotient of two complex numbers in terms of the real and imaginary parts of these numbers. We could just as well have written, for example, $(x_1, y_1)(x_2, y_2) = (x_1x_2 - y_1y_2, x_2y_1 + x_1y_2)$. In particular, we have that $(0, 1)(0, 1) = (-1, 0)$, which means that if we now denote the complex number that is the ordered pair $(0, 1)$ by i, we do indeed have that $i^2 = -1$. Furthermore, for any real numbers x and y written as $(x, 0)$ and $(y, 0)$, we have $x + iy = (x, 0) + (0, 1)(y, 0) = (x, 0) + (0, y) = (x, y)$, which means that every complex number can be written in the form $x + iy$, where $i^2 = -1$. Moreover, the convenience of the representation $x + iy$ results from the following rule for operating with complex numbers (which the student has always used but which he can now readily verify).

In performing the fundamental operations on complex numbers, apply the usual rules of algebra; replace i^2 by -1 whenever it appears and write the result in the form $x + iy$.

EXAMPLE. Determine Re z and Im z if

$$z = \frac{(1 + 2i)(1 - i) - (2 + 3i)}{1 - i}.$$

Solution

$$z = \frac{1 + i - 2i^2 - 2 - 3i}{1 + i} = \frac{1 - 2i}{1 + i}.$$

The simplest way to write this in the form $x + iy$ is to multiply numerator and denominator by $1 - i$ so that $z = -\frac{1}{2} - \frac{3}{2}i$. Hence, Re $z = -\frac{1}{2}$, Im $z = -\frac{3}{2}$. The student should obtain the same results by using the definitions of the operations involved.

The set of complex numbers together with the fundamental operations is called the **complex number system.** It is convenient to extend the complex number system to a system that includes an element called *infinity* (denoted by ∞), for which the following operations are defined: If z is any complex number, then $z + \infty = \infty + z = \infty$; $z \cdot \infty = \infty \cdot z = \infty$, $z \neq 0$; $\infty + \infty = \infty$; $\infty \cdot \infty = \infty$; $z/\infty = 0$; $z/0 = \infty$, $z \neq 0$. The operations $\infty - \infty$, $0 \cdot \infty$, ∞/∞, $0/0$ are undefined. The complex number system together with ∞ and these operations is called the **extended complex number system.** It satisfies A_1 to A_4 and M_1 to M_4.

2. Geometric representation of complex numbers. Since a complex number is an ordered pair of real numbers, we can represent it as a point in a rectangular coordinate system such as the xy-plane. Every point in this plane then represents a unique complex number and every complex number is represented by a unique point in this plane. If $z = x + iy$ denotes any complex number thus represented, we shall now refer to the xy-plane as the **complex plane,** or the z-plane. The x-axis will be called the **real axis** and the y-axis the **imaginary axis.** Since there is a one-to-one correspondence between the points of the z-plane and the set of complex numbers, we shall use the terms *the complex number* z and *the point* z interchangeably. A complex number z is on the real axis if and only if $\operatorname{Im} z = 0$, and it is on the imaginary axis if and only if $\operatorname{Re} z = 0$.

Let P be the point in the z-plane that represents $z = x + iy$. (See Fig. 1.) Every such point P determines a vector $\overrightarrow{OP}$, which could also serve

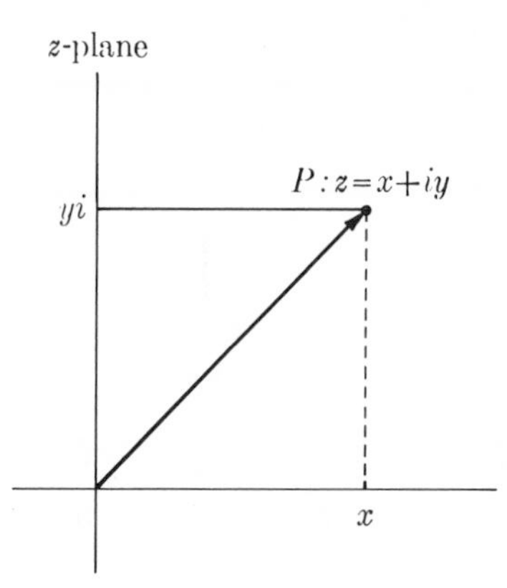

Fig. 1. The complex plane

as a geometric representation of the complex number z. We shall show that addition of vectors according to the parallelogram law is equivalent to the addition of the complex numbers that these vectors represent. Given P_1: $z_1 = x_1 + iy$, and P_2: $z_2 = x_2 + iy_2$, there exists P_3: $z_3 = x_3 + iy_3$ such that $\overrightarrow{OP_1} + \overrightarrow{OP_2} = \overrightarrow{OP_3}$. We shall establish that $z_3 = z_1 + z_2$ by showing that $x_3 = x_1 + x_2$ and $y_3 = y_1 + y_2$. Referring to Fig. 2, since the right triangles OM_2P_2 and P_1NP_3 are congruent (why?),

$$x_3 = OM_3 = OM_1 + M_1M_3 = OM_1 + P_1N = OM_1 + OM_2 = x_1 + x_2$$

and

$$y_3 = M_3P_3 = M_3N + NP_3 = P_1M_1 + P_2M_2 = y_1 + y_2.$$

The student should prove the converse.

We have shown that the definition of the addition of vectors corresponds to the definition of the addition of complex numbers. However, neither the definition of the scalar product nor the vector product of two vectors corresponds to our definition of the product of two complex numbers. For the geometric multiplication of two complex numbers, see p. 188, Exercise 16. Vector analysis affords one method of studying problems involving points in a plane, and complex analysis another. Each has its

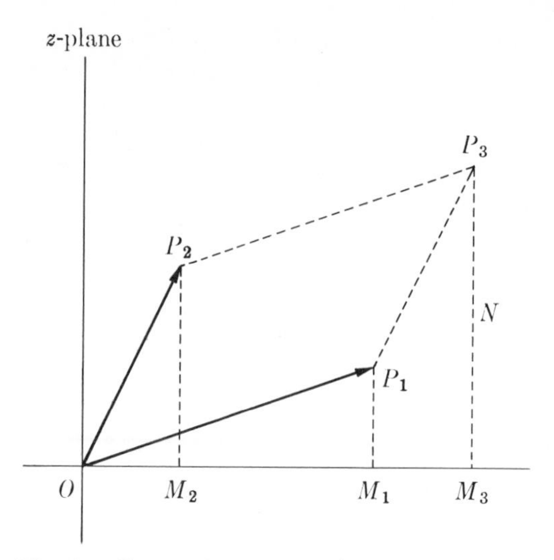

Fig. 2. Geometric addition of complex numbers

advantages, depending on the problem at hand. Vector analysis readily extends to three-dimensional space, whereas complex analysis does not. On the other hand, complex analysis enables us to treat points in the plane analogously to points on the real axis.

Let us now consider another geometric representation of complex numbers. Let the z-plane be the uv-plane in a three-dimensional coordinate system with coordinates (u, v, w). Consider the sphere $u^2 + v^2 + (w - \frac{1}{2})^2 = 1$, tangent to the uv-plane at the origin. Let us denote the point $(0, 0, 1)$ on the sphere as N (the north pole). See Fig. 3. Now any line passing through N and any other point P on the sphere will intersect the z-plane in a point P', representing the complex number z. We shall now represent z as the point P on the sphere. Thus, we can represent the set of complex numbers as points on a sphere; such a sphere will be called the **complex sphere,** the **z-sphere,** or **Riemann sphere.** Hence, to every point in the z-plane there corresponds a point in the z-sphere. The converse is not true, for there is no point in the z-plane that corresponds to N. We shall let N represent the element ∞ and call it the **point at infinity.** The principal advantage in representing complex numbers as points on a sphere is that we can represent ∞ as a point on the sphere. In other words, the z-sphere represents the extended set of complex numbers. Nevertheless, although there is no representation for ∞ in the complex plane, we shall refer to the extended complex plane as consisting of the complex plane and the point at infinity, ∞. We shall always make a careful distinction between the complex plane and the extended complex plane. The student should form the habit of visualizing the complex numbers on the complex sphere, particularly when ∞ is being considered. The procedure of setting up the

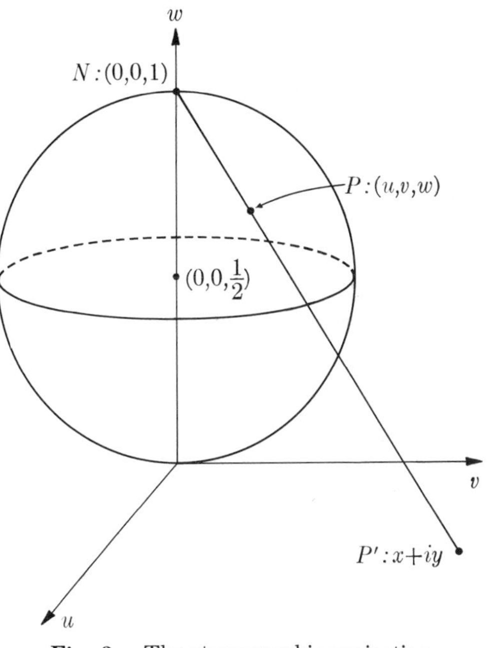

Fig. 3. The stereographic projection

correspondence between points in the z-plane and the z-sphere is actually a projection of points on the z-plane to the z-sphere, with N as the center of projection; this is called the **stereographic projection.**

3. Polar representation, absolute value, and argument. We have seen that a complex number $z = x + iy$ can be represented geometrically as a point with coordinates (x, y) in the xy-plane. If we now transform these rectangular coordinates into polar coordinates, we obtain another representation of z. Under this transformation, $x = r\cos\theta$, $y = r\sin\theta$, so that $z = r(\cos\theta + i\sin\theta)$. This representation of the complex number z is called the **polar form** (or trigonometric form) of z. We shall call the representation $z = x + iy$ the **rectangular form,** to distinguish it from the polar form.

Given a point P with rectangular coordinates (x, y) and polar coordinates (r, θ); Fig. 4 indicates these coordinates geometrically. P represents the complex number z, which can be written in the rectangular form $z = x + iy$ or the polar form $z = r(\cos\theta + i\sin\theta)$. We shall assume that $r \geq 0$, so that r can denote the length of the vector $\overrightarrow{OP}$, which is another representation of z. We shall call r the **absolute value** or **modulus** of the complex number z. We denote the absolute value of z as $|z|$. If z is in the polar form, we can determine $|z|$ by inspection. However, if $z = x + iy$, since $r = \sqrt{x^2 + y^2}$, we have $|z| = \sqrt{x^2 + y^2}$. (Why is this a generalization

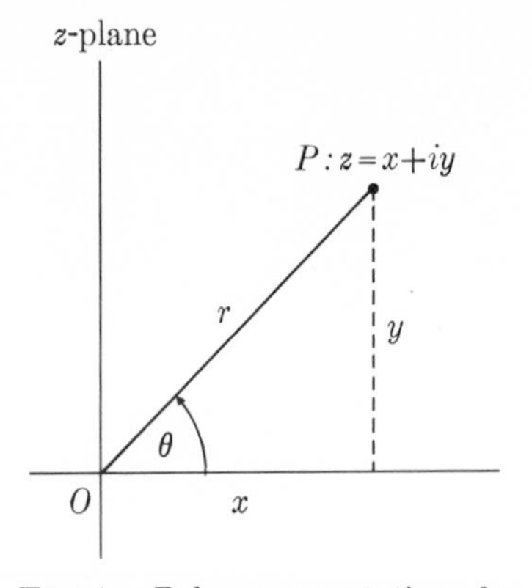

Fig. 4. Polar representation of a complex number

of the absolute value of a real number?) We have the following properties of $|z|$, readily verifiable from the definition,

$\mathbf{A_1}$: $|z| \geq 0$ for all z.
$\mathbf{A_2}$: $|z| = 0$ if and only if $z = 0$.
$\mathbf{A_3}$: $|-z| = |z|$.

Given the complex number $z \neq 0$; we represent it geometrically by the vector $\overrightarrow{OP}$. We denote the angle, measured in radians, which rotates the positive real axis into $\overrightarrow{OP}$ by θ (it is positive if this rotation is in a counterclockwise direction; otherwise it is negative). We call θ the **argument** of the complex number $z \neq 0$ (the terms amplitude and angle are also used) and denote it by $\arg z$. The argument of zero cannot be defined unambiguously and therefore we say that it is undefined. Now, since in polar coordinates $(r, \theta + 2k\pi)$, $k = 0, \pm 1, \pm 2, \cdots$ represent the same point, a complex number z has an infinity of polar forms:

$$z = r[\cos(\theta + 2k\pi) + i \sin(\theta + 2k\pi)], \qquad k = 0, \pm 1, \pm 2, \cdots.$$

Hence, $\arg z = \theta + 2k\pi$, $k = 0, \pm 1, \pm 2, \cdots$ has an infinity of values; i.e., it is multiple-valued. This can be a source of difficulty, and it is necessary to proceed with caution when one is dealing with $\arg z$. For some purposes, one of these values of $\arg z$ is sufficient, whereas for others, it is convenient to consider all of them. To make these ideas precise, let us agree that θ will always be such that $-\pi < \theta \leq \pi$ (any other interval of length 2π with one end point included and the other one not, such as $0 \leq \theta < 2\pi$, could be used). Such a value of θ will be called the **principal value** of the argument of z or the **principal argument** of z. Then we shall call $\theta + 2k\pi$, $k = \pm 1, \pm 2, \cdots$, the kth value of the argument of z, and for simplicity, we shall write $\phi = \theta + 2k\pi$, $-\pi < \theta \leq \pi$. We shall denote the principal value of the argument of z as $\arg z$ and the kth value of arg z as $\arg_k z$, so that $\arg_k z = \arg z + 2k\pi$. If z is given in polar form, then arg z and $\arg_k z$ can be determined by inspection. If, however, $z = x + iy$, then θ is equal to the value of $\tan^{-1} y/x$, which is in the same quadrant as z. The last phrase is essential, since the period of the tangent is π, and this means that for $-\pi < \theta \leq \pi$, $\tan^{-1} y/x$ has two values.

EXAMPLE. Determine $|z|$, arg z, $\arg_k z$ if
(a) $z = 1 + \sqrt{3}i$; (b) $z = -1 - \sqrt{3}i$.

Solution. $|z| = |1 + \sqrt{3}| = |-1 - \sqrt{3}| = 2$. Note that $1 + \sqrt{3}i$ is in the first quadrant and $-1 - \sqrt{3}i$ is in the third quadrant, so that $\tan^{-1}(\sqrt{3}/1) = \tan^{-1}(-\sqrt{3}/-1) = (\pi/3) + k\pi$, $k = 0, \pm 1, \cdots$. Hence, $\arg(1 + \sqrt{3}i) = (\pi/3)$ and $\arg(-1 - \sqrt{3}i) = -\frac{2}{3}\pi$. Then $\arg_k(1 + \sqrt{3}i) = \pi/3 + 2k\pi$,

$$\arg_k(-1 - \sqrt{3}i) = -\tfrac{2}{3}\pi + 2k\pi, \qquad k = \pm 1, \pm 2, \cdots.$$

The polar form of a complex number is advantageous primarily because of the following properties. If

$$z_1 = r_1(\cos\phi_1 + i\sin\phi_1), \quad z_2 = r_2(\cos\phi_2 + i\sin\phi_2), \quad z = r(\cos\phi + i\sin\phi),$$

then

P$_1$: $z_1 z_2 = r_1 r_2[\cos(\phi_1 + \phi_2) + i\sin(\phi_1 + \phi_2)]$.
P$_2$: $z_1/z_2 = r_1/r_2[\cos(\phi_1 - \phi_2) + i\sin(\phi_1 - \phi_2)]$, $z_2 \neq 0$.
P$_3$: $(\cos\phi + i\sin\phi)^n = \cos n\phi + i\sin n\phi$, n an integer. (DeMoivre's formula.)
P$_4$: $|z_1 z_2| = |z_1|\,|z_2|$.
P$_5$: $|z_1/z_2| = |z_1|/|z_2|$, $z_2 \neq 0$.
P$_6$: $|z^n| = |z|^n$, n an integer.
P$_7$: $\arg z_1 z_2 = \arg z_1 + \arg z_2 + 2\delta\pi$, where $\delta = -1$, 0, or 1, $z_1 \neq 0$, $z_2 \neq 0$, according as to whether $\pi < \arg z_1 + \arg z_1 \leq 2\pi$, $-\pi < \arg z_1 + \arg z_2 \leq \pi$, or $-2\pi < \arg z_1 + \arg z_2 \leq -\pi$.
P$_8$: $\arg z_1/z_2 = \arg z_1 - \arg z_2 + 2\delta\pi$, where $\delta = -1$, 0, or 1, $z_1 \neq 0$, $z_2 \neq 0$, according as to whether $\pi < \arg z_1 - \arg z_2 < 2\pi$, $-\pi < \arg z_1 - \arg z_2 < \pi$, or $-2\pi < \arg z_1 - \arg z_2 \leq -\pi$.
P$_9$: $\arg z^n = n\arg z + 2\pi p$, $z \neq 0$, n an integer. $p = [\frac{1}{2} - n\arg z/2\pi]$.
P$_{10}$: $\arg_p z_1 z_2 = \arg_q z_1 + \arg_r z_2$, $z_1 \neq 0$, $z_2 \neq 0$ with the appropriate choice of p, q, r.

Proofs

P$_1$:
$$\begin{aligned} z_1 z_2 &= r_1 r_2(\cos\phi_1 + i\sin\phi_1)\cdot(\cos\phi_2 + i\sin\phi_2) \\ &= r_1 r_2[(\cos\phi_1\cos\phi_2 - \sin\phi_1\sin\phi_2) \\ &\qquad + i(\sin\phi_1\cos\phi_2 + \cos\phi_1\sin\phi_2)] \\ &= r_1 r_2[\cos(\phi_1 + \phi_2) + i\sin(\phi_1 + \phi_2)]. \end{aligned}$$

P$_1$ extends to any finite number of complex numbers so that

$$z_1 z_2 \cdots z_n = r_1 r_2 \cdots r_n[\cos(\phi_1 + \cdots + \phi_n) + i\sin(\phi_1 + \cdots + \phi_n)].$$

If $z_1 = z_2 = \cdots = z_n$, we obtain P_3 for n, a positive integer; for $n = 0$, it is immediate.

$$P_2: \quad \frac{z_1}{z_2} = \frac{r_1}{r_2} \cdot \left[\frac{(\cos \phi_1 \cos \phi_2 + \sin \phi_1 \sin \phi_2) + i(\sin \phi_1 \cos \phi_2 - \cos \phi_1 \sin \phi_2)}{\cos^2 \phi_2 + \sin^2 \phi_2}\right]$$

$$= \frac{r_1}{r_2} [\cos (\phi_1 - \phi_2) + i \sin (\phi_1 - \phi_2)].$$

For n a negative integer, P_3 follows with the use of P_2. P_4 and P_5 are immediate consequences of P_1 and P_2. P_4 extends to any finite number of complex numbers and, in particular if they are equal, we obtain P_6 for n a positive integer. Then, for n a negative integer, P_6 will follow with the use of P_5. P_7 to P_{10} follow from P_1 and P_2. The student should study P_7 to P_9 carefully; otherwise he will make the error of always taking $\delta = 0$ and $p = 0$.

The rectangular form of complex numbers is desirable for addition and subtraction, and the polar form is useful for multiplication (especially for several complex numbers) and division.

EXAMPLE. Given $z_1 = 2(\cos \pi/3 + i \sin \pi/3)$, $z_2 = \sqrt{2}(\cos \frac{3}{4}\pi - i \sin \frac{3}{4}\pi)$, $z = -1 + \sqrt{3}i$. Find $z_1 + z_2$ and z^5.

Solution. $z_1 = 1 + \sqrt{3}i$, $z_2 = -1 + i$ and $z_1 + z_2 = (1 + \sqrt{3})i$. Using $\arg z = 2\pi/3$, $z = 2[\cos (2\pi/3) + i \sin (2\pi/3)]$ and

$$z^5 = 32\left(\cos \frac{10\pi}{3} + i \sin \frac{10\pi}{3}\right) = 32\left(-\frac{1}{2} - \frac{\sqrt{3}}{2}i\right) = -16 - 16\sqrt{3}i.$$

4. Conjugate complex numbers. We define the **conjugate** of $z = x + iy$ as the complex number $x - iy$ and denote it by $\bar{z}$. In other words, $\text{Re}\, \bar{z} = \text{Re}\, z$ and $\text{Im}\, \bar{z} = -\text{Im}\, z$. We have the following properties involving conjugates, which the student can prove readily by using the definition:

C₁: $\bar{\bar{z}} = z$.
C₂: $\bar{z} = z$ if and only if z is real.
C₃: $\overline{z_1 + z_2} = \bar{z}_1 + \bar{z}_2$.
C₄: $\overline{z_1 z_2} = \bar{z}_1 \bar{z}_2$.

C₅: $\overline{(z_1/z_2)} = \dfrac{\bar{z}_1}{\bar{z}_2}, \qquad z_2 \neq 0$.

C₆: $\text{Re}\, \bar{z} = \dfrac{z + \bar{z}}{2}$.

C₇: $\text{Im}\, \bar{z} = \dfrac{z - \bar{z}}{2i}$.

C₈: $|\bar{z}| = |z|$.
C₉: $z\bar{z} = |z|^2 = x^2 + y^2$.

C_3 and C_4 extend to any finite number of complex numbers; in particular, $\overline{z^n} = \bar{z}^n$, n a positive integer.

The conjugate of a complex number is useful in division, for $z_1/z_2 = z_1\bar{z}_2/z_2\bar{z}_2 = z_1\bar{z}_2/|z_2|^2$, which can now be readily written in rectangular form.

Geometrically, if z is not real, z and $\bar{z}$ are symmetric with respect to the real axis, or $\bar{z}$ is the reflection of z about the real axis. On the Riemann sphere, where is $\bar{z}$ located relative to z? How would you define the conjugate of ∞?

EXAMPLE 1. Show that if z is a root of

$$a_n z^n + a_{n-1}z^{n-1} + \cdots + a_1 z + a_0 = 0; \qquad a_n, a_{n-1}, \cdots, a_0 \text{ real},$$

then $\bar{z}$ is also a root of this equation.

Solution

$$\begin{aligned} a_n\bar{z}^n + a_{n-1}\bar{z}^{n-1} + \cdots + a_1\bar{z} + a_0 &= \bar{a}_n\bar{z}^n + \bar{a}_{n-1}\bar{z}^{n-1} + \cdots + \bar{a}_1\bar{z} + \bar{a}_0 \\ &= \overline{a_n z^n} + \overline{a_{n-1}z^{n-1}} + \cdots + \overline{a_1 z} + \bar{a}_0 \\ &= \overline{a_n z^n + a_n a^{n-1} + \cdots + a_1 z + a_0} = \overline{0} = 0. \end{aligned}$$

The student should justify each equation in this chain by citing C_1 to C_9 appropriately. This theorem is often loosely stated as, "the solutions of an equation always occur in conjugate pairs." What was the crucial point in the preceding proof? Illustrate with $(1/\sqrt{2})(1 + i)$ and $(-1/\sqrt{2})(1 + i)$ as the roots of $z^2 - i = 0$.

C_9 will prove to be a very useful property, since it is often much easier to work with $z\bar{z}$ rather than $|z|^2$. This is true for C_6 and C_7 as well.

EXAMPLE 2. Prove that if $|z| < 1$ and $w = i(1 - z)/(1 + z)$, $z \neq -1$, then $\operatorname{Im} w > 0$.

Solution

$$\begin{aligned} \operatorname{Im} w &= \frac{w - \bar{w}}{2i} = \frac{1}{2}i\left[\frac{i(1 - z)}{1 + z} + \frac{i(1 - \bar{z})}{1 + z}\right] \\ &= \frac{1}{2}\left[(1 - z)(1 + \bar{z}) + \frac{(1 - \bar{z})(1 + z)}{(1 + z)(1 + \bar{z})}\right] \\ &= \frac{1 - z\bar{z}}{(1 + z)\overline{(1 + z)}} = \frac{1 - |z|^2}{|1 + z|^2} > 0, \end{aligned}$$

since $|z| < 1$.

5. Inequalities. An important property of the real numbers is that they are ordered; i.e., given the real numbers a and b, either $a = b$, $a < b$, or $b < a$. This property of order does not extend to complex numbers in any simple or useful manner; consequently, we shall not define order for complex numbers and shall say that the set of complex numbers is unordered. Therefore, if ever $z_1 < z_2$ appears, the necessary conclusion is that

z_1 and z_2 are real numbers. As a matter of fact, if in any context we write $z_1 < z_2$, we shall not explicitly state that z_1 and z_2 are real numbers. Since, however, every complex number z determines the three real numbers $|z|$, $\operatorname{Re} z$, $\operatorname{Im} z$, we can consider inequalities involving them. We have the following important inequalities:

I₁: $\operatorname{Re} z \leq |\operatorname{Re} z| \leq |z|$.
I₂: $\operatorname{Im} z \leq |\operatorname{Im} z| \leq |z|$.
I₃: $|z_1 + z_2| \leq |z_1| + |z_2|$ (Triangle inequality).
I₄: $|z_1 - z_2| \geq ||z_1| - |z_2||$.

Proofs: I_1 and I_2 follow immediately from $|z| = \sqrt{(\operatorname{Re} z)^2 + (\operatorname{Im} z)^2}$.

I_3: $|z_1 + z_2|^2 = (z_1 + z_2)(\bar{z}_1 + \bar{z}_2) = z_1\bar{z}_1 + z_2\bar{z}_2 + z_1\bar{z}_2 + z_2\bar{z}_1 = |z_1|^2 + |z_2|^2 + z_1\bar{z}_2 + \overline{z_1\bar{z}_2} = |z_1|^2 + |z_2|^2 + 2 \operatorname{Re} z_1\bar{z}_2 \leq |z_1|^2 + |z_2|^2 + 2|z_1|\,|z_2| = (|z_1| + |z_2|)^2$ (C_9, C_1, C_6, I_1). Taking the square root of both sides of $|z_1 + z_2|^2 \leq (|z_1| + |z_2|)^2$ yields the result.

I_4: $|z_1| = |(z_1 - z_2) + z_2| \leq |z_1 - z_2| + |z_2|$ by I_3, and so (a) $|z_1| - |z_2| \leq |z_1 - z_2|$. Similarly, $|z_2| \leq |z_2 - z_1| + |z_1|$ so that (b) $|z_2| - |z_1| \leq |z_1 - z_2|$. The result follows from (a) and (b).

The student should note under what conditions the equality signs hold.

I_3 extends to any finite number of complex numbers so that

$$\mathbf{I_3'}: \quad \left|\sum_{k=1}^{n} z_k\right| \leq \sum_{k=1}^{n} |z_k.|$$

EXAMPLE. If $|z| = R$, $p(z) = a_n z^n + a_{n-1}z^{n-1} + \cdots + a_0$, $q(z) = b_m z^m + b_{m-1}z^{m-1} + \cdots + b_0$, show that

$$\text{(a)} \qquad \left|\frac{p(z)}{q(z)}\right| \leq \frac{|a_n|R^n + |a_{n-1}|R^{n-1} + \cdots + |a_0|}{||b_m|R^m - |b_{m-1}|R^{m-1} - \cdots - |b_0||},$$

and that for R sufficiently large,

$$\text{(b)} \qquad \left|\frac{p(z)}{q(z)}\right| \leq \frac{K}{R^{m-n}},$$

where K is a constant independent of R.

Solution

$$\left|\frac{p(z)}{q(z)}\right| = \frac{|p(z)|}{|q(z)|},$$

$$|p(z)| \leq |a_n|R^n + |a_{n-1}|R^{n-1} + \cdots + |a_0|$$

with the use of I_3'.

$$\begin{aligned} |q(z)| &= |b_m z^m - (-b_{m-1}z^{m-1} - \cdots - b_0)| \\ &\geq ||b_m|R^m - |b_{m-1}z^{m-1} + \cdots + b_0|| \text{ (using } I_4) \\ &\geq ||b_m|R^m - |b_{m-1}|R^{m-1} - \cdots - |b_0|| \text{ (using } I_3'). \end{aligned}$$

Since taking reciprocals of both sides inverts the inequality, we obtain (a) by considering $|p(z)| \cdot 1/|q(z)|$.

Then (b) follows from the fact that for R sufficiently large,

$$\frac{|a_n|R^n + |a_{n-1}|R^{n-1} + \cdots + |a_0|}{\big||b_m|R^m - |b_{m-1}|R^{m-1} - \cdots - |b_0|\big|} \leq \frac{(|a_n| + \cdots + |a_0|)R^n}{\big||b_m| - |b_{m-1}| - \cdots - |b_0|\big|R^m}.$$

EXERCISES

1. (a) Determine the real values of a and b for which the complex number $(2a + 3b - 5) + i(a + b - 1) = 0$.

(b) Determine the real values of a and b for which $(2a + b) + i(3a + 2b - 1)$ and $(a - b + 5) + i(a - b + 7)$ are equal.

Ans.: (a) $a = -2$, $b = 3$;
(b) $a = 1$, $b = 2$.

2. Express the following complex numbers in the form $x + iy$, where x and y are real: (a) $3 + 2i - (7 + i) + 2i$; (b) $(2 + 3i)(5 - i)$; (c) $3 - 2i/5 + 4i$; (d) $(-\frac{1}{2} + \frac{1}{2}\sqrt{3}i)^{10}$; (e) $\dfrac{1 + i}{1 - 2i} - \dfrac{i}{1 + i}$.

Ans.: (a) $-4 + 3i$; (b) $13 - 17i$; (c) $(7/\sqrt{31}) - (22/\sqrt{31})i$; (d) $-\frac{1}{2} + \frac{1}{2}\sqrt{3}i$; (e) $-(7/10) + (1/10)i$.

3. Find Re z, Im z, $|z|$, arg z of the following:

(a) $z = 1 - 2i$; (b) $z = 3 + 4i$; (c) $z = (1 - 2i)/(3 + 4i)$; (d) $z = (1 + i)^2 - (1 - i)^2$; (e) $z = 5(\cos \frac{9}{4}\pi - i \sin \frac{9}{4}\pi)$; (f) $z = -2i(3 + i)(2 + 4i)(1 + i)$; (g) $z = \dfrac{(3 + 4i)(-1 + 2i)}{(-1 - i)(3 - i)}$.

4. Determine the absolute value and the principal value of the argument of each of the following and express in polar form:

(a) -1; (b) $-2i$; (c) $4 + 2i$; (d) $3 - 3i$; (e) $-4 - 4\sqrt{3}i$.

5. Let $z_1 = 2\sqrt{3} - 2i$, $z_2 = \frac{1}{4} + (\sqrt{3}/4)i$, $z_3 = 4 + 4i$, $z_4 = -2 + 2i$. Express these numbers in polar form and find

(a) z_1z_2; (b) z_2z_3; (c) z_1/z_4; (d) z_3/z_4; (e) $(z_4)^7$; (f) $z_1z_2z_3$; (g) z_1z_3/z_4. Find the absolute values and principal arguments of these numbers.

6. If $z = x + iy$, x and y real, find the real and imaginary parts of

(a) z^3; (b) $1/z^2$; (c) $(z - 1)/(z + 1)$; (d) $z^4 - 2z$; (e) $\frac{1}{2}i[z + (1/z)]$; (f) $z + (|z|/2)$; (g) $z + 2i[\bar{z}/(z + \bar{z})]$.

7. Represent each of the following complex numbers in the complex plane:

(a) i; (b) -1; (c) $-i$; (d) $1 + i$; (e) $\sqrt{2}i$; (f) $i - 1$; (g) $i + 1$; (h) $i + 2$; (i) $2(1 + i)$; (j) $1 + 2i$; (k) $-\sqrt{3}i$; (l) $1 + (\sqrt{3}i/2)$; (m) $\sqrt{3}i - \frac{1}{2}$; (n) $-(1 + \sqrt{3}i/2)$, (o) $(1 - \sqrt{3}i/2)$.

8. If z is any nonzero complex number, represent the following in the complex plane and on the Riemann sphere:

(a) $-z$; (b) $\bar{z}$; (c) $1/z$; (d) $1/\bar{z}$; (e) $z + \bar{z}$; (f) $z - \bar{z}$; (g) iz; (h) $z/\bar{z}$; (i) $\bar{z}/z$; (j) $z + |z|$; (k) $z - |z|$, (l) $z/|z|$; (m) $|z|/z$.

9. Show, without expanding the powers, that

(a) $\left|\left(\dfrac{x + iy}{x - iy}\right)^2\right| = 1$; (b) $\left|\dfrac{(x + iy)^3}{(x - iy)^2}\right| = \sqrt{x^2 + y^2}$.

10. Determine which of the following numbers are real and which are pure imaginary, where z, z_1, z_2 are any complex numbers for which these numbers are defined:

(a) $z + \bar{z}$; (b) $z - \bar{z}$; (c) $iz\bar{z}$; (d) $z^2 - \bar{z}^2$; (e) $[(1/z + 1/\bar{z})(z + \bar{z})]/(z - \bar{z})$; (f) $z_1\bar{z}_2 - z_2\bar{z}_1$; (g) $z_1\bar{z}_2 + \bar{z}_1 z_2$; (h) $(z_1\bar{z}_2 + \bar{z}_1 z_2)/(z_1\bar{z}_1 - 1)$; (i) $(z_1\bar{z}_2 - \bar{z}_1 z_2)/i(z_1\bar{z}_1 + z_2\bar{z}_2)]$; (j) $[i(z_1\bar{z}_2 - \bar{z}_1 z_2)]/(z_1\bar{z}_2 - \bar{z}_1 z_2)$; (k) $(z_1 - z_2)/(1 - z_1 z_2)$.

◇ **11.** Show that (a) $\text{Re}\,(z_1 + z_2) = \text{Re}\, z_1 + \text{Re}\, z_2$; (b) $\text{Im}\,(z_1 + z_2) = \text{Im}\, z_1 + \text{Im}\, z_2$; (c) $\text{Re}\, z_1 z_2 = \text{Re}\, z_1 \,\text{Re}\, z_2 - \text{Im}\, z_1 \,\text{Im}\, z_2$; (d) $\text{Im}\, z_1 z_2 = \text{Re}\, z_1 \,\text{Im}\, z_2 + \text{Im}\, z_1 \,\text{Re}\, z_2$; (e) $\text{Re}\,(-iz) = \text{Im}\, z$; (f) $\text{Im}\, iz = \text{Re}\, z$.

12. Find the real and imaginary parts of the following (see Exercise 11): (a) $(3 + 2i)(-2 + i)$; (b) $z^3 - 2iz^2 + 1$, where $z = x + iy$.

13. Prove that $|z_1 + z_2|^2 + |z_1 - z_2|^2 = 2(|z_1|^2 + |z_2|^2)$ for any complex numbers z_1 and z_2. What is the geometric interpretation of this identity?

14. Solve the equations (a) $z^2 + 3 = 0$; (b) $z^2 + 2iz - 5 = 0$; (c) $z^4 - 16 = 0$; (d) $z^8 - 2z^4 + 1 = 0$; (e) $z^3 + z^2 + z + 1 = 0$. (*Hint:* Multiply both sides by $z - 1$.) *Ans.:* (a) $\pm\sqrt{3}i$; (b) $\pm 2 + i$; (c) ± 2, $\pm 2i$; (d) $\pm i$, ± 1; (e) -1, $\pm i$.

15. Show that the roots of $z^3 + 2z + 4 = 0$ are outside the unit circle. (*Hint:* Show that the maximum value of $|z^3 + 2z|$ is 3 if z is inside the unit circle.)

◇ **16.** Determine a geometric construction for the product of two complex numbers z_1 and z_2 by showing that the triangle whose vertices are 0, 1, z_1 is similar to the triangle whose vertices are 0, z_2, $z_1 z_2$. Also determine a construction for the quotient of z_1 and $z_2 \neq 0$.

17. Prove that

(a) $z + \bar{z} = 0$ if and only if $\text{Re}\, z = 0$.
(b) If $z_1 + z_2$ and $z_1\bar{z}_2$ are both real, either z_1 and z_2 are both real or $z_1 + z_2 = 0$.
(c) $z + (1/z)$ is real if and only if $\text{Im}\, z = 0$ or $|z| = 1$.
(d) If $\text{Im}\, z \neq 0$, $z/(1 + z^2)$ is real if and only if $|z| = 1$.
(e) $\text{Re}\, z_1 z_2 = |z_1|\,|z_2|$ if and only if $\arg z_2 + \arg z_1 = 2p\pi$, $p = -1$, 0, or 1.

18. Use DeMoivre's formula to express $\cos 3\phi$, $\sin 3\phi$, $\cos 4\phi$, $\sin 4\phi$, $\cos 5\phi$, and $\sin 5\phi$ in terms of $\sin\phi$ and $\cos\phi$.

19. If $z_1 \neq z_2$, $z_1 \neq 0$, show that

$$\frac{1}{z_1 - z_2} = \frac{1}{z_1} + \frac{z_2}{z_1^2} + \frac{z_2^2}{z_1^3} + \cdots + \frac{z_2^n}{z_1^{n+1}}(z_1 - z_2).$$

20. If $x_n + iy_n = (1 + i\sqrt{3})^n$, show that $x_{n-1}y_n - x_n y_{n-1} = 4^{n-1}\sqrt{3}$, n a positive integer.

◇ **21.** If z is a complex number with the property that $|z| < \epsilon$ for all $\epsilon > 0$, show that $z = 0$. (*Hint:* Assume $z \neq 0$ and let $\epsilon = |z|/2$.)

22. Show that

(a) $|z_1 - z_2| \le |z_1| + |z_2|$;
(b) $||z_1| - |z_2|| \le |z_1 + z_2|$;

(c) $|z_n - z_1| \le \sum_{k=1}^{n-1} |z_{k+1} - z_k|$;

(d) $\left|\dfrac{z_1}{z_2 + z_3}\right| \le \dfrac{|z_1|}{|z_2| - |z_3|}$, $|z_2| \neq |z_3|$.

23. If $|z_i| < 1$, $\lambda_i \geq 0$, $i = 1, 2, \cdots, n$, and $\lambda_1 + \lambda_2 + \cdots + \lambda_n = 1$, show that $|\lambda_1 z_1 + \lambda_2 z_2 + \cdots + \lambda_n z_n| < 1$.

24. (a) Show that

$$|z_1 + z_2|^2 - |1 + \bar{z}_1 z_2| = (|z_1|^2 - 1)\cdot(1 - |z_2|^2).$$

(b) If $|z_1| \leq 1$ and $|z_2| \leq 1$, show that $|z_1 + z_2| \leq |1 + \bar{z}_1 z_2|$. When does the equality sign hold?

25. Show that if $z = x + iy$, $(1/\sqrt{2})(|x| + |y|) \leq |z| \leq |x| + |y|$. (*Hint:* Assume that the left-hand inequality does not hold.)

26. Show that if $w = (z + i)/(iz + 1)$ and $\operatorname{Im} z \leq 0$, then $|w| \leq 1$.

27. Show that

(a)
$$\sum_{k=0}^{n} z^k = \frac{1 - z^{n+1}}{1 - z}, \qquad z \neq 1,$$

(b)
$$\sum_{k=0}^{n} \cos k\theta = \frac{\frac{1}{2} - \sin (n + \frac{1}{2})\theta}{2 \sin \frac{1}{2}\theta}, \qquad 0 < \theta < 2\pi,$$

(c)
$$\sum_{k=1}^{n} \sin k\theta = \frac{\frac{1}{2}\cos \frac{1}{2}\theta + \cos (n + \frac{1}{2})\theta}{2 \sin \frac{1}{2}\theta}, \qquad 0 < \theta < 2\pi.$$

(d)
$$\sum_{k=0}^{n-1} \cos (2k + 1)\theta = \frac{\sin 2n\theta}{2 \sin \theta}, \qquad 0 < \theta < \pi.$$

28. Show that the equation of the stereographic projection is

$$z = (u + iv)/(1 - w), \qquad w \neq 1,$$

and that

$$u = (z + \bar{z})/[2(|z|^2 + 1)], \quad v = (z - \bar{z})/[2i(|z|^2 + 1)], \quad w = (|z|^2)/(|z|^2 + 1),$$

and thus show that the correspondence between the points in the z-plane and the Riemann sphere, excluding the North pole, is one-to-one.

29. Prove that in the stereographic projection (see Exercise 28) straight lines in the z-plane correspond to small circles on the Riemann sphere, all passing through the center of projection.

30. Prove that if $0 < a_0 < a_1 < \cdots < a_n$, then all the roots of $P(z) = a_0 z^n + a_1 z^{n-1} + \cdots + a_n = 0$ are outside the unit circle. (*Hint:* Show that $|(1 - z)P(z)| \geq a_n - [(a_n - a_{n-1})|z| + (a_{n-1} - a_{n-2})|z|^2 + \cdots + a_0|z|^{n+1}]$. Assume $|z| \leq 1$ and arrive at a contradiction.)

6. Complex analytic geometry. We now consider some plane analytic geometry, employing complex terminology and techniques.

If z_1 and z_2 are any two points, then the distance d between them is $d = |z_1 - z_2|$. This formula can be established by expressing z_1 and z_2 in rectangular form and obtaining the familiar distance formula in rectangular coordinates. However, it is more instructive to proceed as follows: Let $P_1 = z_1$, $P_2 = z_2$, and $P_3 = -z_2$. (See Fig. 5.) P_2 and P_3 are symmetric with respect to O. There exists a point P that forms with O, P_1, P_3 a parallelogram such that $OP = |z_1 - z_2|$. But OPP_1P_2 is a parallelogram. (Why?) Hence, $OP = P_1P_2$, and since P_1P_2 is the distance between z_1 and

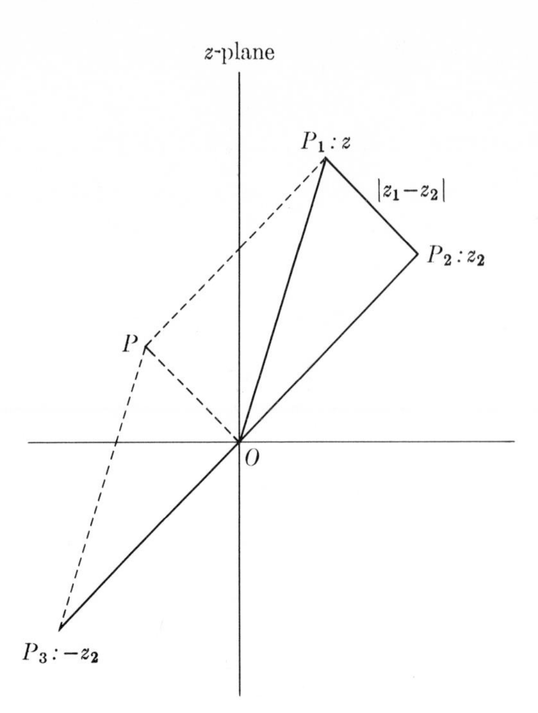

Fig. 5. The distance between two points

z_2, we have the result. Let us note in passing that $\arg(z_1 - z_2)$ is equal to the angle from the positive real axis to $\overrightarrow{P_1P_2}$.

Now let z_0 be a fixed point and $a > 0$, a constant; then the equation $|z - z_0| = a$ is satisfied by those points z, and only those points, whose distance from z_0 is a. Hence $|z - z_0| = a$ is the equation of the circle with center at z_0 and radius a. We shall call this equation the complex equation of the circle. Note the simplicity—it gives the two properties that characterize the circle, center and radius, at a glance.

The inequality $|z - z_0| < a$ is satisfied by those points z, and only those points, whose distance from z_0 is less than a. Hence $|z - z_0| < a$ represents the set of points interior to the circle $|z - z_0| = a$; similarly, $|z - z_0| > a$ represents the set of points exterior to this circle. These sets of points represent regions in the complex plane; many sets of points are conveniently represented by complex expressions such as these. At this point, the student should review p. 69, Section 6, Chapter 3. All the definitions in that section apply to regions in the complex plane, properly translated into complex language if necessary. For example, an ϵ-neighborhood of the point z_0 is the set of points z such that $|z - z_0| < \epsilon$. An ϵ-neighborhood of ∞ is the set of points z such that $|z| > \epsilon$ (can you visualize this on the Riemann sphere?).

EXAMPLES

(1) $3 \le z - i < 5$ is the region whose boundary consists of the concentric circles $|z - i| = 3$ and $|z - i| = 5$. It is neither open (the points of $|z - i| = 3$ belong to it) nor closed (the points of $|z - i| = 5$ do not belong to it). It is a bounded multiply connected region.

(2) $|\text{Re } z| > 1$ is the set of points whose real part is greater than 1 or less than -1. It consists of the half-planes $x > 1$ and $x < -1$. Since this set is not connected, it is not a region.

(3) $\text{Re }(z - iz) \ge 2$. Since $\text{Re }(z - iz) = \text{Re } z + \text{Re } iz = x + y$ (see p. 188, Exercise 11), the complex expression represents the set of points on and above the line $x + y = 2$. It is a closed, simply connected, unbounded region.

We have seen that the complex equation of a circle is $|z - z_0| = a$. Let us now consider some complex equations and determine the curves they represent. We try to avoid translating the equations into familiar rectangular forms; however, this may not always be feasible.

EXAMPLES

(1) $\text{Re }(z + 1) = |z - 3|$. Since $\text{Re }(z + 1)$ is the distance from z to the line $x = -1$ (why?), this equation is satisfied by a point z if and only if its distance from a fixed point 3 is equal to its distance from a fixed line $x = -1$. Hence, the curve is a parabola with focus at $z = 3$ and directrix $x = -1$. The student should show that the rectangular form is $y^2 = 8(x - 1)$.

(2) $|z - 1| = 2|z + 2|$. We may not be able to visualize the set of points z whose distance from 1 is twice their distance from -2. We could replace z by $x + iy$ at once; however, we can avoid calculation if we proceed as follows: $|z - 1|^2 = 4|z + 2|^2$ or $(z - 1)(\bar{z} - 1) = 4(z + 2)(\bar{z} + 2)$ or $|z|^2 + 6 \text{ Re } z + 5 = 0$. Hence, $x^2 + y^2 + 6x + 5 = 0$, which is the equation of a circle. This example illustrates that the same curve may have several complex equations. This one has the simpler equation: $|z - 3| = 2$.

(3) $|z - a| + |z - b| = k$, a and b are complex numbers $a \neq b$. This equation is satisfied by z if and only if the sum of its distances from a and b is a constant, and hence the curve is an ellipse.

(4) $\arg\left(\dfrac{z-1}{z+1}\right) = \dfrac{\pi}{2}$. In order for this to be satisfied, $\text{Re}\left(\dfrac{z-1}{z+1}\right) = 0$ and $\text{Im}\left(\dfrac{z-1}{z+1}\right) > 0$. But

$$\frac{z-1}{z+1} = \frac{z-1}{z+1} \cdot \frac{\bar{z}+1}{\bar{z}+1} = \frac{|z|^2 - 1 + 2i \text{ Im } z}{|z+1|^2}$$

and its real part is $(|z|^2 - 1)/|z + 1|^2$, which can vanish only if $|z| = 1$, and its imaginary part is positive only if $\text{Im } z > 0$. Hence, $\arg [(z - 1)/(z + 1)] = \pi/2$ is the equation of the unit semicircle, $|z| = 1$, $y > 0$.

A more sophisticated solution:

$$\frac{\pi}{2} = \arg (z - 1) - \arg (z + 1).$$

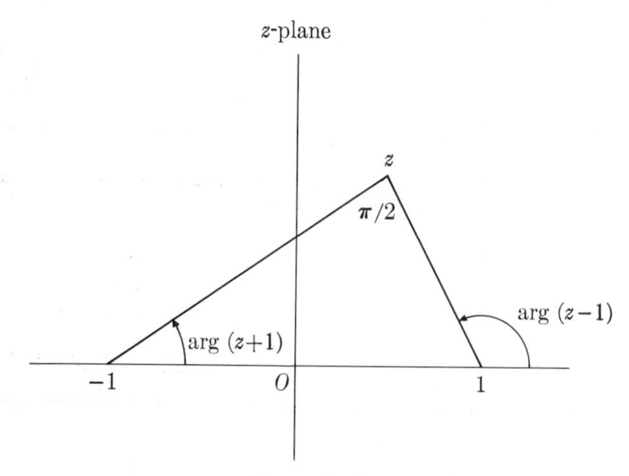

Example 4

(Why?) In the figure are shown $\pi/2$, $\arg(z - 1)$, $\arg(z + 1)$. The right triangle with vertices at -1, 1, z, with hypotenuse on the real axis, must be inscribed in the unit semicircle, and hence z must lie on that semicircle.

Many problems in analytic geometry can be solved more elegantly with the use of complex methods.

EXAMPLE. Prove that the angles at the base of an isosceles triangle are equal.

Solution. Let a be any number on the positive real axis and z_0 a point such that the triangle with vertices O, a, z_0 is an isosceles triangle. This implies that $|z_0| = |z_0 - a|$, which can be written as $z_0\bar{z}_0 = (z_0 - a)(\bar{z}_0 - a)$ or $\operatorname{Re} z_0 = a/2$. We must show that $\arg z_0 = \pi - \arg(z_0 - a)$ or $\arg z_0(z_0 - a) = \pi$. (See figure.) This

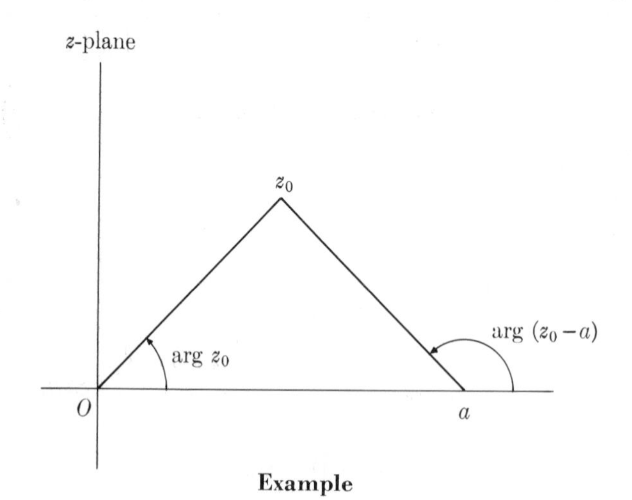

Example

will follow if $\operatorname{Re} z_0(z_0 - a) < 0$ and $\operatorname{Im} z_0(z_0 - a) = 0$. With the use of Exercise 11, p. 188,

$$\begin{aligned}\operatorname{Re} z_0(z_0 - a) &= \operatorname{Re} z_0 \operatorname{Re}(z_0 - a) - \operatorname{Im} z_0 \operatorname{Im}(z_0 - a)\\ &= \frac{-a^2}{2} - (\operatorname{Im} z_0)^2 < 0.\\ \operatorname{Im} z_0(z_0 - a) &= \operatorname{Re} z_0 \operatorname{Im}(z_0 - a) + \operatorname{Im} z_0 \operatorname{Re}(z_0 - a)\\ &= \frac{a}{2}\operatorname{Im} z_0 - \frac{a}{2}\operatorname{Im} z_0 = 0.\end{aligned}$$

The student has now learned a new language for points in the plane, and it should be his primary aim at this time to be as completely conversant as possible in this language. At the outset, he will find himself translating the new language into the old language, representing the points in the plane by the ordered pairs of real numbers (x, y) with which he is familiar and thus exchanging one number for two numbers. However, he should gradually resort to such a translation less and less; only then will the methods of complex analysis assume their full power and elegance of form.

EXERCISES

1. Describe geometrically the set of points given by each of the following inequalities. Indicate whether each set is a region. Determine whether each region is bounded or unbounded; open, closed, neither open nor closed; simply connected or multiply connected.

(a) $|z - 1 + 3i| \le 1$; (b) $\operatorname{Im} z > 1$; (c) $3 \le |z - 2| \le 5$; (d) $|\operatorname{Re} z| \le 2$; (e) $0 \le \arg z \le \pi/4$; (f) $|2z + 3| > 4$; (g) $-\pi < \arg z < \pi$, $|z| > 2$; (h) $\operatorname{Re}(1/z) < \frac{1}{4}$; (i) $\operatorname{Im} z^2 > 0$; (j) $(z - z_0)/(z + z_0) < 1$, $\operatorname{Re} z_0 > 0$; (k) $1/|z| \ge \frac{1}{4}$; (l) $|z - 1| \le 4|z + 1|$; (m) $|z - 1| + |z + i| \ge 5$; (n) $|z - 2| - |z + 2| \le 1$; (o) $0 < \operatorname{Re} iz \le 2$; (p) $0 < \operatorname{Re} z \le \operatorname{Im} z$; (q) $|z - 1| \le \operatorname{Re} z$; (r) $|z - 1|^2 \le 2(\operatorname{Im} z + \operatorname{Re} z)$; (s) $\operatorname{Re}(z + \bar{z})^2 \ge 4$; (t) $\operatorname{Re} z(\bar{z} + 2) > 8$.

2. Determine the curves in the complex plane represented by the following equations:

(a) $|z| = \frac{1}{4}$; (b) $\operatorname{Re} z = 3$; (c) $\arg z = \pi/4$; (d) $|z - 1| = 1$; (e) $|z - 2| = |z - 2i|$; (f) $|z - 1| = 2|z - i|$; (g) $|z - 1| - |z + 1| = 1$; (h) $z\bar{z} + (1 + i)z + (1 - i)\bar{z} + 1 = 0$; (i) $\operatorname{Re} z^2 = 0$; (j) $|z^2 + az + b| = c^2$; (k) $|z^2 - 1| = 4$; (l) $|z + 1|^2 - |z - 1|^2 = 2$; (m) $z - \bar{z} = i$; (n) $\operatorname{Im}(z^2 - 1) = 1$; (o) $\operatorname{Re}(2\bar{z} + |z|^2) = 4 \operatorname{Im}(z - \bar{z})$.

3. Interpret geometrically:

(a) $\operatorname{Re}\left(\dfrac{z - z_1}{z_2 - z_3}\right) = 0$;

(b) $\operatorname{Im} \dfrac{(z - z_2)(z_1 - z_3)}{(z - z_3)(z_1 - z_2)} = 0.$

◇ **4.** Show that the general equation of a straight line is $az + \bar{a}\bar{z} + b = 0$, where b is a real number.

◇ **5.** Show that the general equation of a circle is $z\bar{z} + az + \bar{a}\bar{z} + b = 0$, $\operatorname{Im} b = 0$.

6. Show that the general equation of a circle is $|z|^2 + 2 \operatorname{Re}(z_0 z) = c$, where z_0 is an arbitrary complex number and $c + |z_0|^2 > 0$.

7. Show that the curve determined by the condition $\operatorname{Re} z_0 a^2 = c \neq 0$, where z_0 is complex, is a hyperbola.

8. If a and b are real numbers, $a \neq \pm 1$, show that $|z|^2 + a \operatorname{Re} z^2 = b$ represents either an ellipse or a hyperbola.

9. Show that $(a\bar{z} + \bar{a}z)^2 = 2(b\bar{z} + \bar{b}z) + c$, $\operatorname{Im} c = 0$, represents the most general parabola in the complex plane.

10. Show that the midpoint of the line segment joining z_1 and z_2 is $\frac{1}{2}(z_1 + z_2)$.

11. Let A_1, A_2, A_3, A_4 be the points representing the complex numbers z_1, z_2, z_3, z_4. Show that

(a) $A_1A_2 \perp A_3A_4$ if and only if $(z_1 - z_2)(\bar{z}_3 - \bar{z}_4) + (\bar{z}_1 - \bar{z}_2)(z_3 - z_4) = 0$;
(b) $A_1A_2 \| A_3A_4$ if and only if $(z_1 - z_2)(\bar{z}_3 - \bar{z}_4) = (\bar{z}_1 - \bar{z}_2)(z_3 - z_4)$.

12. $ABCD$ is a rhombus with $AB = 2BD$. If B and D represent $1 + 3i$ and $-3 + i$, find the numbers represented by A and C.

Ans.: $(-1 + \sqrt{15}) - 2i(-1 + \sqrt{15})$,
$(-1 - \sqrt{15}) - 2i(-1 - \sqrt{15})$.

13. Show that the lines joining the midpoints of the adjacent sides of a quadrilateral form a parallelogram.

14. (a) Show that z_1, z_2, z_3 are collinear if and only if $(z_1 - z_2)/(z_1 - z_3)$ is real.
(b) Show that $1 + 4i$, $2 + 7i$, $3 + 10i$ are collinear.

15. Show that the centroid of particles of masses $m_1, m_2, \cdots, m_n$ placed at $z_1, z_2, \cdots, z_n$ is

$$\frac{m_1z_1 + m_2z_2 + \cdots + m_nz_n}{m_1 + m_2 + \cdots + m_n}.$$

16. Show that z_1, z_2, z_3 are the vertices of an equilateral triangle if and only if

$$\begin{vmatrix} z_1 & z_2 & 1 \\ z_2 & z_3 & 1 \\ z_3 & z_1 & 1 \end{vmatrix} = 0.$$

(*Hint:* If the condition holds, show that $|z_1 - z_2|^3 = |z_2 - z_3|^3 = |z_3 - z_1|^3 = |z_1 - z_2|\,|z_2 - z_3|\,|z_3 - z_1|$.)

17. Show that the triangles whose vertices are z_1, z_2, z_3, and z_1', z_2', z_3' are similar if

$$\begin{vmatrix} z_1 & z_1' & 1 \\ z_2 & z_2' & 1 \\ z_3 & z_3' & 1 \end{vmatrix} = 0.$$

18. If the consecutive vertices z_1, z_2, z_3, z_4 of a quadrilateral lie on a circle, prove that $|z_1 - z_3| \cdot |z_2 - z_4| = |z_1 - z_2| \cdot |z_3 - z_4| + |z_2 - z_3| \cdot |z_1 - z_4|$ and interpret the result geometrically.

19. Let $z_1, z_2, \cdots, z_n$ be the vertices of a convex polygon P (a polygon that is the boundary of a convex region R). If $\lambda_1, \cdots, \lambda_n \geq 0$ such that $\lambda_1 + \lambda_2 + \cdots + \lambda_n = 1$, show that a point z can be written in the form

$$z = \sum_{k=1}^{n} \lambda_k z_k \qquad \text{if and only if } z \text{ is on } P \text{ or in } R.$$

20. (a) If $0 \leq \arg z_1 - \arg z_2 < \pi$, show that the area of the triangle whose vertices are O, z_1, z_2 is $\frac{1}{2}\operatorname{Im} \bar{z}_1 z_2$.

(b) If $0 \leq \arg z_1 < \arg z_2 < \cdots < \arg z_n < 2\pi$, show that the area of the polygon whose vertices are $z_1, z_2, \cdots, z_n$ is

$$A = \tfrac{1}{2}\operatorname{Im} \sum_{j=1}^{n} z_j \bar{z}_{j-1}$$

$$= \tfrac{1}{4} \sum_{j=1}^{n} (z_j - z_{j-1}) \cdot (\bar{z}_j + \bar{z}_{j-1}), \qquad z_0 = z_n.$$

(c) Show that the exterior angles of the polygon in (b) are equal to $\arg (z_{j+1} - z_j)/(z_j - z_{j-1})$, $j = 1, 2, \cdots, n$, $(z_{-1} = z_{n-1})$, and then prove that the sum of the exterior angles of the polygon is 2π.

Chapter 6

Complex Functions

1. Functions. Let E denote a given set of complex numbers. If z denotes any one of the complex numbers in E, then z is called a **complex variable.** If to each complex number z of E, we let correspond a unique complex number w, then we say that a **function of the complex variable** z is defined in E, or more accurately, a complex-valued function of the complex variable z is defined in E. We express this correspondence as $w = f(z)$. Since for every z in E, $w = f(z)$ is uniquely determined, the term **function** implies single-valued function. If to each complex number z of E, we let correspond two or more values of w, then we say that a multiple-valued function of z is defined in E, denoted by $w = f(z)$. In short, the term *function* will always imply that w is single-valued and the term *multiple-valued function* will always be used explicitly when w is multiple-valued. Often we encounter the terms *real-valued function of a complex variable* and *complex-valued function of a real variable;* these are self-explanatory. We shall use the term **complex function** to denote a complex-valued function of a complex variable $w = f(z)$, where z or w always assume some nonreal values, and the term **real function,** where z and w assume only real values.

Since in $w = f(z)$, w is a complex number, it can be written in rectangular form: Let $u = \operatorname{Re} w$ and $v = \operatorname{Im} w$; then $w = u + iv$. Since w depends upon z, which in turn depends on x and y, $z = x + iy$, u and v are functions of the real variables x and y, and we write more precisely

$$w = f(z) = u(x, y) + iv(x, y),$$

noting that u and v are real-valued functions of two real variables. Conversely, two given functions u and v of the real variables x and y determine the complex function $w = u + iv$. Therefore, many properties of $w = f(z)$ can be deduced from the corresponding properties of $u(x, y)$ and $v(x, y)$. We shall make effective use of this principle in establishing general results, assuming that the student is familiar with the properties of functions of two real variables. However, once these general results have been obtained, the student should avoid translating every complex function into the two corresponding functions of two real variables.

EXAMPLE 1. If $w = z^2$, we let $z = x + iy$ to obtain $w = z^2 = x^2 - y^2 + 2ixy$ so that $u(x, y) = x^2 - y^2$ and $v(x, y) = 2xy$.

EXAMPLE 2. $w = \arg z$. This is an example of a real-valued function of a complex variable, so that $v(x, y) = 0$; $u(x, y) =$ the value of $\tan^{-1}(y/x)$ in the quadrant of z. $w = \arg_k z = \arg z + 2k\pi$, $k = 1, 2, \cdots$ is a multiple-valued real-valued function of a complex variable.

We have seen that $w = f(z)$ can always be written in the form $w = u + iv$ merely by setting $z = x + iy$ and writing the result in rectangular form. On the other hand, an expression of the form $w = u + iv$ can always be written in the form $w = f(z)$ by letting $x = \operatorname{Re} z = \dfrac{z + \bar{z}}{2}$ and $y = \operatorname{Im} z = \dfrac{z - \bar{z}}{2i}$ and obtaining an expression in z and $\bar{z}$ that will be a function of z, since $\bar{z}$ is a function of z. In practice, a judicious use of complex techniques will eliminate tedious manipulations, as is illustrated in the following examples.

EXAMPLE 3. Express $\dfrac{x}{x^2 + y^2} - \dfrac{iy}{x^2 + y^2}$ as a function of z.

Solution

$$\frac{x - iy}{x^2 + y^2} = \frac{\bar{z}}{z\bar{z}} = \frac{1}{z}.$$

EXAMPLE 4. Express $x + y + i(x - y)$ as a function of z.

Solution. $x + y + i(x - y) = x(1 + i) + y(1 - i) = x(1 + i) - iy(1 + i) = (x - iy)(1 + i) = (1 + i)\bar{z}$. This function cannot be expressed explicitly in terms of z.

Let $w = f(z)$ be defined on the set E. Then every z in E determines a complex number w; let us denote the set of these complex numbers w corresponding to every z in E as F. Let the set E be plotted on the z-plane and the set F plotted on a second complex plane, called the w-plane, whose

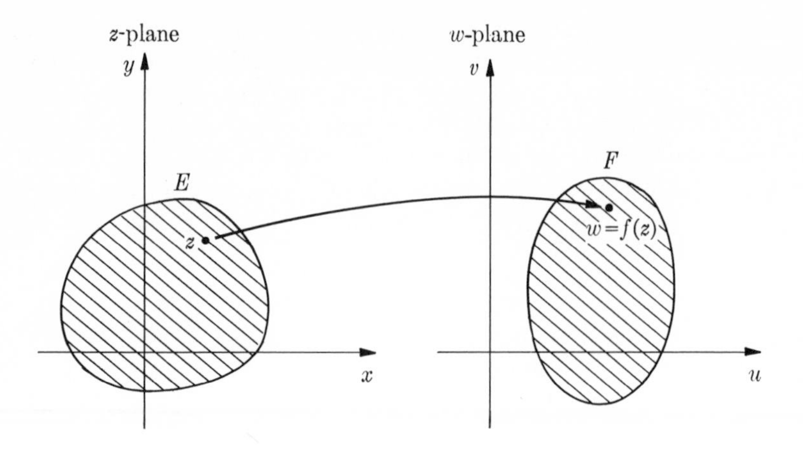

Fig. 1. $w = f(z)$ as a mapping

real and imaginary axes are the u and v axes. (See Fig. 1.) Then $w = f(z)$ is said to define a mapping of the set E in the z-plane into the set F of the w-plane. The set E, the set of z for which $f(z)$ is defined, is called the *domain* of $f(z)$, and the set F, the set of all $f(z)$ for z in E, is called the *range* of $f(z)$. Hence, the domain of $w = f(z)$ is a set in the z-plane, and its range is a set in the w-plane.

EXAMPLE 5. The domain of $f(z) = z^2$ is the entire z-plane, and its range is the entire w-plane. If z is real, what are the domain and range of $f(z)$?

EXAMPLE 6. The domain of $g(z) = |z|$ is the entire z-plane, since the absolute value of every complex number is defined. Since $|z| \geq 0$, the range of z is the nonnegative u-axis.

EXAMPLE 7. The domain of $h(z) = 1/(z^2 + 1)$ is the entire z-plane, except $z = i$ and $z = -i$, since $h(z)$ is not defined at these points. Two distinct values of z determine one value $h(z)$; i.e., $h(-z) = h(z)$, provided $z \neq \pm i$. Then, since $z^2 = (1 - w)/w$, every $w \neq 0$ in the plane corresponds to two points in the z-plane; hence, the range of $h(z)$ is the entire w-plane, except zero.

We have defined the domain and range of a function as subsets of the complex plane. For some purposes, it is convenient to let the domain and range of a function be subsets of the extended complex plane. This means that, given $w = f(z)$, we must define the value w that corresponds to $z = \infty$ and the value z that corresponds to $w = \infty$. We shall say that the value of $w = f(z)$ at the point at infinity, written $f(\infty)$, is the value of $f(1/z)$ at $z = 0$, if this value exists; otherwise, it is undefined. Furthermore, we shall say that the value of $f(z)$ at $z = z_0$ is ∞ if the value of $1/f(z)$ at $z = z_0$ is 0; otherwise, it is undefined.

EXAMPLE 8. If $f(z) = \dfrac{z-1}{z+1}$, then $f(1/z) = \dfrac{1-z}{1+z}$, which is 1 at $z = 0$; hence, $f(\infty) = 1$. On the other hand, $f(-1) = \infty$, since $1/f(z) = \dfrac{z+1}{z-1}$ is 0 at $z = -1$.

The value of a function at a point is a property of the function at that point. We shall have occasion to consider many properties of a function at a point such as limit, continuity, and differentiability. We shall define these properties for points in the complex plane.

We shall extend these definitions so as to include the point at infinity by using the following definition, which we call

The principle of the point at infinity. $f(z)$ has the property P at the point at infinity if $f(1/z)$ has the property P at $z = 0$.

The application of this principle will preclude having to define anew "$f(z)$ has the property P at ∞" every time we encounter a different P.

2. Limits and continuity. Let $f(z)$ be defined in some neighborhood of a point z_0, except possibly at z_0 itself. We say that the **limit of $f(z)$** as z approaches z_0 is c, written $\lim_{z \to z_0} f(z) = c$, means that for every $\epsilon > 0$, there exists $\delta > 0$ such that $0 < |z - z_0| < \delta$ implies $|f(z) - c| < \epsilon$. (Note that the form of the definition is precisely the one for real functions and vector functions.) Geometrically, $\lim_{z \to z_0} f(z) = c$ implies that $f(z)$ can be made to lie within a circle of arbitrarily small radius ϵ and center c merely by letting z lie in a circle of radius δ and center z_0. (See Fig. 2.) If the $\lim_{z \to z_0} f(z) = c$, then c is uniquely determined, for suppose $\lim_{z \to z_0} f(z) = c'$, $c' \neq c$; let $\epsilon = |c' - c|/2$. Then there exists δ_1 such that for $0 < |z - z_0| < \delta_1$,

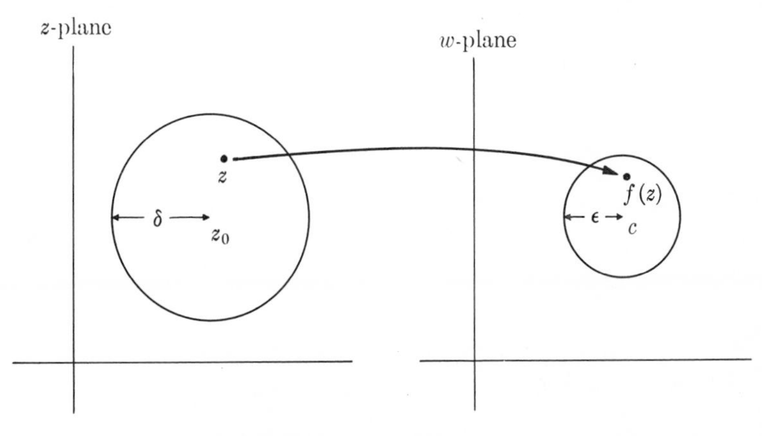

Fig. 2. $\lim_{z = z_0} f(z) = c$

$|f(z) - c| < |c' - c|/2$ and δ_2 such that for $0 < |z - z_0| < \delta_2$, $|f(z) - c'| < |c' - c|/2$. Let $\delta = \min(\delta_1, \delta_2)$. Then, for $0 < |z - z_0| < \delta$, $|c' - c| = |c' - f(z) + f(z) - c| \leq |f(z) - c'| + |f(z) - c| < |c' - c|$. Contradiction: Hence, $c' = c$. The uniqueness of the limit c implies that *no matter along what curve z approaches z_0, if the* $\lim_{z \to z_0} f(z)$ *exists, it will always be c.*

The study of the properties of the limit is facilitated by the

THEOREM. Let $f(z) = u(x, y) + iv(x, y)$, $z_0 = x_0 + iy_0$, $c = c_1 + ic_2$. A necessary and sufficient condition that $\lim_{z \to z_0} f(z) = c$ is that $\lim_{\substack{x \to x_0 \\ y \to y_0}} u(x, y) = c_1$ and $\lim_{\substack{x \to x_0 \\ y \to y_0}} v(x, y) = c_2$.

Proof

Sufficiency. Given $\epsilon > 0$, then there exists $\delta > 0$ such that $|u - c_1| < \epsilon/2$ and $|v - c_2| < \epsilon/2$ whenever $0 < |x - x_0| < \delta/2$ and $0 < |y - y_0| < \delta/2$. Hence, $|f(z) - c| = |u - c_1 + i(v - c_2)| \leq |u - c_1| + |v - c_2| < \epsilon$, whenever $0 < |z - z_0| < \delta$. Hence, $\lim_{z \to z_0} f(z) = c$.

Necessity. Given $\epsilon > 0$, then there exists $\delta > 0$ such that $|f(z) - c| < \epsilon$ whenever $0 < |z - z_0| < \delta$. But

$$|u - c_1| \leq |f(z) - c| \quad \text{and} \quad |x - x_0| \leq |z - z_0|, \quad |y - y_0| \leq |z - z_0|.$$

Hence,

$$\lim_{\substack{x \to x_0 \\ y \to y_0}} u(x, y) = c_1.$$

Similarly,

$$\lim_{\substack{x \to x_0 \\ y \to y_0}} v(x, y) = c_2.$$

With the use of this theorem and the corresponding limit theorem for functions of two real variables, we have the

THEOREM ON LIMITS. If $f(z)$ and $g(z)$ are defined in some neighborhood of z_0 and $\lim_{z \to z_0} f(z) = a$ and $\lim_{z \to z_0} g(z) = b$, then

L_1: $\lim_{z \to z_0} kf(z) = ka$, where k is any complex constant.

L_2: $\lim_{z \to z_0} [f(z) + g(z)] = a + b$.

L_3: $\lim_{z \to z_0} f(z)g(z) = ab$.

L_4: $\lim_{z \to z_0} f(z)/g(z) = a/b, b \neq 0$.

L_2 and L_3 extend to any finite number of functions.

It follows readily from the definition that $\lim_{z \to z_0} z = z_0$ (the student can test his understanding of the definition by proving this). Then the theorem on limits, appropriately extended, yields

$$\lim_{z \to z_0} \sum_{j=0}^{n} a_j z^j = \sum_{j=0}^{n} a_j z_0^j, \qquad a_j \text{ constant}, j = 0, 1, \cdots, n.$$

A function $f(z)$, defined throughout some neighborhood of z_0, is said to be **continuous at z_0** if $\lim_{z \to z_0} f(z) = f(z_0)$. $f(z)$ is **continuous in a region** if it is continuous at every point in the region. Intuitively, continuity implies that the values of $f(z)$ for z close to z_0 will be near to $f(z_0)$.

Here we might apply the principle of the point at infinity: $f(z)$ is continuous at ∞ if $f(1/z)$ is continuous at $z = 0$.

We have the following theorems on continuity.

C_1: $f(z) = u(x, y) + iv(x, y)$ is continuous at $z_0 = x_0 + iy_0$ if and only if u and v are continuous at (x_0, y_0).

C_2: If $f(z)$ and $g(z)$ are continuous at $z = z_0$, then $kf(z)$ (k arbitrary complex constant), $f(z) + g(z)$, $f(z)g(z)$, $f(z)/g(z)(g(z_0) \neq 0)$, $f[g(z)]$ are continuous at $z = z_0$.

C_3: If $f(z)$ is continuous in a closed region R, then there exists $M > 0$ such that $|f(z)| < M$ for every z in R; i.e., $f(z)$ is *bounded* in R.

Proofs. C_1 follows immediately by the definition of continuity and the corresponding theorem for limits. C_2 follows from the definition of continuity and the theorem on limits (except the continuity of $f[g(z)]$, which can be proved by applying the corresponding theorem for composite functions of two real variables). C_3: the continuity of $f(z)$ implies the continuity of u and v, which implies the existence of M_1 and M_2 such that $|u| < M_1$ and $|v| < M_2$. (See Fulks, *Advanced Calculus*, p. 200, for proof.) But $|f(z)| = \sqrt{u^2 + v^2}$ and the proof follows with $M = \sqrt{M_1^2 + M_2^2}$.

EXAMPLE 1. $f(z) = \dfrac{z_2 + 1}{z^4 - 1}$ is continuous everywhere except at $z = -1, 1, i, -i$, since $f(z)$ is not defined at these points.

EXAMPLE 2. $f(z) = \arg z$ is continuous everywhere except $\operatorname{Re} z \leq 0$, $\operatorname{Im} z = 0$; i.e., for all points along the negative real axis and zero, for since $-\pi < \arg z \leq \pi$, if z_0 is such a point, every neighborhood of z_0 will contain points whose argument is close to π and other points whose argument is close to $-\pi$.

We have been studying complex functions in general. Before we proceed with this general study, it will be convenient for purposes of illustration to have available some specific functions and at the same time to study those functions that occur most frequently in practice. According to our definition, a function $w = f(z)$ is defined by indicating the correspondence between z and w. This may be done in many ways. $f(z)$ may be an explicit expression that has been developed by performing well-defined operations. Or $f(z)$ may be defined by specifying its real and imaginary parts.

We shall have occasion to define complex functions in these various ways. The domain, range, and region of continuity should be indicated for each new complex function encountered. For many purposes, it is important to know those values of z that satisfy $f(z) = 0$. We call these values the **zeros** of $f(z)$. Hence, z_0 is a zero of $f(z)$ if $f(z_0) = 0$. All complex functions that we shall consider are those whose domains are an extension of the domains of well-known real functions. As a matter of fact, if $w = f(x + iy)$ and we set $y = 0$, we obtain these real functions. This consideration will often suggest the definition of the corresponding complex function. We shall be interested in those properties of the real functions that are preserved in the extension as well as those that are not; furthermore, we shall note the properties that are peculiar to the complex functions.

3. Rational functions. Let $p(z) = a_n z^n + a_{n-1} z^{n-1} + \cdots + a_1 z + a_0$, $n \geq 0$, an integer, a_j, $j = 0, 1, \cdots, n$, arbitrary complex constants. $p(z)$ is well defined, since it can be obtained from z by a finite number of algebraic operations that have been defined for complex numbers. The domain of $p(z)$ is the entire z-plane, and its range is the entire w-plane. $p(z)$ is continuous everywhere in the z-plane. $p(z)$ is called the **polynomial function.** It reduces to the real polynomial function when $\text{Im}\, z = 0$ and $\text{Im}(a_j) = 0$, $j = 0, 1, \cdots, n$. We note that $p(\infty) = \infty$. Let $p(z)$ and $q(z)$ be any two polynomial functions; the function $r(z) = p(z)/q(z)$ is called a **rational function.** Note that a rational function is a polynomial when $q(z) = 1$. The domain of $r(z)$ is the entire z-plane, except the zeros of $q(z)$; the range is best determined for each specific rational function. $r(z)$ is continuous everywhere in the z-plane except at the zeros of $q(z)$. It is readily seen that a rational function of z is an extension of the definition of a rational function in x from the real axis to the z-plane.

Now that we have seen that rational functions can be extended from the real axis to the z-plane, it is natural to inquire about the extension from the real axis to the z-plane of the familiar functions that we have studied, such as the exponential function, trigonometric functions, hyperbolic functions, logarithmic function, inverse trigonometric functions, and inverse hyperbolic functions. We find that we can define these functions in the z-plane in such a manner that they reduce to the familiar real functions when $\text{Im}\, z = 0$, and furthermore that many of the properties of these complex functions are the same as the ones for the corresponding real functions. The student should be cautioned, however, that some of the properties of the real functions do not extend to the complex functions; furthermore, the complex functions may have properties that are meaningless for the real functions. In the sequel, we shall explicitly indicate these differences. The rational functions, the exponential and logarithmic functions, the trigonometric functions and their inverses, and the hyperbolic functions and their inverses are examples of what we call **elementary functions.**

4. The exponential function. We now extend the definition of the exponential function from the real axis to the complex plane in such a manner that many of the properties of the real exponential function are preserved. We shall see that we can achieve this by defining the **complex exponential function,** denoted by e^z, as $e^z = e^x(\cos y + i \sin y)$. We note immediately that when $y = 0$, this reduces to the real exponential function e^x. The definition of e^z has been given by specifying $\operatorname{Re} e^z = e^x \cos y$ and $\operatorname{Im} e^z = e^x \sin y$.

The domain of e^z is the entire z-plane, since $e^x \cos y$ and $e^x \sin y$ are defined everywhere in the xy-plane. The range of $w = e^z$ is the entire w-plane, except $w = 0$, for if $w_0 = r_0(\cos \phi_0 + i \sin \phi_0)$ is any point in the w-plane, except 0, so that $r_0 > 0$, $e^z = w_0$ always has a solution $z_0 = x_0 + iy_0$, obtained by solving $e^{x_0} \cos y_0 = r_0 \cos \phi_0$ and $e^{y_0} \sin y_0 = r_0 \sin \phi_0$, and it is readily seen that $x_0 = \log r_0$ and $y_0 = \phi_0$. e^z is continuous everywhere in the z-plane.

The exponential function has the following properties.

E$_1$: $|e^z| = e^x$.
E$_2$: $\arg e^z = y, \; -\pi < y \leq \pi$.
E$_3$: $e^z \neq 0$ for any z.
E$_4$: $e^{ti} = \cos t + i \sin t$, t any real number.
E$_5$: $|e^{ti}| = 1$, t any real number.
E$_6$: $e^{x+yi} = e^x e^{yi}$.
E$_7$: $z = re^{\phi i}$, $\phi = \theta + 2\pi k$, $k = 0, \pm 1, \pm 2, \cdots$, z any complex number, $r = |z|$, $\theta = \arg z$.
E$_8$: $e^{z_1+z_2} = e^{z_1}e^{z_2}$ (addition formula).
E$_9$: $e^{-z} = 1/e^z$.
E$_{10}$: $e^{z_1-z_2} = e^{z_1}/e^{z_2}$.
E$_{11}$: $(e^z)^n = e^{nz}$, n any integer.
E$_{12}$: $e^z + 2\pi ki = e^z$, $k = 0, \pm 1, \pm 2, \cdots$; i.e., e^z is periodic with period $2\pi i$.
E$_{13}$: $\overline{e^z} = e^{\bar{z}}$.

Proofs. Writing e^z in polar form and comparing with the definition of e^z yields E$_1$ and E$_2$. E$_3$ follows from E$_1$, since $e^x \neq 0$. E$_4$ follows by letting $x = 0$ and $t = y$ in the definition of e^z, since y is any real number. E$_5$ follows readily from E$_4$. The definition of e^z and E$_4$ yields E$_6$. Expressing z in polar form and using E$_4$ gives E$_7$, which is another representation of a complex number in very compact form called the **exponential form.**

$$\begin{aligned} \text{E}_8\text{:}\quad e^{z_1}e^{z_2} &= e^{x_1}e^{x_2}e^{iy_1}e^{iy_2} \\ &= e^{x_1+x_2}(\cos y_1 + i \sin y_1)(\cos y_2 + i \sin y_2) \\ &= e^{x_1+x_2}[\cos(y_1 + y_2) + i \sin(y_1 + y_2)] \\ &= e^{x_1+x_2}e^{i(y_1+y_2)} \\ &= e^{z_1+z_2}. \end{aligned}$$

$$\text{E}_9\text{:}\quad 1 = e^0 = e^{z-z} = e^z e^{-z} \qquad \text{by E}_8.$$

$$\begin{aligned} \text{E}_{10}\text{:}\quad e^{z_1-z_2} &= e^{z_1}e^{-z_2} \\ &= \frac{e^{z_1}}{e^{z_2}} \qquad \text{by E}_8 \text{ and E}_9. \end{aligned}$$

E_8 extends to $e^{z_1+z_2+\cdots+z_n} = e^{z_1}e^{z_2}\cdots e^{z_n}$ and if $z_1 = z_2 = \cdots = z_n = z$, we obtain E_{11} for n, a positive integer. If n is a negative integer, E_{11} follows from E_9; E_{11} is true for $n = 0$. (Proof?)

$$\begin{aligned} \text{E}_{12}\text{:}\quad e^{z} + 2\pi ki &= e^{x} + i(y + 2\pi k) \\ &= e^x[\cos(y + 2\pi k) + i \sin(y + 2\pi k)] \\ &= e^x(\cos y + i \sin y) \\ &= e^z. \end{aligned}$$

$$\begin{aligned} \text{E}_{13}\text{:}\quad \overline{e^z} &= e^x(\cos y - i \sin y) \\ &= e^x[\cos(-y) + i \sin(-y)] \\ &= e^{x-iy} = e^{\bar{z}}. \end{aligned}$$

We note that E_3, E_8, E_9, E_{10} are properties of the real exponential function, which have been preserved when this function is extended to the complex plane. The other properties have no meaning for the real exponential function.

EXAMPLE 1. Evaluate $|e^{-3iz+5i}|$.

Solution. Let $z = x + iy$. Then $e^{-3iz+5i} = e^{3y+(5-x)i} = e^{3y}e^{(5-x)i}$ by E_8. Then $|e^{-3iz+5i}| = e^{3y}|e^{(5-x)i}| = e^{3y}$, by E_9.

EXAMPLE 2. Solve the equation $e^z = 2 + 2i$ for all z.

Solution. We rewrite the equation in the form

$$e^x e^{iy} = 2\sqrt{2}e^{[(\pi/2)+2\pi k]i},$$

using E_{12}. Then $e^x = 2\sqrt{2}$, or $x = \log 2\sqrt{2}$ and $y = (\pi/2) + 2\pi k$. Hence, *all* solutions of the given equation are $z = \log 2\sqrt{2} + [(\pi/2) + 2\pi k]i$, $k = 0, \pm 1, \pm 2, \cdots$.

5. The trigonometric functions. The real sine and cosine functions can be expressed in terms of the complex exponential function because, by E_4, $e^{ix} = \cos x + i \sin x$ and $e^{-ix} = \cos x - i \sin x$, where x is real; hence, we readily obtain $\sin x = \dfrac{e^{ix} - e^{-ix}}{2i}$ and $\cos x = \dfrac{e^{ix} + e^{-ix}}{2}$. These expressions suggest the following definitions for the **complex sine and**

cosine: $\sin z = \dfrac{e^{iz} - e^{iz}}{2i}$ and $\cos z = \dfrac{e^{iz} + e^{-iz}}{2}$, where z is a complex number. If $z = x + iy$ and $y = 0$, then clearly $\sin z$ and $\cos z$ reduce to the real sine and cosine functions. The domain of $\sin z$ and $\cos z$ is the entire z-plane, since the exponential function has this domain. The range of $w = \sin z$ and $w = \cos z$ is the entire w-plane (which we shall show subsequently). $\sin z$ and $\cos z$ are continuous everywhere in the z-plane, which follows from the continuity of e^z and C_2 in the theorem on continuous functions.

The complex sine and cosine functions have the following properties.

T_1: $\sin z = \sin x \cosh y + i \cos x \sinh y,$
$\cos z = \cos x \cosh y - i \sin x \sinh y \qquad$ (rectangular form).

T_2: The zeros of $\sin z$ are $k\pi$, and the zeros of $\cos z$ are $(2k + 1)(\pi/2)$, $k = 0, \pm 1, \pm 2, \cdots$, i.e., they are real and are the zeros of $\sin x$ and $\cos x$.

T_3: $\sin (z_1 \pm z_2) = \sin z_1 \cos z_2 \pm \cos z_1 \sin z_2,$
$\cos (z_1 \pm z_2) = \cos z_1 \cos z_2 \mp \sin z_1 \sin z_2.$

T_4: $\sin (z + 2\pi k) = \sin z,$
$\cos (z + 2\pi k) = \cos z, \qquad k = 0, \pm 1, \pm 2, \cdots,$

T_5: $\sin^2 z + \cos^2 z = 1.$

T_6: $\sin 2z = 2 \sin z \cos z,$
$\cos 2z = \cos^2 z - \sin^2 z.$

T_7: $|\sin z|^2 = \sin^2 x + \sinh^2 y,$
$|\cos z|^2 = \cos^2 x + \sinh^2 y.$

Proofs

T_1:
$$\sin z = \frac{e^{iz} - e^{-iz}}{2i}$$
$$= \frac{e^{ix}e^{-y} - e^{-ix}e^{y}}{2i} = \frac{e^{-y}(\cos x + i \sin x)}{2i} - \frac{e^{y}(\cos x - i \sin x)}{2i}$$
$$= \frac{e^{y} + e^{-y}}{2} \sin x + i \left(\frac{e^{y} - e^{-y}}{2}\right) \cos x$$
$$= \sin x \cosh y + i \cos x \sinh y,$$
and similarly for $\cos z$.

T_2: $\sin z = \sin x \cosh y + i \cos x \sinh y = 0$ only if (1) $\sin x \cosh y = 0$ and (2) $\cos x \sinh y = 0$. Since $\cosh y \neq 0$, (1) is satisfied only if $x = k\pi$, $k = 0, \pm 1, \pm 2, \cdots$. Since these values do not make $\cos x = 0$, (2) is satisfied only if $\sinh y = 0$ or $y = 0$. Hence, $z = k\pi$ are the zeros of $\sin z$, and similarly for the zeros of $\cos z$.

The proofs of T_3 to T_7 are left to the student.

The range of $w = \sin z$ can be determined from T_1, for if $w_0 = u_0 + v_0 i$ is any point in the w-plane, then $u_0 = \sin x \cosh y$ and $v_0 = \cos x \sinh y$

will always have solutions for x and y. (Why?) Similarly, the range of $w = \cos z$ is the entire w-plane.

An immediate consequence of T_7 is that $\sin z$ and $\cos z$ are not bounded, since $\sinh y$ is not bounded. On the other hand, since $|\sin x| \leq 1$ and $|\cos x| \leq 1$, where x is real (the real sine and cosine functions are bounded); we see that this property does not extend to the complex sine and cosine functions.

The remaining complex trigonometric functions may be defined in terms of $\sin z$ and $\cos z$ as

$$\tan z = \frac{\sin z}{\cos z}, \qquad z \neq (2k+1)(\pi/2),$$

$$\cot z = \frac{\cos z}{\sin z}, \qquad z \neq k\pi,$$

$$\csc z = \frac{1}{\sin z}, \qquad z \neq k\pi,$$

$$\sec z = \frac{1}{\cos z}, \qquad z \neq (2k+1)(\pi/2), \; k = 0, \pm 1, \pm 2, \cdots.$$

EXAMPLE. Solve for all values of z: $\sin z = i$.

Solution. The given equation can be written as $\sin x \cosh y + i \cos x \sinh y = i$, so that (1) $\sin x \cosh y = 0$, and (2) $\cos x \sinh y = 1$. (1) has only the solutions $x = k\pi$, $k = 0, \pm 1, \pm 2, \cdots$. Hence, (2) becomes $\sinh y = \pm 1$ or $y = \sinh^{-1} \pm 1$. Hence, $z = k\pi \pm \sinh^{-1} 1$, $k = 0, \pm 1, \pm 2, \cdots$ are all the solutions of the given equation.

6. The hyperbolic functions. We define the **complex hyperbolic sine and hyperbolic cosine** as

$$\sinh z = \frac{e^z - e^{-z}}{2} \quad \text{and} \quad \cosh z = \frac{e^z + e^{-z}}{2}.$$

If $z = x + iy$, they reduce to the real hyperbolic sine and hyperbolic cosine functions when $y = 0$. The domain of $\sinh z$ and $\cosh z$ is the entire z-plane, and the range of these functions is the entire w-plane. They are continuous everywhere in the z-plane. The following relations, which can be verified readily, indicate that the hyperbolic functions can be expressed as trigonometric functions, and vice versa:

$$\begin{aligned} \mathbf{H_1:} \quad & \sin iz = i \sinh z, \\ & \cos iz = \cosh z. \\ \mathbf{H_2:} \quad & \sinh iz = i \sin z, \\ & \cosh iz = \cos z. \end{aligned}$$

These can be used to prove the following properties analogous to the corresponding ones for trigonometric functions:

H₃: $\sinh z = \sinh x \cos y + i \cosh x \sin y,$
$\cosh z = \cosh x \cos y + i \sinh x \sin y.$

H₄: The zeros of $\sinh z$ are $z = k\pi i$ and the zeros of $\cosh z$ are $z = (2k+1)(\pi/2)\,i,\ k = 0, \pm 1, \pm 2, \cdots.$

H₅: $\sinh(z_1 \pm z_2) = \sinh z_1 \cosh z_2 \pm \cosh z_1 \sinh z_2,$
$\cosh(z_1 \pm z_2) = \cosh z_1 \cosh z_2 \pm \sinh z_1 \sinh z_2.$

H₆: $\cosh^2 z - \sinh^2 z = 1.$

H₇: $\sinh 2z = 2 \sinh z \cosh z,$
$\cosh 2z = \sinh^2 z + \cosh^2 z.$

H₈: $|\sinh z|^2 = \sinh^2 x + \sin^2 y,$
$|\cosh z|^2 = \sinh^2 x + \cos^2 y.$

The proofs are left to the student.

The remaining complex hyperbolic functions may be defined as:

$$\tanh z = \frac{\sinh z}{\cosh z}, \qquad z \neq (2k+1)(\pi/2)k,$$

$$\coth z = \frac{\cosh z}{\sinh z}, \qquad z \neq k\pi i,$$

$$\operatorname{sech} z = \frac{1}{\cosh z}, \qquad z \neq (2k+1)(\pi/2)k,$$

$$\operatorname{csch} z = \frac{1}{\sin z}, \qquad z \neq k\pi i,\ k = 0, \pm 1, \pm 2, \cdots.$$

EXAMPLE 1. If $w = \sinh[\log 2 + (\pi/4)i]$, find $\operatorname{Re} w$ and $\operatorname{Im} w$.

Solution

$$\sinh\left(\log 2 + \frac{\pi}{4} i\right) = \sinh(\log 2) \cos\frac{\pi}{4} + i \cosh(\log 2) \sin\frac{\pi}{4}$$
$$= \frac{\sqrt{2}}{2}\left(\frac{3}{4} + \frac{5}{4} i\right),$$

using the definitions of the real hyperbolic sine and cosine functions. Hence,

$$\operatorname{Re} w = \frac{3\sqrt{2}}{8} \quad \text{and} \quad \operatorname{Im} z = \frac{5\sqrt{2}}{8}.$$

EXAMPLE 2. Solve the equation $\cosh z = -2$.

Solution. The equation can be written as $\cosh x \cos y + i \sinh x \sin y = -2$, whose solution can be found by solving (1) $\cosh x \cos y = -2$, and (2) $\sinh x \sin y = 0$. The solutions of (2) are $x = 0$ or $y = k\pi$, $k = 0, \pm 1, \pm 2, \cdots$, but $x = 0$ does not satisfy (1), since this would mean that $\cos y = -2$, which has no solution. Hence, $\cosh x \cos k\pi = 2$, or $\cosh x = \pm 2$. But $\cosh x \geq 0$, so that $x = \cosh^{-1} 2$. Hence, the solutions of the given equation are $k\pi + i \cosh^{-1} 2$, $k = 0, \pm 1, \pm 2, \cdots$.

EXERCISES

1. If $z = x + iy$ and $w = u + iv$, find u and v for

(a) $w = z^4$; (b) $w = \dfrac{1}{z^2}$; (c) $w = \dfrac{z-1}{z+1}$; (d) $w = ze^z$; (e) $w = \tan z$; (f) $w = \sec z$;

(g) $w = \coth z$; (h) $w = e^z \sin z$; (i) $w = \dfrac{e^z+1}{e^z-1}$; (j) $w = \dfrac{1}{e^z}$; (k) $w = \left(z + \dfrac{1}{z}\right)^2$;

(l) $w = e^{e^z}$; (m) $w = \sin(\cosh z)$; (n) $w = (z-1)^{2n}$, n a positive integer.

2. Determine the points in the z-plane where these functions are not continuous:

(a) $w = z^2 - z$; (b) $w = xy + i(x^3 + y^3)$;

(c) $w = \dfrac{2 - iz^2}{z^2+1}$; (d) $w = |z|$;

(e) $w = \bar{z}$; (f) $w = \operatorname{Re} z$; (g) $w = \cot z$; (h) $w = \csc z$;
(i) $w = \tanh z$; (j) $w = e^{z/(z^2+z+3)}$;

(k) $w = \begin{cases} 0, & \operatorname{Re} z \text{ rational} \\ 1, & \operatorname{Re} z \text{ irrational} \end{cases}$;

(l) $w = \begin{cases} z, & |z| \le 1 \\ |z|, & |z| > 1 \end{cases}$;

(m) $w = \begin{cases} 1, & z \text{ on } |z| = 1 \\ z, & z \text{ not on } |z| = 1. \end{cases}$

3. Express as functions of z, where $z = x + iy$:
(a) $2xy + i(x^2 - y^2)$; (b) $e^x \sin y + ie^x \cos y$;
(c) $x^2 + y^2 + 2xyi$;

(d) $\dfrac{x}{x^2+y^2} + \dfrac{iy}{x^2+y^2}$;

(e) $e^x(x \cos y - y \sin y) + ie^x(y \cos y + x \sin y)$;
(f) $e^{\sin x \cosh y} \cdot [\cos(\cos x \sinh y) + i \sin(\cos x \sinh y)]$;

(g) $\dfrac{\sin x \cosh y - i \cos x \sinh y}{\sin^2 x + \sinh^2 y}$.

Ans.: (a) $i\bar{z}^2$; (b) $ie^{\bar{z}}$; (c) $\dfrac{|z|^2 + 4i \operatorname{Re} z \operatorname{Im} z}{2}$; (d) $1/\bar{z}$; (e) $\bar{z}e^z$; (f) $e^{\sin z}$; (g) $\sin \bar{z}/|\sin z|^2$.

4. Evaluate:
(a) $e^{\pi i}$; (b) $e^{-\pi i}$; (c) $e^{(3/4)\pi i}$;
(d) $e^{-(2/3)\pi i}$; (e) $e^{7 \pm 7\pi i}$; (f) $e^{(3-\pi i)/2}$;
(g) $e^{(2+\pi i)/4}$; (h) $\sin i$; (i) $\cos[(\pi/3) - i]$; (j) $\sinh 3i$;
(k) $\tan(\pi + i)$; (l) $(1 + i)e^{1+\pi i}$.

Ans.: (a) -1; (b) -1; (c) $(\sqrt{2}/2)(-1 + i)$; (d) $-\frac{1}{2}(1 + \sqrt{3}i)$; (e) $-e^7$; (f) $-e^{3/2}i$; (g) $(\sqrt{e}/2)(1 + i)$; (h) $i \sinh 1$; (i) $\frac{1}{2}(\cosh 1 - \sqrt{3} \sinh 1)$; (j) $i \sin 3$; (k) $\tanh 1$; (l) $\sqrt{2}e$.

5. Solve for all values of z:
(a) $e^z = 2$; (b) $e^z = i$; (c) $e^z = 1 + 2i$; (d) $\sin z = 2i$; (e) $\cos z = 2$; (f) $\cot z = 1$; (g) $e^{2z-1} = 1$; (h) $\sin z = \cosh 4$; (i) $\cosh z = \frac{1}{2}$; (j) $\sinh z + \sin z = 0$; (k) $\cos z = 4 + 3i$; (l) $\sin z = 1 - i$.

Ans.: (a) $\log 2 + 2k\pi i$; (b) $[(\pi/2) + 2k\pi)i$; (c) $\frac{1}{2} \log 5 + i \tan^{-1} 2$; (d) $k\pi \pm i \sinh^{-1} 2$; (e) $2k\pi + i \cosh^{-1} 2$; (f) $(\pi/4) + 2k\pi$; (g) $\frac{1}{2} + k\pi i$; (h) $(\pi/2) + 2k \pm 4i$; (i) $\pm[(\pi/3) + 2k\pi]i$; (j) 0.

6. Show that $\cos z_1 = \cos z_2$ if and only if $z_2 = \pm z_1 + 2k\pi$, $k = 0, \pm 1$ $\pm 2, \cdots$. When does $e^{z_1} = e^{z_2}$ and $\sin z_1 = \sin z_2$?

7. Show that $\sinh (z + 2\pi i) = \sinh z$ and $\cosh (z + 2\pi i) = \cosh z$.

8. Show that
(a) $e^{i\bar{z}} = \overline{e^{iz}}$ only if $z = k\pi$, $k = 0, \pm 1, \pm 2, \cdots$.
(b) $\sin \bar{z} = \overline{\sin z}$ for all z.
(c) $\cos \bar{z} = \overline{\cos z}$ for all z.
(d) $\cos i\bar{z} = \overline{\cos iz}$ for all z.
(e) $\sin i\bar{z} = \overline{\sin iz}$ only if $z = k\pi i$, $k = 0, \pm 1, \pm 2, \cdots$.
(f) $\cosh \bar{z} = \overline{\cosh z}$ for all z.

9. Show that
(a) $|\cos z|^2 = \cosh^2 y - \sin^2 x$.
(b) $|\sinh y| \leq |\cos z| \leq \cosh y$.
(c) $|\sin z|^2 = \cosh^2 y - \cos^2 x$.
(d) $|\sinh y| \leq |\sin z| \leq \cosh y$.
(e) $|\sinh z|^2 = \cosh^2 x - \cos^2 y$.
(f) $\sin x \leq |\sinh x| \leq \cosh x$.

10. Show that
(a) e^z is real if and only if $\text{Im } z = k\pi$, and e^z is pure imaginary if and only if $\text{Im } z = (2k + 1)(\pi/2)$, $k = 0, \pm 1, \pm 2, \cdots$.
(b) If $\text{Re } z > 0$, then $|e^z| > 1$ and if $\text{Re } z < 0$, then $|e^z| < 1$.

11. (a) Show that $|e^{4i-z}| = e^{-x}$.
(b) Simplify $|e^{2z+i}|$ and $|e^{iz^2}|$ and show that

$$|e^{2z+i} + e^{iz^2}| \leq e^{2x} + e^{-2xy}.$$

12. Show that if $-(\pi/4) \leq \text{Re } z \leq (\pi/4)$, then $|\tan z| < 1$.

13. Show that $\tan z = i$ has no solutions.

14. If $z_1 \sin z_2 = z_2 \sinh z_1$, show that z_1 and z_2 cannot both be real and non-zero.

◇ **15.** Define $\lim_{z \to \infty} f(z) = c$, $\lim_{z \to z_0} f(z) = \infty$, $\lim_{z \to \infty} f(z) = \infty$.

16. Discuss the behavior of e^z, the trigonometric functions, and the hyperbolic functions at the point at infinity.

17. Show that if we define e^z as $e^x(\cos ky + i \sin ky)$, $k \neq 0$, the properties E_1 to E_{13} hold. We shall show later that if the property $(d/dx)e^x = e^x$ is to be extended to e^z, k must be 1.

18. Show that $e^{z+p} = e^z$ if and only if $p = 2k\pi i$, $k = 0, \pm 1, \pm 2, \cdots$.

7. Inverse functions. Given the function $w = f(z)$ with domain D and range R; this means that to every point z in D there corresponds one and only one point w in R. We can indicate this correspondence by $z \to w$ and think of it as a mapping of D in the z-plane into R in the w-plane. Now let z_0 be any point in D; then there exists a point w_0 in R such that $w_0 = f(z_0)$. We call w_0 the **image** of z_0 under $w = f(z)$ and z_0 the **inverse image** of w_0 under $w = f(z)$. Every point in D has one and only one image in D; however, a point in R may have more than one inverse image in D. In the event that every point in R has only one inverse image in D, we say that the correspondence $z \to w$ is a **one-to-one correspondence;** otherwise, it will be a many-to-one correspondence.

Let us assume that $w = f(z)$ establishes a one-to-one correspondence between its domain D and its range R so that $z \to w$. Then there exists a function with domain R and range D that we call the **inverse function** of $w = f(z)$ and denote it as $z = f^{-1}(w)$. If the correspondence is many-to-one, then the inverse function is a multiple-valued function. If $z = g(w)$ is the inverse function of $w = f(z)$, then $w = f(z)$ is the inverse function of $z = g(w)$. If $z = g(w)$ is the inverse function of $w = f(z)$, then $g[f(z)] = z$ and $f[g(w)] = w$.

We now consider the inverse functions of the elementary functions that we have studied. It is convenient to express all our functions in the form $w = f(z)$, as a mapping from the z-plane into the w-plane. In order to conform to this convention, we shall express the elementary functions whose inverse functions we are about to consider in the form $z = g(w)$, so that the inverse functions can be written as $w = g^{-1}(z) = f(z)$.

We define the **logarithmic function,** $w = \log z$, as the inverse function of the exponential function $z = e^w$. Since the exponential function is periodic, infinitely many points in the w-plane are mapped into each point of the z-plane, except $z = 0$. Hence, the logarithmic function is a multiple-valued function with infinitely many values for each z except $z = 0$. Since $w = \log z$ is the inverse function of $z = e^w$, we have that $e^{\log z} = z$. We now express $w = \log z$ in rectangular form, from which we can deduce many of its properties. Let $\log z = u + iv$ and write $z = re^{i(\theta + 2k\pi)}$, $-\pi < \theta \leq \pi$; then $re^{i(\theta+2k\pi)} = z = e^{\log z} = e^{u+vi} = e^u e^{vi}$, so that $e^u = r$ or $u = \log r$ and $v = \theta + 2k\pi$. Hence, $\log z = \log r + i(\theta + 2k\pi)$. In this expression, $\log r$ has only one value. However, $\log z$ is multiple-valued whether z is real or not. In order to avoid any confusion, we shall write $\log r$ in the preceding expression as $\text{Log}\, r$, so that

$$\log z = \text{Log}\, r + i(\theta + 2k\pi), \qquad -\pi < \theta \leq \pi,\ k = 0, \pm 1, \pm 2, \cdots.$$

This form of $\log z$ exhibits precisely its multiple-valued character.

Many properties of functions are not readily extended to multiple-valued functions; for this reason, multiple-valued functions are problematic and must be approached with caution. In the case of $\log z$, if we fix k we shall have a single-valued function that we shall call the ***k*th branch** of $\log z$. The value of $\log z$ in this branch will be called its kth value.

The branch of $\log z$ corresponding to $k = 0$ will be called its **principal branch** and the value of $\log z$ in this branch its **principal value,** which we denote as $\text{Log}\, z$. If we have to specify the kth value of $\log z$, we shall denote it as $(\log z)_k$. Observe that $(\log z)_k = \text{Log}\, z + 2k\pi i$ and $\text{Log}\, z = \text{Log}\, r + i\theta$. (Note that the notation for $\text{Log}\, r$ is consistent with that of $\text{Log}\, z$, for $\theta = \arg r = 0$, since $r > 0$.) It should be understood that the logarithmic function actually consists of the totality of all the branches, $\text{Log}\, z$, $(\log z)_k$, $k = \pm 1, \pm 2, \cdots$. Expressing the function in terms of branches makes it convenient in the study of its properties. We can write $\text{Log}\, z$ in the form $\text{Log}\, z = \text{Log}\, |z| + i \arg z$. $\text{Log}\, z$ is continuous everywhere except at the point $z = 0$ (since $\text{Log}\, |z|$ is not defined there) and all points along the negative real axis (i.e., all points z such that $\text{Re}\, z < 0$, $\text{Im}\, z = 0$), since $\arg z$ is not continuous at these points. Now, since $(\log z)_k = \text{Log}\, z + 2k\pi i$, each branch of $\log z$ has the same continuity properties as the principal branch. We call the negative real axis a **branch cut.** Of course, if we were to select another interval of length 2π for θ rather than $-\pi < \theta \leq \pi$, we should have another half-line as the branch cut. For some purposes it will be convenient to do so, and we shall have the opportunity to use other branch cuts. The point $z = 0$ is on every branch cut; it is called a **branch point.** The logarithmic function has the following properties for z_1, z_2, z nonzero:

L_1: $\text{Log}\, z = \frac{1}{2} \text{Log}\, (x^2 + y^2) + i \tan^{-1}(y/x)$, the inverse tangent in the same quadrant as z.

L_2: $\text{Log}\, z_1 z_2 = \text{Log}\, z_1 + \text{Log}\, z_2 + 2\pi\delta i$, $\delta = -1$, 0, or 1, depending on whether $\pi < \arg z_1 + \arg z_1 \leq 2\pi$, $-\pi < \arg z_1 + \arg z_2 \leq \pi$, or $-2\pi < \arg z_1 + \arg z_2 \leq -\pi$.

L_3: $\text{Log}\, (z_1/z_2) = \text{Log}\, z_1 - \text{Log}\, z_2 + 2\pi\delta i$, $\delta = -1$, 0, or 1, depending on whether $\pi < \arg z_1 - \arg z_2 < 2\pi$, $-\pi < \arg z_1 - \arg z_2 \leq \pi$, or $-2\pi < \arg z_1 - \arg z_2 \leq -\pi$.

L_4: $\text{Log}\, z^n = n \,\text{Log}\, z + 2\pi p i$, n a positive integer, $p = [\frac{1}{2} - n\,(\arg z/2\pi)]$.

L_5: $(\log z_1 z_2)_p = (\log z_1)_q + (\log z_2)_r$ with the appropriate choice of p, q, r.

L_6: $\text{Log}\, z$ has only the zero $z = 1$; $(\log z)_k$ has no zeros.

L_7: $\text{Log}\, e^z = z + 2\pi p i$, p is the integer that satisfies

$$-\frac{1}{2} - \frac{\text{Im}\, z}{2\pi} < p \leq \frac{1}{2} - \frac{\text{Im}\, z}{2\pi}.$$

L_8: $e^{n \,\text{Log}\, e^z} = e^{nz}$.

The proofs follow readily from the definitions and properties P_7 to P_{10} of the argument (p. 183). L_8 follows from L_7 and the periodicity of the exponential function.

EXAMPLE 1. Express $\text{Log}\, (-4 - 4i)$ and $[\log\, (-4 - 4i)]_k$ in rectangular form.

Solution. With the use of L_1, $\text{Log}(-4-4i) = \text{Log}\,4\sqrt{2} - (3\pi/4)i$. Then

$$[\log(-4-4i)]_k = \text{Log}\,4\sqrt{2} - \left(\frac{3\pi}{4} + 2\pi k\right)i, \qquad k = \pm 1, \pm 2, \cdots.$$

EXAMPLE 2. If $z_1 = 2e^{3\pi i/4}$ and $z_2 = 4e^{\pi i/2}$, find $\text{Log}\, z_1 z_2$.

Solution. By L_2 (since $\arg z_1 + \arg z_2 = 3\pi/4 + \pi/2 = 5\pi/4$), $\text{Log}\, z_1 z_2 = \text{Log}\, z_1 + \text{Log}\, z_2 - 2\pi i = \text{Log}\, 2 + 3\pi i/4 + \text{Log}\, 4 + \pi i/2 - 2\pi i = \text{Log}\, 8 - 3/4\pi i$.
We can also determine $\text{Log}\, z_1 z_2$ directly, for $z_1 z_2 = 8e^{5/4\pi i}$. But $\arg z_1 z_2 = -3\pi/4$, so that $\text{Log}\, z_1 z_2 = \text{Log}\, 8 - 3\pi i/4$.

We have defined z^n for any integer n. It remains to define z^α for any complex number α. Since for any real constant c and x real, we have that $x^c = e^{c \,\text{Log}\, x}$, and with the use of L_8, $z^n = e^{n\,\text{Log}\, z}$ (proof?), we are led to the definition of the **generalized power function** as $z^\alpha = e^{\alpha \log z}$, $z \neq 0$, a complex variable, and α, a complex constant. Since $\log z$ is a multiple-valued function, we should expect z to be multiple-valued in general; however, we know that it is single-valued when α is an integer. As in the case of the logarithm, it will be convenient to study the power function as a set of single-valued functions or branches.

We define the kth value of z^α as $e^{\alpha(\log z)_k}$ and denote it by $(z^\alpha)_k$. If $k = 0$, we call it the principal value of z^α and denote it by $P[z^\alpha]$, so that $P[z^\alpha] = e^{\alpha\,\text{Log}\, z}$. Since $(\log z)_k = \text{Log}\, z + 2\pi k i$, we have that $(z^\alpha)_k = P[z^\alpha]e^{2\pi i k\alpha}$, $k = \pm 1, \pm 2, \cdots$, which means that each value of the power function can be obtained from the principal value by multiplying it by the factor $e^{2\pi i k\alpha}$, $k = \pm 1, \pm 2, \cdots$. These may not be all different; for example, if α is an integer, the factor will be one for all k, as we expect, since we know that z^n, n an integer, is single-valued. Actually, this is a special case of the very important

THEOREM. z^α is n-valued if and only if α is a rational number of the form m/n, where m and n have no common factors, $n \geq 1$.

Proof. Since all the values of z^α can be obtained by multiplying $P[z^\alpha]$ by $e^{2\pi i k\alpha}$, we need consider only the values of $e^{2\pi i k\alpha}$. First, suppose that $e^{2\pi i k\alpha}$ has only n different values, $k = \pm 1, \pm 2, \cdots$. Then there must exist two integers k and k', $k \neq k'$, such that

$$e^{2\pi i k\alpha} = e^{2\pi i k'\alpha} \text{ or } e^{2\pi i\alpha(k-k')} = 1.$$

But this means that $\alpha(k - k')$ is an integer, say, p, so that $\alpha = p\,(k - k')$, which is a rational number.

Conversely, let α be a rational number of the form m/n. Then it is clear that for $k = 0, 1, \cdots, n-1$, the values of $e^{2\pi i mk/n}$ are distinct. We must now show that these n values are the only values of $e^{2\pi i mk/n}$. Let k' be any integer other than $0, 1, \cdots, n-1$. First, suppose $k' > n - 1$. Let

q be an integer such that $nq \le k' < n(q+1)$; then $0 \le k' - nq < n$, so that $k' - nq$ is one of the integers $0, 1, \cdots, n-1$. Now $e^{2\pi im(k'-nq)/n} = e^{2\pi imk'}e^{-2\pi imq} = e^{2\pi imk'}$. This means that k' yields the same value of $e^{2\pi imk/n}$ as does one of the integers $0, 1, \cdots, n-1$. The case $k' < 0$ is left to the student. The proof is complete.

The preceding theorem implies that z^α, $z \ne 0$, has n distinct values if $\alpha = m/n$, m and n integers without common factors, $n \ge 1$ and an infinity of distinct values if α is irrational or if $\operatorname{Im} \alpha \ne 0$. It follows that z^α is single-valued only if α is an integer.

Now let us consider $z^{1/n}$, where n is an integer > 1. We know that it has n distinct values. These values are the roots of z, for $[z^{1/n}]^n = [e^{(1/n)\log z}]^n = e^{\log z} = z$ (by E_{11}, p. 203). We call each of these roots the nth root of z; hence, the complex number z has n nth roots. It is an important problem in practice to determine all these roots for a given complex number z and a given integer $n > 1$. Let us derive a simple formula, which can be applied readily.

$$z^{1/n} = e^{(1/n)\log z} = e^{(1/n)[\operatorname{Log} r + (\theta + 2k\pi)i]} = r^{1/n}e^{[(\theta+2k\pi)/n]i}.$$

It is more convenient from the computational standpoint to write this in polar form. So, if we let $z_0, z_1, \cdots, z_{n-1}$ be the nth roots of z,

$$z_k = r^{1/n}[\cos(\theta + 2k\pi)/n + i \sin(\theta + 2k\pi)/n],$$
$$k = 0, 1, \cdots, n-1, \ r = |z|, \ \theta = \arg z.$$

To determine $z^{m/n}$, m and n integers, $n > 1$, without common factors, we let $z^{m/n} = (z^{1/n})^m$. [See p. 217, Exercise 19(b).]

EXAMPLE. Find all of the fourth roots of $z = -8 + 8\sqrt{3}i$.

Solution. Denote the roots by z_0, z_1, z_2, z_3. Then, since $r = 16$ and $\theta = 2\pi/3$,

$$z_k = 2\left[\cos\frac{(2\pi/3) + 2k\pi}{4} + i\sin\frac{(2\pi/3) + 2k\pi}{4}\right], \qquad k = 0, 1, 2, 3.$$

Hence,

$$z_0 = 2\left[\cos\frac{\pi}{6} + i\sin\frac{\pi}{6}\right] = \sqrt{3} + i,$$

$$z_1 = 2\left[\cos\frac{2\pi}{3} + i\sin\frac{2\pi}{3}\right] = -\sqrt{3} + i,$$

$$z_2 = 2\left[\cos\frac{7\pi}{6} + i\sin\frac{7\pi}{6}\right] = -\sqrt{3} - i,$$

and

$$z_3 = 2\left[\cos\frac{5\pi}{3} + i\sin\frac{5\pi}{3}\right] = \sqrt{3} - i.$$

The generalized power function has the following properties, which are valid for the kth value of the function, $k = 0, \pm 1, \pm 2, \cdots$, provided the kth value in each identity is taken for every power function that occurs in that identity and $z \neq 0$.

P₁: $(z^\alpha)^n = z^{\alpha n}$, n an integer.
P₂: $z^{-\alpha} = 1/z^\alpha$.
P₃: $z^{\alpha+\beta} = z^\alpha z^\beta$.
P₄: $z^{\alpha-\beta} = z^\alpha/z^\beta$.
P₅: $e^{(\log z^\alpha)_k} = e^{\alpha(\log z)_k}$.
P₆: $z_1^\alpha z_2^\alpha = (z_1 z_2)^\alpha e^{2\pi\alpha(k-\delta)i}$, $\delta = -1$, 0, or 1, depending on whether $\pi < \arg z_1 + \arg z_1 \leq 2\pi$, $-\pi < \arg z_1 + \arg z_2 \leq \pi$, or $-2\pi < \arg z_1 + \arg z_2 \leq -\pi$, $k = 0, \pm 1, \pm 2, \cdots$, $z_1 \neq 0$, $z_2 \neq 0$.

The student should prove these properties, using the necessary properties of the exponential and logarithmic functions. Note that P_1 to P_5 are properties of the real power function that extend to the complex power function; and note particularly P_6, where the exponential factor becomes one only if α is an integer. Furthermore, in general, $(z^\alpha)^\beta \neq z^{\alpha\beta}$ [see p. 217, Exercise 19(a)]. The student should now be well aware that all properties of real functions do not extend to the corresponding complex functions.

EXAMPLE 1. Find the principal value of $(-i)^i$ and then all its other values.

Solution

$$\begin{aligned} P[(-i)^i] &= e^{i \operatorname{Log}(-i)} \\ &= e^{i[\operatorname{Log}|-i| - (i\pi/2)]} \\ &= e^{\pi/2}. \end{aligned}$$

$$[(-i)^i]_k = e^{\pi/2}e^{-2k\pi} = e^{\pi/2 - 2k\pi}, \qquad k = \pm 1, \pm 2, \cdots.$$

EXAMPLE 2. Find all values of z that satisfy $z^i = i$.

Solution

$$\begin{aligned} z^i &= e^{i \operatorname{Log} z} e^{-2k\pi} = e^{i[\operatorname{Log} r + i\theta]} e^{-2k\pi} \\ &= e^{-(2k\pi+\theta)} e^{i \operatorname{Log} r}, \end{aligned}$$

so that $z^i = i$ becomes

$$e^{-(2k\pi+\theta)} e^{i \operatorname{Log} r} = e^{(\pi/2)i}.$$

Hence, $e^{-(2k\pi+\theta)} = 1$ and $\operatorname{Log} r = \pi/2$, so that

$$z = re^{i\theta} = e^{\pi/2}e^{-2k\pi i}, \qquad k = 0, \pm 1, \pm 2, \cdots.$$

It remains to consider the inverse functions of the trigonometric and hyperbolic functions. Let us study the inverse sine function, denoted by $w = \sin^{-1} z$, in detail; the remaining ones can be studied in the same way. Since $w = \sin^{-1} z$ is the inverse function of $z = \sin w$, we can obtain an explicit representation for this inverse function by solving

$$z = (e^{iw} - e^{-iw})/2i$$

for w in terms of z. This equation can be written as $e^{2iw} - 2ize^{iw} - 1 = 0$, which is a quadratic in e^{iw} [see p. 216, Exercise 8(a)] whose solution is

$e^{iw} = iz + (1 - z^2)^{1/2}$, $(1 - z^2)^{1/2}$ having two values. Now $w = \sin^{-1} z = -i \log [iz + (1 - z^2)^{1/2}]$. For each value of $(1 - z^2)^{1/2}$, $\sin^{-1} z$ is a multiple-valued function with infinitely many values, since the logarithmic function has this property. We define the principal value of $\sin^{-1} z$ as that value which is determined by the principal value of $(1 - z^2)^{1/2}$ and the principal value of the logarithmic function; it is denoted as $\text{Sin}^{-1} z$.

We merely list the explicit representations of some of the other trigonometric and hyperbolic functions together with that of the inverse sine:

$$\sin^{-1} z = -i \log [iz + (1 - z^2)^{1/2}],$$
$$\cos^{-1} z = -i \log [z + (z^2 - 1)^{1/2}],$$
$$\tan^{-1} z = \frac{i}{2} \log \frac{i + z}{i - z}$$
$$\sinh^{-1} z = \log [z + (z^2 + 1)^{1/2}]$$
$$\cosh^{-1} z = \log [z + (z^2 - 1)^{1/2}]$$
$$\tanh^{-1} z = \frac{1}{2} \log \frac{1 + z}{1 - z}.$$

The student should establish these representations. The principal values of these functions are determined by taking the principal values of all multiple-valued functions occurring in their representation. They are denoted as $\text{Sin}^{-1} z$, $\text{Cos}^{-1} z$, $\text{Tan}^{-1} z$, $\text{Sinh}^{-1} z$, $\text{Cosh}^{-1} z$, $\text{Tanh}^{-1} z$.

EXERCISES

1. Evaluate each of the following:

(a) $\log 1$; (b) $\text{Log } 1$; (c) $\log(-1)$; (d) $\text{Log}(-1)$; (e) $\log i$; (f) $\text{Log } i$; (g) $\log \sqrt{i}$; (h) $\text{Log}(1 + \sqrt{3}i)$; (i) $\text{Log}(-ei)$; (j) $\text{Log}(1 - i)$.

Ans.: (a) $2k\pi i$; (b) 0; (c) $(2k + 1)\pi i$; (d) πi; (e) $[(\pi/2) + 2k\pi]i$; (f) $\pi i/2$; (g) $[(\pi/4) + k\pi]i$; (h) $\text{Log } 2 + (\pi i/3)$; (i) $1 - (\pi i/2)$; (j) $\frac{1}{2} \text{Log } 2 - (\pi i/4)$.

2. Find the principal value and then all other values of

(a) i^i; (b) $(1 + i)^i$; (c) 2^i; (d) $(-1)^{2i}$; (e) $1^{\sqrt{2}}$; (f) $\log i^i$; (g) $i \log i$; (h) $(-1)^{1/\pi}$; (i) $(1 + i)^{1+\sqrt{3}i}$; (j) $[\frac{1}{2}e(-1 - i\sqrt{3})]^{3\pi i}$.

Ans.: Principal values: (a) $e^{-\pi/2}$; (b) $e^{-\pi/4 + i \text{ Log } 2}$; (c) $e^{i \text{ Log } 2}$; (d) $e^{-2\pi}$; (e) $e^{2\sqrt{2}\pi i}$; (f) $-\pi/2$; (g) $-\pi/2$; (h) $e\pi$; (i) $(1 + i)e^{(\sqrt{3}/2)[(-\pi/2) + i \text{ Log } 2]}$; (j) $-e^{2\pi^2}$.

3. Find each of the following:

(a) $\tan^{-1} 2i$; (b) $\tan^{-1}(1 + i)$; (c) $\cosh^{-1}(-1)$; (d) $\tanh^{-1}(0)$; (e) $\cos^{-1} i$.

Ans.: (a) $-(k + \frac{1}{2})\pi + (i/2) \text{ Log } 3$; (b) $-\frac{1}{2}(\theta + 2k\pi) + (i/2) \text{ Log} \sqrt{5}$, $\theta = \tan^{-1} 2$ in the third quadrant; (c) $2k\pi i$; (d) $k\pi i$; (e) $-[(\pi/2) + (2k\pi)] - i \text{ Log } |1 \pm 2|$.

4. Solve:

(a) $\log z = (\pi/2)i$; (b) $e^z = -3$; (c) $\sin z = 2$; (d) $\cos z = \sqrt{2}$; (e) $\sin z = 1 - i$; (f) $\cos z = 2i$; (g) $z^4 = -81$; (h) $i^z = 2$; (i) $z^{2i} = -1$; (j) $\tan^{-1} z = i$.

Ans.: (a) i; (b) $\text{Log } 3 + (2k + 1)\pi i$; (c) $(\pi/2)(1 + 4k) \pm i \text{ Log}(2 + \sqrt{3})$; (d) $2k\pi - i \text{ Log}(\sqrt{2} + 1)$; (f) $(\pi/2) + 2k\pi + \text{Log}(2 \pm \sqrt{5})$;

(h) $-2k'\pi + \dfrac{i \operatorname{Log} 2}{(\pi/2) + 2k\pi}$; (j) $\dfrac{i(e^2 - 1)}{e^2 + 1}$.

5. Find (a) $\sqrt{i}$; (b) $\sqrt{-i}$; (c) $\sqrt{1 + i}$; (d) $\sqrt{\dfrac{1 + i\sqrt{3}}{2}}$;

(e) $\sqrt[3]{i}$; (f) $\sqrt[3]{-i}$; (g) $\sqrt[4]{i}$; (h) $\sqrt[4]{-i}$; (i) $\sqrt[3]{1 + i}$; (j) $\sqrt[3]{1 - i}$.

Ans.: (a) $(1 + i)/\sqrt{2}$; (b) $\pm(-1 + i)/\sqrt{2}$; (c) $\pm\sqrt{2}\left(\cos\dfrac{\pi}{8} + i \sin\dfrac{\pi}{8}\right)$; (d) $\pm\frac{1}{2}(\sqrt{3} + i)$; (e) 1, $(-1 \pm \sqrt{3}i)/2$; (f) i, $(\pm\sqrt{3} - i)/2$; (h) $\pm(\pm 1 + i)/\sqrt{2}$; (i) $\sqrt[6]{2}(\cos\theta + i \sin\theta)$, $\theta = \pi/12, 3\pi/4, 17\pi/12$.

6. (a) Show that the nth roots of unity are $1, \omega, \omega^2, \cdots, \omega^{n-1}$, where $\omega = \cos(2\pi/n) + i \sin(2\pi/n)$.

(b) Show that $1 + \omega + \omega^2 + \cdots + \omega^{n-1} = 0$.

(c) Show that for every integer p, $1 + \omega^p + \omega^{2p} + \cdots + \omega^{(n-1)p} = n$, when p is a multiple of n but otherwise is equal to 0.

(d) Show that the nth roots of unity determine the vertices of a regular polygon of n sides inscribed in a circle of radius 1 and center at the origin.

(e) Show that the nth roots of a, $a > 0$, are $\sqrt[n]{a}\omega^k$, $k = 0, 1, \cdots, n - 1$.

(f) Determine the nth roots of $-a$, $a > 0$.

7. Solve (and retain for future reference) $a > 0$; (a) $z^4 + a^4 = 0$; (b) $z^6 + a^6 = 0$; (c) $z^8 + a^8 = 0$.

8. (a) Show that the roots of the quadratic equation $az^2 + bz + c = 0$ are $z = -b + \sqrt{b^2 - 4ac}/2a$. Since $\sqrt{b^2 - 4ac}$ has two values, the equation has two roots. When is one the negative of the other?

(b) Solve: $2iz^2 - iz + 5 = 0$; $(i + 1)z^2 - \sqrt{3}z + 2i - 1 = 0$.

9. Solve: (a) $z^3 = -\sqrt{2} + \sqrt{2}i$; (b) $z^5 = 16 - 16\sqrt{3}i$; (c) $z^{2/3} + 2 = 0$; (d) $z^4 + 5z^2 = 36$; (e) $z^6 + 7z^3 = 8$; (f) $z^4 - 3(1 + 2i)z^2$.

10. Show that the solutions of $z^4 + 4 = 0$ are $1 + i, -1 + i, -1 - i, 1 - i$, and deduce that $z^4 + 4 = (z^2 + 2z + 2)(z^2 - 2z + 2)$.

11. Find all values of $\sqrt[4]{3 + 4i}$ and hence solve the simultaneous equations $x^4 - 6x^2y^2 + y^4 = 3$, $xy(x^2 - y^2) = 1$ for real values of x and y.

12. (a) Show that if $z \neq 1$, $\operatorname{Re}[\log(z - 1)] = \frac{1}{2}\operatorname{Log}(r^2 - 2r\cos\theta + 1)$, $z = re^{i\phi}$, $\phi = \theta + 2k\pi$, $k = 0, \pm 1, \pm 2, \cdots$.

(b) Show that if $z \neq 1, \pm i$, $\operatorname{Re}(\tan^{-1} z) = \pi(k \pm \frac{1}{4})$.

13. Show that $\log[\sin(x + iy)\csc(x - iy)] = 2i\tan^{-1}(\tanh y \cot x)$.

14. Prove that for $z \neq 0$, $\operatorname{Re}[\log(z/\bar{z})] = 0$.

15. If $p = a + bi$ and $q = a - bi$, where a and b are real, show that $pe^q + qe^p$ is real and $\log(\cos q \sec p) = i\alpha$, where

$$\tan\alpha = \sin 2a \sinh 2b/(1 + \cos 2a \cosh 2b).$$

16. Show that z^{a+bi}, a, b real, $z \neq 0$, is real if and only if $2a$ is an integer and $b \operatorname{Log}|z| + a \arg z$ is a multiple of π.

17. Show that all values of z^α have the same absolute value if and only if $\operatorname{Im}\alpha = 0$. If $\operatorname{Im}\alpha \neq 0$, show that z^α has infinitely many distinct absolute values.

18. Show that all values of z^α lie on a half-line through the origin if and only if $\operatorname{Re} \alpha$ is an integer.

◇ **19.** (a) Show that $(z^\alpha)^\beta = z^{\alpha\beta}e^{2\pi i\beta(p+k)}$, where

$$p = \left[\frac{1}{2} - \frac{\operatorname{Im} \alpha \operatorname{Log} |z| + \operatorname{Re} \alpha \arg z}{2\pi}\right], \qquad k = 0, \pm 1, \pm 2, \cdots.$$

(b) If m and n are integers, $n > 0$, with common factors, show that $z^{m/n} = (z^{1/n})^m = (z^m)^{1/n}$.

20. (a) Show that $(\log z_1)_p + (\log z_2)_q = (\log z_1 z_2)_r$, $r = p + q + \delta$, $\delta = -1$, 0, or 1.

(b) Show that

$$(\log z_1)_k + (\log z_2)_k = (\log z_1 z_2)_k + 2\pi\cdot(k + \delta)i, \qquad \delta = -1, 0, \text{ or } 1.$$

(c) $(\log z^n)_k = n(\log z)_k + 2\pi\cdot[\delta - (n-1)k]i$, $\delta = -1, 0$, or 1.

(d) Show by an example that for a given k there does not exist necessarily k' such that $(\log z^n)_k = n(\log z)_{k'}$.

21. Show that $|z^h| = |z|^h$, h real, for every value of z^h.

22. Generalize DeMoivre's formula (P_3, p. 183) to the case in which n is an arbitrary complex number.

23. Discuss the behavior of the logarithmic function and the inverse trigonometric and hyperbolic functions at the point at infinity.

24. If C is a disk not containing the point ∞, then for each point $a \neq \infty$ not belonging to C, there exists in C a value of $\log (z - a)$. Prove this.

25. Determine all roots of

$$1 + nx - \frac{n(n-1)}{2}x^2 - \frac{n(n-1)(n-2)}{3}x^3 + \cdots + (-1)^{n(n-1)/2}x^n = 0.$$

8. Geometric interpretation of complex functions. The real function $y = f(x)$ can be conveniently represented geometrically as the set of points (x, y) in the xy-plane. Since the complex function $w = f(z)$, $z = x + iy$, $w = u + iv$, involves the quadruple of numbers x, y, u, v, the analogous geometric representation would require a four-dimensional space. Such a representation is difficult to visualize, and it is not very feasible to use it to study the properties of functions. It is simpler and far more useful to interpret the complex function $w = f(z)$ geometrically as the mapping of specific configurations in the z-plane, such as curves and regions into corresponding configurations in the w-plane.

If $w = f(z)$ maps the configuration F in the z-plane into the configuration F' in the w-plane, we call F' the *map* or *image* of F under $w = f(z)$.

On occasion we shall interpret $w = f(z)$ as a mapping of configurations on the z-sphere into configurations on the w-sphere.

We shall be primarily concerned with complex functions that are continuous in a given region in the z-plane; the mappings determined by these functions will be called **continuous mappings.** A continuous function maps curves and regions in the z-plane into curves and regions in the w-plane.

Let us consider the mapping of a given curve in the z-plane under a given function. Closed curves will be mapped into closed curves; however, a simple curve is not necessarily mapped into a simple curve. (Why?) The map of the point of intersection of two curves is the point of intersection of the maps of these curves. The continuous function $w = f(z) = u(x, y) + iv(x, y)$ maps a curve of the form $g(x, y) = 0$ in the z-plane into a curve of the form $h(u, v) = 0$ in the w-plane. An important problem is the following: Given $w = f(z)$ and the curve $g(x, y) = 0$, determine the map of $g(x, y) = 0$ under $f(z)$. This problem can be solved by eliminating x and y from $u = u(x, y)$, $v = v(x, y)$, and $g(x, y) = 0$ to obtain the curve $h(u, v) = 0$, which is the map of $g(x, y) = 0$ under $f(z)$.

EXAMPLE. Find the map of the circle $x^2 + y^2 + ax + by + c = 0$ under $w = 1/z$.

Solution. $w = 1/z = x/(x^2 + y^2) - [iy/(x^2 + y^2)]$. Let $u = x/(x^2 + y^2)$ and $v = -y/(x^2 + y^2)$, so that $x^2 + y^2 = 1/(u^2 + v^2)$, and $x = u/(u^2 + v^2)$, $y = -v/(u^2 + v^2)$. Substituting in $x^2 + y^2 + ax + by + c = 0$ yields $c(u^2 + v^2) + au - bv + 1 = 0$. If $c \neq 0$, this is a circle, and if $c = 0$, it is a straight line; hence circles that do not pass through the origin are mapped into circles, and circles passing through the origin are mapped into straight lines. If we consider a straight line to be a circle passing through the point at infinity, then we can say unreservedly that $w = 1/z$ maps circles into circles. This can be visualized readily if we consider the mapping from the z-sphere to the w-sphere.

Now let us consider the mapping of regions in the z-plane. Let R be a region in the domain of the continuous function $w = f(z)$; let R' be the map of R under this function. Furthermore, if Γ is the boundary of R and $f(z)$ maps Γ into Γ', then Γ' is the boundary of R'. But Γ' is also the boundary of the region that is the complement of R'. An important problem is the following: Given a region R in the domain of the continuous function $w = f(z)$, determine its map R' under $f(z)$.

One method of solving this problem is as follows: We determine the boundary Γ' that is the map of Γ, the boundary of R, under $f(z)$. Now Γ' is the boundary of two regions, say, R_1 and R_2, where R_1 is the complement of R_2. In order to determine whether R_1 or R_2 is R', we consider any point z_0 in R; then if $f(z_0)$ is in R_1, $R' = R_1$; otherwise, $R' = R_2$.

A more elegant method of solving the preceding problem is to represent R by means of appropriate inequalities involving z which, with the use of $z = f^{-1}(w)$ and proper deft manipulation, can be transformed into inequalities involving w that represent R'. Both methods are illustrated in the following examples.

EXAMPLE 1. Determine the map of the region R in the first quadrant of the z-plane bounded by the hyperbolas $x^2 - y^2 = a$, $x^2 - y^2 = b$, $2xy = c$, $2xy = d$, $b > a > 0$, $d > c > 0$, under $w = z^2$.

Solution. $w = z^2 = x^2 - y^2 + 2ixy$. Let $u = x^2 - y^2$ and $v = 2xy$. Then the maps of the given hyperbolas are the straight lines $u = a$, $u = b$, $v = c$, $v = d$. If $z_0 = x_0 + iy_0$ is any point in R, then $a < x_0^2 - y_0^2 < b$ and $c < 2x_0y_0 < d$, so that $a < u < b$ and $c < v < d$. Hence, R is mapped into the rectangle R': $A'B'C'D'$ (see figure).

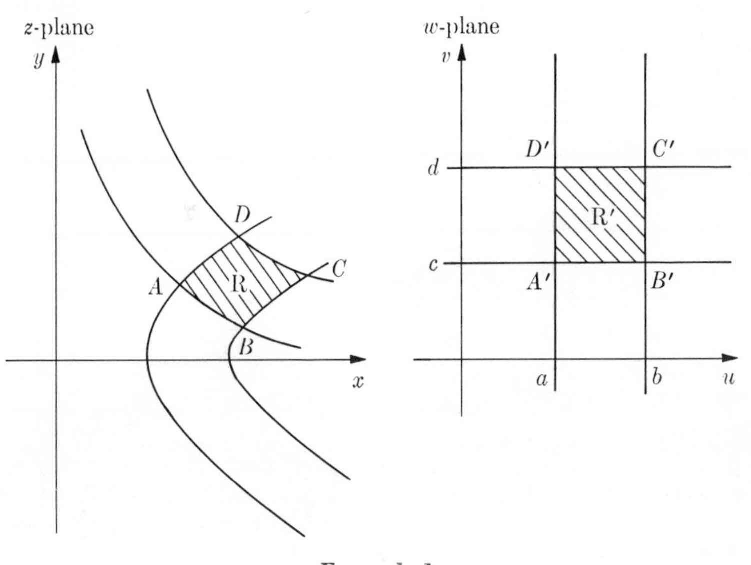

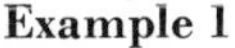
Example 1

Let us examine some of the properties of $w = z^2$ from the foregoing mapping. The angles of intersection of the pairs of curves determining the boundary of R are right angles (why?) and their maps are right angles. The function has no zeros in R, for if it did, R' would have to include the origin. The largest value of $|z^2|$ in R occurs at $z = C$, for it is clear that OC' is the largest line segment from 0 to any point in R'.

EXAMPLE 2. Determine the map of $R: 1 \le \operatorname{Re} z \le 3,\ 0 \le \operatorname{Im} z \le (\pi/2)$ under $w = e^z$.

Solution. Since $w = e^z$, $z = \log w = \operatorname{Log} r + i(\theta + 2k\pi)$. Hence, $\operatorname{Re} z = \operatorname{Log} |w|$ and $\operatorname{Im} z = \arg w + 2k\pi$, so that $1 \le \operatorname{Log} |w| \le 3$ and

$$0 \le \arg w + 2k\pi \le \pi/2.$$

It follows that $e \le |w| \le e^3$ and $-2k\pi \le \arg w \le (\pi/2) - 2k\pi$; these inequalities represent the region R' indicated in the figure. Hence, R' is the map of R.

We see that the values of $|e^z|$ are the same if z is on the line segment BC, and this common value e^3 is the largest value of $|e^z|$ in R; also the values of $|e^z|$ are the same if z is on AD, and this common value e is the smallest value of $|e^z|$ in R. Note that the largest and smallest values of

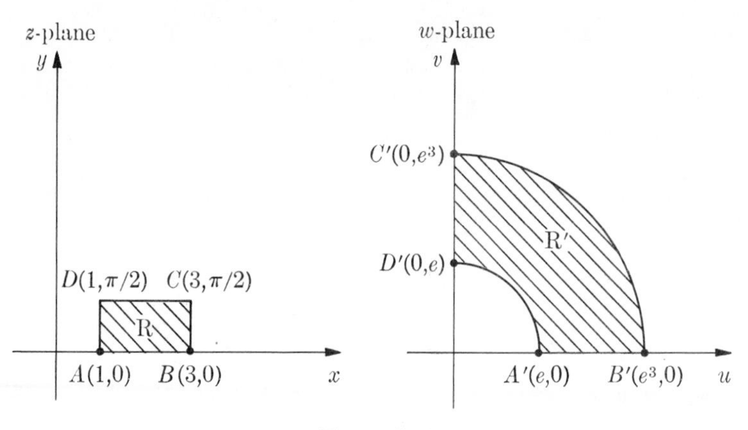

Example 2

$|e^z|$ occur on the boundary of R. Are the angles at A', B', C', D' in R' right angles?

EXAMPLE 3. Determine the map of $|z-1| < 1$ under $w = 1/z$.

Solution. $z = 1/w$ and $z - 1 = (1-w)/w$ so that $|z-1| < 1$ if and only if $|(1-w)/w| < 1$, or $|1-w| < |w|$, or $(1-w)(1-\overline{w}) < w\overline{w}$, or $1 < w + \overline{w}$; i.e., $\text{Re } w > \frac{1}{2}$. Note that a bounded region is mapped into an unbounded region. (See figure.)

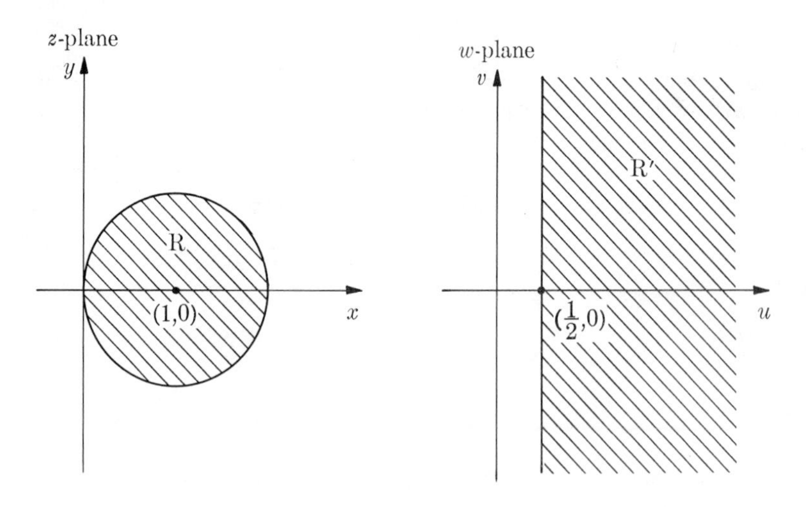

Example 3

EXAMPLE 4. Determine the map of R: $-\pi/2 \le \text{Re } z \le \pi/2$, $\text{Im } z \ge 0$ under $w = \sin z$.

Solution. $w = \sin z = \sin x \cosh y + i \cos x \sinh y$. Let $u = \sin x \cosh y$ and $v = \cos x \sinh y$. For z on AB, $v = 0$ and $u = \sin x$, and as x increases from $-\pi/2$ to $\pi/2$, u increases from -1 to 1. (See figure.) For z on BC, $v = 0$, $u = \cosh y$ and

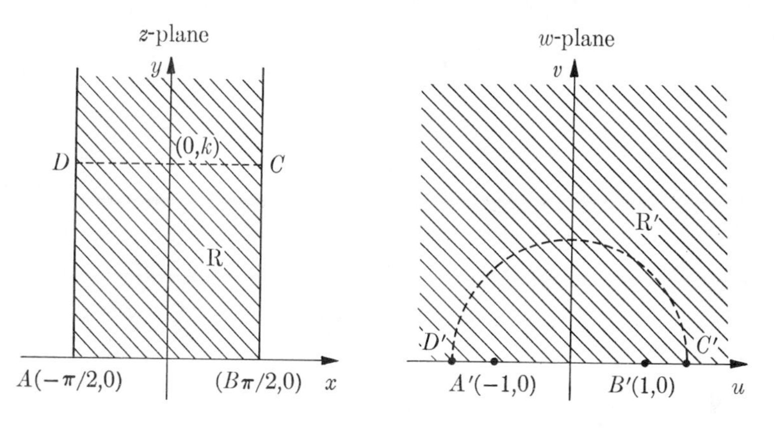

Example 4

as y increases from 0 to ∞, u increases from 1 to ∞; similarly for z on AD, $v = 0$ and $u = -\cosh y$, so that as y increases from 0 to ∞, u decreases from -1 to $-\infty$. Hence, the boundary of R is mapped into the entire real axis of the w-plane. Since $z = i$ is in R, $\sin i = i \sinh 1$, and $\sinh 1 > 0$, the map of R is the upper half of the w-plane.

Let us consider the map of the line segment $y = k$ from D to C under $w = \sin z$. The student should show that it is the upper half of the ellipse $(w^2/\cosh^2 k) + (v^2/\sinh^2 k) = 1$.

EXERCISES

1. Determine the curves in the w-plane that are the maps of the circles $|z| = 1$ and $|z - 1| = 1$ and of the lines $x = 1$ and $y = 1$ under the following:

(a) $w = 2z$; (b) $w = z - 1 + 2i$; (c) $w = 2iz$; (d) $w = z^2$; (e) $w = \dfrac{z + i}{z - i}$.

As z moves from O along $|z| = 1$ in a counterclockwise direction and returns to O, how many times does $w = f(z)$ go around the origin for each of the above functions?

2. Show that under the mapping $w = z^2$, the lines $y = c$ map into parabolas, all of whose foci are at $w = 0$. What are the images of the lines $x = c$?

3. (a) Determine the images of the lines $x = c$, $y = c$, $ax + by = 0$, $ax + by + c = 0$, $c \neq 0$ under $w = 1/z$.

(b) Show that the image of $x^2 - y^2 = 1$, $x > 0$ under $w = 1/z$ is the circle $|z - 1| < 1$. (*Hint:* Use polar coordinates.) What is the image of $x^2 - y^2 = 1$?

4. Show that $w = \sqrt{1 - z^2}$ maps the hyperbola $2x^2 - 2y^2 = 1$ into $2u^2 - 2v^2 = 1$. We say that the hyperbola is *mapped into itself*.

5. Show that $w = z^2$ maps $|z - a| = a$, $a > 0$, into $\rho = 2a^2(1 + \cos \phi)$, $w = \rho e^{i\phi}$.

6. Show that $w = e^z$ transforms the lines $ky = x$ into the spirals $\rho = e^{k\phi}$, $w = \rho e^{i\phi}$.

7. Show that $w = iz + 1$ maps $\text{Re}\, z > 0$ into $\text{Im}\, w > 1$.

8. Show that $w = iz + 1$ maps $\text{Re}\, z > 0$, $0 < \text{Im}\, z < 2$ into $|\text{Re}\, w| < 1$, $\text{Im}\, w > 0$.

9. Determine the regions into which $0 < \theta < (\pi/4)$, $r < 1$, $z = re^{i\theta}$, is mapped under
(a) $w = z^2$; (b) $w = z^3$; (c) $w = z^4$; (d) $w = z^n$, n a positive integer; (e) $w = 1/z$.

10. Show that $w = 1/z$, $z = x + iy$, $w = u + iv$ maps
(a) $0 < y < \frac{1}{2}c$ into $u^2 + (v + c)^2 > c^2$, $v < 0$.
(b) $y > c > 0$ into the interior of a circle.
(c) $x > 1$, $y > 0$ into $|w - \frac{1}{2}| < \frac{1}{2}$, $v < 0$.

11. Show that $w = e^z$ maps $0 \le \text{Im}\, z \le \pi$ into the upper half of the w-plane and R: $\text{Re}\, z < 0$, $0 \le \text{Im}\, z \le \pi$ into R': $|w| \le 1$, $\text{Im}\, w > 0$. What is the largest value of $|e^z|$ in R? At what values of z in R does it occur? What does e^z map $\text{Re}\, z \ge 0$, $0 \le \text{Im}\, z \le \pi$ into?

12. Show that $w = \sin z$ maps R: $|\text{Re}\, z| \le \pi/2$, $\text{Im}\, z \ge 0$ into R': $\text{Im}\, w \ge 0$. What are the images of $z = 0, -\pi/2, \pi/2 + ci$? Does $\sin z$ have any zeros in R?

13. Show that $w = \cosh z$ maps
(a) $z = yi$, $0 \le y \le \pi/2$ into $0 \le \text{Im}\, w \le 1$.
(b) $\text{Re}\, z \ge 0$, $0 \le \text{Im}\, z \le \pi/2$ into the first quadrant of the w-plane. Does $\cosh z$ have any zeros in the given regions in the z-plane? Determine the largest value of $|\cosh z|$ in these regions.

14. Show that $w = \sin^2 z$ maps $0 \le \text{Re}\, z \le \pi/2$, $\text{Im}\, z \ge 0$ into $\text{Im}\, w \ge 0$.

15. Show that $w = z + 1/z$ maps
(a) $|z| = a$ into ellipses and $\arg z = b$ into hyperbolas, a and b constants, with foci at $w = \pm 1$.
(b) $|z| \le 1$ into $\text{Im}\, w \le 0$.
(c) $|z| > 1$, $\text{Im}\, z > 0$ into $\text{Im}\, w > 0$.

16. Show that $w = \dfrac{z}{1 - z}$ maps $|z| < 1$ into $\text{Re}\, w \ge -\frac{1}{2}$.

17. Show that $w = z + e^z$ maps $|\text{Im}\, z| \le \pi$ into the entire w-plane. What can you say about the zeros of $z + e^z$?

18. Show that $w = \text{Log}\, z$ maps $\text{Re}\, z > 0$ into $0 < \text{Im}\, w < \pi$.

19. Show that $w = \text{Log}\, [(1 + z)/(1 - z)]$ maps $|z| \le 1$ into $|\text{Im}\, w| \le \pi/2$.

20. Show that $w = \text{Log}\, [(1 + z^2)/2z]$ maps $|z| < 1$, $\text{Im}\, z > 0$ into $0 < \text{Im}\, w < \pi$.

21. Show that $w = (i - z)/(i + z)$ maps $\text{Im}\, z \ge 0$ into $|w| \le 1$.

22. Show that $w = (1 - \cos z)/(1 + \cos z)$ maps $0 \le \text{Re}\, z \le \pi/2$, $\text{Im}\, z \ge 0$, into $|w| \le 1$, $\text{Im}\, w \ge 0$.

23. Show that $w = \coth (z/2)$ maps $\text{Re}\, z \ge 0$, $|\text{Im}\, z| \le \pi$, into $\text{Re}\, w \ge 0$. What are the images of the points $z = 0, \pi i, -\pi i$?

24. Show that $w = K(z - z_0)/(z - \bar{z}_0)$, $|K| = 1$, maps $\text{Im}\, z > 0$ into $|w| < 1$ if $\text{Im}\, z_0 > 0$ and into $|w| > 1$ if $\text{Im}\, z_0 < 0$.

25. Show that $w = \dfrac{z - a}{az - 1}$, $a = 1 + \sqrt{2}$, maps $|z| < 1$, $|z - \frac{1}{2}| > \frac{1}{2}$ into

$1 < |z| < a$. If

$$a = \frac{1 + x_1x_2 + \sqrt{(1 - x_1^2)(1 - x_2^2)}}{x_1 - x_2}, \qquad -1 < x_2 < x_1 < 1,$$

what is the map of the region indicated in the figure under the given function?

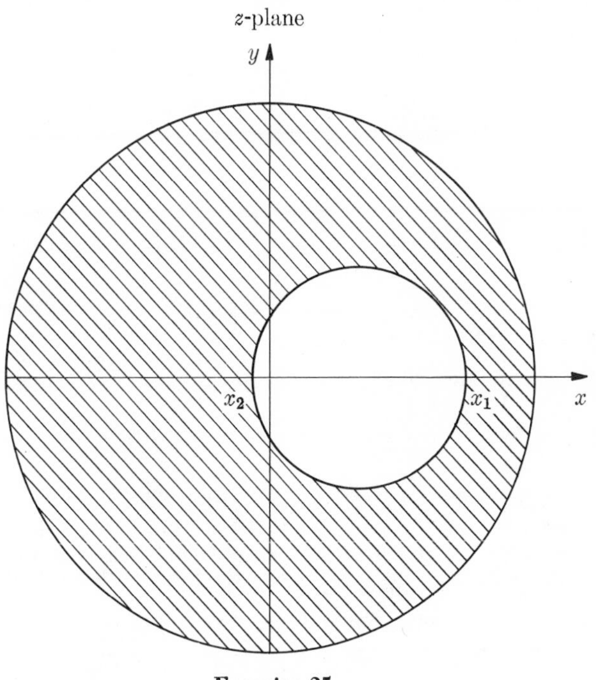

Exercise 25

Chapter 7

The Complex Differential Calculus

1. The complex derivative. Since the operation of differentiation plays a central role in the study of real functions, it is natural to consider such an operation applied to complex functions. We turn to the definition of the derivative of a complex function. Given a complex function $w = f(z)$ with domain D; let z_0 be any fixed point in D and let z be any point in D. Then the **derivative** of $f(z)$ at z_0 is

$$\lim_{z \to z_0} \frac{f(z) - f(z_0)}{z - z_0},$$

provided this limit exists. We denote this derivative by $f'(z_0)$. This definition of the derivative is exactly the same in form as that for real functions. However, we should recall that our definition of limit implies that it is uniquely determined; i.e., the limit must be the same regardless of the path along which z approaches z_0. In other words, *the value of the limit must be the same on all paths from z to z_0*. In moving from the real axis to the complex plane, we acquire another degree of freedom; if we restrict ourselves to the real axis, x can approach x_0 in one of two directions, but in the complex plane, z can approach z_0 along infinitely many paths. It would appear then that we are imposing a rather strong condition that $f'(z_0)$ exist; we shall soon see, however, that it is this very condition that leads to properties of complex functions that are not shared by real functions.

One way of showing that the derivative of a function $f(z)$ does not exist at a point z_0 is to exhibit two different paths along which $[f(z) - f(z_0)]/(z - z_0)$ has two different values as $z \to z_0$.

EXAMPLE 1. Show that $f(z) = \bar{z}$ does not have a derivative anywhere.

Solution. The domain of $f(z)$ is the entire z-plane. Let z_0 be any fixed point and z any point in the plane. Consider

$$Q = \frac{\bar{z} - \bar{z}_0}{z - z_0} = \frac{x - x_0 - (y - y_0)i}{x - x_0 + (y - y_0)i}.$$

We shall first let $z \to z_0$ by letting $y \to y_0$ and then letting $x \to x_0$ (i.e., the dotted path in Fig. 1); then $Q \to 1$. Now letting $z \to z_0$ by letting $x \to x_0$ and then

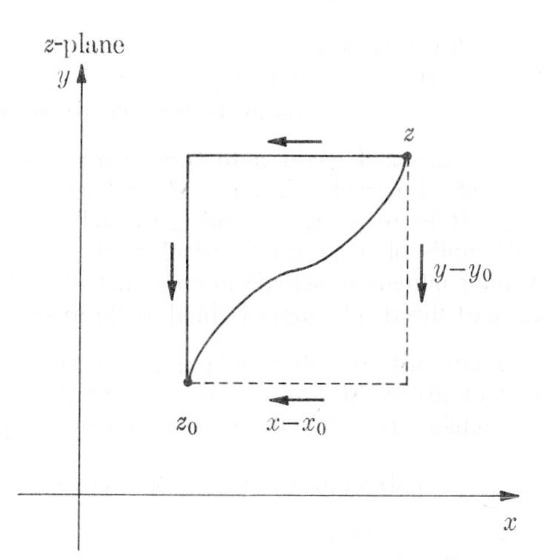

Fig. 1. Paths from z to z_0

$y \to y_0$ (i.e., the solid path in Fig. 1), $Q \to -1$. Since z_0 was any point, the derivative of $\bar{z}$ does not exist at any point.

EXAMPLE 2. Show that $w = |z|^2$ has a derivative only for $z = 0$.

Solution

$$Q = \frac{|z|^2 - |z_0|^2}{z - z_0} = z\frac{\bar{z} - \bar{z}_0}{z - z_0} + \bar{z}_0.$$

The result of Example 1 indicates that for $z_0 \neq 0$, $\lim_{z \to z_0} Q$ does not exist. If $z_0 = 0$, $Q = \bar{z}$, and the student should show that $\lim_{z \to 0} \bar{z} = 0$.

In the case of the real function $y = |x|^2$, since $|x|^2 = x^2$, we have that its derivative exists at every point on the real axis, a result that does not extend to the complex plane. If a function has a derivative at a point, then we say that the function is **differentiable** at that point. Hence, differentiability is a property of a function at a point. Now let D be the set of points z such that $f'(z)$ exists; then D is the domain of a function whose range is the set of $f'(z)$ for z in D. Such a function could be called the **derived function** of $w = f(z)$, but we shall bow to common usage and call it the **derivative** of $f(z)$ and denote it by $f'(z)$, $df(z)/dz$, dw/dz, or w'.

When we are interested in the derivative of $f(z)$ at a point that can be any point z in an open region, then it is often more convenient to use the following alternate definition of the derivative of $f(z)$ at z:

$$f'(z) = \lim_{h \to 0} \frac{f(z + h) - f(z)}{h},$$

if this limit exists. The student should show that this definition is equivalent to the one previously given.

We shall now show that differentiability implies continuity, but continuity does not imply differentiability.

THEOREM. If $f(z)$ is differentiable at z_0, then $f(z)$ is continuous at z_0.

Proof. We must show that $\lim_{z \to z_0} f(z) = f(z_0)$ or $\lim_{z \to z_0} [f(z) - f(z_0)] = 0$. But

$$f(z) - f(z_0) = \frac{f(z) - f(z_0)}{z - z_0} (z - z_0)$$

and since $f'(z_0)$ exists, the limit of the right-hand side is zero.

The converse of the theorem is not true; we have seen that $\bar{z}$ is continuous everywhere, but differentiable nowhere.

The rules for the differentiation of complex functions can be obtained from the definition of the derivative, but since in form this is the same as the real derivative, these rules will be the same as those for real functions. If $f(z)$ and $g(z)$ are differentiable in some region in the z-plane, then in that region,

D₁: $dc/dz = 0$, c any complex constant.

D₂: $\dfrac{d}{dz}[f(z) + g(z)] = \dfrac{df(z)}{dz} + \dfrac{dg(z)}{dz}.$

D₃: $\dfrac{d}{dz}[f(z)g(z)] = f(z)\dfrac{dg(z)}{dz} + g(z)\dfrac{df(z)}{dz}$

D₄: $\dfrac{d}{dz}\left[\dfrac{f(z)}{g(z)}\right] = \dfrac{g(z)[df(z)/dz] - f(z)[dg(z)/dz]}{[g(z)]^2}, \qquad g(z) \neq 0.$

D₅: $dz^n/dz = nz^{n-1}$, $n \neq 0$, an integer; $z \neq 0$ if $n < 0$.

D₆: If $f'(\zeta)$ exists at $\zeta = g(z)$, then

$$\frac{df[g(z)]}{dz} = \frac{df(\zeta)}{d\zeta}\frac{dg(z)}{dz} \qquad \text{(chain rule).}$$

The nth derivative of $f(z)$ can be defined as

$$f^{(n)}(z) = \frac{d}{dz} f^{(n-1)}(z), \qquad n = 2, 3, \cdots.$$

2. Conditions for differentiability. It is not always a simple matter to establish the existence or nonexistence of the derivative of a function at a given point from the definition. We now consider a criterion that will enable us to do so quite simply and readily. First let us prove the

THEOREM. If $f(z) = u(x, y) + iv(x, y)$ is differentiable at the point $z_0 = x_0 + iy_0$, then the first partial derivatives of $u(x, y)$ and $v(x, y)$ exist at (x_0, y_0) and satisfy the equations:

$$\frac{\partial u}{\partial x} = \frac{\partial v}{\partial y} \quad \text{and} \quad \frac{\partial u}{\partial y} = -\frac{\partial v}{\partial x}$$

at (x_0, y_0) and

$$f'(z_0) = \frac{\partial u}{\partial x} + i\frac{\partial v}{\partial x} = \frac{\partial v}{\partial y} - i\frac{\partial u}{\partial y},$$

the partials evaluated at (x_0, y_0).

Proof. Since $f(z)$ is differentiable at z_0,

$$f'(z_0) = \lim_{z \to z_0} \frac{f(z) - f(z_0)}{z - z_0}$$

exists. This implies that if we let $z \to z_0$ along two different paths, $[f(z) - f(z_0)]/(z - z_0)$ approaches the same value $f'(z_0)$. Let one path be (1) the polygonal line from $x + iy$ to $x + iy_0$ to $x_0 + iy_0$, and the other path be (2) the polygonal line from $x + iy$ to $x_0 + iy_0$ to $x_0 + iy_0$ (see Fig. 1). Then

$$\text{(1)} \qquad f'(z_0) = \lim_{z \to z_0} \frac{f(z) - f(z_0)}{z - z_0}$$

$$= \lim_{x \to x_0} \frac{u(x, y_0) - u(x_0, y_0)}{x - x_0} + i \lim_{x \to x_0} \frac{v(x, y_0) - v(x_0, y_0)}{x - x_0}$$

$$= \frac{\partial u}{\partial x} + i\frac{\partial v}{\partial x},$$

evaluated at (x_0, y_0), by the definition of the partial derivative.

$$\text{(2)} \qquad f'(z_0) = \lim_{y \to y_0} \frac{u(x_0, y) - u(x_0, y_0)}{i(y - y_0)} + i \lim_{y \to y_0} \frac{v(x_0, y) - v(x_0, y_0)}{i(y - y_0)}$$

$$= \frac{\partial v}{\partial y} - i\frac{\partial u}{\partial x},$$

evaluated at (x_0, y_0).

Equating the real and imaginary parts of $f'(z_0)$ in (1) and (2) yields

$$\frac{\partial u}{\partial x} = \frac{\partial v}{\partial y} \quad \text{and} \quad \frac{\partial u}{\partial y} = -\frac{\partial v}{\partial x}.$$

(1) and (2) also indicate the two explicit representations of $f'(z_0)$, which enable us to determine $f(z)$ when it is expressed in rectangular form.

The partial differential equations

$$\partial u/\partial x = \partial v/\partial y \quad \text{and} \quad \partial u/\partial y = -(\partial v/\partial x)$$

in the preceding theorem are known as the **Cauchy-Riemann differential equations.** They are a necessary condition for differentiability.

The converse of the preceding theorem is not true. (See p. 234, Exercise 14.) It will be true if we require not only the existence of the partial derivatives but also their continuity; this, then, will be the very criterion that will prove useful for the determination of the differentiability of a given function. We have the

CAUCHY-RIEMANN CRITERION FOR DIFFERENTIABILITY. If $f(z) = u(x, y) + iv(x, y)$, the first partial derivatives of $u(x, y)$ and $v(x, y)$ being continuous at (x_0, y_0), and if $\partial u/\partial x = \partial v/\partial y$ and $\partial u/\partial y = -(\partial v/\partial x)$ at (x_0, y_0), then $f(z)$ is differentiable at $z_0 = x_0 + iy_0$.

Proof. Since the partial derivatives of u and v are continuous at (x_0, y_0), there exists a neighborhood of (x_0, y_0) where u and v as well as their partial derivatives are continuous. Let (x, y) be any point in this neighborhood and let $z = x + iy$. Denoting $\Delta z = z - z_0 = \Delta x + i\,\Delta y$, we have, using the law of the mean,

$$\begin{aligned}
&f(z_0 + \Delta z) - f(z_0) \\
&\quad = u(x_0 + \Delta x, y_0 + \Delta y) - u(x_0, y_0) + i[v(x_0 + \Delta x, y_0 + \Delta y) - v(x_0, y_0)] \\
&\quad = \left.\frac{\partial u}{\partial x}\right]_{p^*} \Delta x + \left.\frac{\partial u}{\partial y}\right]_{p^*} \Delta y + i \left.\frac{\partial v}{\partial x}\right]_{p^{**}} \Delta x + i \left.\frac{\partial v}{\partial y}\right]_{p^{**}} \Delta y \\
&\qquad [p^* = (x_0 + \theta\,\Delta x, y_0 + \theta\,\Delta y), p^{**} = (x_0 + \theta'\,\Delta x, y_0 + \theta'\,\Delta y), 0 < \theta, \theta' < 1] \\
&\quad = \left.\frac{\partial u}{\partial x}\right]_{p^*} \Delta x + i \left.\frac{\partial u}{\partial x}\right]_{p^*} \Delta y + i \left.\frac{\partial v}{\partial x}\right]_{p^{**}} \Delta x - \left.\frac{\partial v}{\partial x}\right]_{p^{**}} \Delta y \\
&\qquad + \left\{ \left.\frac{\partial v}{\partial x}\right]_{p^{**}} + \left.\frac{\partial u}{\partial y}\right]_{p^*} + i \left.\frac{\partial v}{\partial y}\right]_{p^{**}} - i \left.\frac{\partial u}{\partial x}\right]_{p^*} \right\} \Delta y \\
&\quad = \left\{ \left.\frac{\partial u}{\partial x}\right]_{p^*} + i \left.\frac{\partial v}{\partial x}\right]_{p^{**}} \right\} \Delta z + \omega\,\Delta y,
\end{aligned}$$

where

$$\omega = \left.\frac{\partial v}{\partial x}\right]_{p^{**}} + \left.\frac{\partial u}{\partial y}\right]_{p^*} + i \left.\frac{\partial v}{\partial y}\right]_{p^{**}} - i \left.\frac{\partial u}{\partial x}\right]_{p^*}.$$

Now

$$Q = \frac{f(z_0 + \Delta z) - f(z_0)}{\Delta z} = \left.\frac{\partial u}{\partial x}\right]_{p^*} + i \left.\frac{\partial v}{\partial x}\right]_{p^{**}} + \omega \frac{\Delta y}{\Delta z}.$$

As $\Delta z \to 0$, $p^* \to (x_0, y_0)$, $p^{**} \to (x_0, y_0)$. Furthermore, using the Cauchy-Riemann equations, $\omega \to 0$. Since $|\Delta y| \leq |\Delta z|$, we now have that

$$\lim_{\Delta z \to 0} Q = \frac{\partial u}{\partial x} + i\,\frac{\partial v}{\partial x},$$

the partials evaluated at (x_0, y_0). Hence, $\lim_{\Delta z \to 0} Q$ exists. But this limit is $f'(z_0)$, and the theorem is proved.

We now apply the Cauchy-Riemann criterion for differentiability by giving two examples.

EXAMPLE 1. Find the points at which the derivative of $f(z) = x^2 - y^2 - 2xyi$ exists.

Solution. $u(x, y) = x^2 - y^2$, $v(x, y) = -2xy$.

$$\frac{\partial u}{\partial x} = 2x, \quad \frac{\partial v}{\partial y} = -2x, \quad \frac{\partial u}{\partial y} = -2y, \quad \frac{\partial v}{\partial x} = -2y.$$

The partial derivatives are continuous everywhere, but the Cauchy-Riemann differential equations are satisfied only if $x = y = 0$. Hence, $f'(z)$ exists only at the origin and $f'(0) = \dfrac{\partial u(0, 0)}{\partial x} + i\,\dfrac{\partial v(0, 0)}{\partial x} = 0$.

EXAMPLE 2. Show that the derivative of e^z exists everywhere in the z-plane and that $de^z/dz = e^z$.

Solution. Let $u(x, y) = e^x \cos y$, $v(x, y) = e^x \sin y$. Then $\partial u/\partial x = e^x \cos y = \partial v/\partial y$ and $\partial u/\partial y = -e^x \sin y = -\partial v/\partial x$; since these partial derivatives are continuous everywhere, e^z is differentiable everywhere. $de^z/dz = \partial u/\partial x + i\,\partial v/\partial x = e^x \cos y + ie^x \sin y = e^z$.

We list the derivatives of some of the elementary functions:

(1) $de^z/dz = e^z$.
(2) $d \sin z/dz = \cos z$.
(3) $d \cos z/dz = -\sin z$.
(4) $d \tan z/dz = \sec^2 z$.
(5) $d \cot z/dz = -\csc^2/z$.
(6) $d \csc z/dz = \sec z \tan z$.
(7) $d \operatorname{Log} z/dz = 1/z$.
(8) $dz^\alpha/dz = \alpha z^{\alpha-1}$.
(9) $d \sinh z/dz = \cosh z$.
(10) $d \cosh z/dz = \sinh z$.
(11) $d \tanh z/dz = \operatorname{sech}^2 z$.
(12) $d \operatorname{Sin}^{-1} z/dz = 1/\sqrt{1 - z^2}$.
(13) $d \operatorname{Cos}^{-1} z/dz = -i/\sqrt{z^2 - 1}$.
(14) $d \operatorname{Tan}^{-1} z/dz = 1/(1 + z^2)$.

(2), (3), (9), (10) can be proved using equation (1), which we established in the preceding example, and the appropriate rules of differentiation. (4), (5), (6) follow with the use of (2) and (3) and the quotient rule; similarly, for (11).

$$\operatorname{Log} z = \frac{1}{2} \operatorname{Log} (x^2 + y^2) + i \tan^{-1} \frac{y}{x} = u + vi,$$

$$x^2 + y^2 > 0, \ -\pi < \tan^{-1} (y/x) \leq \pi.$$

Then

$$\frac{\partial u}{\partial x} = \frac{x}{x^2 + y^2} = \frac{\partial v}{\partial y} \quad \text{and} \quad \frac{\partial u}{\partial y} = \frac{y}{x^2 + y^2} = -\frac{\partial v}{\partial x}.$$

These partial derivatives are continuous everywhere except at the origin and the negative real axis, and are equal at every point except at the origin. Hence Log z is differentiable everywhere except at the origin and the negative real axis.

$$\frac{d}{dz} \operatorname{Log} z = \frac{x}{x^2 + y^2} - \frac{iy}{x^2 + y^2} = \frac{\bar{z}}{|z|^2} = \frac{1}{z}.$$

The student should note that although $1/z$ is defined for all $z \neq 0$, it is not the derivative of Log z at any point on the negative real axis, since Log z is not differentiable there. (8), (12), (13), (14) can be established with the use of (7).

3. Analytic functions. We are now ready to consider the most significant concept in complex analysis—the concept of analytic function. A function $f(z)$ is said to be **analytic at a point** z_0 if there is a neighborhood of z_0 such that at every point in this neighborhood $f'(z)$ exists. A point z_0 is called a **regular point** of $f(z)$ if $f(z)$ is analytic at z_0. A point z_0 is called a **singular point** or **singularity** of $f(z)$ if $f(z)$ is not analytic at z_0. z_0 is called an **isolated singular point** of $f(z)$ if $f(z)$ is not analytic at z_0, but is analytic throughout some neighborhood of z_0. A function may have a derivative at a point without being analytic at the point, for the existence of the derivative at a point z_0 does not guarantee the existence of the derivative at all points in some neighborhood of z_0. The function $|z|^2$ affords an example, for as we have seen, it has a derivative only at the origin.

A function $f(z)$ is **analytic in an open region** if it is analytic at every point in the region. It is clear that in an open region, differentiability and analyticity are equivalent. Whenever we say that $f(z)$ is analytic, we imply that it is analytic in *some* open region. The necessary condition for differentiability can be translated into the

THEOREM. If $f(z) = u(x, y) + iv(x, y)$ is analytic in an open region, then at any point in this region the first partial derivatives of $u(x, y)$ and $v(x, y)$ exist and satisfy the Cauchy-Riemann equations: $\partial u/\partial x = \partial v/\partial y$ *and* $\partial u/\partial y = -\partial v/\partial x$.

We also have the

CAUCHY-RIEMANN CRITERION FOR ANALYTICITY. If $f(z) = u(x, y) + iv(x, y)$, the first partial derivatives of $u(x, y)$ and $v(x, y)$ being continuous in some open region D, and if $\partial u/\partial x = \partial v/\partial y$ *and* $\partial u/\partial y = -(\partial v/\partial x)$ in D, then $f(z)$ is analytic in D.

EXAMPLE 1. Show that $f(z) = x^2 + iy^2$ has a derivative at every point on the line $y = x$, but that $f(z)$ is analytic nowhere.

Solution. $u = x^2$ and $v = y^2$ have continuous partial derivatives everywhere. Now, $\partial u/\partial x = 2x$, $\partial u/\partial y = 2y$, $\partial u/\partial y = 0$, $\partial v/\partial x = 0$, so that the Cauchy-Riemann equations are satisfied only if $y = x$; hence, $f(z)$ is differentiable at every point on the line $y = x$. But $f(z)$ is analytic nowhere, since if z_0 is any point, there does not exist a neighborhood about z_0 throughout which $f(z)$ is differentiable.

EXAMPLE 2. Determine the points where $f(z) = x^2 - y + ixy^2$ is differentiable and the points where it is analytic.

Solution. $u = x^2 - y$ and $v = xy^2$ have continuous partial derivatives everywhere.

$$\frac{\partial u}{\partial x} = 2x, \quad \frac{\partial v}{\partial y} = 2xy, \quad \frac{\partial u}{\partial y} = -1, \quad \frac{\partial v}{\partial x} = y^2.$$

The Cauchy-Riemann equations are satisfied only if $y = \pm 1$ and any x; i.e., along the two lines $y = 1$ and $y = -1$. $f(z)$ is differentiable at these points and only these points. $f(z)$ is analytic nowhere. Why?

These examples illustrate that analyticity is a stronger property than differentiability; moreover, this property is the basis of the principal theorems of complex analysis, as we shall have ample opportunity to observe.

We shall constantly be confronted with the following problem: Given $f(z)$, where is it analytic? In other words: What are the singular points of $f(z)$? The Cauchy-Riemann criterion for analyticity affords one method of answering these questions; however, it is not always the simplest. Very useful is the following

THEOREM. If $f(z)$ and $g(z)$ are analytic in an open region D, then

(1) $f(z) + g(z)$ and $f(z)g(z)$ are analytic in D.

(2) $f(z)/g(z)$ is analytic in D except at those points z in D such that $g(z) = 0$.

(3) $f[g(z)]$ is analytic in D, if D contains the range of $g(z)$; i.e., *an analytic function of an analytic function is analytic.*

The proof of the theorem is left to the student.

Now we should certainly know where the elementary functions that we have studied are analytic. We list them here, leaving the proofs to the student.

(1) Polynomials, e^z, $\cos z$, $\sin z$, $\sinh z$, $\cosh z$ are analytic everywhere.

(2) Rational functions are analytic everywhere except at the points where the denominators vanish.

(3) $\tan z$ is analytic everywhere except where $\cos z = 0$; i.e., for $z = (2k + 1)\pi/2$; $\cot z$ is analytic everywhere except at $z = k\pi$; $\tanh z$ is analytic everywhere except at

$$(2k + 1)\pi/2i, \; k = 0, \pm 1, \pm 2, \cdots.$$

(4) Log z is analytic everywhere except at the origin and on the negative real axis.

EXAMPLE 1. What are the singular points of $f(z) = e^{\sin z}/z^2 + 1$?

Solution. $e^{\sin z}$ and $z^2 + 1$ are analytic everywhere (why?), and since $f(z)$ is the quotient of two analytic functions, it is analytic everywhere except where the denominator vanishes. Hence, the singular points of $f(z)$ are $z = \pm i$.

EXAMPLE 2. What are the singular points of $f(z) = \text{Log}\,(z^2 + 1)\,\dfrac{\tan z}{z^4 + 4}$ in $R: 0 < \text{Re}\, z < 2$?

Solution. Since $z^2 + 1$ is never zero or a negative number in R, $\text{Log}\,(z^2 + 1)$ is analytic in R; $\tan z$ is analytic everywhere except at $z = (2k + 1)\pi/2$, $k = 0, \pm 1, \pm 2, \cdots$. Furthermore, $f(z)$ is not analytic for those z such that $z^4 + 4 = 0$; i.e., $z = 1 + i, -1 + i, -1 - i, 1 - i$. Hence, the singular points of $f(z)$ in R are $\pi/2, 1 + i, 1 - i$.

A function that is analytic at every point in the z-plane is called an **entire function.** The sum and product of two entire functions is entire, and the entire function of an entire function is an entire function. We have seen that polynomials, e^z, $\sin z$, $\cos z$, $\sinh z$, $\cosh z$ are entire functions.

EXERCISES

1. Use the definition of the derivative of a function to show that each of the following is differentiable nowhere:
(a) $w = \text{Re}\, z$; (b) $w = \text{Im}\, z$; (c) $w = xy + iy$.

2. Determine the values of z for which each of the following are differentiable by applying the Cauchy-Riemann criterion and determine the derivative of the function at these points. At what points are the functions analytic? Which functions are entire?
(a) $w = \arg z$; (b) $w = 3x + y + i(3y - x)$; (c) $w = \sin \bar{z}$;
(d) $w = \cosh z$; (e) $w = ie^y$; (f) $w = x^3 - i(y - 1)^3$;
(g) $w = 2x + xy^2 i$; (h) $w = 3ix$; (i) $w = e^x(\cos y - i \sin y)$;
(j) $w = x^2 + iy$; (k) $w = z\,\text{Im}\, z$; (l) $w = x^2 + y^2 + 2xyi$;
(m) $w = (x^2 - y^2 + zxy)(1 + i)$;
(n) $w = [x^3 + xy^2 + x + i(x^2 y + y^3 - y)]/(x^2 + y^2)$,
(o) $w = 2x - 3y + i(3x + 2y)$;
(p) $w = |x^2 - y^2| + 2i|xy|$; (q) $w = |x^2 - y^2| + 2i|xy|$;
(r) $w = e^y(\cos x + i \sin x)$; (s) $w = [x^2 y(x + iy)]/(x^4 + y^2)$;
(t) $w = [\sin x \cosh y - i \cos x \sinh y]/(\sin^2 x + \sinh^2 y)$.

3. Determine a, b, c, d so that the following are entire functions:
(a) $x^2 + axy + y^2 + i(cx^2 + dxy + y^2)$; (b) $\cos x \cosh y + a \cos x \sinh y + i(b \sin x \sinh y + \sin x \cosh y)$.

4. Determine the singular points of each of the following:
(a) $w = (z + 2)/(z - 2)$; (b) $w = (2z + 1)/[z(z^2 + 1)]$;

(c) $w = \dfrac{z^2 + i}{z^2 - 3z + 2}$; (d) $w = (z + 2)^{-1}(z^2 + 2z + 2)^{-1}$;
(e) $w = (z^2 + 1)\tan z$; (f) $w = \sec(z^2 + 1)$; (g) $w = (\coth z)/(z^2 + 1)^2$;
(h) $w = (z^2 + 5z)/(z^6 + 1)$; (i) $w = \operatorname{Log}(z - 1)/(z + 1)$;
(j) $w = (\sqrt{z} + 1)/(\sqrt{z} - 1)$; (k) $w = \sqrt{1 - z^2}$; (l) $w = e^{1/z}\sin 1/z$;
(m) $w = z^z$; (n) $w = e^{\sin x \cosh y}[\cos(\cos x \sinh y) + i \sin(\cos x \sinh y)]$;
(o) $w = e^{\tan(z+1)}[(z + 1)/\sin(z^2 + z + 2)]$.

5. (a) If $z = r(\cos\theta + i\sin\theta)$, show that the Cauchy-Riemann differential equations in polar coordinates for $w = u + iv$ are

$$\frac{\partial u}{\partial r} = \frac{1}{r}\frac{\partial v}{\partial \theta} \quad \text{and} \quad \frac{\partial v}{\partial r} = -\frac{1}{r}\frac{\partial u}{\partial \theta}.$$

(b) Determine the points of differentiability and analyticity of $w = 2r\sin\theta - (2r\cos\theta)i$.

6. (a) Define two differential operators, denoted by $\partial/\partial z$ and $\partial/\partial \bar{z}$, by

$$\frac{\partial}{\partial z} = \frac{1}{2}\left(\frac{\partial}{\partial x} - i\frac{\partial}{\partial y}\right), \quad \frac{\partial}{\partial \bar{z}} = \frac{1}{2}\left(\frac{\partial}{\partial x} + i\frac{\partial}{\partial y}\right).$$

Show that if $w = f(z)$ is analytic in an open region D, then $\partial w/\partial \bar{z} = 0$, and if $\partial w/\partial x$ and $\partial w/\partial y$ are continuous in D and $\partial w/\partial \bar{z} = 0$ in D, w is analytic in D. $\partial w/\partial \bar{z} = 0$ is referred to as the **complex form of the Cauchy-Riemann equations.** Note that the determination of $\partial w/\partial \bar{z}$ is equivalent to formally taking the partial derivative of w with respect to $\bar{z}$, treating z as a constant. Why do we say "formally"?

(b) Use (a) to determine where the following functions are analytic:

(1) $w = \overline{\cos z}$; (2) $w = \dfrac{x - iy}{x^2 + y^2}$.

7. (a) If $f(z) = u(x, y) + iv(x, y)$ is analytic, then $u(x, y) = c_1$ and $v(x, y) = c_2$, where c_1 and c_2 are constants, determine two curves in the xy-plane. Show that at any point of intersection (x_0, y_0) of these curves, the tangents to the curves are perpendicular if $f'(z_0) \neq 0$, $z_0 = x_0 + iy_0$. If c_1 and c_2 are now made to vary, they will determine two families of curves; we say that an analytic function determines two families of orthogonal curves.

(b) Indicate the two families of orthogonal curves determined by (1) $f(z) = z^2$; (2) $f(z) = 1/z$; (3) $f(z) = (z - 1)/(z + 1)$.

8. Show that if $f(z) = u + iv$ is analytic, then

(a)
$$\frac{\partial(u, v)}{\partial(x, y)} = \begin{vmatrix} \dfrac{\partial u}{\partial x} & \dfrac{\partial u}{\partial y} \\ \dfrac{\partial v}{\partial x} & \dfrac{\partial v}{\partial y} \end{vmatrix} = |f'(z)|^2.$$

(b)
$$\left[\frac{\partial}{\partial x}|f(z)|\right]^2 + \left[\frac{\partial}{\partial y}|f(z)|\right]^2 = |f'(z)|^2.$$

◇ **9.** Prove:
(a) If $f(z)$ is analytic and $\operatorname{Re} f(z)$ or $\operatorname{Im} f(z)$ is constant, then $f(z)$ is constant.
(b) If $f(z)$ and $\overline{f(z)}$ are both analytic, then $f(z)$ is constant.

(c) If $f(z)$ is analytic and $|f(z)|$ is constant, then $f(z)$ is constant.

(d) If $f(z)$ is analytic and all its values are real, then $f(z)$ is constant.

(e) If $f_1(z), f_2(z), \cdots, f_n(z)$ are analytic and $|f_1(z)|^2 + |f_2(z)|^2 + \cdots + |f_n(z)|^2$ is a constant, then $f_1(z), f_2(z), \cdots, f_n(z)$ are all constants.

10. If $f(z) = u + iv$ is analytic, are $g(z) = v + iu$ and $h(z) = -v + iu$ analytic?

11. Apply the principle of the point at infinity to determine when a function is analytic at the point of infinity. Determine whether a polynomial, e^z, $\cos z$, $\sin z$, or any entire function, is analytic at the point of infinity. Determine whether a rational function, $\tan z$, or $\operatorname{sech} z$ is analytic at the point of infinity.

12. Let A be the set of analytic functions, D the set of differentiable functions, and C the set of continuous functions in an open region, E the set of entire functions. If F is a subset of G, we write $F \subset G$. Hence, $E \subset A \subset D \subset C$. Give an example of each of the following that does not occur in the text:

(a) A continuous nondifferentiable function.

(b) A differentiable nonanalytic function.

13. Prove that if $f'(z) = 0$ in an open region D, then $f(z)$ is constant in D.

14. Define $f(z) = [x^3 - y^3 + (x^3 + y^3)i]/(x^2 + y^2)$, $z \neq 0$, $f(0) = 0$. Show that at $z = 0$, $\partial u/\partial x = 1 = \partial v/\partial y$ and $\partial u/\partial y = -1 = -(\partial v/\partial x)$, so that the Cauchy-Riemann equations are satisfied there. Show that $f(0)$ does not exist, by showing that

$$\frac{f(z) - f(0)}{z - 0} \rightarrow \frac{1 - m^3 + i(1 + m^3)}{(1 + m^2)(1 + mi)}$$

along $y = mx$ and that this depends on m. Now show that $\partial u/\partial x$ is not continuous at $z = 0$, thereby showing that it is not sufficient that the partial derivatives of u and v merely exist at a point in order for the function to be differentiable at the point—they must be continuous at the point.

15. Show that $f(z) = |z|$ does not have a derivative anywhere. Show that the limiting values as $z \rightarrow z_0$ along all possible paths of $[f(z) - f(z_0)]/(z - z_0)$ form the circumference of a circle. Determine

$$r = \left[\left(\frac{\partial u}{\partial x} - \frac{\partial v}{\partial y}\right)^2 + \left(\frac{\partial u}{\partial y} + \frac{\partial v}{\partial x}\right)^2\right]^{1/2};$$

r is called the **index of nonanalyticity.** Discuss.

16. Let $w = u(x, y) + iv(x, y)$, where u, v, $\dfrac{\partial u}{\partial x}, \dfrac{\partial u}{\partial y}, \dfrac{\partial v}{\partial x}, \dfrac{\partial v}{\partial y}$ are continuous in some region R. Show that either w or $\overline{w}$ is analytic in any subregion D of R if and only if the surface areas of $z = u(x, y)$, $z = v(x, y)$, $z = \sqrt{u^2(x, y) + v^2(x, y)}$ over D are all equal. [*Hint:* Since

$$S = \iint_D \sqrt{1 + z_x^2 + z_y^2}\, dx\, dy,$$

the theorem may be restated as w or $\overline{w}$ is analytic in D if and only if

$$u_x^2 + u_y^2 = v_x^2 + v_y^2 = \frac{u^2(u_x^2 + u_y^2) + v^2(v_x^2 + v_y^2) + 2uv(u_xv_x + u_yv_y)}{u^2 + v^2}.\Big]$$

Chapter 8

The Complex Integral Calculus

1. The complex integral. Let $C: x = \phi_1(t),\ y = \phi_2(t),\ \alpha \leq t \leq \beta$, be a regular curve in the complex plane. We may now represent C as $z(t) = \phi_1(t) + i\phi_2(t)$ and call this the **complex parametric representation** of C; it is the complex analogue of the vector representation of C. As we have seen, C may have many complex representations, but for the present purpose, we shall find its parametric representation the most convenient. Now let the complex function $f(z)$ be defined on C. We define the (complex) integral of $f(z)$ on C as follows: Divide the interval $\alpha \leq t \leq \beta$ into n parts by the points $\alpha = t_0 < t_1 < \cdots < t_{j-1} < t_j < \cdots < t_n = \beta$. Corresponding to each t_j, there is a point z_j on C. Let t_j^* be a point such that $t_{j-1} \leq t_j^* \leq t_j$; corresponding to t_j^* is a point z_j^* on C. Form the sum

$$\sum_{j=1}^{n} f(z_j^*)\Delta z_j,$$

where $\Delta z_j = z_j - z_{j-1}$. Denote the largest of $|\Delta z_j|$, $j = 1, 2, \cdots, n$, by $||\Delta z||$. Then, if the limit of this sum (as n becomes infinite in such a way that $||\Delta z||$ approaches zero) exists, we call it the **integral of $f(z)$** on C and denote it by $\int_C f(z)\, dz$; i.e.,

$$\int_C f(z)\, dz = \lim_{\substack{n\to\infty \\ ||\Delta z||\to 0}} \sum_{j=1}^{n} f(z_j^*)\, \Delta z_j.$$

If $\int_C f(z)\, dz$ exists, we say that $f(z)$ is integrable on C. This integral may also be denoted by $\int_A^B f(z)\, dz$, where A and B are the initial and terminal points of C, provided it is clear that the integration is on C.

One of our principal problems is to evaluate the integral of a given function on a given curve. To use the definition would be cumbersome, if not impossible; fortunately, this is never necessary. Since the definition of the complex integral is formally the same as that of the line integral, we might expect to utilize our extensive knowledge of the latter to evaluate the former; this thought takes on precise form in the

THEOREM. If $f(z) = u(x, y) + iv(x, y)$, then

$$\int_{\text{C}} f(z)\,dz = \int_{\text{C}} u(x, y)\,dx - v(x, y)\,dy + i\int_{\text{C}} v(x, y)\,dx + u(x, y)\,dy.$$

Proof. With the notation in the definition of the integral, we have that

$$f(z_j^*) = u(x_j^*, y_j^*) + iv(x_j^*, y_j^*)$$

and

$$\begin{aligned}\Delta z_j &= (x_j - x_{j-1}) + i(y_j - y_{j-1})\\ &= \Delta x_j + i\,\Delta y_j.\end{aligned}$$

Then

$$\sum_{j=1}^{n} f(z_j^*)\,\Delta z_j = \sum_{j=1}^{n} u(x_j^*, y_j^*)\,\Delta x_j - \sum_{j=1}^{n} v(x_j^*, y_j^*)\,\Delta y_j + i\left[\sum_{j=1}^{n} v(x_j^*, y_j^*)\,\Delta x_j + \sum_{j=1}^{n} u(x_j^*, y_j^*)\,\Delta y_j\right]\cdot$$

As $||\Delta z|| \to 0$, $||\Delta x||$ and $||\Delta y|| \to 0$; hence, upon taking the limit of both sides of the preceding equation as $n \to \infty$ and $||\Delta z|| \to 0$, we obtain the result.

Note that this representation can be obtained formally by writing

$$\int_{\text{C}} f(z)\,dz = \int_{\text{C}} (u + iv)(dx + i\,dy),$$

expanding the integrand, and expressing the result as two integrals. Hence, a complex integral can be reduced to two real line integrals.

Now the fundamental theorem for line integrals (p. 101) yields the

THEOREM. If $f(z)$ is continuous on C: $z(t)$, $\alpha \leq t \leq \beta$, then $\int_{\text{C}} f(z)\,dz$ exists and

$$\int_{\text{C}} f(z)\,dz = \int_{\alpha} f[z(t)]z'(t)\,dt.$$

The student should have no difficulty in constructing the proof. Note that this theorem can be considered as a "change of variable" from the complex variable z to the real variable t.

The complex integral has the following properties: If $f(z)$ and $g(z)$ are integrable on a regular curve C, and k is any complex constant, then

I₁: $\int_{\text{C}} kf(z)\,dz = k\int_{\text{C}} f(z)\,dz.$

I_2: $\int_C [f(z) + g(z)]\, dz = \int_C f(z)\, dz + \int_C g(z)\, dz.$

I_3: $\int_{C_1+C_2} f(z)\, dz = \int_{C_1} f(z)\, dz + \int_{C_2} f(z)\, dz.$

I_4: $\int_C f(z)\, dz = -\int_{C'} f(z)\, dz,$

where C and C′ have the same points but have opposite directions.

I_5: If C: $z(t)$, $\alpha \leq t \leq \beta$, then

$$\text{Re} \int_C f(z)\, dz = \int_\alpha^\beta \text{Re}\, [f(z)z'(t)]\, dt$$

and

$$\text{Im} \int_C f(z)\, dz = \int_\alpha^\beta \text{Im}\, [f(z)z'(t)]\, dt.$$

I_6: **(Fundamental Integral Inequality).** If $|f(z)| \leq M$, a constant, on C, then $|\int_C f(z)\, dz| \leq ML_C$, where L_C is the length of C.

I_2 extends to any finite number of functions and I_3 to any finite number of curves. I_6 is a result that will be used frequently in the sequel. The proofs of I_1 to I_4 can be obtained either from the definition of the integral or more elegantly from the corresponding properties of line integrals; I_5 may be obtained from the definition.

We prove I_6. Let

$$S_n = \sum_{j=1}^{n} f(z_j^*)\, \Delta z_j.$$

Then

$$|S_n| \leq \sum_{j=1}^{n} |f(z_j^*)|\, |\Delta z_j| \qquad \leq M \sum_{j=1}^{n} |\Delta z_j| \leq ML_C,$$

since the length of the line segment from z_{j-1} to z_j is less than or equal to the curve C between these points. Hence, $|S_n| \leq ML_C$ *for all* n. Let $S = \lim_{n\to\infty} S_n$. It follows that $|S| = \lim_{n\to\infty} |S_n|$. (Proof?) Then $|S| \leq ML_C$.† But $S = \int_C f(z)\, dz$ by definition, and we have the result.

EXAMPLE 1. Evaluate $I = \int_C (xy + ix^2)\, dz$, C: $z(t) = t + t^2 i$, $0 \leq t \leq 1$.

Solution. $x = t$, $y = t^2$;

$$\begin{aligned} I &= \int_0^1 (t^3 + it^2)(1 + 2ti)\, dt \\ &= -\int_0^1 t^3\, dt + i \int_0^1 (t^2 + 2t^4)\, dt \\ &= -\frac{1}{4} + \frac{11}{15} i. \end{aligned}$$

† For, in general, if $|s_n| \leq k$ for all n and $\lim_{n\to\infty} s_n = s$, then $|s| \leq k$. If not, then $|s| - k > 0$; let $\epsilon = |s| - k$. There exists a positive integer N such that for $n > N$, $|s - s_n| \leq |s| - k$, or $|s| - k > |s - s_n| \geq |s| - |s_n|$, implying that $|s_n| > k$, a patent contradiction.

In Example 1, C was given in parametric form with parameter t. In general, every point z on C depends on two real numbers; e.g., $z = x + iy$ or $z = re^{i\theta}$. In these cases, if x and y or r and θ can be expressed as functions of t, then we can proceed as in Example 1. On the other hand, it may happen that for a particular C, x is constant so that y can serve as the parameter, or θ is constant so that r can serve as the parameter. We illustrate these ideas in the following examples.

EXAMPLE 2. Evaluate

$$\text{I} = \int_{\text{C}} \frac{dz}{z - z_0}; \qquad \text{C}: |z - z_0| = a.$$

Solution. We can write $z - z_0 = ae^{i\theta}$, $0 \le \theta < 2\pi$. Here, $r = a$ is constant and θ serves as the parameter. Now

$$\text{I} = \int_0^{2\pi} \frac{iae^{i\theta}}{ae^{i\theta}}\, d\theta = 2\pi i.$$

EXAMPLE 3. $\text{I} = \int_0^{1+i} \bar{z}\, dz$; C: the line segment joining 0 and $1 + i$.

Solution. We can express C as $z = re^{i\pi/4}$, $0 \le r \le \sqrt{2}$, so that r is the parameter. Then

$$\text{I} = \int_0^{1/2} re^{-i\pi/4}(e^{i\pi/4}\, dr) = \int_0^{1/2} r\, dr = 1.$$

EXAMPLE 4. $\text{I} = \int_{\text{C}} |z|^2\, dz$; C: $z = x + iy$, $y = x^2$, from $z = 0$ to $z = 1 + i$.

Solution. We can write C: $z = x + ix^2$, $0 \le x \le 1$. Then

$$\begin{aligned} \text{I} &= \int_0^1 (x^2 + x^4)(1 + 2xi)\, dx \\ &= \int_0^1 (x^2 + x^4)\, dx + 2i \int^1 (x^3 + x^5)\, dx \\ &= \frac{8}{15} + \frac{5}{6} i. \end{aligned}$$

EXAMPLE 5. $\text{I} = \int_0^{1+2i} \text{Im}\,(z^2 + 1)\, dz$; C: the polygonal line from 0 to 1 to $1 + 2i$.

Solution

$$\begin{aligned} \text{I} &= \int_0^1 \text{Im}\,(x^2 + 1)\, dx + \int_0^2 \text{Im}\,[(1 + iy)^2 + 1]\, dy \\ &= 0 + 4 = 4. \end{aligned}$$

EXAMPLE 6. Determine M so that $|\int_{\text{C}} e^z\, dz| \le M$, where C: $z(t) = t + \frac{1}{3}t^{3/2}i$, $1 \le t \le 2$.

Solution. Let $x = t$, $y = \frac{1}{3}t^{3/2}$, $1 \le x \le 2$. Now $|e^z| = e^x \le e^2$, on C, since e^x is an increasing function. Hence, by I_6, $|\int_{\text{C}} e^z\, dz| \le e^2 L_{\text{C}} = \frac{1}{3}(6\sqrt{6} - 5\sqrt{5})e^2$.

2. The Cauchy integral theorem. We now consider a theorem that is the cornerstone in the integration theory of analytic functions. It is the

CAUCHY INTEGRAL THEOREM. If $f(z)$ is analytic in a bounded simply connected region D and on its boundary C, which is a regular closed curve, then $\int_C f(z)\,dz = 0$.

Proof. We shall give Cauchy's proof of the theorem, which requires the additional hypothesis that $f'(z)$ be continuous on C and in D. Goursat proved, however, that this hypothesis is superfluous; consequently, the theorem is often called the **Cauchy-Goursat theorem,** a proof of which can be found in Knopp, *Theory of Functions,* Vol. I, p. 49. We shall see later that the continuity of $f'(z)$ is a consequence of this theorem. If we could establish the continuity of $f'(z)$ by some other method, then the proof we are about to present would have no restrictions; but to the present day, all proofs of this fact follow from the Cauchy integral theorem—this is the intriguing nature of mathematics.

Since $f(z)$ is analytic on C, it is continuous there and $\int_C f(z)\,dz$ exists. Then

$$\int_C f(z)\,dz = \int_C u\,dx - v\,dy + i\int_C v\,dx + u\,dy.$$

$f'(z)$ is continuous on C and D (and here is where we use the superfluous hypothesis), u, v, and their first partial derivatives are continuous there; hence, the conditions of Green's theorem, p. 114, are satisfied so that

$$\oint_C u\,dx - v\,dy = -\iint_D \left(\frac{\partial v}{\partial x} + \frac{\partial u}{\partial y}\right) dx\,dy,$$

$$\oint_C v\,dx + u\,dy = \iint_D \left(\frac{\partial u}{\partial x} - \frac{\partial v}{\partial y}\right) dx\,dy.$$

But $f(z)$ is analytic in D, so that the Cauchy-Riemann equations are satisfied there; hence, the double integrals vanish and we have the result.

If C is a closed regular curve, we shall call the direction in which an observer moves along C, keeping the region enclosed by C to his left, the **positive direction** of C. The integral of $f(z)$ on C, along its positive direction, will be denoted by $\oint_C f(z)\,dz$.

We now consider an extension of the Cauchy integral theorem to multiply connected regions. We have the

CAUCHY INTEGRAL THEOREM FOR MULTIPLY CONNECTED REGIONS. Let D be the bounded open region whose boundary consists of the regular closed nonoverlapping curves $C, C_1, C_2, \cdots, C_n$, where $C_1, C_2, \cdots, C_n$ are in the interior of C. If $f(z)$ is analytic in D and on its boundary, then

$$\oint_C f(z)\,dz = \oint_{C_1} f(z)\,dz + \oint_{C_2} f(z)\,dz + \cdots + \oint_{C_n} f(z)\,dz.$$

The student should prove this, using the Cauchy integral theorem analogously as Green's theorem was used to prove Green's theorem for multiply connected regions.

An immediate consequence of this theorem is that if $f(z)$ is analytic in a region D and on its boundary Γ, which consists of the regular closed curves $C_1, C_2, \cdots, C_n$; then $\oint_\Gamma f(z)\,dz = 0$.

A regular closed curve is often called a **contour.** Another immediate consequence of the preceding theorem is the

THEOREM (DEFORMATION OF CONTOUR PRINCIPLE). If the regular closed curve C can be continuously deformed into another regular closed curve C′ that does not intersect C and if $f(z)$ is analytic in the closed region whose boundary is C + C′, then

$$\oint_C f(z)\,dz = \oint_{C'} f(z)\,dz.$$

The deformation principle enables us very often to replace a complicated C by a simple C′.

EXAMPLE 1. Evaluate

$$I = \oint_C \frac{\operatorname{Log} \cos z}{e^z}\,dz, \qquad C: |z - (\pi/4)| = \pi/8.$$

Solution. I = 0, since its integrand is analytic on C and its interior.

EXAMPLE 2. Evaluate

$$I = \oint_C \frac{dz}{z-1}, \qquad C: \quad z(t) = 3\cos t + 4i \sin t.$$

Solution. C is an ellipse that has $z = 1$ in its interior. But $1/(z-1)$ is analytic everywhere except at $z = 1$. Therefore, the conditions of the Cauchy integral theorem are not satisfied. However, let $C': |z - 1| = 1$. Then, by the deformation of contour principle, $I = \oint_{C'} \frac{dz}{z-1} = 2\pi i$, by Example 2, p. 238.

EXAMPLE 3. Evaluate

$$I = \oint_C \frac{dz}{z(z^2-1)}$$

where C is the boundary of the region D: $|z| < 2$, $|z| > \frac{1}{4}$, $|z - 1| > \frac{1}{2}$, $|z + 1| > \frac{1}{2}$. (See figure.)

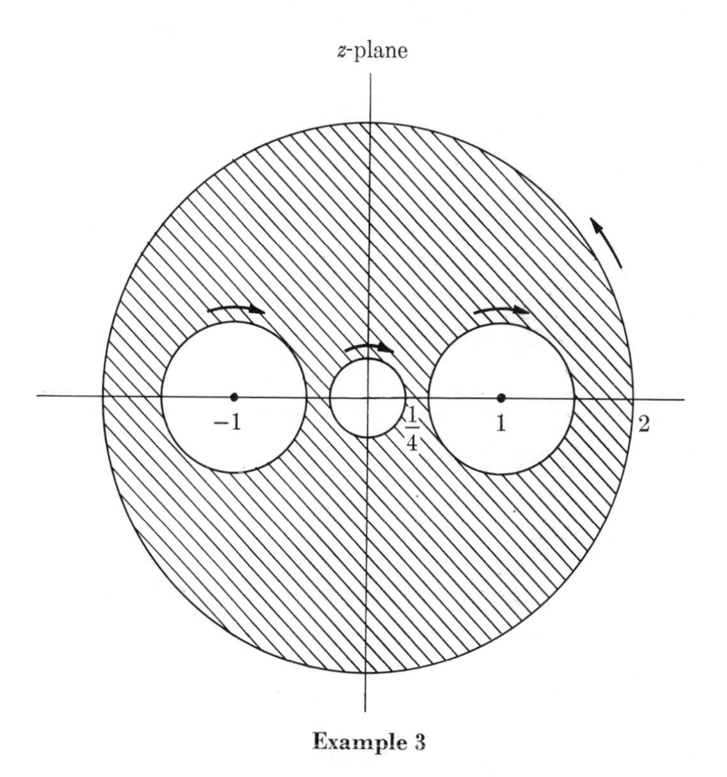

Example 3

Solution. I is to be evaluated along C in a direction such that D remains always to our left as we move along C; in D, $1/z(z^2 - 1)$ is analytic. Hence, I = 0.

3. The fundamental theorem of the calculus. We now extend the fundamental theorem of the real calculus to the complex plane. We first prove two theorems.

THEOREM. If $f(z)$ is analytic in an open simply connected region D and z_0 is a fixed point and z is any point in D, then $\int_{z_0}^{z} f(\zeta)\, d\zeta$ is independent of path in D.

The student can readily establish the independence of path with the use of the Cauchy integral theorem. This theorem implies that $\int_{z_0}^{z} f(\zeta)\, d\zeta$ depends on z only and hence is a function of z, say, $F(z)$. We now prove the

THEOREM. If $f(z)$ is analytic in an open simply connected region and $F(z) = \int_{z_0}^{z} f(\zeta)\, d\zeta$, then $F'(z) = f(z)$ and $F(z)$ is analytic in D.

Proof. Let $f(z) = u(x, y) + iv(x, y)$ and $F(z) = U(x, y) + iV(x, y)$, $z = x + iy$, $z_0 = x_0 + iy_0$.

$$U = \int_{(x_0,y_0)}^{(x,y)} u\,dx - v\,dy \quad \text{and} \quad V = \int_{(x_0,y_0)}^{(x,y)} v\,dx + u\,dy,$$

but these line integrals are independent of path, for $f(z)$ being analytic in D, $\partial u/\partial y = -(\partial v/\partial x)$ and $\partial v/\partial y = \partial u/\partial x$; hence, there exist functions $g(x, y)$ and $h(x, y)$ such that $dg = u\,dx - v\,dy$ and $dh = v\,dx + u\,dy$. Hence, $U = g(x, y) - g(x_0, y_0)$ and $V = h(x,y) - h(x_0, y_0)$; but $\partial U/\partial x = \partial g/\partial x = u$ and $\partial V/\partial x = \partial h/\partial x = v$. Hence, $F'(z) = \partial U/\partial x + i(\partial V/\partial x) = u + iv = f(z)$. Furthermore, $\partial U/\partial x = u = \partial V/\partial y$ and $\partial U/\partial y = -v = -(\partial V/\partial x)$, so that $F(z)$ is analytic in D.

We are now ready to prove the

FUNDAMENTAL THEOREM OF THE CALCULUS. If $f(z)$ is analytic in an open simply connected region D and z_1 and z_2 are any two points in D, then

$$\int_{z_1}^{z_2} f(z)\,dz = F(z_2) - F(z_1)$$

where $F'(z) = f(z)$.

Proof. The existence of $F(z)$ is assured by the previous theorems. Let $f(z) = u(x, y) + iv(x, y)$ and $F(z) = U(x, y) + iV(x, y)$, $z_1 = x_1 + iy_1$, $z_2 = x_2 + iy_2$.

$$\begin{aligned}
\int_{z_1}^{z_2} f(z)\,dz &= \int_{z_1}^{z_2} F'(z)\,dz \\
&= \int_{(x_1,y_1)}^{(x_2,y_2)} \frac{\partial U}{\partial x}\,dx - \frac{\partial V}{\partial x}\,dy + i\int_{(x_1,y_1)}^{(x_2,y_2)} \frac{\partial V}{\partial x}\,dx + \frac{\partial U}{\partial x}\,dy \\
&= \int_{(x_1,y_1)}^{(x_2,y_2)} \frac{\partial U}{\partial x}\,dx + \frac{\partial U}{\partial y}\,dy + i\int_{(x_1,y_1)}^{(x_2,y_2)} \frac{\partial V}{\partial x}\,dx + \frac{\partial V}{\partial y}\,dy \\
&= \int_{(x_1,y_1)}^{(x_2,y_2)} dU + i\int_{(x_1,y_1)}^{(x_2,y_2)} dV \\
&= F(z_2) - F(z_1).
\end{aligned}$$

This theorem can be stated equivalently: *If $f(z)$ is analytic in an open simply connected region D, then $\int_{z_1}^{z_2} f(z)\,dz$ is independent of path in D.* Note that the Cauchy integral theorem is a special case of this theorem.

EXAMPLE. Evaluate $I = \int_0^{\pi i} \sin z\,dz$.

Solution. $\sin z$ is analytic everywhere and $d/dz\,[-\cos z] = \sin z$, so that $I = -\cos \pi i + 1 = 1 - \cosh \pi$.

Given $I = \int_C f(z)\,dz$ to evaluate; if $f(z)$ is analytic in an open simply connected region D containing C, then I $= 0$ if C is a regular closed curve; if C is not closed, we evaluate I by using the fundamental theorem of the calculus. If $f(z)$ is not analytic in D, then we can either make the change in variable $z = z(t)$ or express I in terms of two real line integrals, making use of the deformation principle, where convenient. However, if $f(z)$ has only isolated singular points in D, we shall now consider simpler methods for the evaluation of I.

4. Some properties of analytic functions. We have seen that the Cauchy integral theorem and the fundamental theorem of the calculus are important consequences of the analyticity of a function; we now establish some further consequences. Indeed, we shall find that analytic functions have many significant properties that are not enjoyed by other functions, and it is for this reason that the study of analytic functions is in the forefront of those branches of mathematics that are structurally complete and esthetically satisfying. We first prove the

CAUCHY INTEGRAL FORMULA. If $f(z)$ is analytic in a simply connected open region D, and C is a regular closed curve in D, then for any point in the interior of C,

$$f(z) = \frac{1}{2}\pi i \oint_C \frac{f(\zeta)\, d\zeta}{\zeta - z}.$$

Proof. Let z_0 be any point in the interior of C. Since $f(z)$ is analytic at z_0, it is continuous there, and this implies that for every $\epsilon > 0$ there exists a $\delta > 0$ such that for $0 < |z - z_0| < \delta$, we have $|f(z) - f(z_0)| < \epsilon$. Now let C′ be a circle of radius r and center z_0 that is contained entirely in the interior of C and such that $r < \delta$. (C′ exists because the interior of C is an open region.) Let $z = \eta$ if it is on C′. Then, by the deformation of

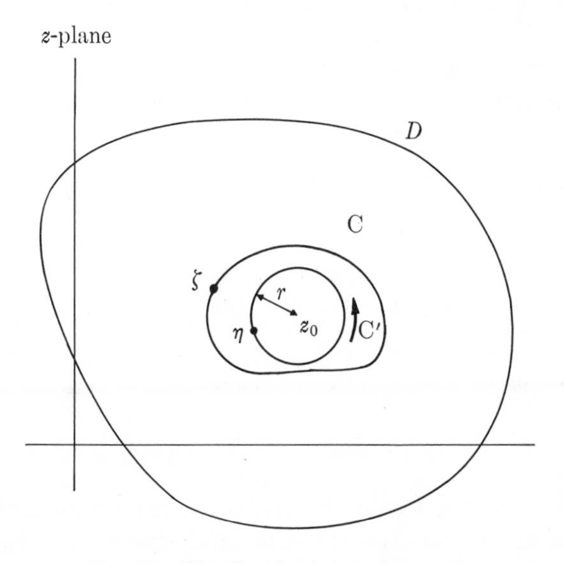

Fig. 1. The Cauchy integral formula

contour principle, since $[f(z)]/(z - z_0)$ is analytic in the region whose boundary consists of C and C′,

$$I = \oint_C \frac{f(\zeta)\, d\zeta}{\zeta - z_0} = \oint_{C'} \frac{f(\eta)\, d\eta}{\eta - z_0}.$$

(Bear in mind that ζ is any point on C and η any point on C′.) See Fig. 1. Now

$$I = \oint_{C'} \frac{f(\eta) - f(z_0)}{\eta - z_0}\, d\eta + f(z_0) \oint_{C'} \frac{d\eta}{\eta - z_0} = I_1 + I_2.$$

But since $I_2 = 2\pi i$ (p. 238, Example 2), it remains to show that $I_1 = 0$. However,

$$\left| \frac{f(\eta) - f(z_0)}{\eta - z_0} \right| < \frac{\epsilon}{r}$$

so that $|I_1| < \epsilon L_C / r = 2\pi\epsilon$ by the fundamental integral inequality. But $|I_1| < 2\pi\epsilon$ for every $\epsilon > 0$, so that (p. 188, Exercise 21) $|I_1| = 0$, and hence $I_1 = 0$. Since z_0 can be any point in the interior of C, we shall now replace it by z and our proof is complete.

The Cauchy integral formula indicates that the value of an analytic function at a point interior to a regular closed curve depends on the values of this function on the curve; this implies that we cannot define the value of a function at a point at will without destroying the analyticity of the function. We see, therefore, that analyticity is a very "binding" property of complex functions.

The Cauchy integral formula may be extended to a multiply connected region, where C now becomes the complete boundary of the region with positive direction.

The Cauchy integral formula may be used to evaluate certain special integrals. For this purpose, it is more convenient to write it as

$$f(z_0) = \frac{1}{2\pi i} \oint_C \frac{f(z)\, dz}{z - z_0}.$$

EXAMPLE. Evaluate

$$I = \oint_C \frac{\cos z\, dz}{z(z^2 + 4)}, \qquad C\colon\ |z| = 1.$$

Solution. Since $\cos z/(z^2 + 4)$ is analytic for $|z| \leq 1$ and $z = 0$ is in this region, we have by the Cauchy integral formula,

$$I = \oint_C \frac{(\cos z/z^2 + 4)\, dz}{z - 0} = 2\pi i \left. \frac{\cos z}{z^2 + 4} \right]_{z=0} = \frac{\pi i}{2}.$$

We now show that we can differentiate under the integral sign in the Cauchy integral formula to obtain an integral expression for the derivative of $f(z)$. We have the

THEOREM. If $f(z)$ is analytic in a simply connected open region D, and C is a closed regular curve in D, then for any point z in the interior of C,

$$f'(z) = \frac{1}{2\pi i} \oint_C \frac{f(\zeta)\, d\zeta}{(\zeta - z)^2}.$$

Proof. Since z is any point in the interior of C, we have

$$f(z) = \frac{1}{2\pi i} \oint_C \frac{f(\zeta)\, d\zeta}{\zeta - z}$$

by the Cauchy integral formula. We determine $f'(z)$ by using the definition of the derivative.

$$\frac{f(z+h) - f(z)}{h} = \frac{1}{2\pi i} \oint_C \frac{f(\zeta)\, d\zeta}{(\zeta - z)(\zeta - z - h)}$$

which approaches

$$f'(z) = \frac{1}{2\pi i} \oint_C \frac{f(\zeta)\, d\zeta}{(\zeta - z)^2}, \qquad \text{as } h \to 0,$$

since

$$\mathrm{I} = \left| \oint_C \frac{f(\zeta)\, d\zeta}{(\zeta - z)(\zeta - z - h)} - \oint_C \frac{f(\zeta)\, d\zeta}{(\zeta - z)^2} \right| \to 0,$$

as we now show. We write

$$\mathrm{I} = |h| \oint_C \frac{f(\zeta)\, d\zeta}{(\zeta - z)^2(\zeta - z - h)^2}.$$

Now let $r = \min\limits_{\zeta \text{ on } C} |\zeta - z|$. Since $f(z)$ is analytic and hence continuous on C, it is bounded there (p. 201, C_3); hence, $|f(\zeta)| \leq M$, a constant, where ζ is on C. Then

$$\left| \frac{f(\zeta)}{(\zeta - z)^2(\zeta - z - h)^2} \right| \leq \frac{M}{r^2(r - |h|)^2},$$

so that by the fundamental integral inequality,

$$|\mathrm{I}| \leq \frac{|h| M L_C}{r^2(r - |h|)^2}, \qquad \text{and } \mathrm{I} \to 0 \text{ as } h \to 0.$$

We now prove a very general theorem, which indicates the conditions under which we can differentiate under the integral sign.

LEIBNIZ'S THEOREM. If $f(\zeta, z)$ is analytic with respect to z for every fixed ζ in an open simply connected region D, which contains a regular curve C and is continuous with respect to ζ for every fixed z on C, and if $|f(\zeta, z)| < M$, for every ζ, z in D, then $F(z) = \int_C f(\zeta, z)\, d\zeta$ is analytic in D and

$$F'(z) = \int_C \frac{\partial f(\zeta, z)}{\partial z}\, d\zeta.$$

Proof. Since $f(\zeta, z)$ is analytic for fixed ζ in D, we have, by the Cauchy integral formula, that

$$f(\zeta, z) = \frac{1}{2\pi i} \oint_{C^*} \frac{f(\zeta, \omega)}{\omega - z} \, d\omega$$

where C^*: $|z| < \rho$ is in D. Then

$$F(z) = \frac{1}{2\pi i} \int_C d\zeta \oint_{C^*} \frac{f(\zeta, \omega)}{\omega - z} \, d\omega.$$

By the preceding theorem,

$$\frac{\partial f(\zeta, z)}{\partial z} = \frac{1}{2\pi i} \oint_{C^*} \frac{f(\zeta, \omega)}{(\omega - z)^2} \, d\omega.$$

Now let $z + h$ be a point such that $|\omega - z - h| > \frac{1}{2}\rho$. Since ω is any point on C^*, $|\omega - z| = \rho$. Then

$$\left| \frac{F(z + h) - F(z)}{h} - \int_C \frac{\partial f(\zeta, z)}{\partial z} \, d\zeta \right|$$

$$= \left| \frac{1}{2\pi i} \int_C d\zeta \int_{C^*} f(\zeta, \omega) \frac{h}{(\omega - z - h)(\omega - z)^2} \, d\omega \right| \leq \frac{2|h| M L_C}{\rho^2},$$

using the fundamental integral inequality twice. But this approaches 0 as $h \to 0$, and we have that

$$F'(z) = \frac{d}{dz} \int_C f(\zeta, z) \, d\zeta = \int_C \frac{\partial f(\zeta, z)}{\partial z} \, d\zeta.$$

Since $F'(z)$ exists in D, $F(z)$ is analytic there.

This theorem enables us to prove readily

THE GENERALIZED CAUCHY INTEGRAL FORMULA. If $f(z)$ is analytic in a simply connected open region D and C is a closed regular curve in D, then for any point z in the interior of C,

$$f^{(n)}(z) = \frac{n!}{2\pi i} \oint_C \frac{f(\zeta) \, d\zeta}{(\zeta - z)^{n+1}}.$$

Proof. Differentiate

$$f'(z) = \frac{1}{2\pi i} \oint_C \frac{f(\zeta) \, d\zeta}{(\zeta - z)^2}$$

$n - 1$ times with respect to z.

The generalized Cauchy integral formula remains valid if D is a multiply connected open region, provided C is the complete boundary of D with positive direction.

EXAMPLE 1. Show that $I = \int_C \frac{dz}{(z - z_0)^n} = 0$, $n = 2, 3, \cdots$, where C is any regular closed curve that encloses z_0.

Solution. I is of the form $\int_C \frac{f(z)\,dz}{(z - z_0)^n}$ with $f(z) = 1$, and by the generalized Cauchy formula this is equal to $\frac{2\pi i}{(n-1)!} f^{(n-1)}(z)$, which is zero.

EXAMPLE 2. Evaluate

$$I = \oint_C \frac{\sin z\, dz}{[z - (\pi/2)]^2(z + 5)}; \qquad C:\ |z| = 2.$$

Solution. $\sin z/(z + 5)$ is analytic in $|z| \le 2$. Furthermore, if

$$f(z) = \frac{\sin z}{(z + 5)}, \quad f'\left(\frac{\pi}{2}\right) = \frac{-1}{[(\pi/2) + 5]^2}.$$

Hence, $I = -2\pi i/[(\pi/2) + 5]^2$.

The generalized Cauchy integral formula together with the theorem on p. 241 implies that if $f(z)$ is analytic, $f'(z)$ exists and is analytic, which in turn implies that $f''(z)$ exists and is analytic, etc. Indeed, we have the

THEOREM. If $f(z)$ is analytic in an open region D, then $f(z)$ has derivatives of all orders in D, each of which is analytic in D.

This remarkable theorem indicates that the property of analyticity is a rather strong one. The existence of the derivative of a real function does not imply the existence of its higher derivatives, even though the derivative may exist throughout an open interval.

If $f(z) = u(x, y) + iv(x, y)$, the preceding theorem can be stated in terms of the partial derivatives of u and v if the student will supply the necessary details:

THEOREM. If $f(z) = u(x, y) + iv(x, y)$ is analytic in an open region D, then $u(x, y)$ and $v(x, y)$ have partial derivatives of all orders in D.

This theorem leads to the very significant

THEOREM. If $f(z) = u(x, y) + iv(x, y)$ is analytic in an open region D, then $u(x, y)$ and $v(x, y)$ are harmonic functions in D.

Proof. By the preceding theorem, the second partial derivatives of u and v are continuous. Since $f(z)$ is analytic, the Cauchy-Riemann equations are valid in D:

$$\frac{\partial u}{\partial x} = \frac{\partial v}{\partial y} \quad \text{and} \quad \frac{\partial u}{\partial y} = -\frac{\partial v}{\partial x};$$

then

$$\frac{\partial^2 u}{\partial x^2} = \frac{\partial^2 v}{\partial x\, \partial y} \quad \text{and} \quad \frac{\partial^2 u}{\partial y^2} = -\frac{\partial^2 v}{\partial x\, \partial y}$$

or

$$\frac{\partial^2 u}{\partial x^2} + \frac{\partial^2 u}{\partial y^2} = 0$$

which means that u is a harmonic function in D. Similarly, we can show that v is harmonic in D.

The significance of this theorem lies in the fact that every analytic function determines two harmonic functions. Furthermore, if u is a harmonic function, then there exists a harmonic function v, called the **harmonic conjugate** of u such that $u + iv$ is analytic (p. 255, Exercise 22). Hence, many properties of harmonic functions may be studied via analytic functions, and conversely. Since harmonic functions play a central role in mathematical physics, it is not too difficult to see why the study of analytic functions is fruitful for practical applications. Most of the theorems for analytic functions have analogs for harmonic functions, and vice versa. We shall now consider a very important harmonic analog of the Cauchy integral formula. It is known as

THE POISSON INTEGRAL FORMULA. If $u(r, \theta)$ is harmonic in $|z| \leq R$, then

$$u(r, \theta) = \frac{R^2 - r^2}{2\pi} \int_0^{2\pi} \frac{u(R, \phi)\, d\phi}{R^2 - 2rR\cos(\phi - \theta) + r^2}.$$

Proof. Let $v(r, \theta)$ be the harmonic conjugate of $u(r, \theta)$ so that $f(z) = u + iv$, $z = re^{i\theta}$. Then the Cauchy integral formula and the Cauchy integral theorem indicate that

$$f(z) = \frac{1}{2\pi i} \oint_C \left[\frac{1}{\zeta - z} - \frac{1}{\zeta - z^*}\right] f(\zeta)\, d\zeta, \quad \mathrm{C}: |\zeta| = R,$$

if $|z| < R$ and $|z^*| > R$. Let $z^* = R^2/z$. (Be sure to show that for this value, $|z^*| > R$.) Then, since $\zeta = Re^{i\phi}$,

$$f(z) = \frac{R^2 - |z|^2}{2\pi} \int_0^{2\pi} \frac{f(Re^{i\phi})\, d\phi}{|Re^{i\phi} - z|^2},$$

$$u(r, \theta) = \operatorname{Re} f(z) = \frac{R^2 - |z|^2}{2\pi} \int_0^{2\pi} \frac{\operatorname{Re} f(Re^{i\phi})\, d\phi}{|Re^{i\phi} - z|^2} \quad \text{(by } \mathrm{I}_5)$$

$$= \frac{R^2 - r^2}{2\pi} \int_0^{2\pi} \frac{u(R, \phi)\, d\phi}{R^2 - 2rR\cos(\phi - \theta) + r^2},$$

since

$$\begin{aligned} |Re^{i\phi} - z|^2 &= (Re^{i\phi} - re^{i\theta})(Re^{-i\phi} - re^{-i\theta}) \\ &= R^2 - Rr(e^{i(\phi-\theta)} + e^{-i(\phi-\theta)}) + r^2 \\ &= R^2 - 2Rr\cos(\phi - \theta) + r^2. \end{aligned}$$

The student might question the artifice of introducing z^* in the proof; he should show that one cannot obtain the result merely by taking the real part of both sides of the Cauchy integral formula.

The Poisson integral formula, then, expresses the value of a harmonic function u at any point (r, θ) in the interior of the circle $|z| = R$ in terms of the value of this function at any point (R, ϕ) on the boundary of $|z| \leq R$.

Now we shall consider a property of analytic functions that follows from the corresponding property for harmonic functions. It is embodied in the theorem known as the

MAXIMUM MODULUS PRINCIPLE. If $f(z)$ is analytic and nonconstant in a bounded open region D, continuous on its boundary C, and $|f(z)| \leq M$ on C, then $|f(z)| < M$ for any point z in D.

Proof. Let $f(z) = u(x, y) + iv(x, y)$. Since $|f(z)| \leq M$ on C and $|u(x, y)| \leq |f(z)|$, we have that $|u(x, y)| \leq M$ on C. But u is a harmonic function, so that [Exercise 9(b), p. 153] $|u(x, y)| < M$ in D. Now $e^{|f(z)|} = e^{u(x,y)} \leq e^{|u(x,y)|} < e^M$ in D, so that $e^{|f(z)|} < e^M$ in D. It follows that $|f(z)| < M$ in D.

The maximum modulus principle asserts that the absolute value of an analytic function cannot attain its maximum at an interior point of a region unless the function is a constant; if the region is bounded, the maximum is attained on the boundary of the region.

5. Cauchy's inequality, Liouville's theorem, and the fundamental theorem of algebra.

An immediate consequence of the generalized Cauchy integral formula is the very useful

CAUCHY'S INEQUALITY. If $f(z)$ is analytic in an open region D and for any z in D, C is a circle of radius r and center z contained in D, and $|f(z)| \leq M$ on C, then $|f^{(n)}(z)| \leq n!M/r^n$, $n = 0, 1, 2, \cdots$.

Proof. From the generalized Cauchy integral formula,

$$f^{(n)}(z) = \frac{n!}{2\pi i} \oint_C \frac{f(\zeta)\, d\zeta}{(\zeta - z)^{n+1}}, \qquad n = 0, 1, 2, \cdots,$$

we obtain, since $|\zeta - z| = r$,

$$|f^{(n)}(z)| \leq \frac{n!}{2\pi} \frac{M}{r^{n+1}} L_C = \frac{n!M}{r^n}.$$

Cauchy's inequality enables us to establish immediately a theorem of far-reaching importance in the theory of analytic functions, known as

LIOUVILLE'S THEOREM. If $f(z)$ is entire and bounded in the z-plane, then $f(z)$ is a constant.

Proof. Cauchy's inequality for $n = 1$ is $|f'(z)| \leq M/r$, r being the radius of a circle whose center is arbitrary. Since $f(z)$ is entire, we can take r to be arbitrarily large. Hence, $|f'(z)| = 0$ and $f'(z) = 0$, which implies that $f(z)$ is a constant. (Proof?)

EXAMPLE. Show that the inequality $|\sin z| \leq 1$, which is valid for all real z, is not true for all complex z, even when 1 is replaced by any positive constant.

Solution. Assume that $|\sin z| \leq M$ for all z. Then, since $\sin z$ is entire, by Liouville's theorem, it would have to be a constant, which it is not. Hence, there exists no M such that $|\sin z| \leq M$.

One of the celebrated theorems of algebra states that *every polynomial equation of positive degree with complex coefficients* (i.e., $P(z) = a_n z^n + a_{n-1}z^{n-1} + \cdots + a_0 = 0$, $n > 1$, $a_n \neq 0$) *has at least one complex root.* It is known as the **fundamental theorem of algebra.** Its proof by purely algebraic methods is exceedingly difficult and involved. On the other hand, it follows immediately with the use of Liouville's theorem. For assume $P(z) = 0$ has no roots; then $f(z) = 1/P(z)$ is an entire function. Since $\lim_{z\to\infty} f(z) = \lim_{z\to\infty} (1/a_n z^n) = 0$, there exist r and M_1 such that for $|z| > r$, $|f(z)| < M_1$ (p. 209, Exercise 15). In the closed region $|z| \leq r$, $|f(z)|$ is continuous and has a maximum value M_2 there [IVAd]. Let $M = \max(M_1, M_2)$; then $|f(z)| \leq M$ for all z. By Liouville's theorem, $f(z)$ is a constant, and therefore $P(z)$ is a constant, which is not the case because $n > 0$ and $a_n \neq 0$.

If a is a complex number such that $P(a) = P'(a) = P''(a) = \cdots = P^{(m-1)}(a) = 0$, $P^{(m)}(a) \neq 0$, then a is called a **zero of order *m*** of the polynomial $P(z)$. With the use of well-known algebraic theorems, one can show that if a is a zero of order m of $P(z)$, then there exists a polynomial $Q(z)$, $Q(a) \neq 0$ such that $P(z) = (z - a)^m Q(z)$. Actually, this result can be extended to any analytic function. We define a zero of order m of an analytic function $f(z)$ as for polynomials. We then have the

THEOREM. If $f(z)$ is analytic in an open region D and a is a zero of order m of $f(z)$ in D, then there exists an analytic function $g(z)$, $g(a) \neq 0$ such that $f(z) = (z - a)^m g(z)$ in D.

The proof follows immediately with the use of Taylor's formula [p. 253, Exercise 14(a)].

EXERCISES

1. Evaluate:

(a) $\oint_C \bar{z}\, dz$, C: $|z| = 1$.

(b) $\int_{-i}^{i} |z|\, dz$ along (1) the straight-line segment joining $-i$ and i; (2) $|z| = 1$, $\operatorname{Re} z \leq 0$; (3) the polygonal line $-i$ to 1 to i.

(c) $\int_C |z|^2\, dz$, C: $|z - i| = 1$.

(d) $\int_0^{3+i} \bar{z}^2\,dz$ along (1) the polygonal line from 0 to i to $3+i$; (2) $x^2 = 9y$.

(e) $\int_1^i (dz/z)$ along $z(t) = \cos t + i \sin t$, $0 \le t \le \pi/2$. Is the fundamental theorem of the calculus applicable?

(f) $\oint_C \frac{dz}{z}$, C: $\left|z - \frac{\sqrt{3}}{2}\right| + \left|z + \frac{\sqrt{3}}{2}\right| = 2$.

(g) $\int_0^{1+i} (y - x - 3x^2 i)\,dz$ along the straight-line segment joining 0 and $1 + i$.

(h) $\int_C \frac{z+2}{z}\,dz$, C: $z = 2e^{i\theta}$, θ from 0 to $-\pi$.

(i) $\oint_C (\text{Re } z + \text{Im } z)\,dz$, C: $|z| = 1$.

(j) $\oint_C (dz/z)$, C: the boundary of the region bounded by $|z| = 1$ and the square with vertices at $\pm 2 \pm 2i$.

Ans.: (a) $2\pi i$; (b) (1) i, (2) 2; (c) $-\pi$; (d) (1) $9 - i/3$, (2) $\frac{42}{5} - \frac{26}{3}i$; (e) $\pi/2$; (f) $2\pi i$; (g) $1 - i$; (h) $4 - 2\pi i$; (i) $-\pi + \pi i$; (j) 0.

2. Evaluate:

(a) $\oint_C e^{\sin z} \cos z\,dz$, C: the cardioid $r = a(1 + \cos\theta)$.

(b) $\oint_C \frac{dz}{z^2+1}$, C: $|z - 1| = 1$.

(c) $\oint_C \tan z\,dz$, C: $|z - 2i| = 1$.

(d) $\oint_C \frac{dz}{z^3+1}$, C: the boundary of the region bounded by $|z| = 2$, $|z+1| = \frac{1}{2}$, $|z - [(1+\sqrt{3}i)/2]| = \frac{1}{2}$, $|z - [(1-\sqrt{3}i)/2]| = \frac{1}{2}$.

(e) $\oint_C (dz/z^4)$, C: the straight line segment from $-3 + 5i$ to $3 + 5i$, the parabola $y + 4 = x^2$ from $-4i$ to $-3 + 5i$, and the straight-line segment from $-4i$ to $3 + 5i$.

3. Evaluate the integrals of each of the following functions along the square, with vertices at $\pm 2 \pm 2i$ in the positive direction:
(a) $e^{-z}/[z - (\pi i/2)]$; (b) $\cos z/[z(z^2 + 8)]$; (c) $z/(2z + 1)$;

(d) $\frac{\tan(z/2)}{(z-1)^2}$; (e) $\frac{\cosh z}{z^4}$.

Ans.: (a) 2π; (b) $\pi i/4$; (c) $-\pi i/2$; (d) $\pi i \sec^2 \frac{1}{2}$; (e) 0.

4. Integrate each of the following functions about $|z| = 3$ in the positive direction:

(a) $(z^3 + 1)/[z(z - 2)]$; (b) $[z(z - 2)]/(z^2 + 1)$;
(c) $(z^2 - 1)/z$; (d) $1/(z^2 - 1)$; (e) $z/(z^4 - 1)$.

Ans.: (a) $8\pi i$; (b) $-4\pi i$; (c) $-2\pi i$; (d) 0; (e) 0.

5. Evaluate:

(a) $\int_0^{1+i} (z + 1)\, dz$.

(b) $\int_0^{2+i} (z^2 - iz + 2)\, dz$.

(c) $\int_{\pi/4}^{i} \tan z\, dz$, along the line segment joining $\pi/4$ and i.

(d) $\oint_C \frac{e^z\, dz}{z - 2}$, C: $|z - 2| = 1$.

(e) $\oint_C \frac{z^2 + 4}{z}\, dz$, C: $|z| = 1$.

(f) $\oint_C \frac{e^z}{z^5}\, dz$, C: $|z| = 1$.

(g) $\oint_C \frac{dz}{(z^2 + 1)(z^2 + 4)}$, C: $|z| = 3/2$.

(h) $\oint_C \frac{\sin z}{z}\, dz$, C: $|z - 1| + |z + 1| = 4$.

(i) $\oint_C \frac{dz}{z^2(z - 3)}$, C: $|z| = 2$.

(j) $\int_0^{(\pi/2)i} \cosh z\, dz$.

Ans.: (a) $1 + 2i$; (b) $\frac{7}{6} + \frac{8}{3}i$; (c) $\text{Log} \sec i - \text{Log}\sqrt{2}$; (d) $2\pi i e^2$; (e) $8\pi i$; (f) $2\pi i$; (g) 0; (h) 0; (i) $-\frac{2}{9}\pi i$; (j) i.

6. If C_1: $|z| = 1$, C_2: $|z - 3| = 1$, C_3: $|z| = 9$, show that the integral of $(2z - 3)/(z^2 - 3z)$ along C_1 or C_2 is $2\pi i$; along C_3 is $4\pi i$; and along $C_3 - C_1 - C_2$ is 0 (in the positive direction along C_1, C_2, C_3).

7. Show that $\oint_C \frac{dz}{\sqrt{1 - z^2}} = \pm 2\pi$, C: $z(t) = a \cos t + b \sin t$, $0 \leq t \leq 2\pi$, $a^2 - b^2 = 1$, the sign depending on the chosen value of $\sqrt{1 - z^2}$.

8. Evaluate $\oint_C \frac{(z + 1)\, dz}{z^3 - 2z^2}$, where C is in turn:

(a) $|z| = 1$; (b) $|z - 2 - i| = 2$; (c) $|z - 1 - 2i| = 2$.

Ans.: (a) $-3\pi i/2$; (b) 0; (c) 0.

9. Evaluate $\oint_C \sec z\, dz$ along (a) $|z| = 1$; (b) $|z| = 2$; (c) $|z| = 10$; (d) $|z - 2| = 4$.

Ans.: (a) 0; (b) 0; (c) 0; (d) 0.

10. Establish the following inequalities:

(a) $\left|\int_0^{1+2i} \bar{z}^2\, dz\right| \leq 5\sqrt{5}$, along the line segment joining 0 and $1 + 2i$.

(b) $\left|\int_i^{2+i} z^2\, dz\right| \leq 10$. Compare the upper bound 10 with the exact value of the absolute value of the integral.

(c) $\left|\int_i^{2+i} \frac{dz}{z^2}\right| < 2$, along line segment from i to $2 + i$.

(d) $\left|\int_{-i}^{i} (x^2 + iy^2)\, dz\right| < 2$, along line segment from $-i$ to i.

(e) $\left|\oint_C \frac{dz}{z^2 + 1}\right| \leq \frac{\pi}{3}$, C: $|z| = 2$.

(f) $\left|\oint_C (e^z - \bar{z})\, dz\right| \leq 60$, C: triangle with vertices at $0, -4, 3i$.

(g) $\left|\oint_C \frac{\text{Log}\, z}{z^2}\, dz\right| < \frac{2\pi}{r}(\pi + \text{Log}\, r)$, C: $|z| = r, r > 1$. Show that the integral tends to 0 as $r \to \infty$

11. If $f(z)$ is analytic in an open region containing a closed regular curve C, find the values of each of the following:

(a) $\oint_C \frac{e^{z-z_0}}{z - z_0} f(z)\, dz$; (b) $\oint_C \frac{z^2 + z_0^2}{z^2 - z_0^2}\, dz$; (c) $\oint_C [f(z)]^n z^{z_0}\, dz$, n a positive integer.

12. If C is a closed regular curve, show that the area of the region enclosed by C is $A = (1/2i) \oint_C \bar{z}\, dz$.

13. (a) Establish the formula for integration by parts:

$$\oint_C f(z)g'(z)\, dz = f(z)g(z)]_C - \oint_C g(z)f'(z)\, dz$$

where $f(z)$ and $g(z)$ are analytic in an open region containing the regular curve C and $f(z)g(z)]_C = f(\beta)g(\beta) - f(\alpha)g(\alpha)$; α is the initial point and β is the terminal point of C.

(b) Evaluate $\int_0^{\pi i} e^z \sin z\, dz$. *Ans.:* (b) $-\frac{1}{2}(\sin \pi i + \cos \pi i + 1)$.

◇ **14.** (a) If $f(z)$ is analytic in an open region D containing $z = a$, show that

$$f(z) = f(a) + f'(a)(z - a) + \frac{f''(a)(z - a)^2}{2!} + \cdots + \frac{f^{(n)}(a)(z - a)^n}{n!} + g(z)(z - a)^{n+1},$$

where $g(z)$ is analytic in D **(Taylor's formula).** (*Hint:* Write the Cauchy integral formula as

$$f(z) = \frac{1}{2\pi i} \int_C \frac{f(\zeta)\, d\zeta}{(\zeta - a)(1 - t)}$$

where $t = \frac{z - a}{\zeta - a}$; now use the identity

$$\frac{1}{1-t} = 1 + t + t^2 + \cdots + t^n + \frac{t^{n+1}}{1-t}$$

and the generalized Cauchy integral formula.)

(b) Prove L'Hospital's rule: If $f'(a)$ and $g'(a)$ exist, $g'(a) \neq 0$ and $f(a) = g(a) = 0$, then

$$\lim_{z \to a} \frac{f(z)}{g(z)} = \frac{f'(a)}{g'(a)}.$$

15. Establish the Cauchy-Schwarz inequality:

$$\left|\int_C f(z)\overline{g(z)}\,dz\right|^2 \leq \left|\int_C |f(z)|^2\,dz\right|\left|\int_C |g(z)|^2\,dz\right|,$$

where $f(z)$ and $g(z)$ are analytic in an open region containing the regular curve C. (*Hint:* $|\int_C |\lambda f(z) + g(z)|^2\,dz| \geq 0$ for any real number λ; hence, when expanded, it becomes a quadratic equation in λ whose discriminant is negative.)

16. If $f(z)$ is analytic on and in the interior of a closed regular curve, show that $\oint_C \overline{f(z)}f'(z)\,dz$ is pure imaginary.

17. If C: $|z| = 1$, C′: $|z| = 1$, $\text{Im}\, z \geq 0$, then show that

(a) $\oint_C f(z)\,dz = \oint_{C'} [f(z) - f(-z)]\,dz.$

(b) $\oint_{C'} f(z)\,dz = 0$, if $f(z)$ is analytic in $|z| \leq 1$ and $f(-z) = -f(z)$.

◇ **18.** The Legendre polynomial of degree n is defined as

$$P_n(z) = \left(\frac{1}{2^n n!}\right)\left(\frac{d^n}{dz^n}\right)(z^2 - 1)^n.$$

(Show that this is a polynomial of degree n.)

(a) Show that

$$P_n(z) = \frac{1}{2^{n+1}\pi i} \cdot \int_C \frac{(\zeta^2 - 1)^n\,d\zeta}{(\zeta - z)^{n+1}}$$

for any closed regular curve C that encloses z.

(b) Let C be the circle with center z and radius $\sqrt{|z^2 - 1|}$. Establish *Laplace's formula:*

$$P_n(z) = \frac{1}{\pi}\int_0^{\pi} (z + \sqrt{z^2 - 1}\cos\theta)^n\,d\theta.$$

(c) Define the associated Legendre function as

$$P_n^m(z) = (-1)^m(1 - z^2)^{m/2}\frac{d^m}{dz^m}P_n(z).$$

Show that

$$P_n^m(z) = \frac{(-1)^m(n+m)!}{2^{n+1}\pi i n!}(1 - z^2)^{m/2} \cdot \oint_C \frac{(\zeta^2 - 1)^n}{(\zeta - z)^{n+m+1}}\,d\zeta$$

$$= \frac{i^m(n+m)!}{2\pi m!} \cdot \int_{-\pi}^{\pi} (z + \sqrt{z^2 - 1}\cos\theta]^n e^{-im\theta}\,d\theta,$$

where C is any closed regular curve that encloses z.

19. Show that if $f(z) = (z - a)/(z + a)$, then $f^{(n)}(0) = [(-1)^n 2n!]/a^n$.

20. (a) Show that if $f(z)$ is analytic, then

$$\frac{\partial^2|f(z)|^2}{\partial x^2} + \frac{\partial^2|f(z)|^2}{\partial y^2} = 4|f'(z)|^2.$$

(b) Show that $|f(z)|^2$ can be harmonic only if it is a constant.

(c) Generalize (a) by replacing $|f(z)|^2$ by $|f(z)|^n$, where n is a positive integer.

(d) Generalize (b) by showing that if $f_1(z), f_2(z), \cdots, f_n(z)$ are analytic, then $|f_1(z)|^2 + \cdots + |f_n(z)|^2$ is harmonic only if all the functions are constants.

21. (a) If u, v, w are real and harmonic, show that $uv = w$ can hold only if v is a constant multiple of the harmonic conjugate of u.

(b) If v is the harmonic conjugate of u, show that $e^u \cos v$ and $e^u \sin v$ are harmonic conjugates.

◇ **22.** (a) Show that the harmonic conjugate of $u(x, y)$, harmonic in the open regular region D, is

$$v(x, y) = \int_{(a,b)}^{(x,y)} -\frac{\partial u}{\partial y}\,dx + \frac{\partial u}{\partial x}\,dy,$$

where the line integral is taken over any path in D from the fixed point (a, b) to the variable point (x, y).

(b) Show that $\cos x \cosh y$ and $x(x^2 + y^2)$ are harmonic in the entire z-plane and determine their harmonic conjugates.

23. Verify the maximum modulus principle for $f(z) = (z + 1)^2$ in the interior of the triangle with vertices at 0, 2, i.

24. Prove the minimum modulus principle: If $f(z)$ is analytic, nonconstant, and nonzero in a bounded open region D, and continuous on its boundary C, then $|f(z)| > M$ for any point z in D. [*Hint:* Consider $1/f(z)$.]

25. Prove the fundamental theorem of algebra by applying the maximum modulus principle to $f(z) = (a_0 + a_1 z + \cdots + a_n z^n)^{-1}$ in the region $|z| \le R$ and letting $R \to \infty$.

26. Let $\overline{PP_j}$ denote the distance from the variable point P to the fixed point P_j.

(a) Prove that for any point z in $|z| \le r$, the maximum value of $\overline{PP_1}\cdot\overline{PP_2}\cdot\overline{PP_3}$ is attained at some point on $|z| = r$. [*Hint:* The product is $|(z - z_1)(z - z_2)(z - z_3)|$.]

(b) Generalize (a) to n arbitrary points P_j, $j = 1, \cdots, n$ in the plane and P a point in a closed region D by showing that

$$\prod_{j=1}^{n} \overline{PP_j}$$

attains its maximum if P is some point on the boundary of D.

(c) Prove that the minimum value of the product in (b) is also attained at some point on the boundary of D if P_j, $j = 1, \cdots, n$ are not in D. What is the minimum if one of these points is in D?

27. (a) Prove **Schwarz's lemma:** If $f(z)$ is analytic in $|z| < 1$, $|f(z)| \le 1$, $f(0) = 0$, then $|f(z)| \le z$ and $|f'(0)| \le 1$, with equality only if $f(z) = e^{i\alpha}z$, α real.

Hint: Apply the maximum modulus principle to $g(z)$ where

$$g(z) = \begin{cases} \dfrac{f(z)}{z}, & z \ne 0 \\ f'(0), & z = 0. \end{cases}$$

(b) Prove the following modification of Schwarz's lemma. If $f(z)$ is analytic in $|z| < r$, $|f(z)| \leq M$, $f(0) = 0$, then $|f(z)| \leq (M/r)|z|$ with equality only if $f(z) = e^{i\alpha}z$, α real. [*Hint:* Apply (a) to $f(rz)/M$.]

28. Let $f(z)$ be analytic in $r_1 \leq |z| \leq r_2$, $|f(z)| \leq M_1$ on $|z| = r_1$ and $|f(z)| \leq M_2$ on $|z| = r_2$. For $r_1 \leq r \leq r_2$, let $M = |f(z)|$ on $|z| = r$.

Prove **Hadamard's three-circle theorem:**

$$\begin{vmatrix} \text{Log}\, r & \text{Log}\, M & 1 \\ \text{Log}\, r_1 & \text{Log}\, M_1 & 1 \\ \text{Log}\, r_2 & \text{Log}\, M_2 & 1 \end{vmatrix} \leq 0.$$

(*Hint:* Apply the maximum modulus principle to $z^\alpha[f(z)]$ where

$$\alpha = \frac{\text{Log}\, M(r_2) - \text{Log}\, M(r_1)}{\text{Log}\, r_1 - \text{Log}\, r_2}.\Bigg)$$

29. Prove the analog of Liouville's theorem for harmonic functions: If $u(x, y)$ is harmonic and bounded from either above or below in the entire xy-plane, then $u(x, y)$ is a constant. (*Hint:* Apply Liouville's theorem to e^{u+iv}, where v is the harmonic conjugate of u.)

30. Prove the generalized Liouville theorem: If n is a positive integer, $f(z)$ is entire and $|f(z)| \leq M|z|^n$ for all z, then $f(z)$ must be a polynomial whose degree is less than or equal to n. (*Hint:* Use the Cauchy inequality for $n + 1$.)

31. Prove the following version of Liouville's theorem: If $f(z)$ is analytic in the extended complex plane, then $f(z)$ is a constant.

32. Show that if $f(z)$ is analytic, then (a) $\nabla^2 \text{Log}\, |f(z)| = 0$ if $f(z) \neq 0$; (b) $\nabla^2|f(z)| > 0$ if $f(z)f'(z) \neq 0$.

◇ **33.** Show that the zeros of an analytic function that does not vanish identically are isolated; i.e., every zero z_0 has a neighborhood throughout which the function is different from zero.

◇ **34.** (a) Prove **Riemann's theorem:**

If $z = a$ is an isolated singular point of $f(z)$ such that $\lim_{z \to a} f(z) = c \neq \infty$, and if we define $f(a) = c$, then the extended function is analytic at $z = a$. We call $z = a$ a **removable singular point** of $f(z)$.

(b) Prove the modified generalized Cauchy integral formula: If $f(z)$ is analytic in a simply connected open region D, except possibly at points that are removable singular points, and C is a closed regular curve in D, then for any point a in the interior of C,

$$\lim_{z \to a} f^{(n)}(z) = \frac{n!}{2\pi i} \int_C \frac{f(\zeta)\, d\zeta}{(\zeta - a)^{n+1}}.$$

What other theorems in this section admit of analogous modification?

35. (a) Show that if $\int_C f(z)\, dz = 0$ for every regular closed curve in an open region D, then the integral of $f(z)$ is independent of path in D.

(b) Show that if $f(z)$ is continuous and $\int_{z_0}^{z} f(\zeta)\, d\zeta$ is independent of path in D, then $F(z) = \int_{z_0}^{z} f(\zeta)\, d\zeta$ is analytic in D and $F'(z) = f(z)$.

(c) Show that the following converse of the Cauchy integral theorem is false: If $\int_C f(z)\, dz = 0$ about *every* closed regular curve C in an open region D, then $f(z)$ is analytic in D; show by citing

$$\int_C \frac{dz}{(z - z_0)^n} = 0, \qquad n = 2, 3, \cdots,$$

where C is a regular closed curve enclosing z_0.

(d) Prove **Morera's theorem:** If $f(z)$ is continuous in an open region D and $\int_C f(z)\, dz = 0$ for every regular closed curve in D, then $f(z)$ is analytic in D. [*Hint:* From (a) and (b), $F(z) = \int_{z_0}^{z} f(\zeta)\, d\zeta$ is analytic. Then $F'(z)$ is analytic. But $F'(z) = f(z)$.]

6. The theory of residues. Let us consider for evaluation the integral $\oint_C f(z)\, dz$, where C is a regular closed curve and $f(z)$ has a finite number of singular points $z_1, z_2, \cdots, z_n$ located in the interior of C and is analytic on C. Now if we enclose these points by nonoverlapping closed regular

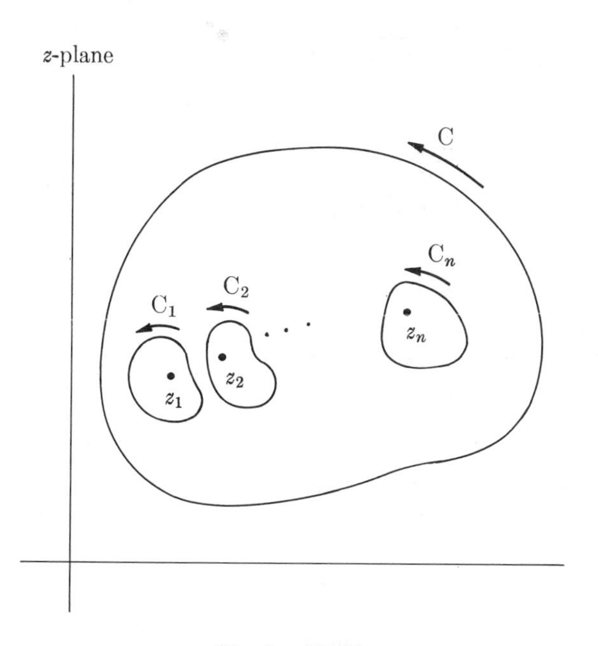

Fig. 2. Residues

curves $C_1, C_2, \cdots, C_n$ (see Fig. 2), then by the Cauchy integral theorem for multiply connected regions, we have

$$\text{(A)} \qquad \oint_C f(z)\, dz = \oint_{C_1} f(z)\, dz + \oint_{C_2} f(z)\, dz + \cdots + \oint_{C_n} f(z)\, dz.$$

If we can evaluate the integrals on the right, then we shall have the value of $\oint_C f(z)\, dz$. However, these integrals very often are as difficult to evaluate as the given integral if we employ the techniques we have considered thus far. If we were able to evaluate these integrals by other means, however, then we would be able to evaluate $\oint_C f(z)\,dz$. This leads us to the following definition: The **residue** of $f(z)$ at an isolated singular point $z = a$ is $(1/2\pi i)\oint_C f(z)\,dz$, where C is any closed regular curve whose interior contains $z = a$ but no other singular point of $f(z)$. We write

$$\operatorname*{Res}_{z=a} f(z) = \frac{1}{2\pi i}\oint_C f(z)\,dz.$$

If z is the point at infinity, then

$$\operatorname*{Res}_{z=\infty} f(z) = -\frac{1}{2\pi i}\oint_C f(z)\,dz,$$

where C is a regular closed curve that encloses all the singular points of $f(z)$. (Why is the residue of $f(z)$ uniquely determined regardless of C?) The definition of residue and (A) lead immediately to the

CAUCHY RESIDUE THEOREM. *If $f(z)$ is analytic in an open region D except at a finite number of points $z_1, z_2, \cdots, z_n$, and C is a closed regular curve in D such that these points are in its interior, then*

$$\oint_C f(z)\,dz = 2\pi i \sum_{k=1}^{n} \operatorname*{Res}_{z=z_k} f(z).$$

The Cauchy residue theorem can be effective only if we have available a simple method for the determination of residues. Since our concern is with residues at singular points, we first study such points. Hitherto, our concern has been merely to determine the singular points of a given function; now it becomes necessary to classify them further. The singular point $z = a$ of $f(z)$ is called a **pole of order m of $f(z)$** if there exists a positive integer m such that $\lim_{z\to a}(z - a)^m f(z) = c$, where c is a nonzero complex number. A pole of $f(z)$ is called a **simple pole** if it is a pole of order 1. If $z = a$ is an isolated singular point of $f(z)$ such that $\lim_{z\to a} f(z) = c \neq \infty$, then $z = a$ is a **removable singular point** of $f(z)$. [See p. 256, Exercise 34, which indicates that $f(z)$ may be defined at a removable singular point in such a manner that $f(z)$ is analytic at that point. We shall *always* define $f(z)$ in this way at such a point.] A nonremovable singular point of $f(z)$ that is not a pole is called an **essential singular point of $f(z)$.**

EXAMPLE. The singular points of $1/z^2 \sin z$ are 0 and $k\pi$, $k = \pm 1, \pm 2, \cdots$. Since

$$\lim_{z\to 0} z^3 \frac{1}{z^2 \sin z} = \lim_{z\to 0} \frac{1/\sin z}{z} = 1$$

[use L'Hospital's rule, p. 253, Exercise 14(b)], $z = 0$ is a pole of order 3. $z = k\pi$, $k = \pm 1, \pm 2, \cdots$ are simple poles, since

$$\lim_{z\to k\pi} \frac{z - k\pi}{z^2 \sin z} = \lim_{z\to k\pi} \frac{1}{2z \sin z + z^2 \cos z} = \frac{(-1)^k}{k^2\pi^2}.$$

The following characterizations of poles are often easier to apply than the definition:

P_1: $z = a$ is a pole of order m of $f(z)$ if and only if there exists a positive integer m and a function $\phi(z)$ such that (1) $\lim_{z\to a} \phi(z) \neq 0$; (2) $\phi(z)$ is either analytic at $z = a$ or has a removable singular point at $z = a$; (3) $f(z) = \phi(z)/(z - a)^m$.

P_2: If $f(z) = \phi(z)/(z - a)^m$, where $\phi(a) \neq 0$ and $\phi(z)$ is analytic at $z = a$, then $z = a$ is a pole of order m of $f(z)$.

P_3: $z = a$ is a pole of order m of $f(z)$ if and only if $z = a$ is a zero of order m of $1/f(z)$.

P_4: If $f(z) = h(z)/g(z)$, where $g(z)$ and $h(z)$ are analytic, then $z = a$ is a pole of order m of $f(z)$ if and only if $h(a) \neq 0$ and $z = a$ is a zero of order m of $g(z)$; i.e., $g(a) = g'(a) = \cdots = g^{(m-1)}(a) = 0$, $g^{(m)}(a) \neq 0$.

P_5: $z = a$ is a pole of $f(z)$ if and only if $\lim_{z\to a} |f(z)| = \infty$.

The proofs of P_1 to P_4 are left to the student. We prove P_5: If $z = a$ is a pole of $f(z)$, then by P_1 we can write

$$f(z) = \frac{\phi(z)}{(z - a)^m}, \qquad \lim_{z\to a} \phi(z) \neq 0, \quad \phi(z) \text{ analytic at } a,$$

and it is clear that $\lim_{z\to a} |f(z)| = \infty$. If $\lim_{z\to a} |f(z)| = \infty$, then there exist r and M such that for $0 < |z - a| < r$, $|f(z)| > M$. Then $g(z) = 1/f(z)$ is analytic and bounded in $0 < |z - a| < r$. By Riemann's theorem (p. 256, Exercise 34), $g(z)$ is analytic at $z = a$. But $g(a) = 0$. Hence,

$$g(z) = (z - a)^n h(z), \qquad h(a) \neq 0$$

for some positive integer n (p. 250). Then $z = a$ is a pole of $f(z)$ by P_3. P_5 is particularly useful in showing that $z = a$ is not a pole; i.e., an essential singularity of $f(z)$.

EXAMPLES

(1) $f(z) = (z^2 - 1)/z(z - 1)^2$, by P_2, has a simple pole at $z = 0$ and a pole of order 2 at $z = 1$. In general, for the rational function $p(z)/q(z)$, the poles can be determined by inspection if $q(z)$ is factored into linear factors.

(2) $f(z) = \tan z$ has simple poles at $z = (2k + 1)(\pi/2)$, $k = 0, \pm 1, \cdots$, by P_4, since $\tan z = \sin z/\cos z$ and $\cos[(2k + 1)(\pi/2)] = 0$, but $\sin[(2k + 1)(\pi/2)] \neq 0$.

(3) $z = 0$ is an essential singular point of $e^{1/z}$, since (by P_5) $\lim_{z\to 0} |e^{1/z}| = \lim_{x,y\to 0} e^{x/(x^2+y^2)}$ does not exist.

If all the singular points of a function are poles, then that function is called a **meromorphic function.** We shall now be primarily concerned with meromorphic functions and especially with the determination of the residues of such functions at their poles. We have defined the residue of a function at an isolated singular point. Poles are always isolated singular points, in view of P_3 and Exercise 33, p. 256. The following expressions for residues facilitate their computation. Note that although the residue of $f(z)$ is an integral, none of these expressions involves any integration.

R_1: If $z = a$ is a simple pole of $f(z)$, then

$$\operatorname*{Res}_{z=a} f(z) = \lim_{z \to a} (z - a)f(z).$$

R_2: If $z = a$ is a pole of order m of $f(z)$, then

$$\operatorname*{Res}_{z=a} f(z) = \frac{1}{(m-1)!} \lim_{z \to a} \frac{d^{m-1}}{dz^{m-1}} (z - a)^m f(z).$$

R_3: If $f(z) = h(z)/g(z)$, $g(z)$ and $h(z)$ analytic at $z = a$, $h(a) \neq 0$, where $z = a$ is a simple pole of $f(z)$, then

$$\operatorname*{Res}_{z=a} f(z) = \frac{h(a)}{g'(a)}.$$

R_4: If $$f(z) = \frac{A_1}{z-a} + \frac{A_2}{(z-a)^2} + \cdots + \frac{A_n}{(z-a)^n} + \phi(z),$$

$\phi(z)$ analytic at $z = a$, then $\operatorname*{Res}_{z=a} f(z) = A_1$.

R_5:

$$\operatorname*{Res}_{z=\infty} f(z) = -\operatorname*{Res}_{z=0} \frac{1}{z^2} f\left(\frac{1}{z}\right).$$

R_6: If $f(z)$ has a finite number of singular points in the z-plane, $z_1, z_2, \cdots, z_n$, then

$$\sum_{k=1}^{n} \operatorname*{Res}_{z=z_k} f(z) + \operatorname*{Res}_{z=\infty} f(z) = 0.$$

Proofs. R_1 is a special case of R_2, which we prove. By P_1, $f(z) = \phi(z)/(z - a)^m$, $\phi(z)$ analytic at $z = a$, $\phi(a) \neq 0$, or $z = a$, a removable singular point of $f(z)$, $\lim_{z \to a} f(z) \neq 0$. By the definition of residue,

$$\operatorname*{Res}_{z=a} f(z) = \frac{1}{2\pi i} \oint_C \frac{\phi(z)\, dz}{(z-a)^m} = \frac{1}{(m-1)!} \lim_{z \to a} \phi^{(m-1)}(z)$$

[by the modified, generalized Cauchy integral formula, Exercise 34(b), p. 256]

$$= \frac{1}{(m-1)!} \lim_{z \to a} \frac{d^{m-1}}{dz^{m-1}} (z - a)^m f(z).$$

Proof of R_3. By P_2 we note that $g(a) = 0$. Now by R_1,

$$\operatorname*{Res}_{z=a} f(z) = \lim_{z\to a} \frac{(z-a)h(z)}{g(z)} = \lim_{z\to a} h(z) \Big/ \left(\frac{g(z)-g(a)}{z-a}\right) = \frac{h(a)}{g'(a)}.$$

Proof of R_4.

$$\begin{aligned}\operatorname*{Res}_{z=a} f(z) &= \frac{1}{2\pi i}\oint_C f(z)\,dz \\ &= \frac{A_1}{2\pi i}\oint_C \frac{dz}{z-a} + \frac{A_2}{2\pi i}\oint_C \frac{dz}{(z-a)^2} \\ &\quad + \cdots + \frac{A_n}{2\pi i}\oint_C \frac{dz}{(z-a)^n} + \oint_C \phi(z)\,dz.\end{aligned}$$

Then the first integral equals $2\pi i$ (Example 2, p. 238) and the others are zero by Example 1, p. 246 and the Cauchy integral theorem.

Proof of R_5. Let C be the circle $|z| = R$ such that all the singularities of $f(z)$ are in the interior of C. Then

$$\operatorname*{Res}_{z=\infty} f(z) = -\frac{1}{2\pi i}\oint_C f(z)\,dz.$$

Let $z = Re^{-i\theta}$ and $r = 1/R$. Then

$$\begin{aligned}\operatorname*{Res}_{z=\infty} f(z) &= \frac{1}{2\pi}\int_0^{2\pi} f\left(\frac{1}{re^{i\theta}}\right) d(re^{i\theta}) \\ &= -\frac{1}{2\pi i}\int_0^{2\pi} f\left(\frac{1}{re^{i\theta}}\right)\frac{d(re^{i\theta})}{(re^{i\theta})^2} \\ &= -\frac{1}{2\pi i}\oint_{C'} \frac{f(1/z)\,dz}{z^2},\end{aligned}$$

where C′ is the circle $|z| = r$, and the result is immediate.

Proof of R_6. There exists a circle C of sufficiently large radius R, $|z| = R$, which encloses all singular points except $z = \infty$. Then

$$-\operatorname*{Res}_{z=\infty} f(z) = \frac{1}{2\pi i}\oint_C f(z)\,dz = \sum_{k=1}^{n} \operatorname*{Res}_{z=z_k} f(z),$$

and the result is immediate.

EXAMPLES

(1) $f(z) = \dfrac{e^z}{z(z-1)^2}$ has singular points $z = 0$, $z = 1$; $z = 0$ is a simple pole and by R_1,

$$\operatorname*{Res}_{z=0} f(z) = \lim_{z\to 0} \frac{e^z}{(z-1)^2} = 1.$$

$z = 1$ is a multiple pole and by R_2,

$$\operatorname*{Res}_{z=1} f(z) = \lim_{z\to 1} \frac{d}{dz}\left(\frac{e^z}{z}\right) = \lim_{z\to 1} \frac{e^z(z-1)}{z^2} = 0.$$

(2) $\operatorname*{Res}_{z=i} \dfrac{\sin z}{z^2+1} = \dfrac{\sin i}{2i} = \dfrac{\sinh 1}{2}$ (by R_3).

(3) $z = \pi/2$ is a simple pole of $\tan z$. Why?

$$\operatorname*{Res}_{z=\pi/2} \tan z = \frac{\sin(\pi/2)}{-\sin(\pi/2)} = -1 \text{ (by } R_3).$$

(4) $\operatorname*{Res}_{z=2} \dfrac{z+2}{(z-1)^2} = 1$ (by R_4),

since

$$\frac{z+2}{(z-1)^2} = \frac{(z-1)+3}{(z-1)^2} = \frac{1}{z-1} + \frac{3}{(z-1)^2}.$$

(5)
$$f(z) = \frac{\sin z}{z^2} = \frac{1}{z}\left(\frac{\sin z}{z}\right)$$

and since $\lim_{z\to 0} (\sin z/z) = 1$, $z = 0$ is a removable singular point of $\sin z/z$. Hence, $z = 0$ is a simple pole of $f(z)$ by P_1.

$$\operatorname*{Res}_{z=0} f(z) = \lim_{z\to 0} z \cdot \frac{\sin z}{z^2} = 1.$$

(6) $\operatorname*{Res}_{z=0} e^{1/z} = 1$. $z = 0$ is the only singular point of $e^{1/z}$, but it is an essential singular point. Although we have no technique at present for determining the residues at essential singular points, in this case we can use R_6 effectively. By R_5,

$$\operatorname*{Res}_{z=\infty} e^{1/z} = -\operatorname*{Res}_{z=0} \frac{e^z}{z^2} = -1.$$

Then by R_6 we have the result.

Now that we have techniques available for the determination of the residues of $f(z)$, the evaluation of $\oint_C f(z)\,dz$, using the Cauchy residue theorem, becomes a fairly straightforward procedure when $f(z)$ is a meromorphic function; the determination of the residue of $f(z)$ at an essential singular point will be considered in the next chapter, "Complex Infinite Series." The Cauchy residue theorem is quite a general theorem; it includes the Cauchy integral theorem if we define

$$\operatorname*{Res}_{z=a} f(z) = \frac{1}{2\pi i} \oint_C f(z)\,dz$$

where C is any closed regular curve such that $f(z)$ is analytic on C and in its interior, and $z = a$ is any point enclosed by C; it also includes the generalized Cauchy integral formula. (Proof?)

EXAMPLE 1. Evaluate

$$I = \oint_C \frac{z^4\,dz}{z^2+1}, \qquad C: \left|z - \frac{i}{2}\right| = 1.$$

Solution: $f(z) = z^4/z^2 + 1$ in the interior of C has the singular point $z = i$, which is a simple pole. Hence, $\operatorname*{Res}_{z=i} f(z) = i^4/2i = -i/2$. By the Cauchy residue theorem, $I = \pi$.

EXAMPLE 2. Evaluate

$$I = \oint_C \frac{dz}{z^3(z-1)^2}, \qquad C: |z| = 2.$$

Solution: In $|z| < 2$, $f(z) = \dfrac{1}{z^3(z-1)^2}$ has two singular points: $z = 0$, a pole of order 3 and $z = 1$, a pole of order 2. $\operatorname*{Res}_{z=0} f(z) = 3$ and $\operatorname*{Res}_{z=1} f(z) = -3$. Hence, $I = 0$. Since all the singular points of $f(z)$ are in $|z| < 2$, this result also follows from the fact that the $\operatorname*{Res}_{z=\infty} f(z) = 0$.

We are now in a position to evaluate a large class of integrals $I = \int_C f(z)\,dz$. Let us review the situation:

(1) If C is a regular closed curve and $f(z)$ has no singular points on C or in its interior, then $I = 0$.

(2) If $f(z)$ is analytic in a bounded region containing the regular curve C, which is not closed, then we evaluate I by the fundamental theorem of the calculus.

(3) If C is a closed regular curve and $f(z)$ has a finite number of poles in the interior of C and no other singular points there, we use the Cauchy residue theorem.

(4) If $f(z)$ has an infinity of singular points, then we either make a change in variable to reduce it to a complex integral of a real variable or reduce it to two real line integrals.

EXERCISES

1. Determine the singular points of each of the following functions and determine whether they are poles (indicate the order) or essential singular points. Find the residues of the functions at the poles and at the point at infinity:

(a) $\dfrac{z^2-1}{z^2+1}$; (b) $\dfrac{1}{(z+1)^3}$; (c) $\dfrac{z+1}{z^2(z-2)}$; (d) $\dfrac{z^4+1}{z^2(z-2)^3}$;

(e) $\dfrac{z}{z^2+2z+5}$; (f) $\dfrac{1}{(z^2+a^2)^2}$; (g) $\dfrac{z^4}{(z^2+a^2)^4}$; (h) $\dfrac{\sin z}{z}$;

(i) $\dfrac{1}{z\sin z}$; (j) $\dfrac{\sin z}{z^3}$; (k) $\dfrac{z}{\sin z}$; (l) $\dfrac{1}{z^2\sin z}$;

(m) $\dfrac{1}{z - z\sin z}$; (n) $\tan \pi z$; (o) $\cot \pi z$; (p) $\sec \pi z$;

(q) $\tanh z$; (r) $\csc^2 \pi z$; (s) $z\cos(1/z)$; (t) $ze^{-1/z}$;

(u) $\dfrac{e^z}{1 - \sin z}$; (v) $\tan z/(1 - e^z)^2$; (w) $z/(\cosh z - \cos z)$;

(x) $e^{\tan z}$; (y) $e^{\sin z}/\text{Log}(1 + z^2)$; $\text{Re}\, z \geq 0$.

2. If $f(z) = h(z)/g(z)$ and $z = a$ is a pole of order 2 of $f(z)$, $h(a) \neq 0$, show that

$$\operatorname*{Res}_{z=a} f(z) = \frac{6h'(a)g''(a) - 2h(a)g'''(a)}{3[g''(a)]^2}.$$

3. (a) Prove that if $f(z) = g(z)h(z)$, $g(z)$ is analytic and $h(z)$ is meromorphic with a simple pole at $z = a$, then

$$\operatorname*{Res}_{z=a} f(z) = g(a) \operatorname*{Res}_{z=a} h(z).$$

(b) Prove that if $g(z)$ is analytic at $z = a$ and $f(z)$ has a pole at $z = a$, then

$$\operatorname*{Res}_{z=a} [f(z) + g(z)] = \operatorname*{Res}_{z=a} f(z).$$

4. Prove that if $f(z)$ has a pole of order m at $z = a$ and if $P(w)$ is a polynomial of degree n, then $P[f(z)]$ has a pole of order nm at $z = a$.

5. Show that $f(z) = (z^3 - z^2 + 1)/z^3$ is analytic at ∞ and $\operatorname*{Res}_{z=\infty} f(z) = 1$. Hence, it does not necessarily follow that the residue of a function analytic at the point of infinity is zero.

6. Evaluate:

(a) $\displaystyle\oint_C \frac{z\,dz}{z+1}$, C: $|z| = 2$; (b) $\displaystyle\oint_C \frac{z^4\,dz}{z^2+1}$ C: $\left|z - \frac{i}{2}\right| = 1$;

(c) $\displaystyle\oint_C \frac{z\,dz}{z^3+1}$, C: $|z| = 2$; (d) $\displaystyle\oint_C \frac{dz}{z^4+1}$, C: $|z - 1| = 2$;

(e) $\displaystyle\oint_C \frac{dz}{2z^2 + 3z - 2}$, C: $|z| = 1$; (f) $\displaystyle\oint_C \frac{dz}{z^2(z+1)}$, C: $|z| = 2$;

(g) $\displaystyle\oint_C \frac{(z^3+1)\,dz}{(z-1)(z^2+4)}$, (1) C: $|z - 2| = 2$, (2) C: $|z - 2| = 4$;

(h) $\displaystyle\oint_C \frac{\sin z\,dz}{z^2 + a^2}$, C: $|z| = 2$, $0 < a < \sqrt{2}$;

(i) $\displaystyle\oint_C \frac{e^z\,dz}{z^2 - 1}$, C: $|z| = 2$; (j) $\displaystyle\oint_C \frac{\sin z\,dz}{[z - (\pi/2)]^2}$, C: $|z| = 2$;

(k) $\displaystyle\oint_C \frac{e^{-z}}{z^2}\,dz$, C: $|z| = 1$; (l) $\displaystyle\oint_C \frac{dz}{z\sin z}$, C: $|z| = 5$;

(m) $\displaystyle\oint_C \frac{e^{\pi z}\,dz}{2z^2 - i}$, C: $|z| = 1$; (n) $\displaystyle\oint_C \frac{\cosh \pi z\,dz}{z(z^2+1)}$, C: $|z| = 2$;

(o) $\oint_C \tan z\, dz$, C: $|z| = 2$; (p) $\oint_C \frac{z\, dz}{1 - e^z}$, C: square with vertices at $\pm 4 \pm 4i$;

(q) $\oint_C \frac{dz}{\cosh z}$, C: $|z - i| = 1$;

(r) $\oint_C \csc z\, dz$, C: $|z - 2| = 4$; (s) $\oint_C \tan^2 z\, dz$, C: $|z| = 2$;

(t) $\oint_C \frac{z + 1}{z^2 - 2z}\, dz$, $C = C_1 + C_2$, where C_1: $|z| = 1$, C_2: $|z| = 3$.

Ans.: (a) $-2\pi i$; (b) $-4\pi i$; (c) 0; (d) 0; (e) $\frac{2}{3}\pi i$; (f) 0; (g) $\frac{2}{5}\pi i$, $2\pi i$; (h) $(2\pi i/a) \sinh a$; (i) $2\pi i \sinh 1$; (j) 0; (k) $-2\pi i$; (l) 0; (m) $(1 - i)\pi \cosh (\pi/2)$; (n) $2\pi i$; (o) 0; (p) 0; (q) 2π; (r) 0; (s) 0; (t) 0.

7. Evaluate as simply as possible:

(a) $\oint_C \frac{e^z}{z^3}\, dz$, C: $|z| = 1$.

(b) $\int_0^{2+i} (z^2 - iz + 2)\, dz$ on the line from 0 to $2 + i$.

(c) $\oint_C \frac{z^2 \cosh z}{e^z}\, dz$, C: square with vertices at ± 1, $\pm i$.

(d) $\oint_C \frac{dz}{2z - 3}$, C: $|z| = 3$.

(e) $\oint_C e^z\, dz$, C: square with vertices at $0, \pi, \pi i, \pi + \pi i$.

(f) $\oint_C \frac{4z^3 + 2z}{z^4 + z^2 + 1}\, dz$, C: $|z| = 2$.

(g) $\oint_C \frac{dz}{(z - 1)^3(z - 7)}$. C: $|z - i| = 1$.

(h) $\oint_C \frac{|z|}{\bar{z}}\, dz$, C: $|z| = 1$; (i) $\oint_C \sin \frac{1}{z}\, dz$, C: $|z| = 1$.

(j) $\oint_C \frac{\sin^2 z}{z(4z^2 - 1)}\, dz$, C: $|z| = 1$.

(k) $\oint_C \sin z^2\, dz$, C: $|z| = 1$.

(l) $\oint_C \frac{e^{\tan z}\, dz}{z^2 + 1}$, C: $|z - 3i| = 1$.

(m) $\int_1^\infty dz$. (Define $\int_a^\infty f(z)\, dz = \lim_{b \to \infty} \int_a^b f(z)\, dz$, if this limit exists.)

(n) $\oint_C \frac{e^{az}}{1 + e^z}\, dz$, $a > 0$, C: $|z| = 4$.

(o) $\int_1^i z \operatorname{Log} z\, dz$, C: $|z| = 1$, $\operatorname{Re} z \geq 0$, $\operatorname{Im} z \geq 0$.

Ans.: (a) $2\pi i$; (b) $\frac{5}{3}(4 + \frac{5}{2}i)$; (c) 0; (d) πi; (e) $2(1 - e\pi)$; (f) 0; (g) 0; (h) $2\pi i$; (i) $2\pi i$; (j) $4\pi i \sin^2 \frac{1}{2}$; (k) 0; (l) 0; (m) 1; (n) $-e^{a\pi i}$; (o) $\frac{1}{4}(1 - \pi i)$.

8. (a) Let

$$f(z) = \frac{p(z)}{(z - z_1)(z - z_2)\cdots(z - z_n)},$$

where $p(z)$ is a polynomial of degree $m < n$, $z_1, z_2, \cdots, z_n$ are distinct. Show that in the partial fraction expansion

$$f(z) = \sum_{k=0}^{n} \frac{A_k}{z - z_k}, \qquad A_k = \operatorname*{Res}_{z=z_k} f(z).$$

(b) Find the partial fraction expansion of $\dfrac{z+1}{(z-1)(z-2)(z-3)}$.

9. (a) Show that the sum of the residues of

$$\frac{a_{n-1}z^{n-1} + a_{n-2}z^{n-2} + \cdots + a_0}{b_n z^n + b_{n-1}z^{n-1} + \cdots + b_0}$$

at the zeros of the denominator is a_{n-1}/b_n and this sum for

$$\frac{c_n z^n + c_{n-1}z^{n-1} + \cdots + c_0}{b_n z^n + b_{n-1}z^{n-1} + \cdots + b_0} \quad \text{is} \quad \frac{b_n c_{n-1} - a_{n-1} b_n}{b_n^2}.$$

(b) Let $p(z)$ be a polynomial of degree n with leading coefficient 1 and distinct zeros $z_1, z_2, \cdots, z_n$ and let $q(z)$ be any polynomial of degree $n - 1$ with leading coefficient 1. Show that

$$\sum_{i=1}^{n} q(z_i)/p'(z_i) = 1.$$

[*Hint:* Consider the residue of $q(z)/p(z)$ at its singular points and at ∞.]

◇ **10.** (a) Show that a polynomial of degree n has a pole of order n at ∞ with residue 0.

(b) Show that a rational function is meromorphic.

(c) Show that for the rational function $r(z) = p(z)/q(z)$, if the degree of $p(z)$ is greater than the degree of $q(z)$, then ∞ is a pole of $r(z)$; otherwise, ∞ is a regular point of $r(z)$.

7. Evaluation of real definite integrals by contour integration. Integration of complex functions along contours (i.e., closed regular curves) is often referred to as **contour integration.** There are certain classes of definite integrals of real functions for which the elementary methods of integration are either inapplicable or are too complicated, and for which contour integration can be used for their evaluation with great success. We now turn to these classes of integrals.

If in any rational function of two real variables $R(x, y)$, x is replaced by $\sin\theta$ and y by $\cos\theta$, we obtain what we shall call a *rational function* in $\sin\theta$ and $\cos\theta$; we denote it by $R(\sin\theta, \cos\theta)$. We shall assume that θ is real. We now consider the class of integrals $\int_0^{2\pi} R(\sin\theta, \cos\theta)\, d\theta$. For the evaluation of such integrals by an elementary method, see Sherwood and Taylor, *Calculus*, p. 299. Here we consider an alternate method, using contour integration. The procedure is to convert the real integral into a complex integral by making the change in variable $z = e^{i\theta}$ so that

$$\sin\theta = \frac{z - (1/z)}{2i}, \quad \cos\theta = \frac{z + (1/z)}{2}, \quad d\theta = \frac{dz}{iz}$$

and as θ varies from 0 to 2π (any interval of length 2π can be used), z traces out the unit circle in the positive direction. Hence,

$$\int_0^{2\pi} R(\sin\theta, \cos\theta)\, d\theta = \oint_{|z|=1} R\left[\frac{z - (1/z)}{2i}, \frac{z + (1/z)}{2}\right] \frac{dz}{iz}.$$

The complex integral can be evaluated by the use of the Cauchy residue theorem, provided the function in the integrand has no singularities on the unit circle. This means that the denominator of $R(\sin\theta, \cos\theta)$ must not vanish for any θ, $0 \leq \theta \leq 2\pi$.

EXAMPLE 1. Evaluate

$$\mathrm{I} = \int_0^{2\pi} \frac{d\theta}{1 + k\cos\theta}, \qquad -1 < k < 1.$$

Solution: We first ensure that $1 + k\cos\theta$ does not vanish in $0 \leq \theta \leq 2\pi$. But $1 + k\cos\theta = 0$ only if $\cos\theta = -(1/k)$, and since $-1 < k < 1$, this would mean that $|\cos\theta| > 1$, which is impossible. Now

$$\mathrm{I} = \frac{2}{i}\oint_{|z|=1} \frac{dz}{kz^2 + 2z + k}.$$

The singularities of $f(z) = \dfrac{1}{kz^2 + 2z + k}$ are $\dfrac{-1 \pm \sqrt{1 - k^2}}{k}$ (real numbers). Only $a = \dfrac{-1 + \sqrt{1 - k^2}}{k}$ is in $|z| = 1$ and $\operatorname*{Res}_{z=a} f(z) = \dfrac{1}{2\sqrt{1 - k^2}}$. Hence,

$$\mathrm{I} = \frac{2\pi}{\sqrt{1 - k^2}}.$$

EXAMPLE 2. Evaluate

$$\mathrm{I} = \int_0^{2\pi} \frac{\cos\theta\, d\theta}{1 + k\cos\theta}.$$

Solution: Suppose we differentiate with respect to k both sides of

$$\int_0^{2\pi} \frac{d\theta}{1 + k\cos\theta} = \frac{2\pi}{\sqrt{1 - k^2}}$$

(see Example 1), by differentiating under the integral sign; we obtain

$$-\int_0^{2\pi} \frac{\cos\theta\, d\theta}{(1 + k\cos\theta)^2} = \frac{2\pi k}{(1 - k^2)^{3/2}}.$$

Then I would equal $\frac{-2\pi k}{(1-k^2)^{3/2}}$. However, is the interchange of integration and differentiation valid? The answer is given by

Leibniz's rule for differentiation under the integral sign. If $f(x, \lambda)$ is continuous and $\partial f/\partial\lambda$ is continuous in an open region that includes the rectangle $a \leq x \leq b$, $\lambda_1 \leq \lambda \leq \lambda_2$, then for $\lambda_1 < \lambda < \lambda_2$,

$$\frac{d}{d\lambda}\int_a^b f(x, \lambda)\, dx = \int_a^b \frac{\partial f(x, \lambda)}{\partial\lambda}\, dx.$$

Proof. Let $g(\lambda) = \int_a^b \frac{\partial f(x, \lambda)}{\partial\lambda}\, dx$. Then

$$\begin{aligned}\int_{\lambda_1}^{\lambda} g(u)\, du &= \int_{\lambda_1}^{\lambda}\int_a^b \frac{\partial f(x, u)}{\partial u}\, dx\, du \\ &= \int_a^b \left(\int_{\lambda_1}^{\lambda} \frac{\partial f(x, u)}{\partial u}\, du\right) dx \\ &= \int_a^b [f(x, \lambda) - f(x, \lambda_1)]\, dx.\end{aligned}$$

Now

$$\frac{d}{d\lambda}\int_{\lambda_1}^{\lambda} g(u)\, du = \frac{d}{d\lambda}\left[\int_a^b f(x, \lambda)\, dx - \int_a^b f(x, \lambda_1)\, dx\right]$$

and

$$g(\lambda) = \frac{d}{d\lambda}\int_a^b f(x, \lambda)\, dx,$$

and we have completed the proof.

We now consider the improper integral $\int_{-\infty}^{\infty} Q(x)\, dx$ for special cases of the real function $Q(x)$. The value of $\int_{-\infty}^{\infty} Q(x)\, dx$ may be defined in various ways. The method of contour integration, which we are about to employ, requires that we define

$$\int_{-\infty}^{\infty} Q(x)\, dx = \lim_{R\to\infty}\int_{-R}^{R} Q(x)\, dx,$$

if this limit exists. This is called the **Cauchy principal value.** It is often identified with such notation as $P\int_{-\infty}^{\infty} Q(x)\, dx$. However, since we shall be using only this value, when we write $\int_{-\infty}^{\infty} Q(x)\, dx$, we imply its Cauchy principal value. The Cauchy principal value of an integral may exist while other values of the integral may not; for example,

$$\int_{-\infty}^{\infty} \frac{x\, dx}{x^2+1} = \lim_{R\to\infty}\int_{-R}^{R} \frac{x\, dx}{x^2+1} = 0,$$

since the integrand in the latter integral is an odd function. However, if we define

$$\int_{-\infty}^{\infty} \frac{x\, dx}{x^2+1} = \lim_{a\to\infty}\int_{a}^{0} \frac{x\, dx}{x^2+1} + \lim_{b\to\infty}\int_0^b \frac{x\, dx}{x^2+1},$$

we find that the integrals on the right are both divergent.

We shall now evaluate $\int_{-\infty}^{\infty} r(x)\,dx$, where $r(x) = p(x)/q(x)$ and $p(x)$, $q(x)$ are real polynomials, by contour integration. This integral can be considered as the integral of $r(z)$, with integration along the real axis. Here we have merely replaced the real variable x in $r(x)$ by the complex variable z, where $\operatorname{Re} z = x$. If R is a real number, we have

$$\int_{-\infty}^{\infty} r(x)\,dx = \lim_{R\to\infty} \int_{-R}^{R} r(x)\,dx,$$

if this limit exists. Now let C_R be the semicircle with center at the origin and radius R. C_R and the line segment $-R \le x \le R$, $y = 0$, form a

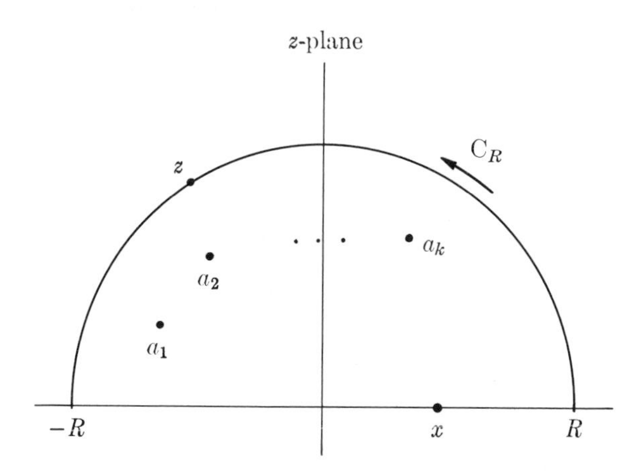

Fig. 3. Contour integration

regular closed curve C (Fig. 3). Now we consider evaluating $\oint_C r(z)\,dz$, using the Cauchy residue theorem. Since $\oint_C r(z)\,dz = \int_{-R}^{R} r(x)\,dx + \int_{C_R} r(z)\,dz$, we have

$$\int_{-R}^{R} r(x)\,dx + \int_{C_R} r(z)\,dz = 2\pi i \sum_{k=1}^{s} \operatorname*{Res}_{z=a_k} r(z),$$

where a_k, $k = 1, 2, \cdots, s$ are the singularities of $r(z)$ in the interior of C. Now, since we are going to let $R \to \infty$, we must take R large enough so that C encloses *all* the singularities of $r(z)$ in the upper half-plane. All these singularities are poles [see Exercise 10(b), p. 266], and since $r(z) = p(z)/q(z)$, these poles are the zeros of $q(z)$ in the upper half-plane. We must be sure that none of these zeros is real, for otherwise we shall have singularities on the path of integration; hence, it is necessary but not sufficient that $q(z)$ be of even degree. Now, if $\lim_{R\to\infty} \int_{C_R} r(z)\,dz$ exists and is I_0, we shall have

$$\int_{-\infty}^{\infty} \frac{p(x)\,dx}{q(x)} = 2\pi i \sum_{k=1}^{s} \operatorname*{Res}_{z=a_k} \frac{p(z)}{q(z)} - \mathrm{I}_0.$$

In general, it is difficult to determine I_0 except in the case when $\mathrm{I}_0 = 0$. We now consider conditions on $p(z)$ and $q(x)$ to ensure that $\mathrm{I}_0 = 0$. Let $p(z) = a_n z^n + \cdots + a_1 z + a_0$, $q(z) = b_m z^m + \cdots + b_1 z + b_0$; then

$$\left| \int_{C_R} \frac{p(z)}{q(z)}\,dz \right| \le \frac{\pi K}{R^{m-n-1}},$$

for some constant K independent of R and R sufficiently large, by the fundamental integral inequality and Example, p. 186. If $m \ge n + 2$, then the right-hand side approaches 0 as $R \to \infty$, and we have that the

$$\lim_{R\to\infty} \int_{C_R} \frac{p(z)}{q(z)}\,dz = 0.$$

Let us state this result as a

THEOREM. If $p(x)$ and $q(x)$ are real polynomials of degree n and m, respectively, $m \ge n + 2$, and $q(x)$ has no real zeros, then

$$\int_{-\infty}^{\infty} \frac{p(x)}{q(x)}\,dx = 2\pi i \sum_{k=1}^{s} \operatorname*{Res}_{z=a_k} \frac{p(z)}{q(z)},$$

where $a_1, a_2, \cdots, a_s$ are the zeros of $q(x)$ in the upper half of the z-plane.

EXAMPLE 1. Evaluate $\mathrm{I} = \displaystyle\int_0^{\infty} \frac{dx}{x^4+1}$.

Solution. Since the integrand is an even function,

$$\mathrm{I} = \frac{1}{2}\int_{-\infty}^{\infty} \frac{dx}{x^4+1}.$$

The degree of $x^4 + 1$ is 4 and the degree of 1 is 0. The only zeros of $x^4 + 1$ in the upper half of the z-plane are $a = (\sqrt{2}/2)(1 + i)$ and $b = (\sqrt{2}/2)(-1 + i)$, and these are simple poles of $f(z) = 1/(z^4 + 1)$. Hence,

$$\operatorname*{Res}_{z=a} f(z) = \frac{-1-i}{4\sqrt{2}}, \qquad \operatorname*{Res}_{z=b} f(z) = \frac{1-i}{4\sqrt{2}}.$$

Hence, $\mathrm{I} = (\pi\sqrt{2})/4$.

EXAMPLE 2. Evaluate

$$\mathrm{I} = \int_{-\infty}^{\infty} \frac{x^2\,dx}{(x^2+a^2)^2}, \qquad a > 0.$$

Solution. We could evaluate I directly as in the preceding example since all the conditions are satisfied. But since ai is a pole of order 2 (by this time the student should be well aware of how tedious it is to calculate the residues at multiple poles), it is simpler to proceed as follows. Consider

$$I' = \int_0^\infty \frac{x^2\,dx}{(x^2 + a^2)(x^2 + b^2)}, \qquad a > 0, b > 0.$$

It is readily seen that $I' = \dfrac{\pi}{2(a + b)}$. If

$$\lim_{b\to a} I' = \int_0^\infty \lim_{b\to a} \frac{x^2\,dx}{(x^2 + a^2)(x^2 + b^2)} = \frac{\pi}{2a},$$

then $I = \pi/2a$. The interchange of the limit operation and integration in the improper integral is not always valid; in this case it is, in view of the following

THEOREM. If $f(x, \lambda)$ is continuous for $a \leq x < \infty$ and $\alpha < \lambda < \beta$, and there exists a function $M(x)$, independent of λ such that $|f(x, \lambda)| \leq M(x)$, $\alpha \leq \lambda \leq \beta$, and if $\int_a^\infty M(x)\,dx$ is convergent, then

$$\lim_{\lambda\to\alpha} \int_a^\infty f(x, \lambda)\,dx = \int_a^\infty \lim_{\lambda\to\alpha} (x, \lambda)\,dx.$$

The proof can be constructed from theorems in Exercise 25, p. 471. Since

$$\frac{x^2}{(x^2 + a^2)(x^2 + b^2)} \leq \frac{1}{x^2 + a^2}, \quad b \geq 0, \qquad \int_0^\infty \frac{dx}{x^2 + a^2} = \frac{\pi}{2a},$$

and the other conditions of the theorem are satisfied, we are justified in our procedure in Example 2.

EXAMPLE 3. Evaluate

$$\int_0^\infty \frac{dx}{(x^4 + 1)^3}.$$

Solution. The singular points of the integrand are poles of order 3; let us therefore consider another method. Let us replace 1 by the parameter λ so that

$$I = \int_0^\infty \frac{dx}{(x^4 + \lambda)}.$$

Let us formally differentiate both sides with respect to λ, differentiating under the integral sign:

$$\frac{dI}{d\lambda} = -\int_0^\infty \frac{dx}{(x^4 + \lambda)^2}$$

and differentiating again

$$\frac{d^2I}{d\lambda^2} = 2\int_0^\infty \frac{dx}{(x^4 + \lambda)^3}.$$

Hence

$$\int_0^\infty \frac{dx}{(x^4 + 1)^3} = \frac{1}{2}\frac{d^2I}{d\lambda^2}\bigg]_{\lambda=1}$$

But, using Example 1, we have that $I = (\lambda^{-3/4}\pi\sqrt{2})/4$. Hence, the value of the given integral appears to be $(21\pi\sqrt{2})/64$.

The technique employed in the last example depends on the possibility of differentiating an improper integral under the integral sign. (Leibniz's rule for differentiation under the integral sign is not valid here. Why?) That this is not always possible is illustrated by:

$$F(\lambda) = \int_0^\infty \lambda^3 e^{-\lambda^2 x}\, dx = \lambda,$$

all λ including $\lambda = 0$. $F'(\lambda) = 1$; but

$$\int_0^\infty \frac{\partial}{\partial\lambda}[\lambda^3 e^{-\lambda^2 x}]\, dx = \int_0^\infty (3\lambda^2 - 2\lambda^4 x)e^{-\lambda^2 x}\, dx = \begin{cases} 1, & \lambda \neq 0 \\ 0, & \lambda = 0 \end{cases}.$$

(The student should supply the details.) A criterion for the validity of differentiation under an improper integral is given in the

THEOREM. If (1) $f(x, \lambda)$ and $\partial f/\partial\lambda$ are continuous in $a \leq x < \infty$, $\alpha \leq \lambda \leq \beta$; (2) $\int_a^\infty f(x, \lambda)\, dx$ is convergent; (3) there exists a continuous function $M(x)$, independent of λ such that $|(\partial/\partial\lambda)f(x, \lambda)| \leq M(x)$, $\alpha \leq \lambda \leq \beta$, where $\int_a^\infty M(x)\, dx$ is convergent, then

$$\frac{d}{d\lambda}\int_a^\infty f(x, \lambda)\, dx = \int_a^\infty \frac{\partial}{\partial\lambda}[f(x, \lambda)]\, dx.$$

A proof of this theorem can be constructed from the definitions and theorems in Exercise 25, p. 471. The conditions in the theorem are sufficient but not necessary; however, this particular theorem has the advantage that the stated conditions are usually readily verified for many integrals. In the example just considered, the student should verify that the conditions of the theorem are satisfied.

We now consider the evaluation of the real integrals $\int_{-\infty}^\infty \frac{p(x)}{q(x)} \sin kx\, dx$ and $\int_{-\infty}^\infty \frac{p(x)}{q(x)} \cos kx\, dx$, $k > 0$, where $p(x)$ and $q(x)$ are polynomials of degree n and m, respectively, $m \geq n + 1$, and $q(x)$ has no real zeros, by contour integration. Since $\sin kx = \operatorname{Im} e^{ikx}$ and $\cos kx = \operatorname{Re} e^{ikx}$, we first integrate $\frac{p(z)}{q(z)} e^{ikz}$ around the contour in Fig. 3 to obtain

$$\int_{-R}^R \frac{p(x)}{q(x)} e^{ikx}\, dx + \int_{C_R} \frac{p(z)}{q(z)} e^{ikz}\, dz = 2\pi i \sum_{j=1}^{s} \operatorname*{Res}_{z=a_j} \frac{p(z)}{q(z)} e^{ikz},$$

where a_j, $j = 1, \cdots, s$, are the zeros of $q(x)$ in the upper half-plane.

In order to show that

$$I_R = \int_{C_R} \frac{p(z)}{q(z)} e^{ikz}\, dz \to 0$$

as $R \to \infty$, let $z = Re^{i\theta}$ on C_R; we shall need an inequality known as the

Jordan inequality. If $0 \leq \theta \leq (\pi/2)$, then $\sin\theta \geq 2\theta/\pi$.

Proof. We shall show that $\sin\theta/\theta$ is decreasing in $0 \le \theta \le \pi/2$ so that its least value in this interval will occur at $\pi/2$ and the inequality will follow immediately. Consider

$$\frac{d}{d\theta}\left(\frac{\sin\theta}{\theta}\right) = \frac{\theta\cos\theta - \sin\theta}{\theta^2} = \frac{\cos\theta}{\theta^2}(\theta - \tan\theta).$$

In $0 \le \theta \le (\pi/2)$, $\cos\theta/\theta^2 \ge 0$ and $\theta - \tan\theta < 0$ $(d/d\theta)(\theta - \tan\theta) = -\tan^2\theta < 0$; hence, $\theta - \tan\theta$ is decreasing and equals 0 at 0 and approaches $-\infty$ as $\theta \to \pi/2$.] Hence, $d/d\theta(\sin\theta/\theta) \le 0$ in $0 \le \theta \le (\pi/2)$.

Now, since

$$|e^{ikz}| = |e^{ikR(\cos\theta + i\sin\theta)}| = e^{-kR}\sin\theta \le e^{-2kR\theta/\pi}$$

in $0 \le \theta \le \pi/2$, and for R sufficiently large, $\left|\dfrac{p(Re^{i\theta})}{q(Re^{i\theta})}\right| \le \dfrac{K}{R^{m-n}}$, K independent of R (see Example, p. 186),

$$|\mathrm{I}_R| \le \frac{K}{R^{m-n-1}}\int_0^{\pi} e^{-kR\sin\theta}\,d\theta$$

$$= \frac{2K}{R^{m-n-1}}\int_0^{\pi/2} e^{-kR\sin\theta}\,d\theta \le \frac{2K}{R^{m-n-1}}\int_0^{\pi/2} e^{-2kR\theta/\pi}\,d\theta$$

$$= \frac{\pi K}{kR^{m-n}}(1 - e^{-kR}) \to 0$$

as $R \to \infty$, since $m > n$, $k > 0$. Hence,

$$\int_{-\infty}^{\infty} \frac{p(x)}{q(x)} e^{ikx}\,dx = 2\pi i \sum_{j=1}^{s} \operatorname*{Res}_{z=a_j} \frac{p(z)}{q(z)} e^{ikz}.$$

Now, if we take the imaginary (or real) part of both sides of this equation (p. 237, I_5) we obtain the value of

$$\int_{-\infty}^{\infty} \frac{p(x)}{q(x)} \sin kx\,dx$$

(or $\int_{-\infty}^{\infty} [p(x)/q(x)] \cos kx\,dx$). Let us state this result as a

THEOREM. If $p(x)$ and $q(x)$ are real polynomials of degree n and m, respectively, $m \ge n + 1$, and $q(x)$ has no real zeros, then for $k > 0$,

$$\int_{-\infty}^{\infty} \frac{p(x)}{q(x)} \begin{Bmatrix}\sin kx\\ \cos kx\end{Bmatrix} dx = \begin{Bmatrix}\mathrm{Im}\\ \mathrm{Re}\end{Bmatrix} 2\pi i \sum_{j=1}^{s} \operatorname*{Res}_{z=a_j} \frac{p(z)}{q(z)} e^{ikz},$$

where a_j, $j = 1, \cdots, s$ are the zeros of $q(x)$ in the upper half-plane.

EXAMPLE 1. Evaluate

$$\mathrm{I} = \int_0^{\infty} \frac{\cos kx\,dx}{x^2 + a^2}, \qquad a > 0,\ k > 0.$$

Solution. Since the integrand is an even function,

$$\mathrm{I} = \frac{1}{2}\int_{-\infty}^{\infty} \frac{\cos kx\, dx}{x^2 + a^2}.$$

The only zero of $x^2 + a^2$ in the upper half of the plane is ai and

$$\operatorname*{Res}_{z=ai} \frac{e^{ikz}}{z^2 + a^2} = \frac{e^{-ka}}{2ai}.$$

Hence,

$$\mathrm{I} = \frac{\pi}{2a} e^{-ka}.$$

EXAMPLE 2. Evaluate

$$\mathrm{I} = \int_0^{\infty} \frac{x \sin kx\, dx}{x^2 + a^2}, \qquad a > 0,\ k > 0.$$

Solution. We can obtain the value of this integral by differentiating I in Example 1 with respect to k (is this valid?) to obtain

$$-\int_0^{\infty} \frac{x \sin kx\, dx}{x^2 + a^2} = -\frac{\pi}{2} e^{-ak}.$$

Hence

$$\mathrm{I} = \frac{\pi}{2} e^{-ak}.$$

EXAMPLE 3. Show that $\displaystyle\int_0^{\infty} \frac{\sin x}{x}\, dx = \frac{\pi}{2}.$

Solution. Let $k = 1$ and let $a \to 0$ in the integral in Example 2. (Show that the passage to the limit is valid.)

We now consider the real definite integral $\int_0^{\infty} x^{\alpha-1} r(x)\, dx$, where $r(x)$ is a rational function and $0 < \alpha < 1$. To evaluate this integral by contour integration, we must employ a special contour along which we can consider one branch of the multiple-valued function $z^{\alpha-1}$; in this way, we essentially have a single-valued function. For this purpose, we let $z = \rho e^{i\phi}$, $0 \leq \phi < 2\pi$, so that the positive real axis is a branch cut. Now we take as the path of integration the contour C consisting of the circles C_r and C_R with center at the origin and radii r and R, $r < R$ (Fig. 4), and the cut along the positive real axis traversed twice. This contour is the boundary of a simply connected region D in which $z^{\alpha-1}$ can be made single-valued. Let us examine the cut along the positive real axis; since we are traversing this cut twice, we can think of it as having two edges, an upper edge and a lower edge. If we move along the upper edge in the direction shown in Fig. 4, then $\arg z = 0$ for any z on the upper edge; then $\arg z = 2\pi$ for any z on the lower edge. Hence, since $|z| = x$ on the cut, $z^{\alpha-1} = x^{\alpha-1}$ on the upper edge and $z^{\alpha-1} = x^{\alpha-1}e^{2\pi\alpha i}$ on the lower edge.

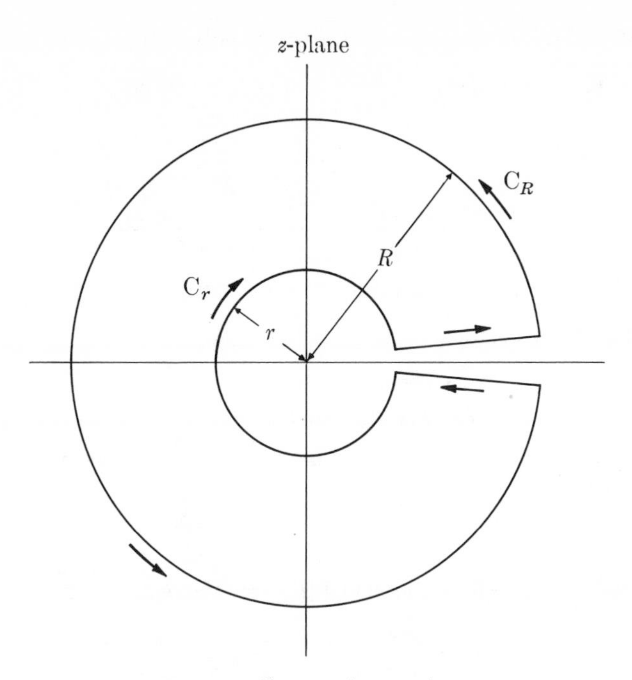

Fig. 4. Contour integration

Now

$$\oint_{C} z^{\alpha-1}r(z)\,dz = \int_{r}^{R} x^{\alpha-1}r(x)\,dx + \int_{C_R} z^{\alpha-1}r(z)\,dz$$

$$+ e^{2\pi\alpha i}\int_{R}^{r} x^{\alpha-1}r(x)\,dx$$

$$+ \int_{C_R} z^{\alpha-1}r(z)\,dz$$

$$= 2\pi i \sum_{j=1}^{s} \operatorname*{Res}_{z=a_j} z^{\alpha-1}r(z)$$

where a_j, $j = 1, \cdots, s$, are the zeros of $q(z)$ $[r(z) = p(z)/q(z)]$ occurring in D. In order to evaluate $\int_0^\infty x^{\alpha-1}r(x)\,dx$, we must let $r \to 0$ and $R \to \infty$; hence, r must be chosen sufficiently small and R sufficiently large so that D contains all the zeros of $q(z)$. $q(z)$ must have no zeros on the positive real axis, for otherwise $r(z)$ would have singular points on the path of integration. Now, if $|z^\alpha r(z)| \to 0$ as $|z| \to 0$ *and* $|z| \to \infty$, then

$$\int_{C_R} z^{\alpha-1}r(z)\,dz \to 0 \quad \text{and} \quad \int_{C_r} z^{\alpha-1}r(z)\,dz \to 0.$$

This leads immediately to the

THEOREM. If $p(x)$ and $q(x)$ are real polynomials, $q(x)$ has no zeros on the positive real axis, $\left|\dfrac{z^\alpha p(z)}{q(z)}\right| \to 0$ as $|z| \to 0$ *and* $|z| \to \infty$, $0 < \alpha < 1$, then

$$\int_0^\infty \frac{x^{\alpha-1}p(x)\,dx}{q(x)} = \frac{2\pi i \sum_{j=1}^{s} \operatorname*{Res}_{z=a_j} \dfrac{z^{\alpha-1}p(z)}{q(z)}}{1 - e^{2\pi i\alpha}}$$

where a_j, $j = 1, \cdots, s$ are the zeros of $q(x)$.

EXAMPLE. Show that

$$\mathrm{I} = \int_0^\infty \frac{x^{\alpha-1}\,dx}{1+x} = \frac{\pi}{\sin \pi\alpha}, \qquad 0 < \alpha < 1.$$

Solution. The only zero of $1 + x$ is $x = -1$, and it does not occur on the positive real axis.

$$\operatorname*{Res}_{z=-1} \frac{z^{\alpha-1}}{1+z} = (-1)^{\alpha-1} = -e^{\pi i\alpha}.$$

Furthermore, $\dfrac{|z|^\alpha}{|1+z|} \to 0$ as $|z| \to 0$ and $|z| \to \infty$. Hence

$$\mathrm{I} = \frac{2\pi i e^{\pi i\alpha}}{1 - e^{2\pi i\alpha}} = \frac{\pi}{\dfrac{e^{\pi i\alpha} - e^{-\pi i\alpha}}{2i}} = \frac{\pi}{\sin \pi\alpha}.$$

Finally, let us consider the real integral $\displaystyle\int_{-\infty}^{\infty} \frac{p(x)\,dx}{q(x)(x-b)}$, where $p(x)$ and $q(x)$ are real polynomials of degree n and m, respectively, $m \geq n + 1$, $q(x)$ having no real zeros, and $b > 0$. We cannot evaluate this integral by the techniques thus far employed, since

$$f(z) = \frac{p(z)}{q(z)(z-b)}$$

has the real pole $z = b$. However, by employing a special contour, we shall succeed in its evaluation. Let the contour C consist of two semicircles C_R and C_r of radii R and r, C_R centered at the origin and C_r at b, $R > b + r$, and the line segments along the real axis from $-R$ to $b - r$ and from $b + r$ to R (Fig. 5). R is chosen sufficiently large and r sufficiently small so that C encloses all the zeros of $q(x)$. Now,

$$\text{(A)} \quad \int_{-R}^{b-r} f(x)\,dx + \int_{\mathrm{C}_r} f(z)\,dz + \int_{b+r}^{R} f(x)\,dx + \int_{\mathrm{C}_R} f(z)\,dz = 2\pi i \sum_{j=0}^{s} \operatorname*{Res}_{z=a_j} f(z),$$

where a_j, $j = 1, \cdots, s$, are the zeros of $q(x)$ in the upper half of the z-plane. As before, $\lim_{R\to\infty} \int_{\mathrm{C}_R} f(z)\,dz = 0$. We now consider $\mathrm{I}_r = \int_{\mathrm{C}_r} f(z)\,dz$. We can write

$$f(z) = \frac{p(z)}{q(z)(z-b)} = \frac{\mathrm{A}}{z-b} + \phi(z)$$

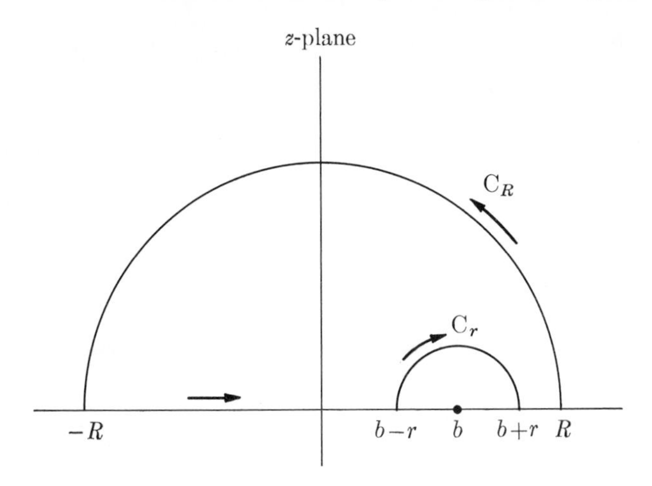

Fig. 5. An indented contour

where $\phi(z)$ is analytic in $0 \leq |z - b| \leq r$. But $A = \operatorname*{Res}_{z=b} f(z)$ (p. 260, R_4). Hence, $I_r = \operatorname*{Res}_{z=b} f(z) + \int_{C_r} \frac{dz}{z-b} + \int_{C_r} \phi(z)\, dz$. However,

$$\left|\int_{C_r} \phi(z)\, dz\right| \leq M\pi r,$$

where M is the maximum value of $\phi(z)$ on C_r; hence, as $r \to 0$, $\int_{C_r} \phi(z)\, dz \to 0$. Now, on C_r, $z - b = re^{i\theta}$, so

$$\int_{C_r} \frac{dz}{z-b} = -\int_{\pi}^{0} d\theta = -\pi i.$$

Hence,

$$\lim_{r\to 0} I_r = -\pi i \operatorname*{Res}_{z=b} f(z).$$

Now returning to (A) and letting $R \to \infty$ and $r \to 0$, we obtain

$$\int_{-\infty}^{\infty} \frac{p(x)\, dx}{q(x)(x-b)} = \pi i \operatorname*{Res}_{z=b} f(z) + 2\pi i \sum_{j=0}^{s} \operatorname*{Res}_{z=a_j} f(z),$$

where a_j, $j = 1, \cdots, s$, are the zeros of $q(x)$ in the upper half of the plane.

The contour we have just employed is sometimes called an **indented contour.** A number of other real definite integrals can be evaluated by contour integration if the appropriate indented contour or a special contour is used. The selection of such contours often requires considerable ingenuity and experience. The student will find examples of these among the exercises, where convenient contours are suggested.

We have indicated that contour integration affords one method of evaluating certain real definite integrals; it may not necessarily be the simplest, so that the student should be on the alert for other methods—some of which we consider in Part IV.

EXERCISES

1. Evaluate:

(a) $\displaystyle\int_0^{2\pi} \frac{d\theta}{5 + 4\sin\theta}$; (b) $\displaystyle\int_{-\pi}^{\pi} \frac{d\theta}{1 + \sin^2\theta}$;

(c) $\displaystyle\int_0^{\pi} \frac{d\theta}{a + b\cos\theta}$, $a > |b|$;

(d) $\displaystyle\int_0^{2\pi} \frac{d\theta}{a + b\sin\theta}$, $a > |b|$;

(e) $\displaystyle\int_0^{\pi} \frac{d\theta}{a^2 + \sin^2\theta}$, $a > 0$;

(f) $\displaystyle\int_0^{\pi} \frac{\sin^2\theta\, d\theta}{a + b\cos\theta}$, $a > |b|$;

(g) $\displaystyle\int_0^{2\pi} \frac{d\theta}{a^2\cos^2\theta + b^2\sin^2\theta}$, $a, b > 0$;

(h) $\displaystyle\int_0^{2\pi} \frac{d\theta}{1 - 2a\sin\theta + a^2}$, $0 < a < 1$;

(i) $\displaystyle\int_0^{2\pi} \frac{\cos n\theta\, d\theta}{1 - 2a\cos\theta + a^2}$, $a < 1$, n a positive integer.

Ans.: (a) $2\pi/3$; (b) $\pi\sqrt{2}$; (c) $\pi/\sqrt{a^2 - b^2}$; (d) $2\pi/\sqrt{a^2 - b^2}$; (e) $\pi/a\sqrt{a^2 + 1}$; (f) $(\pi/b^2)(a - \sqrt{a^2 - b^2})$; (g) $\pi/2ab$; (h) $2\pi/(1 - a^2)$; (i) $[\pi(1 - a + a^2)]/1 - a$; (j) $\pi a^n/(1 - a^2)$.

2. Use results in Exercise 1 with the appropriate operations to evaluate:

(a) $\displaystyle\int_0^{\pi} \frac{d\theta}{(a + b\cos\theta)^2}$, $a > |b|$;

(b) $\displaystyle\int_0^{\pi} \frac{d\theta}{(a^2 + \sin^2\theta)^2}$, $a > 0$;

(c) $\displaystyle\int_0^{\pi} \frac{d\theta}{(a^2\cos^2\theta + b^2\sin^2\theta)^2}$;

(d) $\displaystyle\int_0^{\pi} \frac{\cos^2 n\theta\, d\theta}{1 - 2a\cos 2\theta + a^2}$, $a < 1$, n a positive integer;

(e) $\displaystyle\int_0^{\pi} \frac{\sin^2 n\theta\, d\theta}{1 - 2a\cos 2\theta + a^2}$, $a < 1$, n a positive integer.

Ans.: (a) $\pi a/(a^2 - b^2)^{3/2}$; (b) $\pi(2a + 1)/2a(a^2 + 1)^{3/2}$; (c) $\pi(a^2 + b^2)/4a^3b^3$; (d) $\dfrac{\pi}{2}\dfrac{1 + a^n}{1 - a^2}$; (e) $\dfrac{\pi}{2}\dfrac{1 - a^n}{1 - a^2}$.

3. (a) Establish Wallis' formulas:

$$s_{2n} = \int_0^{\pi/2} \cos^{2n}\theta\, d\theta = \int_0^{\pi/2} \sin^{2n}\theta\, d\theta$$
$$= \frac{\pi}{2}\frac{1\cdot 3\cdot 5\cdots(2n-1)}{2\cdot 4\cdot 6\cdots 2n} = \frac{\pi}{2}\frac{(2n)!}{(2^n n!)^2}$$
$$s_{2n+1} = \int_0^{\pi/2} \cos^{2n+1}\theta\, d\theta = \int_0^{\pi/2} \sin^{2n+1}\theta\, d\theta$$
$$= \frac{(2^n n!)^2}{(2n+1)!}.$$

(b) Use (a) to evaluate $\int_0^1 \frac{x^n\, dx}{\sqrt{1-x^2}}$.

(c) Show that Wallis' formulas can be obtained from the recurrence relation $s_n = \frac{n-1}{n} s_{n-2}$, established by integration by parts.

(d) Show that $\{s_n\}$ is monotonically decreasing. (*Hint:* $0 \le \sin\theta \le 1$, $0 \le \theta \le \pi/2$.) Since $\{s_n\}$ is bounded from below, it has a limit.

(e) Define Wallis' product

$$W_n = \frac{s_{2n+1}}{s_{2n}}\frac{\pi}{2}$$

and show that $\lim_{n\to\infty} W_n = \frac{\pi}{2}$ and that $\lim_{n\to\infty} \frac{(n!)^2 2^{2n}}{(2n)!\sqrt{n}} = \sqrt{\pi}$.

(f) Show that $\frac{2}{2n+1} < \log\left(1+\frac{1}{n}\right)$, and that $e < \left(1+\frac{1}{n}\right)^{n+1/2}$ (compare the area under $y = \frac{1}{x}$ from 1 to $1+\frac{1}{n}$ with the area of the trapezoid whose sides are on the lines $y = 0$, $y = 1$, $y = 1+\frac{1}{n}$, and the tangent to $y = \frac{1}{x}$ at $x = 1+\frac{1}{2n}$. See p. 14, Exercise 7(a).

(g) Show that

$$u_n = \frac{\left(\frac{n}{e}\right)^n \sqrt{n}}{n!} < 1.$$

(Show that the area under $y = \log x$ from 1 to n is $A = \log\left(\frac{n}{e}\right)^n + 1$. Divide the interval $[0, n]$ into subintervals by the points $k - \frac{1}{2}$, $k = 2, \cdots, n$. Construct rectangles with the first and last subintervals as bases and heights 2 and n, respectively; construct trapezoids on the remaining subintervals with nonparallel sides on the tangent lines to $y = \log x$ at the midpoints of the subintervals. Show that the sum of the areas of the rectangles and trapezoids is

$$\begin{aligned} B &= 1 + \log 2 + \cdots \log(n-1) + \tfrac{1}{2}\log n \\ &= 1 + \log n! - \log\sqrt{n}. \end{aligned}$$

Compare A and B.)

(h) Show that $\{u_n\}$ is monotonically increasing by showing that $u_{n+1}/u_n > 1$. It follows that $\lim_{n\to\infty} u_n$ exists.

(i) Show that $\lim_{n\to\infty} u_n^2/u_{2n} = \dfrac{1}{\sqrt{2\pi}}$ and hence that $\lim_{n\to\infty} u_n = \dfrac{1}{\sqrt{2\pi}}$.

(j) Establish **Sterling's formula:**

$$\lim_{n\to\infty} \frac{(n/e)^n\sqrt{2\pi n}}{n!} = 1$$

or $n! \sim n^n\sqrt{2\pi n}e^{-n}$, which gives an approximation to $n!$ for large n.

4. Evaluate:

(a) $\displaystyle\int_{-\infty}^{\infty} \frac{dx}{(a^2+x^2)(b^2+x^2)}$, $a, b > 0$;

(b) $\displaystyle\int_0^{\infty} \frac{dx}{x^4+a^4}$, $a > 0$;

(c) $\displaystyle\int_0^{\infty} \frac{x^2\,dx}{x^6+a^6}$, $a > 0$; (d) $\displaystyle\int_0^{\infty} \frac{dx}{x^6+a^6}$, $a > 0$;

(e) $\displaystyle\int_{-\infty}^{\infty} \frac{dx}{(1+x^2)^3}$; (f) $\displaystyle\int_0^{\infty} \frac{dx}{(x^2+a^2)^2}$, $a > 0$;

(g) $\displaystyle\int_0^{\infty} \frac{dx}{x^4-6x^2+25}$; (h) $\displaystyle\int_{-\infty}^{\infty} \frac{dx}{x^2+2ax+a^2+b^2}$, $b > 0$;

(i) $\displaystyle\int_{-\infty}^{\infty} \frac{(x^2-x+2)\,dx}{x^4+10x^2+9}$; (j) $\displaystyle\int_{-\infty}^{\infty} \frac{dx}{(a^2+x^2)^2(b^2+x^2)^2}$, $a, b > 0$.

Ans.: (a) $\dfrac{\pi}{ab(a+b)}$; (b) $\pi\sqrt{2}/4a^3$; (c) $\pi/6a^3$; (d) $\pi/3a^5$; (e) $3\pi/8$; (f) $\pi/4a^3$; (g) $\pi/20$; (h) π/b; (i) $5\pi/12$; (j) $\dfrac{\pi(a^2+3ab+b^2)}{2a^3b^3(a+b)^3}$.

5. Evaluate: $(a > 0, b > 0)$.

(a) $\displaystyle\int_{-\infty}^{\infty} \frac{\cos kx}{a^4+x^4}\,dx$; (b) $\displaystyle\int_{-\infty}^{\infty} \frac{x\sin kx\,dx}{a^4+x^4}$;

(c) $\displaystyle\int_0^{\infty} \frac{\cos kx\,dx}{(x^2+a^2)(x^2+b^2)}$; (d) $\displaystyle\int_0^{\infty} \frac{x\sin kx\,dx}{(x^2+a^2)(x^2+b^2)}$;

(e) $\displaystyle\int_0^{\infty} \frac{\cos kx\,dx}{(x^2+a^2)^2}$; (f) $\displaystyle\int_0^{\infty} \frac{x^2\cos kx\,dx}{x^2+a^2}$;

(g) $\displaystyle\int_0^{\infty} \frac{\cos kx\,dx}{x^4+4a^4}$; (h) $\displaystyle\int_{-\infty}^{\infty} \frac{\cos kx\,dx}{(x+c)^2+a^2}$;

(i) $\displaystyle\int_0^{\infty} \frac{x^3\sin kx\,dx}{x^4+4a^4}$; (j) $\displaystyle\int_0^{\infty} \frac{x^2\cos 3x\,dx}{(x^2+1)^2}$.

Ans.: (a) $\dfrac{\pi}{2a^3}e^{-ak/2}\left(\cos\dfrac{ak}{\sqrt{2}}+\sin\dfrac{ak}{\sqrt{2}}\right)$; (b) $\dfrac{\pi}{a^2}e^{-ak/\sqrt{2}}\sin\dfrac{ak}{\sqrt{2}}$;

(c) $\dfrac{\pi}{2(a^2 - b^2)}\left[\dfrac{e^{-bk}}{b} - \dfrac{e^{-ak}}{a}\right]$; (d) $\dfrac{\pi}{2(a^2 - b^2)}(e^{-bk} - e^{-ak})$;

(e) $\dfrac{\pi}{4a^3}e^{-ak}(ak + 1)$; (f) $\dfrac{\pi}{4a}e^{-ak}(1 - ak)$; (g) $\dfrac{\pi}{8a^3}e^{-ak}(\cos ak - \sin ak)$;

(h) $\dfrac{\pi}{a}e^{-ak}\cos ck$; (i) $\dfrac{\pi}{2}e^{-ak}\cos ak$; (j) $(-\pi/2)e^3$.

6. Evaluate:

(a) $\displaystyle\int_0^\infty \frac{x^{1/5}\,dx}{1 + x^3}$; (b) $\displaystyle\int_0^\infty \frac{x^{1/2}\,dx}{x^2 + 6x + 10}$;

(c) $\displaystyle\int_0^\infty \frac{x^{\alpha-1}}{1 + x^4}\,dx,\ 0 < \alpha < 1$;

(d) $\displaystyle\int_0^\infty \frac{x^{-\alpha}\,dx}{1 + 2x\cos\theta + x^2},\ -1 < \alpha < 1,\ -\pi < \theta < \pi$;

(e) $\displaystyle\int_0^\infty \frac{x^\alpha\,dx}{a^2 + x^2},\ -1 < \alpha < 1,\ a > 0$;

(f) $\displaystyle\int_0^\infty \frac{x^\alpha\,dx}{(1 + x^2)^2},\ -1 < \alpha < 3$.

Ans.: (a) $\dfrac{\pi}{3}\sin\dfrac{2\pi}{5}$; (b) $\pi 10^{1/4}\sin(\frac{1}{2}\cot^{-1}3)$; (c) $\dfrac{\pi}{8}\sin\dfrac{\pi\alpha}{4}$;

(d) $\dfrac{\pi\sin\alpha\theta}{\sin\pi\alpha\sin\theta}$; (e) $\dfrac{\pi a^{\alpha-1}}{2\cos(\pi\alpha/2)}$; (f) $\dfrac{\pi(1-\alpha)}{4\cos(\pi\alpha/2)}$.

7. (a) Show that

$$\int_0^\infty \frac{x^{\alpha-1}}{x - b}\,dx = \frac{\pi b^{\alpha-1}}{\sin\pi\alpha}, \qquad 0 < \alpha < 1.$$

(b) Differentiate with respect to b in (a) to obtain

$$\int_0^\infty \frac{x^{\alpha-1}\,dx}{(x + b)^2} = \frac{\pi(1-\alpha)b^{\alpha-2}}{\sin\pi\alpha}, \qquad 0 < \alpha < 1.$$

(c) Let $b = ic (c > 0)$ in (b) and establish

$$\int_0^\infty \frac{x^\alpha\,dx}{x^2 + c^2} = \frac{\pi c^{\alpha-1}}{2\cos(\pi\alpha/2)}, \qquad 0 < \alpha < 2.$$

8. Using previously established results, show that

(a) $\displaystyle\int_{-\infty}^\infty \frac{e^{kx}\,dx}{1 + e^x} = \frac{\pi}{\sin k\pi}, \qquad 0 < k < 1$;

(b) $$\int_0^\infty \frac{\sin kx\,dx}{x} = \begin{cases} \dfrac{\pi}{2}, & k > 0 \\ -\dfrac{\pi}{2}, & k < 0; \end{cases}$$

(c) $\displaystyle\int_0^\infty \frac{\sin x^2}{x}\,dx = \frac{\pi}{4};$

(d) $\displaystyle\int_0^\infty \frac{x^{\alpha-1}}{1+x^2}\,dx = \frac{\pi}{2\sin(\pi\alpha/2)}, \qquad 0 < \alpha < 2;$

(e) $\displaystyle\int_0^\infty \frac{(\text{Log } x)^2}{1+x^2}\,dx = \frac{\pi^3}{8};$

(f) $\displaystyle\int_{-\infty}^\infty \frac{e^{2ax}\,dx}{\cosh \pi x} = \sec a, \qquad -\frac{\pi}{2} < a < \frac{\pi}{2}.$

[*Hint:* Let $x = u/2\pi$ in (a).]

9. (a) Prove: If $p(x)$ and $q(x)$ are real polynomials of degree n and m, respectively, $m \geq n+2$, and if $a_1, a_2, \cdots, a_r$ are the nonreal simple zeros of $q(x)$ in the upper half of the z-plane and $b_1, b_2, \cdots, b_s$ are the real simple zeros of $q(x)$, then

$$\int_{-\infty}^\infty \frac{p(x)\,dx}{q(x)} = 2\pi i \sum_{k=1}^{r} \operatorname*{Res}_{z=a_k} \frac{p(z)}{q(z)} + \pi i \sum_{k=1}^{s} \operatorname*{Res}_{z=b_k} \frac{p(z)}{q(z)}.$$

(b) With the same hypothesis as in (a), determine the corresponding evaluations for $\displaystyle\int_{-\infty}^\infty \frac{p(x)\sin kx\,dx}{q(x)}$ and $\displaystyle\int_{-\infty}^\infty \frac{p(x)\cos kx\,dx}{q(x)}$.

Show that:

(c) $\displaystyle\int_{-\infty}^\infty \frac{x^2\,dx}{(x^2+a^2)(x-b)} = \frac{\pi ab}{2(a^2+b^2)}.$

(d) $\displaystyle\int_0^\infty \frac{\sin kx}{x(a^2+x^2)}\,dx = \frac{\pi}{2a^2}(1-e^{-ak}), \qquad a > 0.$

(e) $\displaystyle\int_0^\infty \frac{\sin^2 kx\,dx}{x^2(a^2+x^2)} = \frac{\pi}{4a^3}\left(e^{-2ak} + 1 - ak + \frac{a^2k^2}{2}\right), \qquad a > 0.$

(f) $\displaystyle\int_0^\infty \frac{\sin kx\,dx}{x(a^2+x^2)^2} = \frac{\pi}{2a^4}\left(1 - \frac{ak+2}{2}e^{-ak}\right), \qquad a > 0.$

(g) $\displaystyle\int_0^\infty \frac{\cos \pi x\,dx}{1-4x^2} = \frac{\pi}{4}.$

(h) $\displaystyle\int_0^\infty \frac{x^{\alpha-1}}{1-x}\,dx = \pi \cot \pi\alpha, \qquad 0 < \alpha < 1.$

10. Taking as the contour the semicircle of radius R centered at the origin and the line segment along the real axis from $-R$ to R with a circle of radius r indenting the origin, establish the following:

(a) $\displaystyle\int_0^\infty \frac{\text{Log } x\,dx}{x^2+1} = 0;$ (b) $\displaystyle\int_0^\infty \frac{\text{Log } x}{(x^2+1)^2} = -\frac{\pi}{4};$

(c) $\displaystyle\int_0^\infty \frac{x^{\alpha-1}\,\text{Log } x}{1+x}\,dx = -\pi^2 \cot \pi\alpha \csc \pi\alpha, \qquad 0 < \alpha < 1.$

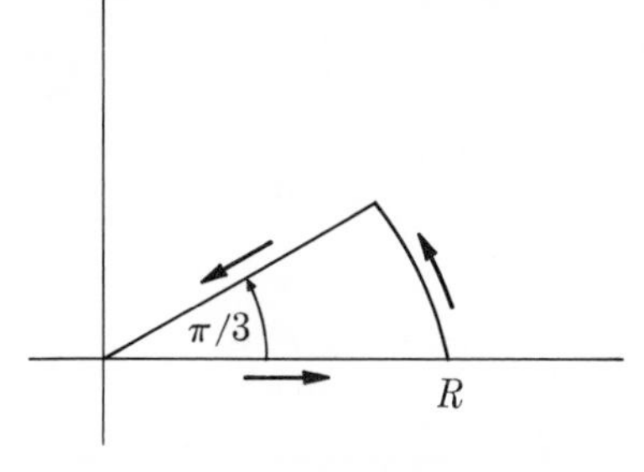

Exercise 11(a)

11. (a) Evaluate $\int_0^\infty \frac{dx}{x^6+1}$ by considering $\int_C \frac{dz}{z^6+1}$, where C is the contour that forms the boundary of the sector of the circle illustrated, R taken sufficiently large so that the sector includes just one pole of the function. (See figure.)

Ans.: $\frac{\pi}{3}$.

(b) Generalize (a) to show that

$$\int_0^\infty \frac{x^m\,dx}{x^n+a} = \frac{\pi}{na^{(n-m-1)/n}\sin\frac{(m+1)\pi}{n}}.$$

12. Establish each of the following by integrating the given function about the suggested contour.

(a) $\int_{-\infty}^\infty e^{-x^2}\,dx = \sqrt{\pi}$, $f(z) = e^{-z^2}$, C: rectangle with sides on $y = 0$, $y = b$, $x = \pm R$.

(b) $\int_0^\infty \frac{\sinh \alpha x}{\sinh \pi x}\,dx = \frac{1}{2}\tan\frac{\alpha}{2}$, $-\pi < \alpha < \pi$, $f(z) = e^{\alpha z}/\sinh \pi z$, C: rectangle on sides $y = 0$, $y = 1$, $x = \pm R$, indented at 0 and i.

(c) $\int_0^\infty \frac{dx}{1-x^4} = \frac{\pi}{4}$, $f(x) = \frac{1}{1-z^4}$, C: positive real axis indented at 1, line $\arg z = \pi/4$, and an arc of a large circle.

(d) $\int_0^\infty \frac{\operatorname{Log} x}{x^2-1}\,dx = \frac{\pi^2}{4}$, $f(z) = \frac{\operatorname{Log} z}{z^2-1}$, C: r to R on positive real axis, along $|z| = R$, $\operatorname{Im} z \geq 0$, $\operatorname{Re} z \geq 0$, along iR to ir, along $|z| = r$, $\operatorname{Im} z \geq 0$, $\operatorname{Re} z \geq 0$.

13. (a) Let $f(z)$ be analytic in the entire plane except at a finite number of points $a_1, a_2, \cdots, a_k$, these points not being integers or of the form $p + \frac{1}{2}$, p an integer. Show that $\operatorname{Res}_{z=n} \pi \cot \pi z f(z) = f(n)$.

(b) Let C_k be the rectangle with vertices at $\pm(k + \frac{1}{2}) \pm ik$. Show that $|\cot \pi z| \leq M$, where M is independent of k, by writing $\cot \pi z = i\,\frac{e^{2\pi iz}+1}{e^{2\pi iz}-1}$ and evaluating its maximum absolute value along each side of C_k.

(c) Show that

$$\frac{1}{2\pi i}\oint_{C_k} \pi \cot \pi z\, f(z)\, dz = \sum_{n=-k}^{k} f(n) + \sum_{j=1}^{k} \operatorname*{Res}_{z=a_j} f(z) \cot \pi a_j$$

where $z = a_j$ is in the interior of C_k.

(d) If $|z^2 f(z)| < N$ for $|z| > kN$, show that $\lim_{k\to\infty} |\int_{C_k} \pi \cot \pi z f(z)\, dz| = 0$, and hence

$$\sum_{n=-\infty}^{\infty} f(n) = -\pi \sum_{j=1}^{k} \operatorname*{Res}_{z=a_j} f(z) \cot \pi a_j.$$

(e) Establish similarly under the same conditions

$$\sum_{n=-\infty}^{\infty} (-1)^n f(n) = -\pi \sum_{j=1}^{k} \operatorname*{Res}_{z=a_j} f(z) \csc \pi a_j.$$

14. Use Exercises 13(d) and (e) to establish the following sums of the given series:

(a) $\sum_{n=0}^{\infty} \frac{1}{n^2} = \frac{\pi^2}{6}$; (b) $\sum_{n=0}^{\infty} \frac{(-1)^{n+1}}{n^2} = \frac{\pi^2}{12}$,

(c) $\sum_{n=-\infty}^{\infty} \frac{1}{(n+a)^2} = \frac{\pi^2}{\sin^2 \pi a}$, $a > 0$, not an integer.

(d) $\sum_{n=1}^{\infty} \frac{1}{n^2 - a^2} = \frac{1}{2a^2} - \frac{\pi}{2a} \cot \pi a$, $a > 0$, not an integer.

(e) $\sum_{n=0}^{\infty} \frac{(-1)^n}{2n+1} = \frac{\pi}{4}$;

(f) $\sum_{n=0}^{\infty} \frac{(-1)^n}{(2n+1)^3} = \frac{\pi^3}{32}$.

15. By integrating $e^{az}/(e^{-2iz} - 1)$ along a suitable contour, show that

$$\int_0^{\infty} \frac{\sin ax\, dx}{e^{2x} - 1} = \frac{1}{4}\pi \coth \frac{1}{2}\pi a - \frac{1}{2} a.$$

8. Logarithmic residues and the argument principle. Let $f(z)$ be analytic at $z = a$ with a zero of order k there. Then there exists $\phi(z)$, $\phi(z)$ analytic at $z = a$, $\phi(a) \neq 0$, such that $f(z) = (z-a)^k \phi(z)$ (p. 250). It follows that

$$\frac{f'(z)}{f(z)} = \frac{k}{z-a} + \frac{\phi'(z)}{\phi(z)}$$

which indicates that k is the residue of $\frac{f'(z)}{f(z)}$ at its simple pole $z = a$ (R_4), p. 260). Since

$$\frac{f'(z)}{f(z)} = \frac{d \operatorname{Log} f(z)}{dz},$$

we say that k is the residue of the logarithmic derivative of $f(z)$ at $z = a$, or more briefly, the **logarithmic residue** of $f(z)$ at $z = a$. Hence, we have shown that the logarithmic residue of $f(z)$ at a zero of $f(z)$ is equal to the order of that zero. Now suppose $z = b$ is a pole of order m of $f(z)$; then there exists a function $\psi(z)$, analytic at $z = b$, $\psi(b) \neq 0$, such that $f(z) = \dfrac{\psi(z)}{(z-b)^m}$. It follows that $\dfrac{f'(z)}{f(z)} = -\dfrac{m}{z-b} + \dfrac{\psi'(z)}{\psi(z)}$, so that $\operatorname*{Res}_{z=b} \dfrac{f'(z)}{f(z)} = -m$. Hence, the logarithmic residue of $f(z)$ at a pole of $f(z)$ is equal to the negative of the order of that pole. An application of the Cauchy residue theorem yields the

THEOREM. If $f(z)$ is meromorphic in a simply connected open region D and C is any regular closed curve C in D such that no zeros or poles of $f(z)$ occur on C, then

$$\frac{1}{2\pi i} \oint_C \frac{f'(z)}{f(z)}\, dz = N - P,$$

where N is the number of zeros of $f(z)$, a zero of order k counted k times, and P is the number of poles of $f(z)$, a pole of order m counted m times, that occur in the interior of C.

If $f(z)$ is analytic in D and $f(z) \neq 0$ on C, this reduces to

$$\frac{1}{2\pi i} \oint_C \frac{f'(z)}{f(z)}\, dz = N,$$

which is an integral formula for the number of zeros, a zero of order k counted k times, in the interior of C.

The preceding theorem indicates that $\dfrac{1}{2\pi i} \oint_C \dfrac{f'(z)\, dz}{f(z)}$ is an integer; this is surprising. However, we shall express this integral in a different form, which will readily exhibit the fact that it is an integer. Furthermore, this new form will be more useful in practice; for suppose we wished to determine the number of zeros N of $z^4 + 6z + 1$ in $|z| = 1$ from the preceding formula. Then

$$N = \frac{1}{2\pi i} \oint_C \frac{4z^3 + 6}{z^4 + 6z + 1}\, dz;$$

but to evaluate this integral by the techniques we have considered, we should have to *know* the zeros of $z^4 + 6z + 1$!

Let $f(z) = Re^{i\phi}$, where $R = |f(z)|$ and $\phi = \arg f(z)$. As z traverses the closed regular curve C, $f(z)$ traverses its map Γ, which is also a closed regular curve. Let z_0 be any point on C and $f(z_0) = R_0e^{i\phi_0}$ be its corresponding point on Γ. As z moves along C from z_0 in a positive direction and back to z_0, $f(z)$ moves from $f(z_0)$ along Γ and back eventually to $f(z_0)$. Now $|f(z)|$ is R_0 at z_0 and may change as z moves along C; nevertheless, it becomes R_0 again when z returns to z_0. The argument of $f(z)$ is ϕ_0 at z_0, but as z moves along C, ϕ_0 will be increased (decreased) by 2π every time

$f(z)$ traces out on Γ in the positive (negative) direction a closed path that has the origin in its interior. Now

$$\frac{1}{2\pi i}\oint_C \frac{f'(z)\,dz}{f(z)} = \frac{1}{2\pi i}\int_\Gamma \frac{e^{i\phi}\,dR + iRe^{i\phi}\,d\phi}{Re^{i\phi}}$$

$$= \frac{1}{2\pi i}\int_\Gamma \frac{dR}{R} + \frac{1}{2\pi}\int_\Gamma d\phi$$

$$= \frac{1}{2\pi i}\operatorname{Log} R\Big]_{R_0}^{R_0} + \frac{1}{2\pi}\phi\Big]_{\phi_0}^{\phi_0+2k\pi}$$

$$= k,$$

where k is the number of times Γ winds around the origin in a positive direction, diminished by the number of times it winds around the origin in a negative direction. We often write $k = (1/2\pi)\,\Delta_C \arg f(z)$ where $\Delta_C \arg f(z)$ can be read as the change or variation in the argument of $f(z)$ as z traverses C. We have established what is known as the

ARGUMENT PRINCIPLE. If $f(z)$ is meromorphic in a simply connected region D, and C is a regular closed curve in D such that no zeros or poles of $f(z)$ occur on C, then $N - P = (1/2\pi)\,\Delta_C \arg f(z)$, where N is the number of zeros of $f(z)$, a zero of order k counted k times, and P is the number of poles of $f(z)$, a pole of order m counted m times, that occur in the interior of C.

EXAMPLE. Determine the number of zeros of $z^4 + 6z + 1$ in (a) $|z| < 2$; (b) $|z| < 1$; (c) $|z| < \frac{1}{8}$.

Solution. Let $f(z) = z^4 + 6z + 1$. We know that $f(z)$ has four zeros. We are interested in determining how many of these occur in the given regions.

(a) Let C: $|z| = 2$. It is a difficult matter to determine the map of C under $f(z)$; fortunately, this is not necessary. First let us determine if all four zeros of $f(z)$ are in $|z| < 2$. We write

$$f(z) = z^4\left(1 + \frac{6}{z^3} + \frac{1}{z^4}\right) = z^4\zeta,$$

where $\zeta = 1 + (6/z^3) + (1/z^4)$. Then $\arg f(z) = \arg z^4 + \arg\zeta$ and $\Delta_C \arg f(z) = 4\Delta_C \arg z + \Delta_C \arg\zeta = 8\pi + \Delta_C \arg\zeta$. In order for

$$N = \frac{1}{2\pi}\Delta_C \arg f(z) = 4,$$

$\Delta_C \arg\zeta$ must vanish. We shall show that this is the case.

$$|\zeta - 1| = \left|\frac{6}{z^3} + \frac{1}{z^4}\right| \le \frac{6}{|z|^3} + \frac{1}{|z|^4} = \frac{13}{16} \qquad \text{for } |z| = 2.$$

Hence, $|\zeta - 1| < 1$, which means that as z traverses $|z| = 2$, ζ traverses a circle with center at 1 and radius less than 1—this circle does not contain the origin in its interior; hence $\Delta_C \arg\zeta = 0$.

(b) All four zeros of $f(z)$ might be in $|z| < 1$. But $|\zeta - 1| \le 7$ for $|z| = 1$, which means that as z traverses $|z| = 1$, ζ traverses a circle that has the origin in its interior, and it is too complicated to determine how many times ζ traverses this circle and in what directions. We now know, however, that all the zeros of $f(z)$ are not in $|z| < 1$. If three of them are there, then $\Delta_C \arg f(z) = 3\Delta_C \arg z + \Delta_C \arg \eta$, where $\eta = z + (6/z^2) + (1/z^2)$. But $|\eta| \leq 8$ for $|z| < 1$. Hence, $f(z)$ does not have three zeros in $|z| < 1$. Similarly, one can show that $f(z)$ does not have two zeros in $|z| < 1$. Let us see if it has one zero there.

$$\Delta_C \arg f(z) = \Delta_C \arg z + \Delta_C \arg \gamma,$$

where $\gamma = z^3 + 6 + (1/z)$. But $|\gamma - 6| \leq 2$; hence, $\Delta_C \arg \gamma = 0$ for $|z| = 1$ and $f(z)$ has one zero in $|z| < 1$.

(c) $|\gamma - 6| \leq 1/512 + 8$. Hence, $f(z)$ has no zeros in $|z| < \frac{1}{8}$; all the zeros of $f(z)$ are in $\frac{1}{8} < |z| < 2$.

Of fundamental importance is the problem of determining how many values of z determine $f(z) = a$. This is equivalent to the number of zeros of $f(z) - a$; if we denote this number by N_a, we have the following

THEOREM. If $f(z)$ is meromorphic in a simply connected open region D and C is a regular closed curve in D such that no zeros or poles of $f(z)$ occur on C, then

$$N_a - P = \frac{1}{2\pi i} \oint_C \frac{f'(z)}{f(z) - a} dz = \frac{1}{2\pi} \Delta_C \arg [f(z) - a],$$

where N_a is the number of values of z that determine $f(z) = a$ and P is the number of poles, a pole of order m counted m times, that occur in the interior of C.

EXAMPLE. Show that if $f(z)$ is analytic on and within a regular closed curve C and $f(z)$ is real for every z in C, then $f(z) =$ constant.

Solution. Let $\alpha = a + ib$, $b \neq 0$. For any z on C, let $w = f(z) - \alpha$. Then, since $f(z)$ is real, $\operatorname{Im} w = -b$. If $b > 0$, $\operatorname{Im} w < 0$, and if $b < 0$, $\operatorname{Im} w > 0$; in either case, $\Delta_C \arg w = 0$. Hence, by the preceding theorem, since $f(z)$ is analytic, $N_\alpha = 0$. Hence, $f(z)$ cannot assume values whose imaginary part is different from zero; i.e., $f(z)$ is also real in the interior of C. Then $f(z) =$ constant [p. 233, Exercise 9(a)].

As another application of the argument principle, we prove the exceedingly useful

ROUCHÉ THEOREM. If $f(z)$ and $g(z)$ are analytic in a simply connected open region D and C is any closed regular curve in D and if for every z on C, $|f(z)| > |g(z)|$, then $f(z) + g(z)$ has exactly as many zeros as $f(z)$ in the interior of C, a zero of order k counted k times.

Proof. We write $f(z) + g(z) = f(z)\left[1 + \dfrac{g(z)}{f(z)}\right]\cdot$ Then

$$\Delta_C \arg [f(z) + g(z)] = \Delta_C \arg f(z) + \Delta_C \arg \left[1 + \frac{g(z)}{f(z)}\right].$$

Let $\zeta = g(z)/f(z)$. Then, since $|f(z)| > |g(z)|$, on C, $|\zeta| < 1$ and $\Delta_C \arg \zeta = 0$, and the theorem follows immediately by the argument principle.

9. Inverse function of an analytic function. We have now progressed to a point in the development of the theory of analytic functions where we can examine the inverse function of an analytic function more carefully. We have yet to answer the question: Is the inverse function of an analytic function analytic under suitable conditions? The answer is *yes*; now let us determine the suitable conditions. If w_0 is the image of the point z_0 under $w = f(z)$, we know that if $f(z)$ is continuous at z_0, for every neighborhood of w_0, $N(w_0)$, there exists a neighborhood of z_0, $N(z_0)$, such that every z in $N(z_0)$ has its image $f(z)$ in $N(w_0)$. Does this mean that every point in $N(w_0)$ is the image of some point in $N(z_0)$? Not necessarily; and surely if we expect the inverse function $f^{-1}(z)$ to be analytic at w_0, it must be defined at every point in some neighborhood of w_0. We have the following

Lemma. If $f(z)$ is analytic at z_0 with value w_0, $f'(z_0) \neq 0$, then there exist neighborhoods $N(z_0)$ and $N(w_0)$ such that every w in $N(w_0)$ is the image of one and only one point in $N(z_0)$.

Proof. Since $f'(z_0) \neq 0$, there exists some neighborhood of z_0 where $f(z)$ is analytic at z_0; z_0 is an isolated zero of $f(z) - w_0$ (p. 256, Exercise 33), which means there exists $\epsilon > 0$ such that for $0 < |z - z_0| \leq \epsilon$,

$$|f(z) - w_0| > 0.$$

Hence, we can find a number $A > 0$ such that for z on C: $|z - z_0| = \epsilon$, $|f(z) - w_0| > A$. Now let w be any point such that $|w - w_0| < A$. Then $|f(z) - w_0| > |w - w_0|$ holds on C. By Rouché's theorem, $f(z) - w_0$ and $f(z) - w_0 + (w_0 - w) = f(z) - w$ have the same number of zeros in the interior of C. But $f(z) - w_0$ has one simple zero there, since $f'(z_0) \neq 0$; hence, $f(z) - w$ has one and only one zero there. This means that for w such that $|w - w_0| < A$, we have found one and only one z in $|z - z_0| < \epsilon$ such that $w = f(z)$. We have found the two required neighborhoods: $N(z_0)$: $|z - z_0| < \epsilon$, and $N(w_0)$: $|w - w_0| < A$.

The preceding lemma indicates that under the prescribed conditions, the inverse function of an analytic function is uniquely defined. We now consider the

INVERSE FUNCTION THEOREM. If $f(z)$ is analytic at z_0, $f'(z_0) \neq 0$, then the inverse function defined in a neighborhood of $w_0 = f(z_0)$ is analytic in that neighborhood.

Proof. There is no loss in generality in assuming that $z_0 = w_0 = 0$. Then, by the lemma, $w = f(z)$ has only one solution z in $|z| < \epsilon$ when $|w| < A$. With the use of Exercise 4(b), p. 289,

$$z = \frac{1}{2\pi i} \oint_C \frac{\zeta f'(\zeta)\, d\zeta}{f(\zeta) - w},$$

where C: $|z| = \epsilon$. If we write $z = F(w)$, this becomes

$$F(w) = \frac{1}{2\pi i} \oint_C \frac{\zeta f'(\zeta)\, d\zeta}{f(\zeta) - w}$$

which is an explicit representation of the inverse function $F(w) = f^{-1}(z)$ in $|w| < A$. That $F(w)$ is analytic in $|w| < A$ now follows by Leibniz's theorem on p. 245.

The derivative of $F(w) = f^{-1}(z)$ at a point w_0 where it exists can be expressed as

$$F'(w_0) = \frac{1}{f'(z_0)}, \qquad w_0 = f(z_0),$$

since

$$F'(w_0) = \lim_{w \to w_0} \frac{F(w) - F(w_0)}{w - w_0}$$

$$= \lim_{z \to z_0} \frac{z - z_0}{f(z) - f(z_0)} = \frac{1}{f'(z_0)}.$$

EXERCISES

1. Determine the number of zeros of each of the following functions in the given regions:

(a) $z^3 + 3z^2 + z + 5$, $|z| < 3$.

(b) $z^5 - 12z^2 + 14$, where (1) $1 < |z| < \frac{5}{2}$; and (2) $|z| < 2$.

(c) $z^4 + 2z^3 + 2z + 4$, $\operatorname{Re} z > 0$, $\operatorname{Im} z > 0$.

[*Hint:* Determine $\Delta_C f(z)$ along $0 \leq x \leq R$, $|z| = R$, $\operatorname{Re} z > 0$, $\operatorname{Im} z > 0$, $R \leq y \leq 0$ for sufficiently large R.]

(d) $z^6 + 6z + 10$ in each quadrant of the z-plane.

(e) $z^4 + z^3 + 4z^2 + 2z + 3 = 0$ in each quadrant.

2. Show that $z^n e^{a-z} - 1$, $a > 0$, n positive integer, has exactly n zeros in $|z| < 1$.

3. Show that $z + e^{-z} - a$, $a > 1$, has one real zero in $\operatorname{Re} z > 0$.

4. (a) Prove that if $f(z)$ is meromorphic and $g(z)$ is analytic in a simply connected open region D, and C is any regular closed curve in D such that no zeros or poles of $f(z)$ occur on C, then

$$\frac{1}{2\pi i} \oint_C \frac{f'(z)}{f(z)} g(z)\, dz = \sum_{j=1}^{m} f_j g(a_j) - \sum_{j=1}^{n} s_j g(b_j),$$

where a_j is a zero of $f(z)$ of order r_j ($j = 1, 2, \cdots, m$) and b_j is a pole of order s_j ($j = 1, 2, \cdots, n$) occurring in the interior of C.

(b) If $f(z)$ is analytic in a simply connected open region D, and C is any regular closed curve in D such that $f(z) \neq 0$ on C and $z_1, z_2, \cdots, z_n$ are the zeros of $f(z)$ in the interior of C, a zero of order k counted k times, show that

$$z_1 + z_2 + \cdots + z_n = \frac{1}{2\pi i} \oint_C \frac{zf'(z)}{f(z)}\, dz.$$

5. (a) Use Rouché's theorem to prove that $a_n z^n + a_{n-1} z^{n-1} + \cdots + a_1 z + a_0$, $a_n \neq 0$, has precisely n zeros in the z-plane, a zero of order k counted k times, by letting $f(z) = a_n z^n$ and $g(z) = a_{n-1} z^{n-1} + \cdots + a_0$ and letting C be $|z| = R$, with R sufficiently large.

(b) Prove that $e^z - kz^n$, $k > e$, has exactly n zeros in $|z| < 1$.

6. If ζ is a complex number such that $|\zeta| < 1$, show that $f(z) = \dfrac{z - \zeta}{1 - \bar{\zeta} z}$ takes in $|z| < 1$ every value a for which $|a| < 1$ exactly once, and it takes no values a such that $|a| > 1$. [*Hint:* Prove that $|f(z)| = 1$ for $|z| = 1$ and apply Rouché's theorem to $f(z) - a$.]

7. Show that $f(z)$ is entire and does not vanish for all z in the complex plane if and only if $f(z) = e^{\phi(z)}$, where $\phi(z)$ is entire.

8. If $f(z)$ is analytic in a simply connected region D and on its boundary C except for P poles, each pole of order m being counted m times and $f(z)$ is real, $f(z) \neq 0$ on C, prove that the number of zeros of $f(z)$ in D, each zero of order k being counted k times, is P.

9. Let $f(z)$ be analytic in a simply connected region D and on its boundary C, and let $|f(z)|$ be constant on C. Prove that $f(z)$ must have at least one zero in D unless it is a constant. [*Hint:* Apply Rouché's theorem to $f(z) - a$.]

10. (a) Show that the number of zeros of $\lambda z - \tan z$, λ a complex constant, in the interior of the square with vertices at $\pm n\pi \pm in\pi$, n a positive integer, is $2n + 1$.

Hints:

(1) Show that from $\tan z = \dfrac{e^{2iz} - 1}{i(e^{2iz} + 1)}$, $|\tan z| < \dfrac{1 + e^{-2n}}{1 - e^{-2n}}$ on C;

(2) $|\lambda z| \geq \pi n|\lambda|$ on C and if $\pi n|\lambda| > \dfrac{1 + e^{-2n}}{1 - e^{-2n}}$, $|\lambda z| > |\tan z|$;

(3) Use Rouché's theorem to show that $N - P$ is the same for λz and $\lambda z - \tan z$;

(4) Show that $N - P = 1$;

(5) Show that $P = 2n$.

(b) Show that if λ is real, $\lambda x - \tan x$ has $2n + 1$ zeros in $-n < x < n$. Hence, if λ is real, all the zeros of $\lambda z - \tan z$ are real.

11. Prove that if $f(z)$ is analytic and has n zeros in a simply connected region D bounded by a regular closed curve C, then $f'(z)$ has $n - 1$ zeros in D.

12. If $f(z)$ is analytic in a simply connected region D and on its boundary C, a regular closed curve, and if $\operatorname{Re} f(z) = 0$ for $2k$ points on C, show that $f(z)$ has at most k zeros in D.

13. If a and b are real, show that $z^{2n} + a^2 z^{2n-1} + b^2$ has $n - 1$ zeros with positive real parts if n is odd, and n zeros with positive real parts if n is even.

14. Show that for every $R > 0$ there exists a number N such that for $n \geq N$ all the zeros of $1 + z + (z^2/2!) + \cdots + (z^n/n!)$ lie outside $|z| = R$.

15. Show that $f(z) = z + (1/z)$ assumes every nonreal value, as well as those real values x such that $x > 2$ or $x < -2$, precisely once in R: $|z| < 1$. [*Hint:* Let $z = e^{i\theta}$; then $f(z) = 2\cos 2\theta$, and as z moves along $|z| = 1$, w traverses $-2 \leq x \leq 2$ twice. Hence, for any w_0 outside this segment,

$$\Delta_C \arg (w - w_0) = 0.$$

Hence, for the function $f(z) - w_0$, $N - P = 0$. But $P = 1$.]

Chapter 9

Complex Infinite Series

1. Sequences and series of complex numbers. **A sequence of complex numbers** or **complex sequence** is a function whose domain is the set of nonnegative integers. This means that to every nonnegative integer n we assign a complex number z_n. Such a sequence will be denoted by $\{z_n\}$ or by $z_0, z_1, \cdots, z_n, \cdots$. The complex number z_n is called the *general* term or nth term of the sequence. We say that the **limit of a sequence** $\{z_n\}$ is the complex number c, written $\lim_{n\to\infty} z_n = c$, if for every $\epsilon > 0$, there exists a positive integer N such that for $n > N$, $|z_n - c| < \epsilon$. Given the sequence $\{z_n\}$, let $\operatorname{Re} z_n = x_n$ and $\operatorname{Im} z_n = y_n$, $n = 0, 1, \cdots$, so that $z_n = x_n + iy_n$; we see that every complex sequence $\{z_n\}$ determines two real sequences $\{x_n\}$ and $\{y_n\}$. The relationship between the limit of the complex sequence and the limits of the real sequences is given in the important

THEOREM. $\lim_{n\to\infty} z_n = c$ if and only if $\lim_{n\to\infty} x_n = a$ and $\lim_{n\to\infty} y_n = b$, where $z_n = x_n + iy_n$, $n = 0, 1, \cdots$ and $c = a + ib$, x_n, y_n, a, b real.

Proof. Since $|x_n - a| \leq |z_n - c|$ and $|y_n - b| \leq |z_n - c|$, $\lim_{n\to\infty} z_n = c$ implies that for every $\epsilon > 0$, there exists a positive integer N such that for $n > N$, $|x_n - a| < \epsilon$ and $|y_n - b| < \epsilon$; hence, $\lim_{n\to\infty} x_n = a$ and $\lim_{n\to\infty} y_n = b$.

Given $\epsilon > 0$, $\lim_{n\to\infty} x_n = a$ implies the existence of a positive integer N_1 such that for $n > N_1$, $|x_n - a| < \epsilon/2$ and $\lim_{n\to\infty} y_n = b$ implies the existence of a positive integer N_2 such that for $n > N_2$, $|y_n - b| < \epsilon/2$. Then for $n > N = \max(N_1, N_2)$,

$$|z_n - c| = |x_n - a + i(y_n - b)| \leq |x_n - a| + |y_n - b| < \epsilon.$$

Hence, $\lim_{n\to\infty} z_n = c$.

If the limit of a sequence exists, we say that the sequence is **convergent;** otherwise, we say that it is **divergent.** The preceding theorem can then be stated: A sequence $\{z_n\}$ is convergent if and only if the sequences $\{x_n\}$ and $\{y_n\}$, $z_n = x_n + iy_n$, $n = 0, 1, \cdots$, are convergent. This theorem enables us to establish many properties of the limits of complex sequences merely by citing the corresponding properties of real sequences. For example, if we define the product of a constant complex number k and a sequence $\{z_n\}$ as the sequence $\{kz_n\}$ and the sum, product, and quotient of the sequences $\{z_n\}$ and $\{\zeta_n\}$ as the sequences $\{z_n + \zeta_n\}$, $\{z_n\zeta_n\}$, and $\{z_n/\zeta_n\}$, respectively, we can establish readily the

THEOREM ON LIMITS. If $\lim_{n\to\infty} z_n = c$ and $\lim_{n\to\infty} \zeta_n = \gamma$, then (1) $\lim_{n\to\infty} kz_n = kc$, k any complex constant; (2) $\lim_{n\to\infty} (z_n + \zeta_n) = c + \gamma$; (3) $\lim_{n\to\infty} z_n\zeta_n = c\gamma$; (4) $\lim_{n\to\infty} z_n/\zeta_n = c/\gamma$, $\gamma \neq 0$.

EXAMPLE 1. Find $\lim_{n\to\infty} (2 + i/n)^4$.

Solution. Let $z_n = 2 + i/n$. Then $\text{Re}\, z_n = 2$ and $\text{Im}\, z_n = 1/n$. Hence, $\lim_{n\to\infty} z_n = 2$ and $\lim_{n\to\infty} z_n^4 = 16$.

EXAMPLE 2. Show that $\lim_{n\to\infty} (1/i)^n$ does not exist.

Solution. Let $z_n = (1/i)^n$. Then $\text{Re}\, z_n = (-1)^n \cos n\pi/2$ and $\text{Im}\, z = (-1)^n \sin n\pi/2$. Since $\lim_{n\to\infty} \text{Re}\, z_n$ and $\lim_{n\to\infty} \text{Im}\, z_n$ do not exist (why?), $\lim_{n\to\infty} z_n$ does not exist.

Given the sequence $\{z_n\}$; the sequence $\{s_n\}$, where

$$s_n = \sum_{k=0}^{n} z_k,$$

$n = 0, 1, \cdots$, is called an **infinite series of complex numbers,** or **complex series,** and is denoted by $\sum_{n=0}^{\infty} z_n$. We shall call z_n the nth *term* and s_n the ***n*th partial sum** of the infinite series. If $\lim_{n\to\infty} s_n = s$, we call s the *sum* of the infinite series and write $\sum_{n=0}^{\infty} z_n = s$. The student should bear in mind that $\sum_{n=0}^{\infty} z_n$ is just another way of denoting the sequence $\{s_n\}$, $s_n = \sum_{k=0}^{n} z_k$, $n = 0, 1, \cdots$, and that statements about sequences can be translated into corresponding statements about series. In view of this, we have the

THEOREM. $\sum_{n=0}^{\infty} z_n$ is convergent if and only if $\sum_{n=0}^{\infty} x_n$ and $\sum_{n=0}^{\infty} y_n$, are convergent, $z_n = x_n + iy_n$. Furthermore,

$$\sum_{n=0}^{\infty} z_n = \sum_{n=0}^{\infty} x_n + i \sum_{n=0}^{\infty} y_n.$$

The significance of this theorem lies in the fact that the determination of the convergence or divergence of a complex series reduces to the determination of the convergence or divergence of two real series for which we have available a variety of tests such as the comparison test, ratio test, integral test, and Leibniz's test for alternating series [VB]. We have an immediate

Corollary. If $\sum_{n=0}^{\infty} z_n$ is convergent, then $\lim_{n\to\infty} z_n = 0$.

We also have the following

THEOREM. If $\sum_{n=0}^{\infty} z_n$ and $\sum_{n=0}^{\infty} \zeta_n$ are convergent and k is any complex constant, then

$$(1)\ \sum_{n=0}^{\infty} kz_n = k \sum_{n=0}^{\infty} z_n;$$

$$(2)\ \sum_{n=0}^{\infty} (z_n + \zeta_n) = \sum_{n=0}^{\infty} z_n + \sum_{n=0}^{\infty} \zeta_n.$$

EXAMPLE 1. Test for convergence or divergence:

$$\sum_{n=2}^{\infty} \frac{i^n}{\operatorname{Log} n}.$$

Solution. Let $z_n = i^n/\operatorname{Log} n$. Then

$$\operatorname{Re} z_n = \frac{\cos n\pi/2}{\operatorname{Log} n} \quad \text{and} \quad \operatorname{Im} z_n = \frac{\sin (n\pi/2)}{\operatorname{Log} n}.$$

Hence

$$\sum_{n=2}^{\infty} \frac{i^n}{\operatorname{Log} n} = \sum_{n=1}^{\infty} \frac{(-1)^n}{\operatorname{Log} 2n} + i \sum_{n=1}^{\infty} \frac{(-1)^n}{\operatorname{Log} (2n+1)}$$

and the series is convergent by Leibniz's test for alternating series.

EXAMPLE 2. Test for convergence or divergence: $\sum_{n=1}^{\infty} \frac{2^n + i}{n}$.

Solution. Since $\sum_{n=1}^{\infty} \frac{2^n}{n}$ is divergent $\left(\lim_{n\to\infty} \frac{2^n}{n} \neq 0\right)$, the given series is divergent.

The complex series $\sum_{n=0}^{\infty} z_n$ is called **absolutely convergent** if $\sum_{n=0}^{\infty} |z_n|$ is convergent. We have the important

THEOREM. If $\sum_{n=0}^{\infty} z_n$ is absolutely convergent, then it is convergent.

Proof. Let $z_n = x_n + iy_n$. Since $|x_n| \leq |z_n|$ and $|y_n| \leq |z_n|$,

$$\sum_{n=0}^{\infty} |x_n| \quad \text{and} \quad \sum_{n=0}^{\infty} |y_n|$$

are convergent by the comparison test. Hence, $\sum_{n=0}^{\infty} x_n$ and $\sum_{n=0}^{\infty} y_n$ are absolutely convergent, and hence convergent. Therefore, $\sum_{n=0}^{\infty} z_n$ is convergent.

This theorem indicates that the convergence of some complex series $\sum_{n=0}^{\infty} z_n$ can be determined from the convergence of the real series $\sum_{n=0}^{\infty} |z_n|$.

EXAMPLE. $\sum_{n=1}^{\infty} \frac{i^n}{n^2}$ is convergent since $\left|\frac{i^n}{n^2}\right| = \frac{1}{n^2}$ and $\sum_{n=1}^{\infty} \frac{1}{n^2}$ is convergent.

We can now generalize the triangle inequality: If $\sum_{n=0}^{\infty} |z_n|$ is convergent, then $|\sum_{n=0}^{\infty} z_n| \leq \sum_{n=0}^{\infty} |z_n|$. Since $\sum_{n=0}^{\infty} z_n$ converges absolutely, it converges. Let $s_n = z_1 + z_2 + \cdots + z_n$ and $t_n = |z_1| + |z_2| + \cdots + |z_n|$. Then $|s_n| \leq t_n$ and $\lim_{n\to\infty} |s_n| \leq \lim_{n\to\infty} t_n$, and we have the result.

2. Power series. A complex series of the form $\sum_{n=0}^{\infty} a_n(z - a)^n$, where z is a complex variable and a and a_n, $n = 0, 1, \cdots$, are constant complex numbers, is called a **power series.** a is called the **center** and a_n, $n = 0, 1, \cdots$, the **coefficients** of the power series. We define the power series with center at ∞ as $\sum_{n=0}^{\infty} \frac{a_n}{z^n}$.

We have the following

THEOREM. If $\sum_{n=0}^{\infty} a_n(z - a)^n$ is convergent for $z = z_0$, $z_0 \neq a$, then it is absolutely convergent for all z such that $|z - a| < |z_0 - a|$.

Proof. It is sufficient to prove the theorem when $a = 0$. Since $\sum_{n=0}^{\infty} a_n z_0^n$ is convergent, $\lim_{n\to\infty} a_n z_0^n = 0$. Then one can easily show that there exists a constant M such that $|a_n z_0^n| < M$. For any z such that $|z| < |z_0|$, $|a_n z^n| = |a_n z_0^n| \cdot \left|\frac{z}{z_0}\right|^n < M\left|\frac{z}{z_0}\right|^n$; but $M\left|\frac{z}{z_0}\right|^n$ is the general term of a convergent geometric series, since $\left|\frac{z}{z_0}\right| < 1$. Hence the theorem is established with the use of the comparison test.

The theorem given above enables us to prove the

FUNDAMENTAL THEOREM OF POWER SERIES. For every power series $P = \sum_{n=0}^{\infty} a_n(z - a)^n$, there exists a number r from the extended set of real numbers $0 \leq r \leq \infty$, such that one of the following holds:

(1) If $r = \infty$, P is convergent for all values of z.
(2) If $r = 0$, P is convergent only for $z = a$.
(3) If $0 < r < \infty$, P is convergent for $|z - a| < r$ and divergent for $|z - a| > r$; for $|z - a| = r$, it may be convergent for no z, some z, or all z.

The proof is left to the student. The latter part of (3) may be proved by exhibiting the three series $\sum_{n=0}^{\infty} z^n$ (divergent for $|z| = 1$), $\sum_{n=1}^{\infty} \frac{z^n}{n}$ (divergent for $|z| = 1$ unless $z = \pm 1$), $\sum_{n=1}^{\infty} \frac{z^n}{n^2}$ (convergent for $|z| = 1$).

The number r in the fundamental theorem is called the **radius of convergence** of $\sum_{n=0}^{\infty} a_n(z - a)^n$, and if $0 < r < \infty$, $|z - a| = r$ is called the **circle of convergence** of the power series. We shall now establish a formula that will express r explicitly in terms of the coefficients of its power series. To do this, we must introduce some new notation and terminology. Given a sequence of real numbers $\{a_n\}$, either $\lim_{n\to\infty} a_n$ exists, or $a_n \to \pm\infty$, or it oscillates about certain points. These points are called limit points. More precisely, a point is a **limit point** of a sequence of points if every neighborhood of that point contains an infinite number of points of the sequence. We define the **limit superior** (also called upper limit) of the real sequence $\{a_n\}$, denoted by $\overline{\lim_{n\to\infty}}\, a_n$, as follows:

$$\overline{\lim_{n\to\infty}}\, a_n = \begin{cases} \lim_{n\to\infty} a_n, \text{ if this limit exists} \\ \pm\infty, \text{ if } a_n \to \pm\infty \\ \text{largest of the limit points, if } \{a_n\} \text{ oscillates.} \end{cases}$$

We now prove

The Cauchy-Hadamard formula. The radius of convergence of $\sum_{n=0}^{\infty} a_n(z - a)^n$ is $r = 1/\mu$, where $\mu = \overline{\lim_{n\to\infty}} \sqrt[n]{|a_n|}$.

Proof. For fixed z, $\overline{\lim_{n\to\infty}} \sqrt[n]{|a_n(z - a)^n|} = \mu|z - a|$. If $|z - a| > 1/\mu$, there will exist an infinity of n such that

$$\sqrt[n]{|a_n(z - a)^n|} > 1 \quad \text{or} \quad |a_n(z - a)^n| > 1.$$

Hence, $\lim_{n\to\infty} a_n(z - a)^n \neq 0$, and it follows that the series is divergent for such values of z.

If $|z - a| < 1/\mu$, we can find an integer N such that for $n > N$, $\sqrt[n]{|a_n(z - a)^n|} < t$, where $\mu|z - a| < t < 1$. Hence, $|a_n(z - a)^n| < t^n$. But t^n is the general term of a convergent geometric series, since $t < 1$. Hence, the series is convergent for $|z - a| < 1/\mu$ by the comparison test.

EXAMPLE 1. Determine the radius of convergence of

$$\sum_{n=1}^{\infty}\left(1+\frac{1}{n}\right)^{-n^2} z^n.$$

Solution

$$r = \frac{1}{\overline{\lim\limits_{n\to\infty}}\sqrt[n]{\left(1+\frac{1}{n}\right)^{-n^2}}} = \lim_{n\to\infty}\left(1+\frac{1}{n}\right)^n = e.$$

EXAMPLE 2. Determine the radius of convergence of $\sum_{n=1}^{\infty} a_n$, where $a_n = 1/3^n$ if n is odd, and $a_n = \sqrt{n}$ if n is even.

Solution. The sequence $\{\sqrt[n]{a_n}\}$ can be written as $\frac{1}{3}$, $\sqrt[2]{2}$, $\frac{1}{3}$, $\sqrt[4]{4}$, $\cdots$, $\frac{1}{3}$, $\sqrt[2n]{2n}$, $\cdots$, from which we see that $\frac{1}{3}$ and 1 are its limit points, since $\lim\limits_{n\to\infty}\sqrt[2n]{2n} = 1$. Hence, $\overline{\lim\limits_{n\to\infty}}\sqrt[n]{a_n} = 1$ and $r = 1$.

The power series $\sum_{n=0}^{\infty} a_n(z-a)^n$ represents a function $f(z)$ in the interior of its circle of convergence of radius r. If we denote this region by $N_r(a)$, we then have

$$f(z) = \sum_{n=0}^{\infty} a_n(z-a)^n, \qquad \text{for } z \text{ in } N_r(a).$$

In the sequel, for purposes of simplicity, we shall let $a = 0$ and shall then denote the circular region of convergence as N_r. However, any result that we obtain in this special case can always be shown to be valid in the general case by replacing z by $z - a$.

Let us now consider the series $\sum_{n=1}^{\infty} na_nz^{n-1}$, which is obtained from $\sum_{n=0}^{\infty} a_nz^n$ by term-by-term differentiation. It is a power series, and hence represents a function in the interior of its circle of convergence; i.e., $g(z) = \sum_{n=1}^{\infty} na_nz^{n-1}$, for z in $N_{r'}$.

We have the following important

THEOREM. If $f(z) = \sum_{n=0}^{\infty} a_nz^n$ for z in N_r and $g(z) = \sum_{n=1}^{\infty} na_nz^{n-1}$ for z in $N_{r'}$, then (1) $r = r'$; i.e., the two series have the same circle of convergence, and (2) $f'(z) = g(z)$ for z in N_r.

Proof. (1) This follows from the Cauchy-Hadamard formula, since

$$\frac{1}{r'} = \overline{\lim_{n\to\infty}}\sqrt[n]{n|a_n|} = \lim_{n\to\infty}\sqrt[n]{n}\ \overline{\lim_{n\to\infty}}\sqrt[n]{|a_n|} = \overline{\lim_{n\to\infty}}\frac{\sqrt[n]{n}}{r} = \frac{1}{r},$$

since $\lim\limits_{n\to\infty}\sqrt[n]{n} = 1$. (Proof?)

(2) Let z be any point in N_r with $|z| = \rho$. Let h be any complex number with $|h| = \epsilon$ such that $\rho + \epsilon < \sigma < r$. Then

$$\left|\frac{f(z+h)-f(z)}{h} - g(z)\right| = \left|\sum_{n=0}^{\infty} a_n \cdot \left[\frac{(z+h)^n - z^n}{h} - nz^n\right]\right|$$

$$= \left|\sum_{n=0}^{\infty} a_n\left[\frac{n(n-1)}{2} z^{n-2}h + \cdots + h^{n-1}\right]\right|$$

$$\leq \sum_{n=0}^{\infty} |a_n|\left[\frac{n(n-1)}{2} \rho^{n-2}\epsilon + \cdots + \epsilon^{n-1}\right]$$

$$= \sum_{n=0}^{\infty} |a_n|\left[\frac{(\rho+\epsilon)^n - \rho^n}{\epsilon} - n\rho^{n-1}\right]$$

$$= \sum_{n=0}^{\infty} |a_n|\sigma^n\left[\frac{\left(\frac{\rho+\epsilon}{\sigma}\right)^n - \left(\frac{\rho}{\sigma}\right)^n}{\epsilon} - \frac{n}{\rho}\left(\frac{\rho}{\sigma}\right)^n\right].$$

Since for $0 < t < 1$,

$$\sum_{n=0}^{\infty} t^n = \frac{1}{1-t} \quad \text{and} \quad \sum_{n=1}^{\infty} nt^{n-1} = \frac{1}{(1-t)^2} \quad \text{and} \quad |a_n|\sigma^n < M \quad \text{(why?)},$$

we have

$$\left|\frac{f(z+h)-f(z)}{h} - g(z)\right| \leq M\left[\frac{1}{\epsilon}\left(\frac{1}{\sigma-\rho+\epsilon} - \frac{1}{\sigma-\rho}\right) - \frac{1}{(\sigma-\rho)^2}\right]$$

$$= \frac{M}{(\sigma-\rho)^2(\sigma-\rho-\epsilon)} \to 0 \qquad \text{as } \epsilon = |h| \to 0$$

Hence, by the definition of the derivative, $f'(z) = g(z)$ in N_r.

Corollary. If $f(z) = \sum_{n=0}^{\infty} a_n z^n$ in N_r, then

$$f^{(k)}(z) = \sum_{n=k}^{\infty} n(n-1)\cdots(n-k+1)a_n z^{n-k}$$

in N_r, $k = 1, 2, \cdots$.

This follows readily from the theorem, since the differentiated series is a power series, which in turn can be differentiated term by term, and this process can be repeated any number of times.

The preceding theorem and its corollary enable us to show that every power series represents an analytic function in its circle of convergence; i.e., the

THEOREM. If $f(z) = \sum_{n=0}^{\infty} a_n(z-a)^n$ in $N_r(a)$, then $f(z)$ is analytic in $N_r(a)$ and

$$a_n = \frac{f^{(n)}(a)}{n!}, \qquad n = 0, 1, \cdots.$$

Proof. Since $f(z)$ is differentiable at every point in N_r, by the theorem given above, it is analytic there. The a_n may be determined by differentiating the power series term by term and evaluating each derivative at $z = a$.

In the next section, we prove the converse of the preceding theorem, which will enable us to represent an analytic function as a power series in a specific circle.

Let us now consider the power series $\sum_{n=0}^{\infty} z^n$. It is readily seen that its radius of convergence is 1. Hence, it represents an analytic function $f(z)$ in $|z| < 1$; i.e.,

$$f(z) = \sum_{n=0}^{\infty} z^n, \qquad |z| < 1.$$

Furthermore

$$f'(z) = \sum_{n=1}^{\infty} nz^{n-1},$$

$|z| < 1$. Thus, $(1 - z)f'(z) = f(z)$, from which we obtain $\operatorname{Log} f(z) = -\operatorname{Log}(1 - z) +$ constant, which yields $f(z) = 1/(1 - z)$, since $f(0) = 1$. Hence

$$\frac{1}{1 - z} = \sum_{n=0}^{\infty} z^n, \qquad |z| < 1.$$

This series, of frequent occurrence, is known as the **geometric series.**

EXERCISES

1. Find the following, if they exist:

(a) $\lim_{n\to\infty} \left(\frac{n}{n+i} - \frac{n+i}{n}\right)$; (b) $\lim_{n\to\infty} \frac{n}{i^n}$;

(c) $\lim_{n\to\infty} \cos n(1 + i)$; (d) $\lim_{n\to\infty} \frac{n^2 + in - 2}{in^2}$;

(e) $\lim_{n\to\infty} i^{1/n}$; (f) $\lim_{n\to\infty} n^{(-1)^n}$; (g) $\lim_{n\to\infty} ni^n$;

(h) $\lim_{n\to\infty} \frac{n^i \sin n!}{n + i}$; (i) $\lim_{n\to\infty} \frac{(3i)^n + (-2i)^n}{(3i)^{n+1} - (-2i)^{n+1}}$;

(j) $\lim_{n\to\infty} n\left(\cos\frac{\theta}{n} + i\sin\frac{\theta}{n} - 1\right)$;

(k) $\lim_{n\to\infty} z_n, \quad z_0 = 1,\ z_1 = i,\ z_n = \frac{1}{2}(z_{n-1} + z_{n-2}),\ n \geq 2$;

(l) $\lim_{n\to\infty} z_n, \quad z_{2n} = \left(\frac{i}{3}\right)^n,\ z_{2n+1} = \left(\frac{i}{2}\right)^n.$ *Ans.:* (a) 0; (d) $-i$; (e) 1; (i) 1; (j) $-i\theta$; (l) 0.

2. Determine whether the following series are convergent or divergent:

(a) $\sum_{n=1}^{\infty} \frac{n}{(4n - i)(4n - 2i)}$;

(b) $\sum_{n=1}^{\infty} \frac{n + 3i + 4}{i^n}$;

(c) $\sum_{n=1}^{\infty} \frac{\text{Log } n}{\sqrt[n]{n+i}}$; (d) $\sum_{n=1}^{\infty} n i^{-n^2}$;

(e) $\sum_{n=1}^{\infty} \frac{1}{\sqrt[n]{n+i}}$; (f) $\sum_{n=1}^{\infty} \frac{i^n n!}{n^n}$;

(g) $\sum_{n=1}^{\infty} \frac{n!}{i^{ni}}$; (h) $\sum_{n=1}^{\infty} \frac{(-1)\sqrt[n]{n}}{n+i}$; (i) $\sum_{n=1}^{\infty} \frac{(-1)^{n-1}}{n^i}$;

(j) $\sum_{n=1}^{\infty} (-1)^n[1 - n \sin (i/n)]$. *Ans.:* Divergent (a), (b), (c), (d), (f), (g), (i), (j); convergent (e), (h).

3. Determine the radius of convergence of $\sum_{n=0}^{\infty} a_n z^n$ where a_n is (a) $n(n+1)$; (b) $n^{\text{Log } n}$; (c) n^2, n even, $1/4^n$, n odd; (d) $[1 + (1/n)]^{n^2}$; (e) $(\text{Log } n)^n$; (f) n^n; (g) $n!$; (h) $1 + ni$; (i) $(1 + i)^n$; (j) $1/4^m$ if $n = 3m$, 0 if $n = 3m + 1$, $(-1)^m/m$ if $n = 3m + 2$; (k) $1/m!$ when $n = 2^m$, $m = 0, 1, \cdots$, otherwise 0; (l) $e^{(-1)^n n}$; (m) $1 + \sin n\pi/2$; (n) $(-1)^{n+1}n - n$; (o) $n \sin (n\pi/2)$.

Ans.: (a) 1; (b) ∞; (c) 1; (d) e; (f) ∞; (g) 0; (h) 1; (i) $\sqrt{2}$; (j) 1; (k) 1; (l) 1; (m) 1; (n) $\sqrt{2}$; (o) ∞.

4. (a) Prove that if

$$\lim_{n\to\infty} \left|\frac{a_{n+1}}{a_n}\right| = t,$$

then the radius of convergence of $\sum_{n=0}^{\infty} a_n z^n$ is $1/t$.

(b) Determine the radius of convergence of

$$\sum_{n=0}^{\infty} \frac{n!}{n^n} z^n, \tag{1}$$

$$\sum_{n=0}^{\infty} \frac{a(a+1)\cdots(a+n)b(b+1)\cdots(b+n)}{n!c(c+1)\cdots(c+n)} z^n, \tag{2}$$

a, b, c arbitrary complex numbers, $c \neq 0, -1, -2, \cdots$. (*Hypergeometric series.*)

Ans.: (b) (1)e; (2) ∞.

5. Show that if $|a_n| < M$ for all n, and r is the radius of convergence of $\sum_{n=0}^{\infty} a_n z^n$, then $r \geq 1$.

6. Show that the radius of convergence of $\sum_{n=1}^{\infty} \frac{(-1)^n}{n} z^n$ is 1. Test for convergence at $z = 1, -1$, and i.

7. Given that the series $\sum_{n=0}^{\infty} a_n z^n$ has radius of convergence r. Find the radius of convergence of each of the following:

(a) $\sum_{n=1}^{\infty} a_n n^p z^n$; (b) $\sum_{n=1}^{\infty} \frac{a_n}{n^p} z^n$;

(c) $\sum_{n=0}^{\infty} \frac{a_n z^n}{n!}$; (d) $\sum_{n=0}^{\infty} a_n n! z^n$.

8. If $\sum_{n=1}^{\infty} a_n z^n$ and $\sum_{n=1}^{\infty} b_n z^n$ have radii of convergence r and r', find the radii of convergence of

(a) $\sum_{n=0}^{\infty} (a_n + b_n) z^n$; (b) $\sum_{n=0}^{\infty} a_n b_n z^n$;

(c) $\sum_{n=0}^{\infty} \frac{a_n}{b_n} z^n$, $b_n \neq 0$.

9. (a) If $|z_0| = 1$, show that $\sum_{n=1}^{\infty} \frac{1}{n}\left(\frac{z}{z_0}\right)^n$ converges for $|z| = 1$, $z \neq z_0$ and diverges for $z = z_0$.

(b) Show that $\sum_{n=1}^{\infty} \frac{1}{n}\left(\frac{1}{z_1^n} + \frac{1}{z_2^n} + \cdots + \frac{1}{z_p^n}\right) z^n$ has radius of convergence 1, is divergent at $z_1, z_2, \cdots, z_p$, and is convergent for all other z, $|z| = 1$.

10. Show that

$$f(z) = 1 + \sum_{n=1}^{\infty} \frac{c(c-1)\cdots(c-m+1)}{n!} z^n$$

is analytic when $|z| < 1$ and that $f'(z) = cf(z)/(1+z)$. Hence, show that $f(z) = (1+z)^c$. Show that when c is a positive integer, this is the binomial theorem.

11. Show that the radius of convergence of $\sum_{n=0}^{\infty} \frac{z^n}{n!}$ is ∞ and determine the analytic function this power series represents in the z-plane.

12. (a) Define the **limit inferior** (or lower limit) of the real sequence $\{a_n\}$, denoted by $\underline{\lim}_{n\to\infty} a_n$.

(b) Show that $\lim_{n\to\infty} a_n$ exists if and only if $\overline{\lim}_{n\to\infty} a_n = \underline{\lim}_{n\to\infty} a_n$.

(c) Show that $\underline{\lim}\, a_n \leq \overline{\lim}\, a_n$, $\underline{\lim}\, a_n + \underline{\lim}\, b_n \leq \underline{\lim}\,(a_n + b_n) \leq \underline{\lim}\, a_n + \overline{\lim}\, b_n \leq \overline{\lim}\,(a_n + b_n) \leq \overline{\lim}\, a_n + \overline{\lim}\, b_n$, as $n \to \infty$.

(d) Show that $\overline{\lim}_{n\to\infty} \cos nx = 1$ if x/π is irrational.

(e) Determine $\overline{\lim}_{n\to\infty} a_n$ and $\underline{\lim}_{n\to\infty} a_n$ where a_n is (1) $(-1)^n n$, (2) $n^2 \sin^2 \frac{1}{2}n\pi$, (3) x^n. *Ans.:* (1) $\infty, -\infty$; (2) $\infty, 0$.

3. Taylor's series. We have seen that a power series $\sum_{n=0}^{\infty} a_n(z-a)^n$ represents an analytic function $f(z)$ in the interior of its circle of convergence and that $a_n = f^{(n)}(a)/n!$. Given a power series, in general it is difficult to determine explicitly the analytic function such a series represents; as a matter of fact, this series is often used to define the analytic function, and its properties are deduced from this definition. However, given an analytic function, the existence and determination of its power series representation is indicated by

TAYLOR'S THEOREM. If $f(z)$ is analytic in an open region D and if a is in D, then there exists a power series $\sum_{n=0}^{\infty} a_n(z-a)^n$ that converges to $f(z)$ in the largest open circular region with center at a, which is entirely contained in D. Furthermore, $a_n = \frac{f^{(n)}(a)}{n!}$.

Proof. Let $C\colon |z-a| = r$ and $N_r(a)$ belong to D. Then, by the Cauchy integral formula,

$$f(z) = \frac{1}{2\pi i} \oint_C \frac{f(\zeta)\, d\zeta}{\zeta - z} \qquad \text{for any } z \text{ in } N_r(a).$$

But

$$\frac{1}{\zeta - z} = \frac{1}{\zeta - a}\left[\frac{1}{1 - \dfrac{z - a}{\zeta - a}}\right]$$

$$= \frac{1}{\zeta - a}\left[\sum_{k=0}^{n-1}\left(\frac{z - a}{\zeta - a}\right)^k + \left(\frac{z - a}{\zeta - a}\right)^n \frac{1}{\zeta - z}\right].$$

Hence,

$$f(z) = \sum_{k=0}^{n-1}\left(\frac{1}{2\pi i}\oint_C \frac{f(\zeta)\, d\zeta}{(\zeta - a)^{k+1}}\right)(z - a)^k + R_n,$$

where

$$R_n = \frac{1}{2\pi i}\oint_C \frac{f(\zeta)(z - a)^n}{(\zeta - a)^{n+1}} \frac{d\zeta}{\zeta - z}.$$

By the generalized Cauchy integral formula,

$$f(z) = \sum_{k=0}^{n-1} \frac{f^{(k)}(a)}{k!}(z - a)^k + R_n.$$

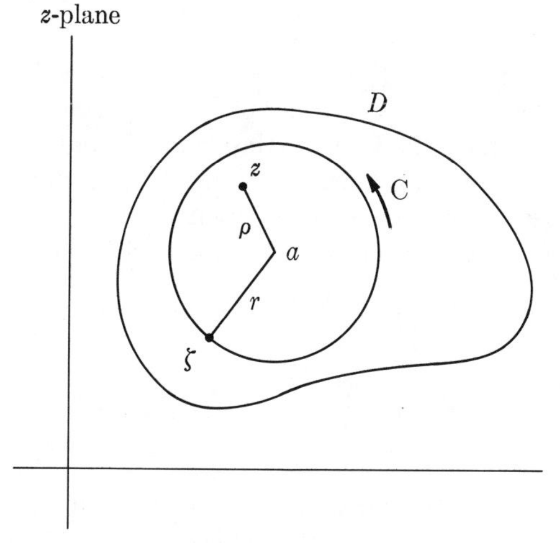

Fig. 1. Taylor's theorem

It remains to show that $\lim_{n\to\infty} R_n = 0$. Let $|z - a| = \rho$. Then for $\rho < r = |\zeta - a|$ (see Fig. 1), since $|f(z)| \leq M$ on C (why?), we have

$$\left|\frac{f(\zeta)(z - a)^n}{(\zeta - a)^{n+1}(\zeta - z)}\right| \leq \frac{M\rho^n}{r^{n+1}|\zeta - a - (z - a)|} \leq \frac{M\rho^n}{r^{n+1}(r - \rho)} = \frac{K\rho^n}{r^{n+1}},$$

K independent of n. (Justify all the inequalities!) Hence

$$|R_n| \leq \frac{1}{2\pi}\frac{K\rho^n}{r^{n+1}}L_C = K\left(\frac{\rho}{r}\right)^n.$$

Now, since $\rho/r < 1$, $|R_n| \to 0$ as $n \to \infty$.

Now consider all the circles with center at a whose interiors are in D. Of all these circles, the one with the largest radius determines the required largest open circular region.

A power series $\sum_{n=0}^{\infty} a_n(z-a)^n$ such that $a_n = \dfrac{f^{(n)}(a)}{n!}$ is called the **Taylor series** of $f(z)$ about $z = a$. In the special case $a = 0$, the series is called the **Maclaurin series** of $f(z)$. We have seen that a power series is always the Taylor series of an analytic function in the interior of its circle of convergence, and conversely, an analytic function can always be represented as a Taylor series about a point, such a representation being valid in the interior of the largest circle centered at the point that is contained wholly in the open region where $f(z)$ is analytic.

EXAMPLE. Determine the Maclaurin series of $f(z) = e^z$.

Solution. Since $f^{(n)}(0) = 1$, $e^z = \sum_{n=0}^{\infty} \dfrac{z^n}{n!}$, the radius of convergence is $r = \infty$, since e^z is an entire function.

Given the power series $\sum_{n=0}^{\infty} a_n(z-a)^n$, we know that it represents an analytic function within its circle of convergence whose radius can always be determined by the Cauchy-Hadamard formula. However, given an analytic function, we can always determine the radius of convergence of its Taylor series about the point a without the use of this formula. It is simply *the distance from a to the nearest singular point of $f(z)$.*

EXAMPLE. Determine the radius of convergence r of the Taylor series of

$$f(z) = \frac{\sin z}{(z^2+1)(z+2)(z-4)}$$

about (a) $z = 0$; (b) $z = 1$; (c) $z = 2$; (d) $z = 5 + 5i$.

Solution. The singular points of $f(z)$ are $\pm i$, -2, 4. (a) $\pm i$ are nearest to 0 and hence $r = 1$; (b) $\pm i$ are nearest to 1 and hence $r = \sqrt{2}$; (c) 4 is nearest to 2 and hence $r = 2$; (d) 4 is nearest to $5 + 5i$ and hence $r = \sqrt{26}$.

For x real, we recall the expansions

(a) $$\frac{1}{1+x} = \sum_{n=0}^{\infty} (-1)^n x^n, \qquad -1 < x < 1$$

(b) $$\frac{1}{1+x^2} = \sum_{n=0}^{\infty} (-1)^n x^{2n}, \qquad -1 < x < 1.$$

The interval of convergence in (a) is not surprising, since the function is not defined for $x = -1$. However, since the function in (b) is defined for all real x, the interval of convergence of its series may be surprising, until we realize that $1/(1 + x^2)$ is Re $(1/(1 + z^2))$ and $1/(1 + z^2)$ has singularities at $z = \pm i$, thereby yielding $|z| = 1$ as the circle of convergence, cutting the x-axis at 1 and -1. This is just another instance illustrating the fact that the full generality of many theorems in function theory can be achieved only when we admit complex functions.

In order to ensure that $f(z)$ has one and only one Taylor series about a point, we prove

THE UNIQUENESS THEOREM FOR TAYLOR SERIES. If $f(z)$ is analytic at a with Taylor series $\sum_{n=0}^{\infty} a_n(z - a)^n$, valid in $N_r(a)$, and $f(z) = \sum_{n=0}^{\infty} b_n(z - a)^n$ in $N_r(a)$, then $a_n = b_n$, $n = 0, 1, 2, \cdots$.

Proof. $\sum_{n=0}^{\infty} b_n(z - a)^n$ is a power series representing $f(z)$ in $N_r(a)$ and is necessarily the Taylor series of $f(z)$. Hence, $b_n = \dfrac{f^{(n)}(a)}{n!} = a_n$, $n = 0, 1, 2, \cdots$.

This theorem is very useful in practice, since it assures us that whatever method we employ for determining a power series

$$\sum_{n=0}^{\infty} a_n(z - a)^n,$$

representing $f(z)$, this series will be its Taylor series about $z = a$. Thus far, in order to determine the Taylor series of $f(z)$ about $z = a$, we have computed

$$a_n = \frac{f^{(n)}(a)}{n!}, \qquad n = 0, 1, \cdots,$$

and then determined the radius of convergence of the series. However, this method in practice is often tedious and laborious. Fortunately, the following theorem enables us to find the Taylor series of many functions without any appeal to the definition of the Taylor series of a function.

THEOREM ON OPERATIONS FOR TAYLOR SERIES. If $f(z)$ and $g(z)$ are analytic in some open circular region $N_r(a)$ and $\sum_{n=0}^{\infty} a_n(z - a)^n$ and $\sum_{n=0}^{\infty} b_n(z - a)^n$ are their Taylor series about $z = a$, then the Taylor series about $z = a$ of

T$_1$: $kf(z) = \sum_{n=0}^{\infty} ka_n(z - a)^n$, k any complex number;

T$_2$: $f(z) + g(z) = \sum_{n=0}^{\infty} (a_n + b_n)(z - a)^n$;

T$_3$: $f(z)g(z) = \sum_{n=0}^{\infty} c_n(z - a)^n$, where $c_n = \sum_{k=0}^{\infty} a_k b_{n-k}$;

$$\mathbf{T_4:}\quad \frac{f(z)}{g(z)} = \sum_{n=0}^{\infty} c_n(z-a)^n,\ a_n = \sum_{k=0}^{\infty} c_k b_{n-k},\ g(z) \neq 0 \text{ in } N_r(a);$$

$$\mathbf{T_5:}\quad \int_a^z f(u)\,du = \sum_{n=0}^{\infty} \frac{a_n}{n+1}(z-a)^{n+1};$$

these series being convergent in $N_r(a)$.

Proof. Let $h(z)$ denote any one of the functions in T_1 to T_4. Then the coefficients of the Taylor series of $h(z)$ about $z = a$ are

$$\frac{h^{(n)}(a)}{n!}, \qquad n = 0, 1, 2, \cdots.$$

Then since

$$\frac{d^n}{dz^n} kf(z)\Big]_{z=a} = kf^{(n)}(a),$$

$$\frac{d^n}{dz^n}[f(z) + g(z)]\Big|_{z=a} = f^{(n)}(a) + g^{(n)}(a)$$

and

$$\frac{d^n}{dz^n}[f(z)g(z)]\Big|_{z=a} = \sum_{k=0}^{n} \frac{n!}{(n-k)!k!} f^{(k)}(a)f^{(n-k)}(a),$$

(**Leibniz's rule for the nth derivative of the product of two functions;** if you are not familiar with it, try proving it by mathematical induction—we shall encounter it again), we immediately obtain T_1, T_2, T_3. Since $f(z) = g(z) \cdot \dfrac{f(z)}{g(z)}$, we obtain the required relation in T_4. The power series in T_5 represents an analytic function $g(z)$ in $N_{r'}(a)$. But $g'(z) = f(z)$ and $f(z)$ is analytic in $N_r(a)$, so $r = r'$; integrating both sides yields the result.

The theorem on operations indicates that we find the Taylor series of the sum of two functions merely by adding corresponding terms in the Taylor series of these functions, and the product or the quotient of two functions by multiplying or dividing their Taylor series in the same manner that we multiply or divide two polynomials. We find the Taylor series of the integral of $f(z)$ by integrating its Taylor series term by term.

If $N_{r_1}(a)$ and $N_{r_2}(a)$ are the interiors of the circles of convergence of the Taylor series of $f(z)$ and $g(z)$, then the preceding theorem implies that $N_r(a)$, $r = \min(r_1, r_2)$, is the interior of the circle of convergence of the Taylor series of $f(z) + g(z)$, $f(z)g(z)$.

Given $f(z) = \sum_{n=0}^{\infty} a_n(z-a)^n$; by making appropriate substitutions for z, we can obtain the Taylor series of other functions. In general, the center of the Taylor series and its radius of convergence will change. We illustrate this situation in the

EXAMPLE. Determine the Taylor series of (a) $1/(1+z^2)$; (b) $1/(1-2iz)$; (c) $1/z$ about an appropriate point, indicating the radius of convergence.

Solution. We substitute for ζ in

$$\frac{1}{1-\zeta} = \sum_{n=0}^{\infty} \zeta^n, \qquad |\zeta| < 1.$$

(a) $\zeta = -z^2$; then

$$\frac{1}{1+z^2} = \sum_{n=0}^{\infty} (-1)^n z^{2n}, \qquad |-z^2| < 1 \quad \text{or} \quad |z| < 1.$$

(b) $\zeta = -2iz$; then

$$\frac{1}{1-2iz} = \sum_{n=0}^{\infty} (2i)^n z^{2n}, \qquad |z| < \tfrac{1}{2}.$$

(c) $\zeta = 1 - z$; then

$$\frac{1}{z} = \sum_{n=0}^{\infty} (-1)^n (z-1)^n, \qquad |z-1| < 1.$$

We now list the Maclaurin series of some of the elementary functions:

$$(1) \qquad e^z = \sum_{n=1}^{\infty} \frac{z^n}{n!}, \qquad \text{all } z.$$

$$(2) \qquad \frac{1}{1-z} = \sum_{n=0}^{\infty} z^n, \qquad |z| < 1.$$

$$(3) \qquad \sin z = \sum_{n=0}^{\infty} \frac{(-1)^n z^{2n+1}}{(2n+1)!}, \qquad \text{all } z.$$

$$(4) \qquad \cos z = \sum_{n=0}^{\infty} \frac{(-1)^n z^{2n}}{(2n)!}, \qquad \text{all } z.$$

$$(5) \qquad \sinh z = \sum_{n=0}^{\infty} \frac{z^{2n+1}}{(2n+1)!}, \qquad \text{all } z.$$

$$(6) \qquad \cosh z = \sum_{n=0}^{\infty} \frac{z^{2n}}{(2n)!}, \qquad \text{all } z.$$

$$(7) \qquad \operatorname{Log}(z+1) = \sum_{n=1}^{\infty} \frac{(-1)^{n+1} z^n}{n}, \qquad |z| < 1.$$

$$(8) \qquad \operatorname{Tan}^{-1} z = \sum_{n=0}^{\infty} \frac{(-1)^n z^{2n+1}}{2n+1}, \qquad |z| < 1.$$

$$(9) \qquad \frac{1}{(1-z)^2} = \sum_{n=0}^{\infty} n z^n, \qquad |z| < 1.$$

$$(10) \qquad \tan z = z + \frac{z^3}{3} + \frac{2z^5}{15} + \cdots, \qquad |z| < \pi/2.$$

We have already established (1) and (2). The series for e^{iz}, e^{-iz}, e^{-z} can be obtained from (1) by making the appropriate substitutions. Then (3) to (6) may be established by using the definitions of the functions involved and T_1 and T_2 of the theorem on operations. Since $\operatorname{Log}(z+1) =$

$\int_1^z \frac{du}{u+1}$, the appropriate substitution in (2) with T_5 yields (7). Similarly, (8) can be obtained with the use of $\text{Tan}^{-1} z = \int_0^z \frac{du}{1+u^2}$. We obtain (9) by multiplying the series in (2) by itself and observing that, using T_3 with $a_n = b_n = 1$, we have $\sum_{k=1}^n 1 = n$. We obtain (10) by dividing the series for $\sin z$ by that of $\cos z$. Since the nearest singular point of $\tan z$ to 0 is $z = \pi/2$, we obtain immediately the radius of convergence. To obtain the general term appears to be impossible; we content ourselves with determining as many terms in the series that we desire. The student should supply all the details in obtaining the series in (3) to (10).

EXERCISES

1. Use the appropriate substitution in known series to obtain the following:

(a) $e^z = e^a \sum_{n=0}^{\infty} \frac{(z-a)^n}{n!}, \quad$ all z.

(b) $\frac{1}{z^2} = \sum_{n=0}^{\infty} (n+1)(z+1)^n, \quad |z+1| < 1.$

(c) $\frac{1}{z^2} = \frac{1}{4} \sum_{n=0}^{\infty} (-1)^n(n+1)\left(\frac{z-2}{2}\right)^n, \quad |z-2| < 2.$

(d) $\frac{1}{(1-z^2)^2} = \sum_{n=0}^{\infty} nz^{2n}, \quad |z| < 1.$

(e) $\text{Log } z = \sum_{n=1}^{\infty} \frac{(-1)^{n+1}(z-1)^n}{n}, \quad |z-1| < 1.$

2. Find the Maclaurin series of each of the following, indicating the radius of convergence:

(a) $\frac{1}{(1-z)^3}$; (b) $\frac{z}{(z-1)(z-2)}$; (*Hint:* Use partial fractions;)

(c) $(\text{Tan}^{-1} z)^2$; (d) $e^z \cos z$; (*Hint:* Use the definition of $\cos z$;)
(e) $\tanh z$; (f) $(z-1)/(z+1)$; (g) $\sin z/z$; (h) $1/e^{1-z}$;
(i) $\sqrt{z^2 - 1}$ (see p. 300, Exercise 10); (j) $\text{Sin}^{-1} z$.

Ans.: (a) $\sum \frac{(n+1)(n+2)}{2} z^n$, $|z| < 1$; (b) $\sum \left(1 - \frac{1}{2^n}\right) z^n$, $|z| < 1$;

(d) $\sum \frac{(1+i)^n + (1-i)^n}{n!} z^n$, all z; (f) $-1 + 2\sum (-1)^{n+1} z^n$; $|z| < 1$

(g) $\sum \frac{(-1)^n z^{2n}}{(2n+1)!}$, all z; (h) $\frac{1}{e} \sum z^n/n!$ all z

3. Find the Taylor series of each of the following, indicating the radius of convergence:
(a) $\cos z$ about $z = \pi/2$; (b) $\sinh z$ about $z = \pi i$;
(c) $1/(z-2)$ about $z = 1$; (d) $1/[z(z-2)]$ about $z = 1$;
(e) $z/(z^2-1)$ about $z = i$; (f) $(z-1)/(z+1)$ about $z = 1$.

4. Determine the radius of convergence of the Taylor series of each of the following functions about the point indicated, without actually determining the series:

(a) $\dfrac{z^2-1}{(z^2+4)(z+2)}$, $z = i$; (b) $\dfrac{\sin z}{z^2+1}$, $z = 2$; (c) $\dfrac{\tan z}{1+z+z^2}$, $z = 1$;

(d) $\dfrac{1}{e^{z^2}-1}$, $z = 5i$; (e) $z \csc z$, $z = \pi$.

Ans.: (a) 1; (b) $\sqrt{5}$; (c) $\sqrt{3}$; (d) 5; (e) π.

5. If $f(z)$ is analytic for $|z| < r$ and if $f(z)$ is an $\left\{\begin{matrix}\text{odd}\\ \text{even}\end{matrix}\right\}$ function; i.e., if $\left\{\begin{matrix}f(-z) = -f(z)\\ f(-z) = f(z)\end{matrix}\right\}$, show that in the Taylor series of $f(z)$, the coefficients of $\left\{\begin{matrix}\text{even}\\ \text{odd}\end{matrix}\right\}$ index are zero.

6. If $a_n = \alpha_n + i\beta_n$, α_n and β_n real, and $f(z) = \sum_{n=0}^{\infty} a_n z^n$ converges for $|z| < r$, show that $f(z) = g(z) + ih(z)$, where $g(z) = \operatorname{Re} f(z) = \sum_{n=0}^{\infty} \alpha_n z^n$ and $h(z) = \operatorname{Im} f(z) = \sum_{n=0}^{\infty} \beta_n z^n$.

7. If $f(z)$ is analytic for $|z| < r$ and if $f(x)$ is real for $-r < x < r$, show that the coefficients of $f(z) = \sum_{n=0}^{\infty} a_n z^n$ must all be real. Show that for $|z| < r$, $f(\bar{z}) = \overline{f(z)}$.

8. Show that if $f(z) = \sum\limits_{n=0}^{\infty} a_n(z-a)^n$, $|z-a| < r$, $|a_n| \le \dfrac{M}{r^n}$, where M is the maximum value of $f(z)$ on $|z-a| = r$. Use this to prove the maximum modulus principle (p. 249).

9. Show that the series $\sum\limits_{m=0}^{\infty} \dfrac{(-1)^m z^{n+2m}}{2^{n+2m} m!(n+m)!}$ represents an entire function. This function is called *Bessel's function of order n* and is denoted by $J_n(z)$. Show that (a) $J_n(z)$ satisfies the differential equation $z^2w''(z) + zw'(z) + (z^2 - n^2)w(z) = 0$.
(b) $2nJ_n(z) = z(J_{n-1}(z) + J_{n+1}(z))$.

10. If $f(z) = \sum_{n=0}^{\infty} a_n z^n$, $|z| < R$, show that for $r < R$,

$$\sum_{n=0}^{\infty} |a_n|^2 r^{2n} = \frac{1}{2\pi} \int_0^{2\pi} |f(re^{i\theta})|^2 d\theta \qquad \textit{(Parseval's identity)}$$

and

$$\sum_{n=0}^{\infty} |a_n|^2 r^{2n} \le M_r^2$$

where $M_r = \max |f(z)|$ on $|z| = r$ (*Bessel's inequality*).

4. Laurent series. If in the power series $\sum_{n=0}^{\infty} b_n \zeta^n$, convergent for $|\zeta| < r$, we replace ζ by $\dfrac{1}{z-a}$, we obtain the series $\sum\limits_{n=0}^{\infty} \dfrac{b_n}{(z-a)^n}$, which is convergent for $|z - a| > 1/r$; i.e., in the exterior of the circle with center at a and radius $1/r = r_1$. In this region, this series represents an analytic function $g(z)$. We have, then,

$$g(z) = \sum_{n=0}^{\infty} \frac{b_n}{(z - a)^n}$$

for $|z - a| > r_1$. Furthermore, if the power series $\sum_{n=0}^{\infty} a_n(z - a)^n$ is convergent for $|z - a| < r_2$, then it represents an analytic function $f(z)$ and

$$f(z) = \sum_{n=0}^{\infty} a_n(z - a)^n$$

for $|z - a| < r_2$. Now, if $r_2 > r_1$, the function $h(z) = f(z) + g(z)$ is analytic in the region common to both $|z - a| < r_2$ and $|z - a| > r_1$, and we have the representation

$$h(z) = \sum_{n=0}^{\infty} a_n(z - a)^n + \sum_{n=0}^{\infty} \frac{b_n}{(z - a)^n}, \qquad r_1 < |z - a| < r_2,$$

which can be written as

$$h(z) = \sum_{n=-\infty}^{\infty} a_n(z - a)^n, \qquad r_1 < |z - a| < r_2,$$

where $b_n = a_{-n}$, $n = 1, 2, \cdots$ and $a_0 + b_0$ has been written as a_0. The region $r_1 < |z - a| < r_2$ is called an **annulus** (or ring) with center at a, inner radius r_1, and outer radius r_2. This annulus is also called the *region of convergence* of the series. We have established the

THEOREM. The series of the form $\sum_{n=-\infty}^{\infty} a_n(z - a)^n$ represents an analytic function in $r_1 < |z - a| < r_2$.

It is the converse of this theorem that we now examine; we ask if a function $f(z)$ that is analytic in a given annulus can be represented as $f(z) = \sum_{n=-\infty}^{\infty} a_n(z - a)^n$ in that annulus? An affirmative answer is afforded by

LAURENT'S THEOREM. If $f(z)$ is analytic in the annulus

$$D: \quad r_1 < |z - a| < r_2,$$

then

$$f(z) = \sum_{n=-\infty}^{\infty} a_n(z - a)^n$$

in D, where

$$a_n = \frac{1}{2\pi i} \oint_C \frac{f(\zeta)\, d\zeta}{(\zeta - a)^{n+1}},$$

with C any closed regular curve in D having a in its interior.

Proof. Denote the circles $|z - a| = r_1 + \epsilon$ and $|z - a| = r_2 - \epsilon$ by C_1 and C_2, where $\epsilon > 0$ is arbitrarily small. Let z be any point in D such

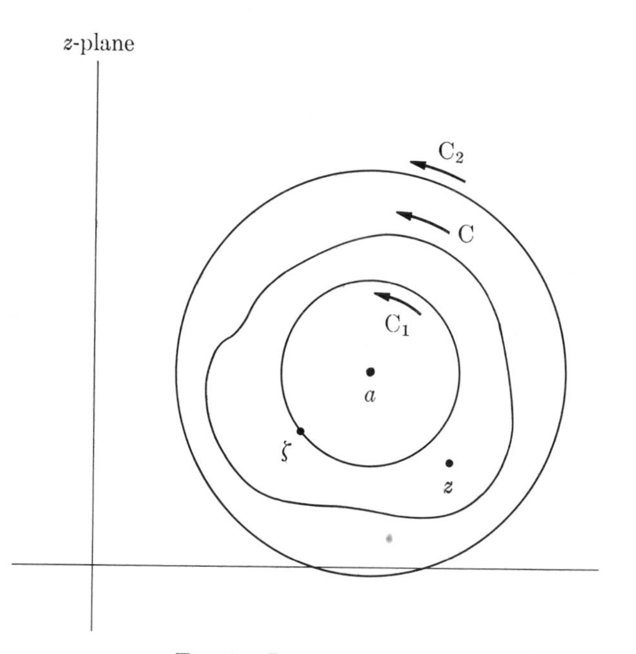

Fig. 2. Laurent's theorem

that $r_1 + \epsilon < |z - a| < r_2 - \epsilon$ (see Fig. 2). Then by the Cauchy integral formula,

$$f(z) = \frac{1}{2\pi i}\oint_{C_2}\frac{f(\zeta)\,d\zeta}{\zeta - z} - \frac{1}{2\pi i}\oint_{C_1}\frac{f(\zeta)\,d\zeta}{\zeta - z}$$

and we can write $f(z) = f_1(z) + f_2(z)$, where

$$f_1(z) = \frac{1}{2\pi i}\oint_{C_2}\frac{f(\zeta)\,d\zeta}{\zeta - z} \quad \text{and} \quad f_2(z) = \frac{1}{2\pi i}\oint_{C_1}\frac{f(\zeta)\,d\zeta}{z - \zeta}.$$

It can be shown, completely analogously to the proof in Taylor's theorem, that

$$f_1(z) = \sum_{n=0}^{\infty} a_n(z - a)^n, \quad a_n = \frac{1}{2\pi i}\int_{C_2}\frac{f(\zeta)\,d\zeta}{(\zeta - a)^{n+1}}, \qquad n = 0, 1, \cdots.$$

We now show that

$$f_2(z) = \sum_{n=1}^{\infty}\frac{a_{-n}}{(z - a)^n},$$

$$a_{-n} = \frac{1}{2\pi i}\oint_{C_1} f(\zeta)(\zeta - a)^{n-1}\,d\zeta, \qquad n = 1, 2, \cdots.$$

We have

$$\frac{1}{z-\zeta} = \frac{1}{z-a-(\zeta-a)} = \frac{1}{z-a}\cdot\frac{1}{1-\dfrac{\zeta-a}{z-a}}$$

$$= \frac{1}{z-a}\left[\sum_{k=0}^{n-1}\left(\frac{\zeta-a}{z-a}\right)^k + \frac{\left(\dfrac{\zeta-a}{z-a}\right)^n}{1-\dfrac{\zeta-a}{z-a}}\right]$$

$$= \sum_{k=1}^{n}\frac{(\zeta-a)^{k-1}}{(z-a)^k} + \frac{1}{z-\zeta}\cdot\left(\frac{\zeta-a}{z-a}\right)^n.$$

Therefore

$$f_2(z) = \frac{1}{2\pi i}\oint_{C_1}\sum_{k=1}^{n}\frac{(\zeta-a)^{k-1}}{(z-a)^k}f(\zeta)\,d\zeta + R_n$$

where

$$R_n = \frac{1}{2\pi i(z-a)^n}\oint_{C_1}\frac{(\zeta-a)^n}{z-\zeta}f(\zeta)\,d\zeta$$

or

$$f_2(z) = \sum_{k=1}^{n}\frac{a_{-k}}{(z-a)^k} + R_n.$$

We now show that $\lim_{n\to\infty} R_n = 0$. First, $|f(z)| \le M$, a constant, on C_1 (why?); we have $|\zeta - a| = r_1 + \epsilon$, and letting $|z - a| = \rho$,

$$|z-\zeta| = |z-a-(\zeta-a)| \ge \rho - r_1 - \epsilon.$$

Now,

$$\left|\frac{(\zeta-a)^n}{z-\zeta}f(\zeta)\right| \le \frac{(r_1-\epsilon)^n M}{\zeta - r_1 - \epsilon} = K(r_1+\epsilon)^n, \qquad K \text{ independent of } n.$$

Then

$$|R_n| \le \frac{K}{2\pi\rho^n}(r_1+\epsilon)^n L_{C_1} = K\left(\frac{r_1+\epsilon}{\rho}\right)^n(r_1+\epsilon) \to 0 \qquad \text{as } n \to 0$$

since $(r_1 + \epsilon)/\rho < 1$. Now, by the deformation of contour principle, C_1 and C_2 can be replaced by C.

The two extreme cases are of importance:

(1) If $r_1 \to 0$, the annulus becomes $0 < |z - a| < r_2$; i.e., the interior of the circle $|z - a| = r_2$ with the center deleted.

(2) if $r_2 \to \infty$, the annulus becomes $r_1 < |z - a|$; i.e., the exterior of the circle $|z - a| = r_1$.

In the proof of Laurent's theorem, we considered the decomposition $f(z) = f_1(z) + f_2(z)$. We then obtained $f_1(z) = \sum_{n=0}^{\infty} a_n(z-a)^n$ as in Taylor's theorem, with one difference; i.e.,

$$a_n = \frac{1}{2\pi i}\oint_{C_2}\frac{f(\zeta)\,d\zeta}{(\zeta-a)^{n+1}}$$

cannot be written as $f^{(n)}(a)/n!$ using the generalized Cauchy integral formula as in the proof of that theorem. Why?

A series of the form $\sum_{n=-\infty}^{\infty} a_n(z-a)^n$, where

$$a_n = \frac{1}{2\pi i}\oint_C \frac{f(\zeta)\,d\zeta}{(\zeta - a)^{n+1}}$$

is called the **Laurent series** of $f(z)$ about $z = a$.

THE UNIQUENESS THEOREM FOR LAURENT SERIES. If $f(z)$ is analytic in $r_1 < |z - a| < r_2$, and both $f(z) = \sum_{n=-\infty}^{\infty} a_n(z-a)^n$ and $f(z) = \sum_{n=-\infty}^{\infty} b_n(z-a)^n$ are valid in that annulus, then $a_n = b_n$, $n = \cdots -1, 0, 1, \cdots$; i.e., $f(z)$ has only one Laurent series at $z = a$ in a given annulus.

Proof. $\sum_{n=-\infty}^{\infty} (a_n - b_n)(z-a)^n$ is the Laurent series of $F(z) \equiv 0$. Hence, by Laurent's theorem, $a_n - b_n = 0$.

It should be noted that the Laurent series of $f(z)$ about $z = a$ in two different annuluses are in general different.

In practice, it is difficult to determine the Laurent series of $f(z)$ about $z = a$ in a given annulus from the definition—i.e., evaluating the integrals

$$\oint_C \frac{f(z)\,dz}{(z-a)^n}, \qquad n = \cdots -1, 0, 1.$$

As a matter of fact, the Laurent series of $f(z)$ about $z = a$ is often used to evaluate these very integrals. Since for any given annulus the Laurent series of $f(z)$ at $z = a$ is unique, we are assured that if we obtain a series expansion for $f(z)$ in the form $\sum_{n=-\infty}^{\infty} a_n(z-a)^n$, it will be the Laurent series of $f(z)$ about $z = a$. We now turn to various techniques for determining such expansions.

THEOREM ON OPERATIONS FOR LAURENT SERIES. If

$$f(z) = \sum_{n=-\infty}^{\infty} a_n(z-a)^n$$

in an annulus R_1 and

$$g(z) = \sum_{n=-\infty}^{\infty} b_n(z-a)^n$$

in an annulus R_2, and R is the annulus that is the region common to R_1 and R_2, then

L_1: $kf(z) = \sum_{n=-\infty}^{\infty} ka_n(z-a)^n$ in R_1, k a complex constant.

L_2: $f(z) + g(z) = \sum_{n=-\infty}^{\infty} (a_n + b_n)(z-a)^n$ in R.

L_3: $f(z)g(z) = \sum_{n=-\infty}^{\infty} c_n(z-a)^n$ in R, where $c_n = \sum_{k=-\infty}^{\infty} a_k b_{n-k}$.

$$\mathbf{L_4}: \quad \frac{f(z)}{g(z)} = \sum_{n=-\infty}^{\infty} c_n(z-a)^n, \; a_n = \sum_{k=-\infty}^{\infty} c_k b_{n-k}$$

in an annulus that is the region common to R and $|z-a| < r_0$, $|z-a| < r_0$ being the smallest circular region containing all the zeros of $g(z)$.

$$\mathbf{L_5}: \quad f'(z) = \sum_{n=-\infty}^{\infty} na_n(z-a)^{n-1} \text{ in } R_1.$$

$\mathbf{L_6}$: $\int_C f(z)\,dz = \sum_{n=-\infty}^{\infty} a_n \int_C (z-a)^n\,dz$ in R_1, where C is any regular curve in R_1.

In some cases the proof parallels the proof of the theorem on operations for Taylor series; in other cases, the details are too involved and will be omitted.

Note that a Taylor series is a special case of a Laurent series; namely, the case where the coefficients of the negative powers of $z - a$ all vanish. This means that in the preceding theorem, one of the series can be a Taylor series. The method of substitution to obtain new series from known ones is very effective, and we shall illustrate with some examples.

EXAMPLE 1. Find the Laurent series of $f(z) = z/(1-z)$ about $z = 0$ in a suitable annulus.

Solution. $f(z)$ is analytic at $z = 0$, and we could expand it in a Taylor series valid in $|z| < 1$. Now, for $|z| > 1$, no Taylor series is valid, but this is an annulus for which, by Laurent's theorem, there exists a Laurent series representing $f(z)$ in this annulus. Since

$$\frac{1}{1-\zeta} = \sum_{n=0}^{\infty} \zeta^n, \qquad |\zeta| < 1,$$

making the substitution $\zeta = 1/z$ yields the Laurent series

$$\frac{z}{1-z} = \sum_{n=0}^{\infty} \frac{1}{z^n}, \qquad |z| > 1.$$

EXAMPLE 2. Find the Laurent series of $e^{1/z}$ about $z = 0$ in a suitable annulus.

Solution. Since $e^{\zeta} = \sum_{n=0}^{\infty} \frac{\zeta^n}{n!}$, all z, making the substitution $\zeta = 1/z$ yields

$$e^{1/z} = \sum_{n=0}^{\infty} \frac{1}{n!z^n}, \qquad |z| > 0.$$

EXAMPLE 3. Find the Laurent series of $(z+2)/(z-1)$ valid in $|z+2| > 1$.

Solution

$$\frac{z+2}{z+1} = \frac{1}{1-[1/(z+2)]}.$$

In

$$\frac{1}{1-\zeta} = \sum_{n=0}^{\infty} \zeta^n, \qquad |\zeta| < 1,$$

making the substitution $\zeta = 1/(z+2)$ yields

$$\frac{z+2}{z+1} = \sum_{n=0}^{\infty} \frac{1}{(z+2)^n}, \qquad |z+2| > 1.$$

One of the fundamental problems in complex analysis is the representation of a function by a series in the neighborhood of a given point. If that point is a regular point of the function, then we know that there exists a neighborhood about that point in which the function has a Taylor series. However, if the point is an isolated singular point of the function, there is no neighborhood about the point in which the function can be represented by a Taylor series. For such points, we represent the function in some annulus about the point by a Laurent series. In practice, therefore, bearing in mind that function implies single-valued function, we expand a function into Laurent series at isolated singular points—such series representing the function in some annulus throughout which the function is analytic. If the boundary of the annulus has singular points of the function, then that annulus will be the largest in which the Laurent series of the function is valid.

If $f(z)$ has a finite number of singular points $z_1, z_2, \cdots, z_n$, then $f(z)$ can be expanded in a Laurent series about each of them. Let us consider all the Laurent series about z_1 valid in the largest possible annuluses. Let us assume that $|z_1 - z_2| < |z_1 - z_3| < \cdots < |z_1 - z_n|$. Then we have Laurent series valid in $0 < |z - z_1| < |z_1 - z_2|$, $|z_1 - z_2| < |z - z_1| < |z_1 - z_3|$, $\cdots$, $|z - z_1| > |z_1 - z_n|$; in general, n of them.

EXAMPLE 1. Determine all the Laurent series at the singular points of

$$f(z) = \frac{1}{z^2(z-1)},$$

each valid in the largest possible annulus.

Solution. The singular points of $f(z)$ are $z = 0$ and $z = 1$. The Laurent series of $f(z)$ about $z = 0$ will have powers of z. There are two possible Laurent series of the required type, one valid in $0 < |z| < 1$ and the other valid in $|z| > 1$, as illustrated in the figure.

For the first, $1/z^2$ is the Laurent series of $1/z^2$, valid for $0 < |z|$, and since

$$\frac{1}{z-1} = \frac{-1}{1-z} = -\sum_{n=0}^{\infty} z^n, \qquad |z| < 1,$$

multiplication of the series yields

$$\frac{1}{z^2(z-1)} = -\sum_{n=0}^{\infty} z^{n-2}, \qquad 0 < |z| < 1,$$

which is the region common to $0 < |z|$ and $|z| < 1$.

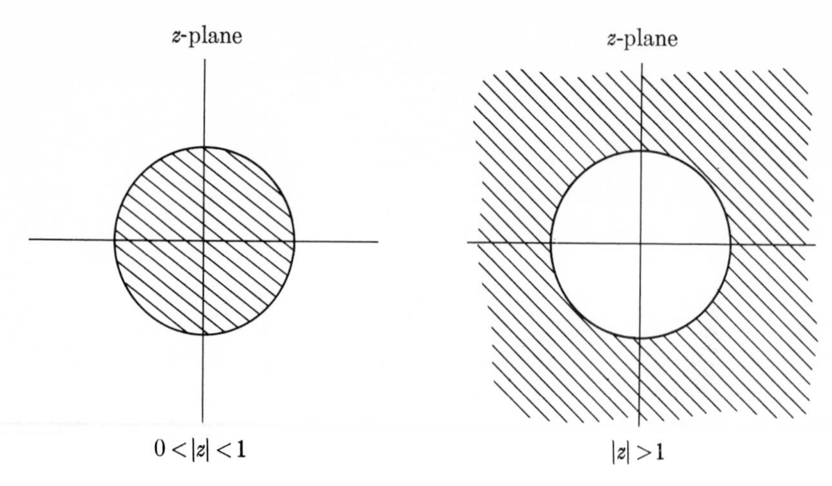

Example 1

Now let us consider the Laurent series of $f(z)$ at $z = 0$ valid in $|z| > 1$. We write

$$f(z) = \frac{1}{z^3[1 - (1/z)]},$$

which is the product of $1/z^3$ whose Laurent series is $1/z^3$, $|z| > 0$, and $1/[1 - (1/z)]$ whose Laurent series is

$$\sum_{n=0}^{\infty} \frac{1}{z^n}, \qquad |z| > 1.$$

Hence,

$$f(z) = \sum_{n=0}^{\infty} \frac{1}{z^{n+3}}, \qquad |z| > 1,$$

which is the region common to $|z| > 1$ and $|z| > 0$.

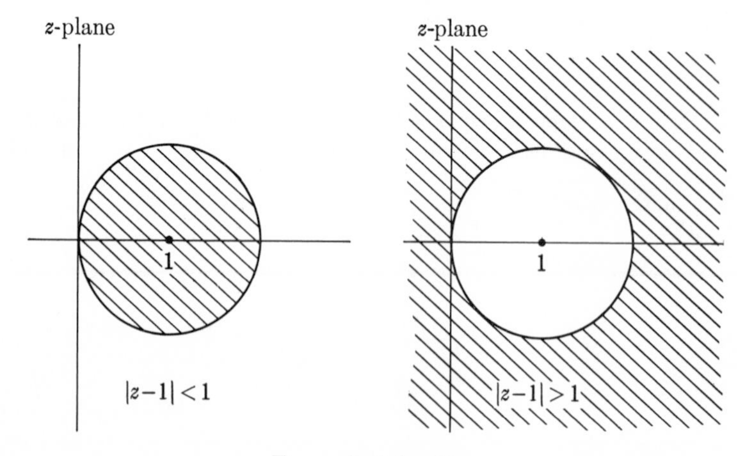

Example 1 (*cont.*)

We now consider the Laurent series of $f(z)$ about $z = 1$. These will have powers of $z - 1$. There are two of the required type, one valid in $0 < |z - 1| < 1$ and the other in $|z - 1| > 1$, as illustrated. We write

$$\frac{1}{z^2} = \frac{1}{(z - 1 + 1)^2} = \sum_{n=0}^{\infty} (-1)^n n(z - 1)^n, \qquad |z - 1| < 1,$$

and since $1/(z - 1)$ is the Laurent series of $1/(z - 1)$ about $z = 1$, $|z - 1| > 0$; we have

$$f(z) = \sum_{n=0}^{\infty} (-1)^n n(z - 1)^{n-1}, \qquad 0 < |z - 1| < 1.$$

Furthermore, if we write

$$\frac{1}{z^2} = \frac{1}{(z - 1 + 1)^2} = \frac{1}{(z - 1)^2} \frac{1}{\left(1 + \dfrac{1}{z - 1}\right)^2}$$

then

$$f(z) = \frac{1}{(z - 1)^3} \frac{1}{\left(1 + \dfrac{1}{z - 1}\right)^2}$$

which is the product of

$$\frac{1}{(z - 1)^3}, \quad |z - 1| > 0, \qquad \text{and} \qquad \sum_{n=0}^{\infty} \frac{(-1)^n}{(z - 1)^n}, \quad |z - 1| > 1.$$

Hence

$$f(z) = \sum_{n=0}^{\infty} \frac{(-1)^n}{(z - 1)^{n+3}}, \qquad 0 < |z - 1| < 1.$$

EXAMPLE 2. Determine all the Laurent series at the singular points of

$$f(z) = \frac{1}{(z - 1)(z - 2)},$$

each valid in the largest possible annulus.

Solution. It is convenient to express $f(z)$ in partial fractions as

$$f(z) = \frac{1}{(z - 1)(z - 2)} = \frac{1}{z - 2} - \frac{1}{z - 1}.$$

The singular points of $f(z)$ are $z = 1$ and $z = 2$. There are two Laurent series of $f(z)$ about $z = 1$ in powers of $z - 1$, one valid in $0 < |z - 1| < 1$ and the other in $|z - 1| > 1$. We write

$$f(z) = \frac{-1}{1 - (z - 1)} - \frac{1}{z - 1} = -\sum_{n=0}^{\infty} (z - 1)^n - \frac{1}{z - 1},$$

the first series valid for $|z - 1| < 1$ and the second for $|z - 1| > 0$. Hence,

$$f(z) = -\sum_{n=0}^{\infty} (z - 1)^{n-1}, \qquad 0 < |z - 1| < 1.$$

Also,

$$
\begin{aligned}
f(z) &= \frac{1}{z-2} - \frac{1}{z-1} \\
&= \frac{1}{(z-1)\left(1 - \dfrac{1}{z-1}\right)} - \frac{1}{z-1} \\
&= \frac{1}{z-1} \sum_{n=0}^{\infty} \frac{1}{(z-1)^n} - \frac{1}{z-1} \\
&\qquad \text{(the first series valid for } |z-1| > 1 \\
&\qquad \text{ and the second for } |z-1| > 0) \\
&= \sum_{n=1}^{\infty} \frac{1}{(z-1)^{n+1}}, \qquad |z-1| > 1.
\end{aligned}
$$

The student should verify the remaining Laurent series:

$$f(z) = \sum_{n=0}^{\infty} (z-2)^{n-1}, \qquad 0 < |z-2| < 1,$$

$$f(z) = -\sum_{n=1}^{\infty} \frac{1}{(z-2)^{n+1}}, \qquad |z-2| > 1.$$

The Laurent series of $f(z)$ at an isolated singular point is often used to study the nature of the singular point. If this series is written as

$$\sum_{n=0}^{\infty} a_n(z-a)^n + \sum_{n=1}^{\infty} \frac{a_{-n}}{(z-a)^n},$$

where a is an isolated singular point of $f(z)$ and the series is valid in the annulus $0 < |z-a| < r$, we call $\sum_{n=1}^{\infty} \frac{a_{-n}}{(z-a)^n}$ the **principal part** of the Laurent series of $f(z)$ at $z = a$. The annulus $0 < |z-a| < r$ is called a **deleted neighborhood** of a, since it is a neighborhood of a with a removed. It is important to note that we have defined the principal part of the Laurent series of $f(z)$ about $z = a$ in a deleted neighborhood of a—not in any other Laurent series of $f(z)$ about $z = a$.

We have the following results:

(1) $\operatorname*{Res}_{z=a} f(z) = a_{-1}$.

(2) $z = a$ is a pole of order m of $f(z)$ if and only if the principal part of the Laurent series of $f(z)$ at $z = a$ is

$$\frac{a_{-1}}{z-a} + \frac{a_{-2}}{(z-a)^2} + \cdots + \frac{a_{-m}}{(z-a)^m}, \qquad a_{-m} \neq 0.$$

(3) $z = a$ is an essential singular point of $f(z)$ if the principal part of the Laurent series of $f(z)$ at $z = a$ has an infinite number of nonzero terms.

Proof. (1) Both $\operatorname*{Res}_{z=a} f(z)$ and a_{-1} are equal to

$$\frac{1}{2\pi i}\oint_C f(z)\,dz$$

where C is any closed curve having a in its interior and completely contained in $0 < |z - a| < r$.

(2) Since $z = a$ is a pole of order m of $f(z)$, $f(z) = (z - a)^{-m}\phi(z)$, either $\phi(a) \neq 0$, $\phi(z)$ analytic at $z = a$, or $z = a$ is a removable singular point of $\phi(z)$ such that $\lim_{z\to a} \phi(z) = 0$ (p. 259, P_1). Then $\phi(z)$ can be expanded in a Taylor series about $z = a$, valid in $0 \leq |z - a| < r$:

$$\phi(z) = \sum_{n=0}^{\infty} b_n(z - a)^n$$

$[\phi(a) = b_0$, if a is a removable singular point of $f(z)]$. Then

$$f(z) = (z - a)^{-m}\sum_{n=0}^{\infty} b_n(z - a)^n = \sum_{n=0}^{\infty} b_n(z - a)^{n-m},$$

which is the Laurent series of $f(z)$ at $z = a$, valid in $0 < |z - a| < r$. Since we can now write

$$f(z) = \frac{a_{-m}}{(z - a)^m} + \cdots + \frac{a_{-1}}{z - a} + \sum_{n=0}^{\infty} a_n(z - a)^n,$$

$$a_{-m} = b_0, \cdots, a_{-1} = b_{m-1}, a_n = b_n, n > m,$$

the result is immediate.

(3) This follows immediately from (2).

(1) indicates an alternate method of determining $\operatorname*{Res}_{z=a} f(z)$. However, if $z = a$ is a pole of $f(z)$, the methods we have considered are in general simpler for the calculation of the residue. However, if $z = a$ is an isolated essential singular point of $f(z)$, then the only general method we have available for calculating $\operatorname*{Res}_{z=a} f(z)$ is to determine a_{-1} in the Laurent series of $f(z)$ at $z = a$, valid in some deleted neighborhood of $z = a$.

EXAMPLE. Evaluate

$$\mathrm{I} = \oint_C \sin\frac{1}{z}\,dz, \qquad C: |z| = 1.$$

Solution

$$\sin\frac{1}{z} = \sum_{n=0}^{\infty} (-1)^n \frac{1}{(2n + 1)!z^{2n+1}}, \qquad |z| > 0.$$

Hence, $z = 0$ is an essential singular point of $f(z) = \sin 1/z$. $\operatorname*{Res}_{z=0} f(z) = a_{-1} = 1$ Hence, by the Cauchy residue theorem, since there are no other singular points of $f(z)$, $\mathrm{I} = 2\pi i$.

5. Analytic continuation. We defined the complex elementary functions in such a manner that they are extensions of the corresponding real elementary functions from the real axis to the complex plane. We then proved that these functions are analytic in certain open regions in the complex plane. In other words, given a real function $f(x)$ defined in $a \le x \le b$, we defined $f(z)$ in some open region D in the z-plane, including $a \le x \le b$ so that for $y = 0$, $f(z) = f(x)$ in $a \le x \le b$ and $f(z)$ is analytic in D.

The question arises as to whether we can define an analytic function $\phi(z)$ in D such that $\phi(z) = f(x)$ in $a \le x \le b$ and $\phi(z) \not\equiv f(z)$ in D; i.e., can two analytic functions assume the same values along a line segment and not be identical? From our knowledge of analytic functions and their strong binding properties, we should expect the answer to be *no*. After all, doesn't the Cauchy integral formula indicate that the values of an analytic function on the boundary of a region determine its values in the interior of that region? As a matter of fact, as our next theorem shows, once we have prescribed the values of an analytic function for a certain set of points, we cannot define its values arbitrarily elsewhere and still preserve its analyticity. We have the

IDENTITY THEOREM FOR ANALYTIC FUNCTIONS. If $f(z)$ and $g(z)$ are analytic in an open region D and if $z_1, z_2, \cdots, z_n, \cdots$ is a sequence of points converging to z_0 in D and such that $f(z_k) = g(z_k)$, $k = 1, 2, \cdots$, then $f(z) \equiv g(z)$ in D.

Proof. Let $h(z) = f(z) - g(z)$. Then $h(z)$ is analytic at z_0 and has a Taylor series:

$$h(z) = \sum_{n=0}^{\infty} a_n(z - z_0)^n$$

converging in $|z - z_0| < r$. Furthermore, $h(z_k) = 0$, $h = 1, 2, \cdots$; hence, since $h(z)$ is continuous at z_0 and $\lim_{k \to \infty} z_k = 0$, $h(z_0) = 0$; i.e., $a_0 = 0$. We now show that the remaining coefficients are zero, for suppose this were not true. Then there would exist an index m such that $a_0 = a_1 = \cdots = a_{m-1} = 0$, $a_m \ne 0$ and $h(z)$ could be written in the form $h(z) = (z - z_0)^m \phi(z)$, where $\phi(z) = a_m + a_{m+1}(z - z_0) + \cdots$, $a_m \ne 0$. Since $h(z_k) = 0$ implies $\phi(z_k) = 0$, $k = 1, 2, \cdots$, and since $\phi(z)$ is continuous at z_0, this means that $a_m = \phi(z_0) = 0$, contrary to our assumption. We have shown, therefore, that $h(z) \equiv 0$ for $|z| < r$, and this means that $f(z) \equiv g(z)$ for $N_r(z_0)$: $|z - z_0| < r$. Suppose ζ is any point in D not in $N_r(z_0)$. (If such a point does not exist, then our proof is complete.) We must show that $f(\zeta) = g(\zeta)$. Let C be any regular curve with initial point z_0 and terminal point ζ lying entirely within D. Let z_1 be a point on C such that z_1 is in $N_r(z_0)$. Then there exists a circle C_1 with center at z_1 and entirely contained in D where $f(z)$ and $g(z)$ are analytic and such that there are points in the interior of C not in $N_r(z_0)$ (see Fig. 3). Then, in the path from z_0 to z_1 on C,

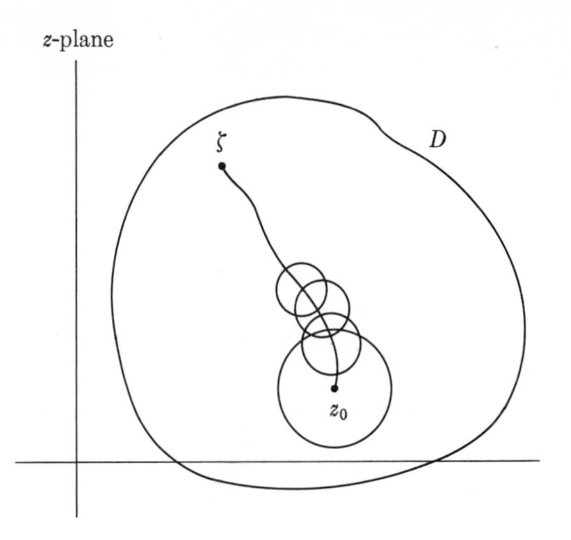

Fig. 3. Analytic continuation

there exists a sequence of points for which $f(z) = g(z)$ and such that it converges to z_1. Application of the previous argument enables us to conclude that $f(z) = g(z)$ in the interior of C_1. We repeat this process successively by considering a chain of circles $C_1, C_2, \cdots, C_k$ such that C_k has its center at ζ, and all the centers of these circles lie on C and are entirely contained in D. Now our proof is complete.

The identity theorem indicates that if a real function is defined in some interval on the real axis (a sequence of points on this interval can then be readily determined so that it converges to an end point of the interval), then its extension to an analytic function defined in some region of the complex plane is uniquely determined. We say that if I is the interval on the real axis and D is the open region in the z-plane, $f(z)$ is the **analytic continuation** of $f(x)$ from I to D or that $f(x)$ has been continued analytically from I to D.

The identity theorem has a very important application. Suppose that $f(x)$ satisfies some algebraic identity or differential equation; then does its analytic continuation into the z-plane satisfy the same identity or equation? For example, we know that $\sin^2 x = 1 - \cos^2 x$ and $d/dx \sin x = \cos x$ for all real x. Now we have proved that these relations are also valid for all complex z. However, with the identity theorem, their validity is immediate, for $\sin^2 z$ and $1 - \cos^2 z$ are two analytic functions that assume equal values on the real axis and hence are identical; similarly for $d/dx \sin z$ and $\cos z$. Therefore, to determine whether a real identity can be extended to the corresponding complex identity, it is sufficient to determine whether all the functions in the complex identity are analytic functions. This in essence is what we call the **principle of permanence of forms of functional identities.** However, this principle is often applied with the phrase, "this complex identity follows by analytic continuation."

EXAMPLE 1. Let $P(w_1, w_2, \cdots, w_n)$ be a polynomial in n variables. Let $w_k = f_k(z)$ be functions analytic in some open region D that contains $a \leq x \leq b$ on the real axis. Now if $P[f_1(x), f_2(x), \cdots, f_n(x)] = 0$ in $a \leq x \leq b$, then

$$P[f_1(z), f_2(z), \cdots, f_n(z)] = 0$$

in D.

EXAMPLE 2. Show that $e^z e^{-z} = 1$ by analytic continuation.

Solution. Since $e^0 = 1$, $e^{x-x} = 1$ or $e^x e^{-x} = 1$. Both e^z and e^{-z} are analytic everywhere, and hence we have the identity.

We now generalize the concept of analytic continuation. Let $f(z)$ be analytic in the open region D_1 and $g(z)$ analytic in the open region D_2. Now suppose D_1 and D_2 overlap; we denote the region common to D_1 and D_2 as $D_1 \cap D_2$—it is called the intersection of D_1 and D_2. If $f(z) = g(z)$ in $D_1 \cap D_2$, then we call $g(z)$ the **analytic continuation** of $f(z)$ into D_2 [or $f(z)$ the analytic continuation of $g(z)$ into D_1].

EXAMPLE. Let

$$f(z) = \sum_{n=0}^{\infty} z^n \quad \text{and} \quad g(z) = \frac{1}{1-z}.$$

Now $f(z)$ is analytic in D_1: $|z| < 1$ and $g(z)$ is analytic in D_2: all $z \neq 1$. D_1 is contained in D_2. $g(z)$ is the analytic continuation of $f(z)$ into D_1.

If the analytic continuation of a function exists, then it is uniquely determined; this follows immediately by the identity theorem.

Now suppose that the analytic function $f(z)$ has a representation that is valid only in some region D. For example, if this representation is its Taylor series about $z = a$, and $f(z)$ has singular points, then this representation is valid only in the interior of a circle with center at a and radius equal to the distance from a to the nearest singular point; in the exterior of this circle, the series is divergent. Given such a representation of $f(z)$, if its analytic continuation exists from D into another region in the complex plane, how do we determine it? This may be done in various ways, but we shall consider only the power series method, which is the standard method. This method is justified in being called standard because it can be proved that all the values of a function obtained by any other method of analytic continuation can also be obtained by means of power series.

We proceed as follows: Let z_0 be any point in D, the region of analyticity of $f(z)$. Let ζ_0 be any point not in D and let C be a regular curve with initial point z_0 and terminal point ζ_0. Since $f(z)$ is analytic in D, there exists $r > 0$ such that the Taylor series of $f(z)$ is valid in the interior of

C_1: $|z - z_0| = r$. This region contains a part of C. Now let z_1 be a point on C and in the interior of C_1. Since $f(z)$ is analytic at z_1, there exists r_2 such that the Taylor series of $f(z)$ is valid in the interior of C_2: $|z - z_1| = r_2$. We continue in this fashion by forming a chain of circles $C_1, C_2, \cdots$, which will ultimately contain ζ_0 in one of its interiors, provided $f(z)$ has no singular points on C. If C has a singular point of $f(z)$, then we consider another curve. There is the possibility, however, that no analytic continuation exists; for example, $f(z)$ may be represented by a Taylor series such that every point on the circle of convergence is a singular point of $f(z)$ and every curve from a point in the interior of such a circle to a point in the exterior will always have a singular point of $f(z)$ on it. Such a circle of convergence is called a **natural boundary.**

Any analytic continuation of $f(z)$ is called a **function element** and the totality of these function elements is called a **complete analytic function.** Such a characterization of a function leads to a unified treatment of analytic functions; the student may wish to consult Ahlfors, *Complex Analysis*, chapter vi.

EXERCISES

1. Using the Taylor series of the appropriate function, determine the Laurent series of each of the following functions at the given point, valid in the given region:

(a) $\sin \frac{1}{z^2}$, $z = 0$, $|z| > 0$; (b) $\cos \frac{1}{z-1}$, $z = 1$, $|z - 1| > 0$;

(c) $\frac{1}{z^2(z-1)^2}$, $z = 0$, $0 < |z| < 1$;

(d) $\frac{(z-1)^2}{z(z-2)}$, $z = 1$, $|z - 1| > 1$; $\left(\textit{Hint: } \frac{(z-1)^2}{z(z-2)} = \frac{1}{1 - [1/(z-1)^2]}\right)$.

(e) $\operatorname{Tan}^{-1} \frac{1}{z}$, $z = 0$, $|z| > 0$.

Ans.: (a) $\sum_{n=0}^{\infty} \frac{(-1)^n}{z^{2n+1}(2n+1)!}$;

(c) $\sum_{n=0}^{\infty} (n+1)z^{n-2}$.

2. Determine the Laurent series of each of the following functions at the given point, valid in the given region, by making use of the theorem on operations for Laurent series:

(a) $\frac{\sinh z}{z^2}$, $z = 0$, $|z| > 0$; (b) $\frac{z-1}{z^2}$, $z = 0$, $|z| > 0$;

(c) $\frac{z^2}{z-1}$, $z = 1$, $|z - 1| > 1$; (d) $\frac{1}{z(1+z^2)}$, $z = 0$, $|z| > 1$;

(e) $\csc z$, $z = 0$, $0 < |z| < \pi$; (f) $\frac{e^z}{z(z^2+1)}$, $z = 0$, $0 < |z| < 1$;

(g) $\dfrac{1}{ze^{z-1}}$, $z = 0$, $|z| > 0$; (h) $\dfrac{1 - \cos z}{z}$, $z = 0$, $|z| > 0$;

(i) $\left(\dfrac{1}{z^2} + \dfrac{1}{z}\right) e^z$, $z = 0$, $|z| > 0$; (j) $\cos \dfrac{1}{z} + \cos z - 1$, $z = 0$, $|z| > 0$;

(k) $\dfrac{1}{(z - b)^m}$, $z = b$, $|z| > b$, $m > 1$; (l) $\cot z$, $z = 0$, $0 < |z| < \pi$;

(m) $\cot z \csc z$, $z = 0$, $0 < |z| < \pi$.

Ans.: (b) $\dfrac{1}{z} - \dfrac{1}{z^2}$; (c) $z - 1 + 2 + \dfrac{1}{z - 1}$; (d) $\displaystyle\sum_{n=0}^{\infty} \frac{(-1)^n}{z^{2n+3}}$;

(e) $\dfrac{1}{z} - \dfrac{z^2}{3!} + \cdots$; (f) $\dfrac{1}{z} + 1 - z + \dfrac{1}{2} z^3 + \cdots$; (g) $e \displaystyle\sum_{n=0}^{\infty} \frac{(-1)^n z^{n-1}}{n!}$;

(k) $1 + b^m \displaystyle\sum_{n=0}^{\infty} \frac{m(m+1)\cdots(m+n-1)}{z^{2m}}$.

3. Determine all the Laurent series at the singular points of each of the following functions, each valid in the largest possible annulus, specifying this annulus in each case:

(a) $\dfrac{1}{z(1 + z^2)}$; (b) $\dfrac{z^3 - 1}{z^2}$; (c) $\dfrac{1}{(z^2 + 1)(z - 2)}$;

(d) $\dfrac{1}{z^2(z - 1)(z + 2)}$; (e) $\dfrac{3z + 1}{z^2 - 1}$; (f) $\dfrac{1}{z(z - 1)(z - 2)}$;

(g) $\dfrac{z^2 - 1}{(z + 2)(z + 3)}$; (h) $\dfrac{\csc (\pi/2)z}{z^2 + 2iz - 5}$; (i) $\dfrac{z}{2z^2 - z - 1}$;

(j) $\dfrac{e^z}{z - 1}$; (k) $e^z + e^{1/z}$.

4. Use Exercises 2 and 3 to evaluate the following:

(a) $\displaystyle\oint_C \frac{dz}{z(1 + z^2)}$, C: $|z| = 2$;

(b) $\displaystyle\oint_C \frac{(3z + 1)\, dz}{z^2 - 1}$, C: triangle with vertices at $-1 + i$, $5 + 7i$, $1 - 3i$;

(c) $\displaystyle\oint_C \frac{dz}{e^z - 1}$, C: $|z| = 1$; (d) $\displaystyle\oint_C \frac{z\, dz}{2z^2 - z - 1}$, C: $|z| = 2$;

(e) $\displaystyle\oint_C (e^z + e^{1/z})\, dz$, C: $|z| = 1$. *Ans.:* (a) 0; (b) $4\pi i$; (c) $2\pi i$; (d) πi; (e) $2\pi i$.

5. Show that $\displaystyle\operatorname*{Res}_{z=0} e^{z+(1/z)} = \sum_{n=0}^{\infty} \frac{1}{n!(n+1)!}$.

6. Show that

$$\cosh\left(z + \frac{1}{z}\right) = a_0 + \sum_{n=1}^{\infty} a_n\left(z^n + \frac{1}{z^n}\right),$$

where

$$a_n = \frac{1}{2\pi} \int_0^{2\pi} \cos n\theta \cosh (2 \cos \theta) \, d\theta.$$

7. (a) What is the characteristic of the Laurent series of $f(z)$ at ∞ if ∞ is a pole? An essential singular point?

(b) Show that ∞ is an essential singular point of e^z and $\sin z$, and determine the residue of each of these functions at ∞.

8. Prove:

(a) If $f(z)$ has no singular points in the complex plane and a pole of order m at infinity, then $f(z)$ is a polynomial of degree m. (*Hint:* $f(1/z)$ has a pole of order m at $z = 0$ and the principal part of its Laurent expansion at this point is of the form $\mathrm{P}(1/z) = (b_1/z) + (b_2/z^2) + \cdots + (b_m/z^n)$, $\quad b_m \neq 0$. Define

$$g\left(\frac{1}{z}\right) = f\left(\frac{1}{z}\right) - \mathrm{P}\left(\frac{1}{z}\right), \quad z \neq 0, \quad \text{and} \quad g\left(\frac{1}{z}\right) = b_0, \qquad \text{for } z = 0.$$

Show that $g(1/z)$ is analytic at $z = 0$ and hence $g(z)$ is analytic at ∞. Also show that $g(z)$ is analytic at every point in the complex plane. Hence, $g(z) = b_0$ (constant) (p. 256, Exercise 31). But $f(z) = g(z) + \mathrm{P}(z)$, and the result is immediate.

(b) If $f(z)$ has no essential singular points in the extended plane, then $f(z)$ is a rational function.

Hint: Show that $f(z)$ can have only a finite number of poles, for if it had an infinite number, the limit point of this set would be an essential singular point. Denote these poles by $a_1, a_2, \cdots, a_r$, and the principal part of the Laurent expansion at each of these poles by

$$\mathrm{P}_j(z) = \frac{a_{-1j}}{z - a_j} + \frac{a_{-2j}}{(z - a_j)^2} + \cdots + \frac{a_{-m_jj}}{(z - a_j)^{m_j}}, \qquad j = 1, 2, \cdots, r.$$

If $z = \infty$ is a pole, write its principal part as $\mathrm{P}_0(z) = b_1 z + b_2 z^2 + \cdots + b_{m_0} z^{m_0}$; if $z = \infty$ is not a pole, then $\mathrm{P}_0(z) = 0$. Let

$$g(z) = f(z) - \sum_{j=0}^{r} \mathrm{P}_j(z), \qquad z \neq a_j,$$

and at $z = a_j$, $g(z) = \infty$, the limit of the right-hand side as z approaches these points. Show that $g(z)$ is analytic in the extended plane.

(c) If $f(z)$ has poles $a_1, a_2, \cdots, a_r$ of order $p_1, p_2, \cdots, p_r$ and zeros $b_1, b_2, \cdots, b_s$ of order $q_1, q_2, \cdots, q_s$,

$$f(z) = C \frac{(z - b_1)^{q_1}(z - b_2)^{q_2} \cdots (z - b_s)^{q_s}}{(z - a_1)^{p_1}(z - a_2)^{p_2} \cdots (z - a_r)^{p_r}},$$

where C is a constant.

(d) If $f(z)$ is a rational function, in the extended complex plane, the number of its zeros (a zero of multiplicity k counted k times) is equal to the number of its poles (a pole of multiplicity m counted m times). This number is called the **degree of the rational function.**

(e) If $f(z)$ has a simple pole at $z = 2i$ and at $z = -2i$ and no other singular points in the extended plane, and if $z = 1$ and $z = 3$ are its simple zeros, and $f(\infty) = 4$, then

$$f(z) = \frac{4(z^2 - 4z + 3)}{z^2 + 4}.$$

(f) If $f(z)$ has a simple pole at $z = 2$ with residue 5 and a pole of order 2 at $z = 0$ with principal part $(4/z^2) - (3/z)$, no other singular points in the extended plane, and $f(\infty) = 0$, then

$$f(z) = \frac{2(z^2 + 5z - 4)}{z^2(z-2)}.$$

(g) (**Partial fractions theorem**). If $f(z)$ is a rational function with poles at $a_1, a_2, \cdots, a_r$ of order $m_1, m_2, \cdots, m_r$, then

$$f(z) = \text{polynomial} + \sum_{j=1}^{\infty} \frac{A_{m_j}}{(z - a_j)^{m_j}}.$$

9. Show that

$$e^{(z/2)[t-(1/t)]} = \sum_{n=-\infty}^{\infty} J_n(z)t^n,$$

where

$$J_n(z) = \frac{1}{\pi}\int_0^{\pi} \cos\,(n\theta - z\sin\theta)\,d\theta.$$

Also show that

$$J_n(z) = \sum_{k=0}^{\infty} \frac{(-1)^k (z/2)^{n+2k}}{k!(n+k)!}.$$

$J_n(z)$ is the **Bessel function of order** $\boldsymbol{n}$.

10. If $f(z)$ is analytic in $r < |z| < 1/r$, where it satisfies the relation $f(1/z) = \overline{f(z)}$, and a_n, $n = \cdots -1, 0, 1, \cdots$ are the coefficients of its Laurent series about $z = 0$, show that $a_{-n} = \bar{a}_n$.

11. Prove, by analytic continuation, assuming the identities to be true when the variables are real:

(a) $\dfrac{d}{dz} e^z = e^z$.

(b) $e^{z_1+z_2} = e^{z_1}e^{z_2}$.

(c) $\sin\,(z_1 + z_2) = \sin z_1 \cos z_2 + \cos z_1 \sin z_2$.

(*Hint:* In (b) and (c), prove the identity first with z_1 real and z_2 complex by analytic continuation on z_2, and then prove it with z_1 and z_2 complex by analytic continuation on z_1).

12. Show that if b is real,

$$\frac{1}{2}\,\text{Log}\,(1 + b^2) + i\tan^{-1} b + \frac{z - ib}{1 + ib} - \frac{1}{2}\left(\frac{z - ib}{1 + ib}\right)^2 + \frac{1}{3}\left(\frac{z - ib}{1 + ib}\right)^3 - \cdots$$

is an analytic continuation of

$$f(z) = \sum_{n=1}^{\infty} \frac{(-1)^{n-1} z^n}{n}.$$

13. Show that

$$f(z) = \sum_{n=1}^{\infty} \frac{z^n}{n} \quad \text{and} \quad g(z) = i\pi + \sum_{n=1}^{\infty} (-1)^n \frac{(z-2)^n}{n}$$

have no common region of convergence, but that they are the analytic continuations of the same function.

14. Show that $|z| = 1$ is a natural boundary of

$$f(z) = z + \sum_{n=1}^{\infty} z^{2^n}, \qquad |z| < 1.$$

(*Hint:* Let S be the sum of the series and let r be any real number. Show that for any real number M there exists a $\delta > 0$ such that when $|r - 1| < \delta$, $|S| > M$. Hence, r cannot be in any analytic continuation of $f(z)$ that contains 1. By showing that $f(z) = z + f(z^2)$, show that this is also true for any point on $|z| = 1$.)

15. Prove the **principle of reflection** (or symmetry principle). If $f(z)$ is analytic in a closed region R_1 in the upper half-plane containing an interval (a, b) of the real axis as part of its boundary, such that $f(z)$ is real and continuous on (a, b), and if R_2 is the region in the lower half-plane that is the reflection of R_1 about the real axis, so that if z is in R_1, $\bar{z}$ is in R_2, then $\overline{f(\bar{z})}$ is the analytic continuation of $f(z)$ from R_1 to R_2. (*Hint:* Show by the Cauchy-Riemann criterion that $\overline{f(\bar{z})}$ is analytic in R_2.)

Chapter 10

Conformal Mapping

1. Transformations. We have interpreted the continuous function $w = f(z)$ geometrically as a mapping of a part of the z-plane into a part of the w-plane. Hence, a given region D in the z-plane is mapped into a region D' in the w-plane and a curve C in the z-plane is mapped into a curve C$'$ in the w-plane by the function $f(z)$, continuous on D and C. D' and C$'$ are called the maps (or images) of D and C under $w = f(z)$.

Given $w = f(z)$ continuous on a curve C or region D in the z-plane, our problem hitherto has been to determine the maps of C and D under $f(z)$ in order to study the nature of $f(z)$. However, a problem of fundamental importance is to determine a function $w = f(z)$ that will map a given region D in the z-plane into a given region D' in the w-plane. In general, this is a more difficult problem. It arises in the following situation: Suppose that we are interested in certain properties of a given region D in the z-plane, but that the nature of D makes the study of these properties difficult. Then it is worth while considering the possibility of mapping or transforming the region D into the region D' in such a way that these properties are preserved and are easier to study in D' than they are in D. We now turn to this problem.

Our concern will be with transformations of one region into another region that are effected by complex functions. We actually will call $w = f(z)$ a **mapping** or **transformation,** and although we use these terms equivalently, the term mapping is usually reserved for geometric considerations, whereas the term transformation often conveys a more general meaning. Let us make it clear at the outset that when we refer to the transformation

$w = f(z)$, we mean the transformation of a part of the z-plane that is contained in the domain of definition of $f(z)$. Our study of transformations is twofold: (1) the determination of the properties of a given part of the z-plane which are preserved or remain invariant under a given transformation; and (2) the determination of a transformation that will map a given region into another given region.

If we were to consider *any* transformation $w = f(z)$ of a region D in the z-plane, we could hardly expect a given property of D to remain invariant under this transformation. It is only when we impose certain conditions on the transformations or restrict them to a certain class that we obtain significant invariants of the transformations. We have already considered continuous functions, which we shall now call continuous transformations. We have seen that under a continuous transformation, a curve is mapped into a curve, or that a curve is invariant under such a transformation. Other invariants of continuous transformations are regions, interior points of regions, boundaries of regions, and simply connected regions. However, a simple curve is not an invariant of all continuous transformations. Furthermore, although a continuous transformation maps a region D into a region D', D' may overlap a part of itself if there exist points in D', each of which is the image of several points in D.

In order that continuous transformations have simple curves and non-overlapping regions as invariants, we must restrict our class of continuous transformations further by considering the class of univalent transformations. A **univalent transformation** is a continuous transformation that transforms a region D into a region D' in a one-to-one manner; i.e., every point in D is mapped into one and only one point in D', and every point in D' is the image of one and only one point in D. (Univalent transformations are often called **schlicht** transformations, "schlicht" being the German word for smooth.) For example, $w = z^2$ is a univalent transformation in the first quadrant of the z-plane, for it maps this quadrant into the upper half of the w-plane in a one-to-one fashion, since $z = \sqrt{w}$ has only one value of z in the first quadrant of the z-plane for every value of w in the upper half of the w-plane. However, $w = z^2$ is not a univalent transformation in the entire z-plane. This example suggests a

Criterion for Univalence. The transformation $w = f(z)$ maps D univalently into D' if its inverse transformation $z = f^{-1}(w)$ exists and is single-valued in D'.

(For other criteria for univalence, see Kaplan, *Advanced Calculus*, p. 581.)

We have considered some of the invariants of continuous transformations and of univalent transformations. However, as we shall soon see, it is the class of univalent transformations that are analytic functions which yields some very significant invariants. In view of the wealth of properties of analytic functions, this should come as no surprise.

2. Conformal mapping. Let C_1 and C_2 be any two regular curves in the z-plane that intersect at the point z_0, and let T_1 and T_2 be the lines tangent to C_1 and C_2 at z_0. We then define the angle from C_1 to C_2 as the angle from T_1 to T_2, and we denote this angle as $\angle(C_1, C_2)$. Now let $w = f(z)$ be a transformation defined in an open region D and let z_0 be any point in D. If C_1 and C_2 are any two regular curves that intersect at z_0 and C_1' and C_2' are their maps under $w = f(z)$ and $\angle(C_1, C_2) = \angle(C_1', C_2')$, then we call $w = f(z)$ a **conformal transformation** or **conformal mapping** in D. In other words, a conformal mapping is one in which the angle between any two curves intersecting at a point is invariant. If $\angle(C_1, C_2) = \angle(C_1', C_2')$ or $\angle(C_1, C_2) = \angle(C_2', C_1')$ under a given transformation, then we say that transformation is **isogonal.** In other words, if a transformation leaves invariant the magnitude of the angle between two curves intersecting at a point, it is isogonal; if it preserves both the magnitude and direction of the angle, it is conformal. The student should show that $w = \bar{z}$ is isogonal but not conformal in the z-plane. A sufficient condition that a transformation be conformal is given in the

THEOREM. If $w = f(z)$ is univalent and analytic in an open region D and $f'(z) \neq 0$ in D, then $w = f(z)$ is conformal in D.

Proof. Let z_0 be any point in D and let C be any regular curve passing through z_0 whose map under $f(z)$ is C' so that $w_0 = f(z_0)$ is on C'. Now let z be any other point on C contained in D. Then

$$w - w_0 = f(z) - f(z_0) = \frac{f(z) - f(z_0)}{z - z_0} \cdot (z - z_0)$$

and

$$\arg(w - w_0) = \arg \frac{f(z) - f(z_0)}{z - z_0} + \arg(z - z_0).$$

Now as $z \to z_0$ along C, $w \to w_0$ along C' (see Fig. 1), $\arg(z - z_0) \to \alpha$, which is the angle from the positive x-axis to the tangent line to C at z_0, measured counterclockwise, $\arg(w - w_0) \to \beta$, which is the angle from the positive u-axis to the tangent line to C' at w_0, measured counterclockwise, and

$$\arg \frac{f(z) - f(z_0)}{z - z_0} \to \arg f'(z_0)$$

which is defined, since $f'(z_0) \neq 0$.

Hence $\beta = \arg f'(z_0) + \alpha$. (***Note:*** If the unit vector tangents to C and C' at z_0 are expressed by the complex numbers u and u', then this equation can be written as $\arg u' = \arg f'(z_0) + \arg u$.)

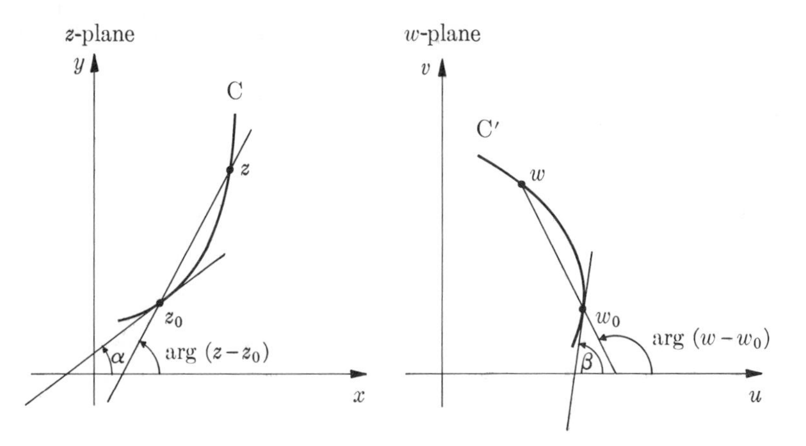

Fig. 1. Map of an angle

Now let C_1 and C_2 be regular curves passing through z_0 with maps C_1' and C_2'. If α_1 and α_2 are the angles from the positive x-axis to the tangent lines to C_1 and C_2 at z_0 and β_1 and β_2 are the angles from the positive u-axis to the tangent lines to C_1' and C_2' at w_0, all angles measured counterclockwise, then $\beta_1 = \arg f'(z_0) + \alpha_1$ and $\beta_2 = \arg f'(z_0) + \alpha_2$. Subtraction yields $\alpha_2 - \alpha_1 = \beta_2 - \beta_1$ or $\angle(C_1, C_2) = \angle(C_1', C_2')$. (See Fig. 2.)

If $f'(z_0) = 0$, the result does not follow, as is illustrated by $w = z^2$ and $z_0 = 0$; for the angle between the lines, $\theta = 0$, and $\theta = \pi/4$ in the z-plane is $\pi/4$, and these lines are mapped into the u and v axes and the angle between these lines is a right angle. A point z_0 where $f'(z_0) = 0$ is called a **critical point** of the transformation $w = f(z)$. For critical points, we have the following

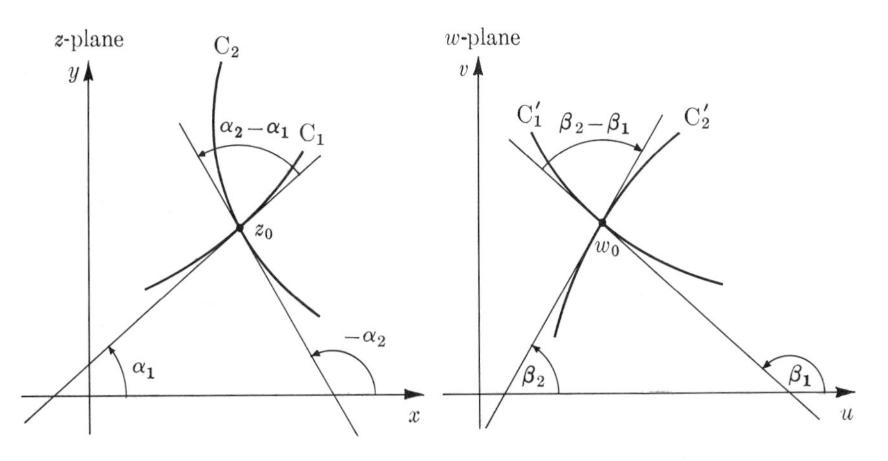

Fig. 2. Preservation of angles

THEOREM. If $w = f(z)$ is univalent and analytic in an open region D, the point z_0 in D is a zero of order m of $f'(z)$, and if C_1 and C_2 are two regular curves intersecting at z_0 with maps C_1' and C_2', then $\angle(C_1', C_2') = (m + 1)\angle(C_1, C_2)$.

Proof. Since z_0 is a zero of order m of $f'(z)$, $f'(z_0) = f''(z_0) = \cdots = f^{(m)}(z_0) = 0$, $f^{(m+1)}(z_0) \neq 0$, and the Taylor expansion of $f(z)$ about $z = z_0$ is $f(z) = f(z_0) + a_{m+1}(z - z_0)^{m+1} + a_{m+2}(z - z_0)^{m+2} + \cdots$, $m \geq 1$, $a_{m+1} \neq 0$. Hence $f(z) - f(z_0) = (z - z_0)^{m+1}g(z)$, where $g(z)$ is analytic at z_0 and $g(z_0) \neq 0$. Now $\arg(w - w_0) = \arg[f(z) - f(z_0)] = (m - 1)\arg(z - z_0) + \arg g(z)$. The proof is now completed, as in the previous theorem; the student should supply the details.

We illustrate the preceding theorem by considering $w = z^4$, which maps the positive x-axis C_1 into the positive u-axis C_1' and C_2: $\theta = \pi/2$ into C_2': $\phi = 2\pi$, so that $\angle(C_1', C_2') = 4\angle(C_1, C_2)$, since $z = 0$ is a zero of order 3 of $4z^3$.

We have seen that a sufficient condition for a univalent transformation without critical points to be conformal is that it be analytic. Under further hypotheses, this condition is also necessary, as is indicated in the following

THEOREM. Let $f(z) = u(x, y) + iv(x, y)$, the first partial derivatives of u and v being continuous in an open region D, and let the Jacobian $\dfrac{\partial(u, v)}{\partial(x, y)} \neq 0$ and $f'(z) \neq 0$ in D. If $f(z)$ is a conformal transformation in D, then $f(z)$ is analytic in D.

The proof of this theorem can be found in Nehari, *Conformal Mapping*, pp. 150–152.

We can now say that a univalent transformation without critical points and with nonvanishing Jacobian is conformal in an open region if and only if it is analytic there. Hence, in a certain sense, analyticity and conformality are equivalent.

A fundamental problem in applied mathematics is the following: Given a simply connected region D bounded by a closed regular curve C, to determine the function $H(x, y)$, which is harmonic in D and assumes prescribed values on C. This is known as the **Dirichlet problem.** It is always possible to determine a function that is analytic in D; its real and imaginary parts then afford two harmonic functions in D. However, it is usually not a simple matter to determine such a function so that either its real or imaginary part assumes prescribed values on C; this may be due to the nature of D. We shall be concerned only with the special case in which C is divided into a finite number of parts and where the harmonic function we are seeking is a constant in each of these parts.

Now suppose that D is transformed into a region D' and C into a curve C′ under $w = f(z)$, and say that this is accomplished in such a manner that we can readily determine a function $G(u, v)$ harmonic in D' and such that $G(u, v) =$ constant on C′. Let us now consider the inverse transformation $z = f^{-1}(w) = x(u, v) + iy(u, v)$, which transforms $G(u, v)$ into a function $H(x, y)$ such that $H(x, y) =$ constant on C′. If $H(x, y)$ is harmonic in D, then the problem is solved. The next theorem shows that $H(x, y)$ is harmonic in D if the mapping $z = f^{-1}(w)$ is conformal and $dz/dw \neq 0$. However, the inverse of a conformal transformation is conformal. (Why?) Therefore, we shall state the theorem in the following form:

THEOREM. If $H(x, y)$ is harmonic in a region D and $w = f(z) = u + iv$ is univalent and analytic in D, $f'(z) \neq 0$ in D, then

$$G(u, v) = H[x(u, v), y(u, v)]$$

is harmonic in D', the map of D under $w = f(z)$.

Proof. The harmonic function $H(x, y)$ determines a conjugate harmonic function $h(x, y)$ so that $H + ih = F(z)$ is analytic in D. Now $w = f(z)$ is analytic in D so that $z = f^{-1}(w)$ is analytic in D'. Then $F[f^{-1}(w)]$ is analytic in D', which implies that its real part is harmonic. But this real part is $G(u, v)$.

This theorem implies that harmonicity is invariant under a univalent transformation that is analytic and free of critical points.

EXAMPLE. Show that $\tan^{-1}(\tanh y/\tan x)$ is harmonic in $0 < x < \pi/2$, $y \geq 0$.

Solution. $\arg w = \text{Im Log } w$, and hence is harmonic for all w except for $\text{Re } w \leq 0$, $\text{Im } w = 0$. Let $w = \sin z$. Then $dw/dz = \cos z$ is not zero for

$$0 < \text{Re } z < \frac{\pi}{2}.$$

Hence, $\sin z$ is univalent, analytic, and free of critical points in $0 < \text{Re } z < \pi/2$, $y \geq 0$. Therefore, by the invariance of harmonicity, $\arg \sin z$ is harmonic in $0 < \text{Re } z < \pi/2$, $y \geq 0$. But $\arg \sin z = \tan^{-1}(\tanh y/\tan x)$.

In the example given above we have made use of the invariance of harmonicity to establish that a given function is harmonic.Thus we have avoided a lengthy computation of second partial derivatives merely by starting with a simple well-known harmonic function and then making the appropriate transformation. This is one practical use of the theorem on the invariance of harmonicity. Its most practical use, however, arises in the solution of the Dirichlet problem. Here we wish to determine a function harmonic in a given region with prescribed values on the boundary of the region. This leads us to the second phase in our study of transformations: the determination of a transformation that maps a given region into another given region. Of course, if it is the Dirichlet problem that we wish to solve, then it is a conformal transformation that we seek, since harmonicity is invariant under such a transformation.

Now the question arises: Given two regions D and D', how do we know that there exists a conformal transformation that maps D into D'? After all, we should like to be assured of the existence of such a transformation; otherwise, we might be seeking something that does not exist. If such a transformation exists, we say that D and D' are conformally equivalent. The answer to the question is given in the

> **RIEMANN MAPPING THEOREM.** If D and D' are two simply connected open regions that do not overlap themselves and such that they have more than one boundary point, then there exists a conformal transformation under which D and D' are conformally equivalent.

This is the fundamental theorem of conformal mapping, a proof of which may be found in Nehari, *Conformal Mapping*, p. 175. Although the Riemann mapping theorem assures us of the existence of a conformal transformation that makes two given regions conformally equivalent under prescribed conditions, it in no way indicates how such a transformation can be determined. In general, this is a difficult problem and can be practically solved only for rather simple transformations.

The Poisson formula, p. 248, is a representation of a harmonic function in a circular region with prescribed values on the boundary; hence, this formula gives a solution to the Dirichlet problem for a circular region. A corresponding Poisson formula for a half-plane can be established. Now suppose we wish to solve the Dirichlet problem for a given region D. Our problem is reduced to the determination of a conformal transformation $w = f(z)$ that maps D into a circular region or a half-plane, evaluating Poisson's formula, and then recovering the required harmonic function with the use of $z = f^{-1}(w)$.

Therefore, the Dirichlet problem for any region can be solved by transforming this region into the region bounded by the unit circle, called the **unit disk,** or into a half-plane—these regions are called **canonical regions.** However, what appears to be a simple procedure is marred by the fact that the evaluation of the Poisson formula very often presents difficulties. An alternate approach is considered in Sokolnikoff and Redheffer, *Mathematics of Physics and Modern Engineering*, p. 595.

We now turn to the problem of the determination of a conformal transformation that makes two given regions conformally equivalent. The solution to this problem can be achieved practically only if we consider particular classes of conformal transformations. However, we have one more general result, which indicates that the conformal mapping of D into D' can be achieved merely by a consideration of the mapping of the boundary of D into the boundary of D'.

THEOREM. If (1) D is a region whose boundary C is a closed regular curve; (2) $w = f(z)$ is a function analytic on D and C; (3) $w = f(z)$ maps C into a closed regular curve C′ in such a way that C′ is described by w once in the positive sense if z traverses C in the positive sense, then $w = f(z)$ maps D into the region D', which is the region that remains to our left as we traverse C′.

Proof. The number of times a value w_0 is taken by $f(z)$ is given by

$$N = \frac{1}{2\pi i} \oint_C \frac{f'(z)\,dz}{f(z) - w_0},$$

provided $f(z) \neq w_0$ on C (p. 287). Substituting $w = f(z)$, $dw = f'(z)\,dz$, we have

$$N = \frac{1}{2\pi i} \oint_{C'} \frac{dw}{w - w_0}.$$

By the Cauchy residue theorem, $N = 1$ if w_0 is a point in the interior of C′, and $N = 0$ if w_0 is in the exterior of C′. Hence, every value in D' is taken exactly once by $w = f(z)$, and values in the exterior of C′ are not taken at all. The image of a point z_0 in D cannot occur on C′, for if it did, $f(z)$ would take all values in a neighborhood of $f(z_0)$, and such a neighborhood includes points in the exterior of C′ where, as we have seen, $f(z)$ takes no values.

The preceding theorem extends readily to unbounded regions whose boundaries consist of regular curves.

EXAMPLE. Determine the region into which $|z - 1| < 1$ is mapped by $w = 1/z$.

Solution. Let C: $|z - 1| = 1$. It is readily seen that the map of C under $w = 1/z$ is C′: $\operatorname{Re} w = \frac{1}{2}$. As z moves in a positive direction along C from $z = 2$ to $z = 0$, w moves along C′ from $w = \frac{1}{2}$ to $w = \infty$, so that $\operatorname{Im} w < 0$, and as z

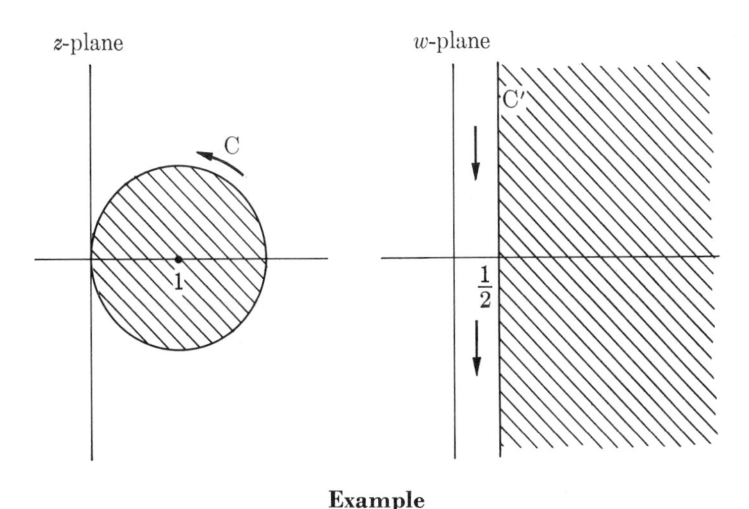

Example

moves from $z = 0$ to $z = 2$ along C in a positive direction, w moves along C′ from $w = \infty$ to $w = \frac{1}{2}$, $\operatorname{Im} w > 0$. Hence, $|z - 1| < 1$ is mapped into $\operatorname{Re} w > \frac{1}{2}$ as illustrated in the figure.

EXERCISES

1. Determine the critical points of the following transformations and the magnification of the angles whose vertices are these points. Determine the regions of conformality.

(a) $w = z^2(z-1)^3$; (b) $w = \sin z$; (c) $w = z + \dfrac{1}{z}$;

(d) $w = \dfrac{z}{1+z}$; (e) $w = \sqrt{z}$; (f) $w = \cosh z$; (g) $w = \operatorname{Log} \dfrac{1-z}{1+z}$;

(h) $w = e^z \cos z$.

2. (a) Show that if $f(z) = u(x, y) + iv(x, y)$ is conformal, then $u(x, y) =$ constant and $v(x, y) =$ constant cut orthogonally at all points of intersection.

(b) If $f(z) = 2x^2 + y^2 + (iy^2/x)$, show that $2x^2 + y^2 = k_1$ and $y^2/x = k_2$ (k_1 and k_2 constants) cut orthogonally, but that $f(z)$ is nowhere conformal. Conclusion? (*Hint:* Determine the slopes of the curves at the points of intersection.)

3. (a) Show that $f(z) = u(x, y) + iv(x, y)$ is univalent in D if $u(x, y) = k_1$ and $v(x, y) = k_2$, for any given constants k_1 and k_2, intersect at most once in D.

(b) Show that $f(z) = x^3 + 4xy^2 + i(x^2y + 4y^3)$ is univalent in the z-plane.

(c) Show that $f(z)$ is conformal at $z = 0$ but $f'(0) = 0$. (Conclusion?)

4. Show that each of the following is univalent in the given region:

(a) $w = \dfrac{1}{z}$, $\operatorname{Re} z > 0$; (b) $w = z + \dfrac{1}{z}$, $\operatorname{Im} z > 0$;

(c) $w = z - \dfrac{1}{z}$, $|z| > 1$; (d) $w = \dfrac{z-i}{z+i}$, $|z| < 1$;

(e) $w = \sqrt{z}$, $z = re^{i\theta}$, $-\pi < \theta < \pi$; (f) $w = \operatorname{Log} z$, $\operatorname{Im} z > 0$;

(g) $w = \operatorname{Log} \dfrac{z-1}{z+1}$, $\operatorname{Im} z > 0$; (h) $w = \operatorname{Log} \dfrac{z}{z+1} - 2 \operatorname{Log} z$, $\operatorname{Im} z > 0$.

5. (a) If $w = f(z)$ is analytic at $z = z_0$, $f'(z_0) \neq 0$, L is the length of a short smooth arc with terminal point z_0, L' is its map under $w = f(z)$, show that

$$\lim_{L \to \infty} \frac{L'}{L} = |f'(z_0)|$$

and hence, approximately, $L' = L|f'(z_0)|$. This means that the infinitesimal length L is magnified by the factor $|f'(z_0)|$.

(b) Determine the length of the map of $|z| = a$, $\operatorname{Im} z > 0$, under the transformation $w = 1/z$.

(c) Determine the locus of points for which the magnification factor is one under the transformation $w = 3z - z^3$. *Ans.:* (b) π/a; (c) $|1 - z^2| = 1/3$.

6. (a) If $w = f(z) = u + iv$ maps D conformally on to D', show that the area of D' is $\iint_D |f'(z)|^2\, dx\, dy$. Show that

$$|f'(z)|^2 = \begin{vmatrix} \dfrac{\partial u}{\partial x} & \dfrac{\partial u}{\partial y} \\ \dfrac{\partial v}{\partial x} & \dfrac{\partial v}{\partial y} \end{vmatrix},$$

which is the Jacobian of the transformation.

(b) Determine the area of the map of the square with vertices at $0, 1, 1 + i, i$ under the transformation $w = z^3$. *Ans.:* 28/5.

7. (a) If $f(z)$ is analytic, show that $w = \overline{f(z)}$ and $w = f(\bar{z})$ are isogonal but not conformal.

(b) If $f(z)$ is analytic in an open region D, show that $\overline{f(\bar{z})}$ is analytic in the open region $\bar{D}$ that consists of all points z such that $\bar{z}$ is in D.

8. Show that if $\lim_{z \to \infty} z^2 f'(z) \neq 0$ or ∞, then ∞ is not a critical point of $w = f(z)$.

9. (a) Show that $c_1 \operatorname{Log} r + c_2$, c_1 and c_2 arbitrary constants, $r = \sqrt{x^2 + y^2}$, is harmonic for $r > 0$.

(b) Show that the function $H(r)$, harmonic for $0 < a < r < b$ and such that $H(a) = A$, $H(b) = B$, is

$$H(r) = \frac{(B - A) \operatorname{Log} r + A \operatorname{Log} b - B \operatorname{Log} a}{\operatorname{Log} b/a}.$$

10. (a) Show that $\arg (a - z)/(a + z)$ is harmonic in any simply connected open region that does not include $z = \pm a$ in its interior.

(b) Show that the function that is harmonic in $|z| < a$ and equals A on $|z| = a$, $\operatorname{Im} z > 0$, and B on $|z| = a$, $\operatorname{Im} z < 0$, is

$$H(x, y) = \frac{A + B}{2} + \frac{A - B}{\pi} \tan^{-1} \frac{2ay}{a^2 - x^2 - y^2},$$

where the value of the inverse tangent is in $-\pi/2 \leq \theta \leq \pi/2$.

11. Determine the maps of the following regions under the given transformation:

(a) $w = \cos z$, D: rectangle with vertices at $\pm ia$, $\pm ia + \pi$.
(b) $w = \sin z$, D: $\operatorname{Im} z > 0$, $-\pi/2 < \operatorname{Re} z < \pi/2$.
(c) $w = e^z$, D: $0 < \operatorname{Im} z < 2\pi$.
(d) $w = e^z$, D: rectangle with vertices at a, $a + ib$, c, $c + ib$.
(e) $w = 1/z$, D: $|z| < a$. (f) $w = z^2$, D: $z = e^{i\theta}$, $0 < \theta < 3\pi/4$.

(g) $w = \dfrac{i - z}{i + z}$, D: $\operatorname{Im} z > 0$. (h) $w = \dfrac{z - 1}{z + 1}$, D: $\operatorname{Re} z > 0$.

(i) $w = z + \dfrac{1}{z}$, D: $|z| > 1$, $\operatorname{Im} z > 0$.

(j) $w = \dfrac{1 - \cos z}{1 + \cos z}$, D: $0 < \operatorname{Re} z < \pi/2$.

(k) $w = \left(\frac{z+1}{z-1}\right)^2$, $D: |z| < 1$, $\text{Im } z > 0$.

(l) $w = \sqrt{z}$, D: exterior of parabola $y^2 = 4c^2(x + c^2)$.

12. Verify that the solutions of the following Dirichlet problems are the given ones:

(a) Determine $H(x, y)$, harmonic for $y > 0$;

$$H(x, 0) = \pi, \quad x < 0; \qquad H(x, 0) = 0, \quad x > 0.$$

$$H(x, y) = \tan^{-1} \frac{y}{x}, \qquad y > 0.$$

(b) Determine $H(x, y)$, harmonic for $y > 0$; $H(x, 0) = c$, constant, $x > a$, $H(x, 0) = 0$, $x < a$.

$$H(x, y) = c\left(1 - \frac{1}{\pi} \tan^{-1} \frac{x - a}{y}\right), \qquad y > 0.$$

(c) Determine $H(x, y)$, harmonic for $y > 0$, $|x| < \pi/2$,

$$H\left(-\frac{\pi}{2}, y\right) = H\left(\frac{\pi}{2}, y\right) = 0, \qquad y > 0;$$

$H(x, 0) = 1$, $|x| < \pi/2$, $H(x, y) = 2/\pi \tan^{-1} (\cos x/\sinh y)$, the inverse tangent taken in the first quadrant.

13. The problem of determining a function $H(x, y)$, harmonic in a given region and such that $\partial H/\partial n = 0$ on the boundary of the region where $\partial H/\partial \mathbf{n}$ is the directional derivative of $H(x, y)$ in the direction of the outward normal $\mathbf{n}$ to the boundary (called the *normal derivative*) is known as a **Neumann problem.**

(a) Show that under an analytic transformation $z = f(w)$, $f'(w) = 0$, the condition $\partial H/\partial \mathbf{n} = 0$ remains invariant.

(b) Show that if $H(x, y)$ is a solution of a Neumann problem, then $H(x, y) + C$ is also a solution of that problem.

(c) Show that if

$$H(x, y) = e^{-x} \cos y + 2y,$$

then

$$\partial H/\partial \mathbf{n} = 2 \text{ along } y = 0.$$

Under the transformation $z = w^2$, show that the normal derivative along the map of $y = 0$ is not constant.

14. Show that $w = \left(\frac{z+i}{z-i} + 1\right)^2$ maps the upper half of the z-plane into the interior of a cardioid.

15. Show that $w = i \sinh z$ maps D: $\text{Re } z \geq 0$, $|\text{Im } z| \leq \pi/2$, into D': $\text{Im } w \geq 0$. Show that the ratio of the area of the rectangle determined by D and $x = a$ and its map is $4a/\sinh 2a$.

3. Linear transformations. We have interpreted $w = f(z)$ geometrically as a transformation or mapping of a part of the z-plane into a part of the w-plane. However, there are some very simple functions which, as transformations, are better described if we think of them as mapping one part of the z-plane into another part of the z-plane. In these cases, the transformation is visualized physically as a motion for which such terms as translation, rotation, stretching, and shrinking become applicable. We consider the following transformations:

L_1: $w = z + b$, b a fixed complex number (translation).
L_2: $w = \alpha z$, α a fixed complex number (rotation and magnification or contraction).
L_3: $w = 1/z$ (reflection and inversion).

By L_1, if $b = \alpha + i\beta$, every point $x + iy$ is translated into a point $x + \alpha + i(y + \beta)$; circles are transformed into circles [Fig. 3(a)].

By L_2, if $\alpha = |\alpha|e^{i\omega}$ and $z = re^{i\theta}$, then $\alpha z = |\alpha|re^{i(\omega+\theta)}$ and every geometric figure will be rotated through an angle ω with a resulting magnification, if $|\alpha| > 1$, or contraction, if $|\alpha| < 1$. In particular, circles are transformed into circles [Fig. 3(b)].

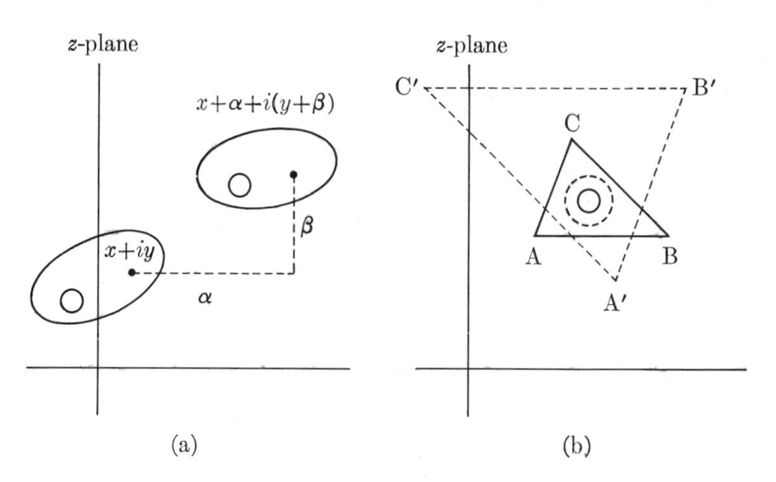

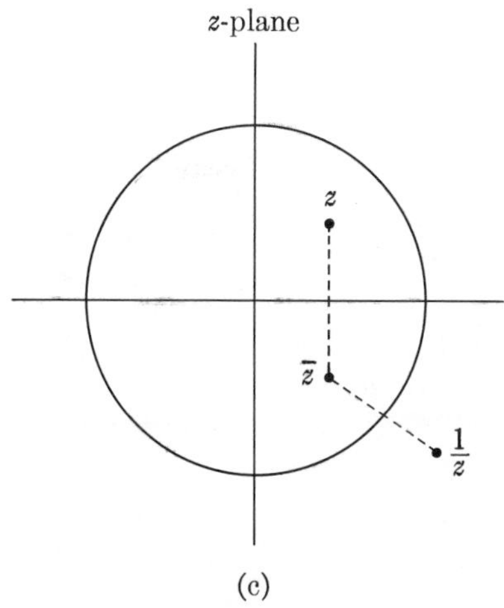

Fig. 3. Linear transformation

By L_3, a point $z = re^{i\theta}$ is transformed into $z' = (1/r)e^{-i\theta}$. This means that $\arg z' = -\arg z$, which indicates a reflection about the real axis, and $|z|\,|z'| = 1$, which indicates an inversion in the unit circle. Hence, if z is in the interior (exterior) of the unit circle, z' is in the exterior (interior) of this circle. The unit circle is invariant under this transformation. Furthermore, since the equation of the general circle is $z\bar{z} + az + az + b = 0$, $\text{Im}\, b = 0$ (p. 194, Exercise 5), and if $b \neq 0$, replacing z by $1/z$ yields $z\bar{z} + (a/b)\bar{z} + (\bar{a}/b)z + (1/b) = 0$, which is also the equation of a circle; if $b = 0$, $z\bar{z} + az + \bar{a}\bar{z} = 0$ is the equation of a circle passing through the origin, and replacing z by $1/z$ in this equation yields $a\bar{z} + \bar{a}z + 1 = 0$, which is the equation of a straight line (p. 193, Exercise 4). If we interpret straight lines as circles passing through the point at infinity, then we can say generally that L_3 transforms circles into circles.

Using the transformations L_1, L_2, L_3 successively, we can generate other transformations. The most significant of these is the transformation

$$\text{L:} \quad w = \frac{az + b}{cz + d} = \frac{a}{c} + \frac{bc - ad}{c(cz + d)}$$

where a, b, c, d are complex constants. This can be obtained as the following succession of transformations: L_2: $t_1 = cz$; L_1: $t_2 = t_1 + d$; L_3: $t_3 = 1/t_2$; L_2: $t_4 = [(bc - ad)/c]t_3$; L_1: $w = t_4 + (a/c)$. In L, we assume that $bc - ad \neq 0$, for $bc - ad = 0$ yields the uninteresting transformation that maps the entire z-plane into the single point $w = a/c$. L is variously referred to as the **linear transformation,** the linear fractional transformation, the bilinear transformation, or the Möbius transformation. Circles are invariant under L, interpreting straight lines as circles, inasmuch as this is a property of L_1, L_2, L_3.

We now turn to a detailed study of the linear transformation

$$\text{L:} \quad w = \frac{az + b}{cz + d}, \qquad bc - ad \neq 0.$$

Although four complex constants occur in L, since it is not altered by dividing numerator and denominator by any one of them that is nonzero, we actually have three essential constants. This means that if we know the images under L of three points z_1, z_2, z_3 in the z-plane to be w_1, w_2, w_3 in the w-plane, then L is uniquely determined. The following expression will enable us to avoid the determination of the constants in L by the tedious process of solving three simultaneous equations:

If z_1, z_2, z_3, z_4 are four distinct points in the z-plane, none of which is equal to $-d/c$, and w_1, w_2, w_3, w_4 are their images under L in the w-plane, then

$$\frac{(w_1 - w_4)(w_3 - w_2)}{(w_1 - w_2)(w_3 - w_4)} = \frac{(z_1 - z_4)(z_3 - z_2)}{(z_1 - z_2)(z_3 - z_4)}.$$

The proof is left to the student. The expression $\dfrac{(z_1 - z_4)(z_3 - z_2)}{(z_1 - z_2)(z_3 - z_4)}$ is called the **cross ratio** of the four points z_1, z_2, z_3, z_4, and is denoted by (z_1, z_2, z_3, z_4). The preceding result can now be stated as:

The cross ratio of four points is invariant under L.

If one of the points, say, z_1, equals $-(d/c)$, then $w_1 = \infty$ and

$$(w_1, w_2, w_3, w_4) = \frac{(w_3 - w_2)}{(w_3 - w_4)}.$$

Now, if z_1, z_2, z_3 are any three distinct points in the z-plane and w_1, w_2, w_3 are their images in the w-plane under L, then if w is the image of any point z in the z-plane under L, we have, in view of the invariance of the cross ratio:

$$\text{L:}\quad \frac{(w_1 - w)(w_3 - w_2)}{(w_1 - w_2)(w_3 - w)} = \frac{(z_1 - z)(z_3 - z_2)}{(z_1 - z_2)(z_3 - z)},$$

and if desired, this can be solved for w in terms of z.

Since L is analytic for all z except $-(d/c)$, and since, as it is readily verified, it has no critical points, L is a conformal transformation. Furthermore, since

$$w_1 - w_2 = \frac{(ad - bc)(z_1 - z_2)}{(cz_1 + d)(cz_2 + d)},$$

w_1 or w_2 not the point at infinity, $z_1 \neq z_2$ implies $w_1 \neq w_2$, and since the point of infinity is the image of $z = -(d/c)$, we have that L is univalent.

What distinguishes one linear transformation from another is the set of constants a, b, c, d, and we could denote

$$\text{L:}\quad w = \frac{az + b}{cz + d}, \qquad bc - ad \neq 0$$

just as well by a notation such as

$$\text{L:}\quad \begin{pmatrix} a & b \\ c & d \end{pmatrix}, \qquad bc - ad \neq 0.$$

$\begin{pmatrix} a & b \\ c & d \end{pmatrix}$ is called a **matrix**, and a, b, c, d are called its elements. We note that for any $\lambda \neq 0$,

$$w = \frac{\lambda az + \lambda b}{\lambda cz + \lambda d}$$

denotes the same transformation as

$$w = \frac{az + b}{cz + d},$$

so that $\begin{pmatrix} a & b \\ c & d \end{pmatrix}$ and $\begin{pmatrix} \lambda a & \lambda b \\ \lambda c & \lambda d \end{pmatrix}$ represent the same transformation. We shall say that these matrices are equivalent; in other words, multiplying each element of a matrix by the same nonzero constant yields an equivalent matrix.

We can obtain the inverse transformation of

$$\text{L}: \quad w = \frac{az + b}{cz + d},$$

denoted by L^{-1}, by solving for z in terms of w so that

$$\text{L}^{-1}: \quad z = \frac{dw - b}{-cw + a}, \qquad bc - ad \neq 0,$$

which is also a linear transformation and can be denoted as

$$\text{L}^{-1}: \quad \begin{pmatrix} d & -b \\ -c & a \end{pmatrix}, \qquad bc - ad \neq 0.$$

We call $\begin{pmatrix} d & -b \\ -c & a \end{pmatrix}$ the **inverse matrix** of $\begin{pmatrix} a & b \\ c & d \end{pmatrix}$; it is obtained from the latter by interchanging a and d and changing the signs of b and c.

Given two linear transformations

$$\text{L}: \quad w = \frac{c\zeta + d}{a\zeta + b} \quad \text{and} \quad \text{L}': \quad \zeta = \frac{a'z + b'}{c'z + d'},$$

we call the transformation obtained by first performing L, and then following it with L′ (a succession of transformations), the product of L and L′, and we write this product as LL′. We have

$$\text{LL}': \quad w = \frac{a\left(\dfrac{a'z + b'}{c'z + d'}\right) + b}{c\left(\dfrac{a'z + b'}{c'z + d'}\right) + d} = \frac{(aa' + bc')z + ab' + bd'}{(ca' + dc')z + cb' + dd'},$$

which is also a linear transformation. If we write

$$\text{L}: \quad \begin{pmatrix} a & b \\ c & d \end{pmatrix} \quad \text{and} \quad \text{L}': \quad \begin{pmatrix} a' & b' \\ c' & d' \end{pmatrix},$$

then if we wish LL′ to be represented by the product of the matrices, we must define this product as

$$\begin{pmatrix} a & b \\ c & d \end{pmatrix} \begin{pmatrix} a' & b' \\ c' & d' \end{pmatrix} = \begin{pmatrix} aa' + bc' & ab' + bd' \\ ca' + dc' & cb' + dd' \end{pmatrix}.$$

The student will readily note what the scheme is for the multiplication of two matrices.

We now are ready to consider the problem of determining a conformal transformation of a given region into another given region in the special case where that transformation is a linear transformation. In many instances, such a transformation can be effected more simply by a succession or product of transformations.

The following transformations are basic:

(1) *Half-plane into unit disk*

$$\tau_1\colon w = e^{i\alpha}\left(\frac{z-\lambda}{z-\bar{\lambda}}\right),\quad \alpha \text{ real},$$

maps $\operatorname{Im} z \geq 0$ into $|w| \leq 1$, if $\operatorname{Im}\lambda > 0$;
$\operatorname{Im} z \leq 0$ into $|w| \leq 1$, if $\operatorname{Im}\lambda < 0$.

(2) *Unit disk into half-plane*

$$\tau_2\colon w = \frac{\bar{\mu}z - e^{i\beta}}{z - e^{i\beta}},\quad \beta \text{ real},$$

maps $|z| \leq 1$ into $\operatorname{Im} w \geq 0$, if $\operatorname{Im}\mu > 0$;
$|z| \leq 1$ into $\operatorname{Im} w \leq 0$, if $\operatorname{Im}\mu < 0$.

(3) *Unit disk into unit disk*

$$\tau_3\colon e^{i\gamma}\left(\frac{z-\nu}{-\bar{\nu}z+1}\right),\quad \gamma \text{ real},$$

maps $|z| \leq 1$ into $|w| \leq 1$, if $|\nu| < 1$;
$|z| \leq 1$ into $|w| \geq 1$, if $|\nu| > 1$.

Proofs. (1) The linear transformation $w = \dfrac{az+b}{cz+d}$ will map the boundary of $\operatorname{Im} z \geq 0$, namely, the real axis, into the unit circle $|w| = 1$ if we map three specific points on the real axis, 0, 1, ∞ into $|w| = 1$. This leads to the following relations:

$$\text{(a)}\quad |b| = |d|;\ \text{(b)}\ |a+b| = |c+d|;\ \text{(c)}\ |a| = |c|.$$

We write

$$w = \frac{a}{c}\left(\frac{z-\lambda}{z-\lambda'}\right)$$

where $\lambda = -(b/a)$, $\lambda' = -(d/c)$ so that it follows from (c) that there exists a real α such that $a/c = e^{i\alpha}$, and from (a) and (c) that $|\lambda| = |\lambda'|$. It remains to show that $\lambda' = \bar{\lambda}$. From (b) it follows that $|1-\lambda| = |1-\lambda'|$, so that $(1-\lambda)(1-\bar{\lambda}) = (1-\lambda')(1-\bar{\lambda}')$, which yields $\operatorname{Re}\lambda = \operatorname{Re}\lambda'$. Now either $\lambda' = \lambda$ (which does not yield the required mapping; why?) or $\lambda' = \bar{\lambda}$. We see that $z = \lambda$ is mapped into $w = 0$, an interior point of $|w| = 1$; hence, if $\operatorname{Im}\lambda > 0$, $\operatorname{Im} z \geq 0$ is mapped into $|w| \leq 1$ and if $\operatorname{Im}\lambda < 0$, $\operatorname{Im} z \leq 0$ is mapped into $|w| \leq 1$.

(2) $\tau_2 = \tau_1^{-1}$. Hence, if

$$\tau_1\colon \begin{pmatrix} e^{i\beta} & -e^{i\beta}\mu \\ 1 & -\bar{\mu} \end{pmatrix},\qquad \tau_2\colon \begin{pmatrix} -\bar{\mu} & e^{i\beta}\mu \\ -1 & e^{i\beta} \end{pmatrix}$$

and the result is immediate.

(3) Let $z = \nu$ map into $w = 0$. Then $z = 1/\bar{\nu}$ must map into $w = \infty$. The point $z = 1$ must map into a point $w = e^{i\gamma}$. Then $(1, \nu, 1/\bar{\nu}, z) = (e^{i\gamma}, 0, \infty, w)$ and the result is immediate.

4. Other special transformations. Of particular importance is the transformation $w = z^n$, where n is a positive integer. If we write $z = re^{i\theta}$, then $w = r^n e^{in\theta}$, and if $\arg z = \theta$, then $\arg w = n\theta$. In order that the transformation be univalent, n must be such that $0 \leq n\theta < 2\pi$.

EXAMPLE 1. Determine a conformal transformation that maps the angular region $0 \leq \theta \leq \pi/4$ into the upper half of the z-plane. (See figure.)

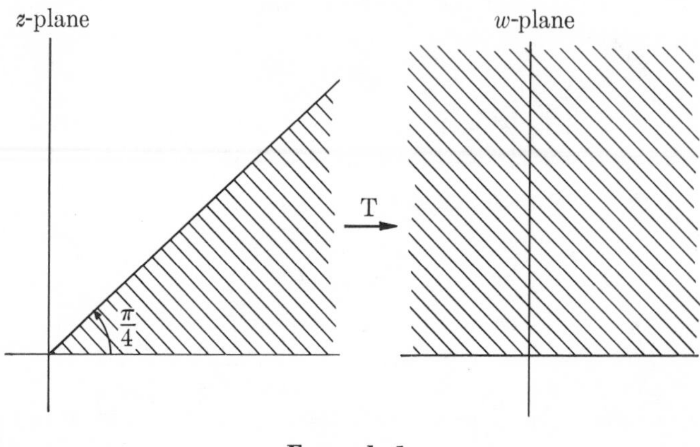

Example 1

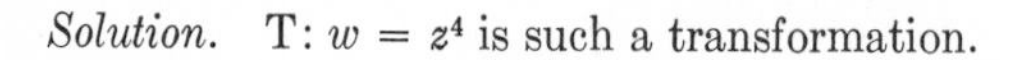

Solution. T: $w = z^4$ is such a transformation.

EXAMPLE 2. Determine a conformal transformation that maps the angular region $0 \leq \theta \leq \pi/6$ into the interior of the unit circle. (See figure.)

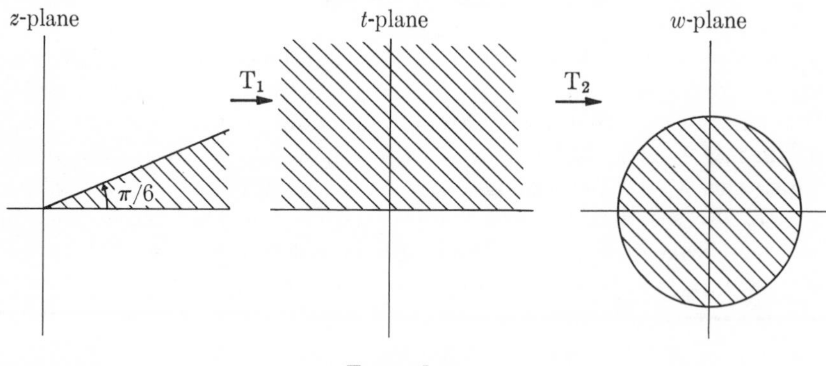

Example 2

Solution. Let $T_1\colon t = z^6, \qquad T_2\colon w = \dfrac{t - i}{t + i}.$

Then one solution is $T_1T_2 = \left(\dfrac{z^6 - i}{z^6 + i}\right).$

EXAMPLE 3. Determine a conformal transformation that maps the upper half of the unit circle into the entire unit circle. (See figure.)

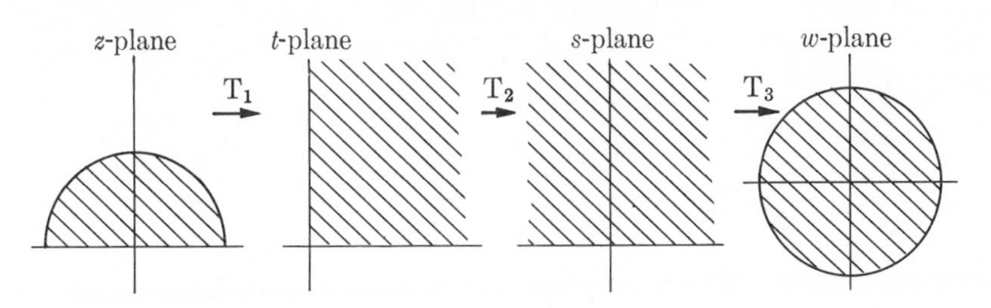

Example 3

Solution. Let T_1: $t = \dfrac{1+z}{1-z}$, T_2: $s = t^2$, T_3: $w = \dfrac{s-i}{s+i}$. Then

$$T_1T_2T_3 = \frac{(z+1)^2 - i(z-1)^2}{(z+1)^2 + i(z-1)^2}$$

is a solution.

Of frequent occurrence are regions whose boundaries consist of polygonal lines; if the region is bounded, the boundary is a closed polygon, and if it is unbounded, part of the boundary will have infinite line segments. Examples of the latter are the regions R_1: $|\text{Re } z| \leq 1$, $\text{Im } z \geq 0$, and R_2: $|\text{Im } z| \leq 1$; we think of R_1 as the limit of the triangular region with vertices at -1, 1, ci, $c > 0$, as $c \to \infty$, and R_2 as the limit of the region whose boundary is the rhombus with vertices at i, $-i$, c, $-c$, $c > 0$, as $c \to \infty$. An important problem in conformal mapping is to determine a conformal transformation that will map such polygonal regions into a canonical region; we shall take the upper half of the complex plane as our canonical region. Actually, it is simpler to determine a transformation that maps the upper half of the complex plane into such a polygonal region and then determine the inverse of this transformation. We shall consider regions whose boundaries are closed polygons and shall treat unbounded regions whose boundaries are polygonal lines as limiting cases of bounded regions (sometimes called *degenerate cases*).

Let P be a closed polygon of n sides with interior angles $\pi\alpha_1$, $\pi\alpha_2$, $\cdots$, $\pi\alpha_n$ and exterior angles $\pi\mu_1$, $\pi\mu_2$, $\cdots$, $\pi\mu_n$, so that $\pi\alpha_k + \pi\mu_k = \pi$ or $\alpha_k + \mu_k = 1$, $k = 1, 2, \cdots, n$. If P is convex, $\alpha_k < 1$ so that $\mu_k > 0$ for all k, but if P is not convex, $\alpha_k > 1$ and $\mu_k < 0$ for some k. Since the sum of the exterior angles of a closed polygon is 2π, we have $\mu_1 + \mu_2 + \cdots + \mu_k = 2$. We wish to determine a conformal transformation $w = f(z)$ that maps the upper half of the z-plane into the interior of P in the w-plane. It is sufficient to determine $w = f(z)$ so that the real axis is mapped into P. Let a_1', a_2', $\cdots$, a_n' be the vertices of P in consecutive order. Then the points $a_1 < a_2 < \cdots < a_n$, $a_n \neq \infty$, on the real axis of the z-plane must be chosen so that $f(a_j) = a'_j$, $j = 1, \cdots, n$, and the line segments $a'_j a'_{j-1}$ are the images of the line segments $a_j a_{j-1}$, $j = 2, \cdots, n$ under $w = f(z)$ and the half-lines $-\infty < x < a_1$ and $a_n < x < \infty$ are mapped into the line segment $a'_n a'_1$ by $w = f(z)$ (see Fig. 4).

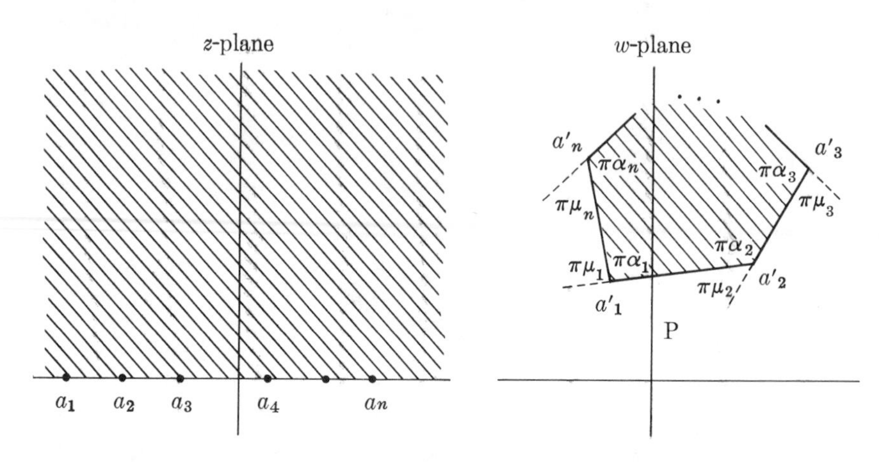

Fig. 4. Schwarz-Christoffel transformation

We shall show that the transformation that will accomplish this is

$$w = f(z) = A \int_{z_0}^{z} (\zeta - a_1)^{-\mu_1} (\zeta - a_2)^{-\mu_2} \cdots (\zeta - a_n)^{-\mu_n} \, d\zeta + B,$$

where A and B are complex constants. We can consider this transformation as the product of the transformations

$$\mathrm{T}_1: \quad t = \int_{z_0}^{z} (\zeta - a_1)^{-\mu_1} (\zeta - a_2)^{-\mu_2} \cdots (\zeta - a_n)^{-\mu_n} \, d\zeta$$

and

$$\mathrm{T}_2: \quad w = At + B,$$

T_2 being a linear transformation. The transformation $w = f(z)$ is known as the **Schwarz-Christoffel transformation.** We refer to its representation as the **Schwarz-Christoffel formula.**

We shall show that the transformation T_1 maps the real axis of the z-plane into a polygon P*, which is similar to the given polygon in the w-plane. Then A and B are so chosen that T_2 maps P* into P; this is always possible, since T_2 involves rotation, magnification or shrinking, and translation.

If the analytic function $w = f(z)$ maps a line segment l on the real axis of the z-plane into a line segment l' in the w-plane, then $\arg f'(z) =$ constant for z on l and equals the angle from the positive u-axis to l'. This follows immediately from the "Note," p. 328. For T_1, we have

$$\frac{dt}{dz} = (z - a_1)^{-\mu_1}(z - a_2)^{-\mu_2} \cdots (z - a_n)^{-\mu_n}$$

so that

$$\arg \frac{dt}{dz} = -\mu_1 \arg (z - a_1) - \mu_2 \arg (z - a_2) - \cdots - \mu_n \arg (z - a_n).$$

Now let a_1 and $a_n \neq \infty$ be any two points on the real axis of the z-plane. If $-\infty < z < a_1$,

$$\arg (z - a_1) = \arg (z - a_2) = \cdots = \arg (z - a_n) = \pi,$$

so that

$$\arg \frac{dt}{dz} = -(\mu_1 + \mu_2 + \cdots + \mu_n)\pi = -2\pi.$$

If $a_n < z < \infty$,

$$\arg (z - a_1) = \arg (z - a_2) = \cdots = \arg (z - a_n) = 0,$$

so that $\arg (dt/dz) = 0$. Let a_1'' and a_n'' be the images of a_1 and a_n under T_1. Then $-\infty < z < a_1$ and $a_n < z < \infty$ are mapped into the line segment $a_1''a_n''$, parallel to the real axis of the t-plane. (See Fig. 5.)

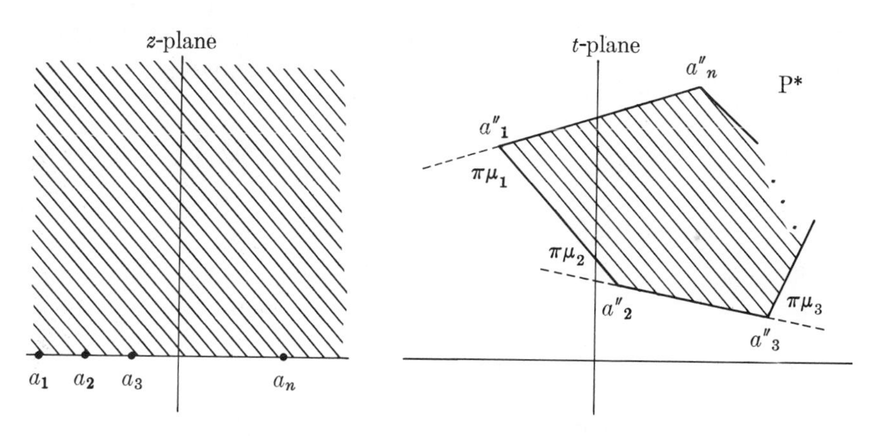

Fig. 5. Schwarz-Christoffel transformation

Now let a_2 be any point on the real axis of the z-plane so that $a_1 < a_2 < a_n$. If $a_1 < z < a_2$, then $\arg (z - a_1) = 0$, while $\arg (z - a_2) = \cdots = \arg (z - a_n) = \pi$, so that

$$\arg (dt/dz) = -(\mu_2 + \cdots + \mu_n)\pi = \pi\mu_1 - 2\pi,$$

or $\pi\mu_1$. Let a_2'' be the image of a_2 under T_1. Then the line segment a_1a_2 is mapped into the line segment $a_1''a_2''$ so that the angle between $a_1''a_n''$ and $a_1''a_2''$ is $\pi - \pi\mu_1 = \pi\alpha_1$, which is the angle between the sides $a_1'a_n'$ of P.

Thus far we have arbitrarily chosen the three points $a_1 < a_2 < a_n$ on the real axis of the z-plane. However, in order that P* be similar to P, the remaining points $a_3 < a_4 < \cdots < a_{n-1}$ will be fixed, since two n-sided polygons are similar if the corresponding angles are equal *and* if $n - 3$ pairs of corresponding sides have the same ratio (proof?). Note that if the polygons are triangles, the equality of the corresponding angles ensures similarity. Now we determine a_3 on the real axis of the z-plane, $a_2 < a_3 < a_n$, so that if a_3'' is its image under T_1, then

$$\frac{a_1''a_2''}{a_2''a_3''} = \frac{a_1'a_2'}{a_2'a_3'}.$$

Since $\arg(z - a_1) = \arg(z - a_2) = 0$, and $\arg(z - a_3) = \cdots = \arg(z - a_n) = \pi$, $\arg(dt/dz) = \pi\mu_1 + \pi\mu_2$, and the angle between $a_1''a_2''$ and $a_2''a_3''$ is $\pi\alpha_2$. Continuing in this fashion, $a_4 < a_5 < \cdots < a_{n-1}$ are determined so that the real axis of the z-plane is mapped into the polygon P*.

The Schwarz-Christoffel transformation is conformal everywhere in the z-plane except at the points $a_1, a_2, \cdots, a_n$. For a proof, see either Copson, *An Introduction to the Theory of Functions of a Complex Variable*, p. 193, or Nehari, *Conformal Mapping*, p. 189.

In the Schwarz-Christoffel transformation, we assumed $a_n \neq \infty$. We now consider a modification of the formula for the case $a_n = \infty$. We achieve this by means of the linear transformation $\zeta = a_n - (1/\zeta')$, which maps the upper half-plane into itself, with a_n as the image of $z = a_n$. Now the Schwarz-Christoffel formula becomes

$$\begin{aligned} f(z) &= A \int_{z_0}^{z} \left(a_n - a_1 - \frac{1}{\zeta'}\right)^{-\mu_1} \left(a_n - a_2 - \frac{1}{\zeta'}\right)^{-\mu_2} \cdots \left(-\frac{1}{\zeta'}\right)^{-\mu_n} \frac{d\zeta'}{(\zeta')^2} + B \\ &= A' \int_{z_0}^{z} (\zeta - b_1)^{-\mu_1}(\zeta - b_2)^{-\mu_2} \cdots (\zeta - b_{n-1})^{-\mu_{n-1}}\, d\zeta + B \end{aligned}$$

where

$$b_j = \frac{1}{a_n - a_j}, \qquad j = 1, \cdots, n - 1,$$

$$A' = A(a_n - a_1)^{-\mu_1} \cdots (a_n - a_{n-1})^{-\mu_{n-1}}$$

and use has been made of the fact that $\mu_1 + \mu_2 + \cdots + \mu_n = 2$. We find that comparing this formula with the Schwarz-Christoffel formula reveals that choosing $a_n = \infty$ has the effect of deleting the term $(\zeta - a_n)^{-\mu_n}$ from the formula. We shall refer to either of these formulas as the Schwarz-Christoffel formula.

It is of importance to note that the Schwarz-Christoffel formula is uniquely determined only if we specify $n - 3$ of the a_j (three of them, as we have seen, can be chosen arbitrarily), $n - 1$ of the μ_j (one of them will be determined by the choice of the three arbitrary a_j), and the constants A and B. Since A and B are complex, each determines two real numbers, and since the a_j and μ_j are real numbers, we must specify $2n$ real numbers. We should expect this, inasmuch as each vertex of the

n-sided polygon is represented by two real numbers. In practice, it is a difficult matter to specify the $(n - 3)$ a_j unless the polygon exhibits a high degree of symmetry. Furthermore, in most cases, the resulting integral cannot be evaluated in terms of elementary functions. The greatest utility of the Schwarz-Christoffel formula actually occurs in the mapping of the upper half-plane into a degenerate polygonal region. However, in these cases the use of the formula has to be justified in each case, since the formula was derived for bounded polygonal regions; in practice, it is simpler to obtain the mapping function heuristically from the formula and then showing that it has the required mapping properties.

EXAMPLE 1. Determine a conformal transformation that maps the upper half-plane into a rectangle.

Solution. Since the vertices of the rectangle have not been specified, we are seeking a conformal transformation that will map $\operatorname{Im} z > 0$ into any rectangle. In the Schwarz-Christoffel formula, we let $a_1 = -k$, $a_2 = -1$, $a_3 = 1$, $a_4 = k$, $k > 1$, the images of these points to be the vertices of the rectangle, and since the exterior angles of the rectangle are all $\pi/2$, $\mu_j = \frac{1}{2}$, $j = 1, 2, 3, 4$. Then

$$f(z) = A \int_0^z \frac{d\zeta}{\sqrt{(1 - \zeta^2)[1 - (\zeta^2/a^2)]}} + B$$

and A and B can be chosen so that the rectangle can be placed in any desired position. The integral is one of a class of integrals referred to as elliptic integrals (see Chapter 14). These cannot be evaluated in terms of elementary functions; however, they have been tabulated.

EXAMPLE 2. Determine a conformal transformation that maps the semi-infinite strip $|\operatorname{Re} z| \leq \pi/2$, $\operatorname{Im} z \geq 0$, into the half-plane $\operatorname{Im} w \geq 0$. (See figure.)

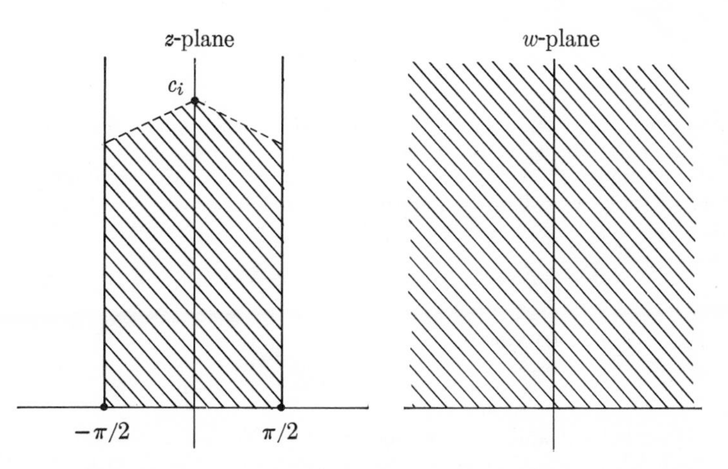

Example 2

Solution. We shall use the Schwarz-Christoffel formula to determine the transformation that will map the upper half of the w-plane into the semi-infinite strip in the z-plane, and then determine the inverse of this transformation. The given region is a degenerate triangular region; it can be considered as the limiting region of the triangular region with vertices at $-\pi/2$, $\pi/2$, ci, $c > 0$, as $c \to \infty$. The limiting values of the interior angles of this triangle are $\pi/2$, $\pi/2$, and 0. Hence, the exterior angles are $\pi/2$, $\pi/2$, and π. In the Schwarz-Christoffel formula, we can pick a_1, a_2, a_3 arbitrarily, and we choose $a_1 = -1$, $a_2 = 1$, and $a_3 = \infty$ so that

$$z = f(w) = A \int_0^w \frac{d\zeta}{\sqrt{\zeta^2 - 1}} + B = A' \int_0^w \frac{d\zeta}{\sqrt{1 - \zeta^2}} + B,$$

where $A' = -iA$. Then $z = A' \sin^{-1} w + B$ or $w = a \sin (z - B)$, $a = 1/A'$. But since $f(1) = \pi/2$ and $f(-1) = -(\pi/2)$, we have that $a = 1$ and $B = 0$, so that the required transformation is $w = \sin z$. The student should verify that this function maps the given region in the z-plane into the given region in the w-plane.

EXAMPLE 3. Determine a conformal transformation that maps the half-plane $\operatorname{Im} z > 0$ into the infinite strip $0 \leq \operatorname{Im} w \leq \pi$. (See figure.)

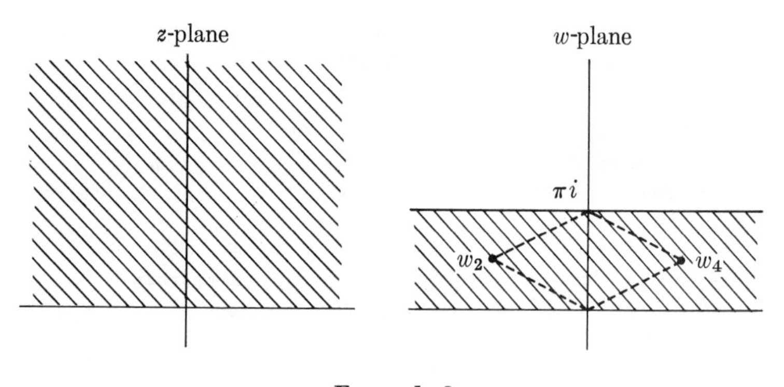

Example 3

Solution. The boundary of the infinite strip is the limit of the rhombus with vertices at πi, w_2, 0, w_4 as $\operatorname{Re} w_1 \to -\infty$ and $\operatorname{Re} w_3 \to \infty$. The limiting values of the exterior angles of the rhombus are 0, π, 0, π. If in the Schwarz-Christoffel formula we leave $a_1 < 0$ to be determined, and let $a_2 = 0$, $a_3 = 1$, and $a_4 = \infty$, we have

$$w = f(z) = A \int_1^z \frac{d\zeta}{\zeta} + B \quad \text{or} \quad w = A \operatorname{Log} z + B.$$

Since $f(1) = 0$, $B = 0$. Now $f(a_1) = \pi i$, $a_1 < 0$, so that

$$\pi i = A \operatorname{Log} a_1 = A (\operatorname{Log} |a_1| + \pi i);$$

hence, $A \operatorname{Log} |a_1| = 0$ and $A\pi = \pi$, from which it follows that $A = 1$ and $a_1 = -1$. The required transformation is $w = \operatorname{Log} z$, subject to verification by the student.

EXAMPLE 4. Determine a function $H(x, y)$, harmonic in the region $-\pi/2 \leq x \leq \pi/2$, $y \geq 0$, such that $H[-\pi/2, y] = H(\pi/2, y) = 0$, $y > 0$, and $H(x, 0) = 1$, $-\pi/2 < x < \pi/2$. (See figure.)

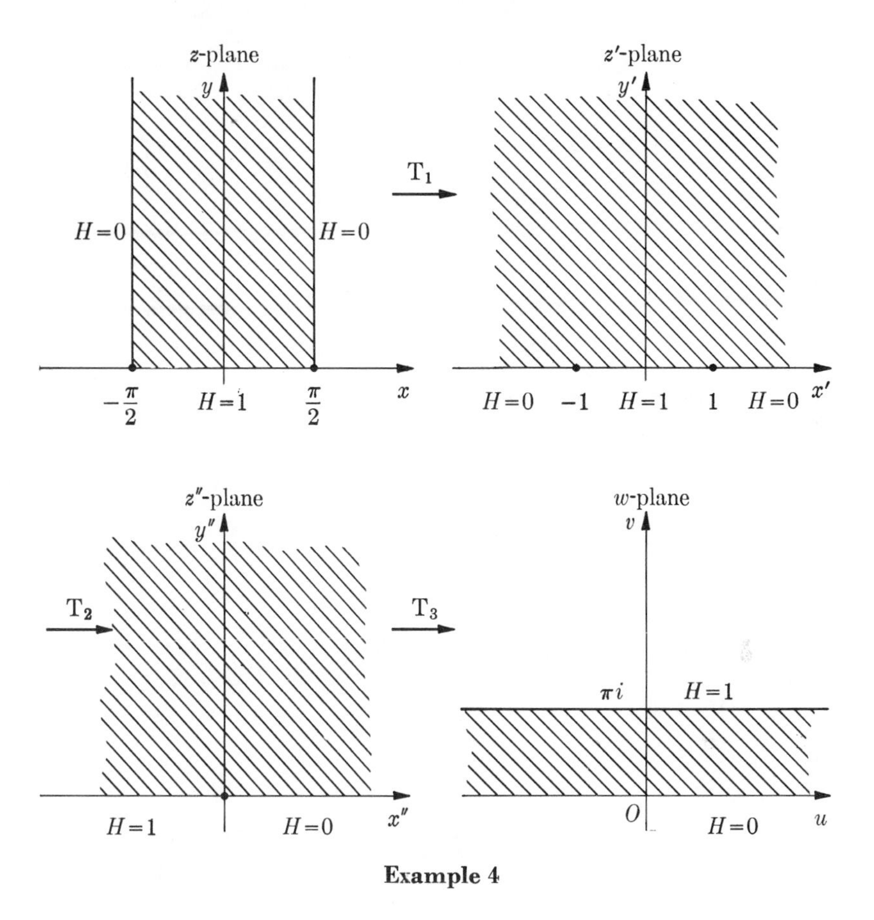

Example 4

Solution. We shall map the given region into a region in which we are able to determine readily a harmonic function having the specified values on the boundary. In order to achieve this, we shall determine a conformal transformation $T: w = f(z)$ that will map the given region into the infinite strip $0 \leq \text{Im } w \leq 0$ in such a way that the line segment $-\pi/2 \leq x \leq \pi/2$, $y = 0$, is mapped into the line $v = \pi$ and the half-lines $x > \pi/2$ and $x < -\pi/2$, $y = 0$, are mapped into the line $v = 0$. Now we are seeking a function that is harmonic in $0 \leq \text{Im } w \leq 0$ and is equal to zero on $v = 0$ and to one on $v = \pi$. Clearly, such a function is

$$H = H[x(u, v), y(u, v)] = \frac{v}{\pi},$$

for it satisfies the conditions on the boundary and is harmonic everywhere since $H = \text{Im } (w/\pi)$ and w/π is an analytic function of w.

Now to determine T; we shall be able to determine it as a product of transformations with which we are familiar and which are illustrated in the figure. Let T_1: $z' = \sin z$. Then T_1 maps the given region into $\text{Im}\, z' \geq 0$ in such a way that $-\pi/2 \leq x \leq \pi/2$, $y = 0$, is mapped into $-1 \leq x' \leq 1$, $y' = 0$ and $x > \pi/2$ and $x < -\pi/2$, $y = 0$, are mapped into $x' > 1$ and $x' < -1$, $y' = 0$ (Example 2). Let T_2: $z'' = (z' - 1)/(z' + 1)$. The student should show that this is a linear transformation that maps $\text{Im}\, z' \geq 0$ into $\text{Im}\, z'' \geq 0$ in such a way that $x' > 1$ and $x' < -1$, $y' = 0$, are mapped into $x'' > 0$, $y'' = 0$, and $-1 \leq x' \leq 1$ is mapped into $x'' < 0$, $y'' = 0$. Finally, let T_3: $w = \text{Log}\, z''$. Then (Example 3) T_3 maps $\text{Im}\, z'' \geq 0$ into $\infty \leq \text{Im}\, w \leq \pi$ in such a way that $x'' > 0$, $y = 0$ is mapped into $v = 0$ and $x'' < 0$, $y = 0$ into $v = \pi$. Now $T = T_1T_2T_3$, so that

$$T\colon \quad w = \text{Log}\,\frac{\sin z - 1}{\sin z + 1}.$$

T is analytic in the given region, and hence T^{-1} is analytic in $0 \leq \text{Im}\, w \leq \pi$. Now transforming the harmonic function $w = \text{Im}\, w/\pi$ under T^{-1} will preserve its harmonicity and its values on the boundary. Now

$$\begin{aligned} H(x, y) &= \text{Im}\,\frac{w}{\pi} = \frac{1}{\pi}\,\text{Im}\left[\text{Log}\,\frac{\sin z - 1}{\sin z + 1}\right] \\ &= \frac{1}{\pi}\arg\frac{\sin z - 1}{\sin z + 1} \\ &= \frac{2}{\pi}\tan^{-1}\left[\frac{\cos x}{\sinh y}\right], \end{aligned}$$

the value of the inverse tangent taken in the upper half-plane, is the required function.

EXERCISES

1. Find the linear transformations that map
(a) $2, i, -2$ into $1, i, -1$; (b) $-i, 0, i$ into $-1, i, 1$;
(c) $0, -1, \infty$ into $-1, -2, -i$;
(d) $\infty, i, 0$ into $0, i, \infty$; (e) z_1, z_2, z_3 into $0, 1, \infty$.

2. Determine the linear transformation that maps the upper half of the z-plane into the upper half of the w-plane in such a way that

(a) $z \geq 0$, $y = 0$ is mapped into $u \leq 0$, $v = 0$ and $x \leq 0$, $y = 0$ into $u \geq 0$, $v = 0$.

(b) $-1 \leq x \leq 1$, $y = 0$ into $u \leq 0$, $v = 0$, and $x > 1$ and $x < -1$ into $u > 0$, $v = 0$.

(c) $0 \leq x \leq 1$, $y = 0$, into $u \leq -1$, $v = 0$; $-1 \leq x < 0$, $y = 0$ into $u \geq 1$, $v = 0$, $x > 1$, $y = 0$ into $0 \leq u < 1$, $v = 0$, and $x < -1$ into $-1 < u \leq 0$, $v = 0$.

(d) $\text{Re}\, z \geq 0$ is mapped into $\text{Re}\, w \leq 0$.

(e) $|z| \leq 1$ is mapped into $|w| \geq 1$.

3. (a) Show that the most general linear transformation that maps $\text{Im } z \geq 0$ into $\text{Im } w \geq 0$ has one of the following forms: (1) $w = h\dfrac{z-a}{z-b}$, $h(a-b) > 0$; (2) $w = -\dfrac{k}{z-b}$; $k > 0$; (3) $w = k(z-a)$, $k > 0$.

(b) Show that every transformation $w = (az+b)/(cz+d)$, a, b, c, d real, such that $ad - bc > 0$, is equivalent to one of the forms in (a).

(c) Show that if $w = (az+b)/(cz+d)$ maps $x = 0$ into $u = 0$, then a, b, c, d are real.

4. Determine the most general linear transformation that maps

(a) the upper half of the z-plane into the lower half of the w-plane.

(b) $|z| < 1$ into $|w - 1| < 1$.

(c) $\text{Re } z > 0$ into $|w| < 1$.

(d) $|z| > 1$ into $\text{Re } w > 0$.

(e) $|z| < 1$ into $|w| < 1$ so that $\text{Re } z > 0$, $\text{Im } z > 0$ maps into $\text{Re } w < 0$, $\text{Im } w < 0$.

(f) $|z - a| \leq R$ into $|w| \leq 1$.

(g) $|z| < 1$ into $\text{Re } z \geq -\frac{1}{2}$.

(h) The region common to $|z - 1| < 1$ and $|z + i| < 1$ into $\text{Re } w > \frac{1}{2}$, $\text{Im } w > \frac{1}{2}$.

5. (a) Determine the cross ratio of the fourth roots of -1 and of the non-real sixth roots of 1. *Ans.:* $-1, -1/3$.

(b) Show that the cross ratio of four distinct points is real if and only if the four points lie on a circle.

6. (a) A point z is called an invariant point (or fixed point) of the linear transformation if $z = (az+b)/(cz+d)$.

Determine the invariant points of

$$w = \frac{-2(z+2i)}{iz+1}. \qquad \textit{Ans.:} \quad -i, 4i.$$

(b) Show that a linear transformation either has 2, 1, or no invariant points.

(c) Show that if a linear transformation has two distinct invariant points α and β, then the transformation can be written in the form

$$\frac{w-\alpha}{w-\beta} = k\left(\frac{z-\alpha}{z-\beta}\right), \qquad k \neq 0,$$

a complex constant.

(d) If the origin is an invariant point of a linear transformation, show that the transformation is $w = z/(cz+d)$, and if the point at infinity is an invariant point, the transformation is $w = az + b$.

7. (a) Given T_1: $t = \dfrac{z+2}{z+3}$, T_2: $w = \dfrac{t}{t+1}$, find T_1T_2, T_2T_1, $T_1^{-1}T_2$, $T_1^{-1}T_2^{-1}$.

(b) Given T_1: $t = z^3$, T_2: $\zeta = \dfrac{1+t}{1-t}$, T_3: $r = \zeta^2$, T_4: $w = \dfrac{r-i}{r+i}$; find $T_1T_2T_3T_4$ and show that it maps $|z| < 1$, $0 < \arg z < \pi/3$ into $|w| < 1$.

(c) Given T_1: $\zeta = (z + \frac{1}{2})\pi i$, T_2: $s = e^{\zeta}$, T_3: $t = \dfrac{1+s}{1-s}$, T_4: $r = t^2$, T_5: $w = \dfrac{r-i}{r+i}$; find $T_1T_2T_3T_4T_5$ and show that it maps $|x| < \frac{1}{2}$, $y \geq 0$ into $|w| \leq 1$.

8. (a) Determine the linear transformation that maps $|z| \leq 1$ into $|w - 1| \leq 1$ such that the images of 0, 1 are $\frac{1}{2}$, 0. Is the transformation uniquely determined?

(b) Determine the linear transformation that maps $|z| \geq 1$ into $\operatorname{Re} w \geq 0$ so that the images of $1, -i, -1$ are $i, 0, -i$. Is the transformation uniquely determined? Find the images of (1) $\arg z =$ constant, $|z| \geq 1$; and (2) $|z| = r$, $r > 1$, under this transformation.

(c) Prove that $w = (iz + 1)/(z + i)$ maps $|x| \leq 1$, $y = 0$ into a semicircle.

9. Determine a conformal transformation that will map

(a) The infinite sector $0 \leq \theta \leq \pi/3$ into $|w| \leq 1$.
(b) The sector $0 \leq \theta \leq \pi/3$, $r \leq 1$ into $\operatorname{Im} w \geq 0$.
(c) The first quadrant of the z-plane into $|w| \leq 1$.
(d) The sector $0 \leq \theta \leq \pi/3$, $r \leq 1$ into the first quadrant of the w-plane.
(e) $|z| \leq 1$, $\operatorname{Im} z \geq 0$ into $|w| \leq 1$.
(f) $|x| \leq \pi/2$, $y = 0$ into the first quadrant of the w-plane.
(g) $|z| \geq 1$, $0 \leq \arg z \leq \pi$ into $0 \leq \operatorname{Im} w \leq \pi$.
(h) $1 < \operatorname{Re} z + \operatorname{Im} z < \infty$ into $\operatorname{Im} w \geq 0$.

10. With the aid of the Schwarz-Christoffel formula, show that

(a) $\displaystyle\int_0^z \zeta^{\alpha-1}(1 - \zeta)^{\beta-1}\,d\zeta$ maps $\operatorname{Im} z \geq 0$ into a triangle with angles $\pi\alpha, \pi\beta, \pi\gamma$.

(b) $\displaystyle\int_0^z \frac{d\zeta}{\sqrt{\zeta(1 - \zeta^2)}}$ maps $\operatorname{Im} z \geq 0$ into a square.

(c) $\displaystyle\int_0^z \frac{d\zeta}{\sqrt{\zeta(1 - \zeta^2)(1 - k^2\zeta^2)}}$, $k > 1$, maps $\operatorname{Im} z \geq 0$ into a region of the type shown in the illustration.

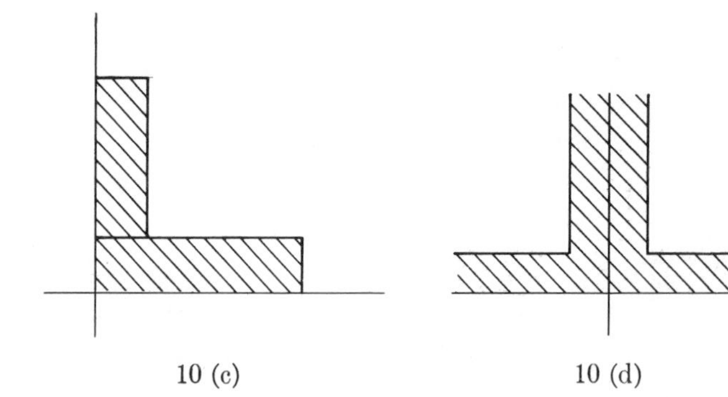

10 (c) 10 (d)

Exercise 10

(d) $\displaystyle\int_0^z \frac{\sqrt{1 - \zeta^2}}{1 - k^2\zeta^2}\,d\zeta$, $k > 1$ maps $\operatorname{Im} z \geq 0$ into a region of the type shown.

11. (a) Show that the Schwarz-Christoffel formula for mapping the upper half-plane into a polygonal region is

$$f(z) = A \int_{z_0}^{z} \frac{d\zeta}{(\zeta - b_1)^{\mu_1} \cdots (\zeta - b_n)^{\mu_n}} + B, \qquad |b_k| = 1, k = 1, \cdots, n.$$

(b) Show that $\int_0^z \frac{\sqrt{1+\zeta^4}}{1-\zeta^4}\, d\zeta$ maps $|z| < 1$ into a region of the type shown in the illustration.

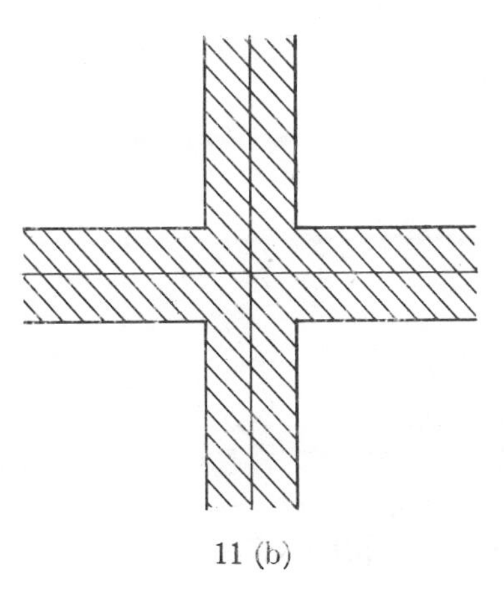

11 (b)

Exercise 11

(c) Show that $\int_0^z (1 - \zeta^n)^{-2/n}\, d\zeta$ maps $|z| < 1$ onto the interior of a regular n-sided polygon.

(d) Show that the Schwarz-Christoffel formula for mapping $|z| < 1$ into the exterior of a polygonal region is

$$f(z) = A \int_0^z (\zeta - b_1)^{\mu_1} \cdots (\zeta - b_n)^{\mu_n} \frac{d\zeta}{\zeta^2}, \qquad |b_k| = 1, k = 1, \cdots, n.$$

(e) Show that $\int_1^z (1 - \zeta^n)^{2/n} \frac{d\zeta}{n^2}$ maps $|z| < 1$ into the exterior of a regular n-sided polygon.

(f) Show that $w = \tan z$ maps $|\text{Re } z| \leq \pi/4$ into $|w| \leq 1$.

(g) Show that $w = z/(1 - z)^2$ maps $|z| \leq 1$ into the w-plane cut along the negative real axis from $-\frac{1}{4}$ to $-\infty$.

12. Show, with the use of the Schwarz-Christoffel formula, that

(a) $w = \text{Cosh}^{-1} z$ maps $\text{Im } z > 0$ into $0 \leq \text{Im } w \leq \pi$, $\text{Re } w \geq 0$.

(b) $w = \text{Log}\,(1 - z^2)$ maps $\text{Im } z \geq 0$ into $|\text{Im } w| \leq \pi$ with a cut along the negative real axis.

13. With the use of the Schwarz-Christoffel formula, determine a conformal transformation of $\text{Im } z \geq 0$ into each of the following regions:

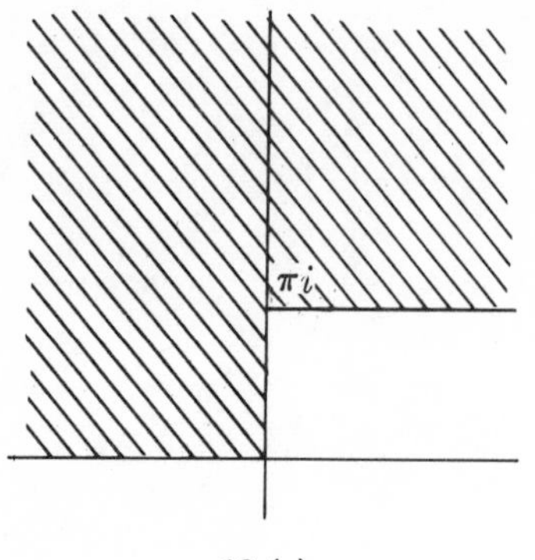

13 (a)

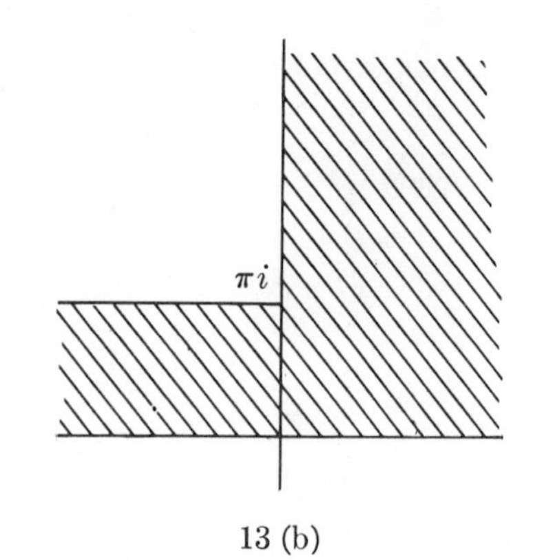

13 (b)

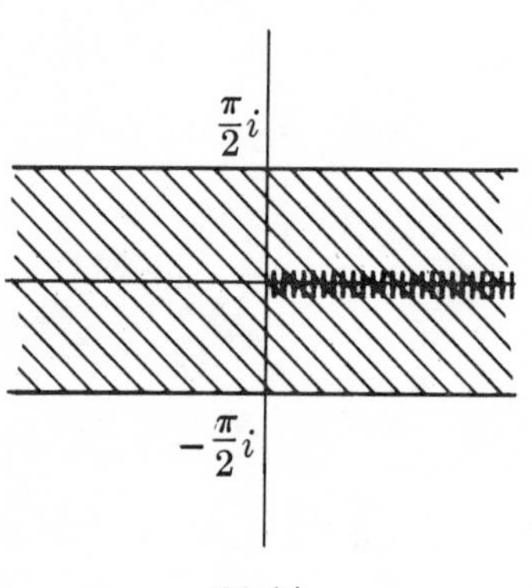

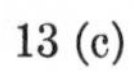
13 (c)

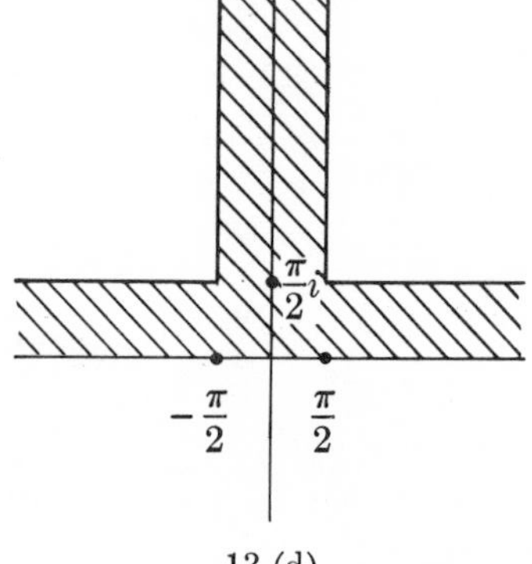

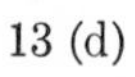
13 (d)

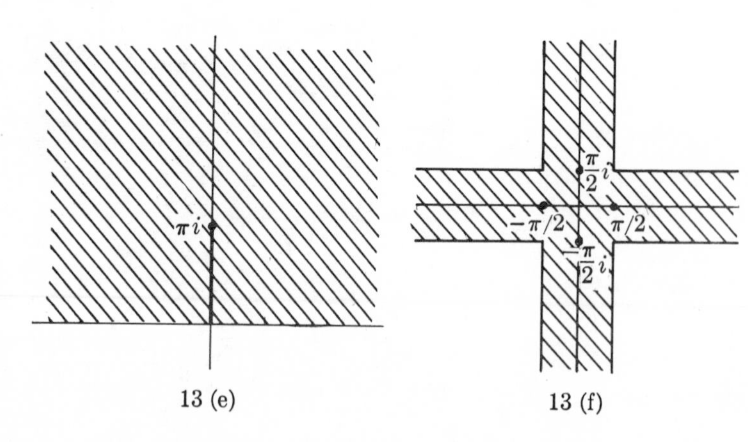

13 (e)

13 (f)

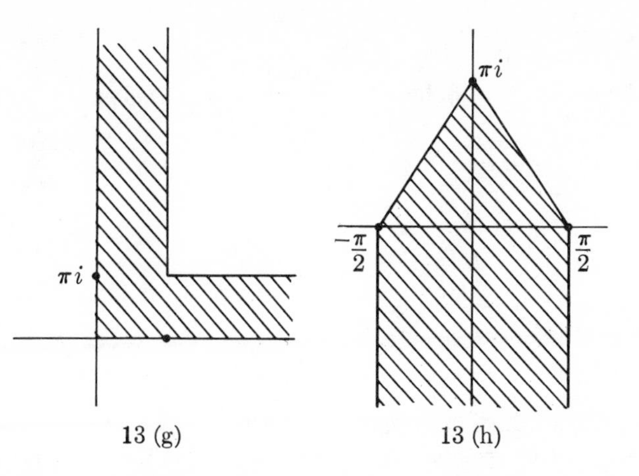

13 (g) 13 (h)

14. Determine the region in the w-plane into which $\operatorname{Im} z \geq 0$ is mapped by the transformation $w = f(z)$, where $f'(z)$ is
(a) $(1 - z^2)^{-2/3}$; (b) $z^{-1/2}(z^2 - 1)^{-3/4}$; (c) $z^{-2/3}(z^2 - 1)^{-2/3}$;
(d) $z^{-1/2}(z - 1)^{-2/3}(z - 1)^{-5/6}$; (e) $z^{-2/3}(z^2 - 1)^{-1/2}$.

15. Show that

(a) $w = \operatorname{Log} \dfrac{1 + z^2}{2z}$ maps $|z| \leq 1$, $\operatorname{Im} z \geq 0$ into $0 \leq \operatorname{Im} w \leq \pi$.

(b) $w = \tan^2 (z/2)$ maps $0 \leq \operatorname{Re} z \leq \pi/2$, $\operatorname{Im} z \geq 0$ into $|w| \leq 1$, $\operatorname{Im} w \geq 0$.

$\left(\textit{Hint: } \tan^2 \dfrac{z}{2} = \dfrac{1 - \cos z}{1 + \cos z}.\right)$

(c) $w = \coth (z/2)$ maps $|\operatorname{Im} z| \leq \pi$, $\operatorname{Re} z \geq 0$ into $\operatorname{Re} w \geq 0$ cut along $0 \leq u \leq 1$, $v = 0$.

(d) $w = \frac{1}{2}[z + (1/z)]$ maps $|z| \leq 1$ and $|z| \geq 1$ into the w-plane cut along $|u| \leq 1$, $v = 0$.

(e) $w = \dfrac{1}{2}\left[(a - b)z + \dfrac{a + b}{z}\right]$ maps $|z| \leq 1$ into the region exterior to the ellipse

$$\frac{u^2}{a^2} + \frac{v^2}{b^2} = 1.$$

(f) $w = \tan^2 \dfrac{\pi\sqrt{z}}{4}$ maps the region inside the parabola $y^2 = 4(1 - x)$ into $|w| \leq 1$. [*Hint:* $t = \sqrt{z}$, $\zeta = \frac{1}{2}\pi t$, $w = \tan^2 (\zeta/2)$.]

16. Solve the following Dirichlet problems by determining $H(x, y)$ harmonic in the given region, with the given values on its boundary.
(a) $x \geq 0$, $y \geq 0$, $H(x, 0) = 0$, $H(0, y) = 1$.
(b) $0 \leq x \leq \pi/2$, $y \geq 0$, $H(0, y) = 1$, $H(\pi/2, y) = 0$, $H(x, 0) = 0$, $0 \leq H(x, y) \leq 1$.
(c) $r \leq 1$, $H(1, \theta) = 1$, $0 \leq \theta \leq \pi$, $H(1, \theta) = 0$, $\pi < \theta < 2\pi$.
(d) $x^2 + y^2 \geq 1$, $y \geq 0$, $H(x, y) = 0$ on $x^2 + y^2 = 1$ and $H(x, y) = 1$ on $|x| > 1$, $y = 0$.

(e) $0 \le y \le \pi$, $x < 0$; $y \ge 0$, $x \ge 0$, $H(x, \pi) = 1$, $x < 0$, $H(0, y) = 2$, $0 \le y \le \pi$, $H(x, 0) = 0$, $x > 0$.

17. Determine $H(x, y)$ harmonic in the given region, and satisfying the given boundary condition.

(a) $x > 0$, $y > 0$, $H(x, 0) = 1$, $x > 1$, $H(0, y) = 0$, $y > 0$, $\left.\dfrac{\partial H}{\partial y}\right]_{y=0} = 0$, $0 < x < 1$.

(b) $r \le r_0$, $0 < \theta < \alpha$, $H(r, 0) = H(r, \alpha) = 0$, $0 \le r \le r_0$, $\left.\dfrac{\partial H}{\partial r}\right]_{r=r_0} = 0$.

(c) $y \ge 0$, $H(x, y) = 1$, $x > 1$, $y = 0$, $H(x, y) = 0$, $x < -1$, $y = 0$; $\partial H/\partial y = 0$, $|x| < 1$, $y = 0$.

18. (a) A set G of elements $a, b, \cdots$, for which there exists a binary operation $\circ$ such that (1) $a \circ b$ is in G for every a and b in G; (2) $a \circ (b \circ c) = (a \circ b) \circ c$; (3) there exists an identity element e in G such that $a \circ e = e \circ a = a$ for every a in G; and (4) there exists for every element a in G an inverse element a^{-1} such that $a \circ a^{-1} = a^{-1} \circ a = e$, is called a **group.** Show that the set of linear transformations with $\circ$ interpreted as "product of transformations" forms a group.

(b) A subset of a group G that is a group is called a *subgroup* of G. Determine whether the following sets of linear transformations are subgroups of the set of all linear transformations: (1) rotations, (2) translations, (3) $w = az + b$, (4) linear transformations with the origin as invariant point, (5) $w = 1/(cz + d)$.

19. Show that if $w = f(z)$ maps $|z| \le 1$ conformally into $|w| \le 1$, then $w = f(z)$ is a linear transformation.

Hint: Let the origin be the image of c. Then $\zeta = \dfrac{z - c}{1 - \bar{c}z}$ maps $|z| \le 1$ conformally into $|w| \le 1$, and this together with $w = f(z)$ yields a function $w = \phi(\zeta)$, which maps $|\zeta| \le 1$ into $|w| \le 1$ so that $\phi(0) = 0$. Show that $\phi(\zeta)$ satisfies the conditions of Schwarz's lemma (Exercise 27, p. 255) so that $|w| \le |\zeta|$ when $|\zeta| \le 1$. The inverse transformation $\zeta = \phi^{-1}(w)$ also satisfies Schwarz's lemma, so that $|\zeta| \le |w|$ when $|w| \le 1$. Hence, $|\zeta| \le |w| \le |\zeta|$ when $|\zeta| \le 1$, which yields $|w| = |\zeta|$. By the second part of Schwarz's lemma, $w = \zeta e^{\alpha i}$, α a real constant. Hence, $w = e^{\alpha i}\dfrac{z - c}{1 - \bar{c}z}$.

20. (a) Show that the stereographic projection (Exercise 28, p. 189) maps the surface of a sphere conformally into a plane.

(b) Show that Mercator's projection $x = \phi$, $y = \operatorname{Log} \tan \frac{1}{2}\theta$ maps the sphere $X = R \sin\theta \cos\phi$, $Y = R \sin\theta \sin\phi$, $Z = R\cos\phi$ into a plane strip.

SUPPLEMENTARY PROBLEMS

ELECTROSTATICS

1. The electrical force of attraction or repulsion between charged particles is $-\nabla u$, where $u(x, y, z)$ is a harmonic function at points free of charges; u is called the *electrostatic potential.* We will assume that u depends only on x and y so that we will consider potential problems in the plane only. Now if u is harmonic in an open region D and v is the harmonic conjugate of u (determined uniquely up to an additive constant), then $f(z) = u(x, y) + iv(x, y)$ is an analytic function in D. We call f the *complex potential* corresponding to the electrostatic potential (real potential u); the curves $u(x, y) =$ constant are called *equipotential lines* and the curves $v(x, y) =$ constant are called *lines of force*. The lines of force are perpendicular to the equipotential lines. (Why?)

(a) Show that the potential between the planes $x = -1$ and $x = 1$ which are kept at potentials u_1 and u_2 is $u = \frac{1}{2}(u_2 - u_1)x + \frac{1}{2}(u_2 + u_1)$. Determine the complex potential, equipotential lines, and lines of force. (*Hint:* u is a function of x only and is a solution of the boundary value problem $u'' = 0$, $u(-1) = u_1$, $u(1) = u_2$.)

(b) Show that the potential between the cylinders $r = a$ and $r = b$, $a < b$, which are kept at potentials u_1 and u_2 is

$$u = \frac{u_2 \operatorname{Log}(r/a) - u_1 \operatorname{Log}(r/b)}{\operatorname{Log}(b/a)}$$

which can be written in the form $u = C_1 \operatorname{Log} r + C_2$, C_1 and C_2 constants. Show that the complex potential is $f(z) = C_1 \operatorname{Log} z + C_2$. Determine the equipotential lines and lines of force. The function $f(z)$ may be considered as the complex potential of a charged line perpendicular to the z-plane at the origin.

(c) Show that the complex potential of two equally but oppositely charged lines at $z = z_1$ and $z = z_2$ is $C \operatorname{Log}[(z - z_2)/(z - z_1)]$, where C is a constant. Determine the equipotential lines and lines of force. (*Hint:* Determine the complex potential due to each line using (b) and then add the two. Why is this valid?)

(d) Determine the equipotential lines and lines of force of the complex potentials $1/z$, $\cos^{-1} z$, $\cosh^{-1} z$.

2. Show that the potential in the region bounded by $r = 1$, $0 \le \theta \le \pi$; $y = 0$, $-1 \le x \le 1$, with the cylinder kept at potential 0 and the plane at potential 1 is $u = (2/\pi) \tan^{-1}(1 - x^2 - y^2/2y)$. Determine the equipotential lines and lines of force. [*Hint:* This is a Dirichlet problem for a semicircular region; map it into a region in the w-plane under $w = (i - z)/(i + z)$].

3. Let R be the region bounded by the planes $y = 0$ and $y = \pi$. Let the half planes $y = 0$, $x > 0$ and $y = \pi$, $x > 0$ be kept at potential 0 and the half planes $y = 0$, $x < 0$ and $y = \pi$, $x < 0$ at potential 1. Show that the potential of R is $u = (1/\pi) \tan^{-1}(\sin y/\sinh x)$. What are the equipotential lines? The lines of force?

4. Determine the potential between two semi-infinite planes intersecting at angle θ both kept at potential 0 if there exists a charged line at z_0. (*Hint:* Use the Schwarz-Christoffel transformation to map the plane angular region determined by the planes into the upper half of the z-plane. Show that the complex potential is $ci \operatorname{Log}[(z^{\pi/\theta} - z_0^{\pi/\theta})/z^{\pi/\theta} - \bar{z}_0^{\pi/\theta}]$.

HYDRODYNAMICS

5. A two-dimensional steady fluid flow is one in which the velocities of all particles of the moving fluid are parallel to one plane (which we choose as the xy-plane), all particles having the same x and y coordinates have equal velocities, and these velocities are independent of time. We assume the fluid to be incompressible (i.e., of constant density) and frictionless (i.e., of zero viscosity). The velocity at any point (x, y) is denoted as $V = V_1(x, y) + iV_2(x, y)$ so that V_1 and V_2 are the components of V in the x and y directions. (See Supplementary Problems, Hydrodynamics, p. 162). Incompressibility implies $\partial V_1/\partial x = -\partial V_2/\partial y$ in any region free of sources and sinks. Now if the flow is irrotational so that $\partial V_2/\partial x = \partial V_1/\partial y$, then V is analytic. There exists a function $\phi(x, y)$ such that $V = -\nabla\phi$;

i.e., $V_1 = -\partial\phi/\partial x$ and $V_2 = -\partial\phi/\partial y$. (Why?) $\phi(x, y)$ is called the *velocity potential* of the motion. Show that ϕ is harmonic. Let ψ be the harmonic conjugate of ϕ. Then $f(z) = \phi(x, y) + i\psi(x, y)$ is analytic; this function is called the *complex potential* of the flow. The curves $\phi(x, y) =$ constant are called *equipotential lines* and the curves $\psi(x, y) =$ constant are called *streamlines*—they are the paths in which the particles of the fluid move.

(a) Show that the complex potential $f(z) = kz$, $k > 0$, describes a uniform parallel flow since its streamlines are $ky =$ constant (parallel to the x-axis) and its velocity $= k =$ constant (parallel to the x-axis).

(b) Determine the equipotential lines and streamlines of $f(z) = z^2$. What is the velocity and speed of the flow? Describe the flow. Determine the point on a streamline where the speed is a minimum.

6. Determine the equipotential lines and streamlines of $f(z) = (c/2\pi)$ Log z, $c \neq 0$ real. Describe the flow. In this flow $z = 0$ is a point source if $c > 0$ and a point sink if $c < 0$; $|c|$ is called the strength of the source or sink. How is the flow directed in each of these cases?

Determine the equipotential lines and streamlines if $c = -ik$, $k > 0$. Describe the flow. The point $z = 0$ is called a *vortex*. Show that the potential of the flow increases by k for every complete turn around the vortex. Symbol k is called the strength of the vortex.

7. (Flow around a cylinder.) Show that the streamlines of $f(z) = z + (1/z)$ are $(r - 1/r) \sin \theta =$ constant (let $z = re^{i\theta}$ in f). Sketch some of these streamlines. Show that the streamline $(r - 1/r) \sin \theta = 0$ consists of the x-axis and the unit circle. Show that the flow can be interpreted as a flow around a long circular cylinder of unit radius. Determine the velocity V of the flow and the points where $V = 0$; these points are called *stagnation points* of the flow. What is their physical interpretation?

8. Describe the flow corresponding to the complex potentials (a) z^3; (b) iz; (c) $-2iz$; (d) $\cosh^{-1} z$; (e) $\cos^{-1} z$; (f) $1/z$; (g) $\sin z$.

9. (a) Determine the complex potential of a flow which has a point source of strength k at $z = -1$ and a sink of strength k at $z = 1$.

(b) Determine the complex potential of a flow with a vortex of strength m at $z = a$ and an equal and opposite vortex at $z = -a$, $a > 0$.

Ans.: (a) $(k/2\pi)$ Log $[(z + 1)/(z - 1)]$;
(b) $(m/2\pi i)$ Log $[(z + a)/(z - a)]$.

10. Show that the complex potential $F(w)$ for the flow over a step in the bed of a deep stream (this bed being the streamline consisting of $v = b$, $u < 0$; $u = 0$, $0 \leq v \leq b$; $v = 0$, $u > 0$) with velocity at infinity equal to q, q real, is bqz/π. (*Hint:* Use the Schwarz-Christoffel transformation to map the upper half z-plane into the step in the w-plane, $\infty \to \infty$, $-1 \to bi$, $1 \to 0$. The transformation is $w = (b/\pi)[\sqrt{z^2 - 1} + \cosh^{-1} z]$. $H(z) = F(w)$ defines a complex potential in Im $z \geq 0$. Now $dH/dz = dF/dw \cdot \dfrac{dw}{dz} = \dfrac{b}{\pi}\sqrt{\dfrac{z + 1}{z - 1}}\dfrac{dF}{dw} \to bq/\pi$ as $z \to \infty$. Then $H(z) = bzq|\pi$.

ADVANCED COMPLEX ANALYSIS

11. Prove the *Casorati-Weierstrass theorem:* If $f(z)$ has an isolated essential singularity at z_0, then, in any neighborhood of z_0 it must come arbitrarily close to any specified number. (*Hint:* Assume false. Then there exists a number α, $\epsilon > 0$,

$\delta > 0$ such that $|f(z) - \alpha| \geq \epsilon$ whenever $|z - z_0| < \delta$. Hence $1/|f(z) - \alpha|$ is bounded for $|z - z_0| < \delta$; its Laurent series about $z = z_0$ shows that either $f(z)$ is analytic or has a pole at z_0.)

12. *Picard's theorem* states that in every neighborhood of an isolated essential singularity an analytic function takes on every value, with one possible exception, an infinite number of times. Illustrate by showing that $e^{1/z} = i$ has an infinite number of solutions in every neighborhood of $z = 0$, an essential singularity of the function, and that $z = 0$ is the exceptional point. Show by an example that the theorem is false if the singularity is a pole.

13. Prove: If $c_{n+1} \leq c_n$, $n = 1, 2, \cdots$, and $\lim_{n\to\infty} c_n = 0$, then $\sum c_n z^n$ converges at all points of $|z| = 1$ except possibly at $z = 1$. (*Hint:* Let

$$R_{n,p}(z) = \sum_{k=n+1}^{n+p} c_k z^k, \quad p \geq 1.$$

Then

$$(z - 1)R_{n,p}(z) = -c_{n+1}z^{n+1} + \sum_{k=n+1}^{n+p-1} (c_k - c_{k+1})z^{k+1} + c_{n+p}z^{n+p+1}.$$

Now

$$|z - 1|\,|R_{n,p}(z)| \leq c_{n+1}|z|^{n+1} + \sum_{k=n+1}^{n+p-1} (c_k - c_{k+1})|z|^{k+1} + c_{n+k}|z|^{n+p+1}.$$

Let $|z| = 1$, $z \neq 1$, then $|R_{n,p}(z)| \leq 2c_{n+1}/|z - 1|$. First let $p \to \infty$ and then $n \to \infty$). Show that Leibniz's test for alternating series is a special case of this theorem.

14. *Analytic definition of argument.* Define $\pi/2 = \int_0^1 (dt/\sqrt{1 - t^2})$. Show that $\int_0^y (dt/\sqrt{1 - t^2})$ is a continuous increasing function of y in $0 \leq y \leq 1$. If $0 \leq \theta \leq \pi/2$, there will therefore exist one and only one value from this interval for which $\int_0^y (dt/\sqrt{1 - t^2}) = \theta$. Define this value to be $\sin\theta$ and define $\cos\theta = \sin[(\pi/2) - \theta]$. Define $e(\theta) = \cos\theta + i\sin\theta$. Show that $e(\theta_1 + \theta_2) = e(\theta_1)e(\theta_2)$, that $e(\theta) = \zeta$ has a solution, and that any two solutions differ by a multiple of 2π. Now define $\arg z$, $z \neq 0$, as any solution of $e(\theta) = z/|z|$. Show that

$$\arg z_1 z_2 = \arg z_1 + \arg z_2 + 2\pi n.$$

15. If C is a contour in the z-plane, we define the *winding number* of C with respect to a to be

$$n(\mathrm{C}, a) = \frac{1}{2\pi i}\int_{\mathrm{C}} dz/(z - a).$$

Why is $n(\mathrm{C}, a)$ an integer?

(a) Show that $n(\mathrm{C}, a) = n(\mathrm{C}_1, a) + n(\mathrm{C}_2, a)$ for $\mathrm{C} = \mathrm{C}_1 + \mathrm{C}_2$ and $n(-\mathrm{C}, a) = -n(\mathrm{C}, a)$.

(b) Show that $n(\mathrm{C}, a)$ is a continuous function of a for a not on C.

(c) Show that if R is a region having no points in common with C, then $n(\mathrm{C}, a)$ is constant for all a in R.

(d) Prove: If $\{a_k\}$ is a sequence of points such that $a_k \to \infty$ as $k \to \infty$, then $n(\mathrm{C}, a_k) \to 0$ as $k \to \infty$.

(e) Show that $n(\mathrm{C}, a) = 0$ for all a exterior to C.

It can be shown that $n(\mathrm{C}, a) = \pm 1$ for all a interior to C. It can be shown that if we take the positive (negative) direction along C, then $n(\mathrm{C}, a) = 1(-1)$.

This means that we could actually determine the positive direction along a contour analytically by means of the winding number.

16. (a) Prove: If $f(z)$ is an entire function having no zeros, then there exists an entire function $g(z)$ such that $f(z) = e^{g(z)}$. (Outline of proof: There is no loss of generality to assume $f(0) = 1$. Then for every δ, $0 < \delta < 1$, there exists $\epsilon > 0$ such that $|f(z) - 1| < \delta$ for $|z| < \epsilon$. For z in this disk, we define $g(z) = \operatorname{Log} f(z)$ and represent $\operatorname{Log} f(z) = -\sum_{n=1}^{\infty} \frac{1}{n}[1 - f(z)]^n$. The series is convergent for $|z| < \epsilon$ and represents an analytic function there. Now $g'(z) = f'(z)/f(z)$. But $g'(z)$ is an entire function, since $f(z)$ is entire without zeros. Hence $g(z)$ is entire.)

(b) *Weierstrass factorization theorem.* If $f(z)$ is an entire function having an increasing sequence $\{a_n\}$ of zeros, $a_0 \neq 0$, a zero of multiplicity m occurring m times in the sequence, and if $\{k_n\}$ is a sequence of nonnegative integers such that $\sum_{\nu=1}^{\infty} |z/a_\nu|^{k_\nu+1}$ is convergent for all z, then

$$f(z) = \exp g(z) \prod_{\nu=1}^{\infty} \left(1 - \frac{z}{a_\nu}\right) \exp\left[\frac{z}{a_\nu} + \frac{1}{2}\left(\frac{z}{a_\nu}\right)^2 + \cdots + \frac{1}{k_\nu}\left(\frac{z}{a_\nu}\right)^{k_\nu}\right],$$

where $g(z)$ is an entire function, the last exponential factor being omitted when the corresponding $k_\nu = 0$. If $a_0 = 0$ is of multiplicity m then the right-hand side has the multiplicative factor z^m.

If there exists a nonnegative integer k such that $\sum_{\nu=1}^{\infty} 1/|a_\nu|^{k+1}$ is convergent, then $\sum_{\nu=1}^{\infty} |z/a_\nu|^{k_\nu+1}$ is convergent if we let $k_n = k$, $n = 1, 2, \cdots$. The smallest such k is called the *rank* of $\{a_n\}$. The representation of $f(z)$ given above where the k_n are equal to the rank is called a *canonical product.*

Construct a canonical product having the same zeros as $(\sin \pi z)/\pi z$ and a canonical product having the same zeros as $\cos \pi z$.

Construct a canonical product having simple zeros at $\pm m \pm in$, m and n integers.

Show that the most general entire function which vanishes at $z = 0, -1, -2, \cdots$ has the form

$$f(z) = e^{g(z)} \prod_{\nu=1}^{\infty} \left(1 + \frac{z}{\nu}\right) e^{-z/\nu},$$

where $g(z)$ is an entire function. (The case in which $g(z) = \gamma z$, γ constant so selected that $f(1) = 1$, is very important. It is $1/\Gamma(z)$, where Γ is the gamma function. See p. 471, Exercise 26.)

SUGGESTED REFERENCES

Books on Complex Analysis

AHLFORS, LARS V. *Complex Analysis.* New York: McGraw-Hill Book Co., Inc., 1953. A highly sophisticated approach to the subject written by an expert in the field. Interesting features are the analytic definition of the argument of a complex number, integration via topological methods, and the general definition of analytic function.

CHURCHILL, RUEL V. *Complex Variables and Applications,* 2nd ed. New York: McGraw-Hill Book Co., Inc., 1960. A satisfactory elementary treatment with emphasis on techniques. Applications in hydrodynamics and electromagnetic theory are considered.

COPSON, E. T. *An Introduction to the Theory of Functions of a Complex Variable.* New York: Oxford University Press, 1935. A standard treatise that emphasizes the theoretical aspects of the subject with considerable attention to special functions, especially elliptic functions for which the author provides a masterly exposition.

DIENES, P. *The Taylor Series.* New York: Dover Publications, 1957. Emphasis is placed on the series approach. Although the style is wordy and the nomenclature is often old-fashioned, there is a great deal that one can learn from this book. The problems are mostly of the "honors" type.

FRANKLIN, PHILIP. *Functions of Complex Variables.* New York: Prentice-Hall, Inc., 1958. A textbook emphasizing the techniques of complex analysis in an elementary setting. Conformal mapping and applications of residues are given prominent treatment.

HILLE, EINAR. *Analytic Function Theory,* vols. 1 and 2. Boston: Ginn & Company, 1959, 1962. A modern treatise that treats the classical aspects of the subject together with topics that are still areas of active research.

KNOPP, KONRAD. *Elements of the Theory of Functions,* 1952; *Theory of Functions I,* 1945; *Theory of Functions II,* 1947; *Problem Book I,* 1948; *Problem Book II,* 1952. These small books contain an astonishing amount of subject matter, eminently readable. The problems are quite challenging.

MACROBERT, THOMAS M. *Functions of a Complex Variable.* New York: The Macmillan Company, 1947. An exposition of complex variable theory, with emphasis on special functions, and giving an extensive treatment of contour integration. Problems galore adorn the text, ranging from those exhibiting techniques to those that are common in English textbooks.

NEHARI, ZEEV. *Introduction to Complex Analysis.* Boston: Allyn and Bacon, Inc., 1961. An excellent introduction to the subject, exhibiting the master's hand at every turn. Interesting problems. Applications in hydrodynamics and electromagnetic theory.

NEHARI, ZEEV. *Conformal Mapping.* New York: McGraw-Hill Book Co., Inc., 1952. A comprehensive treatment of conformal mapping, made self-contained by including the theory of analytic functions. A good chapter on harmonic functions sets the stage.

PENNISI, LOUIS L. *Elements of Complex Variables.* New York: Holt, Rinehart and Winston, Inc., 1963. An excellent introduction to complex analysis, emphasizing technique as well as theory. Good illustrative examples and exercises.

PHILLIPS, E. G. *Functions of a Complex Variable with Applications.* New York: Interscience Publishers, Inc., 1949. This small book is an excellent introduction to the subject, has good problems, and a good elementary treatment of conformal mapping.

SANSONE, GIOVANNI, and GERRETSEN, JOHAN. *Lectures on the Theory of Functions of a Complex Variable.* Groningen, Netherlands: P. Noordhoff, N. V., 1960. A good treatment of the traditional subject matter with occasional interesting deviation from the standard proofs. Emphasis is on special topics such as elliptic functions, integral functions, Dirichlet series, summability, and asymptotic expansions.

THRON, WOLFGANG J. *Introduction to the Theory of Functions of a Complex Variable.* New York: John Wiley & Sons, Inc., 1953. A rigorous treatment of the subject in the "telegraph" style—theorem-proof-remark. Introduces the necessary topology that will yield rigorous proofs. The entire approach is theoretical, with no attention paid to the development of technique.

Other Books of Interest

DEAUX, ROLAND. *Introduction to the Geometry of Complex Numbers.* New York: Frederick Ungar, Inc., 1956. An exposition of the intriguing aspects of complex numbers in the plane.

HILDEBRAND, F. B. *Advanced Calculus for Engineers.* New York: Prentice-Hall, Inc., 1949. A good treatment of the application of conformal mapping to problems of fluid flow.

KAPLAN, WILFRED. *Advanced Calculus.* Reading, Mass.: Addison-Wesley Publishing Company, Inc., 1952. A good one-chapter treatment of the theory and techniques of complex analysis.

KOBER, H. *Dictionary of Conformal Representations.* New York: Dover Publications, 1952. An extensive tabulation of conformal maps, with a great deal of pertinent information.

MILNE-THOMAS, L. M. *Theoretical Hydrodynamics,* 4th ed. New York: The Macmillan Company, 1960. Extensive applications of complex analysis to problems in hydrodynamics, especially the use of the Schwarz-Christoffel transformation.

PIPES, LOUIS A. *Applied Mathematics for Engineers and Physicists,* 2nd ed. New York: McGraw-Hill Book Co., Inc., 1958. Good applications of complex analysis to problems in electrical engineering.

ROTHE, R., OLLENDORFF, F., and POHLHAUSEN, K. *Theory of Functions as Applied to Engineering Problems.* Cambridge, Mass.: Technology Press, MIT, 1951. The engineering problems are mostly in electrical engineering; problems in fluid flow are also considered.

SMITH, LLOYD P. *Mathematical Methods for Scientists and Engineers.* New York: Prentice-Hall, Inc., 1953. A good chapter on applications of complex analysis techniques to potential and fluid flow problems.

Part III

Fourier Analysis

One of the most important problems in the theory of functions is the determination of various representations of a function. A particular representation of a function becomes significant when it enables us to deduce properties of that function which are not readily ascertained from other representations. We shall be primarily concerned in this chapter with real functions; whenever we wish to refer to complex functions, we shall do so explicitly.

The student is familiar with the geometric representation of a function; such a representation affords us the opportunity of determining at a glance the relationships among various values of the function such as its maximum and minimum values, where the values of the function are positive, negative, or zero, the intervals where the function is increasing or decreasing—in short, it gives us a global picture of the function. However, geometric representation is not very effective for the study of the function at a specific point, such as the determination of its value at that point to any desired degree of accuracy. For such a purpose, the representation of a function as an infinite series of functions whose properties are well known is most useful.

The simplest functions that we have encountered are the powers of x: $1, x, x^2, \cdots$ or, to generalize slightly, the powers of x about the constant a: $1, x - a, (x - a)^2, \cdots$. These functions are continuous and differentiable everywhere, and furthermore for any value of x, their values are readily and precisely determined. These functions lead to power series of the form $\sum_{n=0}^{\infty} a_n(x - a)^n$, where a_n, $n = 0, 1, \cdots$ are constants. We say that the function f has a power series or Taylor series about $x = a$ if $a_n = f^{(n)}(a)/n!$ Now, if the series

$$\sum_{n=0}^{\infty} \frac{f^{(n)}(a)}{n!} (x - a)^n$$

converges to $f(x)$ for every x in some interval of the form $a - c < x < a + c$, then the series is a representation of f in the given interval. In view of the simplicity of the powers of x, it would be ideal if every function had a power series that was convergent to this function in some interval. Unfortunately, this is not the case; in order that the power series of f about $x = a$ converge to $f(x)$ in some interval, f must have derivatives of all orders, and the remainder in Taylor's formula must approach zero as $n \to \infty$ [VDd]. The requirement that the function have derivatives of all orders is highly restrictive, indeed; it excludes such a simple function as

$$f(x) = \begin{cases} x, & 0 \leq x \leq 1 \\ 2 - x, & 1 \leq x \leq 2 \end{cases}$$

from being represented as a power series, since f is not differentiable at $x = 1$. Furthermore, many of the functions that we encounter in modern technology are not differentiable at one or more points. Hence, we must seek a representation of such functions as infinite series other than power series. Once we have excluded the powers of x, perhaps the simplest functions are $\sin nx$ and $\cos nx$, $n = 1, 2, 3, \cdots$. It is natural to investigate the possibility of representing a given function in an infinite series of the form

$$A_0 + \sum_{n=1}^{\infty} a_n \cos nx + b_n \sin nx,$$

where A_0, a_n, b_n, $n = 1, 2, \cdots$ are constants. Such an investigation is the main substance of this part. We shall discover that many functions that do not have power series representations do have representations of this form.

Chapter 11

Fourier Series

1. The Fourier series of a function. A series of the form

$$A_0 + \sum_{n=1}^{\infty} a_n \cos nx + b_n \sin nx$$

is called a **trigonometric series.** We shall be concerned with the conditions under which a given function can be represented by such a series. First of all, we note that $\sin nx$ and $\cos nx$ are periodic functions with period 2π. In general, a function f is **periodic** if there exists a number $p \neq 0$ such that $f(x + p) = f(x)$ for all x in the domain of f; the smallest number p having this property is called the **period** of f. If a trigonometric series converges to a function f, then necessarily f is periodic with period 2π, for we have

$$\begin{aligned} f(x) &= A_0 + \sum_{n=1}^{\infty} a_n \cos nx + b_n \sin nx \\ &= A_0 + \sum_{n=1}^{\infty} a_n \cos n(x + 2\pi) + b_n \sin n(x + 2\pi) \\ &= f(x + 2\pi). \end{aligned}$$

Hence, the first condition that we must impose on a given function in order that it be represented by a trigonometric series is that this function be periodic with period 2π. We shall impose further conditions on the function subsequently.

What distinguishes one trigonometric series from another is the set of constants A_0, a_n, b_n, $n = 1, 2, \cdots$, and if a trigonometric series is to represent a function f, then we should be able to express these constants in terms of f. To this end, let us assume that f can be represented as a trigonometric series so that

$$\text{T:}\quad f(x) = A_0 + \sum_{m=1}^{\infty} a_m \cos mx + b_m \sin mx, \qquad -\pi \leq x \leq \pi.$$

We now integrate both sides of T from $-\pi$ to π, integrating the series term by term (we shall show later that if such a series does indeed represent a function, then the series can be integrated term by term to yield a series that is the representation of the integral of the function) to obtain

$$\int_{-\pi}^{\pi} f(x)\, dx = 2\pi A_0,$$

since

$$\int_{-\pi}^{\pi} \begin{Bmatrix} \cos mx \\ \sin mx \end{Bmatrix} dx = 0, \qquad m = 1, 2, \cdots.$$

Hence,

$$A_0 = \frac{1}{2\pi} \int_{-\pi}^{\pi} f(x)\, dx.$$

We now multiply both sides of T by $\cos nx$ and integrate from $-\pi$ to π, integrating the resulting series, term by term, to obtain

$$\int_{-\pi}^{\pi} f(x) \cos nx\, dx = \pi a_n,$$

since

$$\int_{-\pi}^{\pi} \cos mx \cos nx\, dx = \begin{cases} 0, & m \neq n \\ \pi, & m = n, \end{cases} \qquad m, n = 1, 2, \cdots.$$

Hence,

$$a_n = \frac{1}{\pi} \int_{-\pi}^{\pi} f(x) \cos nx\, dx, \qquad n = 1, 2, \cdots.$$

Similarly,

$$b_n = \frac{1}{\pi} \int_{-\pi}^{\pi} f(x) \sin nx\, dx, \qquad n = 1, 2, \cdots.$$

If we let $A_0 = a_0/2$, then we can write

$$a_n = \frac{1}{\pi} \int_{-\pi}^{\pi} f(x) \cos nx\, dx, \qquad n = 0, 1, 2, \cdots,$$

$$b_n = \frac{1}{\pi} \int_{-\pi}^{\pi} f(x) \sin nx\, dx, \qquad n = 1, 2, \cdots.$$

We have shown that if

$$f(x) = \frac{a_0}{2} + \sum_{n=1}^{\infty} a_n \cos nx + b_n \sin nx,$$

then necessarily a_n and b_n have the values given above.

We define the **Fourier series** of f to be the trigonometric series

$$\frac{a_0}{2} + \sum_{n=1}^{\infty} a_n \cos nx + b_n \sin nx,$$

where

$$a_n = \frac{1}{\pi}\int_{-\pi}^{\pi} f(x)\cos nx\,dx, \qquad n = 0, 1, 2, \cdots,$$

$$b_n = \frac{1}{\pi}\int_{-\pi}^{\pi} f(x)\sin nx\,dx, \qquad n = 1, 2, \cdots,$$

if these integrals exist; a_n and b_n are called the **Fourier coefficients** of f. We indicate that this series is the Fourier series of f by writing

$$f(x) \sim \frac{a_0}{2} + \sum_{n=1}^{\infty} a_n \cos nx + b_n \sin nx.$$

At this point it should be made clear that the symbol $\sim$ denotes that a certain trigonometric series is associated with a given function; it does not imply that the series converges to the function for any value of x. As a matter of fact, there exist functions whose Fourier series do not converge to their functions. Of course we shall be interested in the conditions under which $\sim$ can be replaced by $=$, so that the Fourier series of a function will be a representation of that function; but for the present, we merely associate a specific series with a function and call it its Fourier series.

The determination of the Fourier series of a function f reduces itself to the evaluation of three integrals:

$$a_0 = \frac{1}{\pi}\int_{-\pi}^{\pi} f(x)\,dx, \qquad a_n = \frac{1}{\pi}\int_{-\pi}^{\pi} f(x)\cos nx\,dx,$$

$$b_n = \frac{1}{\pi}\int_{-\pi}^{\pi} f(x)\sin nx\,dx.$$

(*Note:* a_0 and a_n, $n = 1, 2, \cdots$ must in general be evaluated separately.) The evaluation of these integrals can be simplified if we consider some properties of even and odd functions. A function f is said to be **even** if $f(-x) = f(x)$ for all x, and **odd** if $f(-x) = -f(x)$ for all x. The student should show that

(1) *If f is even, then*

$$a_n = \frac{2}{\pi}\int_{0}^{\pi} f(x)\cos nx\,dx, \quad n = 0, 1, 2, \cdots \quad \text{and} \quad b_n = 0, n = 1, 2, \cdots.$$

(2) *If f is odd, then*

$$a_n = 0, \quad n = 0, 1, 2, \cdots \quad \text{and} \quad b_n = \frac{2}{\pi}\int_{0}^{\pi} f(x)\sin nx\,dx, \quad n = 1, 2, \cdots.$$

We now consider some examples; in these examples, the functions are defined in the interval $-\pi \le x \le \pi$, with the assumption that they are periodic with period 2π so that their values are automatically determined for every value of x outside this interval.

EXAMPLE 1. Find the Fourier series of the function f, where

$$f(x) = \begin{cases} -1, & -\pi \leq x \leq 0 \\ 1, & 0 < x \leq \pi \end{cases}.$$

Solution. f is an odd function, so that $a_n = 0$, $n = 0, 1, 2, \cdots$ and

$$b_n = \frac{2}{\pi}\int_0^\pi \sin nx \, dx = \frac{2}{\pi n}[-\cos n\pi + 1] = \frac{2}{\pi n}[(-1)^{n+1} + 1].$$

Hence,

$$b_{2n} = 0 \quad \text{and} \quad b_{2n-1} = \frac{4}{\pi(2n-1)},$$

$$f(x) \sim \frac{4}{\pi}\sum_{n=1}^{\infty} \frac{\sin (2n-1)x}{2n-1}.$$

(See figure.)

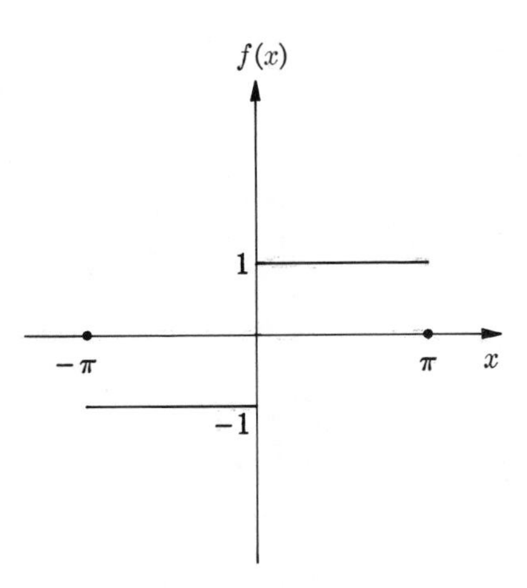

Example 1

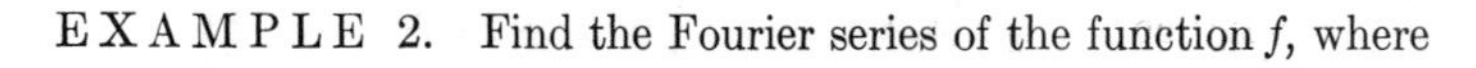

EXAMPLE 2. Find the Fourier series of the function f, where

$$f(x) = \begin{cases} 0, & -\pi \leq x \leq 0 \\ \frac{1}{4}\pi x, & 0 < x \leq \pi \end{cases}.$$

Solution

$$a_0 = \frac{1}{\pi}\int_0^\pi \frac{1}{4}\pi x \, dx = \frac{\pi^2}{8}.$$

$$a_n = \frac{1}{\pi}\int_0^\pi \frac{1}{4}\pi x \cos nx \, dx = \frac{1}{4n^2}(\cos n\pi - 1)$$

$$= \frac{1}{4n^2}[(-1)^n - 1],$$

so that

$$a_{2n} = 0 \quad \text{and} \quad a_{2n-1} = -\frac{1}{2(2n-1)^2}, \qquad n = 1, 2, \cdots,$$

$$b_n = \frac{1}{\pi}\int_0^\pi \frac{1}{4}\pi x \sin nx\, dx = -\frac{1}{4n}\cos n\pi$$

$$= \frac{(-1)^{n+1}}{4n}, \qquad n = 1, 2, \cdots.$$

Hence,

$$f(x) \sim \frac{\pi^2}{16} - \frac{1}{2}\sum_{n=1}^{\infty}\left[\frac{\cos(2n-1)x}{(2n-1)^2} + \frac{(-1)^n}{2n}\sin nx\right].$$

(See figure.)

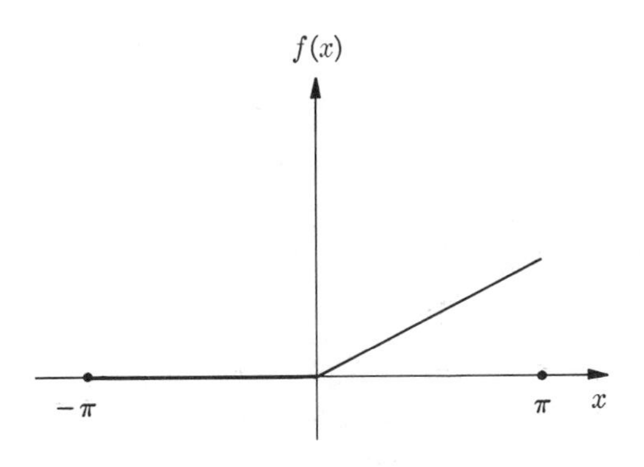

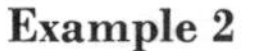

Example 2

2. Other forms of Fourier series. We now express the Fourier series of a function f in other forms, which are more convenient for certain purposes.

Let the Fourier coefficients of f, a_n and b_n, $n = 1, 2, \cdots$, be the sides of a right triangle and let $\theta_n = \tan^{-1}(b_n/a_n)$. Then

$$a_n \cos nx + b_n \sin nx = \sqrt{a_n^2 + b_n^2}\,[\cos nx \cos\theta_n + \sin nx \sin\theta_n]$$
$$= A_n \cos(nx - \theta_n),$$

where $A_n = \sqrt{a_n^2 + b_n^2}$, so that

$$f(x) \sim \frac{a_0}{2} + \sum_{n=1}^{\infty} A_n \cos(nx - \theta_n),$$

$$A_n = \frac{1}{\pi}\int_{-\pi}^{\pi} f(x)\cos(nx - \theta_n)\, dx, \qquad n = 1, 2, \cdots.$$

(The student should establish this expression for A_n.) This form is used extensively by electrical engineers. If $f(x)$ represents a voltage or current, then $A_n \cos(nx - \theta)$ is called the nth harmonic of $f(x)$ and A_n is the amplitude of this harmonic.

Since

$$\cos nx = \frac{e^{inx} + e^{-inx}}{2} \quad \text{and} \quad \sin nx = \frac{e^{inx} - e^{-inx}}{2i},$$

we have that

$$a_n \cos nx + b_n \sin nx = \frac{a_n - ib_n}{2} e^{inx} + \frac{a_n + ib_n}{2} e^{-inx}.$$

Let $c_n = (a_n - ib_n)/2$, so that

$$\bar{c}_n = \frac{a_n + ib_n}{2}, \qquad n = 1, 2, \cdots,$$

and let $c_0 = a_0/2$. Then the Fourier series of f becomes

$$c_0 + \sum_{n=1}^{\infty} c_n e^{inx} + \bar{c}_n e^{-inx},$$

which can be written in the very compact form

$$\sum_{n=-\infty}^{\infty} c_n e^{inx},$$

if we define $c_{-n} = \bar{c}_n$. Now

$$\begin{aligned} c_n &= \frac{a_n - ib_n}{2} \\ &= \frac{1}{2\pi}\left[\int_{-\pi}^{\pi} f(x) \cos nx\, dx - i \int_{-\pi}^{\pi} f(x) \sin nx\, dx\right] \\ &= \frac{1}{2\pi} \int_{-\pi}^{\pi} f(x)\, [\cos nx - i \sin nx]\, dx \\ &= \frac{1}{2\pi} \int_{-\pi}^{\pi} f(x) e^{-inx}\, dx. \end{aligned}$$

Furthermore,

$$c_{-n} = \bar{c}_n = \frac{1}{2\pi} \int_{-\pi}^{\pi} f(x) e^{inx}\, dx,$$

since $\overline{e^{-inx}} = e^{inx}$. Therefore,

$$f(x) \sim \sum_{n=-\infty}^{\infty} c_n e^{-inx}; \quad c_n = \frac{1}{2\pi} \int_{-\pi}^{\pi} f(x) e^{-inx}\, dx, \quad n = \cdots -1, 0, 1 \cdots.$$

This is called the **complex form** of the Fourier series of f or the **complex Fourier series** of f.

Thus far we have considered the Fourier series of functions of period 2π. We now determine the Fourier series of functions of period $2p$, where p is any nonzero real number. In the Fourier series of f:

$$f(x) \sim \frac{a_0}{2} + \sum_{n=1}^{\infty} a_n \cos nx + b_n \sin nx,$$

$$a_n = \frac{1}{\pi} \int_{-\pi}^{\pi} f(x) \cos nx\, dx, \qquad n = 0, 1, 2, \cdots,$$

$$b_n = \frac{1}{\pi}\int_{-\pi}^{\pi} f(x)\sin nx\,dx, \qquad n = 1, 2, \cdots,$$

we make the change in variable $x = \pi t/p$ to obtain

$$f(t) \sim \frac{a_0}{2} + \sum_{n=1}^{\infty} a_n \cos\frac{n\pi t}{p} + b_n \sin\frac{n\pi t}{p},$$

$$a_n = \frac{1}{p}\int_{-p}^{p} F(t)\cos\frac{n\pi t}{p}\,dt, \qquad n = 0, 1, 2, \cdots,$$

$$b_n = \frac{1}{p}\int_{-p}^{p} F(t)\sin\frac{n\pi t}{p}\,dt, \qquad n = 1, 2, \cdots,$$

where

$$F(t) = f\left(\frac{\pi t}{p}\right),$$

so that $F(t + 2p) = F(t)$.

EXAMPLE. Find the Fourier series of the function f where $f(x) = x^2$, $|x| \leq 1$ and $f(x + 2) = f(x)$ for all x.

Solution. $p = 1$. Since f is even, $b_n = 0$, $n = 1, 2, \cdots$ and

$$a_0 = 2\int_0^1 x^2\,dx = \frac{2}{3},$$

$$a_n = 2\int_0^1 x^2 \cos n\pi x\,dx = \frac{4}{n^2\pi^2}(-1)^n, \qquad n = 1, 2, \cdots.$$

Hence,

$$f(x) \sim \frac{1}{3} + \frac{4}{\pi^2}\sum_{n=1}^{\infty}\frac{(-1)^n}{n^2}\cos n\pi x.$$

If often happens that a function f is defined in an interval of length $2p$, not necessarily $-p \leq x \leq p$, and then defined for all other x by $f(x + 2p) = f(x)$. Let us say that this interval is $c \leq x \leq c + 2p$. The student should show that

$$f(x) \sim \frac{a_0}{2} + \sum_{n=1}^{\infty} a_n \cos\frac{n\pi}{p}x + b_n \sin\frac{n\pi}{p}x,$$

$$a_n = \frac{1}{p}\int_c^{c+2p} f(x)\cos\frac{n\pi x}{p}\,dx, \qquad n = 0, 1, 2, \cdots,$$

$$b_n = \frac{1}{p}\int_c^{c+2p} f(x)\sin\frac{n\pi x}{p}\,dx, \qquad n = 1, 2, \cdots.$$

With this form, we are able to find the Fourier series of any function of period $2p$ whose Fourier coefficients exist.

3. Fourier sine and cosine series. For some purposes it is advantageous to have either $a_n = 0$, $n = 0, 1, 2, \cdots$ or $b_n = 0$, $n = 1, 2, \cdots$ in the Fourier series of the function; i.e., a Fourier series with sine terms only or cosine terms only. As we have seen, the Fourier series of an odd function contains only sine terms, whereas that of an even function contains only cosine terms. If the function is neither even nor odd, it will in general contain both sine and cosine terms. Now, suppose that we are interested in a function f defined only in the interval $0 \leq x \leq p$. Then, if we wish the Fourier series of f to contain only sine terms, we define f in $-p \leq x \leq 0$, so that $f(-x) = -f(x)$, and for all other x, $f(x + 2p) = f(x)$. We say that we have defined the **odd periodic extension** of f. The Fourier series of this extended function will have only sine terms; we call it the Fourier **sine series** of f.

On the other hand, if we wish the Fourier series of f to contain only cosine terms, we define f in $-p \leq x \leq 0$, so that $f(-x) = f(x)$, and for all other x, $f(x + 2p) = f(x)$. Here we have defined the **even periodic extension** of f, and its Fourier series will have only cosine terms; we call it the Fourier **cosine series** of f. Now, if we are interested in a function defined in $-p \leq x \leq p$, then we have no control over the nature of the terms in its Fourier series. We can therefore say that if f is defined in $0 \leq x \leq p$, then either

$$f(x) \sim \sum_{n=1}^{\infty} b_n \sin \frac{n\pi}{p} x, \qquad b_n = \frac{2}{p} \int_0^p f(x) \sin \frac{n\pi x}{p}\, dx, \qquad n = 1, 2, \cdots,$$

or

$$f(x) \sim \frac{a_0}{2} + \sum_{n=1}^{\infty} a_n \cos \frac{n\pi x}{p}, \qquad a_n = \frac{2}{p} \int^p f(x) \cos \frac{n\pi x}{p}\, dx,$$
$$n = 0, 1, 2, \cdots.$$

EXAMPLE. Find the Fourier sine and cosine series of f where

$$f(x) = \begin{cases} \dfrac{\pi}{4} x, & 0 \leq x \leq \dfrac{1}{2}\pi \\ \dfrac{\pi}{4} (\pi - x), & \dfrac{1}{2}\pi < x \leq \pi \end{cases}$$

Solution

$$b_n = \frac{2}{\pi} \int_0^\pi f(x)\, dx = \frac{1}{2} \left[\int_0^{\pi/2} x \sin nx\, dx + \int_{\pi/2}^{\pi} (\pi - x) \sin nx\, dx \right]$$
$$= \frac{1}{n^2} \sin \frac{n\pi}{2} = \frac{(-1)^{n+1}}{(2n-1)^2}.$$

Hence,

$$f(x) \sim \sum_{n=1}^{\infty} \frac{(-1)^{n+1} \sin (2n-1)}{(2n-1)^2}, \qquad 0 \leq x \leq \pi.$$

Now,

$$a_0 = \frac{\pi^2}{8}, \qquad a_n = -1/n,$$

and

$$f(x) \sim \frac{\pi^2}{16} - \sum_{n=1}^{\infty} \frac{\cos nx}{n}, \qquad 0 \leq x \leq \pi.$$

4. The convergence of Fourier series. We have seen that if the Fourier coefficients of a function exist, then we can associate a Fourier series with this function. Hitherto, we have been concerned with the determination of the Fourier series of given functions. We have not examined these series for convergence, let alone determining whether they converge to the functions with which they are associated. The Fourier series of a function, even though convergent, may not converge to the function. Our problem is to determine the properties of a function that will ensure the convergence of its Fourier series to that function. We shall then have solved the problem of the representation of a function by its Fourier series.

We noted earlier that one of the properties that a function must have, in order that its Fourier series converge to it, is that it be periodic with period 2π. Henceforth, we shall consider only functions with this property; furthermore, in order to be definite, the functions will be defined in $-\pi \leq x \leq \pi$. Actually, this is no restriction, for given any other finite interval in which a function is defined, we can always transform it to the interval $-\pi \leq x \leq \pi$ by a linear change in variable.

First of all, let us consider under what conditions the Fourier series of a function f actually exists. We have seen that the Fourier series of f is determined by its Fourier coefficients

$$\frac{1}{\pi}\int_{-\pi}^{\pi} f(x) \cos nx \, dx, \qquad n = 0, 1, 2, \cdots,$$

and

$$\frac{1}{\pi}\int_{-\pi}^{\pi} f(x) \sin nx \, dx, \qquad n = 1, 2, \cdots.$$

These Fourier coefficients will exist, provided $f(x) \cos nx$ and $f(x) \sin nx$ are integrable in $-\pi \leq x \leq \pi$. Since $\cos nx$ and $\sin nx$ are bounded integrable functions, $f(x) \cos nx$ and $f(x) \sin nx$ will be integrable in $-\pi \leq x \leq \pi$, provided f is integrable in this interval. (Is the product of two integrable functions always integrable?) We know that if f is continuous in $-\pi \leq x \leq \pi$, then it will be integrable there. However, the condition of continuity is too strong; i.e., the function may be integrable without being continuous. Moreover, if we were to consider only continuous functions, then many of the functions that arise in practice would have to be excluded from consideration. We shall show that a discontinuous function may still be integrable, depending on the nature of its discontinuities.

Let us discuss the discontinuities of a function in general. The limit of f as x approaches x_0 from the left will be denoted by $f(x_0-)$, and the limit of f as x approaches x_0 from the right by $f(x_0+)$. We shall say that the function f has a *finite discontinuity* (or finite jump) at x_0 if $f(x_0-)$ and $f(x_0+)$ both exist, but $f(x_0-) \neq f(x_0+)$. We shall call all other discontinuities of f *infinite discontinuities*. Note that a necessary and sufficient condition that f be continuous at x_0 is that $f(x_0-) = f(x_0+)$.

EXAMPLE 1. The function f such that

$$f(x) = \begin{cases} \dfrac{x}{\pi} + 1, & -\pi \le x \le 0 \\[2ex] \dfrac{x}{\pi} - 1, & 0 < x \le \pi \end{cases}$$

has a finite discontinuity at $x = 0$, for $f(0-) = 1$ and $f(0+) = -1$. (See figure.)

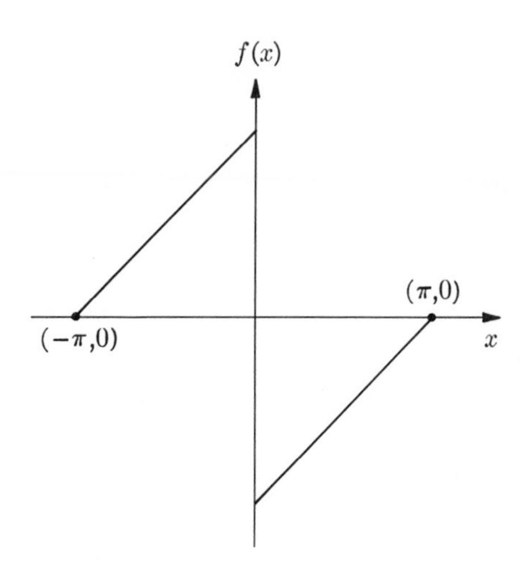

Example 1

EXAMPLE 2. The function f such that

$$f(x) = \begin{cases} 0, & -\pi \le x \le 0 \\[2ex] \dfrac{1}{x}, & 0 < x \le \pi \end{cases}$$

has an infinite discontinuity at $x = 0$, since $f(0+)$ does not exist. (See figure.)

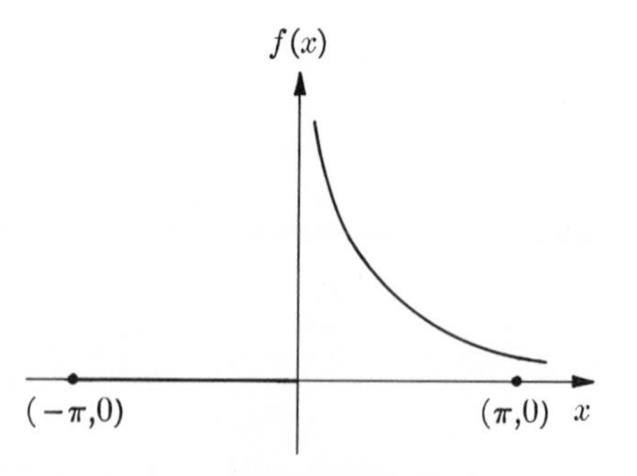

Example 2

We shall say that a function f is **piecewise continuous** in the finite interval $a \leq x \leq b$ if it has only a finite number of finite discontinuities in $a \leq x \leq b$ and $f(a+)$ and $f(b-)$ exist; f is piecewise continuous in an infinite interval if it is piecewise continuous in every finite interval contained in this interval. If f is piecewise continuous in $-\pi \leq x \leq \pi$ and is periodic with period 2π, then f is piecewise continuous in $-\infty < x < \infty$. It will be continuous at $x = k\pi$, $k = \pm 1, \pm 2, \cdots$ only if $f(-\pi) = f(\pi)$; otherwise, these will all be points of discontinuity of f.

EXAMPLE 3. Let f be defined as follows:

$$f(x) = \begin{cases} x^2, & x \leq 0 \\ \left[\dfrac{1}{x}\right], & 0 < x \leq 1 \\ \dfrac{1}{2-x}, & 1 \leq x < 2 \\ 1, & 2 \leq x \leq 3 \end{cases}$$

and $f(x + 1) = f(x)$, $x > 3$. (See figure.) Now f is continuous for $x \leq 0$; it is

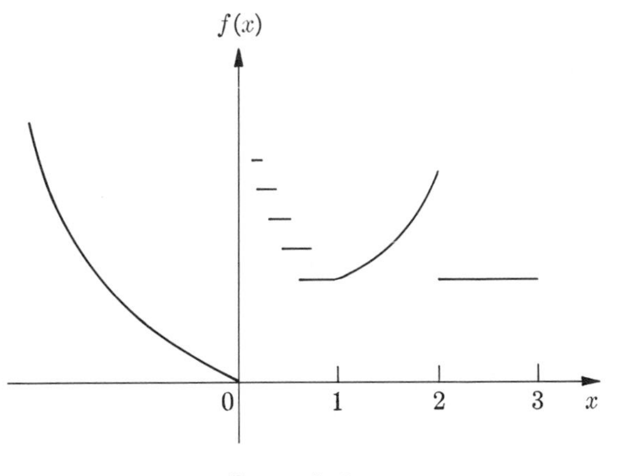

Example 3

piecewise continuous in $2 \leq x \leq 3$; it is not piecewise continuous in $0 \leq x \leq 1$, for it has an infinite number of discontinuities there; it is piecewise continuous in $\frac{1}{2} \leq x \leq 1$; it is not piecewise continuous in $1 \leq x \leq 3$, since it has an infinite discontinuity at $x = 2$; it is piecewise continuous for $x \geq 2$, since every finite interval in this interval has a finite number of finite discontinuities.

Now we shall show that if f is piecewise continuous in $a \leq x \leq b$, then f is integrable in that interval. Let us recall the definition of the integral of f, continuous in $a \leq x \leq b$, a and b finite, except at the points $x_1 < x_2 < \cdots < x_n$ in this interval:

$$\int_a^b f(x)\,dx = \lim_{\substack{\epsilon_i,\eta_i \to 0 \\ i=1,2,\cdots,n}} \int_a^{x_1-\epsilon_1} f(x)\,dx + \int_{x_1+\eta_1}^{x_2-\epsilon_2} f(x)\,dx + \cdots + \int_{x_n-\eta_n}^{b} f(x)\,dx,$$

if this limit exists as $\epsilon_i, \eta_i \to 0$, $i = 1, 2, \cdots, n$, independently of each other; (if a, or b, is a point of discontinuity, we replace it by $a + \eta_0$, or $b - \epsilon_{n+1}$). Now, if $x_1, x_2, \cdots x_n$ are finite discontinuities, we can define f at x_i to be $f(x_i-)$ when x_i is the right-hand end point of an interval, and as $f(x_i+)$ when it is a left-hand end point, since we are assured of the existence of these limits. Hence, f will be continuous in each of the intervals of integration, and it follows that $\int_a^b f(x)\,dx$ exists if f is piecewise continuous in $a \leq x \leq b$.

Note that *the value of* $\int_a^b f(x)\,dx$, *f integrable in* $a \leq x \leq b$, *remains unchanged if we change or redefine the value of f at a finite number of points.*

We can now conclude: If f is piecewise continuous in $-\pi \leq x \leq \pi$, then its Fourier series exists.

Now, if f has a Fourier series, then this series is uniquely determined, since such a series is determined by the Fourier coefficients of the function and these are uniquely determined. However, since we can change the value of an integrable function at a finite number of points without changing the value of its integral, there exist an infinite number of functions having the same Fourier series.

Although the condition that a function be piecewise continuous in $-\pi \leq x \leq \pi$ is sufficient for the existence of the Fourier series of this function, it is not sufficient to ensure that the Fourier series will converge to the function. We must impose another condition on the function. First of all, we define the right-hand derivative of f at x_0 as

$$\lim_{u \to 0+} \frac{f(x_0 + u) - f(x_0+)}{u},$$

if this limit exists, and denote it as $f'_+(x_0)$; we define the left-hand derivative of f at x_0 similarly, and denote it as $f'_-(x_0)$. We shall say that f is **almost differentiable** in $a \leq x_0 \leq b$, if at every point $a < x_0 < b$, $f'_+(x_0)$ and $f'_-(x_0)$ exist, and $f'_+(a)$ and $f'_-(b)$ exist. We say that f is **piecewise smooth** in $a \leq x \leq b$ if both f and f' are piecewise continuous there. To say that f' is piecewise continuous means that if $a < x_0 < b$, $\lim_{x \to x_0+} f'(x)$ and $\lim_{x \to x_0-} f'(x)$ exist and $\lim_{x \to a+} f'(x)$ and $\lim_{x \to b-} f'(x)$ exist. We denote these one-sided limits by $f'(x_0+)$ and $f'(x_0-)$. The student must distinguish carefully between $f'(x_0+)$ and $f'_+(x_0)$ and between $f'(x_0-)$ and $f'_-(x_0)$; they need not be the same. Actually, it can be proved (Exercise 24(a), p. 394) that **if f is piecewise smooth in $a \leq x \leq b$, then it is almost differentiable there.** However, the converse is not true, as the following example shows.

EXAMPLE 4. Let $f(x) = x^2 \sin(1/x)$, $0 < x \le 1$, $f(0) = 0$. Then $f'(x) = 2x \sin(1/x) - \cos(1/x)$ and $f'(0+)$ does not exist. But

$$\lim_{x\to 0+} \frac{x^2 \sin(1/x) - f(0+)}{x - 0} = \lim_{x\to 0+} x \sin\frac{1}{x} = 0.$$

Hence, almost differentiability is a weaker property than piecewise smoothness.

EXAMPLE 5. The function f such that $f(x) = x$, $0 \le x \le 1$, $f(x) = 2 - x$, $1 \le x \le 2$, is continuous in $0 \le x \le 2$; it is piecewise smooth there, and hence it is almost differentiable there. $f'(1+) = f'_+(1) = -1$, $f'(1-) = f'_-(1) = 1$.

EXAMPLE 6. The function f such that $f(x) = x^{1/3}$, $-\pi \le x \le \pi$, is continuous in this interval, but $f'_+(0)$ and $f'_-(0)$ do not exist; hence, f is not almost differentiable in the given interval.

We shall show presently that the Fourier series of a piecewise continuous and almost differentiable function converges to certain values of that function. We do this by determining $\lim_{n\to\infty} s_n(x)$, where $s_n(x)$ is the nth partial sum of the Fourier series of the function.

We now express the nth partial sum $s_n(x)$ of the Fourier series of f in a form such that its limit is easily determined. If a_n, $n = 0, 1, 2, \cdots$, and b_n, $n = 1, 2, \cdots$, are the Fourier coefficients of f, then

$$\begin{aligned} s_n(x) &= \frac{a_0}{2} + \sum_{k=1}^{n} a_k \cos kx + b_k \sin kx, \qquad n = 1, 2, \cdots \\ &= \frac{1}{2\pi}\int_{-\pi}^{\pi} f(t)\,dt + \frac{1}{\pi}\sum_{k=1}^{n}\left[\left(\int_{-\pi}^{\pi} f(t)\cos kt\,dt\right)\cos kx \right. \\ &\qquad \left. + \left(\int_{-\pi}^{\pi} f(t)\sin kt\,dt\right)\sin kx\right] \\ &= \frac{1}{\pi}\int_{-\pi}^{\pi} f(t)\left[\frac{1}{2} + \sum_{k=1}^{n} \cos kt\cos kx + \sin kt \sin kx\right] dt \\ &= \frac{1}{\pi}\int_{-\pi}^{\pi} f(t)\left[\frac{1}{2} + \sum_{k=1}^{n} \cos k(t - x)\right] dt \\ &= \frac{1}{\pi}\int_{-\pi}^{\pi} f(t)\,\frac{\sin(n + \frac{1}{2})(t - x)}{2\sin\left(\frac{t - x}{2}\right)}\,dt \end{aligned}$$

(p. 189, Exercise 27) or, since $2 \sin \frac{1}{2}x \cos kx = \sin(k + \frac{1}{2})x - \sin(k - \frac{1}{2})x$,

$$\begin{aligned} 2\sin\frac{x}{2}\left[\frac{1}{2} + \sum_{k=1}^{n}\cos kx\right] &= \sin\frac{x}{2} + \left[\sin\frac{3x}{2} - \sin\frac{x}{2}\right] + \cdots \\ &\quad + \left[\sin\left(n + \frac{1}{2}\right)x - \sin\left(n - \frac{1}{2}\right)x\right] \\ &= \sin\left(n + \frac{1}{2}\right)x. \end{aligned}$$

With the change in variable $u = t - x$, we have

$$s_n(x) = \frac{1}{\pi}\int_{-\pi-x}^{\pi-x} f(u+x)\,\frac{\sin\,(n+\frac{1}{2})u}{2\sin\,(u/2)}\,du.$$

We let

$$D_n(u) = \frac{\sin\,(n+\frac{1}{2})u}{2\sin\,(u/2)}.$$

$D_n(u)$ is called the **Dirichlet kernel.** It has three important properties:

K$_1$: $D_n(u)$ is periodic with period 2π.
K$_2$: $D_n(-u) = D_n(u)$.
K$_3$: $\dfrac{1}{\pi}\displaystyle\int_{-\pi}^{\pi} D_n(u)\,du = 1.$

K_1 and K_2 are immediate and K_3 follows by integrating both sides of

$$\frac{1}{2} + \sum_{k=1}^{n} \cos ku = D_n(u) \qquad \text{from } -\pi \text{ to } \pi.$$

With K_1 and Exercise 15, p. 391, it follows that

$$s_n(x) = \int_{-\pi}^{\pi} f(u+x)\,D_n(u)\,du.$$

In order to determine $\lim\limits_{n\to\infty} s_n(x)$, we need to establish some properties of the Fourier coefficients of a function—these are significant in their own right. First, we have

Bessel's inequality. If f is piecewise continuous in $-\pi \le x \le \pi$ and a_n, $n = 0, 1, 2, \cdots$, b_n, $n = 1, 2, \cdots$, are its Fourier coefficients, then

$$\frac{a_0^2}{2} + \sum_{k=1}^{n} (a_k^2 + b_k^2) \le \frac{1}{\pi}\int_{-\pi}^{\pi} f^2(x)\,dx, \qquad n = 1, 2, \cdots.$$

Proof. With the use of the definitions of the Fourier coefficients, the nth partial sum $s_n(x)$, and the fact that certain trigonometric integrals vanish, we can establish

$$\text{(1)} \qquad \frac{a_0^2}{2} = \frac{1}{\pi}\int_{-\pi}^{\pi} \frac{a_0}{2} f(x)\,dx = \frac{1}{\pi}\int_{-\pi}^{\pi} \frac{a_0}{2} s_n(x)\,dx.$$

$$\text{(2)} \qquad a_k^2 = \frac{1}{\pi}\int_{-\pi}^{\pi} a_k f(x)\cos kx\,dx = \frac{1}{\pi}\int_{-\pi}^{\pi} a_k s_n(x)\cos kx\,dx.$$

$$\text{(3)} \qquad b_k^2 = \frac{1}{\pi}\int_{-\pi}^{\pi} b_k f(x)\sin kx\,dx = \frac{1}{\pi}\int_{-\pi}^{\pi} b_k s_n(x)\sin kx\,dx,$$

$k = 1, 2, \cdots, n.$

Adding the $2n+1$ equations in (1), (2), (3):

$$\frac{a_0^2}{2} + \sum_{k=1}^{n} (a_k^2 + b_k^2) = \frac{1}{\pi}\int_{-\pi}^{\pi} f(x)\left[\frac{a_0}{2} + \sum_{k=1}^{n} a_k\cos kx + b_k \sin kx\right]dx$$

$$= \frac{1}{\pi}\int_{-\pi}^{\pi} s_n(x)\left[\frac{a_0}{2} + \sum_{k=1}^{n} a_k\cos kx + b_k \sin kx\right]dx,$$

or

$$\frac{a_0^2}{2} + \sum_{k=1}^{n} (a_k^2 + b_k^2) = \frac{1}{\pi} \int_{-\pi}^{\pi} f(x)s_n(x)\, dx = \frac{1}{\pi} \int_{-\pi}^{\pi} s_n^2(x)\, dx.$$

Now,

$$\begin{aligned} 0 &\le \int_{-\pi}^{\pi} [f(x) - s_n(x)]^2\, dx \\ &= \int_{-\pi}^{\pi} f^2(x)\, dx - 2\int_{-\pi}^{\pi} f(x)s_n(x)\, dx + \int_{-\pi}^{\pi} s_n^2(x)\, dx \\ &= \int_{-\pi}^{\pi} f^2(x)\, dx - \int_{-\pi}^{\pi} f(x)s_n(x)\, dx \\ &= \int_{-\pi}^{\pi} f^2(x)\, dx - \frac{a_0^2}{2} - \sum_{k=1}^{n} (a_k^2 + b_k^2), \end{aligned}$$

using the result given above. The required inequality follows immediately. Where did we use the fact that f is piecewise continuous?

It follows immediately from Bessel's inequality that the series

$$\frac{a_0^2}{2} + \sum_{n=1}^{\infty} (a_n^2 + b_n^2)$$

is convergent, for the nth partial sum of this series is less than or equal to a constant for all n; i.e., it is bounded, and clearly it is increasing, so that its limit exists. We use this result to prove the significant

RIEMANN-LEBESGUE THEOREM. If f is piecewise continuous in $-\pi \le x \le \pi$, then

$$\lim_{n\to\infty} \int_{-\pi}^{\pi} f(x) \cos nx\, dx = \lim_{n\to\infty} \int_{-\pi}^{\pi} f(x) \sin nx\, dx = 0.$$

Proof. Since f is piecewise continuous in $-\pi \le x \le \pi$, its Fourier coefficients a_n, $n = 0, 1, \cdots$, $b_n = 1, 2, \cdots$ exist. But since

$$\frac{a_0^2}{2} + \sum_{n=1}^{\infty} (a_n^2 + b_n^2)$$

is convergent,

$$\lim_{n\to\infty} (a_n^2 + b_n^2) = 0 \quad \text{or} \quad \lim_{n\to\infty} a_n = \lim_{n\to\infty} b_n = 0.$$

The result now follows from the definition of the Fourier coefficients.

COROLLARY. If f is piecewise continuous in $-\pi \le x \le \pi$, then

$$\lim_{n\to\infty} \int_{-\pi}^{\pi} f(x) \sin (n + \tfrac{1}{2})x\, dx = 0.$$

Proof.

$$\int_{-\pi}^{\pi} f(x) \sin\left(n + \frac{1}{2}\right) x\, dx = \int_{-\pi}^{\pi} f(x) \sin\frac{x}{2} \cos nx\, dx + \int_{-\pi}^{\pi} f(x) \cos\frac{x}{2} \sin nx\, dx.$$

Since $f(x)\sin(x/2)$ and $f(x)\cos(x/2)$ are piecewise continuous, the result follows with the use of the theorem.

This corollary will now enable us to prove our main theorem, which we call

THE FOURIER EXPANSION THEOREM. If f is periodic with period 2π, piecewise continuous, and almost differentiable in $-\pi \le x \le \pi$, and a_n, $n = 0, 1, 2, \cdots$, b_n, $n = 1, 2, \cdots$, are its Fourier coefficients, then for any x,

$$\frac{1}{2}[f(x+) + f(x-)] = \frac{a_0}{2} + \sum_{n=1}^{\infty} a_n \cos nx + b_n \sin nx.$$

Proof. We show that $\lim_{n\to\infty} s_n(x) = \frac{1}{2}[f(x-) + f(x+)]$. We have that

$$\begin{aligned} s_n(x) &= \frac{1}{\pi}\int_{-\pi}^{\pi} f(x+u)D_n(u)\,du \\ &= \frac{1}{\pi}\int_{-\pi}^{0} f(x+u)D_n(u)\,du + \frac{1}{\pi}\int_{0}^{\pi} f(x+u)D_n(u)\,du = \mathrm{I}_1 + \mathrm{I}_2. \end{aligned}$$

Now

$$\begin{aligned} \mathrm{I}_1 &= \frac{1}{\pi}\int_{-\pi}^{0} f(x+u)D_n(u)\,du \\ &= \frac{1}{\pi}\int_{-\pi}^{0} [f(x+u) - f(x-) + f(x-)]D_n(u)\,du \\ &= \frac{1}{\pi}\int_{-\pi}^{0} [f(x+u) - f(x-)]D_n(u)\,du + \frac{f(x-)}{\pi}\int_{-\pi}^{0} D_n(u)\,du \\ &= \frac{1}{\pi}\int_{-\pi}^{0} [f(x+u) - f(x-)]D_n(u)\,du + \frac{f(x-)}{2}, \end{aligned}$$

by K_2 and K_3. Now

$$[f(x+u) - f(x-)]D_n(u) = \frac{[f(x+u) - f(x-)]\sin(n+\frac{1}{2})u}{2\sin\frac{1}{2}u}.$$

If we can show that $\dfrac{f(x+u) - f(x-)}{2\sin\frac{1}{2}u}$ is piecewise continuous in $-\pi \le x \le \pi$, then

$$\lim_{n\to\infty}\int_{-\pi}^{0} [f(x+u) - f(x-)]D_n(u)\,du = 0,$$

by the corollary to the Riemann-Lebesgue theorem. It is clear that this is true for all $u \neq 0$. Now at $u = 0$,

$$\lim_{u\to 0-}\frac{f(x+u) - f(x-)}{2\sin\frac{1}{2}u} = \lim_{u\to 0-}\frac{f(x+u) - f(x-)}{u}.$$

$$\lim_{u\to 0-}\frac{1/(\sin\frac{1}{2}u)}{\frac{1}{2}u} = \lim_{u\to 0-}\frac{f(x+u) - f(x-)}{u} = f'_-(x),$$

which exists, since f is almost differentiable. Hence, at most,

$$\frac{f(x+u) - f(x-)}{2 \sin \frac{1}{2}u}$$

has a finite discontinuity at $u = 0$, and hence this function is piecewise continuous.

Therefore,

$$\lim_{n\to\infty} \mathrm{I}_1 = \frac{f(x-)}{2}.$$

By considering

$$\mathrm{I}_2 = \frac{1}{\pi}\int_0^\pi [f(x+u) - f(x+) + f(x+)]D_n(u)\,du,$$

it can be shown similarly that

$$\lim_{n\to\infty} \mathrm{I}_2 = \frac{f(x+)}{2}.$$

We therefore have that

$$\lim_{n\to\infty} s_n = \tfrac{1}{2}[f(x-) + f(x+)].$$

If x_0 is a point of continuity of f in $-\pi \le x \le \pi$, then $f(x_0-) = f(x_0+) = f(x_0)$, so that the preceding theorem can be stated as:

The Fourier series of a periodic piecewise continuous and almost differentiable function converges to the value of the function at points of continuity and to the average value (mean value) of the right-hand and left-hand limits at points of discontinuity.

We should hardly expect the Fourier series of a function to converge to the value of the function at points of discontinuity, since we can change the values of the function at these points without changing the Fourier series of the function; however, if we change the value of a function at a point of continuity, this point becomes a point of discontinuity. Note that if a function f is defined only in $-\pi \le x \le \pi$ and satisfies the conditions of the Fourier expansion theorem, then if x is any point outside this interval, the Fourier series of f evaluated at x will be automatically determined as the value of this series at t, $-\pi \le t \le \pi$, such that $f(t + 2k\pi) = f(t)$ for some integer k.

In the Fourier expansion theorem, the piecewise continuity and almost differentiability of the periodic function is a sufficient condition that leads to the result. This condition can be weakened in various ways (see Exercise 30, p. 397). However, the condition we have chosen has the advantage that the theorem can be proved without having to develop extensive mathematical apparatus. The student may be interested in knowing that not one of the sufficient conditions for the convergence of the Fourier series of a function that are known at the present time is also a necessary condition. Also, he may be surprised to discover that even if a function is continuous, its Fourier series need not converge to it.

In practice, however, it is often easier to establish that a function is piecewise smooth rather than almost differentiable; hence, let us strengthen the hypothesis of the Fourier expansion theorem so as to yield:

If f is periodic with period 2π and piecewise smooth in $-\pi \leq x \leq \pi$ and a_n, $n = 0, 1, 2, \cdots$, b_n, $n = 1, 2, \cdots$, are its Fourier coefficients, then for any x:

$$\frac{1}{2}[f(x+) + f(x-)] = \frac{a_0}{2} + \sum_{n=1}^{\infty} a_n \cos nx + b_n \sin nx.$$

EXAMPLE 7. Determine the sum of the series

$$S = \sum_{n=1}^{\infty} \frac{\sin (2n-1)x}{2n-1} \qquad \text{at } x = 0,\ 1,\ \pi,\ 4.$$

Solution. The Fourier series of

$$f(x) = \begin{cases} -1, & -\pi \leq x < 0 \\ 1, & 0 < x < \pi \end{cases} \quad \text{is} \quad \frac{4}{\pi}\sum_{n=1}^{\infty} \frac{\sin (2n-1)x}{2n-1}$$

(Example 1, p. 368). f is piecewise smooth and can be defined outside the given interval so that $f(x + 2\pi) = f(x)$. By the Fourier expansion theorem, $S = (\pi/4)f(x)$, if x is a point of continuity such as $x = 1, 4$, so that for these values $S = (\pi/4)$ and $(-\pi/4)$; $S = (\pi/8)[f(x+) + f(x-)]$ if x is a point of discontinuity such as $x = 1, \pi$, and for both these values, $S = 0$. Note that since each term of the series is 0 at $x = 0$ and π, we know in advance that its sum must be zero, and this example affords us an opportunity to check the theorem.

The Fourier expansion theorem is often very useful in determining the sum of a series of constant terms, as is illustrated in

EXAMPLE 8. Find the sum of $\sum_{n=1}^{\infty} \frac{1}{(2n-1)^2}$.

Solution. The procedure is to find the Fourier series of a function that, when evaluated at some point, will involve the given series. In Example 2, p. 368 we have the Fourier series

$$\frac{\pi^2}{16} - \frac{1}{2}\sum_{n=1}^{\infty} \frac{\cos (2n-1)x}{(2n-1)^2} + \frac{(-1)^n}{2n} \sin nx$$

of

$$f(x) = \begin{cases} 0, & -\pi \leq x \leq 0 \\ \frac{1}{4}\pi x, & 0 < x \leq \pi \end{cases},$$

which, when evaluated at $x = 0$, gives

$$\frac{\pi^2}{16} - \frac{1}{2}\sum_{n=1}^{\infty} \frac{1}{(2n-1)^2}.$$

But $x = 0$ is a point of continuity of f, so that

$$\frac{\pi^2}{16} - \frac{1}{2}\sum_{n=1}^{\infty} \frac{1}{(2n-1)^2} = f(0) = 0.$$

Hence,

$$\sum_{n=1}^{\infty} \frac{1}{(2n-1)^2} = \frac{\pi^2}{8}.$$

The Fourier expansion theorem remains valid for piecewise continuous and almost differentiable periodic functions of arbitrary period; its proof requires only a modification of the proof we have presented. In the sequel, we state and prove theorems concerning periodic functions of period 2π, this period being chosen to simplify our expressions. However, we shall tacitly assume that these theorems remain valid for an arbitrary period, the proofs of which can be obtained by a modification of the proofs of the given theorems. It is a good exercise for the student to restate all these theorems in terms of the arbitrary period.

With the Fourier expansion theorem, we can readily establish the

UNIQUENESS THEOREM. If f and g are continuous in $-\pi \leq x \leq \pi$ and have the same Fourier series, then $f = g$.

5. Operations on Fourier series. The study of the expansion of functions into power series indicates that a very effective method of determining some of these expansions is to perform on known power series of functions operations such as addition, multiplication, division, substitution, differentiation, and integration. However, not all these operations are effective in the case of Fourier series of functions. For example, suppose we are given the Fourier series of f and g and we wish to determine the Fourier series of fg. First of all, it does not necessarily follow that the existence of the Fourier series of f and g implies the existence of the Fourier series of fg. (In other words, if f and g are integrable, then fg is not necessarily integrable. Can you supply an illustrative example?)

However, if the Fourier series of fg does exist, we can determine it by multiplying together the Fourier series of f and g, replacing products of sines and cosines by their sums and differences, and finally collecting similar terms. However, it might be simpler to determine the Fourier coefficients of fg directly. On the other hand, there exists a relation between the Fourier coefficients of f and g and those of fg [see p. 441, Exercise 5(b)] that might prove useful. We shall, however, at this point consider only those operations on Fourier series of functions that are both useful and readily performed.

Since we are primarily concerned with the Fourier series of functions that represent these functions, our notation will be simplified if we "normalize" the function f by defining its value at a point of discontinuity x_0 to be $\frac{1}{2}[f(x_0+) + f(x_0-)]$. First we have the

THEOREM. If f and g are normalized functions such that

$$f(x) = \tfrac{1}{2}a_0 + \sum_{n=1}^{\infty} a_n \cos nx + b_n \sin nx$$

and

$$g(x) = \tfrac{1}{2}c_0 + \sum_{n=1}^{\infty} c_n \cos nx + d_n \sin nx,$$

then

(1) $$kf(x) = \frac{a_0 k}{2} + \sum_{n=1}^{\infty} a_n k \cos nx + b_n k \sin nx,$$

for any constant k.

(2) $$f(x) + g(x) = \tfrac{1}{2}(a_0 + c_0) + \sum_{n=1}^{\infty} (a_n + c_n) \cos nx + (b_n + d_n) \sin nx.$$

The proof is immediate and is left to the student.

We next consider the differentiation of the Fourier series of a function. We prove the

DIFFERENTIATION THEOREM FOR FOURIER SERIES. If f is continuous in $-\pi \leq x \leq \pi$ with $f(-\pi) = f(\pi)$, and if its derivative f' is piecewise continuous and almost differentiable and normalized, then the Fourier series

$$f(x) = \frac{a_0}{2} + \sum_{n=1}^{\infty} a_n \cos nx + b_n \sin nx$$

can be differentiated term by term to yield

$$f'(x) = \sum_{n=1}^{\infty} n(-a_n \sin nx + b_n \cos nx)$$

for those values of x for which $f'(x)$ exists.

Proof. Since f' is piecewise continuous and almost differentiable, its Fourier series converges to it; i.e.,

$$f'(x) = \frac{\alpha_0}{2} + \sum_{n=1}^{\infty} \alpha_n \cos nx + \beta_n \sin nx,$$

where

$$\alpha_n = \frac{1}{\pi}\int_{-\pi}^{\pi} f'(x) \cos nx \, dx \quad \text{and} \quad \beta_n = \frac{1}{\pi}\int_{-\pi}^{\pi} f'(x) \sin nx \, dx.$$

Integrating by parts (the student should show this is valid for piecewise continuous functions),

$$\alpha_n = \frac{1}{\pi}\left[(\cos nx) f(x)\Big|_{-\pi}^{\pi} + n\int_{-\pi}^{\pi} f(x) \sin nx \, dx\right] = nb_n,$$

since $f(\pi) = f(-\pi)$.

$$\beta_n = \frac{1}{\pi}\left[(\sin nx) f(x)\Big|_{-\pi}^{\pi} - n\int_{-\pi}^{\pi} f(x) \cos nx \, dx\right] = -na_n.$$

Note that $\alpha_0 = 0$. Hence,

$$f'(x) = \sum_{n=1}^{\infty} n(-a_n \sin nx + b_n \cos nx),$$

which can be obtained from the Fourier series of f by term-by-term differentiation.

We now turn to the integration of the Fourier series of a function. We have the

INTEGRATION THEOREM FOR FOURIER SERIES. If f is piecewise continuous in $-\pi \leq x \leq \pi$ and

$$f(x) \sim \frac{a_0}{2} + \sum_{n=1}^{\infty} a_n \cos nx + b_n \sin nx$$

then

$$\int_{-\pi}^{x} f(t)\, dt = \frac{a_0}{2}(x + \pi) + \sum_{n=1}^{\infty} \frac{1}{n}(a_n \sin nx + b_n \cos nx + (-1)^n b_n);$$

i.e., the Fourier series of f can be integrated term by term to yield a series that converges to the integral of f.

Proof. Define the function ϕ by $\phi(x) = \int_{-\pi}^{x} f(t)\, dt - \frac{1}{2}a_0 x$. Then ϕ is continuous (Exercise 19, p. 392), and since $\phi'(x) = f(x) - \frac{1}{2}a_0$, ϕ' is piecewise continuous, so ϕ is piecewise smooth. By the Fourier expansion theorem,

$$\phi(x) = \tfrac{1}{2}\alpha_0 + \sum_{n=1}^{\infty} \alpha_n \cos nx + \beta_n \sin nx,$$

where α_n and β_n are the Fourier coefficients of ϕ. Then, for $n \geq 1$,

$$\begin{aligned}
\alpha_n &= \frac{1}{\pi}\int_{-\pi}^{\pi} \phi(x) \cos nx\, dx \\
&= \frac{1}{n\pi}\phi(x) \sin nx \Big|_{-\pi}^{\pi} - \frac{1}{n\pi}\int_{-\pi}^{\pi} \phi'(x) \sin nx\, dx \\
&= -\frac{1}{n\pi}\int_{-\pi}^{\pi} \left(f(x) - \frac{a_0}{2}\right) \sin nx\, dx = -\frac{1}{n} b_n.
\end{aligned}$$

Similarly, $\beta_n = (1/n)a_n$. Hence,

$$\phi(x) = \frac{1}{2}\alpha_0 - \sum_{n=1}^{\infty} \frac{1}{n} a_n \sin nx - \frac{1}{n} b_n \cos nx.$$

But $\phi(\pi) = \pi a_0/2$ (why?), so that

$$\frac{1}{2} a_0 \pi = \frac{1}{2}\alpha_0 - \sum_{n=1}^{\infty} \frac{(-1)^n}{n} b_n.$$

Hence

$$\frac{1}{2}\alpha_0 = \frac{1}{2} a_0 \pi + \sum_{n=1}^{\infty} \frac{(-1)^n}{n} b_n,$$

and we have the result.

The student should carefully note that in the preceding theorem we merely *assumed the existence of the Fourier series of f and not its convergence to f*. As a matter of fact, the Fourier series could be divergent, and integration term by term would yield a convergent series, as is evidenced by the series

$$\sum_{n=1}^{\infty} (-1)^{n+1} \cos nx$$

which is divergent, since the limit of its nth term does not approach zero; however, integration term by term yields the convergent series

$$\sum_{n=1}^{\infty} \frac{(-1)^{n+1} \sin nx}{n}.$$

Note that integrating the Fourier series of f, term by term, will yield the Fourier series of the integral of f only if $a_0 = 0$, for otherwise the integrated series has the term x.

EXAMPLE 1. Determine the Fourier series of f where

$$f(x) = \begin{cases} \frac{1}{4}, & -\pi \leq x \leq 0 \\ \frac{1}{4}(\pi x - 1), & 0 < x \leq \pi \end{cases}.$$

Solution. Let

$$g(x) = \begin{cases} -1, & -\pi \leq x \leq 0 \\ 1, & 0 < x \leq \pi \end{cases} \quad \text{and} \quad h(x) = \begin{cases} 0, & -\pi \leq x \leq 0 \\ \frac{1}{4}\pi x, & 0 < x \leq \pi \end{cases}.$$

Then $f(x) = -\frac{1}{4}g(x) + h(x)$, and by Examples 1 and 2, p. 368, normalizing f,

$$f(x) = \frac{\pi^2}{16} - \sum_{n=1}^{\infty} \left[\frac{\cos(2n-1)x}{2(2n-1)^2} + \left(\frac{1}{4} - \frac{1}{\pi}\right)\frac{\sin(2n-1)x}{2n-1} - \frac{\sin 2nx}{8n}\right].$$

EXAMPLE 2. Determine the Fourier series of f, where $f(x) = |x|$, $-\pi \leq x \leq \pi$.

Solution

$$f(x) = \int_{-\pi}^{\pi} g(x)\, dx$$

where

$$g(x) = \begin{cases} -1, & -\pi \leq x \leq 0 \\ 1, & 0 < x \leq \pi \end{cases}.$$

Hence, with the use of the integration theorem for Fourier series, and Example 1, p. 368,

$$|x| = -\frac{4}{\pi}\left[\sum_{n=1}^{\infty} \frac{\cos(2n-1)x}{(2n-1)^2} + \sum_{n=1}^{\infty} \frac{1}{(2n-1)^2}\right].$$

But by Example 8, p. 382,

$$\sum_{n=1}^{\infty} \frac{1}{(2n-1)^2} = \frac{\pi^2}{8}$$

so that

$$|x| = -\frac{\pi}{2} - \frac{4}{\pi}\sum_{n=1}^{\infty} \frac{\cos(2n-1)x}{(2n-1)^2}.$$

EXERCISES

1. Determine the Fourier series of the following functions, defined in $-\pi \leq x \leq \pi$, and having period 2π:

(a) $f(x) = 0,\ -\pi \leq x < 0;\quad f(x) = 1,\ 0 \leq x \leq \pi$.
(b) $f(x) = x,\ -\pi \leq x \leq \pi$. (c) $f(x) = e^x,\ -\pi \leq x \leq \pi$.
(d) $f(x) = 0,\ -\pi \leq x \leq 0;\quad f(x) = \sin x,\ 0 < x < \pi$.
(e) $f(x) = -\frac{1}{2} - (x/2\pi),\ -\pi \leq x \leq 0;\quad f(x) = \frac{1}{2} - (x/2\pi),\ 0 < x \leq \pi$.
(f) $f(x) = -1,\ -\pi < x < 0;\ f(x) = 2,\ 0 < x < \pi;\ f(x) = \frac{1}{2},\ x = -\pi, 0, \pi$.
(g) $f(x) = \cosh x,\ -\pi \leq x \leq \pi$.
(h) $f(x) = x \cos x,\ -\pi < x < \pi;\quad f(x) = 0,\ x = \pm\pi$.
(i) $f(x) = x + x^2,\ -\pi \leq x \leq \pi$.
(j) $f(x) = \sin \alpha x,\ -\pi \leq x \leq \pi$, α not an integer.
(k) $f(x) = 0,\ -\pi \leq x < 0;\ f(x) = 1,\ 0 \leq x < \pi/2;\ f(x) = -1,\ \pi/2 \leq x \leq \pi$.
(l) $f(x) = -\cos x,\ -\pi \leq x < 0;\quad f(x) = \cos x,\ 0 \leq x \leq \pi$.
(m) $f(x) = x + \pi,\ -\pi \leq x \leq 0;\ f(x) = x - \pi,\ 0 < x \leq \pi$.
(n) $f(x) = \operatorname{Log}\,[2 \cos (x/2)],\ -\pi < x < \pi$.
(o) $f(x) = \sin x + 3 \sin 2x + 2 \sin 3x,\ -\pi \leq x \leq \pi$.

Ans.: (a) $\dfrac{1}{2} + \dfrac{2}{\pi} \sum_{n=1}^{\infty} \dfrac{\sin (2n - 1)x}{2n - 1}$; (b) $2 \sum_{n=1}^{\infty} \dfrac{(-1)^{n+1} \sin nx}{n}$;

(c) $\dfrac{2 \sinh \pi}{\pi} \left[\dfrac{1}{2} + \sum_{n=1}^{\infty} \dfrac{(-1)^n}{1 + n^2} (\cos nx - n \sin nx)\right]$;

(d) $\dfrac{1}{\pi} + \dfrac{1}{2} \sin x - \dfrac{2}{\pi} \sum_{n=1}^{\infty} \dfrac{\cos 2nx}{4n^2 - 1}$; (e) $\dfrac{1}{\pi} \sum_{n=1}^{\infty} \dfrac{\sin nx}{n}$;

(f) $\dfrac{1}{2} + \dfrac{6}{\pi} \sum_{n=1}^{\infty} \dfrac{\sin (2n - 1)x}{2n - 1}$; (g) $\dfrac{2 \sinh \pi}{\pi} \left(\dfrac{1}{2} - \sum_{n=1}^{\infty} \dfrac{\cos nx}{n^2 + 1}\right)$;

(h) $-\dfrac{1}{2} \sin x + 2 \sum_{n=2}^{\infty} \dfrac{(-1)^n n}{n^2 - 1} \sin nx$;

(i) $\dfrac{\pi^2}{3} + 4 \sum_{n=1}^{\infty} \dfrac{(-1)^n \cos nx}{n^2} + \dfrac{(-1)^{n+1} \sin nx}{2n}$; (j) $\dfrac{2}{\pi} \sin \alpha\pi \sum_{n=1}^{\infty} \dfrac{n \sin nx}{n^2 - \alpha^2}$;

(k) $\dfrac{2}{\pi} \sum_{n=1}^{\infty} \dfrac{(-1)^{n+1} \cos (2n - 1)x}{2n - 1} + \dfrac{\sin (4n - 2)x}{2n - 1}$; (l) $\dfrac{8}{\pi} \sum_{n=1}^{\infty} \dfrac{(n + 1) \sin 2nx}{4n^2 - 1}$;

(m) $-2 \sum_{n=1}^{\infty} \dfrac{\sin n\pi}{n}$; (n) $\sum_{n=1}^{\infty} (-1)^{n+1} \dfrac{\cos nx}{n}$.

2. The following functions are defined in a given finite interval; they are periodic with period equal to the length of this interval. Determine their Fourier series.

(a) $f(x) = 2x - 1,\ -1 \leq x \leq 1$.
(b) $f(x) = 1 + \sin x,\ -1 \leq x \leq 1$.
(c) $f(x) = 2,\ -2 \leq x \leq 0;\ f(x) = x,\ 0 < x \leq 2$.
(d) $f(x) = x^2,\ -L \leq x \leq L$.
(e) $f(x) = 0,\ -2 \leq x \leq -1;\ f(x) = 1 + x,\ -1 < x < 0;\ f(x) = 1 - x,\ 0 \leq x < 1;\ f(x) = 0,\ 1 \leq x \leq 2$.
(f) $f(x) = x \sin x,\ 0 \leq x \leq 2\pi$.

(g) $f(x) = x^2,\ 0 \le x \le \pi;\ f(x) = -x^2,\ \pi \le x \le 2\pi$.
(h) $f(x) = 4x - x^2,\ 4 \le x \le 8$.
(i) $f(x) = \cos x,\ -\pi/2 \le x \le \pi/2$.
(j) $f(x) = \cos a,\ |x| \le a \ne 0;\ f(x) = \cos x,\ |x| > a$.

3. Determine the complex form of the Fourier series of the following functions, periodic with the length of the given interval as period:
(a) $f(x) = -x,\ -\pi \le x < 0;\ f(x) = 1,\ 0 \le x \le \pi$.
(b) $f(x) = -x,\ -1 < x \le 0;\ f(x) = x^2,\ 0 < x \le 1$.
(c) $f(x) = \cos \pi x,\ -1 \le x \le 1$.
(d) $f(x) = \sinh x,\ 0 \le x \le 2\pi$.
(e) $f(x) = \sin x + |\sin x|,\ -\pi/4 \le x \le \pi/4$.

4. Determine the Fourier series of the following functions without performing any integrations:
(a) $f(x) = \cos^2 x,\ -\pi \le x \le \pi$.
(b) $f(x) = \sin^3 x,\ 0 \le x \le 2\pi$.
(c) $f(x) = \sqrt{1 - \cos 2x},\ -\pi \le x \le \pi$.
(d) $f(x) = \sin 3x + \sin 5x,\ -\pi \le x \le \pi$.
(e) $f(x) = \sin 2x \cos 4x,\ 0 \le x \le 2\pi$.

5. (a) Show that the Fourier coefficients of f have the indicated properties if f satisfies the given condition:

(1) $f(\pi - x) = f(x)$, $\quad a_{2n+1} = 0,\quad b_{2n} = 0$.
(2) $f(\pi - x) = -f(x)$, $\quad a_{2n} = 0,\quad b_{2n+1} = 0$.
(3) $f(\pi + x) = f(x)$, $\quad a_{2n+1} = 0,\quad b_{2n+1} = 0$.

(4) $f\left(\frac{\pi}{2} - x\right) = f(x)$, $\quad a_{4n+2} = 0,\quad b_{4n} = 0,\quad a_{4n+1} = b_{4n+1},\ a_{4n+3} = -b_{4n+3}$.

(5) $f\left(\frac{\pi}{2} + x\right) = f(x)$, $\quad a_n = b_n = 0$

except for a_0, a_{4n}, b_{4n}. What can you say about the coefficients if

$$f\left(\frac{\pi}{k} + x\right) = f(x),$$

where k is a positive integer?
(6) $f(x) = f(2x)$, $\quad a_n = b_n = 0,\ n = 1, 2, \cdots$.

(b) Using (a) appropriately, determine the Fourier series of the following functions, defined in $-\pi \le x \le \pi$ and periodic with period 2π:

(1) $f(x) = 0,\ -\pi \le x < 0;\ f(x) = \cos x,\ 0 \le x \le \pi$.
(2) $f(x) = 1,\ -\pi \le x \le \pi$.
(3) $f(x) = \sin 2x,\ -\pi \le x \le 0;\ f(x) = \cos 2x,\ 0 \le x \le \pi$.
(4) $f(x) = x,\ -\pi \le x < 0;\ f(x) = \pi - x,\ 0 \le x \le \pi$.

6. Determine the sine series and the cosine series of each of the following functions, defined in the given interval:
(a) $f(x) = \sin x,\ 0 \le x \le \pi$.
(b) $f(x) = \pi - x,\ 0 \le x \le \pi$.
(c) $f(x) = 1,\ 0 \le x \le \pi/2;\ f(x) = 0,\ \pi/2 < x \le \pi$.
(d) $f(x) = x,\ 0 \le x \le \frac{1}{2};\ f(x) = 1,\ \frac{1}{2} < x \le 1$.
(e) $f(x) = \text{Log}\,[2 \sin (x/2)],\ 0 \le x \le \pi$.
(f) $f(x) = e^x,\ 0 \le x \le 1$.

(g) $f(x) = x^2,\ 0 \le x \le 1;\ f(x) = 2 - x,\ 1 \le x \le 2.$
(h) $f(x) = 0,\ 0 \le x \le 1;\ f(x) = 1,\ 1 < x \le 2;\ f(x) = 2,\ 2 < x \le 3.$
(i) $f(x) = (L/2) - x^2,\ 0 \le x \le L.$
(j) $f(x) = mx,\ 0 \le x \le a/2;\ f(x) = m(a - x),\ a/2 < x \le a.$

7. Determine the points of discontinuity of the following functions in the given intervals and indicate whether they are finite or infinite discontinuities. Indicate whether the functions are piecewise continuous and piecewise smooth in those intervals.

(a) $f(x) = x,\ -\pi \le x \le 0;\ f(x) = \pi,\ 0 < x \le \pi.$
(b) $f(x) = \sqrt{|x|},\ -1 \le x \le 1.$
(c) $f(x) = \tan x,\ -\pi \le x \le \pi.$

(d) $f(x) = \dfrac{x^2 - 1}{x - 1},\ x \ne 1;\ f(1) = 0,\ 0 \le x \le 2.$

(e) $f(x) = \dfrac{x^2 - 1}{x - 1},\ x \ne 1;\ f(1) = 2,\ 0 \le x \le 2.$

(f) $f(x) = e^{-1/x},\ x \ne 0;\ f(0) = 0,\ -1 \le x \le 1.$
(g) $f(x) = xe^{-1/x},\ x \ne 0;\ f(0) = 0,\ -1 \le x \le 1.$
(h) $f(x) = x \sin(1/x),\ x \ne 0;\ f(0) = 0,\ -\pi \le x \le \pi.$
(i) $f(x) = x \sin(1/x),\ 0 < x \le \pi;\ f(x) = 1,\ -\pi \le x \le 0.$
(j) $f(x) = [\pi x]$ where $[\pi x]$ denotes the largest integer $\le \pi x,\ -2\pi \le x \le 2\pi.$

(k) $f(x) = c > 0,\ \dfrac{\pi}{2^{2k+1}} < x < \dfrac{\pi}{2^{2k}};\ f(x) = -c,\ \dfrac{\pi}{2^{2k}} < x < \dfrac{\pi}{2^{2k-1}},\ k = 0, 1, 2, \cdots,$
$f\left(\dfrac{\pi}{2^p}\right) = 0,\ p = 0, 1, 2, \cdots;\ f(x) = -f(-x),\ -\infty < x < \infty.$

(l) $f(x) = \dfrac{1}{\sqrt{|x|}},\ \dfrac{\pi}{2^{2k+1}} < x < \dfrac{\pi}{2^{2k}};\ f(x) = -\dfrac{1}{\sqrt{|x|}},\ \dfrac{\pi}{2^{2k}} < x < \dfrac{\pi}{2^{2k-1}},\ k = 0, 1,$
$2, \cdots;\ f\left(\dfrac{\pi}{2^p}\right) = 0,\ p = 0, 1, 2, \cdots;\ f(x) = -f(-x),\ -\infty < x < \infty.$

8. Determine the sum of the Fourier series corresponding to each function in Exercise 1 at the following points:

(a) $-\pi,\ -\pi/2,\ 0,\ \pi,\ 5\pi$; (b) $-\pi,\ 0,\ \pi,\ 2$; (c) $-\pi,\ 0,\ \pi,\ 5$;
(d) $-\pi,\ 0,\ \pi,\ \frac{3}{2}\pi$; (e) $-\pi,\ 0,\ \pi,\ 4$; (f) $-\frac{3}{2}\pi,\ -\pi,\ 0,\ \pi,\ \frac{5}{2}\pi$;
(g) $-\pi,\ 0,\ \pi$; (h) $-\pi,\ \pi$; (i) $-\pi,\ \pi,\ \frac{3}{2}\pi$; (j) $-\pi,\ \pi,\ \frac{5}{2}\pi$.

9. Graph the sum of the first three nonzero terms of the Fourier series of the functions in Exercise 1(a), (b), (e), (f), and (i).

10. With the use of previously determined Fourier series of appropriate functions, establish the following:

(a) $\displaystyle\sum_{n=1}^{\infty} \frac{1}{n^2} = \frac{\pi^2}{6}$; (b) $\displaystyle\sum_{n=1}^{\infty} \frac{(-1)^{n+1}}{n^2} = \frac{\pi^2}{12}$;

(c) $\displaystyle\sum_{n=1}^{\infty} \frac{1}{n^2 + 1} = \frac{1}{2}\left(1 - \frac{\pi}{\sinh \pi}\right)$;

(d) $\displaystyle\sum_{n=1}^{\infty} \frac{1}{4n^2 - 1} = 1$; (e) $\displaystyle\sum_{n=1}^{\infty} \frac{(-1)^n}{2n - 1} = \frac{\pi}{4}$.

11. (a) Show that the equation

$$y^2 = \frac{2c^3}{3d} + \sum_{n=1}^{\infty} \frac{4d}{n^3\pi^3}\left(d \sin\frac{n\pi c}{d} - n\pi c \cos\frac{n\pi c}{d}\right)\cos\frac{n\pi x}{d}$$

is satisfied by the set of points (x, y) on the circle $x^2 + y^2 = c^2$ and on all the circles of radius c with centers on the x-axis having a distance $2nd$, $d > c$, $n = 1, 2, \cdots$, from the origin, as well as all the points on the x-axis exterior to these circles.

(b) Show that the equation

$$y = \frac{2}{3}h + \frac{4h}{\pi^2}\left[\cos\frac{\pi x}{k} + \sum_{n=2}^{\infty}\frac{1}{n^2}\cos\frac{(n-1)\pi x}{k}\right]$$

is satisfied by the set of points (x, y) on the parabolic arcs whose vertices are on the x-axis, the height of each h, and the span of each $2k$.

(c) A point moves in a straight line with an initial velocity u that increases by nu at intervals $n\tau$, $n = 1, 2, \cdots$. Show that the velocity at any time $t > 0$ is

$$v = \frac{1}{2}u + \frac{ut}{\tau} + \frac{u}{\pi}\sum_{n=1}^{\infty}\frac{1}{n}\sin\frac{2n\pi t}{\tau}$$

and the distance traversed is

$$s = \frac{ut}{2\tau}(t + \tau) + \frac{u\tau}{12} - \frac{u\tau}{2\pi^2}\sum_{n=1}^{\infty}\frac{1}{n^2}\cos\frac{2n\pi t}{\tau}.$$

12. Perform the necessary operations on the Fourier series of functions in Exercises 1 and 2 to determine the Fourier series of the following functions:

(a) $f(x) = 1$, $-\pi \le x < 0$; $f(x) = 0$, $0 \le x \le \pi$.
(b) $f(x) = x^2$, $-\pi \le x \le \pi$.
(c) $f(x) = \cos x$, $-\pi \le x \le 0$; $f(x) = 0$, $0 < x \le \pi$.
(d) $f(x) = 2e^x - x\cos x$, $-\pi \le x \le \pi$.
(e) $f(x) = \sin x + \cos x$, $0 \le x \le 2\pi$.
(f) $f(x) = 4 + x$, $-2 \le x \le 0$; $f(x) = 2 + x$, $0 < x \le 2$.

13. (a) Show that

$$\cos\alpha x = \frac{2\alpha\sin\alpha\pi}{\pi}\left[\frac{1}{2\alpha^2} + \sum_{n=1}^{\infty}(-1)^n\frac{\cos nx}{\alpha^2 - n^2}\right],$$

$-\pi \le x \le \pi$, α not an integer.

(b) Let $x = \pi$ in (a) and divide by $\sin\alpha\pi$ to obtain

$$\cot\alpha\pi = \frac{1}{\alpha\pi} + \frac{2\alpha}{\pi}\sum_{n=1}^{\infty}\frac{1}{\alpha^2 - n^2}.$$

(c) Let $0 < \alpha < 1$ in (b) and integrate from 0 to x, $0 < x < 1$, assuming that the series can be integrated term by term, to obtain

$$\operatorname{Log}\frac{\sin\pi x}{\pi x} = \sum_{n=1}^{\infty}\operatorname{Log}\left(1 - \frac{x^2}{n^2}\right)$$

or

$$\sin\pi x = \pi x\prod_{n=1}^{\infty}\left(1 - \frac{x^2}{n^2}\right).$$

(d) Let $x = \frac{1}{2}$ in (c) to obtain Wallis' product:

$$\frac{\pi}{2} = \frac{2^2 \cdot 4^2 \cdot 6^2 \cdots}{1^2 \cdot 3^2 \cdot 5^2 \cdots}.$$

(e) Establish

$$\frac{\pi}{\sin \alpha\pi} = \frac{1}{\alpha} + 2\alpha \sum_{n=1}^{\infty} \frac{(-1)^n}{\alpha^2 - n^2},$$

α not an integer, by letting $x = 0$ in (a).

(f) Show that

$$\int_0^\infty \frac{x^{\alpha-1}}{1+x}\,dx = \int_0^1 \frac{x^{\alpha-1} - x^{-\alpha}}{1+x}\,dx = \frac{1}{\alpha} + 2\alpha \sum_{n=1}^{\infty} \frac{(-1)^n}{\alpha^2 - n^2},$$

$0 < \alpha < 1$. [*Hint:* Express the integral as the sum of two integrals, the first having $(0, 1)$ as the interval of integration and the second $(1, \infty)$; let $x = 1/y$ in the second integral. Use

$$\frac{1}{1+x} = \sum_{n=0}^{\infty} (-1)^n x^n, \ |x| < 1.$$

(g) Show that

$$\int_0^\infty \frac{x^{\alpha-1}}{1+x} = \frac{\pi}{\sin \alpha\pi}.$$

14. (a) Show that

$$x^2 - \frac{\pi^2}{3} = 4 \sum_{n=1}^{\infty} \frac{(-1)^n \cos nx}{n^2}.$$

(b) Integrate both sides of (a) and choose x appropriately to establish the sum

$$\sum_{n=1}^{\infty} \frac{1}{n^2} = \frac{\pi}{32}.$$

(c) Show that

$$\sum_{n=1}^{\infty} \frac{1}{(2n-1)^4} = \frac{\pi^4}{96}.$$

◇ **15.** (a) Prove that if f is piecewise continuous in $-\pi \le x \le \pi$ and periodic with period 2π, then for any a,

$$\int_{-\pi}^{\pi} f(x)\,dx = \int_{a-\pi}^{a+\pi} f(x)\,dx.$$

(b) Let f be periodic and integrable. Define the *moving average* of f by

$$f_h(x) = \frac{1}{2h} \int_{x-h}^{x+h} f(t)\,dt.$$

Show that $f_h(x)$ is periodic. Under what conditions does $[f_h(x)]' = [f'(x)]_h$?

16. Establish the following:

(a) $\lim\limits_{n\to\infty} \int_0^\pi \sqrt{\sin x}\, \sin^2 nx\,dx = 0.$

(b) $\lim\limits_{n\to\infty} \int_0^\pi \frac{\sin x \cos nx}{x^{2/3}}\,dx = 0.$

(c) $\lim\limits_{n\to\infty} \int_{-\pi}^{\pi} [x] \cos^2 (n + \frac{1}{2})x\,dx = 0.$

17. (a) Show that if

$$b_n = \frac{1}{\pi}\int_{-\pi}^{\pi} f(x) \sin nx \, dx,$$

and f is continuous in $-\pi \leq x \leq \pi$, then the series $\sum_{n=1}^{\infty} \frac{b_n}{n}$ is convergent. (*Hint:* Integrate the Fourier series of f and evaluate at $x = 0$.)

(b) Show that $\sum_{n=2}^{\infty} \frac{\sin nx}{\operatorname{Log} n}$ is convergent to some $f(x)$ for all x, but that the series is not the Fourier series of f. (*Hint:* To show convergence of the series, rewrite it as an alternating series and use Leibniz's test; to show it is not a Fourier series, integrate, and show that $\sum_{n=2}^{\infty} \frac{1}{n \operatorname{Log} n}$ is divergent.)

18. Show that if the rth derivative of f is continuous in $-\pi \leq x \leq \pi$ and $f^{(n)}(-\pi) = f^{(n)}(\pi)$, $n = 0, 1, \cdots, r - 1$, then there exists a constant M such that the Fourier coefficients of f satisfy the inequalities:

$$|a_n| \leq \frac{M}{n^r}, \qquad |b_n| \leq \frac{M}{n^r}, \qquad n = 1, 2, \cdots.$$

◇ **19.** Show that if f is piecewise continuous in $-\pi \leq x \leq \pi$, then $\int_{-\pi}^{x} f(t)\, dt$ is continuous in $-\pi < x < \pi$.

20. Show that if f and g are piecewise continuous in $-\pi \leq x \leq \pi$ and periodic with period 2π, then the function h such that

$$h(x) = \frac{1}{2\pi}\int_{-\pi}^{\pi} f(x - t) g(t)\, dt$$

is continuous and periodic with period 2π. Furthermore, show that if

$$f(x) \sim \sum_{n=-\infty}^{\infty} c_n e^{inx} \quad \text{and} \quad g(x) \sim \sum_{n=-\infty}^{\infty} d_n e^{inx},$$

then

$$h(x) \sim \sum_{n=-\infty}^{\infty} c_n d_n e^{inx}.$$

h is called the *convolution* of f and g.

21. (a) Show that the nth partial sum of the Fourier series in Example 1, p. 368, can be written as

$$s_n(x) = \frac{2}{\pi}\int_0^x \frac{\sin 2nt}{\sin t}\, dt.$$

(b) Show that in $(0, \pi)$, s_n has relative maxima at $x = \frac{1}{2}(2m - 1)(\pi/n)$ and relative minima at $x = m\pi/n$, $m = 1, 2, \cdots, 2n - 1$, and that the largest of the relative maxima is $s_n(\pi/2n)$.

Hint: Differentiate

$$s_n(x) = \frac{4}{\pi}\left(\sin x + \frac{\sin 3x}{3} + \cdots + \frac{\sin (2n - 1)x}{2n - 1}\right).$$

(c) Show that if we set $h = \pi/n$,

$$s_n\left(\frac{\pi}{2n}\right) = \frac{1}{2}h\left(\frac{\sin\frac{h}{2}}{\frac{h}{2}} + \frac{\sin\frac{3}{2}h}{\frac{3}{2}h} + \cdots + \frac{\sin\frac{2n-1}{2}h}{\frac{2n-1}{2}h}\right)$$

can be interpreted as the sum in the definition of the definite integral, and hence that

$$\lim_{n\to\infty} s_n\left(\frac{\pi}{2n}\right) = \frac{2}{\pi}\int_0^\pi \frac{\sin t}{t}\,dt.$$

(d) Show by the series method that

$$\frac{2}{\pi}\int_0^\pi \frac{\sin t}{t}\,dt = 1.179 \quad \text{approximately.}$$

(e) Show that the "approximating curves" $y = s_n(x)$ in a neighborhood of the origin tend toward a line segment of length 2.358 rather than 2, which is the length of the jump. This paradox is known as **Gibb's phenomenon** and indicates that the approximation of a function at a point of discontinuity by the partial sums of its Fourier series is not very accurate.

22. In practical applications, a function represented by a Fourier series is approximated by taking as many terms in the series as will yield the desired accuracy. This means that it is desirable to have Fourier coefficients that converge rapidly to zero. In some cases, it is possible to replace a series by an equivalent series whose coefficients converge more rapidly.

(a) Improve the convergence of

$$f(x) = \sum_{n=2}^{\infty} (-1)^n \frac{n^3}{n^4 - 1}\sin nx.$$

Hint:

$$\frac{n^3}{n^4-1} = \frac{1}{n^5 - n} + \frac{1}{n};$$

$$f(x) = \sum_{n=2}^{\infty} (-1)^n \frac{\sin nx}{n} + \sum_{n=2}^{\infty} (-1)^n \frac{\sin nx}{n^5 - n}$$

$$= -\frac{x}{2} + \sin x + \sum_{n=2}^{\infty} (-1)^n \frac{\sin nx}{n^5 - n},$$

$$-\pi < x < \pi.$$

$1/(n^5 - n)$ converges more rapidly than $n^3/(n^4 - 1)$.

(b) Show that

$$\sum_{n=1}^{\infty} \frac{n^4 - n^2 + 1}{n^2(n^4+1)}\cos nx = \frac{3x^2 - 6\pi x - 2\pi^2}{12} - \sum_{n=1}^{\infty} \frac{\cos nx}{n^4+1}, \qquad 0 \le x \le 2\pi.$$

Hint:

$$\frac{n^4 - n^2 + 1}{n^2(n^4+1)} = \frac{1}{n^2} + \frac{1}{n^4+1}.$$

(c) Show that

$$\sum_{n=1}^{\infty} \frac{\sin nx}{n+a} = \frac{\pi - x}{2} + a \int_0^x \operatorname{Log}\left(2 \sin \frac{u}{2}\right) du$$
$$+ \frac{a^2}{12}(x^3 + 3\pi x^2 - 2\pi^2 x)$$
$$- a^3 \sum_{n=1}^{\infty} \frac{\sin nx}{n^3(n-a)}, \qquad a > 0, \quad \text{constant}.$$

Hint: Show that

$$\frac{1}{n+a} = \frac{1}{n} - \frac{a}{n^2} + \frac{a^2}{n^3} - \frac{a^3}{n^3(n+a)}.$$

23. Find the sum of the following series:

(a) $\displaystyle\sum_{n=0}^{\infty} \frac{\cos nx}{p^n}$ and $\displaystyle\sum_{n=1}^{\infty} \frac{\sin nx}{p^n}$, $|p| > 1$.

Hint: $$\sum_{n=0}^{\infty} \frac{\cos nx}{p^n} + i \sum_{n=0}^{\infty} \frac{\sin nx}{p^n} = \sum_{n=0}^{\infty} \frac{e^{inx}}{p^n} = \sum_{n=0}^{\infty} \left(\frac{z}{p}\right)^n = \frac{p}{p-z}.$$

Hence, $$\sum_{n=0}^{\infty} \frac{\cos nx}{p^n} = \operatorname{Re} \frac{p}{p-z} = \frac{p(p - \cos x)}{p^2 - 2p \cos x + 1}.$$

(b) $\displaystyle\sum_{n=0}^{\infty} \frac{(-1)^n \cos (2n+1)x}{(2n+1)!}$ and $\displaystyle\sum_{n=0}^{\infty} \frac{(-1)^n \sin (2n+1)x}{(2n+1)!}$.

(c) $\displaystyle\sum_{n=1}^{\infty} \frac{\cos (n+1)x}{n(n+1)}$ and $\displaystyle\sum_{n=1}^{\infty} \frac{\sin (n+1)x}{n(n+1)}$.

(d) $\displaystyle\sum_{n=2}^{\infty} \frac{(-1)^n n \cos nx}{n^2 - 1}$ and $\displaystyle\sum_{n=2}^{\infty} \frac{(-1)^n n \sin nx}{n^2 - 1}$.

24. (a) Show that if f is continuous and f' is piecewise continuous in $a \le x \le b$, then f is almost differentiable there.

Hint: Let x_0, $a < x_0 < b$, be such that f' is continuous in $a < x < x_0$. Why must x_0 exist? By the law of the mean,

$$\frac{f(x_0) - f(a)}{x_0 - a} = f'(\xi), \qquad a < \xi < x_0.$$

Let $x_0 \to a+$. Then $f'_+(a) = f'(a+)$. Similarly, $f'_-(b) = f'(b-)$. Now divide $a < x < b$ into subintervals such that f' is continuous in the interior of each of these. Can you extend this to f piecewise smooth?

(b) Let $f(x) = 1$, $-\pi \le x < 0$; $f(x) = 0$, $x = 0$; $f(x) = -1$, $-\pi \le x \le 0$. Show that $f'_+(0) = f'_-(0) = 0$, but that $f'(0)$ does not exist.

(c) Show that if $f'(x_0+) = f'(x_0-)$ for $a < x_0 < b$, then $f'(x_0)$ equals this value.

25. Let f be a piecewise continuous function such that in every subinterval where it is continuous, it is a polynomial. Let $x_1, x_2, \cdots, x_m$ be the points of discontinuity and $j_i = f(x_i+) - f(x_i-)$, $j_i^{(k)} = f_i^{(k)}(x_i+) - f_i^{(k)}(x_i-)$, $i = 1, 2, \cdots, m$; $k = 1, 2, \cdots$. Show that the Fourier coefficients of f are

$$a_n = \frac{1}{n\pi}\left[-\sum_{i=1}^{m} j_i \sin nx_i - \frac{1}{n}\sum_{i=1}^{m} j_i' \cos nx_i + \frac{1}{n^2}\sum_{i=1}^{m} j_i'' \sin nx_i + \frac{1}{n^3}\sum_{i=1}^{m} j_i''' \cos nx_i - - + + \cdots\right],$$

$$b_n = \frac{1}{n\pi}\left[\sum_{i=1}^{m} j_i \cos nx_i - \frac{1}{n}\sum_{i=1}^{m} j_i' \sin nx_i - \frac{1}{n^2}\sum_{i=1}^{m} j_i'' \cos nx_i + \frac{1}{n^3}\sum_{i=1}^{m} j_i''' \sin nx_i + - - + + \cdots\right].$$

Find the Fourier coefficients of the functions in Exercise 1(a), (b), (e), (f), (i), using these formulas.

26. Let f be a function of period 2π defined for $-\pi \le x \le \pi$, whose Fourier series is

$$\frac{a_0}{2} + \sum_{n=1}^{\infty} a_n \cos nx + b_n \sin nx;$$

let

$$f_e(x) = \frac{f(x) + f(-x)}{2}, \quad f_0(x) = \frac{f(x) - f(-x)}{2}.$$

(a) Show that $f_e(x)$ is an even function and $f_0(x)$ is an odd function with Fourier series

$$\frac{a_0}{2} + \sum_{n=1}^{\infty} a_n \cos nx, \quad \sum_{n=1}^{\infty} b_n \sin nx,$$

respectively.

(b) Show that $f(x - \pi)$ has the Fourier series

$$\frac{a_0}{2} + \sum_{n=1}^{\infty} (-1)^n(a_n \cos nx + b_n \sin nx).$$

(c) Show that

$$|\sin x| = \frac{2}{\pi}\left(1 - \sum_{n=1}^{\infty} \frac{\cos 2nx}{4n^2 - 1}\right).$$

$|\sin x|$ is called the full-wave rectification of $\sin x$.

(d) Determine the Fourier series of the half-wave rectification of $\sin x$: $f(x) = \sin x$, $\sin x \ge 0$; $f(x) = 0$, $\sin x < 0$.

27. If $f(z)$ is analytic in $r_1 < |z - z_0| < r_2$, show that

$$f(z) = \sum_{n=-\infty}^{\infty} c_n e^{in\theta}, \quad c_n = \frac{1}{2\pi}\int_0^{2\pi} f(re^{i\theta})e^{-in\theta}\, d\theta.$$

[*Hint:* Let $z - z_0 = re^{i\theta}$ in the Laurent expansion of $f(z)$ in the given annulus.]

28. If the function $\dfrac{te^{xt}}{e^t - 1}$ is expanded in a power series in t, the coefficients of the series are functions of x. We write

$$\frac{te^{xt}}{e^t - 1} = \sum_{n=0}^{\infty} \frac{B_n(x)t^n}{n!}.$$

(a) The numbers $B_n = B_n(0)$ are called **Bernoulli numbers.** Show that

$$B_0 = 1, \quad \binom{n}{0} B_0 + \binom{n}{1} B_1 + \cdots + \binom{n}{n-1} B_{n-1} = 0,$$

where

$$\binom{n}{k} = \frac{k!}{(n-k)!k!}, \qquad n \geq 2,$$

and that $B_{2n+1} = 0$, $n \geq 1$.

(b) Show that

$$B_n(x) = B_0 x^n + \binom{n}{1} B_1 x^{n-1} + \cdots + \binom{n}{k} B_k x^{n-k} + \cdots + \binom{n}{n-1} B_{n-1} x + B_n.$$

Hence, $B_n(x)$ is a polynomial of degree n. It is called the **Bernoulli polynomial.**

Hint:

$$\frac{te^{xt}}{e^t - 1} = \sum_{n=0}^{\infty} \frac{(xt)^n}{n!} \sum_{n=0}^{\infty} \frac{B_n t^n}{n!}.$$

(c) Show that

$$B_{n+1}(x) = B_{n+1} + (n+1) \int_0^x B_n(t)\, dt,$$

$$B'_{n+1}(x) = (n+1) B_n(x) \int_0^1 B_n(x)\, dx = 0.$$

(d) Establish the following sine and cosine series for $B_n(x)$, valid in $0 \leq x \leq 1$:

$$B_{2n}(x) = (-1)^{n+1} \frac{2(2n)!}{(2\pi)^{2n}} \sum_{k=1}^{\infty} \frac{\cos 2k\pi x}{k^{2n}}, \qquad n \geq 1.$$

$$B_{2n+1}(x) = (-1)^{n+1} \frac{2(2n+1)!}{(2\pi)^{2n+1}} \sum_{k=1}^{\infty} \frac{\sin 2k\pi x}{k^{2n+1}}, \qquad n \geq 1.$$

(e) Show that

$$\sum_{k=1}^{\infty} \frac{1}{k^{2n}} = (-1)^{n+1} \frac{(2\pi)^{2n} B_{2n}}{2(2n)!}.$$

The series is $\sum_{k=1}^{\infty} \frac{1}{k^z}$, evaluated at $z = 2n$, n a positive integer. Since this series is convergent for $\operatorname{Re} z > 1$ (why?), it defines a function of z, known as the **Riemann zeta function,** and is denoted by $\zeta(z)$. We have, therefore, an explicit evaluation for $\zeta(2n)$.

29. Let $f(x, y)$ be periodic of period 2π in both x and y. If y is held fixed, then the Fourier series of $f(x, y)$ can be written

$$f(x, y) \sim \sum_{n=0}^{\infty} A_n(y) \cos nx + B_n(y) \sin nx.$$

If we now consider the Fourier series of $A_n(y)$ and $B_n(y)$, we can write the "double Fourier series" of $f(x, y)$ in the form

$$f(x, y) \sim \sum_{n=0}^{\infty} \sum_{m=0}^{\infty} (a_{nm} \cos nx \cos my + b_{nm} \cos nx \sin my + c_{nm} \sin nx \cos my + d_{nm} \sin nx \sin my).$$

(a) Assuming that the Fourier series of $f(x, y)$ converges to $f(x, y)$, determine the coefficients

$$\begin{Bmatrix} a_{mn} \\ b_{mn} \end{Bmatrix} = \frac{1}{\pi^2} \int_{-\pi}^{\pi} \int_{-\pi}^{\pi} f(x, y) \cos mx \begin{Bmatrix} \cos ny \\ \sin ny \end{Bmatrix} dx\, dy,$$

$$\begin{Bmatrix} c_{mn} \\ d_{mn} \end{Bmatrix} = \frac{1}{\pi^2} \int_{-\pi}^{\pi} \int_{-\pi}^{\pi} f(x, y) \sin mx \begin{Bmatrix} \cos ny \\ \sin ny \end{Bmatrix} dx\, dy,$$

$m, n = 1, 2, 3, \cdots$, and also the coefficients when m or n is zero. (*Hint:* To determine a_{mn}, multiply both sides of the expansion of $f(x, y)$ in its Fourier series by $\cos mx \cos ny$ and consider the indicated double integral.)

(b) Find the Fourier series of

(1) $$f(x, y) = xy, \qquad -\pi \le x \le \pi,\ -\pi \le y \le \pi;$$

(2) $$f(x, y) = \begin{cases} k, & 0 \le x \le \pi,\ 0 \le y \le \pi; \\ & -\pi \le x \le 0,\ -\pi \le y \le 0; \\ -k, & 0 < x \le \pi,\ -\pi \le y < 0; \\ & -\pi \le x < 0,\ 0 < y \le \pi. \end{cases}$$

30. The Fourier expansion theorem can be proved under weakened hypotheses. We consider some of these proofs.

(a) A function satisfies a *Lipschitz condition* at x if there exists a constant M and $\delta > 0$ such that $|f(y) - f(x)| < M|y - x|$ if $|y - x| < \delta$. Prove: If f satisfies a Lipschitz condition at x, then the Fourier series of f converges to $f(x)$.

Hint:

$$s_n(x) - f(x) = \int_{-\pi}^{\pi} [f(x + t) - f(x)]D_n(t)\, dt.$$

Hence, $|s_n(x) - f(x)| \le M\delta$ for every n.

(b) Show that if f is differentiable at x, then f satisfies a Lipschitz condition at x. Give an example to show that the converse is not true; hence, differentiability is a stronger property than that of the Lipschitz condition.

(c) A function f is of **bounded variation** in $a \le x \le b$ if it can be expressed in the form $f(x) = \phi(x) - \psi(x)$ in this interval where ϕ and ψ are nondecreasing bounded functions. The following theorem can be proved (e.g., in Titchmarsh, *Theory of Functions*, p. 406): If f is periodic and of bounded variation in $-\pi \le x \le \pi$, then the Fourier series of f converges to $\frac{1}{2}[f(x+) + f(x-)]$ at x. Give an example to show that the property of a function having a Lipschitz condition is stronger than the property of bounded variation.

(d) Show that if f is periodic, piecewise continuous, and has a finite number of relative maxima and minima in $-\pi \le x \le \pi$, then its Fourier series converges to $\frac{1}{2}[f(x+) + f(x-)]$. These are known as the **Dirichlet conditions.** (*Hint:* Show that f is of bounded variation.) Show that the Dirichlet conditions are weaker than the conditions in the Fourier expansion theorem.

6. Uniform convergence. We have seen that the Fourier series of a function can be integrated term by term to yield a series that converges to the integral of the function, and under certain conditions, differentiating the Fourier series term by term yields the Fourier series of the derivative of the function. These extremely useful properties of Fourier series are not enjoyed by all series, as is evidenced by the following examples.

EXAMPLE 1. The series

$$S = \sum_{k=1}^{\infty} kxe^{-kx^2} - (k-1)xe^{-(k-1)x^2}$$

is convergent for all x; since if $S_n(x)$ is the nth partial sum of S, it is readily seen that

$$S_n(x) = nxe^{-nx^2}$$

and

$$\lim_{n\to\infty} S_n(x) = 0, \qquad \text{for all } x.$$

Hence,

$$0 = \sum_{k=1}^{\infty} kxe^{-kx^2} - (k-1)xe^{-(k-1)x^2}$$

for all x. The integral of the left-hand side from 0 to 1 is 0, while that of the right-hand side is

$$\tfrac{1}{2}\sum_{k=1}^{\infty} e^{-(k-1)} - e^{-k} = \tfrac{1}{2} \neq 0.$$

Hence, integration of S from 0 to 1, term by term, is not valid. Consider the interval $a \leq x \leq b$; the student should show that term-by-term integration of S from a to b is valid if and only if $a \neq 0$ and $b \neq 0$.

EXAMPLE 2. The series

$$S = \sum_{k=1}^{\infty} \frac{\sin k^2 x}{k^2}$$

is absolutely convergent (and hence convergent for all x) by the comparison test, since $\left|\dfrac{\sin k^2 x}{k^2}\right| \leq \dfrac{1}{k^2}$ and $\sum_{k=1}^{\infty} \dfrac{1}{k^2}$ is convergent.

If we differentiate S term by term, we obtain the series

$$\sum_{k=1}^{\infty} \cos k^2 x,$$

which is divergent for all x, since

$$\lim_{k\to\infty} \cos k^2 x \begin{cases} \text{does not exist, } x \neq 0 \\ = 1,\ x = 0. \end{cases}$$

EXAMPLE 3. It is readily seen that

$$x = \sum_{k=1}^{\infty} \frac{x^k}{k} - \frac{x^{k+1}}{k+1}$$

for all x. The derivative of x is 1 for all x, but the term-by-term derivative of the series is

$$\sum_{k=1}^{\infty} x^{k-1} - x^k$$

which is equal to $\begin{cases} 1,\ x \neq 1 \\ 0,\ x = 1 \end{cases}$.

These examples amply illustrate the fact that it is not always permissible to integrate or differentiate an infinite series term by term in the manner of finite sums. We can express this situation in another way. Let $S_n(x)$ be the nth partial sum of the series $\sum_{n=1}^{\infty} u_n(x)$ that is convergent in $a \leq x \leq b$ so that

$$S(x) = \lim_{n\to\infty} S_n(x), \qquad a \leq x \leq b.$$

Then

$$S'(x) = \frac{d}{dx}\,[\lim_{n\to\infty} S_n(x)]$$

is not necessarily equal to

$$\lim_{n\to\infty} \frac{d}{dx} S_n(x)$$

or

$$\int_a^b S(x)\,dx = \int_a^b \lim_{n\to\infty} S_n(x)\,dx$$

is not necessarily equal to

$$\lim_{n\to\infty} \int_a^b S_n(x)\,dx.$$

Since differentiation and integration are limit operations, this means that the interchange of limit operations is not always permissible.

Now suppose that in $\sum_{n=1}^{\infty} u_n(x)$, $u_n(x)$ is continuous in $a \leq x \leq b$ for every n. Then does it follow that $S(x)$ is continuous in $a \leq x \leq b$? Not necessarily. We have ample evidence in the Fourier series of functions; the terms of every Fourier series are continuous, but Fourier series often converge to discontinuous functions. Actually, inferring the continuity of $S(x)$ from the continuity of $S_n(x)$ involves an interchange of limit operations, for if x_0 is any point in $a \leq x \leq b$, then since $S_n(x)$ is continuous at x_0 for every n, we have

$$\lim_{x\to x_0} S_n(x) = S_n(x_0).$$

Now, from

$$\lim_{n\to\infty} \lim_{x\to x_0} S_n(x) = \lim_{n\to\infty} S_n(x_0),$$

we *cannot* infer that

$$\lim_{x\to x_0} \lim_{n\to\infty} S_n(x) = S(x_0)$$

or

$$\lim_{x\to x_0} S(x) = S(x_0),$$

which implies the continuity of $S(x)$ at x_0.

The foregoing discussion leads us to the conclusion that in order to ensure the validity of the interchange of certain limit operations, we must impose other conditions on sequences, and hence series, in addition to their convergence. Actually, the condition that a sequence be convergent is too weak to ensure the validity of the interchange of these limit operations. We now consider a stronger type of convergence. We first recall that the sequence of functions $\{s_n(x)\}$ converges to $s(x)$ at the point x_0 if for every $\epsilon > 0$ there exists a positive integer N such that $n > N$ implies

$$|s_n(x_0) - s(x_0)| < \epsilon.$$

The sequence of functions $\{s_n(x)\}$ converges to $s(x)$ in a set E (consisting of points on the real line or the complex plane) if it converges to $s(x)$ at every point x in E. Let us combine the last two definitions into one definition. The sequence of functions $\{s_n(x)\}$ converges pointwise to $s(x)$ on the set E if for every $\epsilon > 0$ and every x in E, there exists a positive integer N, *depending both on* ϵ *and* x, such that $n > N$ implies

$$|s_n(x) - s(x)| < \epsilon.$$

The italicized phrase in this definition suggests how we may strengthen the concept of convergence. We say that the sequence of functions $\{s_n(x)\}$ **converges uniformly** to $s(x)$ in E, if for every $\epsilon > 0$ there exists a positive integer N, depending on ϵ only, such that for every $n > N$ and every x in E, we have that

$$|s_n(x) - s(x)| < \epsilon.$$

We first note that uniform convergence is a property of a sequence of functions on a set of points and not of a single point in that set, as is pointwise convergence. It is clear that the uniform convergence of $\{s_n(x)\}$ on E implies pointwise convergence of $\{s_n(x)\}$ on E. That the converse is not true is indicated in

EXAMPLE 4. The sequence $\{nxe^{-nx^2}\}$ converges pointwise to 0 in $0 \leq x \leq 1$. It does *not* converge uniformly to 0 in $0 \leq x \leq 1$. For assume that it does; then for $\epsilon = 1$, there must exist a positive integer N such that

$$nxe^{-nx^2} < 1, \qquad n > N.$$

But

$$\max_{0 \leq x \leq 1} nxe^{-nx^2} = \sqrt{\frac{n}{2e}} \qquad \text{(proof?)}$$

so that

$$\sqrt{\frac{n}{2e}} < 1, \qquad n > N.$$

However, as n becomes infinite, the left-hand side becomes infinite, and we have a contradiction.

Hence, uniform convergence is a stronger condition than pointwise convergence.

It is readily seen that if $s_n(x) \to s(x)$ uniformly in E, then $s_n(x) \to s(x)$ uniformly in F, F any subset of E. (Proof?)

We can interpret uniform convergence geometrically as follows: Suppose that $s_n(x) \to s(x)$ uniformly in $a \le x \le b$. Let $\epsilon > 0$ be given. We now graph the functions $s(x) + \epsilon$ and $s(x) - \epsilon$ in $a \le x \le b$. (See Fig. 1.)

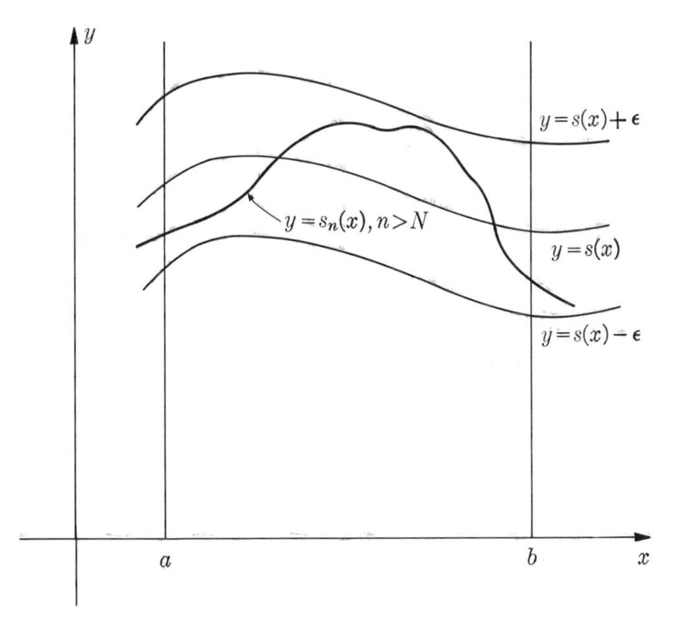

Fig. 1. Geometric interpretation of uniform convergence

The positive integer N determined by ϵ will yield the sequence $s_{N+1}(x)$, $s_{N+2}(x), \cdots$. Uniform convergence implies that each of these functions in $a \le x \le b$ will lie between $s(x) + \epsilon$ and $s(x) - \epsilon$, the latter functions serving as an envelope. The student should illustrate graphically why the sequence in Example 4 is not uniformly convergent in $0 \le x \le 1$.

Since the series $\sum_{k=1}^{\infty} u_k(x)$ is a special sequence, namely, the sequence of partial sums $\{u_1(x) + u_2(x) + \cdots + u_n(x)\}$, to say that the series is uniformly convergent on a set E is merely another way of saying that the sequence of its partial sums is uniformly convergent on E.

EXAMPLE 5. Show that the geometric series $\sum_{k=0}^{\infty} x^k$ converges uniformly to $\dfrac{1}{1-x}$ in $-r \le x \le r$, $0 < r < 1$.

Solution. The nth partial sum is

$$S_n(x) = \sum_{k=0}^{n} x^k = \frac{1-x^n}{1-x}.$$

Now

$$\left|\frac{1-x^n}{1-x} - \frac{1}{1-x}\right| = \frac{|x|^n}{|1-x|} \le \frac{r^n}{1-r}, \qquad |x| \le r.$$

Let $\epsilon > 0$ be given. We wish to determine for what values of n

$$\frac{r^n}{1-r} < \epsilon.$$

Since $r^n/(1-r) > 0$,

$$\log \frac{r^n}{1-r} < \log \epsilon$$

or

$$n > -\frac{\log [\epsilon(1-r)]}{\log (1/r)},$$

using the fact that $0 < r < 1$. If we let N = the greatest integer in $\dfrac{-\log [\epsilon(1-r)]}{\log (1/r)}$, then it is clear that N is independent of x, and for $n > N$,

$$\left| S_n(x) - \frac{1}{1-x} \right| < \epsilon.$$

By definition, $S_n(x) \to \dfrac{1}{1-x}$ uniformly in $-r \leq x \leq r$, $0 < r < 1$.

To establish the uniform convergence of a given sequence of functions on a given set, using the definition, we must know the limit function of the sequence. In many problems, we are interested only in whether a given sequence of functions is or is not uniformly convergent on a given set. As a matter of fact, the actual determination of the limit function may be difficult. This is particularly the case for series. Fortunately, we have the

CAUCHY CONVERGENCE CRITERION FOR UNIFORM CONVERGENCE. The sequence of functions $\{s_n(x)\}$ converges uniformly on the set E if and only if for every $\epsilon > 0$ there exists a positive integer N such that $m > N$, $n > N$, and every x in E implies

$$|s_n(x) - s_m(x)| < \epsilon.$$

Proof. Assume $\{s_n(x)\}$ converges uniformly to $s(x)$ on E. Let $\epsilon > 0$. Then $\epsilon/2 > 0$, for which there exists a positive integer N such that $n > N$ and every x in E implies

$$|s_n(x) - s(x)| < \frac{\epsilon}{2}.$$

Now

$$\begin{aligned} |s_n(x) - s_m(x)| &= |s_n(x) - s(x) + s(x) - s_m(x)| \\ &\leq |s_n(x) - s(x)| + |s(x) - s_m(x)| < \frac{\epsilon}{2} + \frac{\epsilon}{2} = \epsilon, \end{aligned}$$

for $n > N$ and every x in E.

Now let us assume that the condition holds. By the Cauchy convergence criterion, $\{s_n(x)\}$ converges to some limit function, say $s(x)$, for every x in E. Given $\epsilon > 0$, there exists a positive integer N such that $n > N$, $m > N$, and every x in E implies

$$|s_n(x) - s_m(x)| < \epsilon.$$

Let n be fixed and let $m \to \infty$. Since $s_m(x) \to s(x)$ as $m \to \infty$, we have

$$|s_n(x) - s(x)| < \epsilon$$

for $n > N$ and every x in E. Hence, $\{s_n(x)\}$ converges uniformly on E.

For the uniform convergence of series we have the extremely useful test known as the

WEIERSTRASS *M*-TEST FOR UNIFORM CONVERGENCE. Given the series $\sum_{n=1}^{\infty} u_n(x)$. If there exists a sequence of constants $\{M_n\}$ such that (1) $|u_n(x)| \leq M_n$, $n = 1, 2, 3, \cdots$, and every x in a set E, and (2) $\sum_{n=1}^{\infty} M_n$ is convergent, then $\sum_{n=1}^{\infty} u_n(x)$ is uniformly convergent on E.

Proof. Let

$$S_n(x) = \sum_{k=1}^{n} u_k(x) \quad \text{and} \quad V_n = \sum_{k=1}^{n} M_n.$$

Then, since $\sum_{k=1}^{\infty} M_n$ is convergent, given $\epsilon > 0$, there exists a positive integer N such that $n > m > N$ implies

$$V_n - V_m < \epsilon,$$

or

$$\sum_{k=m}^{n} M_k < \epsilon.$$

But by (1),

$$\left| \sum_{k=m}^{n} u_k(x) \right| \leq \sum_{k=m}^{n} |u_k(x)| \leq \sum_{k=m}^{n} M_k < \epsilon,$$

$n > m > N$, and every x in E, or

$$|S_n(x) - S_m(x)| < \epsilon, \qquad n > m > N$$

and every x in E. Uniform convergence follows by the Cauchy convergence criterion.

EXAMPLE 6. Show that $\sum_{n=1}^{\infty} \frac{\sin nx}{n^2}$ converges uniformly for all x.

Solution. Since $\left|\frac{\sin nx}{n^2}\right| \leq \frac{1}{n^2}$ for all x, $n = 1, 2, \cdots$ and $\sum_{n=1}^{\infty} \frac{1}{n^2}$ is convergent, the conditions of the Weierstrass M-test are satisfied and the given series is uniformly convergent for all x.

The Weierstrass M-test indicates a sufficient condition for uniform convergence of series. The condition is not necessary, as the following example indicates. Let

$$s_n(x) = \begin{cases} 0, & x \neq \dfrac{1}{n} \\ \dfrac{1}{n}, & x = \dfrac{1}{n} \end{cases}, \qquad 0 \leq x \leq 1.$$

The sequence $\{s_n(x)\}$ converges uniformly in $0 \leq x \leq 1$ (why?). Let $\{M_n\}$ be any sequence of constants such that $s_n(x) \leq M_n$; i.e., $\frac{1}{n} \leq M_n$, $n = 1, 2, \cdots$. But by the comparison test for divergence, $\sum_{n=1}^{\infty} M_n$ is divergent.

We now establish the main properties of uniformly convergent sequences and series:

(1) **Uniform convergence and continuity**

U₁: If $\{s_n(x)\}$ is a sequence of continuous functions converging uniformly to $s(x)$ on E, then $s(x)$ is continuous in E.

U₁*: If $\sum_{n=1}^{\infty} u_n(x)$ is a uniformly convergent series of functions on E with sum $S(x)$, then $S(x)$ is continuous on E.

(2) **Uniform convergence and integration**

U₂: If $\{s_n(x)\}$ is a sequence of functions integrable and uniformly convergent in $a \leq x \leq b$, a and b finite, then

$$\lim_{n\to\infty} \int_a^b s_n(x)\, dx = \int_a^b \lim_{n\to\infty} s_n(x)\, dx.$$

U₂*: If $\sum_{n=1}^{\infty} u_n(x)$ is a series of functions integrable and uniformly convergent in $a \leq x \leq b$, a and b finite, then

$$\int_a^b \left(\sum_{n=1}^{\infty} u_n(x)\right) dx = \sum_{n=1}^{\infty} \left(\int_a^b u_n(x)\, dx\right).$$

(3) **Uniform convergence and differentiation**

U₃: If $\{s_n(x)\}$ is a sequence of functions continuously differentiable in $a \leq x \leq b$ converging pointwise to $s(x)$, and if $\{s_n'(x)\}$ converges uniformly in $a \leq x \leq b$, then

$$s'(x) = \lim_{n\to\infty} s_n'(x).$$

U₃*: If $\sum_{n=1}^{\infty} u_n(x)$ is a pointwise convergent series of functions continuously differentiable in $a \leq x \leq b$ with sum $S(x)$, and if $\sum_{n=1}^{\infty} u_n'(x)$ is uniformly convergent in $a \leq x \leq b$, then

$$S'(x) = \sum_{n=1}^{\infty} u_n'(x).$$

Proofs. We need prove only U_1, U_2, U_3.

U_1: Let any $\epsilon > 0$ be given. Since $s_n(x) \to s(x)$ uniformly on E, there exists a positive integer N such that $n > N$ and every x in E implies $|s_n(x) - s(x)| < \epsilon/3$. Now let $n > N$ be fixed and let x_0 be any point in E; then $s_n(x)$ is continuous at x_0. Hence, for the given ϵ, there exists $\delta > 0$ such that $|x - x_0| < \delta$ implies $|s_n(x) - s_n(x_0)| < \epsilon/3$. Now

$$\begin{aligned}|s(x) - s(x_0)| &= |s(x) - s_n(x) + s_n(x) - s_n(x_0) + s_n(x_0) - s(x_0)| \\ &\leq |s(x) - s_n(x)| + |s_n(x) - s_n(x_0)| + |s_n(x_0) - s(x_0)| \\ &< \frac{\epsilon}{3} + \frac{\epsilon}{3} + \frac{\epsilon}{3} = \epsilon,\end{aligned}$$

provided $|x - x_0| < \delta$. This implies that $s(x)$ is continuous at x_0. Since x_0 was any point in E, $s(x)$ is continuous in E.

U_2: Let any $\epsilon > 0$ be given. Since $s_n(x) \to s(x)$ uniformly in $a \leq x \leq b$, there exists a positive integer N such that $n > N$ and every x in $a \leq x \leq b$ implies

$$|s_n(x) - s(x)| < \frac{\epsilon}{b - a}.$$

Now, for any $n > N$ and every x in $a \leq x \leq b$,

$$\begin{aligned}&\left|\int_a^b s_n(x)\,dx - \int_a^b s(x)\,dx\right| \\ &\quad = \left|\int_a^b [s_n(x) - s(x)]\,dx\right| \leq \int_a^b |s_n(x) - s(x)|\,dx < \frac{\epsilon}{b - a}\int_a^b dx = \epsilon.\end{aligned}$$

Hence,

$$\lim_{n\to\infty} \int_a^b s_n(x)\,dx = \int_a^b s(x)\,dx.$$

U_3: Let $s^*(x) = \lim_{n\to\infty} s_n'(x)$. We wish to show that $s^*(x) = s'(x)$. Since $s_n'(x) \to s^*(x)$ uniformly in $a \leq x \leq b$, the same is true in $a \leq t \leq x$, and by U_2:

$$\lim_{n\to\infty} \int_a^x s_n'(t)\,dt = \int_a^x s^*(t)\,dt.$$

Then

$$\lim_{n\to\infty} [s_n(x) - s_n(a)] = \int_a^x s^*(t)\,dt.$$

But $s_n(x) \to s(x)$ as $n \to \infty$, so that

$$s(x) = \int_a^x s^*(t)\,dt + s(a),$$

and since $s^*(t)$ is continuous in $a \leq t \leq x$ by U_1, differentiating both sides yields

$$s'(x) = s^*(x).$$

We now illustrate these properties by examples.

EXAMPLE 7. Show that

$$\text{I} = \int_0^\pi \left(\sum_{n=1}^{\infty} \frac{n \sin nx}{e^n}\right) dx = \frac{2e}{e^2 - 1}.$$

Solution. We first see whether it is valid to integrate term by term. Since $\left|\frac{n \sin nx}{e^n}\right| \leq \frac{n}{e^n}$ and $\sum \frac{n}{e^n}$ is convergent by the ratio test, the given series is uniformly convergent for all x by the Weierstrass M-test. Hence, applying U_2^*,

$$\begin{aligned} I &= \sum_{n=1}^{\infty} \frac{n}{e^n} \int_0^{\pi} \sin nx \, dx \\ &= 2 \sum_{n=0}^{\infty} \frac{1}{e^{2n+1}} = 2e \sum_{n=0}^{\infty} \left(\frac{1}{e^2}\right)^{n+1} \\ &= 2e \sum_{n=-1}^{\infty} \left(\frac{1}{e^2}\right)^n = \frac{2e}{e^2 - 1}, \end{aligned}$$

since the series is a geometric series.

EXAMPLE 8. Show that

$$\frac{1}{(1-x)^2} = \sum_{n=0}^{\infty} nx^{n-1}, \qquad -1 < x < 1.$$

Solution. Formally, we can obtain the result by differentiating both sides of

$$\text{(A)} \qquad \frac{1}{1-x} = \sum_{n=0}^{\infty} x^n, \qquad -1 < x < 1,$$

the series, term by term. Let us justify this procedure.

Let $0 < r < 1$. $\sum_{n=0}^{\infty} x^n$ is a pointwise convergent series of continuously differentiable functions in $|x| \leq r$. Furthermore, the differentiated series $\sum_{n=0}^{\infty} nx^{n-1}$ is uniformly convergent in $|x| \leq r$ by the Weierstrass M-test, since $|nx^{n-1}| \leq nr^{n-1}$ in $|x| \leq r$ and $\sum nr^{n-1}$ is convergent by the ratio test. Hence, by U_3^*, the term-by-term differentiation of the series in (A) is valid.

EXAMPLE 9. Show that the series $1 + \sum_{n=1}^{\infty} \frac{(-1)^n x(x-1)\cdots(x-n+1)}{n!}$ is not uniformly convergent in $0 \leq x \leq 1$.

Solution

$$1 + \sum_{n=1}^{\infty} \frac{(-1)^n x(x-1)\cdots(x-n+1)}{n!} t^n = (1-t)^x, \qquad |t| \leq 1.$$

Now, at $t = 1$,

$$(1-t)^x = \begin{cases} 0, & 0 < x \leq 1 \\ 1, & x = 0 \end{cases}.$$

Hence, the sum of the given series is discontinuous in $0 \leq x \leq 1$ and hence, by U_1^*, cannot be uniformly convergent there.

This example suggests the possibility of using U_1 to U_3, U_1^* to U_3^* to prove that a given sequence or series does not converge uniformly in a given interval, and this method may be more effective than an appeal to the definition. The series in Example 1 does not converge uniformly in $0 \leq x \leq 1$.

The conditions given in U_1 to U_3, U_1^* to U_3^* are sufficient for the interchange of limit operations; they are not necessary, as the following examples show.

EXAMPLE 10. Show that if $s_n(x) = \dfrac{e^{-n^2x^2}}{n}$ and $s(x) = \lim_{n\to\infty} s_n(x)$, then $s'(x) = \lim_{n\to\infty} s_n'(x)$, but $\{s_n'(x)\}$ does not converge uniformly in $0 \le x \le 1$.

Solution. $s(x) = 0$, all x, and $\lim_{n\to\infty} s_n'(x) = \lim_{n\to\infty} [-2xne^{-n^2x^2}] = 0$, all x. Now see Example 4.

EXAMPLE 11. Show that if

$$s_n(x) = \frac{n^2x^2}{1 + n^2x^2} \quad \text{and} \quad s(x) = \lim_{n\to\infty} s_n(x),$$

then

$$\int_{-1}^{1} s(x)\,dx = \lim_{n\to\infty} \int_{-1}^{1} s_n(x)\,dx,$$

but $\{s_n(x)\}$ does not converge uniformly in $-1 \le x \le 1$.

Solution

$$s(x) = \begin{cases} 0, & x = 0 \\ 1, & x \neq 0 \end{cases},$$

and

$$\int_{-1}^{1} s(x)\,dx = 2.$$

Now

$$\int_{-1}^{1} s_n(x)\,dx = \int_{-1}^{1} \left[1 - \frac{1}{n^2\left(\dfrac{1}{n^2} + x^2\right)}\right] dx$$

$$= 2\left(1 - \frac{\tan^{-1} n}{n}\right) \to 2 \qquad \text{as } n \to \infty.$$

Proof of nonuniform convergence is left to the student.

EXAMPLE 12. Show that if $s_n(x) = nxe^{-nx^2}$ and $s(x) = \lim_{n\to\infty} s_n(x)$, then $s(x)$ is continuous in $0 \le x \le 1$ but that $\{s_n(x)\}$ does not converge uniformly in $0 \le x \le 1$.

Solution. $s(x) = 0$, $0 \le x \le 1$. See Example 4.

EXERCISES

1. Show that each of the following series is uniformly convergent in the given interval, using the Weierstrass M-test:

(a) $\sum_{n\ 1}^{\infty} (2n + 3)^{3/2} \sin (2n + 1)x$, all x.

(b) $\sum_{n=0}^{\infty} \frac{x^n}{n!}$, $|x| \leq r$.

(c) $\sum_{n=1}^{\infty} \frac{x^n}{n \log^2 n}$, $|x| \leq 1$.

(d) $\sum_{n=0}^{\infty} \frac{\cos (2n + 1)x}{(2n + 1)(2n + 2)}$, all x.

(e) $\sum_{n=1}^{\infty} \frac{1}{n}\left(\frac{x - 1}{x}\right)^n$, $\frac{1}{2} \leq x \leq 1$.

(f) $\sum_{n=0}^{\infty} \left(\frac{\log x}{x}\right)^n$, $x \geq 1$.

(g) $\sum_{n=1}^{\infty} ne^{-nx}$, $x \geq \epsilon > 0$.

(h) $\sum_{n=0}^{\infty} (x \log x)^n$, $0 < x \leq 1$.

2. Show, using the definition of uniform convergence, that

(a) $\sum_{n=1}^{\infty} \frac{x}{(1 + nx)[1 + (n - 1)x]}$ is uniformly convergent in any interval not containing $x = 0$ and not uniformly convergent in every other interval. (*Hint:* Express the nth term in partial fractions.)

(b) $\{n^2x^2e^{-nx}\}$ converges uniformly in $0 < \epsilon \leq x$ but not uniformly in $x \geq 0$.

3. Determine the intervals in which each of the following are uniformly convergent:

(a) $\sum_{n=1}^{\infty} \left(\frac{x}{4}\right)^n$; (b) $\sum_{n=0}^{\infty} \frac{x}{(1 + x)^n}$, $x \geq 0$; (c) $\sum_{n=1}^{\infty} \frac{\sin^m nx}{2^n - 1}$.

(*Hint:* A series cannot be uniformly convergent in an interval where it is not pointwise convergent.)

4. (a) Show that if $\sum_{n=1}^{\infty} a_n$ is absolutely convergent, then $\sum_{n=1}^{\infty} a_n \sin nx$ and $\sum_{n=1}^{\infty} b_n \cos nx$ are uniformly convergent for all x.

(b) Given $\{a_n\}$ such that $0 < a_{n+1} < a_n$, $n = 1, 2, \cdots$, prove that $\sum_{n=1}^{\infty} a_n \sin nx$ and $\sum_{n=1}^{\infty} a_n \cos nx$ converge uniformly if and only if $\lim_{n\to\infty} na_n = 0$.

5. (a) Prove: If $|s_{n+1}(x) - s_n(x)| \leq M_n$, every x in E, $n = 1, 2, \cdots$, and $\sum_{n=1}^{\infty} M_n$ is convergent, then $\{s_n(x)\}$ is uniformly convergent in E.

(b) Show that $\left\{\frac{x^n}{n!}\right\}$ is uniformly convergent in $0 \leq x \leq 1$ and $\{n/e^{nx^2}\}$ in $\frac{1}{2} \leq x \leq 1$.

6. (a) Show that $\sum_{n=0}^{\infty} \frac{x^2}{(1 + x^2)^n}$ is absolutely convergent for all x, but that it is not uniformly convergent in any interval containing zero.

(b) Show that $\sum_{n=1}^{\infty} \frac{(-1)^{n-1}}{n + x^2}$ converges uniformly for all x, but not absolutely.

(c) Show that if a series satisfies the conditions of the Weierstrass M-test, then it is absolutely convergent. This implies that this test is inapplicable to conditionally convergent series that, in view of (b), may be uniformly convergent.

(d) Show that if $\sum_{n=1}^{\infty} v_n(x)$ is uniformly convergent on E and $|u_n(x)| \leq v_n(x)$ all x in E, $n = 1, 2, \cdots$, then $\sum_{n=1}^{\infty} u_n(x)$ is uniformly convergent on E. Why is this a generalization of the Weierstrass M-test?

(e) Show that if $0 < u_n(x) < \dfrac{1}{n}$ and $u_{n+1}(x) \leq u_n(x)$, $a \leq x \leq b$, $n = 1, 2, \cdots$, then $\sum_{n=1}^{\infty} (-1)^n u_n(x)$ is uniformly convergent in $a \leq x \leq b$.

(f) Show that $\sum_{n=2}^{\infty} \dfrac{(-1)^n e^{-nx}}{n(n-1)}$ is uniformly convergent in $0 \leq x \leq R$.

(g) Show that if $0 \leq u_{n+1}(x) \leq u_n(x)$, $n = 1, 2, \cdots$, and $u_n(x) \to 0$ uniformly in $a \leq x \leq b$, then $\sum_{n=1}^{\infty} (-1)^n u_n(x)$ converges uniformly in $a \leq x \leq b$.

(h) Show that $\sum_{n=1}^{\infty} \dfrac{(-1)^n x^{2n}}{1 + x^{2n}}$ converges uniformly in $-1 + \epsilon \leq x \leq 1 - \epsilon$ $\epsilon > 0$. Does it converge absolutely?

(i) Show that $\sum_{n=1}^{\infty} \dfrac{(-1)^n x e^{-x^2/n^2}}{n}$ converges uniformly in $a \leq x \leq b$. Does it converge absolutely?

(j) Show that $\sum_{n=1}^{\infty} u_n(x)$, $u_n(x) = \dfrac{1}{x}$, $\dfrac{1}{n+1} \leq x \leq \dfrac{1}{n}$ and $u_n(x) = 0$ for all other x, is uniformly convergent for all x. Why can't uniform convergence be proved by the Weierstrass M-test?

7. (a) Show that if $\{s_n(x)\}$ and $\{t_n(x)\}$ converge uniformly on E, then $\{s_n(x) + t_n(x)\}$ converges uniformly on E.

(b) A sequence $\{s_n(x)\}$ is **uniformly bounded** on E if there is a constant M such that $|s_n(x)| \leq M$ for all x in E and $n = 1, 2, \cdots$. Show that if $s_n(x) \to s(x)$ uniformly on E and $s(x)$ is bounded, then $\{s_n(x)\}$ is uniformly bounded.

(c) Show that if $\{s_n(x)\}$ and $\{t_n(x)\}$ are uniformly convergent and uniformly bounded in E, then $\{s_n(x)t_n(x)\}$ is uniformly convergent in E. Give an example to show that "uniformly bounded" cannot be deleted from this statement.

(d) Prove **Abel's test** for uniform convergence: If $\sum_{n=1}^{\infty} u_n(x)$ has uniformly bounded partial sums in E, $s_n(x) \to 0$ uniformly on E, $s_{n+1}(x) \leq s_n(x)$, for every x in E, $n = 1, 2, \cdots$ then $\sum_{n=1}^{\infty} s_n(x) u_n(x)$ converges uniformly in E. Show that $\sum_{n=1}^{\infty} a_n \cos nx$ and $\sum_{n=1}^{\infty} b_n \cos nx$ are uniformly convergent in any closed interval not containing a multiple of 2π, if $0 < a_{n+1} < a_n$, $n = 1, 2, \cdots$.

Hint:

$$\sum_{k=1}^{n} \sin kx = \frac{\cos(x/2) - \cos(n + \frac{1}{2})x}{2 \sin \frac{1}{2}x}.$$

(e) Prove: If $\{s_n(x)\}$ is a pointwise convergent sequence of continuously differentiable functions in $a \leq x \leq b$ and $\{s_n'(x)\}$ is uniformly bounded in $a \leq x \leq b$, then $\{s_n(x)\}$ is uniformly convergent in $a \leq x \leq b$.

(f) Prove the **ratio test for uniform convergence:** If $u_n(x)$, $n = 1, 2, \cdots$, are bounded and have no zeros in a set E and if there exists constants N and r, $r < 1$, such that $\left|\dfrac{u_{n+1}(x)}{u_n(x)}\right| \leq r$ for every $n > N$ and all x in E, then $\sum_{n=1}^{\infty} u_n(x)$ is uniformly convergent on E. Apply this test to the binomial series

$$1 + \sum_{n=1}^{\infty} \frac{x(x-1)\cdots(x-n+1)}{n!} t^n, \qquad |t| < 1,$$

t fixed.

When are tests for pointwise convergence applicable to uniform convergence?

(g) Prove: If $s_n(x) \to s(x)$ uniformly on E and there exists a sequence of constants $\{M_n\}$ such that $|s_n(x)| \le M_n$, $n = 1, 2, \cdots$, for all x in E, then $\{s_n(x)\}$ is uniformly bounded in E.

8. (a) Show that if a sequence converges uniformly on E, then any subsequence converges uniformly on E. Is the converse true?

(b) Prove: If $s_{n+1}(x) \le s_n(x)$, $n = 1, 2, \cdots$, for every x in E and $\{s_n(x)\}$ is pointwise convergent in E but contains a uniformly convergent subsequence on E, then $\{s_n(x)\}$ converges uniformly on E.

(c) Prove: If $\{s_n(x)\}$ is uniformly convergent on sets E and F, then it is uniformly convergent on $E \cup F$; i.e., the set of points belonging either to E or F.

(d) Show that if $\{s_n(x)\}$ is convergent on a finite set E, then it is uniformly convergent on E. Why can't this be extended to infinite sets?

(e) Show that if $\{s_n(x)\}$ is uniformly convergent in $a < x < b$ and convergent at $x = a$ and $x = b$, then $\{s_n(x)\}$ is uniformly convergent in $a \le x \le b$.

(f) Prove or disprove: If $\sum_{n=1}^{\infty} u_n(x)$ is convergent on E and $u_n(x) \to 0$ uniformly on E, then $\sum_{n=1}^{\infty} u_n(x)$ converges uniformly on E.

9. Show that

(a) $$\lim_{n\to\infty} \int_{\pi/2}^{\pi} \frac{\sin nx}{nx}\, dx = 0.$$

(b) $$\int_0^{\pi} \left(\sum_{n=1}^{\infty} \frac{\sin nx}{nk} \right) dx = \sum_{n=1}^{\infty} \frac{2}{(2n-1)^{k+1}}, \qquad k > 1.$$

(c) $$\int_1^2 \left(\sum_{n=1}^{\infty} ne^{-nx} \right) dx = \frac{e}{e^2 - 1}.$$

(d) $$\lim_{n\to\infty} \int_1^2 e^{-nx^2}\, dx = 0.$$

10. Determine if the following series can be differentiated term by term in the given interval:

(a) $$\sum_{n=1}^{\infty} \left(\frac{x}{x-1} \right)^n, \qquad -2 \le x \le -1.$$

(b) $$\sum_{n=1}^{\infty} \frac{\sin nx}{n^3 x}, \qquad x > 0.$$

(c) $$\sum_{n=1}^{\infty} e^{-nx} \sin knx, \qquad x > 0.$$

(d) $$\sum_{n=1}^{\infty} \frac{1}{n^3(1 + nx^2)}, \qquad \text{all } x.$$

11. Show that the following sequences and series are not uniformly convergent in the given intervals by showing that the limit functions and sums are discontinuous:

(a) $$\sum_{n=0}^{\infty} x^n(1-x), \qquad 0 \le x \le 1.$$

(b) $\{e^{-nx^2}\}$, $|x| \le 1$.

(c) $\sum_{n=0}^{\infty} \frac{x^2}{(1+x^2)^n}$, $|x| \le 1$.

(d) $\left\{\frac{x^n}{1+x^n}\right\}$, $0 \le x \le 1$.

(e) $\{\sin^n x\}$, $0 \le x \le \pi$.

(f) $\{x^{1/2n-1}\}$, all x.

12. (a) Show that $\sum_{n=1}^{\infty} \frac{x}{1+n^2x}$ converges uniformly in $x \ge 0$ and that its sum is an increasing function.

(b) Show that $\sum_{n=1}^{\infty} \frac{x}{n(x+n)}$ converges uniformly in $0 \le x \le a$ and that its sum is an increasing function $S(x)$. Show that $S'(0) = \pi^2/6$.

13. (a) Let $s_n(x) = \frac{e^{-n^2x^2}}{n}$, $\lim_{n\to\infty} s_n(x) = s(x)$. Show that $\{s_n(x)\}$ converges uniformly for all x, $\lim_{n\to\infty} s_n'(x) = s'(x)$ for all x, but $\{s_n'(x)\}$ is not uniformly convergent in any interval containing zero.

(b) Show that if $s_n(x) = \frac{2nx}{1+n^2x^4}$ and $s(x) = \lim_{n\to\infty} s_n(x)$, then $\int_0^1 s(x)\,dx = 0$ and $\lim_{n\to\infty} \int_0^1 s_n(x)\,dx = \frac{\pi}{2}$. What do you conclude about the uniform convergence of $\{s_n(x)\}$ in $0 \le x \le 1$?

(c) Show that $\frac{\sin nx}{n} \to 0$ uniformly for all x, but $\left\{\left(\frac{\sin nx}{n}\right)'\right\}$ is pointwise convergent only for integral multiples of 2π.

14. (a) Show that the power series $\sum_{n=0}^{\infty} a_n x^n$ with radius of convergence R is uniformly convergent for $-R < x < R$. What do you conclude if the power series is convergent at R or $-R$?

(b) Show that a power series can be integrated term by term within its interval of convergence.

(c) Show that a power series can be differentiated term by term within its interval of convergence. (*Hint:* The radii of convergence of a power series and the differentiated series are equal; see p. 296.)

(d) Restate the preceding theorems if x is a complex variable.

15. (a) Let $s_n(x) = \begin{cases} 1/n, & 0 \le x \le n \\ 0, & x > n \end{cases}$. Then $s_n(x) \to 0$ uniformly for all x. Show that $\lim_{n\to\infty} \int_0^{\infty} s_n(x)\,dx = 1$. Conclusion?

(b) Show that if $u_n(x)$ is integrable on $a \le x < \infty$, $n = 1, 2, \cdots$, and that there exists a sequence of constants $\{M_n\}$ such that $|x^k u_n(x)| \le M_n$, $n = 1, 2, \cdots$, $a \le x \le \infty$, $k > 1$, and $\sum_{n=1}^{\infty} M_n$ is convergent, then

$$\int_a^{\infty} \left(\sum_{n=1}^{\infty} u_n(x)\right) dx = \sum_{n=1}^{\infty} \int_a^{\infty} u_n(x)\,dx.$$

16. (a) Show that

$$\sum_{n=0}^{\infty} r^n \cos nx = \frac{1 - r\cos x}{1 - 2r\cos x + r^2}$$

and

$$\sum_{n=1}^{\infty} r^n \sin nx = \frac{r \sin x}{1 - 2r\cos x + r^2}, \qquad |r| < 1,$$

and deduce $1 + 2\sum_{n=1}^{\infty} r^n \cos nx = \dfrac{1 - r^2}{1 - 2r\cos x + r^2}$, $|r| < 1$. (*Hint:* Let $z = Re^{ix}$ in $\dfrac{1}{1-z} = \sum_{n=0}^{\infty} z^n$, $|z| < 1$, and equate real and imaginary parts.)

(b) Establish the following:

$$\int_0^{\pi} \frac{\cos mx\, dx}{1 - 2r\cos x + r^2} = \frac{\pi r^m}{1 - r^2},$$

$$\int_0^{\pi} \frac{x \sin x\, dx}{1 - 2r\cos x + r^2} = \frac{\pi \log(1 + r)}{r},$$

$$\int_0^{\pi} \frac{\sin x \sin mx\, dx}{1 - 2r\cos x + r^2} = \frac{\pi}{2} r^{m-1}, \qquad m \text{ an integer, } |r| < 1.$$

(c) Show that

$$\int_0^{\pi} \log(1 - 2r\cos x + r^2)\, dx = 0, \qquad |r| < 1.$$

(*Hint:* Integrate twice $\dfrac{r - \cos x}{1 - 2r\cos x} = -\sum_{n=1}^{\infty} r^{n-1} \cos nx$.)

17. Determine the sets of points on which the following are uniformly convergent:

(a) $\sum_{n=0}^{\infty} \dfrac{1}{2n+1}\left(\dfrac{x-1}{x+1}\right)^{2n+1}$; (b) $\sum_{n=1}^{\infty} \dfrac{x^n}{\sqrt{n}}$; (c) $\sum_{n=1}^{\infty} \dfrac{x^{3/2}}{1 + n^2x^2}$;

(d) $\sum_{n=1}^{\infty} \dfrac{\sin^3 nx}{nk}$; (e) $\sum_{n=1}^{\infty} \dfrac{1}{n^x}$; (f) $\{\tan^{-1}(nx)\}$; (g) $\left\{\dfrac{nx}{n^2x^2 + nx + 4}\right\}$;

(h) $\sum_{n=1}^{\infty} \dfrac{\cos^n x \sin nx}{n}$; (i) $\sum_{n=1}^{\infty} (-1)^{n-1} e^{-nx}/n^k$; (j) $\{\sqrt[n]{x \sin x}\}$.

18. (a) Show that if $\dfrac{a_0}{2} + \sum_{n=1}^{\infty} a_n \cos nx + b_n \sin nx$ converges uniformly to $f(x)$ in $-\pi \le x \le \pi$, then it is the Fourier series of $f(x)$.

(b) Show that if $f(x)$ is continuous, $f(-\pi) = f(\pi)$, and $f'(x)$ is piecewise continuous in $-\pi \le x \le \pi$, then the Fourier series of $f(x)$ converges uniformly to $f(x)$ in $-\pi \le x \le \pi$.

Hint: Let $S_n(x)$ be the nth partial sum of the Fourier series of $f(x)$. If $m > n$,

$$|S_m(x) - S_n(x)| = \sum_{k=n+1}^{m} a_k \cos kx + b_k \sin k\pi$$

$$\leq \sum_{k=n+1}^{m} \sqrt{a_k^2 + b_k^2} = \sum_{k=n+1}^{m} \frac{\sqrt{a_k'^2 + b_k'^2}}{k}$$

(a_k' and b_k' the Fourier coefficients of $f'(x)$)

$$\leq \left(\sum_{k=n+1}^{m} \frac{1}{k^2}\right)^{1/2} \left(\sum_{k=n+1}^{m} a_k'^2 + b_k'^2\right)^{1/2}$$

(by the Schwarz inequality).

But

$$\sum_{k=n+1}^{\infty} a_k'^2 + b_k'^2 \leq \frac{1}{\pi} \int_{-\pi}^{\pi} [f'(x)]^2 \, dx$$

and

$$\sum_{k=n+1}^{\infty} \frac{1}{k^2} \leq \sum_{k=n+1}^{\infty} \frac{1}{k^2} \leq \int_{n}^{\infty} \frac{dx}{x^2} = \frac{1}{n}.$$

Hence

$$|S_m(x) - S_n(x)| \leq \frac{C}{\sqrt{n}},$$

where

$$C^2 = \frac{1}{\pi} \int_{-\pi}^{\pi} [f'(x)]^2 \, dx.$$

19. Let the graph of $f_n(x)$ consist of line segments with slope ± 1 such that

$$f_n(x) = \begin{cases} 0, & x = \pm m/4^n \\ \dfrac{1}{2 \cdot 4^n}, & x = m + \frac{1}{2}/4^n \end{cases} \qquad m = 0, 1, 2, \cdots.$$

(Sketch $f_1(x), f_2(x), f_3(x)$). Let $f(x) = \sum_{n=0}^{\infty} f_n(x)$. Show that $f(x)$ is **everywhere continuous** but **nowhere differentiable.**

Hint: Show that the series is uniformly convergent for all x. Let x_0 be any fixed point; show that for any $n = 1, 2, \cdots$ a number h_n can be chosen as one of the numbers 4^{-n-1} or -4^{-n-1} so that

$$f_n(x_0 + h_n) - f_n(x_0) = \pm h_n.$$

Now

$$f_m(x_0 + h_n) - f_m(x_0) = \pm h_n, \qquad m \leq n,$$

and is zero for $m > n$. Therefore, $f(x_0 + h_n) - f(x_0)$ (h_n is an integer, odd or even, according as to whether n is odd or even, and hence becomes infinite as $n \to \infty$).

20. Define

$$\phi(t) = \begin{cases} 0, & 0 \leq t \leq \frac{1}{3}, \frac{5}{3} \leq t \leq 2 \\ 3t - 1, & \frac{1}{3} \leq t \leq \frac{2}{3} \\ 1, & \frac{2}{3} \leq t \leq \frac{4}{3} \\ -3t + 5, & \frac{4}{3} \leq t \leq \frac{5}{3} \end{cases}, \quad \phi(t + 2) = \phi(t).$$

Define

$$g_1(t) = \sum_{n=1}^{\infty} \frac{\phi(3^{2n-2}t)}{2^n}, \quad g_2(t) = \sum_{n=1}^{\infty} \frac{\phi(3^{2n-1}t)}{2^n}.$$

Let $\mathbf{g}(t) = g_1(t)\mathbf{i} + g_2(t)\mathbf{j}$. If C is the curve of $\mathbf{g}(t)$, show that if (a, b) is any point in the square, $0 \le x \le 1$, $0 \le y \le 1$, then (a, b) is on C. (This is an example of a **space-filling curve.**)

Solution in outline: Show that both series are uniformly convergent for all t, since $|\phi(t)| \le 1$. Show that $g_1(t)$ and $g_2(t)$ are continuous for all t. Since $0 \le g_1(t) \le 1$, $0 \le g_2(t) \le 1$, C is a subset of the unit square. Express a and b in the binary system; i.e., $a = \sum_{n=1}^{\infty} \frac{a_n}{2^n}$, $b = \sum_{n=1}^{\infty} \frac{b_n}{2^n}$, where each a_n and b_n is either 0 or 1. Let $C = 2\sum_{n=1}^{\infty} \frac{C_n}{3^n}$, where $C_{2n-1} = a_n$, $C_{2n} = b_n$, $M = 1, 2, \cdots$. Then $0 \le C \le 1$. Now $3^kC = 2\sum_{n=1}^{k} \frac{C_n}{3^{n-k}} + 2\sum_{n=k+1}^{\infty} \frac{C_n}{3^{n-k}}$ = even integer $+ d_k$, $d_k = 2\sum_{n=1}^{\infty} C_{n+k}/3^n$. Hence, $\phi(3^kC) = \phi(d_k)$. If $C_{k+1} = 0$, $0 \le d_k \le 2\sum_{n=2}^{\infty} 3^{-n} = \frac{1}{3}$ and $\phi(d_k) = 0$, so that $\phi(3^kC) = C_{k+1}$; if $C_{k+1} = 1$, $\frac{2}{3} \le d_k \le 1$ and $\phi(d_k) = 1$, so that $\phi(3^kC) = 1$. Hence, $\phi(3^kC) = C_{k+1}$ in all cases; therefore, $g_1(C) = a$ and $g_2(C) = b$.

Chapter 12

The Fourier Integral and Fourier Transforms

1. The Fourier integral. We have seen that a piecewise smooth function can be represented by its Fourier series in an infinite interval only if it is periodic. However, if we are interested in the representation of such a function only in some finite interval, then we can also represent it by its Fourier series; if this function is not periodic, then the Fourier series will represent its periodic extension outside the given interval and not the function, but this does not matter because our interest in the function lies in the given interval. If we are interested in the representation of a function in an infinite interval and this function is not periodic, then it cannot be represented by a Fourier series. Nevertheless, we seek a representation of such a function that is analogous to a Fourier series. This might be achieved formally by considering a function defined in a finite interval, representing it as a Fourier series, and then allowing the interval to become infinite. Let us follow this procedure in order to obtain some notion as to the type of representation we are seeking for the function defined in an infinite interval. We consider the Fourier series of f defined in the interval $-p \leq x \leq p$:

$$\frac{a_0}{2} + \sum_{n=1}^{\infty} a_n \cos \frac{n\pi x}{p} + b_n \sin \frac{n\pi x}{p},$$

and use the definitions of the Fourier coefficients to obtain

$$\frac{1}{2p} \int_{-p}^{p} f(t)\, dt + \sum_{n=1}^{\infty} \frac{1}{p} \int_{-p}^{p} f(t) \left[\cos \frac{n\pi t}{p} \cos \frac{n\pi x}{p} + \sin \frac{n\pi t}{p} \sin \frac{n\pi x}{p} \right] dt$$

$$= \frac{1}{2p} \int_{-p}^{p} f(t)\, dt + \sum_{n=1}^{\infty} \frac{1}{p} \int_{-p}^{p} f(t) \cos \frac{n\pi (x - t)}{p}\, dt.$$

Now let us see what happens if we let $p \to \infty$.

$$\left|\frac{1}{2p}\int_{-p}^{p} f(t)\,dt\right| \le \frac{1}{2p}\int_{-p}^{p} |f(t)|\,dt \le \frac{1}{2p}\int_{-\infty}^{\infty} |f(t)|\,dt \to 0.$$

Here we have made use of the fact that $\int_{-\infty}^{\infty} |f(t)|\,dt$ exists; i.e., that f is absolutely integrable in $-\infty < t < \infty$. We shall soon see that f must have this property if it is to have the representation we are seeking.

In the series, we let $n\pi/p = y_n$ and $\Delta y = \pi/p$, so that it becomes

$$\frac{1}{\pi}\sum_{n=1}^{\infty}\left[\int_{-p}^{p} f(t)\cos y_n(x-t)\,dt\right]\Delta y.$$

Now let us consider the function g such that

$$g(y) = \frac{1}{\pi}\int_{-p}^{p} f(t)\cos y(x-t)\,dt.$$

We can now write the series in the form

$$\lim_{k\to\infty}\sum_{n=1}^{k} g(y_n)\,\Delta y.$$

Now $\sum_{n=1}^{k} g(y_n)\,\Delta y$ is the Riemann sum of $g(y)$ in $0 \le y \le k\pi/p$, so that as $k \to \infty$, this sum formally approaches $\int_0^{\infty} g(y)\,dy$. Finally, we can write the series as

$$\frac{1}{\pi}\int_0^{\infty}\int_{-p}^{p} f(t)\cos y(x-t)\,dt\,dy,$$

which, as $p \to \infty$, becomes

$$\frac{1}{\pi}\int_0^{\infty}\int_{-\infty}^{\infty} f(t)\cos y(x-t)\,dt\,dy,$$

if $\int_{-\infty}^{\infty} f(t)\,dt$ exists.

The student must not be led to believe that we have established a representation for f; the limit processes that have been employed must be justified, for in some cases they are not valid. All that we have done is to obtain an expression that can be explored further for possible representation of f.

We have thus motivated the following definition: Given a function f defined in $-\infty < x < \infty$ such that $\int_{-\infty}^{\infty} f(x)\,dx$ and $\int_{-\infty}^{\infty} |f(x)|\,dx$ exist, then corresponding to f is the integral $\frac{1}{\pi}\int_0^{\infty}\int_{-\infty}^{\infty} f(t)\cos y(x-t)\,dt\,dy$, called the **Fourier integral** of f. We write

$$f(x) \sim \frac{1}{\pi}\int_0^{\infty}\int_{-\infty}^{\infty} f(t)\cos y(x-t)\,dt\,dy.$$

Sufficient conditions under which the Fourier integral of f converges to $f(x)$ for $-\infty < x < \infty$ are given in the

FOURIER INTEGRAL THEOREM. If f is piecewise continuous and almost differentiable in $-\infty < x < \infty$ and $\int_{-\infty}^{\infty} |f(x)|\, dx$ exists, then

$$\frac{1}{2}[f(x+) + f(x-)] = \frac{1}{\pi}\int_0^{\infty}\int_{-\infty}^{\infty} f(t)\cos y(x-t)\, dt\, dy.$$

The proof of this theorem will be omitted; it can be found in Churchill, *Fourier Series and Boundary Value Problems*, p. 115. Note that since f is piecewise continuous in $-\infty < x < \infty$, then the existence of $\int_{-\infty}^{\infty} |f(x)|\, dx$ implies the existence of $\int_{-\infty}^{\infty} f(x)\, dx$ (see p. 433, Exercise 14(c)). If $\int_{-\infty}^{\infty} |f(x)|\, dx$ exists, we say that f is absolutely integrable in $-\infty < x < \infty$; hence, for piecewise continuous functions, absolute integrability implies integrability.

EXAMPLE 1. Find the Fourier integral of f where

$$f(x) = \begin{cases} 1, & |x| \le 1 \\ 0, & |x| > 1 \end{cases}.$$

Solution. We have

$$\begin{aligned} f(x) \sim \frac{1}{\pi}\int_0^{\infty}\int_{-1}^{1}\cos y(x-t)\, dt\, dy &= \frac{1}{\pi}\int_0^{\infty} dy \int_{-1}^{1} (\cos xy \cos yt + \sin xy \sin yt)\, dt \\ &= \frac{1}{\pi}\left[\int_0^{\infty}\cos xy\, dy \int_{-1}^{1}\cos yt\, dt \right. \\ &\quad \left. + \int_0^{\infty}\sin xy\, dy\int_{-1}^{1}\sin yt\, dt\right] \\ &= \frac{2}{\pi}\int_0^{\infty}\frac{\cos xy \sin y}{y}\, dy. \end{aligned}$$

By the Fourier integral theorem, we have that (do all the conditions hold?)

$$\frac{2}{\pi}\int_0^{\infty}\frac{\cos xy\sin y}{y}\, dy = \begin{cases} 1, & |x| < 1 \\ 0, & |x| > 1. \\ \frac{1}{2}, & |x| = 1 \end{cases}$$

Note that for $x = 0$, we obtain

$$\int_0^{\infty}\frac{\sin y}{y}\, dy = \frac{\pi}{2},$$

which was also obtained in Example 3, p. 274. The fact that

$$\frac{2}{\pi}\int_0^{\infty}\frac{\cos y\sin y}{y}\, dy = \frac{1}{2}$$

can be verified directly, since the integral may be written

$$\frac{1}{\pi}\int_0^{\infty}\frac{\sin 2y}{y}\, dy = \frac{1}{\pi}\int_0^{\infty}\frac{\sin u}{u}\, du = \frac{1}{2}.$$

EXAMPLE 2. Determine the function f such that

$$f(x) = \int_0^{\infty}\int_{-\pi}^{\infty} e^{-t}\cos t\cos y(x-t)\, dt\, dy.$$

Solution. This is the Fourier integral of f where

$$f(x) = \begin{cases} 0, & -\infty < x < -\pi \\ -e^{\pi/2}, & x = -\pi \\ e^{-x}\cos x, & -\pi < x < \infty, \end{cases}$$

since f satisfies the conditions of the Fourier integral theorem.

We now express the Fourier integral of f in complex form analogous to the complex Fourier series. We replace $\cos y(x - t)$ by $\frac{1}{2}[e^{iy(x-t)} + e^{-iy(x-t)}]$ in that integral, and write it as two integrals

$$\frac{1}{2\pi}\left[\int_0^\infty \int_{-\infty}^\infty f(t)e^{iy(x-t)}\,dt\,dy + \int_0^\infty \int_{-\infty}^\infty f(t)e^{-y(x-t)}\,dt\,dy\right],$$

and now replace $-y$ by y in the second integral to obtain

$$\frac{1}{2\pi}\int_{-\infty}^\infty \int_{-\infty}^\infty f(t)e^{iy(x-t)}\,dt\,dy.$$

Hence,

$$f(x) \sim \frac{1}{2\pi}\int_{-\infty}^\infty e^{iyx}\,dy \int_{-\infty}^\infty f(t)e^{-yt}\,dt.$$

We can also write the Fourier integral of f as

$$f(x) \sim \int_0^\infty [a(y)\cos xy + b(y)\sin xy]\,dy,$$

where

$$a(y) = \frac{1}{\pi}\int_{-\infty}^\infty f(t)\cos yt\,dt, \quad b(y) = \frac{1}{\pi}\int_{-\infty}^\infty f(t)\sin yt\,dt,$$

which is analogous to the form of the Fourier series we have used most frequently. If f is odd in $-\infty < x < \infty$, or f is defined only in $0 \le x < \infty$, so that its odd extension is defined in $-\infty < x < 0$, then $a(y) = 0$, so that

$$f(x) \sim \frac{2}{\pi}\int_0^\infty \sin xy\,dy \int_0^\infty f(t)\sin yt\,dt,$$

which is called the **Fourier sine integral** of f. Similarly, if f is even in $-\infty < x < \infty$ or is defined only in $0 \le x < \infty$, and its even extension is defined in $-\infty < x < 0$, we have the **Fourier cosine integral** of f:

$$f(x) \sim \frac{2}{\pi}\int_0^\infty \cos xy\,dy \int_0^\infty f(t)\cos yt\,dt.$$

2. Fourier transforms. Let us now assume that the function f satisfies the conditions in the Fourier integral theorem and that it is normalized. Then we can write the complex Fourier integral as

$$f(x) = \frac{1}{\sqrt{2\pi}}\int_{-\infty}^\infty \phi(y)e^{iyx}\,dy,$$

where

$$\phi(y) = \frac{1}{\sqrt{2\pi}}\int_{-\infty}^\infty f(t)e^{-iyt}\,dt.$$

We can now interpret these two equations in the following way: Starting with the function f, the second equation indicates that we "operate" on it by multiplying $f(t)$ by $(1/\sqrt{2\pi})e^{-iyt}$ and then integrating from $-\infty$ to ∞—the result is $\phi(y)$. We say that we have transformed the function f into the function ϕ. This particular transformation is called a **Fourier transformation.** We shall call

$$\frac{1}{\sqrt{2\pi}}\int_{-\infty}^{\infty} f(t)e^{-iyt}\,dt$$

the **Fourier transform** of $f(t)$ and denote it by $\phi(y)$. We shall also write

$$\mathfrak{F}[f(t)] = \phi(y).$$

On the other hand, starting with ϕ, the first equation indicates that we "operate" on it by multiplying $\phi(y)$ by $(1/\sqrt{2\pi})e^{iyx}$ and integrating from $-\infty$ to ∞ to obtain $f(t)$. To achieve symmetry, we shall now write the first equation as

$$f(t) = \frac{1}{\sqrt{2\pi}}\int_{-\infty}^{\infty} \phi(y)e^{iyt}\,dy.$$

This transformation, therefore, is the inverse transformation of the Fourier transformation, and will be called the **inverse Fourier transformation.** We call

$$\frac{1}{\sqrt{2\pi}}\int_{-\infty}^{\infty} \phi(y)e^{iyt}\,dy$$

the **inverse Fourier transform** of $\phi(y)$ and will indicate this as

$$\mathfrak{F}^{-1}[\phi(y)] = f(t).$$

Hence, we have a pair of transforms:

$$\mathfrak{F}[f(t)] = \frac{1}{\sqrt{2\pi}}\int_{-\infty}^{\infty} f(t)e^{-iyt}\,dt = \phi(y);$$

$$\mathfrak{F}^{-1}[\phi(y)] = \frac{1}{\sqrt{2\pi}}\int_{-\infty}^{\infty} \phi(y)e^{iyt}\,dy = f(t).$$

The Fourier sine and cosine integrals of a function f lead to the following definitions: The **Fourier sine transform** of $f(t)$ is

$$\sqrt{\frac{2}{\pi}}\int_{0}^{\infty} f(t)\sin yt\,dt = \phi(y)$$

and will be denoted by

$$\mathfrak{F}_s[f(t)] = \phi(y);$$

and the **inverse Fourier sine transform** of $\phi(y)$ is

$$\sqrt{\frac{2}{\pi}}\int_{0}^{\infty} \phi(y)\sin yt\,dy$$

and will be denoted by

$$\mathfrak{F}_s^{-1}[\phi(y)] = f(t).$$

The **Fourier cosine transform** of $f(t)$ is

$$\sqrt{\frac{2}{\pi}}\int_0^\infty f(t)\cos yt\,dt = \phi(y)$$

and will be denoted by

$$\mathfrak{F}_c[f(t)] = \phi(y);$$

and the **inverse Fourier cosine transform** of $\phi(y)$ is

$$\sqrt{\frac{2}{\pi}}\int_0^\infty \phi(y)\cos yt\,dy$$

and will be denoted by

$$\mathfrak{F}_c^{-1}[g(y)] = f(t).$$

Note that the Fourier sine (cosine) transform and the inverse Fourier sine (cosine) transform are completely symmetrical. It follows that if $\mathfrak{F}_s[f(t)] = \phi(y)$, then $\mathfrak{F}_s[\phi(t)] = f(y)$, or if $\mathfrak{F}_c[f(t)] = \phi(y)$, then $\mathfrak{F}_c[\phi(t)] = f(y)$; i.e., the inverse sine (cosine) transform of a function is the sine (cosine) transform of that function. *Warning*: Various authors do not agree as to what the coefficients of the Fourier transforms should be.

Let us state the following theorem, which assures us of the existence of Fourier transforms and their inverses and is actually a restatement of the Fourier integral theorem.

FOURIER TRANSFORM THEOREM. If f is piecewise continuous and absolutely integrable in $-\infty < t < \infty$ $(0 < t < \infty)$, then its Fourier (sine or cosine) transform exists.

If f is piecewise continuous and almost differentiable in $-\infty < t < \infty$ $(0 < t < \infty)$, then its inverse Fourier (sine or cosine) transform exists.

EXAMPLE. Find $\mathfrak{F}_s[e^{-kt}]$ and $\mathfrak{F}_c[e^{-kt}]$, $t \geq 0$, and evaluate

$$\int_0^\infty \frac{\cos yt}{t^2+k^2}\,dt \quad\text{and}\quad \int_0^\infty \frac{y\sin yt}{t^2+k^2}\,dt.$$

Solution

$$\mathfrak{F}_s[e^{-kt}] = \sqrt{\frac{2}{\pi}}\int_0^\infty e^{-kt}\sin yt\,dt \quad\text{and}\quad \mathfrak{F}_c[e^{-kt}] = \sqrt{\frac{2}{\pi}}\int_0^\infty e^{-kt}\cos yt\,dt.$$

Integrating by parts,

$$\mathrm{I}_1 = \int_0^\infty e^{-kt}\sin yt\,dt = \left.\frac{-e^{-kt}\cos yt}{y}\right]_0^\infty - \frac{k}{y}\,\mathrm{I}_2,$$

where

$$\mathrm{I}_2 = \int_0^\infty e^{-kt}\cos yt\,dt,$$

so that

$$\mathrm{I}_1 = \frac{1}{y} - \frac{k}{y}\mathrm{I}_2.$$

Similarly, if we integrate I_2 by parts, we obtain

$$\mathrm{I}_2 = \frac{k}{y}\mathrm{I}_1.$$

Solving these equations for I_1 and I_2 yields

$$\mathrm{I}_1 = \frac{y}{y^2 + k^2} \quad \text{and} \quad \mathrm{I}_2 = \frac{k}{y^2 + k^2},$$

so that

$$\mathfrak{F}_s[e^{-kt}] = \sqrt{\frac{2}{\pi}}\frac{k}{y^2 + k^2} \quad \text{and} \quad \mathfrak{F}_c[e^{-kt}] = \sqrt{\frac{2}{\pi}}\frac{y}{y^2 + k^2}.$$

Now

$$\mathfrak{F}_s\left[\sqrt{\frac{2}{\pi}}\frac{y}{t^2 + k^2}\right] = e^{-ky}$$

so that

$$\int_0^\infty \frac{y \sin yt}{t^2 + k^2}\, dt = \frac{\pi e^{-ky}}{2}$$

and

$$\mathfrak{F}_c\left[\sqrt{\frac{2}{\pi}}\frac{k}{t^2 + k^2}\right] = e^{-ky}$$

so that

$$\int_0^\infty \frac{\cos yt}{t^2 + k^2}\, dt = \frac{\pi}{2k}e^{-ky}.$$

The complex Fourier series for normalized functions satisfying the conditions of the Fourier expansion theorem, written in the form

$$f(t) = \frac{1}{2\pi}\sum_{n=-\infty}^{\infty} c_n e^{int}, \qquad c_n = \int_{-\pi}^{\pi} f(t)e^{-int}\, dt,$$

can be interpreted as a pair of transformations: The second equation indicates that $f(t)$ is transformed into the sequence $\{c_n\}$, and the first equation indicates the inverse transformation from the sequence $\{c_n\}$ to $f(t)$. The transformation is an integral transformation, and its inverse is a series transformation. We define the **finite Fourier transform** of $f(t)$ as

$$\int_{-\pi}^{\pi} f(t)e^{-int}\, dt = \phi(n)$$

and denote it by

$$F[f(t)] = \phi(n),$$

and the **inverse finite Fourier transform** of $\phi(n)$ as

$$\frac{1}{2\pi}\sum_{n=-\infty}^{\infty} \phi(n)e^{int} = f(t)$$

and denote it by

$$F^{-1}[\phi(n)] = f(t).$$

From the Fourier sine and cosine series we are led to the following definitions. The **finite Fourier sine transform** of $f(t)$ is

$$\int_0^\pi f(t) \sin nt \, dt = \phi(n),$$

which we denote by

$$F_s[f(t)] = \phi(n),$$

and the **inverse finite Fourier sine transform** of $\phi(n)$ is

$$\frac{2}{\pi} \sum_{n=1}^{\infty} \phi(n) \sin nt = f(t)$$

which we denote by

$$F_s^{-1}[\phi(n)] = f(t).$$

The **finite Fourier cosine transform** of $f(t)$ is

$$\int_0^\pi f(t) \cos nt \, dt = \phi(n)$$

and is denoted by

$$F_c[f(t)] = \phi(n),$$

and the **inverse finite Fourier cosine transform** of $\phi(n)$ is

$$\frac{\phi(0)}{\pi} + \frac{2}{\pi} \sum_{n=1}^{\infty} \phi(n) \cos nt = f(t)$$

and is denoted by

$$F_c^{-1}[\phi(n)] = f(t).$$

The finite Fourier transforms of a function defined in any finite interval can be defined by making the appropriate substitutions in our definitions. The Fourier expansion theorem can be restated as the

FINITE FOURIER TRANSFORM THEOREM. If f is piecewise continuous in $-\pi \leq t \leq \pi$ $(0 \leq t \leq \pi)$, then its finite Fourier (sine or cosine) transform exists.

If f is piecewise continuous and almost differentiable in $-\pi \leq t \leq \pi$ $(0 \leq t \leq \pi)$, then its inverse finite Fourier (sine or cosine) transform exists.

EXAMPLE. Find $F_s[t]$ and $F_c[t]$.

Solution

$$\begin{aligned} F_s[t] &= \int_0^\pi t \sin nt \, dt \\ &= -\frac{\pi}{n}(-1)^n + \frac{1}{n}\int_0^\pi \cos nt \, dt \\ &= \frac{\pi(-1)^{n+1}}{n} \end{aligned}$$

$$F_c[t] = \int_0^\pi t \cos nt \, dt = \frac{1}{n}\int_0^\pi \sin nt \, dt = \frac{1}{n}[1 - (-1)^n].$$

We can think of the Fourier transformation as transforming the class of piecewise continuous, absolutely integrable functions L into the class of functions L'. One of the reasons for the importance of the transformation is that we may be confronted with a problem involving functions in class L that may be difficult to solve but that the corresponding problem involving functions in class L' may be easy to solve. We need merely "transform" the problem by determining the Fourier transforms of the functions involved, solving this problem, and finally finding the inverse transform of this solution. In order that we may know what problems can be most effectively solved in this fashion, we must know more about the properties of the functions in class L'. We now determine some of these properties.

First, if every function in L' is to have an inverse Fourier transform, then every function in L' must be piecewise continuous and absolutely integrable. Note that in the case of Fourier sine or cosine transforms, we have that $L = L'$.

We now consider two properties of the transforms of functions, whether they be Fourier transforms, Fourier sine or cosine transforms, or any of the finite Fourier transforms—we shall use the symbol T to denote any one of these transforms.

F_1 (Linearity property): If $\mathrm{T}[f(t)]$ and $\mathrm{T}[g(t)]$ exist, then for any constants c_1 and c_2,

$$\mathrm{T}[c_1 f(t) + c_2 g(t)] = c_1 \mathrm{T}[f(t)] + c_2 \mathrm{T}[g(t)].$$

F_2 (Riemann-Lebesgue theorem): If $\mathrm{T}[f(t)]$ exists and equals $\phi(y)$, then $\lim_{|y|\to\infty} \phi(y) = 0$.

F_1 follows immediately from the definition of the transforms and the fact that integrals have the linearity property. Any transformation that has this linearity property is called a *linear transformation.* To prove F_2 simply would involve the introduction of concepts that would take us too far afield; its proof can be found in Titchmarsh, *Theory of Fourier Integrals*, p. 11, and Bochner and Chandrasekharan, *Fourier Transforms*, p. 3. It is interesting to note that as a result of F_2, if the function f has a Fourier sine or cosine transform, then necessarily $\lim_{t\to\infty} f(t) = 0$ as well as $\lim_{y\to\infty} \phi(y) = 0$, $\phi(y) = \mathfrak{F}_s[f(t)]$ or $\mathfrak{F}_c[f(t)]$.

The next set of properties indicates the nature of the Fourier transforms of the derivatives of functions in class L, these derivatives also belonging to L.

F_3: If $\mathfrak{F}[f(t)] = \phi(y)$ and $\mathfrak{F}[f'(t)]$ exist, and $\lim_{t\to\pm\infty} f(t) = 0$, then

$$\mathfrak{F}[f'(t)] = -iy\phi(y).$$

F_4: If $\mathfrak{F}_s[f(t)] = \phi(y)$ and $\mathfrak{F}_c[f(t)] = \psi(y)$ and $\mathfrak{F}_s[f'(t)]$ and $\mathfrak{F}_c[f'(t)]$ exist, then

$$(1) \quad \mathfrak{F}_s[f'(t)] = -y\psi(y),$$

$$(2) \quad \mathfrak{F}_c[f'(t)] = y\phi(y) - \sqrt{\frac{2}{\pi}}\, f(0).$$

F$_5$: If $\mathfrak{F}_s[f(t)] = \phi(y)$ and $\mathfrak{F}_c[f(t)] = \psi(y)$ and $\mathfrak{F}_s[f'(t)]$, $\mathfrak{F}_c[f'(t)]$, $\mathfrak{F}_s[f''(t)]$, $\mathfrak{F}_c[f''(t)]$ exist, then

$$(1) \quad \mathfrak{F}_s[f''(t)] = -y^2\phi(y) + \sqrt{\frac{2}{\pi}}\, yf(0),$$

$$(2) \quad \mathfrak{F}_c[f''(t)] = -y^2\psi(y) - \sqrt{\frac{2}{\pi}}\, f'(0).$$

F$_6$: If $F_s[f(t)] = \phi(n)$ and $F_c[f(t)] = \psi(n)$ and $F_s[f'(t)]$, $F_c[f'(t)]$, $F_s[f''(t)]$, $F_c[f''(t)]$ exist, then

$$(1) \quad F_s[f''(t)] = -n^2\phi(n) + n[f(0) - (-1)^n f(\pi)],$$

$$(2) \quad F_c[f''(t)] = -n^2\psi(n) - f'(0) + (-1)^n f'(\pi).$$

Proofs. F$_3$: Integrating by parts,

$$\begin{aligned} \mathfrak{F}[f'(t)] &= \frac{1}{\sqrt{2\pi}} \int_{-\infty}^{\infty} f'(t) e^{iyt}\, dt \\ &= \frac{1}{\sqrt{2\pi}}\, e^{iyt} f(t) \Big]_{-\infty}^{\infty} - \frac{iy}{\sqrt{2\pi}} \int_{-\infty}^{\infty} f(t) e^{iyt}\, dt \\ &= -iy\phi(y), \end{aligned}$$

since $f(t) \to 0$ as $t \to \pm\infty$.

F$_4$, (1) Integrating by parts,

$$\begin{aligned} \mathfrak{F}_s[f'(t)] &= \sqrt{\frac{2}{\pi}} \int_0^{\infty} f'(t) \sin yt\, dt \\ &= \sqrt{\frac{2}{\pi}}\, f(t) \sin yt \Big]_0^{\infty} - \sqrt{\frac{2}{\pi}}\, y \int_0^{\infty} f(t) \cos yt\, dt \\ &= -y\phi(y), \end{aligned}$$

by the Riemann-Lebesgue theorem. Similarly, we obtain (2).

F$_5$, (1)

$$\begin{aligned} \mathfrak{F}_s[f''(t)] &= -y\mathfrak{F}_c[f'(t)] = -y[y\phi(y) - f(0)] \\ &= -y^2\phi(y) + yf(0), \end{aligned}$$

by F$_4$. Similarly, we obtain (2).

The proof of F$_6$ is left to the student.

We shall now illustrate the use of the Fourier transform in the solution of certain differential equations and Dirichlet problems. To apply this technique effectively, one should have available a table that lists the commonly occurring functions together with their Fourier transforms, if these exist. The Bateman Manuscript Project, edited by Erdélyi, et al., *Tables of Integral Transforms*, vol. 1, Campbell and Foster, *Fourier Integrals for*

Practical Applications, and Oberhettinger, *Tabellen zur Fourier Transformation*, offer excellent tables. Short tables of finite sine and cosine transforms appear on p. 450.

EXAMPLE 1. Find the solution of $3x''(t) + 2x'(t) + tx = 0$.

Solution. This is a linear differential equation whose coefficients are not all constants. The student has very likely solved such an equation hitherto by means of series. We now consider another approach. Let $\mathfrak{F}[x(t)] = \phi(y)$. Then $\mathfrak{F}[x'(t)] = -iy\phi(y)$ and $\mathfrak{F}[x''(t)] = -y^2\phi(y)$, provided $\lim_{|t|\to\infty} x(t) = \lim_{|t|\to\infty} x'(t) = 0$. Therefore, we shall determine a solution with this property, if it exists. The student should show that $\mathfrak{F}[tx] = -i\phi'(y)$. Now taking the Fourier transform of both sides of the differential equation, we obtain

$$\begin{aligned}\mathfrak{F}[3x'' + 2x' + tx] &= 3\mathfrak{F}[x''] + 2\mathfrak{F}[x'] + \mathfrak{F}[tx]\\ &= -3y^2\phi(y) - 2iy\phi(y) - i\phi'(y) = 0.\end{aligned}$$

Hence, we have the first-order linear differential equation

$$\phi'(y) = (3iy^2 - 2y)\phi(y),$$

whose solution is readily determined as

$$\phi(y) = Ce^{iy^3 - y^2},$$

where C is an arbitrary constant [VIBb]. Now

$$\begin{aligned}x(t) = \mathfrak{F}^{-1}[\phi(y)] &= \frac{C}{\sqrt{2\pi}} \int_{-\infty}^{\infty} e^{iy^3 - y^2} e^{-ity}\, dy\\ &= \frac{C}{\sqrt{2\pi}} \int_{-\infty}^{\infty} \cos\,(y^3 - ty) e^{-y^2}\, dy\\ &\quad + \frac{iC}{\sqrt{2\pi}} \int_{-\infty}^{\infty} \sin\,(y^3 - ty) e^{-y^2}\, dy.\end{aligned}$$

Hence,

$$x(t) = \frac{C}{\sqrt{2\pi}} \int_{-\infty}^{\infty} \cos\,(y^3 - ty) e^{-y^2}\, dy,$$

since the integrand in the second integral is an odd function. The student should verify directly that this is a solution of the differential equation. It can be shown (see Martin and Reissner, *Elementary Differential Equations*, p. 116) that if we denote this solution by u_1, we can obtain a solution u_2, which is linearly independent to it, where

$$u_2 = u_1 \int \frac{e^{-2t/3}}{u_1^2}\, dt.$$

However, $\lim_{|t|\to\infty} u_2 \neq 0$, and we could not have obtained this solution using the transform method.

EXAMPLE 2. Determine the function $H(x, y)$, harmonic in $0 < x,\ y < \infty$, such that $H(x, 0) = e^{-x}$, $H(0, y) = \cos y$, and $\lim_{x\to\infty} H(x, y) = 0$.

Solution. We must determine a function $H(x, y)$ that satisfies Laplace's equation

$$\frac{\partial^2 H}{\partial x^2} + \frac{\partial^2 H}{\partial y^2} = 0$$

and the given conditions. If in $H(x, y)$ we let x be fixed, then we can consider it as a function of the single variable y. Now we assume that the Fourier sine transform of this function exists, and we denote it by $h(x, t)$, which indicates that x remains fixed and that the variable y is transformed into the new variable t. Now let us apply the Fourier sine transformation to both sides of Laplace's equation; we have

$$\mathfrak{F}_s\left[\frac{\partial^2 H}{\partial x^2} + \frac{\partial^2 H}{\partial y^2}\right] = \mathfrak{F}_s[0] = 0,$$

or

$$\mathfrak{F}_s\left[\frac{\partial^2 H}{\partial x^2}\right] + \mathfrak{F}_s\left[\frac{\partial^2 H}{\partial y^2}\right] = 0,$$

by F_1. Since we are transforming with respect to y, $\partial^2 H/\partial y^2$ can be thought of as an ordinary second derivative of H with respect to y, and hence by F_5,

$$\mathfrak{F}_s\left[\frac{\partial^2 H}{\partial y^2}\right] = -t^2 h(x, t) + tH(x, 0) = -t^2 h(x, t) + te^{-x}.$$

Now

$$\mathfrak{F}_s\left[\frac{\partial^2 H}{\partial x^2}\right] = \sqrt{\frac{2}{\pi}} \int_0^\infty \frac{\partial^2 H}{\partial x^2} \sin yt \, dy,$$

in which we shall assume that we can interchange the operations of integration and differentiation so as to obtain

$$\mathfrak{F}_s\left[\frac{\partial^2 H}{\partial x^2}\right] = \sqrt{\frac{2}{\pi}} \frac{\partial^2}{\partial x^2} \int_0^\infty H(x, y) \sin yt \, dy = \frac{\partial^2 h(x, t)}{\partial x^2}.$$

Hence, the transformed Laplace's equation is

$$\frac{\partial^2 h(x, t)}{\partial x^2} - t^2 h(x, t) = -te^{-x}$$

and if we now consider t as fixed and x as varying, $h(x, t) = h$ can be considered as a function of the single variable x, and the equation can be written

$$\mathbf{T_1:} \quad \frac{d^2 h}{dx^2} - t^2 h = -te^{-x}.$$

Now transforming $H(0, y) = \cos y$ and $\lim_{x \to \infty} H(x, y) = 0$, we obtain

$$\mathbf{T_2:} \quad h(0, t) = \frac{-t}{1 - t^2},$$

$$\mathbf{T_3:} \quad \lim_{x \to \infty} h(x, t) = 0,$$

where we have obtained $\mathfrak{F}_s[\cos y]$ from the definition and have assumed that the limit and integration operations can be interchanged.

Our problem now is to find the function h that satisfies T_1, T_2, T_3. But this is a problem in ordinary differential equations. The general solution of T_1 is

$$h(x, t) = Ae^{-tx} + Be^{tx} - \frac{te^{-x}}{1 - t^2},$$

A and B constants; applying first T_3 and then T_2 yields $A = B = 0$. Hence, the function satisfying T_1, T_2, T_3 is

$$h(x, t) = -\frac{te^{-x}}{1 - t^2}.$$

Now let us take the inverse Fourier sine transform of both sides of this equation; we obtain

$$H(x, y) = e^{-x} \cos y.$$

Our problem appears to be solved, but inasmuch as we made several assumptions regarding the interchange of certain operations, it is imperative that we actually verify that $H(x, y)$ satisfies all the conditions. This is a simple matter; note that the harmonicity of $H(x, y)$ is readily established from the fact that $e^{-x} \cos y$ is the real part of the analytic function e^{-z}.

Critique of Example 1. Why did we use the Fourier sine transform in this example? First, the region in which $H(x, y)$ is defined has $0 \leq x < \infty$ and $0 \leq y < \infty$ as its boundary, and this suggests either the Fourier sine or cosine transform. Although we transformed with respect to y, we could just as easily have transformed with respect to x. If the region had been the upper half-plane, and we still wanted to use the Fourier sine or cosine transform, then we would have to transform with respect to y. We used the Fourier sine transform because the transform of the derivative of a function (F_5) involves the value of that function at zero, whereas the Fourier cosine transform involves the value of the derivative of that function at zero; one of our conditions is that $H(x, 0) = e^{-x}$.

EXAMPLE 3. Determine the harmonic function $H(x, y)$ bounded in $0 < x < \pi, y > 0$ and such that $H(0, y) = 0, H(\pi, y) = 1, y > 0$, and $H(x, 0) = 0$, $0 < x < \pi$.

Solution. Since the finite interval $0 < x < \pi$ is part of the boundary of the region, we use the finite Fourier transform, transforming with respect to x. Furthermore, we use the finite Fourier sine transform, since the values of H are given at 0 and π. We let $h(n, y) = F_s[H(x, y)]$. Transforming Laplace's equation, with the use of F_6, and interchanging the operations of integration and differentiation, we obtain

$$-n^2 h(n, y) - n(-1)^n + \frac{\partial^2 h(n, y)}{\partial y^2} = 0.$$

Letting n be fixed, we can write this as

$$T_1\colon \quad \frac{d^2 h}{dy^2} - n^2 h(n, y) = n(-1)^n.$$

Transforming $H(x, 0) = 0$, we obtain

$$T_2: \quad h(n, 0) = 0.$$

Furthermore, since $H(x, y)$ is bounded, there exists a constant M such that $|H(x, y)| < M$, $0 < x < \pi$, $y > 0$. Since $0 < \sin nx \leq 1$ in $0 < x < \pi$, $|h(n, y)| \leq \int_0^\pi |H(x, y)| \sin nx \, dx < M \int_0^\pi dx = M\pi$. Hence

$$T_3: \quad |h(n, y)| < M\pi.$$

The general solution of T_1 is

$$h(n, y) = Ae^{-ny} + Be^{ny} + \frac{1}{n}(-1)^{n-1}.$$

Applying T_3 indicates that $B = 0$; otherwise, $h(n, y)$ would be unbounded, since $e^{ny} \to \infty$ as $y \to \infty$. T_2 indicates that $A = (1/n)(-1)^n$. Hence,

$$T: \; h(n, y) = \frac{1}{n}(-1)^n[e^{-ny} - 1].$$

The definition of the inverse finite sine transform yields

$$H(x, y) = \sum_{n=1}^{\infty} \frac{1}{n}(-1)^n[e^{-ny} - 1] \sin nx.$$

This solution, however, may be expressed in another form (a closed form rather than an infinite series). From T, we have that

$$H(x, y) = F_s^{-1}\left[\frac{1}{n}(-1)^{n+1}\right] + F_s^{-1}\left[\frac{1}{n}(-1)^n e^{-ny}\right].$$

Now

$$F_s^{-1}\left[\frac{1}{n}(-1)^{n+1}\right] = \frac{x}{\pi}$$

(see Example, p. 422), and from any convenient table

$$F_s^{-1}\left[\frac{1}{n}(-1)^{n+1}e^{-ny}\right] = \frac{2}{\pi}\tan^{-1}\frac{\sin x}{e^y + \cos x}$$

so that

$$H(x, y) = \frac{x}{\pi} + \frac{2}{\pi}\tan^{-1}\frac{\sin x}{e^y + \cos x}.$$

The verification that this is the required function is left to the student. Can you verify that $H(x, y)$ in series form satisfies all the requirements?

EXERCISES

1. (a) Express $f(x)$ as a Fourier cosine integral where

$$f(x) = \begin{cases} 1, & 0 \leq x \leq 1 \\ 0, & x > 1 \end{cases}$$

and evaluate

$$\int_0^\infty \frac{\sin y \cos yx}{y}\, dy.$$

(b) Express $f(x)$ as a Fourier sine integral where

$$f(x) = \begin{cases} \sin x, & 0 \leq x \leq \pi \\ 0, & x > \pi \end{cases}$$

and evaluate

$$\int_0^\infty \frac{\sin yx \sin \pi x}{1 - y^2}\, dy.$$

(c) Express $f(x)$ as a Fourier integral where

$$f(x) = \begin{cases} 0, & x < 0 \\ e^{-x}, & x \geq 0 \end{cases}$$

and evaluate

$$\int_0^\infty \frac{\cos xy + y \sin xy}{1 + y^2}\, dy.$$

(d) Express $f(x)$ as a Fourier integral where

$$f(x) = \begin{cases} 0, & x < 0,\ x > 1 \\ 1, & 0 \leq x \leq 1 \end{cases}$$

and evaluate

$$\int_0^\infty \frac{\sin t \cos xt + \sin xt - \cos t \sin xt}{t}\, dt.$$

(e) Express $f(x)$ as a Fourier integral where

$$f(x) = \begin{cases} \cos x, & |x| < \pi \\ 0, & |x| \geq \pi \end{cases}$$

and evaluate

$$\int_0^\infty \frac{x \sin \pi x \cos xy}{1 - x^2}\, dx.$$

2. Determine the functions represented by the following Fourier integrals:

(a) $\displaystyle\int_0^\infty \int_{-\infty}^\infty \frac{\sin^2 t}{t^2} \cos y(x - t)\, dt\, dy.$ (b) $\displaystyle\int_0^\infty \int_0^1 t^2 \cos ty \cos xy\, dt\, dy.$

(c) $\displaystyle\int_0^\infty \int_0^1 t^2 \sin ty \sin xy\, dt\, dy.$

3. Establish the following:

(a) $\mathfrak{F}_s[e^{-kt}] = \sqrt{\dfrac{2}{\pi}} \dfrac{y}{y^2 + k^2}.$ (b) $\mathfrak{F}_c[e^{-kt}] = \sqrt{\dfrac{2}{\pi}} \dfrac{k}{y^2 + k^2}.$

(c) $\mathfrak{F}_s[xe^{-\frac{1}{2}t^2}] = e^{-\frac{1}{2}y^2}.$ (d) $\mathfrak{F}_c[e^{-t^2}] = e^{-y^2}.$

(e) $\mathfrak{F}\left[\dfrac{1}{|x|}\right] = \dfrac{1}{|y|}.$ (f) $\mathfrak{F}_c[\operatorname{sech} \pi t] = \dfrac{1}{1 + y^4}.$

(g) $\mathfrak{F}_c[f(t)] = \sqrt{\dfrac{2}{\pi}} \dfrac{\sin ay}{y},\ f(t) = 1,\ 0 < t < a,\ f(t) = 0,\ t > a.$

(h) $\mathfrak{F}_s\left[\dfrac{\sin t}{t}\right] = \dfrac{1}{\sqrt{2\pi}} \operatorname{Log}\left|\dfrac{1 + y}{1 - y}\right|.$ (i) $\mathfrak{F}\left[\dfrac{\sin at}{t}\right] = \begin{cases} \sqrt{\pi/2}, & |y| < a \\ 0, & |y| > a \end{cases}.$

(j) $\mathfrak{F}_c\left[\sin\frac{1}{2}t^2\right] = \frac{1}{\sqrt{2}}\left[\cos\frac{1}{2}y^2 - \sin\frac{1}{2}y^2\right]$.

4. Establish the following:

(a) $F_s(\pi - t) = \frac{\pi}{n}$. (b) $F_s[\sin kt] = \begin{cases} 0, & k \neq n \\ \pi/2, & k = n \end{cases}$.

(c) $F_s[\cos \alpha t] = \frac{n}{n^2 - \alpha^2}[1 - (-1)^n \cos \alpha\pi]$.

(d) $F_s[t^3] = \pi(-1)^n\left(\frac{6}{n^3} - \frac{\pi^2}{n}\right)$.

(e) $F_s\left[\tan^{-1}\frac{2\alpha \sin t}{1 - \alpha^2}\right] = \frac{\pi\alpha^n}{2n}[1 - (-1)^n]$.

(f) $F_c[t^2] = \begin{cases} \frac{2\pi(-1)^n}{n^2}, & n = 1, 2, \cdots \\ 0, & n = 0 \end{cases}$

(g) $F_c[e^{\alpha t}] = \frac{\alpha}{n^2 + \alpha^2}[(-1)^n e^{\alpha\pi} - 1]$. (h) $F_c[\cosh \alpha(\pi - t)] = \frac{\alpha \sinh \alpha\pi}{n^2 + \alpha^2}$.

(i) $F_c\left[\frac{\cos t - b}{1 - 2b\cos t + b^2}\right] = \begin{cases} \frac{\pi}{2}b^{n-1}, & n = 1, 2, \cdots, |b| < 1 \\ 0, & n = 0 \end{cases}$

(j) $F_c\left[\left(1 - \frac{t}{a}\right)^2\right] = \begin{cases} \frac{2a}{\pi^2 n^2}, & n = 1, 2, \cdots \\ \frac{a}{3}, & n = 0 \end{cases}$

5. (a) Show that the Fourier cosine transform of

$$f(t) = \begin{cases} 1 - t^2, & |t| < 1 \\ 0, & |t| \geq 1 \end{cases} \quad \text{is } 2\sqrt{\frac{2}{\pi}}\left(\frac{y\cos y - \sin y}{y^3}\right)$$

and that

$$\int_0^\infty \left(\frac{x\cos x - \sin x}{x^3}\right)\cos\frac{x}{2}\,dx = \frac{3\pi}{16}.$$

(b) Show that

$$f(x) = \frac{2(1 - \cos x)}{\pi x^2}$$

is a solution of the integral equation

$$\int_0^\infty f(x)\cos yx\,dx = \begin{cases} 1 - y, & 0 \leq y \leq 1 \\ 0, & y > 1 \end{cases}$$

and use this result to show that

$$\int_0^\infty \frac{\sin^2 x}{x^2}\,dx = \frac{\pi}{2}.$$

(c) Show that $\mathfrak{F}[e^{-t^2/2}] = e^{-y^2/2}$; we say that $e^{-t^2/2}$ is its own Fourier transform.

(d) Show that the Fourier sine and cosine transforms of

$$f(t) = \begin{cases} 1, & 0 \le t < 1 \\ 0, & t \ge 1 \end{cases} \quad \text{are} \quad \sqrt{\frac{2}{\pi}}\left(\frac{1 - \cos y}{y}\right) \quad \text{and} \quad \sqrt{\frac{2}{\pi}}\frac{\sin y}{y}.$$

6. If $\mathfrak{F}[f(t)] = \phi(y)$ exists, show that

(a) $\mathfrak{F}[f(t)e^{it\alpha}] = \phi(y + \alpha)$. (b) $\mathfrak{F}[f(t + \alpha)] = e^{-iy\alpha}\phi(y)$.

(c) $\mathfrak{F}[f(\alpha t)] = \dfrac{1}{\alpha}\phi\left(\dfrac{y}{\alpha}\right)$. (d) $\mathfrak{F}\overline{[f(t)]} = \overline{\phi(-y)}$.

7. Establish the following:

(a) If $\mathfrak{F}\left[\dfrac{d^k f(t)}{dt^k}\right]$, $k = 0, 1, \cdots, r$, exist,

$$\mathfrak{F}[f(t)] = \phi(y) \quad \text{and} \quad \lim_{|t|\to\infty} \frac{d^k f(t)}{dt^k} = 0, \qquad k = 0, 1, \cdots, r - 1,$$

then

$$\mathfrak{F}\left[\frac{d^r f(t)}{dt^r}\right] = (-iy)^r\phi(y).$$

(b) If $\mathfrak{F}_c\left[\dfrac{d^k f(t)}{dt^k}\right]$, $k = 0, 1, \cdots, 2r + 1$, exist,

$$\mathfrak{F}_c[f(t)] = \phi(y) \quad \text{and} \quad \mathfrak{F}_s[f(t)] = \psi(y),$$

then

$$\mathfrak{F}_c\left[\frac{d^{2r}f(t)}{dt^{2r}}\right] = (-1)^r y^{2r}\phi(y) - \sqrt{\frac{2}{\pi}}\sum_{n=0}^{r-1}(-1)^n y^{2n} f^{(2r-2n-1)}(0),$$

and

$$\mathfrak{F}_c\left[\frac{d^{2r+1}f(t)}{dt^{2r+1}}\right] = (-1)^r y^{2r+1}\psi(y) - \sqrt{\frac{2}{\pi}}\sum_{n=0}^{r}(-1)^n y^{2n} f^{(2r-2n)}(0).$$

(c) The corresponding formulas in (b) for the Fourier sine transform.

8. If $F_s[f(t)] = \phi(n)$ and $F_c[f(t)] = \psi(n)$, show that for any constant k,

(a) $\phi(n + k) = F_s[f(t) \cos kt] + F_c[f(t) \sin kt]$.

(b) $\psi(n + k) = F_c[f(t) \cos kt] - F_s[f(t) \sin kt]$.

(c) $\phi(n - k) + \phi(n + k) = 2F_s[f(t) \cos kt]$.

(d) $\psi(n - k) + \psi(n + k) = 2F_c[f(t) \cos kt]$.

9. Solve the following Dirichlet problems:

(a) Determine the harmonic function $H(x, y)$ in $x > 0$, $y > 0$ such that

$$\partial H(0, y)/\partial x = 0, \; H(x, 0) = e^{-2x}.$$

(b) Determine the harmonic function $H(x, y)$ in $0 < x < \pi$, $0 < y < \pi$, such that $H(0, y) = H(\pi, y) = 0$ and $H(x, 0) = H(x, \pi) = 1$.

(c) Determine the harmonic function $H(x, y)$ in $0 < x < a$, $0 < y < b$, such that $H(0, y) = H(a, y) = 0$, $H(x, 0) = k_1$, $H(x, b) = k_2$.

10. Determine $T(x, t)$ for each of the following set of conditions:

(a) $\dfrac{\partial T}{\partial t} = \dfrac{\partial^2 T}{\partial x^2}$, $\quad T(0, t) = 0$, $T(x, 0) = \begin{cases} 1, & 0 < x < 1 \\ 0, & x \ge 1 \end{cases}$. $|T(x, t)| < M$, a constant, $x, t > 0$.

(b) $\dfrac{\partial T}{\partial t} = a^2 \dfrac{\partial^2 T}{\partial x^2}$, $\quad T(0, t) = 0, T(x, 0) = e^{-x}, x > 0, |T(x, t)| < M, x, t > 0.$

(c) $\dfrac{\partial T}{\partial t} = \dfrac{\partial^2 T}{\partial x^2}, \dfrac{\partial T(0, t)}{\partial x} = 0, \quad T(x, 0) = \begin{cases} x, & 0 \le x \le 1 \\ 0, & x > 1 \end{cases}, |T(x, t)| < M, x, t > 0.$

Ans.: (a) $\dfrac{2}{\pi} \displaystyle\int_0^\infty \frac{1 - \cos y}{y} e^{-y^2 t} \sin yx \, dy;$

(b) $\dfrac{2}{\pi} \displaystyle\int_0^\infty \frac{y e^{-a^2 y^2 t} \sin yx}{y^2 + 1} dy;$

(c) $\dfrac{2}{\pi} \displaystyle\int_0^\infty \left(\frac{\sin y}{y} + \frac{\cos y - 1}{y^2}\right) e^{-y^2 t} \cos yx \, dy.$

11. (a) Prove the *Fourier convolution theorem:* If $\phi(y) = \mathfrak{F}[f(t)]$ and $\psi(y) = \mathfrak{F}[g(t)]$, then

$$\mathfrak{F}^{-1}[\phi(y)\psi(y)] = \int_{-\infty}^{\infty} f(\lambda) g(t - \lambda) \, d\lambda.$$

Hint: $\phi(y)\psi(y) = \dfrac{1}{2\pi} \displaystyle\int_{-\infty}^{\infty} \int_{-\infty}^{\infty} e^{iy(u+v)} f(u) g(u) \, du \, dv$; let $x = u + v$.

(b) Solve the integral equation

$$f(x) = h(x) + \int_{-\infty}^{\infty} f(\lambda) r(x - \lambda) \, d\lambda$$

for $f(x)$; $h(x)$ and $r(x)$ are given. Assume that the Fourier transforms of $f(x)$, $h(x)$, $r(x)$ exist.

Ans.: (b) $f(x) = \dfrac{1}{\sqrt{2\pi}} \displaystyle\int_{-\infty}^{\infty} \frac{\phi(y) e^{-iyx}}{1 - \sqrt{2\pi}\psi(y)} dy;$

$\phi(y) = \mathfrak{F}[h(x)]$ and $\psi(y) = \mathfrak{F}[r(x)]$.

12. (a) Prove Parseval's identities:

(1) $\displaystyle\int_{-\infty}^{\infty} \mathfrak{F}[f(t)]\overline{\mathfrak{F}[g(t)]} \, dy = \int_{-\infty}^{\infty} f(t)\overline{g(t)} \, dt.$

(2) $\displaystyle\int_{-\infty}^{\infty} |\mathfrak{F}[f(t)]|^2 \, dy = \int_{-\infty}^{\infty} |f(t)|^2 \, dt.$

(3) $\displaystyle\int_0^{\infty} \mathfrak{F}_c[f(t)]\mathfrak{F}_c[g(t)] \, dy = \int_0^{\infty} f(t) g(t) \, dt.$

(4) $\displaystyle\int_0^{\infty} \mathfrak{F}_s[f(t)]\mathfrak{F}_s[g(t)] \, dy = \int_0^{\infty} f(t) g(t) \, dt.$

Hint: Multiply both sides of

$$f(t) = \frac{1}{\sqrt{2\pi}} \int_{-\infty}^{\infty} \mathfrak{F}[f(t)] e^{-iyt} \, dy$$

by $\overline{g(t)}$ and integrate both sides from $-\infty$ to ∞.

(b) Show that

$$\int_0^\infty \frac{dx}{(x^2 + 1)^2} = \int_0^\infty \frac{x^2 \, dx}{(x^2 + 1)^2} = \frac{\pi}{4}.$$

(*Hint:* Use $\mathfrak{F}_s[e^{-t}]$ and $\mathfrak{F}_c[e^{-t}]$ and (3) and (4) in (a).)

13. Solve the following integral equations for $f(x)$:

(a) $\displaystyle\int_0^x f(x-y)e^{-y}\,dy = \begin{cases} 0, & x < 0 \\ x^2e^{-x}, & x \geq 0 \end{cases}.$

(b) $\displaystyle\int_{-\infty}^{\infty} e^{-|x-y|}f(y)\,dy = e^{-|x|}(1 + |x|).$

Ans.: (a) $f(x) = \begin{cases} 0, & x < 0 \\ 2xe^{-x}, & x \geq 0 \end{cases}$; (b) $e^{-|x|}$.

14. (a) We know that

$$\int_0^{\infty} \frac{\sin x}{x}\,dx = \frac{\pi}{2},$$

i.e., $\dfrac{\sin x}{x}$, is integrable in $0 \leq x \leq \infty$. Show that it is not absolutely integrable in that interval. (*Hint:* For $k\pi \leq x \leq (k+1)\pi$, $k = 0, 1, 2, \cdots$, $\dfrac{|\sin x|}{x} \geq \dfrac{|\sin x|}{(k+1)\pi}$, so that

$$\int_{k\pi}^{(k+1)\pi} \frac{|\sin x|}{x}\,dx \geq \frac{1}{(k+1)\pi}\int_{k\pi}^{(k+1)\pi} |\sin x|\,dx = \frac{2}{(k+1)\pi}.$$

If $n\pi \leq b < (n+1)\pi$,

$$\int_0^b \frac{|\sin x|}{x}\,dx \geq \frac{2}{\pi}\sum_{k=0}^{n-1}\frac{1}{k+1};$$

$n \to \infty$ as $b \to \infty$, and the sum becomes a divergent infinite series.)

(b) Give an example to show that $\int_{-\infty}^{\infty} |f(x)|\,dx$ may exist while $\int_{-\infty}^{\infty} f(x)$ does not exist.

(c) Show that if f is continuous in $-\infty < x < \infty$, and $\int_{-\infty}^{\infty} |f(x)|\,dx$ exists, then $\int_{-\infty}^{\infty} f(x)\,dx$ exists.

Hint:

$$\left|\int_a^b f(x)\,dx\right| \leq \int_a^b |f(x)|\,dx \leq \int_{-\infty}^{\infty} |f(x)|\,dx.$$

Generalize to piecewise continuous functions.

15. (a) Show that the Fourier cosine integral of $\sin t/t$ is equal to this function.

(b) Show that the Fourier cosine integral of $1/\sqrt{|t|}$ is equal to this function.

(c) With the use of (a) and (b) and Exercise 9, show that the conditions in the Fourier integral theorem are not necessary.

Chapter 13

Orthogonal Functions

Our study of the representation of functions as Fourier series should lead us to inquire as to whether it is possible to represent functions in a series of a given set of functions other than sines and cosines. We could hardly expect this set of functions to be completely arbitrary; surely, these functions must have certain properties that enable them to play such a significant role. In order to answer these questions, let us retrace the steps that led to the definition of the Fourier series of a given function f, to see if we can determine the properties of sines and cosines that were crucial to our development. Starting with a sequence of functions:

$$1, \cos x, \sin x, \cos 2x, \sin 2x, \cdots, \cos nx, \sin nx, \cdots,$$

which we shall now call the **trigonometric system,** we assumed that f could be represented in a series involving these functions; i.e.,

$$f(x) = \frac{a_0}{2} + \sum_{n=1}^{\infty} a_n \cos nx + b_n \sin nx,$$

with the a_n and b_n as coefficients to be determined. In order to relate these coefficients to f, we multiplied both sides of this equation by $\cos mx$, $m = 0, 1, \cdots$, and $\sin mx$, $m = 1, 2, \cdots$, in turn, and then integrated both sides from $-\pi$ to π. It was at this point that a certain property of the sines and cosines made it possible to obtain explicit expressions for the coefficients. This property is that if $\phi_n(x)$ and $\phi_m(x)$ are any two functions in the trigonometric system, then

$$\int_{-\pi}^{\pi} \phi_n(x)\phi_m(x)\,dx = \begin{cases} 0, & n \neq m \\ \pi, & n = m \end{cases}.$$

With this property, all the terms in the integrated series, except one, vanish; this nonvanishing term is πa_m (or πb_m), which equals $\int_{-\pi}^{\pi} f(x) \cos mx \, dx$ (or $\int_{-\pi}^{\pi} f(x) \sin mx \, dx$) and we have explicit expressions for the coefficients. If we are to generalize the Fourier series of a function f by replacing the trigonometric system involved in this series by a more general system of functions, then this latter system must necessarily have the analogous property mentioned above. This, then, will be our point of departure. We say that a sequence of functions

$$\phi_0, \phi_1, \phi_2, \cdots, \phi_n, \cdots$$

is an **orthogonal system** of functions in $a \leq x \leq b$ if

$$\int_a^b \phi_n(x)\phi_m(x) \, dx = 0, \qquad n \neq m, \quad n, m = 0, 1, 2, \cdots.$$

We shall denote this system by $\{\phi_m\}$. This definition is meaningful only if no function in the system is identically zero.

(Since in geometry the term *orthogonal* is equivalent to *perpendicular*, the student may be curious as to the choice of this word to indicate the aforementioned property. This will become clear if we motivate the definition as in Supplementary Problem 11, p. 447.)

In addition to the trigonometric system that is orthogonal in $-\pi \leq x \leq \pi$, we are familiar with the systems

$$1, \cos x, \cos 2x, \cdots, \cos nx, \cdots$$

and

$$\sin x, \sin 2x, \cdots, \sin nx, \cdots,$$

which are orthogonal in $0 \leq x \leq \pi$.

Now let us assume that a given function f can be represented as follows:

$$f(x) = \sum_{n=0}^{\infty} c_n \phi_n(x), \qquad a \leq x \leq b,$$

where $\{\phi_n\}$ is an orthogonal system in $a \leq x \leq b$. If we multiply both sides by $\phi_m(x)$, integrate from a to b, we obtain (in view of the orthogonality property) that

$$\int_a^b f(x)\phi_m(x) \, dx = c_m \int_a^b \phi_m^2(x) \, dx.$$

Since $\int_a^b \phi_m^2(x) \, dx \neq 0$, we obtain

$$c_m = \frac{\int_a^b f(x)\phi_m(x) \, dx}{\int_a^b \phi_m^2(x) \, dx}, \qquad m = 1, 2, \cdots.$$

The value of $\sqrt{\int_a^b \phi_n^2(x) \, dx}$ is called the **norm** of the orthogonal system $\{\phi_n\}$. We denote it by δ_n, which indicates that in general it depends on n; it is clear that $\delta_n > 0$ for all n. The theory is greatly simplified if we consider orthogonal systems whose norm is 1. We say that the sequence of functions $\{\phi_n\}$ is an **orthonormal system** in $a \leq x \leq b$ if

$$\int_a^b \phi_n(x)\phi_m(x)\,dx = \begin{cases} 0, & m \neq n \\ 1, & m = n \end{cases}.$$

Any orthogonal system $\{\phi_n\}$ with norm δ_n can be converted into the orthonormal system $\{\phi_n/\delta_n\}$. We say that the orthogonal system has been normalized, or that the orthonormal system is the normalization of the orthogonal system. Hence, $1/\sqrt{2\pi}$, $\cos x/\sqrt{\pi}$, $\sin x/\sqrt{\pi}$, $\cdots$ is an orthonormal system in $-\pi \leq x \leq \pi$.

Given an orthonormal system $\{\phi_n\}$ in $a \leq x \leq b$ and a function f such that $c_n = \int_a^b f(x)\phi_n(x)\,dx$ exists, then f determines the series $\sum_{n=0}^{\infty} c_n\phi_n(x)$, which we call the **orthogonal series** of f. We write

$$f(x) \sim \sum_{n=0}^{\infty} c_n\phi_n(x), \qquad c_n = \int_a^b f(x)\phi_n(x)\,dx.$$

The notation indicates that the series corresponds to f merely because the coefficients are determined by f; it does not indicate that the series even converges, let alone that it converges to f. The coefficients c_n, $n = 0, 1, \cdots$ are called the **generalized Fourier coefficients** of f, or the Fourier coefficients of f with respect to $\{\phi_n\}$.

The generalized Fourier coefficients of f are defined as

$$c_n = \int_a^b f(x)\phi_n(x)\,dx, \qquad n = 0, 1, \cdots.$$

We now examine other relationships between a function and its generalized Fourier coefficients.

First we consider the following

THEOREM. If $\{\phi_n\}$ is an orthonormal system in $a \leq x \leq b$, $s_n(x) = \sum_{k=0}^{n} c_k\phi_k(x)$ is the nth partial sum of the orthogonal series of f, and

$$t_n(x) = \sum_{k=0}^{n} \gamma_k\phi_k(x), \qquad \gamma_k,\ k = 0, 1, \cdots, n, \quad \text{arbitrary},$$

then

$$\int_a^b [f(x) - s_n(x)]^2\,dx \leq \int_a^b [f(x) - t_n(x)]^2\,dx,$$

with equality only if $\gamma_k = c_k$, $k = 0, 1, \cdots, n$.

Proof.

$$\begin{aligned}
\int_a^b [f(x) - t_n(x)]^2\,dx &= \int_a^b f^2(x)\,dx - 2\int_a^b f(x)t_n(x)\,dx + \int_a^b t_n^2(x)\,dx \\
&= \int_a^b f^2(x)\,dx - 2\sum_{k=0}^{n} \gamma_k \int_a^b f(x)\phi_k(x)\,dx + \int_a^b t_n^2(x)\,dx \\
&= \int_a^b f^2(x)\,dx - 2\sum_{k=0}^{n} \gamma_k c_k + \sum_{k=0}^{n} \gamma_k^2 \\
&= \int_a^b f^2(x)\,dx - \sum_{k=0}^{n} c_k^2 + \sum_{k=0}^{n} (c_k - \gamma_k)^2.
\end{aligned}$$

The only quantities in this equation that are not fixed are the γ_k, and these determine $t_n(x)$. Now the minimum value of the right-hand side of this equation occurs when $\sum_{k=0}^{n} (c_k - \gamma_k)^2$ is a minimum and this minimum value is zero, which occurs only if $c_k = \gamma_k$, $k = 0, 1, \cdots, n$. The inequality in the theorem is now immediate.

In the proof of the preceding theorem, we have incidentally established that

$$\int_a^b [f(x) - s_n(x)]^2 \, dx = \int_a^b f^2(x) \, dx - \sum_{k=0}^{n} c_k^2,$$

and since the left-hand side is nonnegative, we obtain immediately that

$$\sum_{k=0}^{n} c_k^2 \leq \int_a^b f^2(x) \, dx,$$

and since this is true for all n, we have

Bessel's inequality. If $\{\phi_n\}$ is an orthonormal system in $a \leq x \leq b$ and $f(x) \sim \sum_{n=0}^{\infty} c_n\phi_n(x)$, then

$$\sum_{n=0}^{\infty} c_n^2 \leq \int_a^b f^2(x) \, dx.$$

Bessel's inequality implies that the series $\sum_{n=0}^{\infty} c_n^2$ is convergent and hence that $\lim_{n\to\infty} c_n^2 = 0$ or $\lim_{n\to\infty} c_n = 0$. This is known as the

RIEMANN-LEBESGUE THEOREM. If $\{c_n\}$ is the sequence of generalized Fourier coefficients of f, then $\lim_{n\to\infty} c_n = 0$.

If we define the **mean square error** to $f(x)$, given by

$$t_n(x) = \sum_{k=0}^{n} \gamma_n\phi_n(x)$$

as $\int_a^b [f(x) - t_n(x)]^2 \, dx$, then the above theorem can be stated as follows:

The smallest mean square error to $f(x)$ is given by s_n, where $s_n(x) = \sum_{k=0}^{n} c_k\phi_k(x)$, the nth partial sum of the orthogonal series of f.

We might expect that $\lim_{n\to\infty} \int_a^b [f(x) - s_n(x)]^2 \, dx = 0$. However, this is not always the case. We say that the orthonormal sequence of functions $\{\phi_n\}$ in $a \leq x \leq b$ is **complete** with respect to a given class of functions, or has the **completeness property,** if for every function f in this class,

$$\lim_{n\to\infty} \int_a^b [f(x) - s_n(x)]^2 \, dx = 0,$$

at points of continuity of f, where

$$s_n(x) = \sum_{k=0}^{n} c_n\phi_n(x), \qquad c_n = \int_a^b f(x)\phi_n(x) \, dx.$$

This limit is often indicated as

$$\underset{n\to\infty}{\text{l.i.m.}}\ s_n(x) = f(x)$$

and read as the **limit in the mean** of $s_n(x)$ is $f(x)$ as $n \to \infty$. The limit in the mean does not imply ordinary convergence; i.e., $\lim_{n\to\infty} s_n(x) = f(x)$; nor does ordinary convergence imply the existence of the limit in the mean. For examples, see Wiener, *The Fourier Integral and Certain of Its Applications*, p. 29.

The class of functions that determines the completeness property of an orthonormal sequence of functions cannot be arbitrary. First of all, let us consider the necessary restrictions on an orthonormal sequence of functions, $\{\phi_n\}$ in $a \le x \le b$. Since

$$\int_a^b \phi_n^2(x)\,dx = 1, \qquad n = 0, 1, \cdots,$$

it necessarily follows that ϕ_n^2 must be integrable in $a \le x \le b$, or as we say, ϕ_n must be **square-integrable** in $a \le x \le b$. Now, since

$$|\phi_n(x)\phi_m(x)| \le \tfrac{1}{2}[\phi_n^2(x) + \phi_m^2(x)],$$

it follows that if $\phi_n(x)$ is square-integrable, $n = 0, 1, 2, \cdots$; then

$$\int_a^b \phi_n(x)\phi_m(x)\,dx$$

exists. In other words, all that we require is that $\{\phi_n\}$ belongs to the class of square-integrable functions. It seems reasonable, then, to consider the completeness of an orthonormal sequence of functions with respect to the class of square-integrable functions. In particular, if f is square-integrable, then f is integrable in $a \le x \le b$ if a and b are finite (let $g(x) \equiv 1$ in $|f(x)g(x)| \le \frac{1}{2}[f^2(x) + g^2(x)]$). Can you cite an example to disprove the converse? Actually, every bounded Riemann integrable function is square-integrable, and these are the functions with which we are primarily concerned; in the generalization of the Riemann integral to the Lebesgue integral (which is indispensable in the modern theory of functions), we could replace "bounded Riemann" by "Lebesgue" and have a valid statement. Hence, if f belongs to the class of square-integrable functions, we are assured of the existence of its generalized Fourier coefficients.

It is readily seen that an orthonormal system is complete with respect to the class of square-integrable functions if and only if the equality sign in Bessel's inequality holds at points of continuity of f. The resulting equation is called **Parseval's equation.** In other words, the orthonormal sequence $\{\phi_n\}$ in $a \le x \le b$ is complete with respect to the class of square-integrable functions if and only if for every function f in this class, Parseval's equation:

$$\sum_{n=0}^{\infty} c_n^2 = \int_a^b f^2(x)\,dx, \quad c_n = \int_a^b f(x)\phi_n(x)\,dx, \qquad n = 0, 1, \cdots$$

is valid at points of continuity of f.

It is shown in Supplementary Problem 10, p. 447, that if f is continuous, then the trigonometric system is complete. It then follows that Parseval's equation for the trigonometric system,

$$\frac{a_0^2}{2} + \sum_{n=1}^{\infty} (a_n^2 + b_n^2) = \frac{1}{\pi}\int_{-\pi}^{\pi} f^2(x)\,dx,$$

is valid at points of continuity of f.

Given an orthonormal system of functions, we are interested in what functions can be represented by their orthogonal series determined by this orthonormal system. An important class of functions that occurs frequently in practice is the class of piecewise continuous functions. However, as we have seen in the case of Fourier series, this class of functions is not sufficiently restrictive to ensure that every function in this class can be represented by its orthogonal series. In general, other conditions must be imposed on the functions. In practice, this is most feasibly accomplished for specific orthogonal series. Therefore, given an orthogonal sequence of functions, we are led to an **expansion theorem** that imposes sufficient conditions on functions which will ensure their expansion into their orthogonal series determined by the given orthogonal sequence. The Fourier expansion theorem is such an expansion theorem. In the next chapter, we shall introduce some important examples of orthogonal series, and for each of these we shall consider an expansion theorem.

We mention, in passing, that modern mathematicians have established some very elegant expansion theorems, known as *equiconvergence expansion theorems.* Two series

$$\sum_{n=0}^{\infty} a_n f_n(x) \quad \text{and} \quad \sum_{n=0}^{\infty} b_n f_n(x)$$

are called **equiconvergent** if the convergence of one of them at a point implies the convergence of the other at that point. An equiconvergence expansion theorem, then, would be of the form: If $\{\phi_n\}$ is a given orthogonal system with prescribed properties, then the orthogonal series of a given function f will converge to that function if and only if the Fourier series of that function converges to it; in other words, that the given orthogonal series of f and its Fourier series are equiconvergent. Hence, such an equiconvergence theorem together with the Fourier expansion theorem would yield an expansion theorem for the given orthogonal series.

Now suppose that we are given an orthonormal system $\{\phi_n\}$ in $a \leq x \leq b$ and a function $f \neq \phi_n$, for any n such that

$$c_n = \int_a^b f(x)\phi_n(x)\,dx = 0, \qquad n = 0, 1, \cdots.$$

Then it would follow that if

$$f(x) = \sum_{n=0}^{\infty} c_n\phi_n(x),$$

$f(x)$ is represented by a series that converges to zero—a contradictory state of affairs unless $f(x) \equiv 0$. We avoid this situation by requiring that the orthonormal system be **closed** (or **maximal**) with respect to the class of square-integrable functions, which means that if f is any function in that class not equal to any function in the orthonormal system but is orthogonal to every function in the system, then $f(x) \equiv 0$. This is equivalent to saying that an orthonormal system is closed with respect to the class of square-integrable functions if that system has enough functions to ensure that every nonzero function in the class of square-integrable functions has an orthogonal series that does not converge to zero. If the orthonormal system is complete with respect to the class of square-integrable functions, then it is closed with respect to that class. (See Exercise 6, p. 441.) The converse is not true. See Olmsted, "Completeness and Parseval's Equation," *American Mathematical Monthly*, Vol. 65, pp. 343–345.

Given a sequence of functions $\{\psi_n\}$, which are not orthogonal in $a \leq x \leq b$. However, there may exist a nonnegative function w such that the sequence $\{\sqrt{w}\psi_n\}$ is orthogonal in $a \leq x \leq b$. This suggests the following generalization of an orthogonal system of functions: A sequence of functions $\{\psi_n\}$ is **orthogonal with respect to the weight function** w in $a \leq x \leq b$ if

$$\int_a^b w(x)\psi_n(x)\psi_m(x)\,dx = 0, \qquad n \neq m$$

for every distinct pair of functions in $\{\psi_n\}$.

EXERCISES

1. Show that each of the following sequences of functions is an orthogonal system in the given interval:

(a) $\left\{\cos \dfrac{n\pi(x-a)}{b-a}\right\}$, $a \leq x \leq b$.

(b) $\left\{\sin \dfrac{n\pi(x-a)}{b-a}\right\}$, $a \leq x \leq b$.

(c) $\{\sin \lambda_n\}$, $0 \leq x \leq l$, where $\lambda_n = z_n/l$, $\{z_n\}$ is the sequence of zeros of $\tan z + \alpha z = 0$, α a constant. (See p. 290, Exercise 10.)

(d) $\{\phi_n(x)\}$, $0 \leq x \leq 1$, where $\phi_n(x) =$ the sign ($+$, $-$ or 0) of $\sin 2^{n+1}\pi x$ (Rademacher's functions). (Show that this system is orthonormal.)

2. Show that the trigonometric system is not orthogonal in any interval whose length is not 2π.

3. If $\{\phi_n\}$ is a sequence of complex-valued functions of the real variable t, define this to be an orthonormal system in $a \leq t \leq b$ if

$$\int_a^b \phi_n(t)\overline{\phi_m(t)}\,dt = \begin{cases} 0, & n \neq m \\ 1, & n = m \end{cases}$$

for every pair of functions in the sequence, where $\overline{\phi_m(t)}$ denotes the conjugate of $\phi_m(t)$.

(a) Prove that $\{e^{int}/2\pi\}$ is an orthonormal system in $0 \leq t \leq 2\pi$.

(b) Prove that $\left\{\dfrac{(1-it)^n}{\sqrt{\pi}(1+it)^{n+1}}\right\}$ is orthonormal in $-\infty < t < \infty$. (*Hint:* Use the Cauchy residue theorem in the upper half of the complex plane.)

4. Use Parseval's equation and the Fourier series of functions, which have been established in previous problems, to establish the following:

(a) $\displaystyle\sum_{n=1}^{\infty} \frac{1}{n^2} = \frac{\pi^2}{6}$; (b) $\displaystyle\sum_{n=1}^{\infty} \frac{1}{n^4} = \frac{\pi^4}{90}$.

5. (a) Show that if f and g are continuous and

$$f(x) \sim \frac{a_0}{2} + \sum_{n=1}^{\infty} a_n \cos nx + b_n \sin nx,$$

$$g(x) \sim \frac{\alpha_0}{2} + \sum_{n=1}^{\infty} \alpha_n \cos nx + \beta_n \sin nx,$$

then

$$\frac{a_0\alpha_0}{2} + \sum_{n=1}^{\infty} a_n\alpha_n + b_n\beta_n = \frac{1}{\pi}\int_{-\pi}^{\pi} f(x)g(x)\,dx.$$

(*Hint:* $2f(x)g(x) = [f(x) + g(x)]^2 - f^2(x) - g^2(x)$. Now apply Parseval's equation to f, g, $f + g$.)

(b) Show that if A_n, $n = 0, 1, 2, \cdots$, and B_n, $n = 1, 2, \cdots$ are the Fourier coefficients of $f(x)g(x)$, then

$$A_n = \frac{a_0\alpha_n}{2} + \frac{1}{2}\sum_{m=1}^{\infty} [a_m(\alpha_{m+n} + \alpha_{m-n}) + b_m(\beta_{m+n} + \beta_{m-n})],$$

$$B_n = \frac{a_0\beta_n}{2} + \frac{1}{2}\sum_{m=1}^{\infty} [a_m(\beta_{m+n} - \beta_{m-n}) - b_m(\alpha_{m+n} - \alpha_{m-n})]$$

where $\alpha_{-k} = \alpha_k$ and $\beta_{-k} = -\beta_k$.

6. Prove that if $\{\phi_n\}$ is a complete orthonormal system in $a \leq x \leq b$ with respect to the class of square-integrable functions, then it is closed with respect to that class of functions.

Hint: Assume $f \not\equiv \phi_n$ for any n and that

$$\int_a^b f(x)\phi_n(x)\,dx = 0 \qquad \text{for all } n.$$

Expand $\int_a^b [f(x) - s_n(x)]^2\,dx$, use the preceding equation, take the limit of both sides as $n \to \infty$, use Parseval's equation, and finally establish that $f(x) \equiv 0$.

7. The orthonormal system $\{\phi_n\}$ in $a \leq x \leq b$ is said to have the **uniqueness property** with respect to the class of square-integrable functions if the Fourier coefficients of any function in this class are uniquely determined. Show that completeness implies the uniqueness property. (*Hint:* Use Exercise 6.)

8. A set of functions $\phi_1, \phi_2, \cdots, \phi_n$ is said to be linearly independent if

$$c_1\phi_1(x) + c_2\phi_2(x) + \cdots + c_n\phi_n(x) = 0$$

implies $c_i = 0$, $i = 1, \cdots, n$. A sequence of functions is said to be linearly independent if every finite subset of the sequence is linearly independent. Show that an orthogonal system is linearly independent.

9. (a) Show that a sequence of linearly independent functions $\{\psi_n\}$ determine the orthogonal system $\{\phi_n\}$ in $a \leq x \leq b$ as follows:

$$\phi_0 = \psi_0, \qquad \phi_1 = \mu_{10}\phi_0 + \psi_1, \cdots,$$
$$\phi_n = \mu_{n0}\phi_0 + \mu_{n1}\phi_1 + \cdots + \mu_{n,n-1}\phi_{n-1} + \psi_n,$$

where

$$\mu_{ij} = -\frac{\int_a^b \psi_i(x)\phi_j(x)\,dx}{\int_a^b \phi_j^2(x)\,dx}.$$

We say that $\{\psi_n\}$ has been orthogonalized by the **Gram-Schmidt process of orthogonalization.**

(b) Orthogonalize the sequence of functions $\{x^n\}$ in $0 \leq x \leq 1$.

(c) Orthogonalize the sequence of functions $\{e^{nx}\}$ in $0 \leq x \leq 1$.

10. Show that among all the closed regular curves with fixed length L, the one that encloses the largest area A is a circle (isoperimetric problem).

Hint: Let $x = x(t)$, $y = y(t)$ be the parametric equations of any one of the curves and let $t = 2\pi s/L$, where s is the arc length calculated from some fixed point. Then

$$x(t) = \frac{a_0}{2} + \sum_{n=1}^{\infty} a_n \cos nt + b_n \sin nt$$

and

$$y(t) = \frac{\alpha_0}{2} + \sum_{n=1}^{\infty} \alpha_n \cos nt + \beta_n \sin nt.$$

Since

$$[x'(t)]^2 + [y'(t)]^2 = s^2(t) = \left(\frac{L}{2\pi}\right)^2,$$

show that

$$\frac{1}{\pi}\int_0^{2\pi} [x'(t)]^2 + [y'(t)]^2 = \frac{L^2}{2\pi^2} = \sum_{n=1}^{\infty} n^2(a_n^2 + \alpha_n^2 + b_n^2 + \beta_n^2).$$

(See Exercise 5.) Also show that

$$A = \int_0^2 x(t)y'(t)\,dt = \pi \sum_{n=1}^{\infty} n(a_n\beta_n - b_n\alpha_n).$$

Hence,

$$L^2 - 4\pi A = 2\pi^2 \sum_{n=1}^{\infty} [(na_n - \beta_n)^2 + (n\alpha_n + b_n)^2 + (n^2 - 1)(b_n^2 + \beta_n^2)].$$

Hence, $A \leq L^2/4\pi$ with equality only if

$$a_1 = \beta_1, \quad \alpha_1 = -b_1, \quad a_n = \alpha_n = b_n = \beta_n = 0, \qquad n > 1,$$

which yields

$$\left(x - \frac{a_0}{2}\right)^2 + \left(y - \frac{\alpha_0}{2}\right)^2 = a_1^2 + b_1^2,$$

which is the equation of a circle.

SUPPLEMENTARY PROBLEMS

HARMONIC ANALYSIS

1. (a) Show by the trapezoidal rule that the Fourier coefficients of $f(x)$, $-L \leq x \leq L$, can be approximated as

$$a_n \sim \frac{2}{k} \sum_{i=0}^{k-1} f_i \cos \frac{n\pi x_i}{L}, \quad b_n \sim \frac{2}{k} \sum_{i=0}^{k-1} f_i \sin \frac{n\pi x_i}{L},$$

where $x_0 = -L$, x_1, x_2, $\cdots$, $x_k = L$ are equally spaced points in $-L \leq x \leq L$ with ordinates $f_0, f_1, \cdots, f_k = f_0$. (If $f_0 \neq f_k$, f_0 must be replaced by $(f_0 + f_k)/2$.)

(b) Approximate the Fourier coefficients of $f(x)$, $-1 \leq x \leq 1$, tabulated as follows:

x	$f(x)$
−1.000	−0.115
−0.833	−0.254
−0.677	−0.288
−0.500	−0.316
−0.333	−0.542
−0.167	−0.755
0.000	−0.604
0.167	−0.413
0.333	−0.089
0.500	0.122
0.667	0.205
0.883	0.053
1.000	0.115

MECHANICS

2. A simply supported beam of length L has a load $p(x) = P_0(x)/L$, $P_0 > 0$. If the weight of the beam is neglected, the deflection $y(x)$ satisfies

$$EI\ d^4y/dx^4 = p(x),\ y(0) = y(L) = y''(0) = y''(L) = 0,$$

EI constant. Show that

$$y(x) = \frac{2P_0L^4}{\pi^5 EI} \sum_{n=1}^{\infty} \frac{(-1)^{n+1}}{n^5} \sin \frac{n\pi x}{L}.$$

Show that the deflection at the midpoint is approximately $0.0065356 P_0L^4/EI$. Is this the maximum deflection? (*Hint:* Expand $p(x)$ in a Fourier sine series and assume that $y(x)$ can be expanded in a Fourier sine series. Substitute the series in the differential equation and equate coefficients.)

3. An infinitely long beam rests on an elastic foundation with a concentrated load at its center. We wish to determine the deflection $y(x)$. If a load of $p(x)$ lb/ft is placed on a beam resting on an elastic foundation, $y(x)$ satisfies $EIy^{(4)} = p(x) - Ky, \quad K > 0$. Let

$$y(x) = \frac{1}{\pi}\int_0^\infty [a(t)\cos tx + b(t)\sin tx]\,dx$$

and

$$p(x) = \frac{1}{\pi}\int_0^\infty [A(t)\cos tx + B(t)\sin tx]\,dx,$$

$A(t) = \int_{-\infty}^{\infty} p(x)\cos tx\,dx$, $B(t) = \int_{-\infty}^{\infty} p(x)\sin wt\,dx$ are known. Determine them for $p(x) = \dfrac{P}{2L}$ and let $L \to 0$ so that $A(t) = P$ and $B(t) = 0$. Now substitute the Fourier integrals in the differential equation and equate coefficients to obtain the solution

$$y(x) = \frac{P}{\pi}\int_0^\infty \frac{\cos tx\,dt}{EIt^4 + K}.$$

ELECTRIC CIRCUITS

4. Let $x(t)$ be a periodic function of period T that represents a current flowing through an electric circuit. We define the mean square value of $x(t)$ as

$$\rho = \frac{1}{T}\int_0^T x^2(t)\,dt.$$

It indicates the power determined when the current passes through a unit resistance. If the Fourier coefficients of $x(t)$ are a_n and b_n, show that

$$\rho = \frac{a_0^2}{4} + \frac{1}{2}\sum_{n=1}^{\infty}(a_n^2 + b_n^2).$$

(*Hint:* Use Parseval's identity.)

5. Find the steady-state current flowing in the circuit of the figure if

$$E(t) = \begin{cases} 0, & -\pi/50 < t < 0 \\ E_0 \sin 50t, & 0 < t < \pi/50 \end{cases}$$

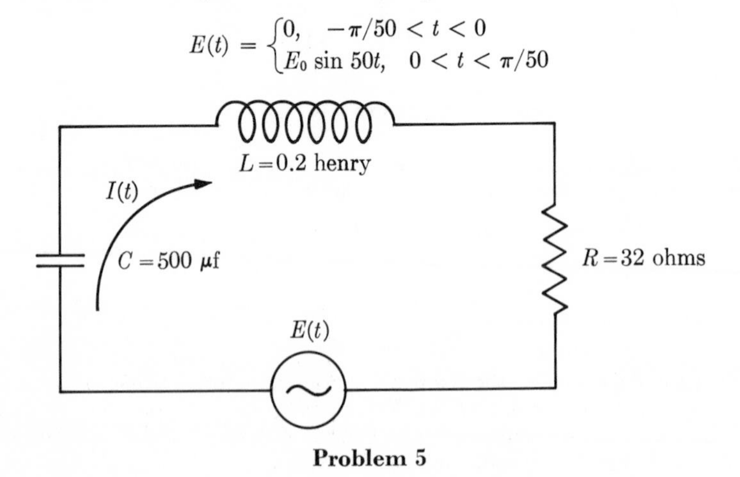

Problem 5

Determine its mean square value. (*Hint:* Determine the differential equation and express the current and voltage as Fourier series and equate coefficients.)

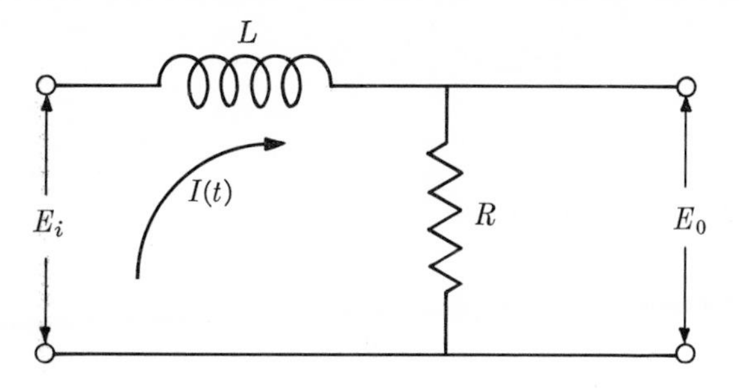

Problem 6

6. Find $I(t)$ in the circuit of the figure if $E_0 = RI$, $E_i = Ee^{-|t|}$. (*Hint:* $LI' + RI = E_i$. Take the Fourier transform of both sides and solve to obtain $\mathfrak{F}(I) = \dfrac{2E}{\sqrt{2\pi}} \dfrac{1}{1 + y^2} \dfrac{1}{iyL + R}$ and $I = \dfrac{E}{\pi} \displaystyle\int_{-\infty}^{\infty} \dfrac{e^{iyt}\,dy}{(1 + y^2)(iyL + R)}$. Evaluate by contour integration to obtain $I(t) = \dfrac{Ee^t}{L + R}$.) Add a capacitor C to the circuit. Determine $I(t)$ for this circuit.

7. Let $x(t)$ be a continuous function depending on time t, $0 \le t < \infty$, and define it as an even function in $-\infty < t < \infty$. Let $x(t)$ have the property that its Fourier transform $g(\omega) = 0$ for $|\omega| > 2\pi W$. (In electrical parlance, the signal $x(t)$ has no frequencies above W cycles per second.) Then

$$x(t) = \frac{1}{\sqrt{2\pi}} \int_{-2\pi W}^{2\pi W} g(\omega) e^{i\omega t}\, d\omega.$$

Now $g(\omega) = \sum_{n=-\infty}^{\infty} c_n e^{in\omega/2W}$, $c_n = \dfrac{1}{4\pi W} \displaystyle\int_{-2\pi W}^{2\pi W} g(\omega) e^{-in\omega/2W}\, d\omega$ for $|\omega| \le 2\pi W$. (Why?) Show that

$$x(t) = 2W \sum_{n=-\infty}^{\infty} c_n \frac{\sin \pi(2Wt + n)}{\pi(2Wt + n)}.$$

Now let $t_k = k/2W$, $k = 0, \pm 1, \pm 2, \cdots$. Then $x(t_n) = \dfrac{1}{\sqrt{2\pi}} \displaystyle\int_{-2\pi W}^{2\pi W} g(\omega) e^{i\omega n/2W}\, d\omega$ and $c_n = \dfrac{1}{2W} x(-n/2W)$ so that

$$x(t) = \sum_{n=-\infty}^{\infty} x\left(\frac{n}{2W}\right) \frac{\sin \pi(2Wt - n)}{\pi(2Wt - n)}.$$

Hence, if we know the value of $x(t)$ at $t = \dfrac{n}{2\pi}$, $n = 0, 1, \cdots$ (since x is even), we know $x(t)$ for all t. In other words, we can determine the signal $x(t)$ merely by "sampling" it at the points given above.

ADVANCED FOURIER ANALYSIS

8. If $s_n(x)$ is the nth partial sum of the Fourier series of a function f, then

$$\sigma_n(x) = \frac{s_0(x) + s_1(x) + \cdots + s_n(x)}{n+1}$$

is called the *arithmetic mean* of the sums $s_0(x), s_1(x), \cdots, s_n(x)$.

Prove *Fejér's theorem:* If f is continuous and periodic with period 2π, then $\lim_{n\to\infty} \sigma_n(x) = f(x)$ uniformly for all x.

Outline of Proof. If

$$D_n(t) = \frac{\sin (n + \frac{1}{2})t}{2 \sin (t/2)},$$

then

$$K_n(t) = \frac{1}{n+1}[D_0(t) + \cdots + D_n(t)] = \frac{1}{2(n+1)}\left[\frac{\sin (n+1)(t/2)}{\sin (t/2)}\right]^2$$

and

$$\sigma_n(x) = \frac{1}{\pi}\int_{-\pi}^{\pi} f(x+t)K_n(t)\, dt.$$

$K_n(t)$ has the following properties:

(1) $K_n(t) \geq 0$.

(2) $\frac{1}{\pi}\int_{-\pi}^{\pi} K_n(t)\, dt = 1$.

(3) $K_n(t) \leq \frac{1}{2(n+1)\sin^2(\delta/2)}, \quad 0 < \delta \leq |t| \leq \pi$.

Now

$$\sigma_n(x) - f(x) = \frac{1}{\pi}\int_{-\pi}^{\pi} [f(x+t) - f(x)]K_n(t)\, dt,$$

using (2), and

$$|\sigma_n(x) - f(x)| \leq \frac{1}{\pi}\int_{-\pi}^{\pi} |f(x+t) - f(x)|K_n(t)\, dt.$$

Let $\epsilon > 0$ be given; then the continuity of f implies that there exists a $\delta > 0$ such that for $|t| < \delta$, $|f(x+t) - f(x)| < \epsilon/2$. The continuity of f also implies that for all x in $-\pi \leq x \leq \pi$, there exists a constant M such that $|f(x)| \leq M$. Property (3) indicates that we can choose a positive integer N such that for $n \geq N$ and $\delta \leq |t| \leq \pi$, $K_n(t) \leq \epsilon/8M$. Now

$$\begin{aligned}|\sigma_n(x) - f(x)| &\leq \frac{1}{\pi}\int_{-\pi}^{-\delta} |f(x+t) - f(x)|K_n(t)\, dt \\ &\quad + \frac{1}{\pi}\int_{-\delta}^{\delta} |f(x+t) - f(x)|K_n(t)\, dt \\ &\quad + \int_{\delta}^{\pi} |f(x+t) - f(x)|K_n(t)\, dt \\ &= \mathrm{I}_1 + \mathrm{I}_2 + \mathrm{I}_3.\end{aligned}$$

But $\quad \mathrm{I}_1 + \mathrm{I}_3 \le \frac{\epsilon}{8M\pi} \int_{-\pi}^{\pi} 2M\, dt = \frac{\epsilon}{2} \quad$ and $\quad \mathrm{I}_2 < \frac{\epsilon}{2\pi} \int_{-\pi}^{\pi} K_n(t)\, dt = \frac{\epsilon}{2},$

so that $|\sigma_n(x) - f(x)| < \epsilon$ for $n > N$, and hence $\lim_{n\to\infty} \sigma_n = f(x)$.

9. Prove *Weierstrass's approximation theorem.* First form: If f is continuous on a closed interval I of length $2p$ and any $\epsilon > 0$ is given, then there exists a trigonometric polynomial

$$\mathrm{T}(x) = \frac{1}{2} a_0 + \sum_{k=1}^{n} a_k \cos \frac{k\pi x}{p} + b_k \sin \frac{k\pi x}{p}$$

such that for all x in I, $|f(x) - \mathrm{T}(x)| < \epsilon$. (*Hint:* Use Problem 1.)

Second form: If f is continuous in a closed interval I and if any $\epsilon > 0$ is given, then there exists a polynomial $\mathrm{P}(x)$ such that for all x in I, $|f(x) - \mathrm{P}(x)| < \epsilon$. (*Hint:* Find the trigonometric polynomial $\mathrm{T}(x)$ such that $|f(x) - \mathrm{T}(x)| < \epsilon/2$. Represent $\mathrm{T}(x)$ as a Maclaurin series; then we can find a partial sum $\mathrm{P}(x)$ of this series such that $|\mathrm{T}(x) - \mathrm{P}(x)| < \epsilon/2$. Combine the two inequalities.)

10. Prove Parseval's theorem for the trigonometric system: If f is continuous, then the trigonometric system is complete.

Hint: Given $\epsilon > 0$, choose N such that for $n > N$, $|f(x) - \sigma_n(x)| < \epsilon$ for all x (see Problem 1). Then $\mathrm{I}_n = \int_{-\pi}^{\pi} [f(x) - \sigma_n(x)]^2\, dx < 2\pi\epsilon^2$ for $n > N$. By the theorem on p. 436,

$$\int_{-\pi}^{\pi} [f(x) - s_n(x)]^2\, dx \le \int_{-\pi}^{\pi} [f(x) - \sigma_n(x)]^2\, dx,$$

and the two inequalities yield $\lim_{n\to\infty} \mathrm{I}_n = 0$.

11. Let R_2 be the set of functions square-integrable in $a \le x \le b$. We call R_2 a **function space.** Define the inner product of two functions f and g in R_2 by

$$(f, g) = \int_a^b f(x)g(x)\, dx$$

and the length of f by $\sqrt{(f, f)}$. Show that R_2 is a vector space. (See Problem 20, p. 168.) If $(f, g) = 0$, we say that f and g are orthogonal. Since in a three-dimensional space of vectors, two vectors are orthogonal or perpendicular if and only if the inner product of these vectors vanishes, the term *orthogonal* is used to designate two vectors in any vector space whose inner product vanishes, although it may have no geometric significance. Starting with the definition of the inner product of $\bar{a} = (a_1, a_2, \cdots, a_n)$ and $\bar{b} = (b_1, b_2, \cdots, b_n)$ in n-dimensional vector space as $(\bar{a}, \bar{b}) = \sum_{i=1}^{n} a_i b_i$ and employing a suitable limiting process, motivate our definition of the inner product of two functions.

SUGGESTED REFERENCES

Books on Fourier Analysis

BOCHNER, S. *Lectures on Fourier Integrals.* Princeton, N. J.: Princeton University Press, 1959. A rigorous exposition of the theory of the Fourier integral. The beginner may find the treatment too high-powered; however, a diligent study of this book will be amply rewarded.

Bochner, S. and Chandrasekharan, K. *Fourier Transforms.* Princeton, N. J.: Princeton University Press, 1949. A good concise and rigorous treatment of Fourier transforms.

Byerly, W. E. *Fourier's Series.* New York: Dover Publications, 1959. A reprint of the 1893 edition, which is still serviceable because of its elementary treatment and wealth of problems, especially those occurring in applications.

Campbell, G. A., and Foster, R. M. *Fourier Integrals for Practical Applications.* New York: Van Nostrand, Inc., 1948. The main feature of this book is the table of Fourier transforms.

Carslaw, H. S. *Introduction to the Theory of Fourier's Series and Integrals.* New York: Dover Publications, 1930. A substantial part of real analysis is developed before the Fourier analysis, and although this is an older work, it is still eminently readable, since it is well documented with illustrative examples, graphs, and problems.

Churchill, R. V. *Fourier Series and Boundary Value Problems,* 2nd ed. New York: McGraw-Hill Book Co., Inc., 1963. The main emphasis is on the application of various orthogonal systems to boundary value problems.

Davis, H. F. *Fourier Series and Orthogonal Functions.* Boston: Allyn and Bacon, Inc., 1963. The classical theory is presented with a modern flavor, giving a valuable insight into the fundamentals of the subject.

Franklin, P. *Fourier Methods.* New York: Dover Publications, 1960. The techniques and applications of Fourier analysis is the main substance of this book.

Hardy, G. H. and Rogosinski, W. W. *Fourier Series.* Cambridge, Mass.: Cambridge University Press, 1944. Some significant theorems on Fourier series are rigorously presented.

Jackson, D. *Fourier Series and Orthogonal Polynomials.* Mathematical Association of America, 1941. A good elementary introduction to Fourier series and other orthogonal systems.

Kaczmarz, S. and Steinhaus, H. *Theorie der Orthogonalreihen.* New York: Chelsea Publishing Company, 1951. The standard work on the theory of general orthogonal systems with the principal systems serving as illustrations.

Rogosinski, W. W. *Fourier Series.* New York: Chelsea Publishing Company, 1950. This little book on the theory of Fourier series contains a wealth of material, including the Fourier integral theorem and divergent Fourier series.

Sansone, G. *Orthogonal Functions.* New York: Interscience Publishers, Inc., 1959. An exposition of general orthogonal systems is followed by a detailed treatment of the principal systems; emphasis is placed on the development of the many formulas associated with these systems.

Titchmarsh, E. C. *Introduction to the Theory of Fourier Integrals.* New York: Oxford University Press, 1948. This is the standard work on Fourier integrals and transforms. It is written completely from the mathematical point of view.

Wiener, N. *The Fourier Integral and Certain of Its Applications.* New York: Dover Publications, 1933. This little book exhibits the tremendous influence that Fourier analysis has had on real analysis.

Zymund, A. *Trigonometric Series,* Vols. I and II. Cambridge, Mass.: Cambridge University Press, 1959. This is a monumental work on Fourier series. It is rigorous, all-encompassing, modern, and stimulating.

Other Books of Interest

BOCHNER, S. *Harmonic Analysis and the Theory of Probability.* Berkeley, Cal.: University of California Press, 1955. Applications of Fourier analysis to probability theory—a subject of extreme interest in present-day technology.

COURANT, R., and HILBERT, D. *Methods of Mathematical Physics.* Vol. 1. New York: Interscience Publishers, Inc., 1953. An excellent one-chapter treatment of general orthogonal systems, Fourier series and integrals, and other orthogonal systems.

ERDÉLYI, A., et al. *Tables of Integral Transforms,* Vol. 1. New York: McGraw-Hill Book Co., Inc., 1954. The most comprehensive table of Fourier transforms and other transforms in existence.

GASKELL, R. E. *Engineering Mathematics.* New York: The Dryden Press, Inc., 1958. A rudimentary treatment of the methods of Fourier series and harmonic analysis.

GREENSPAN, D. *Introduction to Partial Differential Equations.* New York: McGraw-Hill Book Co., Inc., 1961. A good proof of the Fourier expansion theorem in an intermediate setting is presented.

KÁRMÁN, T., and BIOT, M. A. *Mathematical Methods in Engineering.* New York: McGraw-Hill Book Co., Inc., 1940. Applications of Fourier series to structural, electrical, and mechanical problems. Numerical, graphical, and mechanical methods for the determination of Fourier coefficients and harmonic analysis are principal features.

PAGE, C. H. *Physical Mathematics.* New York: D. Van Nostrand Company, Inc., 1955. Applications of Fourier integrals and transforms.

SAGAN, H. *Boundary and Eigenvalue Problems in Mathematical Physics.* New York: John Wiley & Sons, Inc., 1961. A good introduction to Fourier series and its application to boundary value problems. A formal treatment of Fourier series is followed by a rigorous development of the principal theorems.

STEWART, J. L. *Fundamentals of Signal Theory.* New York: McGraw-Hill Book Co., Inc., 1960. Applications of Fourier analysis to electrical wave phenomena.

WHITTAKER, E. T., and WATSON, G. N. *A Course of Modern Analysis.* Cambridge, Mass.: Cambridge University Press, 1945. A typical British exposition of Fourier series together with the customary challenging problems.

WIDDER, D. V. *Advanced Calculus.* Princeton, N. J.: Prentice-Hall, Inc., 1961. A good one-chapter rigorous development of Fourier analysis written in the author's winning style.

FINITE SINE TRANSFORMS

	$F_s[f(t)]$	$f(t)$
1.	$1/n$	$(\pi - t)/\pi$
2.	$(-1)^{n+1}/n + 1$	t/π
3.	$n[1 - (-1)^n e^{c\pi}]/(n^2 + c^2)$	e^{ct}
4.	$\pi \sin nc/n^2, \quad 0 < c < \pi$	$(\pi - c)t, \quad t \leq c; \qquad c(\pi - t), \quad t \geq c$
5.	$\pi \cos nc/n, \quad 0 \leq c \leq \pi$	$-t, \quad t < c; \qquad \pi - t, \quad t > c$
6.	$[1 - (-1)^n]/n^3$	$t(\pi - t)/2$
7.	$n/(n^2 - p^2), \quad \|p\| \neq n$	$\sinh p(\pi - t)/\sin p\pi$
8.	$0 \ (n \neq m); \qquad \pi/2, \quad n = m$	$\sin mt, \quad m = 1, 2, \cdots$
9.	$n[1 - (-1)^n \cos p\pi]/(n^2 - p^2)$, $\|p\| \neq n$	$\cos pt$
10.	$b^n/n, \quad \|b\| \leq 1$	$(2/\pi) \tan^{-1} [b \sin t/(1 - b \cos t)]$

FINITE COSINE TRANSFORMS

	$F_c[f(t)]$	$f(t)$
1.	$0, \quad n \neq 0; \qquad \pi, \quad n = 0$	1
2.	$[(-1)^n - 1]/n^2; \qquad n \neq 0;$ $\pi^2/2, \quad n = 0$	t
3.	$(-1)^n/n^2, \quad n \neq 0; \qquad \pi^2/6, \quad n = 0$	$t^2/2\pi$
4.	$[(-1)^n e^{c\pi} - 1]/(n^2 + c^2), \quad c \neq 0$	e^{ct}/c
5.	$1/(n^2 + c^2), \quad c \neq 0$	$\cosh c(\pi - t)/c \sinh c\pi$
6.	$[(-1)^n \cos p\pi - 1]/(n^2 - p^2), \quad \|p\| \neq n$	$\sin pt/p$
7.	$[(-1)^{n+m} - 1]/(n^2 - m^2); \qquad n \neq 0;$ $0, \quad n = 0$	$\sin mt/m, \quad m = 1, 2, \cdots$
8.	$0, \quad n \neq m; \qquad \pi/2, \quad n = m$	$\cos mt$
9.	$b^n, \quad n \neq 0; \qquad 0, \quad n = 0, \quad \|b\| < 1$	$2b(\cos t - b)/\pi(1 - 2b \cos t + b^2)$
10.	$2 \sin nc/n, \quad n \neq 0; \qquad 2c - \pi, \quad n = 0$	$1, \quad 0 < t < c; \qquad -1, \quad c < t < \pi$

Part IV

Special Functions

$\int \int \int$

Most of the specific functions that we have encountered thus far belong to a class of functions that is designated as the class of **elementary functions.** We shall define this class of functions by specifying the functions that belong to it. First of all, every algebraic function is an elementary function, where by an **algebraic function** we mean any function $y = f(x)$ that satisfies the equation

$$P_n(x)y^n + P_{n-1}(x)y^{n-1} + \cdots + P_1(x)y + P_0(x) = 0$$

for some integer n and polynomials $P_0, P_1, \cdots, P_n$.

Next, certain transcendental functions (nonalgebraic functions) are elementary functions. These are the exponential function, the logarithmic function, the trigonometric functions, and the inverse trigonometric functions. We now complete our class of elementary functions by defining the sum, product, and quotient of two elementary functions to be elementary functions, and an elementary function of an elementary function to be an elementary function. For example,

$$y = \sqrt{\frac{x^2 + 1}{x^2 - 1}}$$

is an algebraic function, since it satisfies the equation

$$(x^2 - 1)y^2 - (x^2 + 1) = 0,$$

and hence is an elementary function. The function

$$y = xe^x \cos \sqrt{x^2 + 1} + \frac{5 \tan^{-1} (\log x)}{\sqrt{\sin x + \sec x}}$$

is an elementary function. Why?

In our study of mathematics, hitherto it has sufficed to consider only elementary functions. However, many problems in applied mathematics cannot be solved if we restrict ourselves to the elementary functions. As a matter of fact, many functions have been expressly defined in order to solve just such problems. For example, there are certain definite integrals that cannot be evaluated in terms of elementary functions, and there are differential equations whose solutions are not elementary functions. In order that such definite integrals can be evaluated and such differential equations can be solved, new functions must be defined. There are certain nonelementary functions that occur so frequently in practice that they have come to enjoy the designation of **special functions.** This part is devoted to a detailed study of the most prominent of these. These special functions are defined in a variety of ways, such as a definite integral with a parameter, a solution to a differential equation, a solution to a difference equation, or by assigning prescribed properties to the function.

We shall be primarily concerned with special functions that are defined for real values; however, we shall usually mention, in passing, the extension of these functions to the complex domain.

Chapter 14

The Gamma Function and Other Definite Integrals

1. The gamma function. The definite integral $\int_0^\infty t^{x-1}e^{-t}\,dt$ with the parameter x occurs frequently in mathematics. This is an improper integral, since the upper limit is infinite and for $0 < x < 1$, the integrand becomes infinite. We shall show presently that for $x > 0$, this integral is convergent and hence defines a function in this interval. It can be shown, however, that this is not an elementary function; i.e., this is a function that is new to us and one that is defined by means of a definite integral with parameter. First of all, let us demonstrate that the integral actually defines a function in $x > 0$. For this purpose we write

$$\int_0^\infty t^{x-1}e^{-t}\,dt = \text{I} + \text{J}$$

where

$$\text{I} = \int_0^1 t^{x-1}\,dt \quad \text{and} \quad \text{J} = \int_1^\infty t^{x-1}e^{-t}\,dt.$$

Now, for $0 < x < 1$, I is improper, since the integrand becomes infinite at these values; however, I is proper for $x \geq 1$. J is improper for $x > 0$, since the upper limit is infinite. If we let $t = 1/u$ in I, it becomes $\int_1^\infty u^{-(x+1)}e^{1/u}\,du$, which is an improper integral of the same type as J. We must now show that I is convergent for $0 < x < 1$ and J is convergent for $x > 0$. Since $\text{J}(b) = \int_1^b t^{x-1}e^{-t}\,dt$ cannot be expressed in terms of elementary functions, we cannot determine the convergence of J by demonstrating the existence of $\lim_{b\to\infty} \text{J}(b)$, as has been our procedure hitherto for establishing convergence. We must resort to other methods such as the one indicated in the

THEOREM (COMPARISON TEST FOR CONVERGENCE). If f and g are continuous for $t \geq a$, $0 \leq f(t) \leq g(t)$ for $t \geq t_0 \geq a$, t_0 a fixed number, and $\int_a^\infty g(t)\,dt$ is convergent, then $\int_a^\infty f(t)\,dt$ is convergent.

Proof. Let $A = \int_{t_0}^\infty g(t)\,dt$. Then $F(b) = \int_{t_0}^b f(t)\,dt \leq \int_{t_0}^b g(t)\,dt \leq A$ (justify these inequalities!); i.e., $F(b)$ is bounded from above. Furthermore, F is an increasing function of b, since $f(t) \geq 0$ for $t \geq t_0$. Hence $\lim_{b\to\infty} F(b)$ exists, and the theorem is proved. (Note the analogy between this theorem and the comparison test for convergence of infinite series.)

With this theorem, we readily establish the convergence of I for $0 < x < 1$ and J for $x > 0$, since $0 < u^{-(x+1)}e^{-1/u} < u^{-(x+1)}$, $u \geq 1$, $x > 0$, and $0 < t^{x-1}e^{-t} < 1/t^2$ for t sufficiently large and $x > 0$ (why?); the convergence of $\int_1^\infty u^{-(x+1)}\,du$ and $\int_1^\infty (dt/t^2)$ can be verified by direct integration. Incidentally, for $x \leq 0$, $\int_0^\infty t^{x-1}e^{-t}\,dt$ is divergent, as the student should show with use of Exercise 24(a), p. 470.

We have seen that $\int_0^\infty t^{x-1}e^{-t}\,dt$ is defined for $x > 0$ and hence defines a function in that interval. This function is almost universally denoted by Γ, and this accounts for it being called the **gamma function.** If we were unaware of the fact that the gamma function is not an elementary function, we might very likely attempt to integrate it by parts, so that

$$\Gamma(x) = \int_0^\infty t^{x-1}e^{-t}\,dt = \left.\frac{e^{-t}t^x}{x}\right]_0^\infty + \frac{1}{x}\int_0^\infty t^x e^{-t}\,dt$$

$$= \frac{1}{x}\int_0^\infty t^x e^{-t}\,dt = \frac{1}{x}\Gamma(x+1),$$

and thus establish the most significant property of the gamma function:

$$\Gamma(x+1) = x\Gamma(x).$$

Why is this property significant? First of all, it indicates that we need know the functional values of Γ only in the interval $0 < x \leq 1$; such values then determine the functional values for $x > 1$. Such a relationship, which expresses certain values of a function in terms of other values of that function, is called a *functional relationship* or functional equation. Another way of stating this is to say that Γ is a solution of the functional equation $f(x+1) = xf(x)$ for $x > 0$. It is of interest to determine whether this functional equation has solutions other than Γ. As a matter of fact, the student actually knows such a function. It is the factorial function, denoted by $n!$ and defined as $n! = 1\cdot 2\cdots n$, where n is a positive integer. This function has the property that $n! = n(n-1)!$ If we let $f(n+1) = n!$, then this equation can be written as $f(n+1) = nf(n)$, which indicates that the factorial function satisfies the functional relationship $f(x+1) = xf(x)$ for x a positive integer. It appears that we have discovered two different solutions to this functional equation. As a matter of fact, this is not the case, for we shall soon see that $\Gamma(n + 1) = n!$, which means that for positive integral values, the gamma function reduces to the factorial function. In other words the gamma function can be thought of as a generalization of the factorial function from the domain of positive integers (its definition having meaning only in this domain) to the domain of positive real numbers.

The functional equation $\Gamma(x + 1) = x\Gamma(x)$ is also significant, for it enables us to extend the definition of Γ from the set of positive real numbers to the set of real numbers, excluding the nonpositive integers. This situation is of frequent occurrence in mathematics: The nature of the definition of a function imposes restrictions on the domain of the function, but some property of the function enables us to extend the domain of this function. Since we defined the gamma function in terms of an improper integral, the values for which this integral is convergent dictated the domain of the function. However, from this definition we established the property $\Gamma(x + 1) = x\Gamma(x)$, which will enable us to extend the domain of the gamma function. For if we write

$$\Gamma(x) = \frac{\Gamma(x+1)}{x},$$

then if $-1 < x < 0$, $\Gamma(x + 1)$ is defined, and hence $\Gamma(x)$ is defined for these negative values of x. In general, repeated use of the functional relationship yields

$$\Gamma(x + n) = (x + n - 1)(x + n - 2)\cdots x\Gamma(x),$$

where n is a positive integer, so that

$$\Gamma(x) = \frac{\Gamma(x+n)}{x(x+1)\cdots(x+n-1)}, \qquad x \neq 0, -1, \cdots, -n,$$

defines Γ if $-n < x < -n + 1$.

We now have the complete definition of the gamma function Γ:

$$\begin{aligned} \Gamma(x) &= \int_0^\infty t^{x-1}e^{-t}\,dt, && \text{if } x > 0, \\ &= \frac{\Gamma(x+n)}{x(x+1)\cdots(x+n-1)}, && -n < x < -n+1,\ n = 1, 2, \cdots \end{aligned}$$

Γ is not defined for the nonpositive integers.

The gamma function Γ has the following properties:

G₁: $\Gamma(x + 1) = x\Gamma(x), \qquad x \neq 0, -1, -2, \cdots.$

G₂: $\Gamma(x + n) = (x + n - 1)(x + n - 2)\cdots x\Gamma(x),$
$\qquad x \neq 0, -1, -2, \cdots, n = 1, 2, \cdots.$

G₃: $\Gamma(1) = 1.$

G₄: $\Gamma(n + 1) = n!, \qquad n = 1, 2, \cdots.$

G_5: $\Gamma(x)\Gamma(y) = \Gamma(x+y)B(x, y)$,

where $B(x,y) = 2\int_0^{\pi/2} \sin^{2x-1}\theta \cos^{2y-1}\theta\, d\theta, \qquad x > 0,\ y > 0.$

G_6: $\Gamma(x)\Gamma(1-x) = \dfrac{\pi}{\sin \pi x}, \qquad x$ nonintegral.

G_7: $\Gamma(\frac{1}{2}) = \sqrt{\pi}$.

Proofs. G_1 has been proved for $x > 0$; the student should prove it for the remaining indicated values of x.

The proof of G_2 is left to the student.

G_3: $\Gamma(1) = \int_0^\infty e^{-t}\,dt = 1.$

G_4 follows from G_2 and G_3. Note that the mystery of the definition $0! = 1$ is completely dissolved.

G_5: Let $t = r^2$ in $\Gamma(x) = \int_0^\infty t^{x-1}e^{-t}\,dt$ to obtain

$$(A) \quad \Gamma(x) = 2\int_0^\infty e^{-r^2}r^{2x-1}\,dr.$$

Then

$$\Gamma(x+y)B(x, y) = 4\int_0^\infty e^{-r^2}r^{2x+2y-1}\,dr \int_0^{\pi/2} \sin^{2x-1}\theta \cos^{2y-1}\theta\,d\theta.$$

Introducing polar coordinates $u = r\cos\theta$, $v = r\sin\theta$, so that $du\,dv = r\,dr\,d\theta$, we have

$$\Gamma(x+y)B(x, y) = 4\int_0^\infty e^{-u^2}u^{2x-1}\,du \int_0^\infty e^{-v^2}v^{2y-1}\,dv = \Gamma(x)\Gamma(y)$$

in view of (A).

G_6: The example, p. 276, indicates that

$$\int_0^\infty \frac{u^{x-1}\,du}{u+1} = \frac{\pi}{\sin \pi x}, \qquad 0 < x < 1.$$

Let $u = \tan^2\theta$. Then

$$2\int_0^{\pi/2} \sin^{2x-1}\theta \cos^{2(1-x)-1}\theta\,d\theta = \frac{\pi}{\sin \pi x}$$

or $B(x, 1-x) = \Gamma(x)\Gamma(1-x)$ by G_5 and G_3, and hence

$$\Gamma(x)\Gamma(1-x) = \frac{\pi}{\sin \pi x}.$$

The student should prove this result for all other nonintegral x.

G_7: Let $x = \frac{1}{2}$ in G_6.

In view of G_1, any tabulation of the gamma function need be made only in an interval of length 1. Such a tabulation may be found in many standard mathematical tables. We have included one such tabulation on p. 558 for easy reference.

The function of two variables in G_5, $B(x, y)$, is called the **beta function.** This is an important function in its own right, but since G_5 indicates that it can be reduced to gamma functions, its detailed study is not necessary. We merely list:

$$\mathbf{B_1:} \quad B(x, y) = 2 \int_0^{\pi/2} \sin^{2x-1} \theta \cos^{2y-1} \theta \, d\theta, \qquad x, y > 0.$$

$$\mathbf{B_2:} \quad B(x, y) = \int_0^1 t^{x-1}(1 - t)^{y-1} \, dt, \qquad x, y > 0.$$

$$\mathbf{B_3:} \quad B(x, y) = \frac{\Gamma(x)\Gamma(y)}{\Gamma(x + y)}, \qquad x, y > 0.$$

B_2 is just as important a representation of $B(x, y)$ as is B_1 and may be obtained from the latter by the change in variable $t = \sin^2 \theta$.

We now consider some further properties of Γ, which will enable us to sketch the graph of $y = \Gamma(x)$.

G_8: Γ is continuous for $x > 0$ and $-n < x < -n + 1$, $n = 1, 2, \cdots$.

G_9: $\lim_{x \to 0+} \Gamma(x) = \infty$.

G_{10}: $$\lim_{x \to -(2n-1)\pm} \Gamma(x) = \pm\infty$$

and

$$\lim_{x \to -2n\pm} \Gamma(x) = \pm\infty, \qquad n = 1, 2, \cdots.$$

G_{11}: $$\frac{d^2}{dx^2} \Gamma(x) = \int_0^\infty e^{-t} t^{x-1} (\log t)^2 \, dt > 0, \qquad x > 0;$$

$$\left.\begin{aligned} &\frac{d^2}{dx^2} \Gamma(x) > 0, \qquad -2n < x < -(2n - 1); \\ &\frac{d^2}{dx^2} \Gamma(x) < 0, \qquad -(2n - 1) < x < -(2n - 2) \end{aligned}\right\} \quad n = 1, 2, \cdots.$$

Proofs. G_8: Continuity for $x > 0$ can be found in Widder, *Advanced Calculus*, p. 369. Then, for the other intervals, it follows immediately from this result and the definition of Γ in these intervals.

G_9 follows from the inequalities

$$\Gamma(x) > \int_0^1 t^{x-1} e^{-t} \, dt > \frac{1}{e} \int_0^1 t^{x-1} \, dt = \frac{1}{ex}, \qquad x > 0.$$

The proofs of G_{10} and G_{11} are left to the student. To establish the expression for $(d^2/dx^2)\Gamma(x)$, the student should justify the interchange of differentiation and integration by applying the theorem on p. 404. Properties G_8 to G_{11} serve to indicate the nature of the graph of the gamma function, which occurs in Fig. 1.

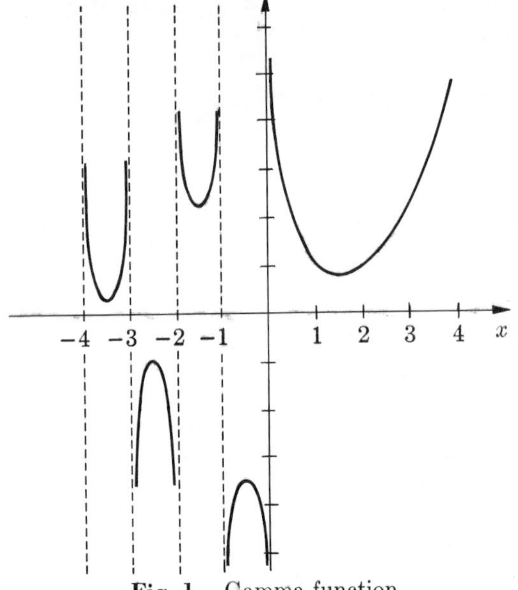

Fig. 1. Gamma function

EXAMPLE 1. Evaluate $\Gamma(4)$, $\Gamma\left(\frac{-5}{2}\right)$, $B\left(\frac{2}{3}, \frac{1}{3}\right)$, $\Gamma\left(\frac{7}{2}\right)$.

Solution. $\Gamma(4) = 3! = 6$. Since $-3 < -5/2 < -2$, we let $n = 3$ in the definition so that

$$\Gamma\left(\frac{-5}{2}\right) = \frac{\Gamma(\frac{1}{2})}{(-\frac{5}{2})(-\frac{3}{2})(-\frac{1}{2})} = \frac{-8\sqrt{\pi}}{15}.$$

$$B\left(\frac{2}{3}, \frac{1}{3}\right) = \frac{\Gamma(\frac{2}{3})\Gamma(\frac{1}{3})}{\Gamma(1)} = \frac{\pi}{\sin(\pi/3)} = \frac{2\pi}{\sqrt{3}} \qquad (B_3, G_3, G_6).$$

$$\Gamma(\tfrac{7}{2}) = \Gamma(\tfrac{1}{2} + 3) = \tfrac{5}{2}\cdot\tfrac{3}{2}\cdot\tfrac{1}{2}\Gamma(\tfrac{1}{2}) = \tfrac{15}{8}\sqrt{\pi}.$$

One of the most important applications of the gamma function is in the evaluation of certain definite integrals. If a given definite integral can be expressed as an integral that represents the gamma function or beta function, then it can be evaluated. In addition to the definition of Γ as a definite integral for $x > 0$, we have other integral representations of Γ, such as

$$\mathbf{G_{12}}: \quad \Gamma(x) = 2\int_0^\infty e^{-t^2} t^{2x-1}\, dt, \qquad x > 0.$$

$$\mathbf{G_{13}}: \quad \Gamma(x) = \int_0^1 \left(\log \frac{1}{t}\right)^{x-1} dt, \qquad x > 0.$$

We have already encountered G_{12} in the proof of G_5, and G_{13} may be obtained by letting $u = \log 1/t$ in $\int_0^\infty u^{x-1}e^{-u}\,du$.

EXAMPLE 2. Evaluate $I = \int_0^\infty e^{-t^2}\,dt$.

Solution. Let $x = \frac{1}{2}$ in G_{12} to obtain

$$\Gamma\left(\frac{1}{2}\right) = 2\int_0^\infty e^{-t^2}\,dt; \quad I = \frac{\sqrt{\pi}}{2}$$

by G_7. This definite integral occurs frequently in probability theory and is called the *probability integral.*

EXAMPLE 3. Evaluate $I = \int_0^\infty e^{-st}t^\lambda\,dt, \quad s > 0, \lambda > -1$.

Solution. Let $u = st$. Then

$$I = \frac{1}{s^{\lambda+1}}\int_0^\infty u^\lambda e^{-u}\,du = \frac{\Gamma(\lambda+1)}{s^{\lambda+1}}.$$

This integral is called a *Laplace integral* and we shall encounter it again.

EXAMPLE 4. Evaluate $I = \displaystyle\int_0^\infty \frac{dx}{1+x^4}$.

Solution. With $x^2 = \tan\theta$,

$$I = \frac{1}{2}\int_0^{\pi/2} \sin^{-1/2}\theta\cos^{1/2}\theta\,d\theta = \frac{1}{4}B\left(\frac{3}{4},\frac{1}{4}\right) = \frac{1}{4}\Gamma\left(\frac{3}{4}\right)\Gamma\left(\frac{1}{4}\right) = \frac{\pi}{2}\sqrt{2}.$$

(B_3, G_3, G_6).

Note the simplicity of this method versus contour integration.

The gamma function is very useful for the simplification of notation.

EXAMPLE 5. Express

$$\frac{r(r+1)\cdots(r+m-1)}{2\cdot4\cdot6\cdots2(m-1)}$$

more compactly, m a positive integer and r real but not a nonpositive integer.

Solution. Since $2\cdot4\cdot6\cdots2(m-1) = 2^{m-1}(m-1)!$, the expression can be written as

$$\frac{r(r+1)\cdots(r+m-1)}{2^{m-1}(m-1)!}.$$

Multiplying numerator and denominator by $\Gamma(r)$, we obtain (by G_2)

$$\frac{\Gamma(r+m)}{2^{m-1}(m-1)!\Gamma(r)}.$$

We now introduce some useful notation. We write

$$\binom{\alpha}{\beta} = \frac{\Gamma(\alpha+1)}{\Gamma(\beta+1)\Gamma(\alpha-\beta+1)}.$$

EXAMPLE 6. Express the binomial series

$$(1 + x)^\alpha = 1 + \sum_{n=1}^{\infty} \frac{\alpha(\alpha - 1)\cdots(\alpha - n + 1)}{n!} x^n, \qquad |x| < 1,$$

where α is any real number, in simpler notation.

Solution. Multiply numerator and denominator under the summation sign by $\Gamma(\alpha - n + 1)$ and use G_2 and $0! = 1$ to obtain

$$(1 + x)^\alpha = \sum_{n=0}^{\infty} \frac{\Gamma(\alpha + 1)}{n!\Gamma(\alpha - n + 1)} x^n,$$

which can be written as

$$(1 + x)^\alpha = \sum_{n=0}^{\infty} \binom{\alpha}{n} x^n, \qquad |x| < 1, \quad \alpha \text{ any real number.}$$

The gamma function can be defined for complex values as

$$\Gamma(z) = \int_0^\infty t^{z-1}e^{-t}\,dt, \qquad \operatorname{Re} z > 0,$$

from which it follows that $\Gamma(z + 1) = z\Gamma(z)$, and this functional relationship enables us to define Γ for values of z other than $\operatorname{Re} z > 0$. It can be shown that $\Gamma(z)$ is a meromorphic function with simple poles at $z = -n$, $n = 0, 1, \cdots$, and

$$\operatorname*{Res}_{z=-n} \Gamma(z) = \frac{(-1)^n}{n!}.$$

By analytic continuation we obtain the various identities involving $\Gamma(z)$ from the corresponding ones for $\Gamma(x)$. A full treatment of the complex gamma function occurs in Copson, *Theory of Functions of a Complex Variable*, chapter ix.

2. Other functions defined by definite integrals. The gamma function can be written as

$$\Gamma(\alpha) = \int_0^x e^{-t}t^{\alpha-1}\,dt + \int_x^\infty e^{-t}t^{\alpha-1}\,dt,$$

each of these integrals defining a function of the two variables α and x. The student should show that for $\alpha > 0$ and $x > 0$, these improper integrals are convergent. Many definite integrals that define functions of considerable importance can be expressed in terms of these integrals. These integrals are called **incomplete gamma functions** and are denoted by

$$\Gamma(\alpha, x) = \int_x^\infty e^{-t}t^{\alpha-1}\,dt, \qquad \gamma(\alpha, x) = \int_0^x e^{-t}t^{\alpha-1}\,dt.$$

We have immediately that $\gamma(\alpha, x) = \Gamma(\alpha) - \Gamma(\alpha, x)$.

We define the following functions:

I Error Function:

$$\operatorname{erf}(x) = \frac{2}{\sqrt{\pi}} \int_0^x e^{-t^2}\,dt = \frac{1}{\sqrt{\pi}}\, \gamma\left(\frac{1}{2}, x^2\right).$$

II Complementary Error Function:

$$\operatorname{erfc}(x) = \frac{2}{\sqrt{\pi}} \int_x^\infty e^{-t^2}\,dt = \frac{1}{\sqrt{\pi}}\,\Gamma\left(\frac{1}{2}, x^2\right)$$

III Exponential Integral Functions:

$$ei(x) = \int_x^\infty e^{-t}t^{-1}\,dt = \Gamma(0, x),$$

$$Ei(x) = \int_0^x e^{-t}t^{-1}\,dt = \gamma(0, x).$$

IV Logarithmic Integral Function:

$$Li(x) = \int^x \frac{dt}{\log t} = -ei(-\log x)$$

V Integral Sine Functions:

$$si(x) = \int_x^\infty \frac{\sin t}{t}\,dt = \frac{1}{2i}\,[ei(-ix) - ei(ix)],$$

$$Si(x) = \int_0 \frac{\sin t}{t}\,dt = \frac{1}{2i}\,[Ei(-ix) - Ei(ix)].$$

VI Integral Cosine Function:

$$Ci(x) = \int_x^\infty \frac{\cos t}{t}\,dt = \frac{1}{2}\,[ei(-ix) + ei(ix)].$$

VII Fresnel Integral Functions:

$$C(x) = \int_0^x \cos t^2\,dt = \frac{1}{2\sqrt{i}}\left[\gamma\left(\frac{1}{2}, ix\right) + i\gamma\left(\frac{1}{2}, -ix\right)\right]$$

$$S(x) = \int_0^x \sin t^2\,dt = \frac{1}{2i^{3/2}}\left[\gamma\left(\frac{1}{2}, ix\right) - i\gamma\left(\frac{1}{2}, -ix\right)\right].$$

Note the following properties that follow immediately:

$\mathbf{I_1}$: $\operatorname{erf}(\infty) = 1.$

$\mathbf{I_2}$: $\operatorname{erfc}(x) = 1 - \operatorname{erf}(x).$

$\mathbf{I_3}$: $si(0) = \dfrac{\pi}{2}.$

$\mathbf{I_4}$: $Si(x) = \dfrac{\pi}{2} - si(x).$

Tabulations of the error function can be found in "Tables of the Error Function and Its Derivative," National Bureau of Standards, *Applied Mathematics Series 41*; and for the integral sine and cosine functions in "Table of Sine and Cosine Integrals for Arguments from 10 to 100," National Bureau of Standards, *Applied Mathematics Series 32*. Tabulations for the exponential integral functions and Fresnel integral functions in Flügge, *Four-Place Tables of Transcendental Functions.*

3. Elliptic integrals. The length of the elliptic arc $x = a\cos\theta$, $y = b\sin\theta$, $0 \le \theta \le \phi$, $b > a > 0$, can be expressed as

$$\int_0^\phi \sqrt{a^2\sin^2\theta + b^2\cos^2\theta}\,d\theta$$

and this integral can be written as $b\int_0^\phi \sqrt{1 - e^2\sin^2\theta}\,d\theta$; the eccentricity of the ellipse, $e < 1$, is

$$e = \frac{\sqrt{b^2 - a^2}}{b}.$$

It can be shown that this integral cannot be evaluated in terms of elementary functions. Because of its origin, it is called an **elliptic integral.** Two similar integrals

$$\int_0^\phi \frac{d\theta}{\sqrt{1 - k^2\sin^2\theta}} \quad \text{and} \quad \int_0^\phi \frac{d\theta}{\sqrt{1 - k^2\sin^2\theta}\,(1 + a^2\sin^2\theta)},$$

$0 < k < 1$, $a \ne k$, are also referred to as elliptic integrals, and these cannot be evaluated in terms of elementary functions.

It is standard practice to distinguish among these three types of elliptic integrals according to the following classification:

I Elliptic Integral of the First Kind:

$$F(k, \phi) = \int_0^\phi \frac{d\theta}{\sqrt{1 - k^2\sin^2\theta}}, \qquad 0 < k < 1.$$

II Elliptic Integral of the Second Kind:

$$E(k, \phi) = \int_0^\phi \sqrt{1 - k^2\sin^2\theta}\,d\theta, \qquad 0 < k < 1.$$

III Elliptic Integral of the Third Kind:

$$\Pi(k, \phi, a) = \int_0^\phi \frac{d\theta}{\sqrt{1 - k^2\sin^2\theta}(1 + a^2\sin^2\theta)}, \qquad 0 < k < 1, a \ne k, a \ne 0.$$

ϕ is called the **amplitude** and k the **modulus** in these elliptic integrals. $F(k, \pi/2)$ is called a **complete elliptic integral** of the first kind, and is denoted by $K(k)$, or simply K. $E(k, \pi/2) = E$ and $\Pi(k, \pi/2) = \Pi$ are complete elliptic integrals of the second and third kind.

Tabulation of these elliptic integrals may be found in Flügge, *Four-Place Tables of Transcendental Functions;* and Byrd and Friedman, *Handbook of Elliptic Integrals for Engineers and Physicists.*

A primary reason for the importance of these elliptic integrals lies in the

THEOREM. If $R(x, y)$ is a rational function in x and y and $P(x)$ is a polynomial of degree at most 4, with real coefficients, then

$$\int R[x, \sqrt{P(x)}]\, dx$$

can be expressed as an elementary function plus elliptic integrals of the first, second, and third kinds.

A proof of this theorem may be found in Franklin, *Treatise on Advanced Calculus*, p. 219. The significance of this theorem lies in the fact that a large class of integrals can be expressed in terms of only three integrals, which have been tabulated. The techniques for actually expressing integrals of the given class in terms of elliptic integrals may be found in Smith, *Mathematical Methods for Scientists and Engineers*, p. 53, or in Karman and Biot, *Mathematical Methods in Engineering*, p. 119.

EXERCISES

1. Evaluate:
(a) $\Gamma(6)$; (b) $\Gamma(1.5)$; (c) $\Gamma(\frac{5}{2})$; (d) $\Gamma(-\frac{3}{2})$; (e) $\Gamma(\frac{9}{2})$; (f) $B(1, \frac{1}{2})$; (g) $B(\frac{1}{2}, \frac{7}{2})$;

(h) $\Gamma(1.93)$; (i) $\Gamma(-0.12)$; (j) $\Gamma(-5.5)$; (k) $\dfrac{\Gamma(\frac{8}{3})}{\Gamma(\frac{2}{3})}$; (l) $B(\frac{1}{3}, \frac{2}{3})$.

Ans.: (a) 750; (b) $\dfrac{\sqrt{\pi}}{2}$; (c) $\frac{3}{4}\sqrt{\pi}$; (d) $\frac{4}{3}\sqrt{\pi}$; (e) $\frac{105}{16}\sqrt{\pi}$; (f) 2; (g) $\dfrac{5\pi}{16}$; (h) 0.9724; (i) 9.07; (j) $\dfrac{2^6\sqrt{\pi}}{3\cdot5\cdot7\cdot9\cdot11}$; (k) $\frac{10}{9}$; (l) $\dfrac{2\pi}{\sqrt{3}}$.

2. Establish each of the following:

(a) $$\frac{1}{n!(\alpha+1)(\alpha+2)\cdots(\alpha+n)} = \frac{\Gamma(\alpha+1)}{n!\Gamma(\alpha+n+1)} = (n!)^{-2}\binom{\alpha+n}{n}^{-1}.$$

(b) $$\frac{(2\alpha+1)(2\alpha+3)\cdots(2\alpha+2r+1)}{2\cdot4\cdot6\cdots2r} = \frac{\Gamma(2\alpha+2r+2)\Gamma(\alpha+1)}{2^{2r}r!\Gamma(2\alpha+1)\Gamma(\alpha+r+1)}.$$

(c) $$\frac{1\cdot3\cdot5\cdots2n-3}{n!(n-3)!} = \frac{(2n-3)!}{2^{n-1}(n!)^2(n-2)!} = \frac{1}{2^{n-1}n!}\binom{2n-3}{n}.$$

(d) $$\binom{\alpha}{\beta} + \binom{\alpha}{\beta+1} = \binom{\alpha+1}{\beta+1}.$$

(e) $$\binom{-\beta}{n} = (-1)^n\binom{\beta+n-1}{n},$$ n a positive integer.

(f) $$\sum_{k=0}^{\infty}\binom{n}{k}\binom{n-k}{\alpha-n}t^k = \binom{n}{\alpha}(1+t)^\alpha.$$

(g) $$\frac{\Gamma(n+\frac{1}{2})}{\Gamma(\frac{1}{2})} = \frac{(2n)!}{n!2^{2n}}.$$

(h) $\sum_{k=0}^{n} \binom{\alpha - k}{r} = \binom{\alpha + 1}{r + 1} - \binom{\alpha - n}{r + 1}$.

(i) $\sum_{k=0}^{n} (-1)^k \binom{\alpha}{k} = (-1)^n \binom{\alpha - 1}{n}$.

3. Evaluate:

(a) $\int_0^\infty \frac{e^{-t}}{\sqrt{t}}\, dt$; (b) $\int_0^\infty e^{-t} t^4\, dt$; (c) $\int_0^\infty e^{-t} t^{5/2}\, dt$;

(d) $\int_0^1 \left(\log \frac{1}{t}\right)^{1/2} dt$; (e) $\int_0^1 \left(\log \frac{1}{t}\right)^{-1/2} dt$; (f) $\int_0^\infty x^3 e^{-x^2}\, dx$;

(g) $\int_0^\infty x^8 e^{-x^2}\, dx$; (h) $\int_0^1 t^4(1 - t)^4\, dt$; (i) $\int_0^1 \sqrt{x(1 - x)}\, dx$;

(j) $\int_0^1 \sqrt[3]{\frac{x}{1 - x}}\, dx$; (k) $\int_0^1 \left(1 - \frac{1}{t}\right)^{1/4} dt$; (l) $\int_0^{\pi/2} \sqrt{\tan x}\, dx$;

(m) $\int_0^{\pi/2} \sqrt{\sin 2x}\, dx$; (n) $\int_0^\infty \frac{e^{-2x}}{\sqrt{x}}\, dx$; (o) $\int_0^\infty x^{3/2} e^{-4x}\, dx$;

(p) $\int_0^{\pi/2} \sin^6 \theta\, d\theta$; (q) $\int_0^{\pi/2} \sin^4 \theta \cos^5 \theta\, d\theta$; (r) $\int_0^\pi \sin^5 \theta\, d\theta$.

Ans.: (a) $\sqrt{\pi}$; (b) 120; (c) $\frac{15\sqrt{\pi}}{8}$; (d) $\frac{\sqrt{\pi}}{2}$; (e) $\sqrt{\pi}$; (f) $\frac{1}{2}$; (g) $\frac{105\sqrt{\pi}}{32}$; (h) $\frac{1}{42}$; (i) $\frac{\pi}{8}$; (j) $\frac{2\pi}{3\sqrt{3}}$; (k) $\frac{\pi}{2\sqrt{2}}$; (l) $\frac{\pi}{4}$; (m) $\sqrt{\frac{2}{\pi}}\, \Gamma^2\left(\frac{3}{4}\right)$; (n) $\sqrt{\frac{\pi}{2}}$; (o) $\frac{3\sqrt{\pi}}{128}$; (p) $\frac{5\pi}{32}$; (q) $\frac{8}{315}$; (r) $\frac{16}{15}$.

4. Evaluate by first making an appropriate substitution:

(a) $\int_0^\infty e^{-x^4}\, dx$; (b) $\int_0^1 \frac{dx}{\sqrt{x \log (1/x)}}$; (c) $\int_0^1 \sqrt{\frac{x}{\log (1/x)}}\, dx$;

(d) $\int_0^1 \left(\frac{x}{\log x}\right)^{1/3} dx$; (e) $\int_0^1 (\log x)^n\, dx$, n a positive integer;

(f) $\int_0^\infty \frac{dt}{\sqrt{t}(1 + t)}$; (g) $\int_0^\infty \frac{dt}{(1 + t)^2 \sqrt{t + (1/t)}}$; (h) $\int_0^\infty \frac{t\, dt}{(1 + t)^3}$;

(i) $\int_0^1 \frac{dx}{\sqrt[3]{1 - x^2}}$; (j) $\int_0^1 \frac{x^5\, dx}{\sqrt{1 - x^4}}$; (k) $\int_0^\infty \frac{x\, dx}{1 + x^6}$; (l) $\int_0^2 (4 - x^2)^{3/2}\, dx$.

Ans.: (a) $\frac{1}{4}\Gamma\left(\frac{1}{4}\right)$; (b) $\sqrt{2\pi}$; (c) $\sqrt{\frac{2\pi}{3}}$; (d) $-\left(\frac{3}{4}\right)^{2/3} \Gamma\left(\frac{2}{3}\right)$; (e) $(-1)^n n!$; (f) π; (g) $\frac{\pi}{2}$; (h) $\frac{1}{2}$; (i) $\frac{\sqrt{\pi}\,\Gamma(\frac{2}{3})}{\Gamma(\frac{7}{6})}$; (j) $\frac{\pi}{8}$; (k) $\frac{\pi}{3\sqrt{3}}$; (l) 3π.

5. Show that

$$\int_0^{\pi/2} \sin^{2n}\theta\, d\theta = \int_0^{\pi/2} \cos^{2n}\theta\, d\theta = \frac{1\cdot 3\cdot 5\cdots 2n-1}{2\cdot 4\cdot 6\cdots 2n}\frac{\pi}{2}$$

and

$$\int_0^{\pi/2} \sin^{2n+1}\theta\, d\theta = \int_0^{\pi/2} \cos^{2n+1}\theta\, d\theta = \frac{2\cdot 4\cdot 6\cdots 2n}{1\cdot 3\cdot 5\cdots 2n+1}.$$

6. Establish each of the following:

(a) $\displaystyle\int_0^\infty x^a b^{-x}\, dx = \frac{\Gamma(a+1)}{(\log b)^{a+1}}, \qquad a > -1,\ b > 0.$

(b) $\displaystyle\int_0^\infty x^{p-1} e^{-qx^r}\, dx = \frac{\Gamma(p/r)}{rq^{p/r}}, \qquad p,\ q,\ r > 0.$

(c) $\displaystyle\int_0^1 x^{r-1}\left(\log\frac{1}{x}\right)^{s-1} dx = \frac{\Gamma(s)}{r^s}, \qquad r,\ s > 0.$

7. Show that

(a) $\displaystyle\Gamma(x)\Gamma(-x) = \frac{-\pi}{x\sin\pi x}$, x not an integer.

(b) $\displaystyle\Gamma(1+x)\Gamma(1-x) = \frac{\pi x}{\sin\pi x}$, x not an integer.

(c) $\displaystyle\Gamma\left(\frac{1}{2}+x\right)\Gamma\left(\frac{1}{2}-x\right) = \frac{\pi}{\cos\pi x},\ x \neq \frac{2n+1}{2},\ n = 0, 1, \cdots.$

(d) $\displaystyle\Gamma(1+ix)\Gamma(1-ix) = \frac{\pi x}{\sinh\pi x}.$

(e) $\displaystyle\Gamma\left(\frac{1}{2}+ix\right)\Gamma\left(\frac{1}{2}-ix\right) = \frac{\pi}{\cosh\pi x}.$

8. (a) Prove that $B(x, x) = 2^{1-2x}B(x, \frac{1}{2}),\ x > 0.$

Hint: $\displaystyle B(x, x) = 2^{-2x+2}\int_0^{\pi/2} \sin^{2x-1} 2\theta\, d\theta.$

(b) Prove Legendre's duplication formula:

$$\Gamma(2x) = \frac{1}{\sqrt{\pi}}2^{2x-1}\Gamma(x)\Gamma\left(x+\frac{1}{2}\right), \qquad x > 0.$$

9. Prove the following identities involving the beta function, $x, y, z, u > 0$:

(a) $\displaystyle B(x, y+1) = \frac{y}{x}B(x+1, y) = \frac{y}{x+y}B(x, y).$

(b) $B(x, y)B(x+y, z) = B(y, z)B(y+z, x) = B(z, x)B(x+z, y).$

(c) $\displaystyle B(x, y)B(x+y, z)B(x+y+z, u) = \frac{\Gamma(x)\Gamma(y)\Gamma(z)\Gamma(u)}{x+y+z+u}.$

(d) $B(x, y) = B(x+1, y) + B(x, y+1).$

10. Show that

(a) $\displaystyle\int_0^1 x^{p-1}(1-x^r)^{q-1}\,dx = \frac{1}{r}B\left(\frac{p}{r}, q\right), \quad p, q, r > 0.$

(b) $\displaystyle\int_0^1 \frac{x^p\,dx}{\sqrt{1-x^2}} = \frac{\sqrt{\pi}}{2}\frac{\Gamma\left(\frac{p+1}{2}\right)}{\Gamma\left(\frac{p+2}{2}\right)}, \quad p > 0.$

(c) $\displaystyle\int_0^1 \frac{dx}{\sqrt{1-x^p}} = \frac{\Gamma\left(\frac{1}{p}\right)}{p\Gamma\left(\frac{1}{p}+\frac{1}{2}\right)}, \quad p > 0.$

11. Show that each of the following is equivalent to $B(x, y)$, $x, y > 0$:

(a) $\displaystyle\frac{1}{2}\int_0^1 \frac{t^{x-1}+t^{y-1}}{(1+t)^{x+y}}\,dt.$

Hint: Let $u = t/(1+t)$.

(b) $\displaystyle\int_0^\infty \frac{t^{y-1}\,dt}{(1+t)^{x+y}}.$

(c) $\displaystyle\frac{1}{2^{x+y-2}}\int_{-1}^1 \frac{(1+u)^{2x-1}(1-u)^{2y-1}}{(1+u^2)^{x+y}}\,du.$

Hint: Let $t = \dfrac{(1+u)^2}{2(1+u^2)}$ in B_2.

(d) $\displaystyle\frac{3^x}{2^{x+y-1}}\int_{-1}^1 \frac{(t+1)^{x-1}(1-t)^{y-1}}{(t+2)^{x+y}}\,dt.$

(e) $\displaystyle\frac{1}{(b-a)^{x+y-1}}\int_a^b (t-a)^{x-1}(b-t)^{y-1}\,dt.$

12. Use Exercise 11 appropriately to evaluate:

(a) $\displaystyle\int_0^{\pi/2} \frac{d\theta}{\sqrt{1+\sin^2\theta}};$ (b) $\displaystyle\int_0^{\pi/2} \frac{d\theta}{\sqrt{a\cos^4\theta + b\sin^4\theta}};$

(c) $\displaystyle\int_{-1}^1 \frac{(1+x)^{2m-1}}{(1+x^2)^{m+(1/2)}}\,dx, \quad m > 0.$

Ans.: (a) $\displaystyle\frac{1}{8}\sqrt{\frac{2}{\pi}}\,\Gamma^2\left(\frac{1}{4}\right)$; (b) $\displaystyle\frac{\Gamma^2(\frac{1}{4})}{4(ab)^{1/4}\sqrt{\pi}}$; (c) $\displaystyle\frac{\sqrt{\pi}\,2^{m-(3/2)}\Gamma(m)}{\Gamma(m+\frac{1}{2})}$.

13. (a) Show that

$$\int_0^{\pi/2} \tan^p x\,dx = \int_0^{\pi/2} \cot^p x\,dx = \frac{1}{2}B\left(\frac{1+p}{2}, \frac{1-p}{2}\right) = \frac{\pi}{2\cos(p\pi/2)}, \quad 0 < p < 1.$$

(b) Evaluate $\displaystyle\int_0^{\pi/2} \tan^{3/4} x\,dx$ and $\displaystyle\int_0^{\pi/2} \cot^{2/3} x\,dx.$

14. (a) Show that

$$I = \int_0^\infty \frac{\cos x}{x^\alpha}\,dx = \frac{\pi}{2\Gamma(\alpha)\cos(\alpha\pi/2)}, \qquad 0 < \alpha < 1.$$

Hint: $\dfrac{1}{x^\alpha} = \dfrac{1}{\Gamma(\alpha)}\displaystyle\int_0^\infty u^{\alpha-1}e^{-xu}\,du$. Then

$$I = \frac{1}{\Gamma(\alpha)}\int_0^\infty\int_0^\infty u^{\alpha-1}e^{-xu}\cos x\,du\,dx = \frac{1}{\Gamma(\alpha)}\int_0^\infty \frac{u^\alpha}{1+u^2}\,du.$$

(b) Show that

$$\int_0^\infty \cos x^2\,dx = \int_0^\infty \sin x^2\,dx = \frac{1}{2}\frac{\sqrt{\pi}}{2}.$$

(c) Show that

$$\int_0^\infty \frac{x^{\alpha-1}\operatorname{Log} x\,dx}{1+x} = -\pi^2\csc\alpha\pi\cot\alpha\pi, \qquad 0 < \alpha < 1.$$

15. Show that

(a) $$\int_0^1 \frac{t^{x-1}(1-t)^{y-1}}{(t+p)^{x+y}} = \frac{B(x, y)}{p^x(1+p)^{x+y}}, \qquad x, y, p > 0.$$

Hint: Let $t = \dfrac{(p+1)u}{p+u}$.

(b) $$\int_0^\infty \frac{x^a\,dx}{(1+x^b)^c} = \frac{1}{b}B\left(\frac{a+1}{b}, c - \frac{a+1}{b}\right), \qquad a > -1, b > 0, bc > a+1.$$

(c) $$\int_0^\infty \frac{x^a\,dx}{1+x^b} = \frac{\pi}{b\sin\left(\dfrac{a+1}{b}\pi\right)}, \qquad 0 < a+1 < b.$$

(d) $$\int_0^{\pi/2} \frac{\sin^{2m-1}\theta\cos^{2n-1}\theta\,d\theta}{(a\sin^2\theta + b\cos^2\theta)^{m+n}} = \frac{B(m, n)}{2a^nb^m}, \qquad m, n > 0.$$

Hint: Let $t = \sin^2\theta$ in (a).

16. (a) Find the area inside the curve

$$x^{2/3} + y^{2/3} = 1.$$

(b) Find the volume in the first octant below the surface

$$x^{1/2} + y^{1/2} + z^{1/2} = a^{1/2}.$$

(c) Find the total length of the lemniscate

$$r^2 = a^2\cos 2\theta.$$

(d) Find the area of the loop in the curve

$$x^5 + y^5 = 5ax^2y^2.$$

(e) Find the volume in the first octant below the surface

$$x^\alpha + y^\beta + z^\gamma = 1, \qquad \alpha, \beta, \gamma > 0.$$

(f) Find the distance from the origin to the centroid of volume in the first octant below the surface

$$\left(\frac{x}{a}\right)^m + \left(\frac{y}{b}\right)^m + \left(\frac{z}{c}\right)^m = 1, \qquad m > 0.$$

Ans.: (a) $\dfrac{3\pi}{8}$; (b) $\dfrac{a^3}{90}$; (c) $\dfrac{a\sqrt{\pi}\,\Gamma(\frac{1}{4})}{\Gamma(\frac{3}{4})}$; (d) $\dfrac{5}{2}a^2$;

(e) $\dfrac{\Gamma\left(1+\frac{1}{\alpha}\right)\Gamma\left(1+\frac{1}{\beta}\right)\Gamma\left(1+\frac{1}{\gamma}\right)}{\Gamma\left(1+\frac{1}{\alpha}+\frac{1}{\beta}+\frac{1}{\gamma}\right)}$; (f) $\dfrac{3aB\left(\frac{2}{m},\frac{3}{m}\right)}{4B\left(\frac{1}{m},\frac{4}{m}\right)}$.

17. A particle starts from rest at $x = a$ and moves along the x-axis toward the origin under the law of force $F = -k/x$. The energy equation is

$$\frac{m}{2}\left(\frac{dx}{dt}\right)^2 + k \operatorname{Log} x = k \operatorname{Log} a.$$

Show that

$$t = -\sqrt{\frac{m}{2k}} \int_a^x \left(\operatorname{Log}\frac{a}{x}\right)^{-(1/2)}$$

and show that the time required to reach the origin is $a\sqrt{m\pi/2k}$.
Hint: Let $a/x = 1/u$ in the integral.

18. Show that

(a) $\displaystyle\int_{-\infty}^{\infty} \frac{e^{-a^2x^2}}{b^2 + x^2}\,dx = \frac{\pi}{b} e^{a^2b^2} \operatorname{erfc}(ab), \qquad ab > 0.$

(b) $\displaystyle\int_0^{\pi/2} e^{-a^2\tan^2 x}\,dx = \int_0^{\pi/2} e^{-a^2\cot^2 x}\,dx = \frac{\pi}{2} e^{a^2} \operatorname{erfc} a, \qquad a \geq 0.$

19. Show that if $G(k, \phi)$ is any elliptic integral, then
(a) $G(k, n \pm \phi) = 2nG(k, \pi/2) \pm G(k, \phi)$.
(b) $G(k, -\phi) = -G(k, \phi)$.

20. Show that

(a) $\displaystyle\int_0^x \frac{dt}{(1 - t^2)(1 - k^2t^2)} = F(k, x).$

(b) $\displaystyle\int_0^x \sqrt{\frac{1 - k^2t^2}{1 - t^2}}\,dt = E(k, x).$

(c) $\displaystyle\int_0^x \frac{dt}{(1 + at^2)\sqrt{(1 - t^2)(1 - k^2t^2)}} = \Pi(k, x, a).$

21. Show that

(a) $\displaystyle\int_0^{\phi} \frac{\sin^2 x\,dx}{\sqrt{1 - k^2\sin^2 x}} = \frac{F(k, \phi) - E(k, \phi)}{k^2}, \qquad k < 1.$

(b) $$\int_0^\phi \sqrt{1 - k^2 \sin^2 x}\, dx = kE\left(\frac{1}{k}, \sin^{-1}(k \sin \phi)\right) + \frac{1 - k^2}{k} F\left(\frac{1}{k}, \sin^{-1}(k \sin \phi)\right), \qquad k > 1.$$

(c) $$\int_0^\phi \frac{dx}{\sqrt{1 - k^2 \sin^2 x}} = \frac{1}{k} F\left(\frac{1}{k}, x\right), \qquad k > 1.$$

(d) $$\int_0^\phi \frac{dx}{\sqrt{c + \cos x}} = \frac{2}{\sqrt{c + 1}} F\left(\sqrt{\frac{2}{c + 1}}, \frac{\phi}{2}\right), \qquad c > 1.$$

22. Find:
(a) The perimeter of the ellipse

$$8x^2 + 9y^2 = 72.$$

(b) The length of the arc of the lemniscate

$$r^2 = \cos 2\theta,$$

form $\theta = 0$ to $\theta = \pi/2$.
(c) The area enclosed by one loop of the curve

$$y^2 = 1 - 4 \sin^2 x.$$

(d) The length of the curve

$$y = \sin x,$$

form $x = 0$ to $x = \pi/3$.
(e) The surface area of a right circular cylinder intercepted by a sphere of radius r whose center lies on the cylinder.

Ans.: (a) $12E(\frac{1}{3}) = 18.314$; (b) 0.584; (c) 1.625; (d) $2E\left(\frac{\sqrt{2}}{2}, \frac{\pi}{3}\right)$; (e) $2.935r^2$.

23. (a) Show that $F(k, \phi)$ is a continuous increasing function of ϕ such that

$$F(k, \phi + \pi) - F(k, \phi) = 2K \quad \text{and} \quad \lim_{\phi \to \pm\infty} F(k, \phi) = \pm\infty.$$

(b) Define the inverse of $u = F(k, \phi)$ to be $\phi = am(u)$ and show that $am(u)$ is a continuous increasing function of u and $am(u + 2K) = am(u) + \pi$.
(c) Define the **Jacobian elliptic functions**

$$sn\, u = \sin\,[am(u)], \quad cn\, u = \cos\,[am(u)], \quad dn\, u = \sqrt{1 - k^2 \sin^2 u}.$$

Prove:

(1) $sn^2 u + cn^2 u = 1$.

(2) $\dfrac{d}{du}\, sn\, u = cn\, u\, dn\, u$.

(3) $\dfrac{d}{du}\, cn\, u = -sn\, u\, dn\, u$.

(4) $sn(u + 4K) = sn\, u$.
(5) $cn(u + 4K) = cn\, u$.
(6) $dn(u + 2K) = dn\, u$.

(7) $sn(u + v) = \dfrac{sn\, u\, cn\, v\, dn\, v + sn\, v\, cn\, u\, dn\, u}{1 - k^2\, sn^2 u\, sn^2 v}$.

(8) $sn(-u) = -sn\, u, \quad cn(-u) = cn\, u, \quad dn(-u) = dn\, u.$

(9) $E(k, \sin^{-1} x) = \displaystyle\int_0^x \sqrt{\frac{1 - k^2x^2}{1 - x^2}}\, dx = sn^{-1}x - k^2 \int_0^{sn^{-1}x} sn^2 u\, du.$

(10) If $k = 0$, $u = \phi$,

$$sn\, u = \sin u, \quad cn\, u = \cos u, \quad dn\, u = 1.$$

◇ **24.** (a) Prove the comparison test for divergence of improper integrals: If f and g are continuous and $0 \le f(x) \le g(x)$ in $\begin{cases} a < x \le b \\ a \le x \end{cases}$, and

$$\begin{cases} \displaystyle\int_a^b g(x)\, dx \\ \displaystyle\int_a^\infty g(x)\, dx \end{cases} \text{is divergent,}$$

then

$$\begin{cases} \displaystyle\int_a^b f(x)\, dx \\ \displaystyle\int_a^\infty f(x)\, dx \end{cases} \text{is divergent.}$$

(b) Prove the limit test for convergence of improper integrals: If f is continuous in $\begin{cases} a < x \le b \\ a \le x \end{cases}$ and

$$\begin{cases} \lim\limits_{x \to a} (x - a)^p f(x) \\ \lim\limits_{x \to \infty} x^p f(x) \end{cases} = A, \qquad 0 < p < 1,$$

then

$$\begin{cases} \displaystyle\int_a^b f(x)\, dx \\ \displaystyle\int_a^\infty f(x)\, dx \end{cases} \text{is convergent.}$$

(c) Prove the limit test for divergence of improper integrals: If f is continuous in $\begin{cases} a < x \le b \\ a \le x \end{cases}$ and

$$\begin{cases} \lim\limits_{x \to a} (x - a) f(x) \\ \lim\limits_{x \to \infty} x f(x) \end{cases} = A \ne 0 \text{ (or } \pm\infty\text{)},$$

then

$$\begin{cases} \displaystyle\int_a^b f(x)\, dx \\ \displaystyle\int_a^\infty f(x)\, dx \end{cases} \text{is divergent.}$$

The test fails if $A = 0$.

(d) Test for convergence or divergence:

$$(1) \int_0^\infty \frac{dx}{1+x^4}; \; (2) \int_0^1 \frac{\operatorname{Log} x \, dx}{x}; \; (3) \int_{-1}^1 e^{1/x}\, dx;$$

$$(4) \int_0^1 \sqrt[3]{x \operatorname{Log} \frac{1}{x}}\, dx; \; (5) \int_1^\infty x\left(1 - \cos\frac{1}{x}\right)^\beta dx.$$

◇ **25.** (a) The integral $\int_a^\infty f(x, t)\, dt$ converges uniformly to $F(x)$ in $A \le x \le B$ if for every $\epsilon > 0$ there exists Q independent of x such that $R > Q$ implies

$$\left| F(x) - \int_a^R f(x, t)\, dt \right| < \epsilon.$$

Show that if $f(x, t)$ is continuous in $a \le t < \infty$, $A \le x \le B$, $|f(x, t)| \le M(t)$, $a \le t < \infty$, $A \le x \le B$, $\int_a^\infty M(t)\, dt < \infty$, then $\int_a^\infty f(x, t)\, dt$ converges uniformly in $A \le x \le B$ (the ***Weierstrass M-test*** for improper integrals).

(b) Show that $\displaystyle\int_0^\infty \frac{x\, dt}{x^2 + t^2}$ is uniformly convergent in $1 \le x \le 2$ and $\displaystyle\int_1^\infty \frac{\sin(xt)\, dt}{t^2}$ in $A \le x \le B$.

(c) Prove: If $f(x, t)$ is continuous in $a \le t < \infty$, $A \le x \le B$ and $\int_a^\infty f(x, t)\, dt$ converges uniformly to $F(x)$ in $A \le x \le B$, then $F(x)$ is continuous in $A \le x \le B$.

(d) Prove: If $f(x, t)$ is continuous in $a \le t < \infty$, $A \le x \le B$ and $\int_a^\infty f(x, t)\, dt$ converges uniformly to $F(x)$ in $A \le x \le B$, then $\int_A^B F(x)\, dx = \int_a^\infty dt \int_A^B f(x, t)\, dx$.

Hint: $|\int_A^B dx \int_R^\infty f(x, t)\, dt| < \epsilon(B - A)$ for $R > Q$ or

$$\lim_{R\to\infty} \int_A^B \left[F(x) - \int_a^R f(x, t)\, dt \right] dx = 0.$$

$$\begin{aligned} \int_A^B F(x)\, dx &= \lim_{R\to\infty} \int_A^B dx \int_a^R f(x, t)\, dt \\ &= \lim_{R\to\infty} \int_a^R dt \int_A^B f(x, t)\, dx = \int_a^\infty dt \int_A^B f(x, t)\, dx. \end{aligned}$$

(e) Prove: If $f(x, t)$ and $g(x, t)$ are continuous in $a \le t < \infty$, $A \le x \le B$, $\int_a^\infty f(x, t)\, dt$ converges to $F(x)$ in $A \le x \le B$ and $\int_a^\infty g(x, t)\, dt$ converges uniformly in $A \le x \le B$, then $F'(x) = \int_a^\infty g(x, t)\, dt$.

26. (a) Show that $\displaystyle\lim_{n\to\infty} \left(\sum_{k=1}^n \frac{1}{n} - \operatorname{Log} n \right)$ exists. It is called **Euler's constant** and is denoted by γ.

Hint:

$$\frac{1}{k} \le \int_{k-1}^k \frac{dx}{x} \le \frac{1}{k-1}, \qquad k = 2, 3, \cdots, n$$

and

$$\sum_{k=2}^n \frac{1}{k} \le \int_1^n \frac{dx}{x} \le \sum_{k=1}^{n-1} \frac{1}{k}.$$

Let

$$C_n = \sum_{k=1}^n \frac{1}{k} - \int_1^n \frac{dx}{x}.$$

Show that $0 \leq C_n \leq 1$ and $C_n \leq C_{n-1}$; hence, $\lim_{n\to\infty} C_n$ exists.

(b) By repeated integration by parts, show that

$$\int_0^n t^{x-1}\left(1 - \frac{t}{n}\right)^n dt = \frac{n!n^x}{x(x+1)\cdots(x+n)}, \qquad x > 0.$$

(c) Show that $\Gamma(x) = \lim_{n\to\infty} \dfrac{n!n^x}{x(x+1)\cdots(x+n)}$.

(d) Show that $\dfrac{1}{\Gamma(x)} = xe^{\gamma x} \prod_{n=1}^{\infty} \left(1 + \dfrac{x}{n}\right) e^{-x/n}$.

(e) By taking the logarithm of each side of the equation in (d) and differentiating term by term, show that

$$\psi(x) = \frac{\Gamma'(x)}{\Gamma(x)} = -\gamma + (x-1) \sum_{n=0}^{\infty} \frac{1}{(n+1)(x+n)}.$$

(f) Show that $\psi(1) = -\gamma = -\int_0^\infty e^{-t} \log t\, dt$. Approximate $\gamma = 0.57721\cdots$.

(g) Show that $\psi(x) = \psi(1+x) - (1/x)$; $\psi(x) - \psi(1-x) = -\pi \cot \pi x$; $\psi(\frac{1}{2} + x) - \psi(\frac{1}{2} - x) = \pi \tan \pi x$.

27. (a) Show that $|\text{erf}\, x| \leq 1$ and $\text{erf}\,(-x) = -\text{erf}\, x$.

(b) Show that $\text{erf}\,(ix) = \dfrac{2i}{\sqrt{\pi}} \int_0^x e^{t^2}\, dt$, $i = \sqrt{-1}$.

(c) Show that $\text{erf}\, x = \dfrac{2}{\sqrt{\pi}} \sum_{n=0}^{\infty} \dfrac{(-1)^n x^{2n+1}}{n!(2n+1)}$ and that for small x, the series converges rapidly.

(d) By repeated integration by parts, show that

$$\text{erf}\, x = 1 - \frac{2}{\sqrt{\pi}} \frac{e^{-x^2}}{2\pi}\left(1 - \frac{1}{2x^2} + \frac{1-3}{2^2x^4} + \cdots\right)$$

and show that convergence is rapid for large x. This type of series is called an **asymptotic series.**

28. (a) Show that

$$C(x) = \frac{1}{2}\int_0^{x^2} \frac{\cos t}{\sqrt{t}}\, dt \quad \text{and} \quad S(x) = \frac{1}{2}\int_0^{x^2} \frac{\sin t}{\sqrt{t}}\, dt.$$

(b) Show that if

$$A(x) = \frac{\sqrt{\pi}}{4} e^{i\pi/4}\, \text{erf}\,(xe^{-i\pi/4}) \quad \text{and} \quad B(x) = \frac{\sqrt{\pi}}{4} e^{-i\pi/4}\, \text{erf}\,(xe^{i\pi/4}),$$

then the Fresnel integral functions become

$$C(x) = A(x) + B(x), \quad S(x) = \frac{A(x) - B(x)}{i}.$$

(c) Show that $C(-x) = -C(x)$ and $S(-x) = -S(x)$.

(d) Find the Maclaurin series of $C(x)$ and $S(x)$.

29. (a) Show that $Si(-x) = -Si(x)$, $si(-x) = \pi - si(x)$.

(b) Show that the only real zero of $Si(x)$ is zero.

(c) Show that if μ_n is the nth extremum (relative maximum or relative minimum) of $Si(x)$, $x > 0$, then $\{|\mu_n|\}$ is a decreasing sequence.

(d) Show that $ei(\pm ix) = ci(x) \pm isi(x)$.

(e) Show that

$$ci(x) = \int_0^x \frac{1 - \cos t}{t}\,dt - \log x - \gamma,$$

where γ is Euler's constant (see Exercise 25), and hence that

$$ci(-x) = cix + i\pi.$$

30. Establish:

(a) $\displaystyle\int_0^\infty \sin x\, si(x)\,dx = \frac{\pi}{4}.$

(b) $\displaystyle\int_0^\infty si(x)ci(x)\,dx = -\text{Log}\ 2.$

(c) $\displaystyle\int_0^\infty e^{-st}ci(t)\,dt = \frac{1}{2^s}\text{Log}\,(1 + s^2), \qquad s > 0.$

(d) $\displaystyle\int_0^\infty e^{-st}si(t)\,dt = \frac{1}{s}\tan^{-1} s, \qquad s > 0.$

(e) $\displaystyle\int_0^\infty e^{-st}t^{-1}\,\text{Log}\,(1 + t^2)\,dt = [ci(s)]^2 + [si(s)]^2, \qquad s > 0.$

31. (a) Show that $T(x, t) = C \operatorname{erf}(x/\sqrt{4kt})$ satisfies the following conditions:

(1) $T(0, t) = 0$; (2) $T(x, 0) = C$; (3) $\partial T/\partial t = k(\partial^2 T/\partial t^2)$.

(b) Show that
$$\begin{aligned} T(x, t) &= C \operatorname{erfc}\frac{x}{2\sqrt{kt}}, & t \le t_0, \\ &= C\left[\operatorname{erf}\frac{x}{2\sqrt{k(t - t_0)}} - \operatorname{erf}\frac{x}{2\sqrt{kt}}\right], & t > t_0, \end{aligned}$$

is a solution of

(1) $T(0, t) = \begin{cases} C, & 0 < t < t_0 \\ 0, & t > t_0 \end{cases}$; (2) $T(x, 0) = 0$; (3) $\partial T/\partial t = k(\partial^2 T/\partial t^2)$.

32. Establish:

(a) $\displaystyle\int_0^{\pi/2} \frac{dx}{\sqrt{\sin x}} = \int_0^{\pi/2} \frac{dx}{\sqrt{\cos x}} = \sqrt{2}K\left(\frac{1}{\sqrt{2}}\right).$

(b) $\displaystyle\int_0^{\pi/2} \sqrt{1 + 4\sin^2 x}\,dx = \sqrt{5}E\left(\frac{2}{\sqrt{5}}\right).$

(c) $\displaystyle\int_0^{\pi/2} \frac{dx}{\sqrt{2 - \cos x}} = \frac{2}{\sqrt{3}}\left[F\left(\frac{\sqrt{2}}{3}, \frac{\pi}{2}\right) - F\left(\frac{\sqrt{2}}{3}, \frac{\pi}{4}\right)\right].$

(d) $\displaystyle\int_0^2 \frac{dx}{\sqrt{(4 - x^2)(9 - x^2)}} = \frac{1}{3}K\left(\frac{2}{3}\right).$

(*Hint:* Let $x = 2\sin\theta$.)

(e) $\displaystyle\int_0^1 \frac{dx}{\sqrt{(1+x^2)(1+2x^2)}} = \frac{1}{\sqrt{2}}\left[K\left(\frac{1}{\sqrt{2}}\right) - F\left(\frac{1}{\sqrt{2}}, \frac{\pi}{4}\right)\right].$

(f) $\displaystyle\int_4^6 \frac{dx}{\sqrt{(x-1)(x-2)(x-3)}} = \sqrt{2}\left[F\left(\frac{1}{\sqrt{2}}, \frac{\pi}{3}\right) - F\left(\frac{1}{\sqrt{2}}, \frac{\pi}{4}\right)\right].$

[*Hint:* Let $x = 3 + u^2$ and use (e).]

(g) $\displaystyle\int_1^\infty \frac{dx}{\sqrt{(x^2-1)(x^2+3)}} = \frac{1}{2}K\left(\frac{\sqrt{3}}{2}\right).$

(*Hint:* Let $x = \sec\theta$.)

(h) $\displaystyle\int_1^\infty \frac{dx}{(3x^2+1)\sqrt{(x^2-1)(x^2+3)}} = \frac{1}{2}K\left(\frac{\sqrt{3}}{2}\right) - \frac{3}{8}\Pi\left(\frac{\sqrt{3}}{2}, -\frac{1}{4}\right).$

(*Hint:* Let $x = \sec\theta$.)

(i) $\displaystyle\int_1^\infty \frac{dx}{\sqrt{x^4-1}} = \frac{1}{\sqrt{2}}K\left(\frac{1}{\sqrt{2}}\right).$

(j) $\displaystyle\int_2^3 \frac{dx}{\sqrt{(x-1)(x-2)(x-3)(x-4)}} = \frac{1}{2}K\left(\frac{\sqrt{3}}{2}\right).$

[*Hint:* Let $x = (at+b)/(ct+d)$, choosing a, b, c, d so that $x = 1, 2, 3$ correspond to $t = 0, 1, \infty$. Let $u^2 = t$ in the resulting integral and then use (g).]

33. Show that if F and G are two solutions of $f(x+1) = xf(x)$, then there exists a function ω such that $\omega(x+1) = \omega(x)$ and $F(x) = \omega(x)G(x)$. Prove the converse. Show that every solution of $f(x+1) = xf(x)$ is of the form $f(x) = \omega(x)\Gamma(x)$, where $\omega(x)$ is a periodic function of period 1.

34. If $\int_a^\infty |f(t)|\,dt$ is convergent, then $\int_a^\infty f(t)\,dt$ is said to be absolutely convergent.

(a) Show that if $\int_a^\infty f(t)\,dt$ is absolutely convergent, then it is convergent. (*Hint:* Use $0 \le |f(t)| + f(t) \le 2|f(t)|$ and the comparison test for convergence.)

(b) Discuss absolute convergence for improper integrals of the second kind.

Chapter 15

Orthogonal Polynomials

1. General orthogonal polynomials. One of the fundamental problems in the study of functions is the determination of a representation of these functions, one that will enable us to establish as simply as possible some of their properties. One of the most useful of such representations is a series of functions that converges to the given function in a specified interval. Let $\phi_0, \phi_1, \cdots \phi_n, \cdots$ be a sequence of functions defined in $a \leq x \leq b$. Then, if f is the given function, the problem resolves itself to the determination of constants $a_0, a_1, \cdots, a_n, \cdots$ so that $\sum_{n=0}^{\infty} a_n\phi_n(x)$ converges to $f(x)$ in $a \leq x \leq b$; this series, then, is a representation of f in $a \leq x \leq b$. In any particular situation, the question arises as to which specific sequence of functions will be the most effective. We could hardly expect any arbitrary sequence of functions to yield significant results. It is only when we characterize this sequence in some fashion that we are able to consider the possibility of its application to the series expansions of functions. In our study of Fourier analysis, we saw that the trigonometric system of functions proved to be effective because it is an orthogonal system. This may lead us to suspect that other orthogonal systems could be used advantageously in series expansions of functions. Let us, therefore, characterize our sequences of functions by requiring that they be orthogonal systems of functions in specified intervals.

Now the question arises as to the choice of a specific orthogonal system in a given problem. What are some of the reasons why we may select one orthogonal system and not another? First of all, if we are interested in the representation of a given function in a series expansion of orthogonal functions, we must choose the orthogonal system that will yield an orthogonal series which will actually converge to the function in a given interval. Although several orthogonal systems may be available for this, it may turn out that one orthogonal series converges more rapidly than the others, meaning that fewer terms of the series are required to approximate the function accurately. This, then, may influence the choice of an orthogonal system. In some instances, as we shall have occasion to encounter, the problem at hand dictates the choice. Finally, the nature of the functions constituting the orthogonal system is an important factor; it is easier to work with functions whose properties are well known and which exhibit a simple structure. This was one of the principal reasons why the trigonometric system was singled out for detailed study—the properties of the sine and cosine functions are, indeed, well known. However, there are functions which are even simpler than these functions, namely, polynomials. Therefore, we shall consider orthogonal systems whose functions are polynomials, and shall study their significant properties.

Let us make our ideas precise. We recall that a polynomial of the nth degree is of the form

$$a_nx^n + a_{n-1}x^{n-1} + \cdots + a_1x + a_0, \qquad a_n \neq 0$$

(a nonzero constant is a polynomial of degree zero and the degree of the zero polynomial is undefined). Now let $p_0, p_1, \cdots, p_n, \cdots$ be a sequence of polynomials such that the degree of p_n is n, $n = 0, 1, 2, \cdots$, and let w be a function such that $w(x) \geq 0$ in $a \leq x \leq b$. Then we shall say that these polynomials are **orthogonal polynomials** with respect to the weight function w in $a \leq x \leq b$ if

$$\int_a^b w(x)p_m(x)p_n(x)\,dx = 0, \qquad m \neq n, \quad m, n = 0, 1, 2, \cdots.$$

We now show that every weight function in the interval $a \leq x \leq b$ (i.e., a function w such that $w(x) \geq 0$ in $a \leq x \leq b$) determines a sequence of orthogonal polynomials $\{p_n\}$ uniquely up to an arbitrary multiplicative constant. This means that if $\{p_n\}$ is a sequence of orthogonal polynomials with respect to the weight function w in $a \leq x \leq b$, then every sequence of orthogonal polynomials with respect to the weight function w in $a \leq x \leq b$ is of the form $\{c_np_n\}$, where $c_0, c_1, \cdots, c_n, \cdots$ are arbitrary nonzero constants. First, p_0 must be a polynomial of degree zero, and hence is a nonzero constant; say, $p_0(x) = c_0 \neq 0$. Next, p_1 is a polynomial of degree 1 whose general form is $k_1x + k_0$, $k_1 \neq 0$, k_1 and k_0 being constants that must satisfy

$$\text{(O)} \int_a^b w(x)c_0(k_1x + k_0)\,dx = 0,$$

or

$$\int_a^b w(x)(k_1 + k_2)\,dx = 0,$$

or

$$Ak_1 + Bk_0 = 0,$$

where $A = \int_a^b w(x)x\,dx$ and $B = \int_a^b w(x)\,dx \neq 0$. Hence $k_0 = -Ak_1/B$, which implies that all first-degree polynomials that satisfy (O) are constant multiples of one another. (When is $A = 0$ and what does this imply?) Now p_2 is a polynomial of the form $k_2x^2 + k_1x + k_0$, which can be uniquely determined up to an arbitrary multiplicative constant as the solution of the equations

$$\int_a^b w(x)p_0(x)p_2(x)\,dx = 0$$

and

$$\int_a^b w(x)p_1(x)p_2(x)\,dx = 0.$$

Continuing in this fashion, we can determine uniquely p_n, where $p_n(x) = k_nx^n + k_{n-1}x^{n-1} + \cdots + k_0$, up to an arbitrary multiplicative constant, once $p_0, p_1, \cdots, p_{n-1}$ have been determined, as the solution of the n equations

$$\int_a^b w(x)p_i(x)p_n(x)\,dx = 0, \qquad i = 0, 1, \cdots, n-1,$$

in the $n + 1$ unknowns $k_n, k_{n-1}, \cdots, k_0$.

We have seen that a weight function in a given interval determines uniquely a sequence of orthogonal polynomials up to an arbitrary multiplicative constant (bear in mind that each polynomial in the sequence can be multiplied by a different constant). In order that the sequence of orthogonal polynomials may be uniquely determined, another condition must be imposed so that all these multiplicative constants are fixed. This may be done in a variety of ways. Those of frequent occurrence are (1) the coefficient of x^n in $p_n(x)$ has a prescribed value such as 1; (2) for a given x_0 (very often a or b) in $a \leq x \leq b$, $p_n(x_0)$ has a prescribed value; (3) the sequence is required to be orthonormal, i.e., in addition to being orthogonal, it must satisfy

$$\int_a^b w(x)p_n^2(x)\,dx = 1, \qquad n = 0, 1, \cdots,$$

and the coefficient of x^n in $p_n(x)$ must be positive. We say that the sequence of orthogonal polynomials has been **normalized** or has a **normalization** when the multiplicative constant is determined. We also say that the imposed condition that fixes this multiplicative constant is a normalization of the orthogonal sequence. Hence, *a weight function in a given interval together with a given normalization uniquely determines a sequence of orthogonal polynomials with respect to that weight function in the given interval.* The student should show that $\{p_n\}$ are orthogonal with respect to $w(x)$ in $a \leq x \leq b$ if and only if

$$\int_a^b w(x)x^k p_n(x)\,dx = 0, \qquad k = 0, 1, \cdots, n-1,$$

which indicates that we could have defined orthogonal polynomials in this manner.

If $p_0, p_1, \cdots, p_n$ are arbitrary polynomials such that p_k is of degree k, $k = 0, 1, \cdots, n$, and r_n is an arbitrary polynomial of degree n, then there exist constants c_k, $k = 0, 1, \cdots, n$, such that

$$r_n(x) = c_0 p_0(x) + c_1 p_1(x) + \cdots + c_n p_n(x).$$

We say that $r_n(x)$ can be represented as a linear combination of $p_0(x)$, $p_1(x), \cdots, p_n(x)$. The proof is left to the student. In particular, if $\{p_n\}$ is a sequence of orthogonal polynomials and r_n is an arbitrary polynomial of degree n, we have the representation

$$(R){:}\quad r_n(x) = c_0 p_0(x) + c_1 p_1(x) + \cdots + c_n p_n(x).$$

This leads to the

THEOREM. If $\{p_n\}$ is a sequence of orthogonal polynomials with respect to the weight function w, and r_n is an arbitrary polynomial of degree n, then

$$\int_a^b w(x) r_n(x) p_m(x)\,dx = 0, \qquad \text{if } m > n.$$

Proof. Multiply both sides of (R) by $w(x)p_n(x)$, integrate from a to b, and use the definition of orthogonality.

The converse of the preceding theorem is particularly significant.

THEOREM. If $\{p_n\}$ is a sequence of orthogonal polynomials determined by the weight function w in $a \le x \le b$ and $\{\phi_n\}$ is a sequence of polynomials such that

$$\int_a^b w(x)\phi_n(x) r(x)\,dx = 0, \qquad n = 1, 2, \cdots,$$

for every polynomial r of degree $\le n-1$, then

$$\phi_n(x) = c_n p_n(x), \qquad n = 0, 1, \cdots, \quad c_1, c_2, \cdots, \text{constants}.$$

Proof. We can always determine c_0 so that $\phi_0 = c_0 p_0$. Now let

$$\phi_n(x) = c_0 p_0(x) + c_1 p_1(x) + \cdots + c_n p_n(x).$$

Multiplying both sides by arbitrary polynomials of degree $0, 1, \cdots, n-1$ successively, and using the preceding theorem and the hypothesis, it follows that $c_0 = c_1 = \cdots = c_{n-1} = 0$. Hence,

$$\phi_n(x) = c_n p_n(x).$$

We shall now show that there exists a relationship between any three consecutive orthogonal polynomials. In order to state this relationship simply and precisely, we introduce some notation that will be used throughout this section. Given the sequence of orthogonal polynomials $\{p_n\}$, we denote the coefficients of x^n and x^{n-1} in $p_n(x)$ by k_n and k_n', respectively. Then we let $s_n = k_n'/k_n$. Also, $h_n = \int_a^b w(x)p_n^2(x)\,dx$. Now we are ready to prove one of the most important results in the general theory of orthogonal polynomials.

THEOREM (RECURRENCE FORMULA). If p_{n-1}, p_n, p_{n+1} are three consecutive polynomials in a sequence of orthogonal polynomials, then

$$p_{n+1}(x) = (A_n x + B_n)p_n(x) - C_n p_{n-1}(x), \qquad n \geq 1,$$

where

$$A_n = \frac{k_{n+1}}{k_n}, \quad B_n = A_n(s_{n+1} - s_n), \quad C_n = \frac{A_n h_n}{A_{n-1}h_{n-1}}.$$

Proof. The polynomial $p_{n+1}(x) - A_n x p_n(x)$ is of degree $\leq n$ (why?) and therefore can be represented as

$$p_{n+1}(x) - A_n x p_n(x) = \gamma_0 p_0(x) + \cdots + \gamma_{n-1}p_{n-1}(x) + \gamma_n p_n(x),$$

where $\gamma_0, \cdots, \gamma_{n-1}, \gamma_n$ are constants. Multiplying both sides of this equation by $w(x)p_k(x)$, $k = 0, 1, \cdots, n-2$, integrating from a to b, and using the definition of orthogonality and the next to the last theorem, we find that

$$\gamma_0 = \gamma_1 = \cdots = \gamma_{n-2} = 0.$$

Hence,

$$p_{n+1}(x) - A_n x p_n(x) = \gamma_{n-1}p_{n-1}(x) + \gamma_n p_n(x),$$

or

$$p_{n+1}(x) = (A_n x + \gamma_n)p_n(x) + \gamma_{n-1}p_{n-1}(x).$$

It remains to show that $\gamma_{n-1} = -C_n$ and $\gamma_n = B_n$. Multiplying both sides of the above equation by $w(x)p_{n-1}(x)$ and integrating from a to b yields

$$\gamma_{n-1}h_{n-1} = -A_n \int_a^b w(x)xp_n(x)p_{n-1}(x)\,dx.$$

On the other hand, we can write

$$xp_{n-1}(x) - \frac{k_{n-1}}{k_n}p_n(x) = \delta_0 p_0(x) + \cdots + \delta_{n-1}p_{n-1}(x),$$

where $\delta_0, \cdots, \delta_{n-1}$ are constants, since the degree of the polynomial on the left-hand side is $\leq n - 1$ (why?). Multiplying both sides of this equation by $w(x)p_n(x)$ and integrating from a to b yields

$$\int_a^b w(x)xp_n(x)p_{n-1}(x)\,dx = \frac{h_n k_{n-1}}{k_n}.$$

Therefore,

$$\gamma_{n-1}h_{n-1} = -A_n \frac{h_n k_{n-1}}{k_n} \quad \text{or} \quad \gamma_{n-1} = -C_n.$$

We now have

$$p_{n+1}(x) = (A_n x + \gamma_n)p_n(x) - C_n p_{n-1}(x).$$

Now, by equating the coefficients of x^n on both sides of this equation, we find that $\gamma_n = B_n$.

A simple application of the recurrence formula leads to the

THEOREM (CHRISTOFFEL-DARBOUX FORMULA). If $\{p_n\}$ is a sequence of orthogonal polynomials, then

$$\sum_{j=0}^{n} \frac{p_j(x)p_j(y)}{h_j} = \frac{k_n}{k_{n+1}h_n} \frac{p_{n+1}(x)p_n(y) - p_n(x)p_{n+1}(y)}{x - y}.$$

Proof

$$\begin{aligned} p_{j+1}(x)p_j(y) - p_j(x)p_{j+1}(y) &= [(A_j x + B_j)p_j(x) - C_j p_{j-1}(x)]p_j(y) \\ &\quad -[(A_j y + B_j)p_j(y) - C_j p_{j-1}(y)]p_j(x) \\ &= A_j(x - y)p_j(x)p_j(y) \\ &\quad + C_j[p_j(x)p_{j-1}(y) - p_{j-1}(x)p_j(y)], \end{aligned}$$

or

$$\frac{k_j}{k_{j+1}h_j} \frac{p_{j+1}(x)p_j(y) - p_j(x)p_{j+1}(y)}{x - y} - \frac{k_{j-1}}{k_j h_{j-1}} \frac{p_j(x)p_{j-1}(y) - p_{j-1}(x)p_j(y)}{x - y} = \frac{p_j(x)p_j(y)}{h_j}.$$

Now this formula holds for $j = 0, 1, \cdots, n$, with the definition $p_{-1}(x) = 0$ and k_{-1} and h_{-1} arbitrary constants. Summing both sides from $j = 0$ to $j = n$ yields the result.

We now prove the interesting

THEOREM. If $\{p_n\}$ is a sequence of orthogonal polynomials with respect to the weight function w in $a \le x \le b$, then the zeros of p_n are real, distinct, and are located in the open interval $a < x < b$.

Proof. Since $\int_a^b w(x)p_0(x)p_n(x)\,dx = 0$ and $p_0(x)$ is a constant, and $w(x) \ge 0$, $p_n(x)$ must change sign at least once in $a \le x \le b$. Let x_1, x_2, $\cdots$, x_m be the points in this interval where $p_n(x)$ changes sign. Then

$$\phi(x) = p_n(x)(x - x_1)(x - x_2) \cdots (x - x_m)$$

has a constant sign throughout the interval. (Why?) If $m < n$, then $\int_a^b w(x)\phi(x)\,dx = 0$, which is impossible because $\phi(x)$ is of constant sign in $a \le x \le b$. Hence, $m \ge n$. But since $p_n(x)$ is of degree n, we cannot have $m > n$. Hence, $m = n$.

Thus far we have considered some important properties of orthogonal polynomials in general, using essentially nothing but the definition of orthogonality. The nature of these properties indicates that the orthogonality condition is a strong one. Now, however, we shall consider certain particular sequences of orthogonal polynomials that are of considerable importance in practice, and we shall study them in detail. Bear in mind that a particular sequence of polynomials will be uniquely determined by merely specifying a weight function in an interval, and a normalization.

2. Legendre polynomials. We define the **Legendre polynomials** $P_n(x)$, $n = 0, 1, \cdots$, to be the orthogonal polynomials with weight function 1 in $-1 \leq x \leq 1$ and normalization $P_n(1) = 1$.

The Legendre polynomials satisfy the following identities:

L1: $\int_{-1}^{1} P_n(x)P_m(x)\,dx = 0, \qquad n \neq m, \quad n, m = 0, 1, \cdots.$

L2: $P_n(x) = \dfrac{1}{2^n n!}\dfrac{d^n}{dx^n}(x^2 - 1)^n.$
(Rodrigues' formula.)

L3: $P_n(-x) = (-1)^n P_n(x).$

L4: $\int_{-1}^{1} [P_n(x)]^2\,dx = \dfrac{2}{2n+1}.$

L5: $(n+1)P_{n+1}(x) = (2n+1)xP_n(x) - nP_{n-1}(x), \qquad n \geq 1.$
(Recurrence formula.)

L6: $\sum_{k=0}^{n} (2k+1)P_k(x)P_k(y) = \dfrac{n+1}{x-y}[P_{n+1}(x)P_n(y) - P_n(x)P_{n+1}(y)].$
(Christoffel-Darboux formula.)

L7: $\sum_{n=0}^{\infty} P_n(x)t^n = (1 - 2xt + t^2)^{-1/2}, \quad |x| \leq 1, \quad |t| < 1.$
(Generating function.)

L8: $P_n(x) = \dfrac{1}{2^n}\sum_{k=0}^{[(1/2)n]} (-1)^k \binom{n}{k}\binom{2n-2k}{n} x^{n-2k}.$

L9: $P_n'(x) = xP_{n-1}'(x) + nP_{n-1}(x).$

L10: $xP_n'(x) = nP_n(x) + P_{n-1}'(x).$

L11: $(1 - x^2)P_{n-1}'(x) = n[xP_{n-1}(x) - P_n(x)].$

L12: $P_{n+1}'(x) - P_{n-1}'(x) = (2n+1)P_n(x).$

L13: $(1 - x^2)P_n''(x) - 2xP_n'(x) + n(n+1)P_n(x) = 0.$
(Differential equation.)

L14: $(2n+1)\int_x^1 P_n(t)\,dt = P_{n-1}(x) - P_{n+1}(x).$

L_{15}: $\mathrm{P}_n(x) = \dfrac{1}{\pi}\displaystyle\int_0^\pi [x + \sqrt{x^2 - 1}\cos\theta]^n\, d\theta.$

(Laplace integral representation.)

Proofs.

L_1 is the definition of orthogonality.

L_2: Let $r(x)$ be an arbitrary polynomial of degree $\leq n - 1$. Then

$$\int_{-1}^{1} \frac{d^n}{dx^n}(x^2 - 1)^n r(x)\, dx = 0, \qquad n = 1, 2, \cdots$$

by successive integration by parts, since

$$\frac{d^{n-k}}{dx^{n-k}}(x^2 - 1)^n = 0$$

for $x = \pm 1$, $1 \leq k \leq n$. Hence,

$$\frac{d^n}{dx^n}(x^2 - 1)^n = C_n \mathrm{P}_n(x)$$

where the C_n, $n = 0, 1, \cdots$, are constants, by the theorem on p. 478. Since $\mathrm{P}_n(1) = 1$, by Leibniz's rule for the nth derivative of a product (see p. 304),

$$\begin{aligned} C_n &= \frac{d^n}{dx^n}(x^2 - 1)^n \Big]_{x=1} \\ &= (x + 1)^n \frac{d^n}{dx^n}(x - 1)^n + n^2(x + 1)^{n-1}\frac{d^{n-1}}{dx^{n-1}}(x - 1)^n + \cdots \Big]_{x=1} \\ &= 2^n \frac{d^n}{dx^n}(x - 1)^n \Big]_{x=1} = 2^n n! \end{aligned}$$

and the result is immediate.

L_3: Replace x by $-x$ in L_2.

L_4: By L_2 and successive integration by parts,

$$\begin{aligned} h_n &= \int_{-1}^{1} [\mathrm{P}_n(x)]^2\, dx \\ &= \frac{1}{2^{2n}(n!)^2}\int_{-1}^{1} \frac{d^n(x^2 - 1)^n}{dx^n}\frac{d^n(x^2 - 1)^n}{dx^n}\, dx \\ &= \frac{(-1)^n}{2^{2n}(n!)^2}\int_{-1}^{1} \frac{d^{2n}(x^2 - 1)^n}{dx^{2n}}(x^2 - 1)^n\, dx \\ &= \frac{(-1)^n(2n)!}{2^{2n}(n!)^2}\int_{-1}^{1} (x^2 - 1)^n\, dx. \end{aligned}$$

But

$$\begin{aligned} \int_{-1}^{1} (x^2 - 1)^n\, dx &= \int_{-1}^{1} (x + 1)^n (x - 1)^n\, dx \\ &= \frac{(-1)^n n! 2^{2n+1}}{(n + 1)(n + 2)\cdots(2n + 1)} = \frac{(-1)^n (n!)^2 2^{2n+1}}{(2n)!(2n + 1)} \end{aligned}$$

by successive integration by parts, so that

$$h_n = \frac{2}{2n + 1}.$$

L_5 is established from the recurrence formula for general orthogonal polynomials (p. 479), since $h_n = \dfrac{2}{2n+1}$ by L_4,

$$k_n = \frac{(2n)!}{2^n(n!)^2} \quad \text{and} \quad k_n' = 0 \text{ by } L_2.$$

Hence,

$$A_n = \frac{2n+1}{n+1}, \quad B_n = 0, \quad C_n = \frac{n}{n+1}.$$

L_6 is the special case for Legendre polynomials of the general Christoffel-Darboux formula, p. 480.

L_7: Multiply L_5 throughout by t^n and sum to obtain

$$\sum_{n=0}^{\infty} (n+1)P_{n+1}(x)t^n = \sum_{n=0}^{\infty} (2n+1)xP_n(x)t^n - \sum_{n=0}^{\infty} nP_{n-1}(x)t^n,$$

defining $P_{-1}(x) = 0$. With $G(t) = \sum_{n=0}^{\infty} P_n(x)t^n$, this can be written as

$$\begin{aligned} G'(t) &= 2xt^{1/2}[t^{1/2}G(t)]' - t[tG(t)]' \\ &= 2xtG'(t) + xG(t) - t^2G'(t) - tG(t). \end{aligned}$$

Then

$$\frac{G'(t)}{G(t)} = \frac{x - t}{1 - 2xt + t^2} = -\frac{1}{2}\left(\frac{2t - 2x}{1 - 2xt + t^2}\right).$$

Integrating,

$$\text{Log } G(t) = -\tfrac{1}{2} \text{Log } (1 - 2xt + t^2),$$

the constant of integration being zero, since $G(0) = 1$. The result is now immediate.

L_8: If $|t^2 - 2xt| < 1$, we have the binomial series

$$\begin{aligned} G(t) &= (1 - 2xt + t^2)^{-1/2} = \sum_{n=0}^{\infty} \binom{-\frac{1}{2}}{n} (t^2 - 2xt)^n \\ &= \sum_{n=0}^{\infty} \frac{(2n)!}{2^{2n}(n!)^2} (2x - t)^n t^n. \end{aligned}$$

Since, by the binomial theorem,

$$(2x - t)^n = \sum_{k=0}^{n} (-1)^k \binom{n}{k} (2x)^{n-k} t^k,$$

we have

$$G(t) = \sum_{n=0}^{\infty} \sum_{k=0}^{n} \frac{(-1)^k (2n)! x^{n-k}}{2^{n+k} n!(n-k)!k!} t^{n+k}.$$

Since

$$\sum_{n=0}^{\infty} \sum_{k=0}^{n} f(k, n) = \sum_{n=0}^{\infty} \sum_{k=0}^{[\frac{1}{2}n]} f(k, n - k),$$

[see p. 497, Exercise 15(c)],

$$G(t) = \sum_{n=0}^{\infty} \sum_{k=0}^{[\frac{1}{2}n]} \frac{(-1)^k(2n-2k)!x^{n-2k}}{2^n(n-k)!(n-2k)!k!} t^n.$$

But, by L_7,

$$G(t) = \sum_{n=0}^{\infty} P_n(x)t^n$$

so that

$$P_n(x) = \frac{1}{2^n} \sum_{k=0}^{[\frac{1}{2}n]} \frac{(-1)^k(2n-2k)!}{(n-k)!(n-2k)!k!} x^{n-2k}$$

which is equivalent to the desired result.

L_9: Let $u = x^2 - 1$. Then L_2 and Leibniz's rule yield

$$\begin{aligned} P_n'(x) &= \frac{1}{2^n n!} \frac{d^{n+1}}{dx^{n+1}} u^n = \frac{1}{2^n n!} 2n \frac{d^n}{dx^n} u^{n-1} x \\ &= \frac{1}{2^{n-1}(n-1)!} \left(x \frac{d^n}{dx^n} u^{n-1} + n \frac{d^{n-1}}{dx^{n-1}} u^{n-1} \right) \\ &= xP_{n-1}' + nP_{n-1}. \end{aligned}$$

L_{10}: In L_7, let $u = 1 - 2xt + t^2$ and $G(x, t) = H(u)$. Then $\partial G/\partial x = -H'(u) \cdot 2t$ and $\partial G/\partial t = H'(u)(2t - 2x)$. Hence

$$(x - t) \frac{\partial G}{\partial t} = t \frac{\partial G}{\partial t}.$$

But

$$G(x, t) = \sum_{n=0}^{\infty} P_n(x)t^n$$

so that

$$\begin{aligned} (x - t) \frac{\partial G}{\partial x} - t \frac{\partial G}{\partial t} &= x \sum_{n=0}^{\infty} P_n'(x)t^n - \sum_{n=0}^{\infty} P_n'(x)t^{n+1} - \sum_{n=0}^{\infty} nP_n(x)t^n \\ &= x \sum_{n=0}^{\infty} P_n'(x)t^n - \sum_{n=0}^{\infty} P_{n-1}'(x)t^n - \sum_{n=0}^{\infty} nP_n(x)t^n \\ &= \sum_{n=0}^{\infty} [xP_n'(x) - P_{n-1}'(x) - nP_n(x)]t^n = 0. \end{aligned}$$

Since the coefficient of t^n is zero, we have the result.

L_{11}: Multiply L_9 throughout by x and replace $xP_n'(x)$ by the right-hand side of L_{10}.

L_{12}: Replace $n - 1$ by n in L_9 and replace $xP_n'(x)$ by the right-hand side of L_{10}.

L_{13}: Replace $n - 1$ by n in L_{11}, differentiate, and use L_{10} and L_{12} successively.

L_{14} follows immediately from L_{12}.

L_{15}: A proof occurs on p. 254, Exercise 18. We consider an alternate proof. Let

$$y_n(x) = \int_0^\pi [x + \sqrt{x^2 - 1} \cos \theta]^n \, d\theta, \qquad n = 0, 1, \cdots.$$

Then it is readily seen that $y_0(x) = P_0(x)$ and $y_1(x) = P_1(x)$. We now show that $(n + 1)y_{n+1}(x) = (2n + 1)xy_n(x) - ny_{n-1}(x)$, which indicates that $y_n(x)$ satisfies the recurrence formula L_5, and hence $y_n(x) = P_n(x)$, $n = 0, 1, \cdots$. By a straightforward calculation, we have

$$(n + 1)y_{n+1}(x) - (2n + 1)xy_n(x) + ny_{n-1}(x) = \frac{1}{\pi} \int_0^\pi wz^{n-1} \, d\theta$$

where $z = x + \sqrt{x^2 - 1} \cos \theta$ and $w = -n(x^2 - 1) \sin^2 \theta + (z - x)z$. Now

$$\frac{1}{\pi} \int_0^\pi wz^{n-1} \, d\theta = -\frac{1}{\pi} n(x^2 - 1) \int_0^\pi \sin^2 \theta z^{n-1} \, d\theta + \frac{1}{\pi} \int_0^\pi (z - x)z^n \, d\theta$$

$$= I_1 + I_2.$$

Integrating I_1 by parts yields $I_1 = -I_2$, and we have the result. For other proofs of L_{15} see p. 496, Exercises 12 and 13.

Remarks. We see from L_3 that if n is even, P_n is an even function, and hence is a polynomial with even powers of x only, while if n is odd, P_n is an odd function and has odd powers of x only.

The identities indicate a variety of ways in which specific Legendre polynomials may be obtained. From L_1 and the normalization, $P_0, P_1, \cdots$ can be obtained successively, but for large n, this is tedious. Having obtained P_0 and P_1 in this manner, P_n, $n \geq 2$, can be obtained successively by the use of the recurrence formula L_5. Or P_n, $n \geq 0$, can be obtained by using Rodrigues' formula, L_2, which also becomes tedious for large n. On the other hand, the generating function L_7 may be used by expanding the right-hand side in a power series in t and determining the coefficients of the powers of t. Since L_8 is an explicit representation of P_n, the determination of P_n, $n \geq 0$, does not require an iterative process and is probably the most advantageous to use in determining explicit polynomials, especially for large n. The Laplace integral representation can also be used to determine P_n, $n \geq 0$; however, for large n, the integration becomes difficult. We list the first six Legendre polynomials; the student should obtain them by each of the methods indicated, where feasible:

$$P_0(x) = 1.$$

$$P_1(x) = x.$$

$$P_2(x) = \tfrac{1}{2}(3x^2 - 1).$$

$$P_3(x) = \tfrac{1}{2}(5x^3 - 3x).$$

$$P_4(x) = \tfrac{1}{8}(35x^4 - 30x^2 + 3).$$

$$P_5(x) = \tfrac{1}{8}(63x^5 - 70x^3 + 15x).$$

Rodrigues' formula, the recurrence formula, the generating function, and the differential equation each characterizes the Legendre polynomials in the sense that the only polynomials p_n, such that $p_n(1) = 1$, that satisfy these equations are the Legendre polynomials. This means, for example, that the only normalized polynomial solution of the differential equation

$$(1 - x^2)y'' - 2xy' + n(n + 1)y = 0,$$

n a nonnegative integer, is $y = \mathrm{P}_n(x)$. Also, the only normalized polynomial solution of the difference equation

$$(n + 1)y_{n+1} - (2n + 1)xy_n + ny_{n-1} = 0,$$

$n \geq 2$, with $y_0 = 1$, $y_1 = x$, is $y_n = \mathrm{P}_n(x)$. This implies that the Legendre polynomials can be defined by Rodrigues' formula, or as the coefficients of the powers of t in the generating function, or as polynomial solutions of the differential equation or difference equation. This is done by various authors, and it becomes a great sport to list the remaining properties of the Legendre polynomials in such an order that they can be established as simply and elegantly as possible. The student will have an opportunity to join in this sport in the exercises.

EXAMPLE 1. Show that

$$\int_{-1}^{1} x\mathrm{P}_n(x)\mathrm{P}_{n-1}(x)\,dx = \frac{2n}{4n^2 - 1}.$$

Solution. By the recurrence formula L_5,

$$x\mathrm{P}_n(x) = \frac{(n + 1)\mathrm{P}_{n+1}(x) + n\mathrm{P}_{n-1}(x)}{2n + 1}$$

so that

$$\int_{-1}^{1} x\mathrm{P}_n(x)\mathrm{P}_{n-1}(x)\,dx = \frac{n + 1}{2n + 1}\int_{-1}^{1} \mathrm{P}_n(x)\mathrm{P}_{n+1}(x)\,dx + \frac{n}{2n + 1}\int_{-1}^{1} \mathrm{P}_{n-1}^2(x)\,dx$$

$$= 0 + \frac{n}{2n + 1} \cdot \frac{2}{2(n - 1) + 1}$$

by L_1 and L_4, and the result is immediate.

EXAMPLE 2. Show that

$$\mathrm{P}'_{2n}(x) = \sum_{k=0}^{n-1} (4k + 3)\mathrm{P}_{2k+1}(x) \quad \text{and} \quad \mathrm{P}'_{2n+1}(x) = \sum_{k=0}^{n} (4k + 1)\mathrm{P}_{2k}(x).$$

Solution. $\mathrm{P}'_{2n}(x)$ is odd and of degree $2n - 1$, and hence can be expressed as

$$\mathrm{P}'_{2n}(x) = \sum_{k=0}^{n-1} c_{2k+1}\mathrm{P}_{2k+1}(x).$$

Multiplying both sides of this equation by $\mathrm{P}_{2m+1}(x)$, $m = 0, \cdots, n - 1$, integrating from -1 to 1, and using L_1 and L_4 yields

$$c_{2m+1} = \frac{4m + 3}{2}\int_{-1}^{1} \mathrm{P}'_{2n}(x)\mathrm{P}_{2m+1}(x)\,dx.$$

Integrating by parts,

$$c_{2m+1} = \frac{4m+3}{2}\left\{\mathrm{P}_{2n}(x)\mathrm{P}_{2m+1}(x)\Big]_{-1}^{1} - \int_{-1}^{1} \mathrm{P}_{2n}(x)\mathrm{P}'_{2m+1}(x)\,dx\right\}.$$

Now,

$$\mathrm{P}'_{2m+1}(x) = \sum_{k=0}^{m} \gamma_{2k}\mathrm{P}_{2k}(x)$$

so that by L_1,

$$\int_{-1}^{1} \mathrm{P}_{2n}(x)\mathrm{P}'_{2m+1}(x)\,dx = 0,$$

since $m < n$. Hence,

$$c_{2m+1} = \frac{4m+3}{2}\,[1 - (-1)^{2n}(-1)^{2m+1}] = 4m+3$$

and we have

$$\mathrm{P}'_{2n}(x) = \sum_{k=0}^{n-1} (4k+3)\mathrm{P}_{2k+1}(x).$$

The second expression is established similarly. The student should show that these two expressions can be combined into the one expression:

$$\mathrm{P}'_n(x) = (2n-1)\mathrm{P}_{n-1}(x) + (2n-5)\mathrm{P}_{n-3}(x) + (2n-9)\mathrm{P}_{n-5}(x) + \cdots.$$

We now prove two inequalities for Legendre polynomials, which furnish certain bounds on these polynomials.

L16: $|\mathrm{P}_n(x)| \le 1$, $|x| \le 1$, with equality only for $x = \pm 1$, $n = 0, 1, 2, \cdots$.

L17: $|\mathrm{P}_n(x)| < \left[\dfrac{\pi}{2n(1-x^2)}\right]^{1/2}$, $|x| < 1$, $n = 1, 2, \cdots$.

Proofs. The integrand in the Laplace integral representation of $\mathrm{P}_n(x)$, L_{15}, is not real for $|x| < 1$, so that

$$|\mathrm{P}_n(x)| \le \frac{1}{\pi}\int_0^{\pi} |x + i\sqrt{1-x^2}\cos\theta|^n\,d\theta$$

$$= \frac{1}{\pi}\int_0^{\pi} [x^2 + (1-x^2)\cos^2\theta]^{n/2}\,d\theta$$

$$= \frac{1}{\pi}\int_0^{\pi} [1 - (1-x^2)\sin^2\theta]^{n/2}\,d\theta.$$

Now L_{16} follows from the inequality

$$\frac{1}{\pi}\int_0^{\pi} [1 - (1-x^2)\sin^2\theta]^{n/2}\,d\theta < \frac{1}{\pi}\int_0^{\pi} d\theta = 1, \qquad \theta \ne 0, \pi,$$

and the fact that $\mathrm{P}_n(\pm 1) = \pm 1$.

To establish L_{17}, we employ two elementary inequalities: (1) $\sin\theta > 2\theta/\pi$, $0 < \theta < \pi/2$ (Jordan's inequality, see p. 272), and (2) $1 - y < e^{-y}$, $y > 0$, which the student should establish. Then

$$
\begin{aligned}
|P_n(x)| &\le \int_0^\pi [1-(1-x^2)\sin^2\theta]^{n/2}\,d\theta \\
&= \frac{2}{\pi}\int_0^{\pi/2} [1-(1-x^2)\sin^2\theta]^{n/2}\,d\theta \\
&< \frac{2}{\pi}\int_0^{\pi/2}\left[1-\frac{4\theta^2(1-x^2)}{\pi^2}\right]^{n/2} d\theta \qquad \text{[by inequality (1)]} \\
&< \frac{2}{\pi}\int_0^{\pi/2} e^{-2n\theta^2(1-x^2)/\pi^2}\,d\theta \qquad \text{[by inequality (2)]} \\
&= \frac{2}{\pi}\,\frac{\pi}{[2n(1-x^2)]^{1/2}}\int_0^\infty e^{-t^2}\,dt
\end{aligned}
$$

(change in variable $t = (\theta/\pi)[2n(1-x^2)]^{1/2}$). But the integral equals $\sqrt{\pi}/2$ (p. 459, Example 2) and the result is immediate.

Since one of the primary applications of orthogonal polynomials is the representation of functions in a series of such polynomials, we now turn to this problem in the case of Legendre polynomials.

First, let us assume that the function f can be represented as

$$f(x) = \sum_{n=0}^{\infty} c_n P_n(x), \qquad -1 \le x \le 1,$$

where $c_0, c_1, \cdots$ are constants. Of course we have no assurance that this is valid for any function f; i.e., that the series will converge to $f(x)$ for any x in the given interval. But if it is valid, then we shall be able to determine an explicit representation of the coefficients c_n, $n = 0, 1, \cdots$. For if we multiply both sides of this equation by $P_m(x)$, integrate from -1 to 1, use L_1 and L_4, and replace m by n, then we have

$$c_n = \frac{2n+1}{2}\int_{-1}^{1} f(x)P_n(x)\,dx, \qquad n = 0, 1, \cdots.$$

The series

$$\sum_{n=0}^{\infty} c_n P_n(x)\,dx \quad \text{with} \quad c_n = \frac{2n+1}{2}\int_{-1}^{1} f(x)P_n(x)\,dx$$

is called the **Legendre series** of f and the c_n, $n = 0, 1, \cdots$ are called the **Legendre coefficients** of f. Sufficient conditions that the Legendre series of f converges to $f(x)$ in $-1 \le x \le 1$ will now be considered. They are similar to the conditions for Fourier series. Furthermore, the proof of the corresponding theorem is analogous to the proof of the Fourier expansion theorem.

Let $s_n(x) = \sum_{k=0}^{n} c_k P_k(x)$ be the nth partial sum of the Legendre series of f. Now using the definition of the Legendre coefficients,

$$s_n(x) = \sum_{k=0}^{n}\left[\frac{2k+1}{2}\int_{-1}^{1} f(y)\mathrm{P}_k(y)\,dy\right]\mathrm{P}_k(x)$$

$$= \frac{1}{2}\int_{-1}^{1} f(y)\sum_{k=0}^{n}(2k+1)\mathrm{P}_k(x)\mathrm{P}_k(y)\,dy$$

$$= \frac{n+1}{2}\int_{-1}^{1} f(y)\left[\frac{\mathrm{P}_{n+1}(x)\mathrm{P}_n(y) - \mathrm{P}_n(x)\mathrm{P}_{n+1}(y)}{x-y}\right]dy$$

(by the Christoffel-Darboux formula, L_6). This is an integral representation of $s_n(x)$.

In order to prove the main theorem, we need several lemmas.

Lemma 1 (Riemann-Lebesgue). If ϕ and ϕ^2 are integrable in $-1 \le y \le 1$, then

$$\lim_{n\to\infty}(n+\tfrac{1}{2})^{1/2}\int_{-1}^{1}\phi(y)\mathrm{P}_n(y)\,dy = 0.$$

Proof. Apply the Riemann-Lebesgue theorem for general orthogonal functions, p. 437, to the orthonormal sequence of polynomials

$$\{(n+\tfrac{1}{2})^{1/2}\mathrm{P}_n(x)\}.$$

Lemma 2

$$\frac{n+1}{2}\int_{-1}^{1}\frac{\mathrm{P}_{n+1}(x)\mathrm{P}_n(y) - \mathrm{P}_n(x)\mathrm{P}_{n+1}(y)}{x-y}\,dy = 1.$$

Proof. Let $f(x) = 1$ for $-1 \le x \le 1$. Then f is a constant polynomial and $s_n(x) = 1$, and the result follows from the integral representation of $s_n(x)$.

Lemma 3

$$\lim_{n\to\infty}\frac{n+1}{2}\int_{x}^{1}\frac{\mathrm{P}_{n+1}(x)\mathrm{P}_n(y) - \mathrm{P}_n(x)\mathrm{P}_{n+1}(y)}{x-y}\,dy = \frac{1}{2}.$$

Proof. Let x be any point $-1 < x < 1$. Define

$$f(y) = \begin{cases} 0, & -1 < y \le x \\ 1, & x < y < 1 \end{cases}.$$

Then

$$c_k = \frac{(2k+1)}{2}\int_{x}^{1}\mathrm{P}_k(y)\,dy = \frac{1}{2}\,[\mathrm{P}_{k-1}(x) - \mathrm{P}_{k+1}(x)],$$

by L_{14}, $k \ge 1$.

$$c_0 = \tfrac{1}{2}\int_{x}^{1}\mathrm{P}_0(x)\,dx = \tfrac{1}{2}(1-x) = \tfrac{1}{2} - \tfrac{1}{2}\mathrm{P}_1(x).$$

Now

$$s_n(x) = \tfrac{1}{2} - \tfrac{1}{2}P_1(x) - \tfrac{1}{2}\sum_{k=1}^{n}[P_{k+1}(x) - P_{k-1}(x)]P_k(x)$$
$$= \tfrac{1}{2} - \tfrac{1}{2}P_{n+1}(x)P_n(x).$$

Since $\lim_{n\to\infty} P_{n+1}(x) = \lim_{n\to\infty} P_n(x) = 0$, by L_{17}, $\lim_{n\to\infty} s_n(x) = \tfrac{1}{2}$. But

$$s_n(x) = \frac{n+1}{2}\int_x^1 \frac{P_{n+1}(x)P_n(y) - P_n(x)P_{n+1}(y)}{x - y}\,dy,$$

and hence the result.

Lemma 4

$$\lim_{n\to\infty} \frac{n+1}{2}\int_{-1}^{x} \frac{P_{n+1}(x)P_n(y) - P_n(x)P_{n+1}(y)}{x - y}\,dy = \frac{1}{2}.$$

Proof. This follows immediately from Lemmas 2 and 3.
We are now ready to prove the

LEGENDRE EXPANSION THEOREM. If f is piecewise continuous and almost differentiable in $-1 \le x \le 1$, then

$$\tfrac{1}{2}[f(x+) + f(x-)] = \sum_{n=0}^{\infty} c_n P_n(x)$$

in $-1 \le x \le 1$, where

$$c_n = \frac{2n+1}{2}\int_{-1}^{1} f(y)P_n(y)\,dy.$$

Proof. Let

$$s_n(x) = \underline{s}_n(x) + \bar{s}_n(x)$$
$$= \frac{n+1}{2}\int_{-1}^{x} f(y)\left[\frac{P_{n+1}(x)P_n(y) - P_n(x)P_{n+1}(y)}{x - y}\right]dy$$
$$+ \frac{n+1}{2}\int_{x}^{1} f(y)\left[\frac{P_{n+1}(x)P_n(y) - P_n(x)P_{n+1}(y)}{x - y}\right]dy.$$

The theorem will be proved if we can show that $\lim_{n\to\infty} \underline{s}_n(x) = \tfrac{1}{2}f(x-)$ and $\lim_{n\to\infty} \bar{s}_n(x) = \tfrac{1}{2}f(x+)$. We shall show that $\lim_{n\to\infty} \bar{s}_n(x) = \tfrac{1}{2}f(x+)$ (the other limit is established analogously), which is equivalent to showing that $\lim_{n\to\infty} [\bar{s}_n(x) - \tfrac{1}{2}f(x+)] = 0$. Now multiplying both sides of the equation in Lemma 3 by $f(x+)$ and using the preceding integral representation of $\bar{s}_n(x)$,

$$\bar{s}_n(x) - \frac{1}{2}f(x+)$$
$$= \frac{n+1}{2}\int_x^1 \frac{f(y) - f(x+)}{y - x}[P_{n+1}(y)P_n(x) - P_{n+1}(x)P_n(y)]\,dy.$$

Now define

$$\phi(y) = \begin{cases} \dfrac{f(y) - f(x+)}{y - x}, & x \le y \le 1 \\ 0, & -1 \le y < x \end{cases}.$$

Since

$$\lim_{y \to x+} \frac{f(y) - f(x+)}{y - x} = f'(x+)$$

exists, f being almost differentiable, ϕ is piecewise continuous; hence, ϕ and ϕ^2 are integrable in $-1 \le y \le 1$. Now

$$\begin{aligned} \bar{s}_n(x) - \frac{1}{2} f(x+) &= \frac{n+1}{2} \int_{-1}^{1} \phi(y)[P_{n+1}(y)P_n(x) - P_{n+1}(x)P_n(y)]\, dy \\ &= \frac{n+1}{2}\left(n + \frac{3}{2}\right)^{-(1/2)} P_n(x) \left[\left(n + \frac{3}{2}\right)^{1/2} \int_{-1}^{1} \phi(y) P_{n+1}(y)\, dy\right] \\ &\quad - \frac{n+1}{2}\left(n + \frac{1}{2}\right)^{-1/2} P_{n+1}(x) \left[\left(n + \frac{1}{2}\right)^{1/2} \int_{-1}^{1} \phi(y) P_n(y)\, dy\right]. \end{aligned}$$

Since by Lemma 1, the quantities in brackets approach zero as $n \to \infty$, it remains to show that

$$\frac{n+1}{2}\left(n + \frac{3}{2}\right)^{-1/2} P_n(x)$$

and

$$\frac{n+1}{2}\left(n + \frac{1}{2}\right)^{-1/2} P_{n+1}(x)$$

are bounded as $n \to \infty$. However, by L_{17},

$$\begin{aligned} \left|\frac{n+1}{2}\left(n + \frac{1}{2}\right)^{-1/2} P_{n+1}(x)\right| &< \left[\frac{(n+1)^2}{4(n + \frac{1}{2})} \frac{\pi}{2(n+1)(1 - x^2)}\right]^{1/2} \\ &< \left[\frac{\pi(n+1)}{4(2n+1)(1 - x^2)}\right]^{1/2} < \left[\frac{\pi}{4(1 - x^2)}\right]^{1/2}. \end{aligned}$$

which is independent of n. Similarly,

$$\left|\frac{n+1}{2}\left(n + \frac{3}{2}\right)^{-1/2} P_n(x)\right| < \left[\frac{\pi}{4(1 - x^2)}\right]^{1/2}.$$

EXAMPLE. Expand the function f, where

$$f(x) = \begin{cases} -1, & -1 \le x \le 0 \\ 1, & 0 < x \le 1 \end{cases},$$

in a Legendre series.

Solution. Since f is an odd function,

$$c_{2n} = \frac{4n+1}{2} \int_{-1}^{1} f(x) P_{2n}(x)\, dx = 0,$$

for $P_{2n}(x)$ is even. Hence,

$$f(x) = \sum_{n=0}^{\infty} c_{2n+1}P_{2n+1}(x)$$

(i.e., the Legendre series of an odd function has Legendre polynomials of odd order only; similarly, that of an even function has Legendre polynomials of even order only), where

$$\begin{aligned} c_{2n+1} &= \frac{4n+3}{2}\int_{-1}^{1} f(x)P_{2n+1}(x)\,dx \\ &= \frac{4n+3}{2}\left[-\int_{-1}^{0} P_{2n+1}(x)\,dx + \int_{0}^{1} P_{2n+1}(x)\,dx\right] \\ &= \frac{1}{2}\left[P_{2n}(0) - P_{2n+2}(0) + P_{2n}(0) - P_{2n+2}(0)\right] \end{aligned}$$

(by integrating both sides of L_{12} from -1 to 0 and letting $x = 0$ in L_{14})

$$= P_{2n}(0) - P_{2n+2}(0) = \frac{(-1)^n(2n)!}{2^{2n+1}(n+1)!n!},$$

[p. 493, Exercise 1(a)]. Hence, if we normalize f,

$$f(x) = \sum_{n=0}^{\infty} \frac{(-1)^n(2n)!}{2^{2n+1}(n+1)!n!} P_{2n+1}(x), \qquad -1 \leq x \leq 1.$$

Note that $f(0) = 0$, as we expect.

In practice, the determination of the general coefficient in the Legendre series of f by evaluating $\frac{1}{2}(2n+1)\int_{-1}^{1} f(x)P_n(x)\,dx$ may be difficult, and we content ourselves with approximating $f(x)$ by as many terms in its Legendre series as will give a desired accuracy. A few Legendre series of functions are listed in Erdélyi, et al., *Higher Transcendental Functions*, Vol. 2, p. 214.

The Legendre polynomial $P_n(z)$ of degree n for complex z can be defined by means of Rodrigues' formula (L_2):

$$P_n(z) = \frac{1}{2^n n!}\frac{d^n}{dz^n}(z^2-1)^n$$

by analytic continuation. The recurrence formula, the generating function, and the differential equation that hold for $P_n(x)$ when x is real are still valid if x is replaced by complex z. Also, we have that

$$\int_{|z|=1} P_n(z)\,\overline{P_m(z)}\,dz = 0, \qquad m \neq n.$$

In general, the sequence of complex polynomials $\{p_n(z)\}$ is said to be orthogonal on a curve C with respect to a weight function $w(z)$, $|w(z)| \geq 0$, integrable on C, if $\int_C w(z)p_n(z)\overline{p_m(z)}\,dz = 0$. Why do you suppose $\overline{p_m(z)}$ rather than $p_m(z)$ is used in this definition?

EXERCISES

◇ **1.** Show that

(a) $P_{2n+1}(0) = 0; \qquad P_{2n}(0) = \dfrac{(-1)^n}{2^{2n}}\dbinom{2n}{n}.$

(b) $P'_{2n}(0) = 0; \qquad P'_{2n+1}(0) = \dfrac{(-1)(2n+1)}{2^{2n}}\dbinom{2n}{n}.$

(c) $P'_n(1) = \dfrac{n(n+1)}{2}.$

(d) $P'_n(-1) = \dfrac{(-1)^{n+1}n(n+1)}{2}.$

(e) $P_n^{(k)}(1) = \dfrac{k!}{2^k}\dbinom{2k}{k}\dbinom{n+k}{n-k}.$

2. Show that

(a) $\dfrac{1-x^2}{n^2}\{[P'_n(x)]^2 - [P'_{n-1}(x)]^2\} = P^2_{n-1}(x) - P^2_n(x).$

(b) $(1-x)[P'_n(x) + P'_{n+1}(x)] = (n+1)[P_n(x) - P_{n+1}(x)].$
(c) $(2n+1)(1-x^2)P'_n(x) = n(n+1)[P_{n-1}(x) - P_{n+1}(x)].$
(d) $(n+1)[(2n+3)P^2_{n+1}(x) - (2n+1)P^2_n(x)]$

$$= \frac{d}{dx}[(1-x^2)(P_n(x)P'_n(x) - P_{n+1}(x)P'_n(x))].$$

(e) $\dfrac{d}{dx}[(1-x^2)P_n(x)P'_n(x)] = (1-x^2)[P'_n(x)]^2 - n(n+1)P^2_n(x).$

3. Graph the Legendre polynomials P_0, P_1, P_2, P_3, P_4 on one coordinate system.

(a) What is the sign of $P_n(x)$, $n = 0, 1, 2, 3, 4$, for $x > 1$? $x < -1$?

(b) Where are the zeros of $P_3(x)$ located with reference to the zeros of $P_2(x)$ and $P_4(x)$?

(c) If $\mu_{r,n}$ is the rth relative maximum of $|P_n(x)|$, is it true that $\mu_{1,4} < \mu_{2,4} < \mu_{3,4}$? $\mu_{1,2} < \mu_{1,3} < \mu_{1,4}$?

4. Show that

(a) $xP'_n(x) = nP_n(x) + (2n-3)P_{n-2}(x) + (2n-7)P_{n-4}(x) + \cdots.$

(b) $\displaystyle\sum_{k=0}^{n}(2k+1)P_k(x) = P'_{n+1}(x) + P'_n(x).$

(c) $(1-x^2)P''_n(x) = -n(n-1)P_n(x) + 2(2n-3)P_{n-2}(x)$
$\qquad\qquad + 2(2n-7)P_{n-4}(x) + \cdots.$

(d) $(1-x)\displaystyle\sum_{k=0}^{n}(2k+1)P_k(x) = (n+1)[P_n(x) - P_{n+1}(x)].$

5. Given the differential equation $(1-x^2)y'' - 2xy' + \lambda(\lambda+1)y = 0$.

(a) Show that by assuming a solution of the form $y = \sum_{k=0}^{\infty} a_k x^k$ that the differential equation has a polynomial solution only if $\lambda = n$, $n = 0, 1, \cdots$, and that this solution is of the form $c_nP_n(x)$, where c_n is an arbitrary constant.

(b) Define P_n as the polynomial solution of the differential equation such that $P_n(1) = 1$. Establish L_1, L_2, L_4, L_5, L_7, L_9, L_{10}, L_{11}, L_{13}, in the order that is most feasible.

Hint: To prove L_1, write the differential equation in the form

$$\frac{d}{dx}[(1 - x^2)P_n'(x)] + n(n + 1)P_n(x) = 0$$

and a second equation replacing n by m. Multiply the first equation by $P_m(x)$ and the second by $P_n(x)$. Subtract the second equation from the first and integrate both sides from -1 to 1.

◇ **6.** (a) Show that if $W_{n-1}(x) = \sum_{k=1}^{n} \frac{1}{k} P_{k-1}(x)P_{n-k}(x)$, $n = 1, 2, \cdots$, and $W_{-1}(x) = 0$, then

$$(1 - x^2)W_{n-1}''(x) - 2xW_{n-1}'(x) + n(n + 1)W_{n-1}(x) = 2P_n'(x).$$

(b) Show that

$$Q_n(x) = \frac{1}{2} P_n(x) \operatorname{Log} \frac{1 + x}{1 - x} - W_{n-1}(x), \qquad n = 0, 1, \cdots$$

is a solution of Legendre's differential equation in Exercise 5, and that $P_n(x)$ and $Q_n(x)$ are linearly independent. Q_n is called the **Legendre function of the second kind.**

(c) Show that if $P_n(x)$ is replaced by $Q_n(x)$ in L_5, L_6, L_9, L_{10}, L_{11}, L_{12}, the identities remain valid.

7. (a) Define the Legendre polynomials by Rodrigues' formula and establish the remaining identities on p. 481 in the order that is most feasible.

(b) Define the Legendre polynomials by means of the recurrence formula for $n \geq 2$, $P_0(x) = 1$, $P_1(x) = x$ and establish the remaining identities on p. 481 in the order that is most feasible.

(c) Define the Legendre polynomials as the coefficients in the power series expansion of $(1 - 2xt + t^2)^{-1/2}$ and establish the remaining identities on p. 481 in the order that is most feasible.

8. Show that

(a) $$\int_{-1}^{1} (x^2 - 1)P_{n+1}(x)P_n'(x)\,dx = \frac{2n(n + 1)}{(2n + 1)(2n + 3)}.$$

(b) $$\int_{-1}^{1} (1 - x^2)[P_n'(x)]^2\,dx = \frac{2n(n + 1)}{2n + 1}.$$

(c) $$\int_{0}^{1} x^2P_{n+1}(x)P_{n-1}(x)\,dx = \frac{n(n + 1)}{(2n - 1)(2n + 1)(2n + 3)}.$$

(d) $$\int_{-1}^{1} (1 - x^2)P_n'(x)P_m'(x)\,dx = 0, \qquad n \neq m.$$

What does this imply about the sequence $\{P_n'\}$?

(e) $$\int_{-1}^{1} x^2P_n^2(x)\,dx = \frac{1}{8(2n - 1)} + \frac{3}{4(2n + 1)} + \frac{1}{8(2n + 3)}.$$

(f) $\int_{-1}^{1} (1 - x)^{-1/2} P_n(x)\, dx = \frac{2\sqrt{2}}{2n + 1}.$

(*Hint:* Let $t \to 1$ in the generating function.)

(g) $\int_{-1}^{1} P_n(x) P'_m(x)\, dx = \begin{cases} 0, & m \leq n \\ 0, & m > n,\ m + n \text{ even.} \\ 2, & m > n,\ m + n \text{ odd} \end{cases}$

(*Hint:* Use theorem on p. 478 for $m \leq n$ and integration by parts for $m > n$.)

(h) $\int_{-1}^{1} P'_n(x) P'_m(x)\, dx = \begin{cases} 0, & n + m \text{ even} \\ m(m + 1), & n + m \text{ odd}, \end{cases} \quad m \leq n.$

(i) $\int_{0}^{1} x^k P_n(x)\, dx = \frac{k(k - 1) \cdots (k - n + 2)}{(k + n + 1)(k + n - 1) \cdots (k - n + 3)}, \quad k > n - 1.$

(j) $\int_{0}^{\pi} P_{2n}(\cos \theta)\, d\theta = \frac{\pi}{2^{2n}} \binom{2n}{n}.$

(k) $\int_{0}^{2\pi} P_{2n}(\cos \theta)\, d\theta = 2\pi \left[\frac{1}{2^{2n}} \binom{2n}{n} \right]^2.$

(l) $\int_{0}^{2\pi} P_{2n}(\cos \theta) \cos \theta\, d\theta = \frac{1}{2^{4n+1}} \binom{2n}{n} \binom{2n + 2}{n + 1}.$

(m) $\int (1 - x^2)[P'_n(x)]^2\, dx = n(n + 1) \int P_n^2(x)\, dx.$

(n) $\int_{-1}^{1} f(x) P_n(x)\, dx = \frac{(-1)^n}{2^n n!} \int_{-1}^{1} (x^2 - 1)^n \frac{d^n f(x)}{dx^n}\, dx.$

Why may this be useful?

(o) $\int_{0}^{\pi} P_n(\cos \theta) \cos n\theta\, d\theta = B(n + \tfrac{1}{2}, \tfrac{1}{2}).$

(p) $\int_{-1}^{1} (1 - 2xt + t^2)^{-1/2} P_n(x)\, dx = \frac{2t^n}{2n + 1}, \quad |t| < 1.$

(q) $\int_{0}^{1} P_n(x^2)\, dx = \frac{(-1)^{[n/2]}}{2n + 1}.$

9. Expand in Legendre series:

(a) $f(x) = |x|, \ -1 < x < 1.$

(b) $f(x) = \begin{cases} 0, & -1 < x < 0 \\ 1, & 0 < x < 1 \end{cases}, \quad f(0) = \tfrac{1}{2}.$

(c) $f(x) = \begin{cases} 0, & -1 < x \leq 0 \\ x, & 0 < x < 1 \end{cases}.$

(d) $f(x) = x, \ 0 \leq x < 1$ in Legendre polynomials of even degree and also in Legendre polynomials of odd degree.

(e) $f(x) = \begin{cases} x + a, & -a < x \leq 0 \\ x - a, & 0 < x < a \end{cases}.$

Hint: Show that the Legendre series of f in $-a < x < a$ is

$$\sum_{n=0}^{\infty} c_n P_n\left(\frac{x}{a}\right), \quad c_n = \left(n + \frac{1}{2}\right) a \int_{-a}^{a} f(x) P_n\left(\frac{x}{a}\right) dx.$$

10. (a) If $f(x) = \sum_{n=0}^{\infty} c_n P_n(x)$, show that

$$\int_1^x f(t)\, dt = -c_0 - \frac{1}{3} c_1 + \sum_{n=0}^{\infty} \left(\frac{c_{n-1}}{2n-1} - \frac{c_{n+1}}{2n+3}\right) P_n(x).$$

(b) Show that

$$\sin^{-1} x = \frac{\pi}{2} \sum_{n=0}^{\infty} \left[\frac{1}{2^{2n}} \binom{2n}{n}\right]^2 [P_{2n+1}(x) - P_{2n-1}(x)].$$

11. Show that

$$(1 - x)^n P_n\left(\frac{1+x}{1-x}\right) = \sum_{k=0}^{n} \binom{n}{k}^2 x^k.$$

(*Hint:* Use Rodrigues' formula and Leibniz's rule.)

12. (a) Show that

$$\int_0^{\pi} \frac{d\theta}{1 + \lambda \cos\theta} = \frac{\pi}{\sqrt{1 - \lambda^2}}, \qquad |\lambda| < 1,\ \lambda \text{ complex}.$$

Hint: Write

$$\cos\theta = \frac{e^{i\theta} + e^{-i\theta}}{2}$$

and show that

$$\frac{1}{1 + \lambda\cos\theta} = \frac{1}{\sqrt{1 - \lambda^2}} \left[1 + 2 \sum_{n=1}^{\infty} \lambda^n \cos n\theta\right] = \frac{-1 + \sqrt{1 - \lambda^2}}{\lambda}.$$

Integrate term by term.

(b) In (a) let

$$\lambda = \frac{-t\sqrt{x^2 - 1}}{1 - tx},$$

expand both sides in powers of t, and thus establish Laplace's integral formula for $P_n(x)$, L_{15}.

13. (a) Show that

$$P_n(x) = n! \sum_{k=0}^{[\frac{1}{2}n]} \frac{(x^2 - 1)^k x^{n-2k}}{2^{2k}(k!)^2(n - 2k)!}.$$

Hint: Write

$$(1 - 2xt + t^2)^{-(1/2)} = (1 - xt)^{-1} \left[1 - \frac{t^2(x^2 - 1)}{(1 - xt)^2}\right]^{-(1/2)},$$

expand in powers of t; the coefficient of t^n is $P_n(x)$.

(b) Show that

$$\frac{1}{2^{2k}(k!)^2} = \frac{1}{(2k)!\,\pi} B\left(\frac{1}{2}, \frac{1}{2} + k\right) = \frac{1}{(2k)!\,\pi} \int_0^{\pi} \cos^{2k}\theta\, d\theta$$

and thus use (a) to establish Laplace's integral formula, L_{15}.

14. Show that
(a) $P_n(x) < P_{n+1}(x), \quad x > 1, n = 0, 1, \cdots.$
(b) $P_0(x) + P_1(x) + \cdots + P_n(x) > 0, \quad x > -1.$

(c) $|P_n'(x)| \leq \dfrac{n(n+1)}{2}.$

(d) $[P_n(\cos\theta)]^2 > \dfrac{\sin(2n+1)\theta}{(2n+1)\sin\theta}, \quad 0 < \theta < \pi.$

(e) $|P_n(x)| \leq |2x|^n, \quad |x| \geq 1.$

(f) $|P_n'(x)| \leq \dfrac{n}{\sqrt{1-x^2}}, \quad |x| < 1.$

(g) $\left|\int_a^b P_n(x)\,dx\right| \leq \dfrac{2}{n+1}, \quad -1 \leq a \leq b \leq 1.$

[*Hint:* for (f) and (g), use Exercise 2(a).]

◇ **15.** (a) Show that

$$\sum_{n=0}^{\infty}\sum_{k=0}^{\infty} g(k, n) = \sum_{n=0}^{\infty}\sum_{k=0}^{n} g(k, n-k).$$

(*Hint:* Collect powers of t in $\sum_{n=0}^{\infty}\sum_{k=0}^{\infty} g(k, n)t^{n+k}$ by letting $k = j$, $n = m - j$, so that $m - j \geq 0$ and $j \geq 0$, or $0 \leq j \leq m$; then let $t = 1$, $j = k$, $m = n$.)

(b) Show that $\sum_{n=0}^{\infty}\sum_{k=0}^{\infty} h(k, n) = \sum_{n=0}^{\infty}\sum_{k=0}^{[1/2n]} h(k, n-2k)$.
(c) Use (a) and (b) to show that

$$\sum_{n=0}^{\infty}\sum_{k=0}^{n} f(k, n) = \sum_{n=0}^{\infty}\sum_{k=0}^{[\frac{1}{2}n]} f(k, n-k).$$

16. (a) Show that

$$\sum_{n=0}^{\infty} [xP_n'(x) - nP_n(x)]t^n = t^2(1 - 2xt + t^2)^{-3/2}.$$

(b) Show that

$$\sum_{n=0}^{\infty}\sum_{k=0}^{[\frac{1}{2}n]} (2n - 4k + 1)P_{n-2k}(x)t^n = (1 - 2xt + t^2)^{-3/2}.$$

(c) Use (a) and (b) to show that

$$xP_n'(x) - nP_n(x) = \sum_{k=0}^{[(n-2)/2]} (2n - 4k - 3)P_{n-2-2k}(x).$$

17. The **Legendre transform** of $f(x)$ is defined as

$$L[f(x)] = \int_{-1}^{1} f(x)P_n(x)\,dx = F(n).$$

(a) Show that $L^{-1}[F(n)] = \frac{1}{2}\sum_{n=0}^{\infty} (2n+1)F(n)P_n(x)$.

(b) Show that $L\left[\dfrac{d}{dx}\{(1 - x^2)f'(x)\}\right] = -n(n+1)F(n).$

18. (a) In the Christoffel-Darboux formula, p. 480, let $y \to x$ to obtain

$$\sum_{j=0}^{n} \frac{p_j^2(x)}{h_j} = \frac{k_n}{k_{n+1}h_n} [p_n(x)p'_{n+1}(x) - p_{n+1}(x)p'_n(x)].$$

(b) Show that

$$p_n(x)p'_{n+1}(x) - p_{n+1}(x)p'_n(x) > 0.$$

(c) Show that $p_n(x)$ and $p_{n+1}(x)$ cannot have a common zero.

(d) Let $x_1 < x_2 < \cdots < x_n$ be the zeros of $p_n(x)$, $x_0 = a$, $x_{n+1} = b$. Show that each interval (x_k, x_{k+1}), $k = 0, 1, \cdots$, contains exactly one zero of $p_{n+1}(x)$.

(e) Establish the partial fraction decomposition

$$\frac{p_n(x)}{p_{n+1}(x)} = \sum_{k=0}^{n} \frac{l_k}{x - x_k},$$

where

$$l_k = \frac{p_n(x_k)}{p'_{n+1}(x_k)} \quad \text{and} \quad x_k,\ k = 0, 1, \cdots, n$$

denote the zeros of $p_{n+1}(x)$. Show that $l_k > 0$.

(f) Prove the **Gauss-Jacobi quadrature formula:**

$$\int_a^b \rho(x)w(x)\,dx = \sum_{k=1}^{n} \lambda_k \rho(x_k),$$

where x_k, $k = 1, 2, \cdots, n$ are the zeros of $p_n(x)$, $\{p_n\}$ a sequence of orthogonal polynomials in $[a, b]$ with weight function w,

$$\lambda_k = \int_a^b \frac{p_n(x)w(x)\,dx}{p'_n(x_k)(x - x_k)} \quad \text{(called the } \textit{weights}\text{)},$$

$\rho(x)$ is a polynomial of degree $\leq 2n - 1$.

Hint: Define the polynomials

$$l_k(x) = \frac{p_n(x)}{(x - x_k)p'_n(x_k)}, \quad k = 1, 2, \cdots, n.$$

Show that $l_k(x_m) = \delta_{km}$, $k, m = 0, 1, \cdots, n$, and if $L_{n-1}(x) = \sum_{k=1}^{n} l_k(x)\rho(x_k)$, then $L_{n-1}(x_k) = \rho(x_k)$, $k = 1, 2, \cdots, n$. $L_{n-1}(x) - \rho(x)$ is of degree $\leq 2n - 1$ and the zeros of $p_n(x)$ are among its zeros. Hence, there exists a polynomial $r(x)$ of degree $\leq n - 1$ such that $\rho(x) - L_{n-1}(x) = p_n(x)r(x)$. Then

$$\int_a^b \rho(x)w(x)\,dx = \int_a^b L_{n-1}(x)w(x)\,dx + \int_a^b p_n(x)r(x)w(x)\,dx$$
$$= \int_a^b L_{n-1}(x)w(x)\,dx.$$

19. Prove that if the weight function w of the sequence of orthogonal polynomials $\{p_n\}$ is even in $-a \leq x \leq a$, then

$$p_n(-x) = (-1)^n p_n(x).$$

Hint:

$$\int_{-a}^{a} p_n(x)x^k w(x)\,dx = (-1)^k \int_{-a}^{a} p_n(x)x^k w(x)\,dx = 0, \qquad k = 0, 1, \cdots, n - 1.$$

$\{p_n(-x)\}$ is orthogonal with respect to $w(x)$ in $-a \leq x \leq a$. Then $p_n(-x) = c_n p_n(x)$, c_n constant. But $c_n = (-1)^n$.

20. Let $\{M_n\}$ be the sequence of orthogonal polynomials determined by the weight function $w(x) = |x|$ in $-1 \le x \le 1$, with the normalization $M_n(1) = 1$. Determine the recurrence formula for $\{M_n\}$. Determine M_0, M_1, M_2, M_3.

21. If $\{p_n\}$ is a sequence of orthogonal polynomials, show that

$$p_n(x) = K \begin{vmatrix} c_0 & c_1 & \cdots & c_n \\ c_1 & c_2 & \cdots & c_{n-1} \\ \cdots & \cdots & \cdots & \cdots \\ c_{n-1} & c_n & \cdots & c_{2n-1} \\ 1 & x & \cdots & x^n \end{vmatrix}$$

where $c_k = \int_a^b w(x)x^k\,dx$, $k = 0, 1, \cdots, 2n - 1$ and K is a constant. Evaluate K if $\{p_n\}$ are orthonormal.

22. Prove that if w is an infinitely differentiable function, $w(x) \ge 0$, in $a \le x \le b$, and $\{G_n\}$ is a sequence of functions such that

$$\frac{d^{n+1}}{dx^{n+1}}\left[\frac{1}{w(x)}\frac{d^nG_n(x)}{dx^n}\right] = 0$$

and

$$G_n(a) = G_n'(a) = \cdots = G_n^{(n-1)}(a) = 0,$$

$$G_n(b) = G_n'(b) = \cdots = G_n^{(n-1)}(b) = 0,$$

then

$$p_n(x) = \frac{1}{w(x)}\frac{d^nG_n(x)}{dx^n}, \qquad n = 0, 1, \cdots$$

is the sequence of orthogonal polynomials with respect to w in $a \le x \le b$. This is the generalized Rodrigues' formula.

23. Given the sequence of orthonormal polynomials $\{p_n\}$ with respect to the weight function w in $a \le x \le b$. Let $s_n(x) = \sum_{k=0}^n c_kp_n(x)$, where

$$c_k = \int_a^b w(x)p_n(x)f(x)\,dx.$$

Show that a necessary and sufficient condition that $\lim_{n\to\infty} [s_n(x) - f(x)] = 0$ is

$$\lim_{n\to\infty} \frac{k_n}{k_{n+1}} \int_a^b [f(y) - f(x)]\,\frac{p_n(y)p_{n+1}(x) - p_n(x)p_{n+1}(y)}{x - y}\,w(x)\,dy.$$

It can be shown that if ξ is the largest zero of $p_{n-1}(x)$, then $k_n/k_{n+1} < \xi$. Improve the foregoing condition for polynomials orthonormal in a finite interval.

24. Prove:

(a) $$\int_{-1}^1 P_n(x)x^{n+2k}\,dx = \frac{1}{2^n}\frac{(n+2k)!}{(2k)!}\frac{\Gamma(k+\frac{1}{2})}{\Gamma(n+k+\frac{3}{2})}, \qquad k = 0, 1, 2, \cdots.$$

(b) $$\sum_{k=0}^n \binom{n}{k} P_k(x)t^{n-k} = (1 + 2xt + t^2)^{n/2}P_n\{(1 + 2xt + t^2)^{-1/2}(x + t)\}.$$

25. (a) Prove that the zeros of the polynomial in t,

$$P_0(x) + \binom{n}{1}P_1(x)t + \binom{n}{2}P_2(x)t^2 + \cdots + P_n(x)t^n, \qquad -1 < x < 1,$$

are real. [*Hint:* Use Exercise 24(b).]

(b) If $t_1, t_2, \cdots, t_n$ are real, show that

$$\left(\frac{t_1 + t_2 + \cdots + t_n}{n}\right)^2 \geq \frac{t_1t_2 + t_1t_3 + \cdots}{\binom{n}{2}}$$

(c) Let $t_1, t_2, \cdots, t_n$ be the zeros of the polynomial in (a). Use (b) to establish **Turán's inequality:**

$$\mathrm{P}_{n-1}^2(x) - \mathrm{P}_n(x)\mathrm{P}_{n-2}(x) \geq 0, \qquad -1 \leq x \leq 1.$$

When does the equality sign hold?

26. Show that the recurrence relation for general orthogonal polynomials can be written in the form

$$xp_n(x) = c_{n,n+1}p_{n+1}(x) + c_{nn}p_n(x) + c_{n,n-1}p_{n-1}(x),$$

where

$$c_{nk} = \int_a^b xw(x)p_n(x)p_k(x)\,dx.$$

3. Jacobi polynomials. The Legendre polynomials are a special case of the orthogonal polynomials with weight function $(1 - x)^\alpha(1 + x)^\beta$, $\alpha > -1$, $\beta > -1$, in the interval $-1 \leq x \leq 1$, denoted by $\mathrm{P}_n^{(\alpha,\beta)}(x)$, $n = 0, 1, \cdots$, and having the normalization $\mathrm{P}_n^{(\alpha,\beta)}(1) = \binom{n+\alpha}{n}$. These polynomials are called the **Jacobi polynomials** and reduce to the Legendre polynomials when $\alpha = \beta = 0$. α and β are called the parameters of $\mathrm{P}_n^{(\alpha,\beta)}(x)$ and are restricted by the conditions $\alpha > -1$ and $\beta > -1$ in order that the weight function be nonnegative and integrable in $-1 \leq x \leq 1$.

Many of the properties of Legendre polynomials are preserved when we generalize them to Jacobi polynomials. In particular, the Jacobi polynomials also satisfy a second-order linear differential equation. We list some of these properties:

J₁: $$\int_{-1}^1 (1 - x)^\alpha(1 + x)^\beta \mathrm{P}_n^{(\alpha,\beta)}(x)\mathrm{P}_m^{(\alpha,\beta)}(x)\,dx = 0,$$
$$m \neq n,\ m, n = 0, 1, \cdots.$$

J₂: $$\mathrm{P}_n^{(\alpha,\beta)}(x) = \frac{(-1)^n}{2^n n!}(1 - x)^{-\alpha}(1 + x)^{-\beta}\frac{d^n}{dx^n}[(1 - x)^{\alpha+n}(1 + x)^{\beta+n}].$$

(Rodrigues' formula.)

J₃: $$\mathrm{P}_n^{(\alpha,\beta)}(-x) = (-1)^n\mathrm{P}_n^{(\beta,\alpha)}(x).$$

J₄: $$\int_{-1}^1 (1 - x)^\alpha(1 + x)^\beta[\mathrm{P}_n^{(\alpha,\beta)}(x)]^2\,dx = \frac{2^{\alpha+\beta+1}\Gamma(n + \alpha + 1)\Gamma(n + \beta + 1)}{(2n + \alpha + \beta + 1)n!\Gamma(n + \alpha + \beta + 1)}.$$

J₅: $$\begin{aligned} 2(n + 1)(n + \alpha + \beta + 1)(2n + \alpha + \beta)\mathrm{P}_{n+1}^{(\alpha,\beta)}(x) &= (2n + \alpha + \beta + 1)[(2n + \alpha + \beta)(2n + \alpha + \beta + 2)x \\ &+ \alpha^2 - \beta^2]\mathrm{P}_n^{(\alpha,\beta)}(x) - 2(n + \alpha)(n + \beta)(2n + \alpha + \beta + 2)\mathrm{P}_{n-1}^{(\alpha,\beta)}(x). \end{aligned}$$

(Recurrence formula.)

$\mathbf{J_6}$: $\sum_{n=0}^{\infty} P_n^{(\alpha,\beta)}(x)t^n = 2^{\alpha+\beta}R^{-1}(1 - t + R)^{-\alpha}(1 + t + R)^{-\beta},$

$$|t| < 1,\ |x| \leq 1,\ R = (1 - 2xt + t^2)^{1/2}.$$

(Generating function.)

$\mathbf{J_7}$: $P_n^{(\alpha,\beta)}(x) = \sum_{k=0}^{n} \binom{n+\alpha}{n-k}\binom{n+\beta}{k}\left(\frac{x-1}{2}\right)^k\left(\frac{x+1}{2}\right)^{n-k}.$

$\mathbf{J_8}$: $(2n + \alpha + \beta)(1 - x^2)\dfrac{d}{dx}P_n^{(\alpha,\beta)}(x)$

$$= n[\alpha - \beta - (2n + \alpha + \beta)x]P_n^{(\alpha,\beta)}(x) + 2(n + \alpha)(n + \beta)P_{n-1}^{(\alpha,\beta)}(x).$$

$\mathbf{J_9}$: $(1 - x^2)\dfrac{d^2}{dx^2}P_n^{(\alpha,\beta)}(x) + [\beta - \alpha - (\alpha + \beta + 2)x]\dfrac{d}{dx}P_n^{(\alpha,\beta)}(x)$

$$+ n(n + \alpha + \beta + 1)P_n^{(\alpha,\beta)}(x) = 0.$$

(Differential equation.)

These properties can be established in essentially the same way as the corresponding properties of Legendre polynomials. We also state the

JACOBI EXPANSION THEOREM. If f is piecewise continuous and almost differentiable in $-1 \leq x \leq 1$, then

$$\frac{f(x+) + f(x-)}{2} = \sum_{n=0}^{\infty} c_n P_n^{(\alpha,\beta)}(x),$$

where $c_n = \binom{n+\alpha}{n}^{-1} \int_{-1}^{1} (1 - y)^{\alpha}(1 + y)^{\beta} f(y) P_n^{(\alpha,\beta)}(y)\, dy.$

J_3 indicates that $P_n^{(\alpha,\beta)}(-x) = (-1)^n P_n^{(\alpha,\beta)}(x)$ if and only if $\alpha = \beta$. We say in this case that the polynomials are symmetric (see p. 498, Exercise 19). The Legendre polynomials are symmetric, but this property is in general not preserved when we generalize these polynomials to Jacobi polynomials.

4. Ultraspherical polynomials. The generating function for Legendre polynomials, L_7, suggests another possibility for generalizing these polynomials. If we replace the constant $\frac{1}{2}$ by the parameter λ (mathematicians abhor numerical constants) and expand $(1 - 2xt + t^2)^{-\lambda}$ in a power series in t, then it can be shown that if $\lambda > -\frac{1}{2}$, the coefficient of t^n is a polynomial in x of degree n containing the parameter λ. We call this polynomial the **ultraspherical polynomial** of degree n and order λ (also called a **Gegenbauer** polynomial) and denote it by $P_n^{(\lambda)}(x)$. Hence, we have

$\mathbf{U_1}$: $\sum_{n=0}^{\infty} P_n^{(\lambda)}(x)t^n = (1 - 2xt + t^2)^{-\lambda}, \qquad |t| < 1,\ |x| \leq 1,\ \lambda > -\frac{1}{2}.$

Now the question arises as to whether the orthogonality property of the Legendre polynomials is preserved when we generalize them to ultraspherical polynomials. We shall show that the sequence $\{P_n^{(\lambda)}\}$ is orthogonal with respect to $(1 - x^2)^{\lambda - 1/2}$, $\lambda > -\frac{1}{2}$, in $-1 \leq x \leq 1$. First,

$$\mathbf{U_2:}\quad P_n^{(\lambda)}(x) = \sum_{k=0}^{[\frac{1}{2}n]} \frac{(-1)^k \Gamma(n-k+\lambda)}{\Gamma(\lambda)k!(n-2k)!}(2x)^{n-2k},$$

which is a generalization of L_8 for Legendre polynomials, can be established by the same technique used for L_8. Multiplying both sides of this equation by $(1 - x^2)^{\lambda-1/2}x^p$, $p = 0, 1, \cdots, n - 1$, and integrating from -1 to 1 will yield

$$\int_{-1}^{1} (1 - x^2)^{\lambda-1/2} P_n^{(\lambda)}(x) x^p\, dx = 0, \qquad p = 0, 1, \cdots, n-1,$$

since as can be shown by successive integration by parts,

$$\int_{-1}^{1} x^{n-2k+p}(1 - x^2)^{\lambda-1/2}\, dx = 0.$$

Hence,

$$\mathbf{U_3:}\quad \int_{-1}^{1} (1 - x^2)^{\lambda-1/2} P_n^{(\lambda)}(x) P_m^{(\lambda)}(x)\, dx = 0, \qquad m \neq n,\ m, n = 0, 1, \cdots.$$

But $(1 - x^2)^{\lambda-1/2}$ is the special case of the weight function $(1 - x)^\alpha(1 + x)^\beta$ for Jacobi polynomials in $-1 \leq x \leq 1$, with $\alpha = \beta = \lambda - \frac{1}{2}$. Hence,

$$P_n^{(\lambda)}(x) = c_n P_n^{(\alpha,\alpha)}(x),$$

where c_n, $n = 0, 1, \cdots$ is constant. To determine c_n, we let $x = 1$, so that

$$P_n^{(\lambda)}(1) = c_n P_n^{(\alpha,\alpha)}(1).$$

Now,

$$P_n^{(\alpha,\alpha)}(1) = \binom{n+\alpha}{n} \qquad \text{while} \qquad P_n^{(\lambda)}(1) = \binom{n+2\lambda-1}{n},$$

which can be established readily from the definition of $P_n^{(\lambda)}(x)$ in U_1.

Hence, we can write

$$\begin{aligned} P_n^{(\lambda)}(x) &= \frac{\Gamma(\alpha+1)\Gamma(n+2\alpha+1)}{\Gamma(2\alpha+1)\Gamma(n+\alpha+1)} P_n^{(\alpha,\alpha)}(x) \\ &= \frac{\Gamma(\lambda+\frac{1}{2})\Gamma(n+2\lambda)}{\Gamma(2\lambda)\Gamma(n+\lambda+\frac{1}{2})} P_n^{(\lambda-1/2,\lambda-1/2)}(x). \end{aligned}$$

From this we see that every symmetric Jacobi polynomial can be expressed as a constant times an ultraspherical polynomial. We list further properties of the ultraspherical polynomials, which can be obtained from the corresponding properties of Jacobi polynomials, using the above expressions.

$\mathbf{U_4:}$ $(n+1)P_{n+1}^{(\lambda)}(x) = 2(n+\lambda)xP_n^{(\lambda)}(x) - (n+2\lambda-1)P_{n-1}^{(\lambda)}(x)$.
(Recurrence formula.)

$\mathbf{U_5:}$ $(1 - x^2)\dfrac{d^2}{dx^2}P_n^{(\lambda)}(x) - (2\lambda+1)x\dfrac{d}{dx}P_n^{(\lambda)}(x) + n(n+2\lambda)P_n^{(\lambda)}(x) = 0.$
(Differential equation.)

$$\mathbf{U_6}: \quad nP_n^{(\lambda)}(x) = x\frac{d}{dx}P_n^{(\lambda)}(x) - \frac{d}{dx}P_{n-1}^{(\lambda)}(x).$$

$$\mathbf{U_7}: \quad (n+2\lambda)P_n^{(\lambda)}(x) = \frac{d}{dx}P_{n+1}^{(\lambda)}(x) - x\frac{d}{dx}P_n^{(\lambda)}(x).$$

$$\mathbf{U_8}: \quad \frac{d}{dx}[P_{n+1}^{(\lambda)}(x) - P_{n-1}^{(\lambda)}(x)] = 2(n+\lambda)P_n^{(\lambda)}(x).$$

$$\mathbf{U_9}: \quad \int_{-1}^{1}(1-x^2)^{\lambda-(1/2)}[P_n^{(\lambda)}(x)]^2\,dx = 2^{1-2\lambda}\pi[\Gamma(\lambda)]^{-2}\frac{\Gamma(n+2\lambda)}{(n+\lambda)\Gamma(n+1)}.$$

5. Tchebichef polynomials. The ultraspherical polynomials become the Legendre polynomials when $\lambda = \frac{1}{2}$. Two other special cases of frequent occurrence are

(1) **Tchebichef† polynomials of the first kind:**

$$T_n(x) = \frac{n}{2}\lim_{\lambda\to 0}\frac{P_n^{(\lambda)}(x)}{\lambda}, \qquad n \geq 1,\ T_0(x) = 1.$$

(2) **Tchebichef polynomials of the second kind:**

$$U_n(x) = P_n^{(1)}(x).$$

Note that the definition of $P_n^{(\lambda)}(x)$ indicates that $P_n^{(0)}(x) = 0$, $n \geq 1$, and hence we cannot define $T_n(x)$ as $P_n^{(0)}(x)$, as some authors carelessly do. The Tchebichef polynomials have the distinction of being the simplest polynomials orthogonal in $-1 \leq x \leq 1$. The orthogonality condition for $\{T_n\}$ indicates that

$$\int_{-1}^{1}(1-x^2)^{-1/2}T_n(x)T_m(x)\,dx = 0, \qquad n \neq m.$$

If we let $x = \cos\theta$ (why is this possible?), this becomes

$$\int_0^{\pi} T_n(\cos\theta)T_m(\cos\theta)\,d\theta = 0.$$

This means that $\{T_n(\cos\theta)\}$ is a sequence of orthogonal polynomials in $\cos\theta$, with weight function 1 in $0 \leq \theta \leq \pi$. But since $\int_0^{\pi}\cos n\theta\cos m\theta\,d\theta = 0$ and $\cos n\theta$ is a polynomial of degree n in $\cos\theta$ (show this with the use of De Moivre's theorem and the binomial theorem), $T_n(\cos\theta) = c_n\cos n\theta$, where c_n is constant, $n = 0, 1, \cdots$. Since $T_n(1) = 1$ (for $\theta = 0$), $c_n = 1$. Hence,

$$T_n(x) = \cos n\theta = \cos n(\cos^{-1}x).$$

Similarly,

$$U_n(x) = \frac{\sin[(n+1)\cos^{-1}x]}{\sqrt{1-x^2}}.$$

† Spellings vary with different authors; however, the initial letter is always T or C.

Hence, the properties of the sine and cosine functions can be used to establish properties of the Tchebichef polynomials. In particular, we have

T₁: $z_{n+1}(x) = 2xz_n(x) - z_{n-1}(x), \qquad z_n(x) = \mathrm{T}_n(x) \text{ or } \mathrm{U}_n(x).$

(Recurrence formula.)

T₂: $\mathrm{T}_n(x) = \mathrm{U}_n(x) - x\mathrm{U}_{n-1}(x).$

T₃: $(1 - x^2)\mathrm{U}_n(x) = x\mathrm{T}_n(x) - \mathrm{T}_{n+1}(x).$

These can be readily established, as can other properties that will be left for the exercises.

The Tchebichef polynomials have various properties that make them particularly useful for the approximation of certain definite integrals and functions; **Tchebichef approximation** plays a highly significant role in present-day numerical analysis. Let us consider some aspects of this subject.

The Gauss-Jacobi quadrature formula (p. 498, Exercise 18(f)) becomes, for the Tchebichef polynomials, $\mathrm{T}_n(x)$:

$$\int_{-1}^{1} \frac{\rho(x)\,dx}{\sqrt{1 - x^2}} = \frac{\pi}{n} \sum_{k=1}^{n} \rho\left[\cos \frac{2k - 1}{2n}\,\pi\right],$$

where $\rho(x)$ is a polynomial of degree $\leq 2n - 1$. Such a formula enables us to evaluate the given definite integral to a high degree of accuracy. $x_k = \cos \dfrac{2k - 1}{2n}\,\pi$, $k = 1, 2, \cdots, n$ are the zeros of $\mathrm{T}_n(x)$ [readily determined by writing $\mathrm{T}_n(x) = \cos(n \cos^{-1} x)$], and among the Jacobi polynomials, the Tchebichef polynomials are the only ones that have an explicit formula for their zeros—all that is needed to calculate them is a table of cosines. Furthermore, the weights λ_k are all constant and equal to π/n in this quadrature formula; in most other cases, these weights are not so readily determined.

Now we consider a property of the polynomials $\mathrm{T}_n(x)$ that accounts for their usefulness in the approximation of functions. It is known as the

Minimax property. If $\mu = \max\limits_{-1 \leq x \leq 1} |p_n(x)|$, where $p_n(x)$ is any polynomial of degree n with leading coefficient 1, then the polynomial having the smallest μ is $\mathrm{T}_n(x)/2^{n-1}$, and this smallest μ is $1/2^{n-1}$.

Proof. $\phi_{n-1}(x) = \dfrac{\mathrm{T}_n(x)}{2^{n-1}} - p_n(x)$ is a polynomial of degree $n - 1$ (why?). Now the extreme values of $\mathrm{T}_n(x)$ in $-1 \leq x \leq 1$ occur at the $n + 1$ values $x = \cos k\pi/n$, $k = 0, 1, \cdots, n$, and are alternately 1 and -1, since $\mathrm{T}_n(x) = \cos(n \cos^{-1} x)$. Now suppose that the extreme values of $p_n(x)$ are less than those of $p_n(x)/2^{n-1}$; then, $\phi_{n-1}(x)$ will have its extreme values at the indicated $n + 1$ values of x, alternatively positive and negative, which means that $\phi_{n-1}(x)$ must have n zeros in $-1 \leq x \leq 1$. But this is impossible; hence, the extreme values of $p_n(x)$ cannot be less than those of $T_n(x)/2^{n-1}$, and the result is immediate. Since $|T_n(x)| \leq 1$, we have that the smallest μ is $1/2^{n-1}$.

It can be shown (see National Bureau of Standards, *Applied Mathematics Series 9*, "Tables of Chebyshev Polynomials," p. 7) that *a series of Tchebichef polynomials converges more rapidly than any other series of ultraspherical polynomials* and *converges much more rapidly than power series.* For example, let us approximate $f(x)$ by its truncated power series $a_0 + a_1x + \cdots + a_nx^n$, $-1 \leq x \leq 1$. Now suppose we express x^i, $i = 1, \cdots, n$, in terms of Tchebichef polynomials, using Exercise 7(a), p. 512. Then we obtain $b_0 + b_1T_1(x) + \cdots + b_nT_n(x)$ as an approximation of $f(x)$. However, $b_n \to 0$ far more rapidly than $a_n \to 0$.

Let $x_0, x_1, \cdots, x_n$ be the zeros of $T_{n+1}(x)$ and $f(x)$, an $n + 1$ times differentiable function in $-1 \leq x \leq 1$. Then, in $-1 \leq x \leq 1$,

$$f(x) = \sum_{i=0}^{n} c_iT_i(x) + \frac{1}{2^n(n+1)!}T_{n+1}(x)f^{(n+1)}(\xi), \qquad -1 < \xi < 1,$$

$$c_0 = \frac{1}{n+1}\sum_{k=0}^{n} f(x_k),$$

$$c_i = \sum_{k=0}^{n} f(x_k)T_i(x_k),$$

is the Tchebichef interpolation formula. (See Hildebrand, *Introduction to Numerical Analysis*, p. 389, for a proof.) It expresses $f(x)$ as a linear combination of Tchebichef polynomials and a remainder term, which vanishes when x is any zero of $T_{n+1}(x)$. One of the advantages of the Tchebichef interpolation formula over other polynomial interpolation formulas is the ease with which the zeros of $T_{n+1}(x)$ can be calculated. Furthermore, note that $T_{n+1}/2^n$ occurs in the remainder; the minimax property indicates a least maximum error in $f(x)$ if the remainder term is dropped. However, the maximum error is not minimized exactly, for it is influenced by $f^{(n+1)}(\xi)$.

6. The hypergeometric function. The Jacobi differential equation (see J_9)

$$(1 - x^2)y'' + [\beta - \alpha - (\alpha + \beta + 2)x]y' + \gamma(\gamma + \alpha + \beta + 1)y = 0$$

can be obtained from the differential equation

$$x(1 - x)y'' + [c - (a + b + 1)x]y' - aby = 0$$

by replacing x by $(1 - x)/2$, and letting $a = -\gamma$, $b = \gamma + \alpha + \beta + 1$, $c = \alpha + 1$. This differential equation is known as the **hypergeometric differential equation** and a, b, c are called its parameters. The hypergeometric differential equation plays a central role in the study of differential equations inasmuch as many important differential equations are either special cases of it or can be reduced to it by an appropriate change in variable. The hypergeometric differential equation has regular singular points at $x = 0$ and $x = 1$. Let us determine the series solution about $x = 0$ in the form

$$x^{\nu} \sum_{n=0}^{\infty} a_n x^n.$$

One readily finds that the indicial equation is $\nu(\nu + c - 1) = 0$; its roots are 0 and $1 - c$. Each of these roots leads to a solution, provided c is not an integer. On the other hand, one solution is always obtained if c is not a negative integer or zero. In this case, we readily obtain the recursion formula

$$(n + 1)(c + n)a_{n+1} = (a + n)(b + n)a_n, \qquad n \geq 0,$$

and by setting $a_0 = 1$, we obtain the series

$$1 + \frac{ab}{c}x + \frac{a(a+1)b(b+1)}{c(c+1)}\frac{x^2}{2!} + \frac{a(a+1)(a+2)b(b+1)(b+2)}{c(c+1)(c+2)}\frac{x^3}{3!} + \cdots,$$

which is known as the **hypergeometric series.** This term indicates that this is a generalization of the geometric series to which it reduces when $a = b = c = 1$. Introducing the notation

$$(a)_n = \frac{\Gamma(a+n)}{\Gamma(a)} = a(a+1)\cdots(a+n-1),$$

the hypergeometric series can be written compactly as

$$\sum_{n=0}^{\infty} \frac{(a)_n(b)_n}{(c)_n}\frac{x^n}{n!}.$$

By the ratio test, we find that this series converges for $|x| \leq 1$ if a, b, $c(c \neq 0)$ are not negative integers. Hence, the hypergeometric series represents a function in $|x| \leq 1$, which is known as the **hypergeometric function** and is denoted by

$$F(a, b; c; x) = \sum_{n=0}^{\infty} \frac{(a)_n(b)_n}{(c)_n}\frac{x^n}{n!}, \qquad |x| \leq 1.$$

This function has a vast literature. The standard works on the subject are Klein, *Vorlesungen über die Hypergeometrische Funktion*, and Kampé de Fériet, *La Fonction Hypergéométrique*. A serviceable chapter on this function occurs in Erdélyi, et al., *Higher Transcendental Functions*, Vol. 1, chapter ii.

First of all, let us note the representation of certain functions with which we are familiar in terms of the hypergeometric function. The student should verify these.

(1) $P_n^{(\alpha,\beta)}(x) = \binom{n+\alpha}{n} F\left(-n, n+\alpha+\beta+1; \alpha+1; \frac{1-x}{2}\right).$

(2) $P_n^{(\lambda)}(x) = \frac{(2\lambda)n}{n!} F\left(-n, n+2; \lambda+\frac{1}{2}; \frac{1-x}{2}\right).$

(3) $P_n(x) = F\left(-n, n+2; 1; \frac{1-x}{2}\right).$

(4) $T_n(x) = F\left(-n, n; \frac{1}{2}; \frac{1-x}{2}\right).$

(5) $\operatorname{Log}(1+x) = xF(1, 1; 2; -x).$

(6) $(1+x)^n = F(-n, 1, 1; -x).$

(7) $\sin^{-1} x = xF(\frac{1}{2}, \frac{1}{2}, \frac{3}{2}; x^2).$

The representation of a given function in terms of the hypergeometric function is very useful inasmuch as a large number of identities and relations are known for this function. This means that the corresponding identities and relations can be very readily established for the given function.

The six hypergeometric functions $F(a \pm 1, b; c; x)$, $F(a, b \pm 1; c; x)$, $F(a, b; c \pm 1; x)$ are said to be *contiguous* to $F(a, b; c; x)$. It can be shown that between $F(a, b; c; x)$ and any two functions contiguous to it, there exists a linear relation with coefficients that are linear functions of x. There are 15 such relations and they are known as **Gauss's recursion formulas.** They may be found in Erdélyi, et al., *Higher Transcendental Functions,* Vol. 1, p. 103, (31) to (45). One of them is

$$(b-a)F(a, b; c; x) + aF(a+1, b; c; x) = bF(a, b+1; c; x),$$

which can be verified by expanding both sides in a power series so that the coefficient of x^n of the term on the left-hand side is

$$\frac{(b-a)(a)_n(b)_n}{(c)_n n!} + \frac{a(a+1)_n(b)_n}{(c)_n n!} = \frac{(b)_n(a)_n(b+n)}{(c)_n n!} = \frac{b(a)_n(b+1)_n}{(c)_n n!},$$

which is the coefficient of x^n of the term on the right-hand side. Translated in terms of the Jacobi polynomials, this becomes

$$(2n+\alpha+\beta+1)P_n^{(\alpha,\beta)}(x) - (n+\alpha)P_{n-1}^{(\alpha+1,\beta)}(x) = (n+\alpha+\beta+1)P_n^{(\alpha,\beta+1)}(x).$$

Two differential formulas for the hypergeometric function are useful:

(1) $$\frac{d^n}{dx^n} F(a, b; c; x) = \frac{(a)_n(b)_n}{(c)_n} F(a+n, b+n; c+n; x)$$

(2) $$\frac{d^n}{dx^n} [x^{a+n-1}F(a, b; c; x)] = (a)_n x^{a-1}F(a+n, b; c; x),$$

which the student should verify. From (1), we obtain the important identity for Jacobi polynomials,

$$\mathbf{J_{10}}: \quad \frac{d^m}{dx^m} \mathrm{P}_n^{(\alpha,\beta)}(x) = 2^{-n}(n + \alpha + \beta + 1)_m \, \mathrm{P}_{n-m}^{(\alpha+m,\beta+m)}(x), \qquad n \geq m,$$

which indicates that the derivatives of Jacobi polynomials can be expressed in terms of Jacobi polynomials. For ultraspherical polynomials, this becomes

$$\mathbf{U_{10}}: \quad \frac{d^m}{dx^m} \mathrm{P}_n^{(\lambda)}(x) = 2^m(\lambda)_m \, \mathrm{P}_{n-r}^{(\lambda+m)}(x), \qquad n \geq m.$$

7. The associated Legendre functions. Let us consider the sequence of the derivatives of the Legendre polynomials, $\{\mathrm{P}_n'\}$, so that $\mathrm{P}_1'(x) = 1$, $\mathrm{P}_2'(x) = 3x$, $\mathrm{P}_3'(x) = \frac{3}{2}(5x^2 - 1)$, $\cdots$. An example will show that

$$\int_{-1}^{1} \mathrm{P}_n'(x)\mathrm{P}_m'(x)\, dx \neq 0$$

for all positive integers n and m, $n \neq m$; hence, this sequence of polynomials is not orthogonal in $-1 \leq x \leq 1$ with respect to the unit weight function. However, as Exercise 8(d), p. 494, indicates, they are orthogonal with respect to the weight function $1 - x^2$ in $-1 \leq x \leq 1$. We can say that the sequence of functions $\{\sqrt{1 - x^2}\mathrm{P}_n'(x)\}$ is orthogonal with respect to the unit weight function in $-1 \leq x \leq 1$.

Now let us consider the sequence of polynomials $\left\{\frac{d^m}{dx^m} \mathrm{P}_n(x)\right\}$, $n \geq m$. We shall determine a weight function so that this sequence is orthogonal with respect to this weight function in $-1 \leq x \leq 1$.

Differentiating the Legendre differential equation

$$(1 - x^2)\mathrm{P}_n''(x) - 2x\mathrm{P}_n'(x) + n(n + 1)\mathrm{P}_n(x) = 0$$

m times, we obtain

$$(1 - x^2)\frac{d^{m+2}}{dx^{m+2}} \mathrm{P}_n(x) - 2(m + 1)x \frac{d^{m+1}}{dx^{m+1}} \mathrm{P}_n(x) + (n - m)(n + m + 1)\frac{d^m}{dx^m} \mathrm{P}_n(x) = 0.$$

Let $u(x) = \frac{d^m}{dx^m} \mathrm{P}_n(x)$; then this equation becomes

$$(1 - x^2)u''(x) - 2(m + 1)xu'(x) + (n - m)(n + m + 1)u(x) = 0.$$

If we multiply throughout by $(1 - x^2)^m$, this equation can be written as

$$(1) \quad \frac{d}{dx}[(1 - x^2)^{m+1}u'(x)] + (n - m)(n + m + 1)(1 - x^2)^m u(x) = 0.$$

Let $v(x) = (d^m/dx^m)\mathrm{P}_k(x)$; then we also have

$$(2) \quad \frac{d}{dx}[(1 - x^2)^m v(x)] + (k - m)(k + m + 1)(1 - x^2)^m v(x) = 0.$$

Now, multiplying (1) by $v(x)$, (2) by $u(x)$, subtracting the results, and integrating from -1 to 1 yields

$$(n-k)(n+k+1)\int_{-1}^{1}(1-x^2)^m u(x)v(x)\,dx$$
$$= \int_{-1}^{1} v(x)\left[\frac{d}{dx}(1-x^2)^{m+1}u'(x)\right]dx$$
$$- \int_{-1}^{1} u(x)\left[\frac{d}{dx}(1-x^2)^{m+1}v'(x)\right]dx.$$

Integration by parts in both integrals on the right shows that this side is equal to zero, since $u(x)$ and $v(x)$ are bounded at $x = -1$ and $x = 1$ (proof?). Hence,

$$\int_{-1}^{1}(1-x^2)^m u(x)v(x)\,dx = 0, \qquad n \neq k,$$

or

$$\int_{-1}^{1}(1-x^2)^m \frac{d^m}{dx^m}\mathrm{P}_n(x)\frac{d^m}{dx^m}\mathrm{P}_k(x)\,dx = 0, \qquad n \neq k.$$

Hence, the sequence of polynomials $\{(d^m/dx^m)\mathrm{P}_n(x)\}$ is orthogonal with respect to the weight function $(1-x^2)^m$ in $-1 \le x \le 1$. The functions $(1-x^2)^{m/2}(d^m/dx^m)\mathrm{P}_n(x)$, $n \ge m$, are called the **associated Legendre functions** of *degree* n and *order* m and are denoted by $\mathrm{P}_n^m(x)$. Note that $\mathrm{P}_n^m(x)$ is a polynomial only if m is even; if m is odd and $|x| > 1$, then $\mathrm{P}_n^m(x)$ is complex-valued; we shall be concerned, however, only with these functions for $|x| \le 1$. We have just shown that

A₁: $\displaystyle\int_{-1}^{1}\mathrm{P}_n^m(x)\mathrm{P}_k^m(x)\,dx = 0, \qquad n \neq k,\ n,\ k = 0, 1, \cdots;$

i.e., the associated Legendre functions of the same order are orthogonal with respect to the unit weight function in $-1 \le x \le 1$.

We have seen that $u(x) = (d^m/dx^m)\mathrm{P}_n(x)$ satisfies the differential equation

$$(1-x^2)u''(x) - 2(m+1)xu'(x) + (n-m)(n+m+1)u(x) = 0.$$

Now, letting $u(x) = (1-x^2)^{-(m/2)}\mathrm{P}_n^m(x)$, we obtain

A₂: $$(1-x^2)\frac{d^2}{dx^2}\mathrm{P}_n^m(x) - 2x\frac{d}{dx}\mathrm{P}_n^m(x) + \left[n(n+1) - \frac{m^2}{1-x^2}\right]\mathrm{P}_n^m(x) = 0.$$

This is known as the **associated Legendre differential equation,** and as we expect, becomes the Legendre differential equation for $m = 0$.

The next property indicates that the associated Legendre functions can be expressed in terms of ultraspherical polynomials.

A₃: $\mathrm{P}_n^m(x) = 2^m(\tfrac{1}{2})_m(1-x^2)^{m/2}\mathrm{P}_{n-m}^{(m+(1/2))}(x).$

This follows immediately from the definition of $P_n^m(x)$ and the expression for the mth derivative of the ultraspherical polynomial (p. 508, U_{10}). A_3 enables us to establish the properties of $P_n^m(x)$, which correspond to properties of the ultraspherical polynomials. The student should establish the following:

A₄: $$(n - m + 1)P_{n+1}^m(x) = (2n + 1)xP_n^m(x) - (n + m)P_{n-1}^m(x), \qquad 0 \le m \le n - 1.$$

A₅: $$P_n^{m+2}(x) - 2(m + 1)\frac{x}{\sqrt{1 - x^2}}P_n^{m+1}(x) + (n - m)(n + m + 1)P_n^m(x) = 0, \qquad 0 \le m \le n - 1.$$

A₆: $$(x^2 - 1)\frac{dP_n^m(x)}{dx} + (n - m + 1)P_{n+1}^m(x) - (n + 1)xP_n^m(x) = 0, \qquad 0 \le m \le n - 1.$$

A₇: $$P_{n-1}^m(x) - P_{n+1}^m(x) = -(2n + 1)\sqrt{1 - x^2}P_n^{m-1}(x), \qquad 0 \le m \le n - 1.$$

A₈: $$\int_{-1}^{1} [P_n^m(x)]^2\, dx = \frac{2}{2n + 1}\frac{(n + m)!}{(n - m)!}.$$

A₉: $$P_n^m(\cos\theta) = \frac{(n + m)!}{2\pi i^m n!}\int_{-\pi}^{\pi} [\cos\theta + i\sin\theta\cos\phi]^n e^{-im\phi}\, d\phi.$$

[Laplace's integral formula, see p. 254, Exercise 17(c)]

The associated Legendre function $P_n^m(x)$ has been defined only for m an integer, $0 \le m \le n$, $n = 0, 1, \cdots$. However, if $m > n$, we can define $P_n^m(x) = 0$. If m is an integer, $0 < m < n$, we can define $P_n^{-m}(x)$ by Laplace's integral formula A_9. One can show readily, then, that

$$P_n^{-m}(x) = \frac{(-1)^m(n - m)!}{(n + m)!}P_n^m(x).$$

If, in the associated Legendre differential equation A_2, we replace m by μ and n by ν, where μ and ν are arbitrary real numbers, we obtain the differential equation

$$(1 - x^2)y'' - 2xy' + \left[\nu(\nu + 1) - \frac{\mu^2}{1 - x^2}\right]y = 0,$$

whose solutions are called **spherical harmonics.** The standard treatise on spherical harmonics is Hobson, *The Theory of Spherical and Ellipsoidal Harmonics.*

EXERCISES

1. Show that

(a) $\tan^{-1} x = x\,F(\frac{1}{2}, 1; \frac{3}{2}; -x^2)$.

(b) $\operatorname{Log}\dfrac{1 + x}{1 - x} = 2x\,F(\frac{1}{2}, 1; \frac{3}{2}; x^2)$.

(c) $\cos(n \sin^{-1} x) = F\left(\frac{n}{2}, \frac{-n}{2}; \frac{1}{2}; x^2\right).$

(d) $\sin nx = n \sin x\, F\left(\frac{1+n}{2}, \frac{1-n}{2}; \frac{3}{2}; \sin^2 x\right), \qquad -\frac{\pi}{2} \le x \le \frac{\pi}{2}.$

(e) $\dfrac{\operatorname{Log}(1-x)}{x} = -F(1, 1; 2; x).$

(f) $\sum_{n=m+1}^{\infty} \binom{a}{n} x^n = \dfrac{x^{m+1}\Gamma(a+1)}{\Gamma(a-m)(m+1)!} F(m+1-a, 1; m+2; -x)$, a not an integer.

2. Show that

(a) $F(a, b; c; x)$

$$= \frac{\Gamma(c)}{\Gamma(b)\Gamma(c-b)} \int_0^1 t^{b-1}(1-t)^{c-b-1}(1-xt)^{-a}\, dt, \qquad c > b > 0,\ |x| < 1.$$

Hint: Expand $(1 - xt)^{-a}$ in a binomial series in powers of x, integrate term by term to obtain

$$\sum_{n=0}^{\infty} \frac{(a)_n}{n!} x^n B(b+n, c-b).$$

Now express the beta function in terms of gamma functions.

(b) $F(a, b; c; 1) = \dfrac{\Gamma(c)\Gamma(c-a-b)}{\Gamma(c-a)\Gamma(c-b)}, \qquad c > a + b.$

(c) $F(-n, b; c; 1) = \dfrac{(c-b)_n}{(c)_n}, \qquad c > b - n.$

(d) $F(a, b; c; x) = (1-x)^{-a} F\left(a, c-b; c; \dfrac{x}{x-1}\right).$

[*Hint:* Replace t by $1 - t$ in (a).]

(e) $F(a, b; c; x) = (1-x)^{-b} F\left(b, c-a; c; \dfrac{x}{x-1}\right).$

(f) $F(a, b; c; x) = (1-x)^{c-a-b} F(c-a, c-b; c; x).$

(g) $F(a, b; 1 + a - b; -1)$

$$= \frac{\sqrt{\pi}\,\Gamma(1+a-b)}{\Gamma[1-b+(a/2)]\Gamma[(a+1)/2]}, \qquad 1 + a - b \ne 0, -1, -2, \cdots.$$

(h) $F\left(a + \frac{1}{3}, 3a; 2a + \frac{2}{3}; e^{i(\pi/3)}\right) = \dfrac{\Gamma(2a + \frac{2}{3})}{\Gamma(a + \frac{1}{3})\Gamma(a + \frac{2}{3})\Gamma(\frac{2}{3})}.$

(i) $F(1, a; a + 1; -1) = 2a\left[\psi\left(\frac{a+1}{2}\right) - \psi\left(\frac{a}{2}\right)\right].$

For the definition of ψ, see p. 471, Exercise 26.

(j) $F\left(a, b; a + b + \frac{1}{2}; \sin^2\theta\right) = F\left(2a, 2b; a + b + \frac{1}{2}; \sin^2\frac{\theta}{2}\right).$

3. If K and E are the complete elliptic integrals of the first and second kind, show that

(a) $K = \frac{\pi}{2} F\left(\frac{1}{2}, \frac{1}{2}; 1; k^2\right)$.

(b) $E = \frac{\pi}{2} F\left(\frac{1}{2}, -\frac{1}{2}; 1; k^2\right)$.

4. Show that

(a) $(c - a - 1)F(a, b; c; x) + a\,F(a + 1, b; c; x)$
$\quad - (c - 1)F(a, b; c - 1, x) = 0.$

(b) $c(1 - x)F(a, b; c; x) - c\,F(a - 1, b; c; x)$
$\quad + (c - b)x\,F(a, b; c + 1; x) = 0.$

and translate these into the corresponding recurrence relations for Jacobi polynomials.

5. Show that

$$\mathrm{P}_n^m(x) = \frac{(n + m)!}{2^m(n - m)!m!} (1 - x^2)^{(1/2)m} F\left(1 + m + n, m - n; 1 + m; \frac{1 - x}{2}\right),$$

and translate the recurrence relations in Exercise 4 to the corresponding ones for $\mathrm{P}_n^m(x)$.

6. Show that for Tchebichef polynomials:

(a) $2\mathrm{T}_m(x)\mathrm{T}_n(x) = \mathrm{T}_{n+m}(x) + \mathrm{T}_{n-m}(x)$.

(b) $2(x^2 - 1)\mathrm{U}_{m-1}(x)\mathrm{U}_{n-1}(x) = \mathrm{T}_{n+m}(x) - \mathrm{T}_{n-m}(x)$.

(c) $\mathrm{T}_n'(x) = n\mathrm{U}_{n-1}(x)$.

(d) $2\mathrm{T}_n(x)\mathrm{U}_{m-1}(x) = \mathrm{U}_{n+m-1}(x) - \mathrm{U}_{n-m-1}(x)$.

(e) $2\mathrm{T}_n^2(x) = 1 + \mathrm{T}_{2n}(x)$.

(f) $\sum_{k=0}^{n} \mathrm{T}_{2k}(x) = \frac{1 + \mathrm{U}_{2n}(x)}{2}$.

(g) $\mathrm{T}_n^2(x) - \mathrm{T}_{n+1}(x)\mathrm{T}_{n-1}(x) = 1 - x^2$.

(h) $\mathrm{U}_n^2(x) - \mathrm{U}_{n+1}(x)\mathrm{U}_{n-1}(x) = 1$.

(i) $\mathrm{T}_m(\mathrm{T}_n(x)) = \mathrm{T}_n(\mathrm{T}_m(x)) = \mathrm{T}_{mn}(x)$.

(j) $\mathrm{U}_{n-1}(\mathrm{T}_m(x))\mathrm{U}_{m-1}(x) = \mathrm{U}_{m-1}(\mathrm{T}_n(x))\mathrm{U}_{n-1}(x) = \mathrm{U}_{mn-1}(x)$.

◇ **7.** Use the recurrence relation to show that

(a) $x^n = \frac{1}{2^{n-1}} \sum_{k=0}^{[n/2]} \binom{n}{k} \mathrm{T}_{n-2k}(x)$.

(b) $x^n = \frac{1}{2^n} \sum_{k=0}^{[n/2]} \binom{n + 1}{k} \mathrm{U}_{n-2k}(x)$.

8. (a) Use the Gauss-Jacobi quadrature formula for Tchebichef polynomials to approximate

$$\int_{-1}^{1} \frac{x^3 + 2x^2 + x + 2}{\sqrt{1 - x^2}}\,dx.$$

(b) Log $(1 + x)$ is approximately equal to

$$x - \frac{x^2}{2} + \frac{x^3}{3} - \frac{x^4}{4} + \frac{x^5}{5}, \qquad -1 \leq x \leq 1.$$

Express the powers of x in terms of Tchebichef polynomials [Exercise 7(a)]. Show that Log $(1 + x)$ can be approximated more accurately by $-\frac{11}{32}T_0(x) + \frac{11}{8}T_1(x) - \frac{3}{8}T_2(x) = \frac{1}{32} + (11x/8) - (3x^2/4)$ than by the given truncated power series.

(c) Solve $xy'' + y = 0$, $y(0) = 0$, $y'(0) = 1$, using the expansion $y = \sum_{n=0}^{\infty} a_n T_n(x)$. With the use of the appropriate identities, eliminate all derivatives of $T_n(x)$ so as to express the final series as a series of Tchebichef polynomials.

(d) Determine, to four decimal places, the coefficients in the approximation $e^x \simeq \sum_{i=0}^{5} c_i T_i(x)$, $-1 \le x \le 1$, if the approximation is to be exact at the zeros of $T_6(x)$, and show that the error is smaller than $e/23{,}040$ everywhere in $-1 \le x \le 1$.

9. Show that the Christoffel-Darboux formula for Tchebichef polynomials is

$$\tfrac{1}{2} + \sum_{k=0}^{n} z_k(x)z_k(y) = (x - y)^{-1}[z_{k+1}(x)z_k(y) - z_k(x)z_{k+1}(y)],\ z_k(x)$$
$$= T_k(x) \quad \text{or} \quad U_k(x).$$

Translate this to obtain an identity involving the trigonometric functions.

10. (a) Use the Fourier expansion theorem to prove the *Tchebichef expansion theorem:* If f is piecewise continuous and almost differentiable in $|x| < 1$, then

$$\frac{f(x+) + f(x-)}{2} = \sum_{n=0}^{\infty} c_n z_n(x), \qquad |x| < 1,$$

where

$$c_n = \frac{2}{\pi}\int_{-1}^{1} f(y)z_n(y)\,dy.$$

(b) Show that

$$(1 - x)^\gamma = \frac{2^{\gamma+1}}{\sqrt{\pi}}\Gamma\left(\gamma + \frac{3}{2}\right)\sum_{n=0}^{\infty} \frac{(n+1)(-\gamma)_n}{(n + \gamma + 2)} U_n(x), \qquad \gamma > -1,\ |x| < 1.$$

11. Show that

$$\sum_{k=0}^{n} (n + \lambda)P_k^{(\lambda)}(x) = \frac{1}{2}\frac{(n + 2\lambda)P_n^{(\lambda)}(x) - (n+1)P_{n+1}^{(\lambda)}(x)}{1 - x}.$$

12. Show that

(a) $\displaystyle\int_0^1 [P_n^m(x)]^2\,dx = \frac{(n+m)!}{(2n+1)(n-m)!}.$

(b) $\displaystyle\int_{-1}^1 (1 - x^2)^{-1}[P_n^m(x)]^2\,dx = \frac{(n+m)!}{m(n-m)!}.$

(c) $\displaystyle\int_{-1}^1 (1 - x^2)^{-1}P_n^l(x)P_n^k(x)\,dx = 0, \qquad k \ne l.$

13. Show that $r^n(\cos m\phi + \sin m\phi)P_n^m(\cos\theta)$ and $(1/r^{n+1})(\cos m\phi + \sin m\phi)P_n^m(\cos\theta)$, where (r, θ, ϕ) are spherical coordinates, are harmonic functions. [*Hint:* Use Supplementary Problem 18(d), p. 164.]

14. The **generalized hypergeometric function** is defined as

$$\sum_{n=0}^{\infty} \frac{(a_1)_n(a_2)_n\cdots(a_p)_n x^n}{(b_1)_n(b_2)_n\cdots(b_q)_n n!}, \qquad b_i \ne 0,\ i = 1, 2, \cdots, q,$$

and is denoted by

$$ {}_pF_q\left[\begin{matrix} a_1, & a_2, & \cdots, & a_p & \\ & & & & x \\ b_1, & b_2, & \cdots, & b_q & \end{matrix}\right], $$

or ${}_pF_q$ for short.

(a) Show that if $p \leq q$, the series converges for all x; if $p = q + 1$, the series converges for $|x| < 1$ and diverges for $|x| > 1$; if $p > q + 1$, the series diverges for $x \neq 0$, unless the series terminates.

(b) Show that $(1 - x)^{-a} = {}_1F_0(a; 0; x)$.

(c) Show that

$$ {}_pF_q\left[\begin{matrix} a_1, & a_2, & \cdots, & a_{k+1}, & \cdots, & a_p & \\ & & & & & & x \\ b_1, & b_2, & \cdots, & b_q & & & \end{matrix}\right] = \sum_{n=0}^{\infty} \frac{a_{k+n}}{a_k} \frac{(a_1)_n \cdots (a_p)_n\, x^n}{(b_1)_n \cdots (b_q)_n\, n!}. $$

(d) Show that

$$ \left(x\frac{d}{dx} + a_k\right) {}_pF_q = {}_pF_q\left[\begin{matrix} a_1, & a_2, & \cdots, & a_{k+1}, & \cdots, & a_p & \\ & & & & & & x \\ b_1, & b_2, & \cdots, & b_q & & & \end{matrix}\right]. $$

(e) Show that

$$ y'' + \left[\frac{1 - a_1 - b_1}{x} + \frac{1 - a_3 - b_3}{x - 1}\right]y' + \left[\frac{-a_1b_1}{x} + \frac{a_3b_3}{x - 1} + a_2b^2\right]\frac{y}{x(x - 1)} = 0, $$

where $y = {}_3F_3$.

15. The hypergeometric differential equation is a special case of **Riemann's differential equation:**

$$ \begin{aligned} u''(x) &+ \left[\frac{1 - \alpha - \alpha'}{x - a} + \frac{1 - \beta - \beta'}{x - b} + \frac{1 - \gamma - \gamma'}{x - c}\right]u' \\ &+ \left[\frac{\alpha\alpha'(a - b)(a - c)}{x - a} + \frac{\beta\beta'(b - c)(b - a)}{x - b}\right. \\ &+ \left.\frac{\gamma\gamma'(c - a)(c - b)}{x - c}\right]\frac{u}{(x - a)(x - b)(x - c)} = 0. \end{aligned} $$

$\alpha, \alpha'; \beta, \beta'; \gamma, \gamma'$ are called the **exponents** belonging to the poles a, b, c, and must satisfy $\alpha + \alpha' + \beta + \beta' + \gamma + \gamma' = 1$. Riemann's differential equation is denoted by the following scheme:

$$ u = p\left\{\begin{matrix} a & b & c & \\ \alpha & \beta & \gamma & x \\ \alpha' & \beta' & \gamma' & \end{matrix}\right\}. $$

Represent the hypergeometric, Jacobi, and Legendre differential equations in this form.

8. Laguerre and Hermite polynomials. The orthogonal polynomials that we have considered up to this point have finite intervals of orthogonality. Functions defined in intervals such as $0 \leq x < \infty$ and $-\infty < x < \infty$ cannot be expanded in a series of polynomials orthogonal in a finite interval. We now define two sequences of polynomials, one orthogonal in the semi-infinite interval $0 \leq x < \infty$ and the other in the infinite interval $-\infty < x < \infty$.

The **Laguerre polynomials** are defined as the orthogonal polynomials with weight function $x^\alpha e^{-x}$, $\alpha > -1$, in $0 \leq x < \infty$, are denoted by $L_n^{(\alpha)}(x)$, and have the normalization $L_n^{(\alpha)}(0) = \binom{n+\alpha}{n}$; n is called the **degree,** and α the *order* of the polynomials. The polynomials with order $\alpha = 0$ are of particular importance and are denoted simply as $L_n(x)$—these are often called **Laguerre polynomials;** the term **generalized** Laguerre polynomials is then used for arbitrary $\alpha > -1$. The Laguerre polynomials have the following properties:

La₁: $\int_0^\infty x^\alpha e^{-x} L_n^{(\alpha)}(x) L_m^{(\alpha)}(x)\, dx = 0, \qquad m \neq n,\ m, n = 0, 1, \cdots.$

La₂: $L_n^{(\alpha)}(x) = \dfrac{e^x}{n!} \dfrac{d^n}{dx^n} (e^{-x} x^{n+\alpha}).$

(Rodrigues' formula.)

La₃: $\int_0^\infty e^{-x} x^\alpha [L_n^{(\alpha)}(x)]^2\, dx = \dfrac{\Gamma(\alpha + n + 1)}{n!}.$

La₄: $(n+1) L_{n+1}^{(\alpha)}(x) = (2n + \alpha + 1 - x) L_n^{(\alpha)}(x) - (n + \alpha) L_{n-1}^{(\alpha)}(x).$

(Recurrence formula.)

La₅: $\sum_{n=0}^{\infty} L_n^{(\alpha)}(x) t^n = (1 - x)^{-\alpha - 1} e^{xt/t-1}, \quad |t| < 1.$

(Generating function.)

La₆: $L_n^{(\alpha)}(x) = \sum_{k=0}^{n} (-1)^k \binom{n+\alpha}{n-k} \dfrac{x^k}{k!}.$

La₇: $L_n^{(\alpha)}(x) = \lim_{\beta \to \infty} P_n^{(\alpha,\beta)} \left(1 - \dfrac{2x}{\beta}\right).$

La₈: $x \dfrac{d}{dx} L_n^{(\alpha)}(x) = n L_n^{(\alpha)}(x) - (n + \alpha) L_{n-1}^{(\alpha)}(x).$

La₉: $\dfrac{d}{dx} [L_n^{(\alpha)}(x) - L_{n+1}^{(\alpha)}(x)] = L_n^{(\alpha)}(x).$

La₁₀: $\dfrac{d^m}{dx^m} L_n^{(\alpha)}(x) = (-1)^m L_{n-m}^{(\alpha-m)}(x), \qquad n \geq m.$

La₁₁: $xy'' + (\alpha + 1 - x) y' + ny = 0, \qquad y = L_n^{(\alpha)}(x).$

(Differential equation.)

Proofs. La₁ is the orthogonality condition that follows from definition.

La₂, La₃, La₄, La₅, La₆ can be established analogously to the corresponding properties for Legendre polynomials.

La_5 indicates that the Laguerre polynomials can be considered as a limiting case of the Jacobi polynomials. This has a very important application: it may be used to establish for Laguerre polynomials many of the corresponding properties of Jacobi polynomials. It can be established by replacing x by $1 - (2x/\beta)$ in J_7 so that

$$\mathrm{P}_n^{(\alpha,\beta)}\left(1 - \frac{2x}{\beta}\right) = \sum_{k=0}^{n} (-1)^k \binom{n+\alpha}{n-k}\binom{n+\beta}{k}\frac{1}{\beta^k}\left(1 - \frac{x}{\beta}\right)^{n-k} x^k.$$

Now letting $\beta \to \infty$, the result is immediate, since

$$\frac{1}{\beta^k}\binom{n+\beta}{k} = \frac{1}{k!}\frac{\Gamma(n+\beta+1)}{\beta^k\Gamma(n+\beta-k+1)}$$

$$= \frac{(\beta+n)(n+n-1)\cdots\beta\Gamma(\beta)}{k!(\beta+n-k-1)\cdots\beta\Gamma(\beta)\beta^k} \to \frac{1}{k!}.$$

La_8 to La_{11} can now be established with the use of La_7 and the corresponding properties for Jacobi polynomials.

We define the **Hermite polynomials** to be the orthogonal polynomials with weight function e^{-x^2} in the interval $-\infty < x < \infty$. The nth degree Hermite polynomial is denoted by $\mathrm{H}_n(x)$, and these polynomials are normalized by

$$\int_{-\infty}^{\infty} e^{-x^2}\mathrm{H}_n^2(x)\,dx = \sqrt{\pi}\,2^n n!,$$

and requiring that the coefficient of x_n in $\mathrm{H}_n(x)$ be positive. The Hermite polynomials have the following properties:

H₁: $\int_{-\infty}^{\infty} e^{-x^2}\mathrm{H}_n(x)\mathrm{H}_m(x)\,dx = 0, \qquad n \neq m,\ n, m = 0, 1, \cdots.$

H₂: $\int_{-\infty}^{\infty} e^{-x^2}\mathrm{H}_n^2(x)\,dx = \sqrt{\pi}\,2^n n!.$

H₃: $\mathrm{H}_n(x) = (-1)^n e^{x^2}\dfrac{d^n}{dx^n}e^{-x^2}.$

(Rodrigues' formula.)

H₄: $\mathrm{H}_n(-x) = (-1)^n\mathrm{H}_n(x).$

H₅: $\mathrm{H}_{2n}(x) = (-1)^n 2^{2n} n!\mathrm{L}_n^{-(1/2)}(x^2).$

$\mathrm{H}_{2n+1}(x) = (-1)^n 2^{2n+1} n! x\mathrm{L}_n^{1/2}(x^2).$

H₆: $\mathrm{H}_n(x) = n!\displaystyle\sum_{k=0}^{[n/2]}\frac{(-1)^k(2x)^{n-2k}}{k!(n-2k)!}.$

H₇: $\mathrm{H}_n(x) = n!\lim_{\lambda\to\infty}\lambda^{-n/2}\mathrm{P}_n^{(\lambda)}(\lambda^{-(1/2)}x).$

H₈: $\mathrm{H}_{n+1}(x) = 2x\mathrm{H}_n(x) - 2n\mathrm{H}_{n-1}(x).$

(Recurrence formula.)

H₉: $\sum_{n=0}^{\infty} \frac{\mathrm{H}_n(x)t^n}{n!} = e^{2xt-t^2}.$

(Generating function.)

H₁₀: $\mathrm{H}_n'(x) = 2n\mathrm{H}_{n-1}(x).$

H₁₁: $\mathrm{H}_n''(x) - 2x\mathrm{H}_n'(x) + 2n\mathrm{H}_n(x) = 0.$

(Differential equation.)

Proofs. H_1 follows from the definition of orthogonality and H_2 from the normalization.

H_3 and H_4 may be established analogously to the corresponding properties for Legendre polynomials.

H_5 may be established with the use of H_3 and La_2.

H_6 follows from H_5 applied to La_6.

H_7 follows from H_6 and H_{10}.

The remaining properties may be established by use of either H_5 or H_7 and the corresponding properties of Laguerre or ultraspherical polynomials. It should be pointed out that the Hermite polynomials are often defined with weight function $e^{-x^2/2}$ (especially in statistics). If these are denoted by $h_n(x)$, we have the relation

$$\mathrm{H}_n(x) = (\sqrt{2})^n h_n(\sqrt{2}x).$$

(Proof?)

Since La_7 and H_7 indicate that the Laguerre polynomials and Hermite polynomials are limiting cases of polynomials that can be expressed in terms of the hypergeometric function, we might expect that $\mathrm{L}_n^{(\alpha)}(x)$ and $\mathrm{H}_n(x)$ cannot be expressed in terms of the hypergeometric function itself, but in terms of some limit of this function. We define the **confluent hypergeometric function** as

$$\lim_{b\to\infty} F\left(a, b, c; \frac{x}{b}\right)$$

and denote it by $\Phi(a, c; x)$. We have

La₁₂: $\mathrm{L}_n^{(\alpha)}(x) = \binom{n+\alpha}{n} \Phi(-n, \alpha+1; x);$

H₁₂: $\mathrm{H}_{2n}(x) = \frac{(-1)^n(2n)!}{n!} \Phi\left(-n, \frac{1}{2}; x^2\right);$

$$\mathrm{H}_{2n+1}(x) = \frac{(-1)^n(2n+1)!}{n!} 2x\Phi\left(-n, \frac{3}{2}; x^2\right);$$

which the student should verify.

We state the

LAGUERRE EXPANSION THEOREM. If f is piecewise continuous and almost differentiable in $0 \leq x < \infty$, then

$$\frac{f(x+) + f(x-)}{2} = \sum_{n=0}^{\infty} c_n \mathrm{L}_n^{(\alpha)}(x), \qquad 0 \le x < \infty,$$

where

$$c_n = \frac{n!}{\Gamma(\alpha + n + 1)} \int_0^{\infty} y^{\alpha} e^{-y} f(y) \mathrm{L}_n^{(\alpha)}(y)\, dy,$$

and the

HERMITE EXPANSION THEOREM. If f is piecewise continuous and almost differentiable in $-\infty < x < \infty$, then

$$\frac{f(x+) + f(x-)}{2} = \sum_{n=0}^{\infty} c_n \mathrm{H}_n(x), \qquad -\infty < x < \infty,$$

where

$$c_n = \frac{1}{\sqrt{\pi}\, n!2^n} \int_{-\infty}^{\infty} e^{-y^2} f(y) \mathrm{H}_n(y)\, dy.$$

9. The classical orthogonal polynomials. The student may have had occasion to wonder why the Jacobi polynomials, particularly their special cases (the ultraspherical polynomials, the Legendre polynomials, the Tchebichef polynomials), and the limiting cases (the Laguerre polynomials and the Hermite polynomials) were singled out for detailed study. There are several reasons for this. First it should be noted that they all have certain analogous properties which facilitate their study. If $\{p_n\}$ denotes any one of these sequences of orthogonal polynomials, then (1) $p_n(x)$ satisfies a second-order linear differential equation of the form: $A(x)y'' + B(x)y' + \lambda_n y = 0$, where $A(x)$ and $B(x)$ are independent of n and λ_n is independent of x; (2) $p_n(x) = \dfrac{1}{K_n w(x)} \dfrac{d^n}{dx^n} [w(x)\rho^n(x)]$, where K_n is independent of x, w is the weight function, and ρ is a polynomial whose coefficients are independent of n (Rodrigues' formula). It can also be shown that (3) $\left\{\dfrac{d^m}{dx^m} p_n(x)\right\}$ is a sequence of orthogonal polynomials. (We have shown this in the case of the Legendre polynomials and it can be shown similarly for Jacobi, Laguerre, and Hermite polynomials.) Moreover, it can be shown that properties (1), (2), (3) are characteristic of these polynomials in the sense that if a sequence of orthogonal polynomials has the property (1), (2), or (3), then that sequence is the sequence of Jacobi polynomials, Laguerre polynomials, or Hermite polynomials. These polynomials are referred to as the **classical orthogonal polynomials.** We shall note in our final part that the fact that they are the only ones that satisfy a second-order linear differential equation is highly significant. Furthermore, the classical orthogonal polynomials are adequate for any expansion problem, since they accommodate a finite interval, a semi-infinite interval, or an infinite interval.

EXERCISES

1. Show that

(a) $H_{2n}(0) = \dfrac{(-1)^n(2n)!}{n!}, \qquad H_{2n+1}(0) = 0.$

(b) $\sum_{n=0}^{\infty} (-1)^n H_{2n}(x) \dfrac{t^{2n}}{(2n)!} = e^{t^2} \cos (2^{1/2}\, xt).$

(c) $\sum_{n=0}^{\infty} (-1)^n H_{2n+1}(x) \dfrac{t^{2n+1}}{(2n+1)!} = e^{t^2} \sin (2^{1/2}\, xt).$

(d) $e^{-x^2} H_n(x) = 2^{n+1}\pi^{-1/2} \int_0^{\infty} e^{-t^2} t^n \cos (2xt - \tfrac{1}{2}n\pi)\, dt.$

(e) $\int_0^x H_n(t)\, dt = \dfrac{1}{2(n+1)} [H_{n+1}(x) - H_{n+1}(0)].$

(f) $\int_0^x e^{-t^2} H_n(t)\, dt = H_{n-1}(0) - e^{-x^2} H_{n-1}(x).$

(g) $\int_{-\infty}^{\infty} e^{-t^2} H_{2n}(xt)\, dt = \pi^{1/2} \dfrac{(2n)!}{n!} (x^2 - 1)^n.$

(h) $\int_{-\infty}^{\infty} e^{-t^2} t H_{2n+1}(xt)\, dt = \dfrac{\pi^{1/2}(2n)!}{n!} (x^2 - 1)^n.$

(i) $\int_{-\infty}^{\infty} e^{-t^2} t^n H_n(xt)\, dt = \pi^{1/2} n! P_n(x), \quad P_n(x)$ the Legendre polynomial.

(j) $H_n(x) = (-1)^n 2^{n/2} \pi^{-1/2} \int_{-\infty}^{\infty} (x\sqrt{2} + it)^n e^{-t^2}\, dt.$

(k) $H_n(x) = \dfrac{1}{2\pi i} \oint_C \dfrac{e^{2xt - t^2}}{t^{n+1}}\, dt,$

C any contour enclosing the origin. (*Hint:* Use H_9 and Cauchy's integral formula.)

(l) $\Gamma(n + \alpha + 1) \int_{-1}^{1} (1 - t^2)^{\alpha - (1/2)} H_{2n}(x^{1/2} t)\, dt$
$= (-1)^n (2n)! \sqrt{\pi}\, \Gamma(\alpha + \tfrac{1}{2}) L_n^{(\alpha)}(x).$

2. Show that

(a) $x \dfrac{d}{dx} L_n^{(\alpha)}(x) = (n+1) L_{n+1}^{(\alpha)}(x) - (n + \alpha + 1 - x) L_n^{(\alpha)}(x).$

(b) $(xy')' + \left(n + \dfrac{\alpha + 1}{2} - \dfrac{x}{4} - \dfrac{\alpha^2}{4x}\right) y = 0,\ y = e^{-(1/2)x} x^{(1/2)\alpha} L_n^{(\alpha)}(x).$

(c) $\sum_{n=0}^{\infty} L_n^{(\alpha - n)}(x) t^n = e^{-xt}(1 + t)^{\alpha}.$

(*Hint:* Use La_6.)

(d) $n! \dfrac{d^m}{dx^m} [e^{-x} x^{\alpha} L_n^{(\alpha)}(x)] = (m + n)!\, x^{\alpha - m} L_{m+n}^{(\alpha - m)}(x).$

(e) $\int_x^\infty e^{-t}\mathrm{L}_n^{(\alpha)}(t)\,dt = e^{-x}[\mathrm{L}_n^{(\alpha)}(x) - \mathrm{L}_{n-1}^{(\alpha)}(x)].$

(f) $\Gamma(\alpha+\beta+n+1)\int_0^x (x-t)^{\beta-1}t^\alpha \mathrm{L}_n^{(\alpha)}(t)\,dt$
$= \Gamma(\alpha+n+1)\Gamma(\beta)x^{\alpha+\beta}\mathrm{L}_n^{(\alpha+\beta)}(x), \qquad \alpha > -1, \beta > 0.$

(g) $\int_0^\infty e^{-x}x^n \mathrm{L}_n(x)\,dx = (-1)^n n!.$

(h) $\int_0^x \mathrm{L}_m(t)\mathrm{L}_n(x-t)\,dt = \int_0^x \mathrm{L}_{m+n}(t)\,dt = \mathrm{L}_{m+n}(x) - \mathrm{L}_{m+n+1}(x).$

3. Prove:

(a) $\sum_{k=0}^{n} \frac{\mathrm{H}_k(x)\mathrm{H}_k(y)}{2^k k!} = \frac{\mathrm{H}_{n+1}(x)\mathrm{H}_n(y) - \mathrm{H}_n(x)\mathrm{H}_{n+1}(y)}{2^{n+1}n!(x-y)}.$

(b) $\sum_{k=0}^{n} (2^k k!)^{-1}\mathrm{H}_k^2(x) = (2^{n+1}n!)^{-1}[\mathrm{H}_{n+1}^2(x) - \mathrm{H}_n(x)\mathrm{H}_{n+2}(x)].$

(c) $\sum_{k=0}^{n} \binom{n}{k} \mathrm{H}_k(2^{1/2}x)\mathrm{H}_{n-k}(2^{1/2}y) = 2^{1/2n}\mathrm{H}_n(x+y).$

(d) $\sum_{k=0}^{n} \binom{2m}{2k} \mathrm{H}_{2k}(2^{1/2}x)\mathrm{H}_{2m-2k}(2^{1/2}y).$
$= 2^{m-1}[\mathrm{H}_{2m}(x+y) + \mathrm{H}_{2m}(x-y)].$

(e) $\sum_{k=0}^{n} \mathrm{L}_k^{(\alpha)}(x) = \mathrm{L}_n^{(\alpha+1)}(x) = \frac{1}{x}[(x-n)\mathrm{L}_n^{(\alpha)}(x) + (\alpha+n)\mathrm{L}_{n-1}^{(\alpha)}(x)].$

(f) $\sum_{k=0}^{n} \mathrm{L}_k^{(\alpha)}(x)\mathrm{L}_{n-k}^{(\beta)}(y) = \mathrm{L}_n^{(\alpha+\beta+1)}(x+y).$

(g) $\mathrm{L}_n^{(\alpha)}(x) = \sum_{k=0}^{n} (k!)^{-1}(\alpha-\beta)_m \mathrm{L}_{n-m}^{(\beta)}(x).$

(h) $n!\mathrm{L}_n^{(\alpha)}(x)\mathrm{L}_n^{(\alpha)}(y)$
$= \Gamma(\alpha+n+1)\sum_{m=0}^{n} m![\Gamma(\alpha+m+1)]^{-1}(xy)^m \mathrm{L}_{n-m}^{(\alpha+2m)}(x+y).$

4. Define the Hermite functions

$$E_n(x) = (\sqrt{\pi}2^n n!)^{-1/2}e^{-x^2/2}\mathrm{H}_n(x), \qquad n = 0, 1, 2, \cdots.$$

Show that

(a) $xE_n(x) = \sqrt{2n}E_{n-1}(x) - E_n'(x).$

(b) $E_{n+1}(x) = \sqrt{\frac{2}{n+1}}\,xE_n(x) + \sqrt{\frac{n}{n+1}}\,E_{n-1}(x).$

(c) $E_n''(x) + (2n+1-x^2)E_n(x) = 0.$

(d) $(2n-x)E_n^2(x) + [E_n'(x)]^2 = 2\sum_{i=0}^{n-1} E_i^2(x).$

(e) $\int_{-\infty}^\infty [E_n'(x)]^2\,dx = \frac{2n+1}{2}.$

5. Show that

(a) $xy'' + (c - x)y' - ay = 0, \qquad y = \Phi(a, c; x).$

(b) $\Phi(a, c; x) = \sum_{n=0}^{\infty} \frac{(a)_n}{(c)_n} \frac{x^n}{n!}.$

(c) $\frac{d}{dx} \Phi(a, c; x) = \frac{a}{c} \Phi(a + 1, c + 1; x).$

(d) $\Phi(a, c; x) = e^x \Phi(c - a, c; -x).$

(Kummer's transformation.)

(e) $\Phi(a, c; x) = \frac{\Gamma(c)}{\Gamma(a)\Gamma(c - a)} \int_0^1 e^{xu} u^{a-1}(1 - u)^{c-a-1}, \qquad c > a > 0.$

(f) $\frac{d^n}{dx^n} \Phi(a, c; x) = \frac{(a)_n}{(c)_n} \Phi(a + n, c + n; x).$

(g) $\frac{d^n}{dx^n} [x^{a+n-1}\Phi(a, c; x)] = (a)_n x^{a-1}\Phi(a + n, c; x).$

(h) $\frac{d^n}{dx^n} [e^{-x}\Phi(a, c; x)] = (-1)^n \frac{(c - a)_n}{(c)_n} e^{-x}\Phi(a, c + n; x).$

(i) $\Phi(a, c; x) = {}_1F_1(a, c; x).$

(See p. 513, Exercise 14.)

6. Let $\Phi(a+) \equiv \Phi(a + 1, c; x)$, $\Phi(a-) \equiv \Phi(a - 1, c; x)$, $\Phi(c+) \equiv \Phi(a, c + 1; x)$, $\Phi(c-) \equiv \Phi(a, c - 1; x)$, $\Phi = (a, c; x)$. Prove:
(a) $(c - a)\Phi(a-) + (2a - c + x)\Phi - a\Phi(a+) = 0.$
(b) $(a - c + 1)\Phi - a\Phi(a+) + (c - 1)\Phi(c-) = 0.$
(c) $c(c - 1)\Phi(c-) - c(c - 1 + x)\Phi + (c - a)x\Phi(c+) = 0.$
(d) $c\Phi - c\Phi(a-) - x\Phi(c+) = 0.$
(e) $c(a + x)\Phi - (c - a)\Phi(a-) - (c - 1)\Phi(c-) = 0.$

7. Use Exercise 6 to establish:
(a) $x\mathrm{L}_n^{(\alpha+1)}(x) = (n + \alpha + 1)\mathrm{L}_n^{(\alpha)}(x) - (n + 1)\mathrm{L}_{n+1}^{(\alpha)}(x).$
(b) $\mathrm{L}_n^{(\alpha-1)}(x) = \mathrm{L}_n^{(\alpha)}(x) - \mathrm{L}_{n-1}^{(\alpha)}(x).$
(c) $(n + \alpha)\mathrm{L}_n^{(\alpha-1)}(x) = (n + 1)\mathrm{L}_{n+1}^{(\alpha)}(x) - (n + 1 - x)\mathrm{L}_n^{(\alpha)}(x).$

8. Show that $\Psi(a, c; x) = \frac{1}{\Gamma(a)} \int_0^{\infty} e^{-xt} t^{a-1}(1 + t)^{c-a-1}\, dt$, $a > 0$, satisfies $xy'' + (c - x)y' - ay = 0$. It can be shown (see Erdélyi et al., *Higher Transcendental Functions*, p. 257) that

$$\Psi(a, c; x) = \frac{\Gamma(1 - c)}{\Gamma(a - c + 1)} \Phi(a, c; x) + \frac{\Gamma(c - 1)}{\Gamma(a)} x^{1-c}\Phi(a - x + 1; 2 - c; x).$$

Prove that (see Exercise 6):
(a) $\Psi(a-) - (2a - c + x)\Psi + a(a - c + 1)\Psi(a+) = 0.$
(b) $(c - a - 1)\Psi(c-) - (c - 1 + x)\Psi + x\Psi(c+) = 0.$
(c) $\Psi - a\Psi(a+) - \Psi(c-) = 0.$

9. Prove:
(a) $\operatorname{erf} x = x\Phi(\frac{1}{2}, \frac{3}{2}; -x^2)$.
(b) $\operatorname{erfc} x = e^{-x^2}\Psi(\frac{1}{2}, \frac{1}{2}; x^2)$.
(c) $Si(x) = \frac{1}{2}\pi - \frac{1}{2}ie^{-ix}\Psi(1, 1; ix) + \frac{1}{2}ie^{ix}\Psi(1, 1; -ix)$.
(d) $Ci(x) = -\frac{1}{2}e^{-ix}\Psi(1, 1; ix) - \frac{1}{2}e^{ix}\Psi(1, 1; -ix)$.
(e) $H_n(2^{-1/2}x) = 2^{n-(1/2)}x\Psi(\frac{1}{2} - \frac{1}{2}n, \frac{3}{2}; \frac{1}{2}x^2)$.
(f) $\Gamma(a) - \Gamma(a, x) = a^{-1}x^a\Phi(a, a+1; -x) = e^{-x}\Psi(1-a, 1-a; x)$,
where

$$\Gamma(a, x) = \int_x^\infty e^{-t}t^{a-1}\,dt.$$

10. Define the difference operator by $\Delta_\alpha F(\alpha) = F(\alpha+1) - F(\alpha)$, $\Delta_\alpha^n F(\alpha) = \Delta_\alpha[\Delta_\alpha^{n-1}F(\alpha)]$, $n = 2, 3, \cdots$. Show that:

(a) $\Delta_\alpha^n F(\alpha) = \sum_{k=0}^{n} (-1)^{n-k}\binom{n}{k} f(\alpha+k)$.

(b) $L_n^{(\alpha)}(x) = \dfrac{(-1)^n\Gamma(\alpha+n+1)}{n!x^\alpha}\Delta_\alpha^n \dfrac{x^\alpha}{\Gamma(\alpha+1)}$.

11. Tchebichef's polynomials of a discrete variable are defined as

$$t_n(x) = n!\Delta^n\binom{x}{n}\binom{x-N}{n}, \qquad n = 0, 1, \cdots, N-1.$$

Show that

(a) $\sum_{x=0}^{N-1} t_m(x)t_n(x) = 0, \qquad m \neq n,\ m, n = 0, 1, \cdots, N-1.$

(b) $t_n(N-1-x) = (-1)^n t_n(x)$.

(c) $(x+2)(x-N+2)\,\Delta^2 t_n(x) + [(2x-N+3) - n(n+1)]\,\Delta t_n(x) - n(n+1)t_n(x) = 0.$

(d) $\lim_{N\to\infty} N^{-n}t_n(Nx) = P_n(2x-1)$, where $P_n(x)$ is the Legendre polynomial.

12. Establish the following series expansions:

(a) $f(x) = \frac{1}{2} + \sum_{n=1}^{\infty} H_{n-1}(0)H_n(x);\ f(x) = \begin{cases} 0, & x \le 0 \\ 1, & x > 0 \end{cases}$, $f(x)$ normalized.

(b) $|x| = \dfrac{1}{\sqrt{\pi}}\sum_{n=0}^{\infty}\dfrac{(-1)^n(-\frac{1}{2})_n}{(2n)!}H_{2n}(x)$.

(c) $x^2 = \Gamma(\alpha+3)\sum_{n=0}^{\infty}\dfrac{(-2)_n L_n^{(\alpha)}(x)}{\Gamma(\alpha+n+1)}$.

13. Show that

(a) $1 + \sum_{n=1}^{\infty}[L_n(x) - L_{n-1}(x)]^2 = e^x$.

(b) $\sum_{n=0}^{\infty}\left[\int_0^t L_n(x)\,dx\right]^2 = e^t - 1$.

(c) $[L_n^{(\alpha)}(x)]^2 = \dfrac{\Gamma(1+\alpha+n)}{n!}\sum_{k=0}^{\infty}\dfrac{(2n-2k)!(2k)!L_{2k}^{(2\alpha)}(2x)}{\Gamma(1+\alpha+k)k!(n-k)!}$.

(d) $$\mathrm{L}_n^{(\alpha)}(x)\mathrm{L}_n^{(\alpha)}(y) = \frac{\Gamma(1+\alpha+n)}{n!}\sum_{k=0}^{\infty}\frac{\mathrm{L}_{n-k}^{(\alpha+2k)}(x+y)(xy)^k}{\Gamma(1+\alpha+k)k!}.$$

14. Show that the most general solution of the functional equation

$$2^{n/2}f_n(x\sqrt{2}) = \sum_{r=0}^{n}\binom{n}{r}f_r(x)f_{n-r}(x)$$

is $f_n(x) = c^n e^{ax^2}\mathrm{H}_n(bx/c)$, a, b, c constants.

Hint: Let

$$g(x, y) = \sum_{n=0}^{\infty}\frac{f_n(x)y^n}{n!}, \qquad |y| < 1.$$

Show that $g(\sqrt{2}x, \sqrt{2}y) = g^2(x, y)$. The general continuous function satisfying this equation is $e^{ax^2+2bxy-c^2y^2}$.

15. Show that if $h_n(x) = 2^{-n/2}(-1)^n\mathrm{H}_n\,(x/\sqrt{2})$, then if $a_{rs} = h_{r+s}(x)$, where a_{rs} is the element occurring in the rth row and sth column, $r, s = 0, 1, \cdots, n$, of a determinant of order $n+1$, such a determinant represented as $|a_{rs}|$, then

$$|h_{r+s}(x)| = (-1)^{1/2n(n+1)}2!3!\cdots n!$$

Chapter 16

Bessel Functions

1. Bessel's differential equation. If in the associated Legendre differential equation (A_2, p. 509):

$$(1 - t^2)y'' - 2ty' + \left[n(n+1) - \frac{m^2}{1-t^2}\right]y = 0,$$

we let $t = \cos\theta$, the equation may be written in the form

$$\frac{1}{\sin\theta}\frac{d}{d\theta}\left(\sin\theta\frac{dy}{d\theta}\right) + \left[n(n+1) - \frac{m^2}{\sin^2\theta}\right]y = 0.$$

Now let $\theta = x/n$ and let $n \to \infty$. Since for n sufficiently large, θ is small, and hence equal to $\sin\theta$, we can let $n \to \infty$ in

$$\frac{1}{x}\frac{d}{dx}\left(x\frac{dy}{dx}\right) + \left(1 + \frac{1}{n} - \frac{m^2}{x^2}\right)y = 0,$$

to obtain

$$x^2y'' + xy' + (x^2 - m^2)y = 0.$$

This equation is known as **Bessel's differential equation.** For the present, m is a parameter of the differential equation that assumes only integral values. This second-order linear differential equation has two linearly independent solutions. We shall obtain one of them as the limit of the associated Legendre function. For this purpose, we use the integral representation (A_9, p. 510).

$$P_n^m(x) = \frac{(n+m)!}{2\pi i^m n!}\int_{-\pi}^{\pi}[\cos\theta + i\sin\theta\cos\phi]^n e^{-im\phi}\,d\phi.$$

We let $\theta = x/n$, and write

$$\frac{n!P_n^m(x)}{(n+m)!} = \frac{1}{2\pi i^m}\int_{-\pi}^{\pi}\left[\cos\frac{x}{n} + i\sin\frac{x}{n}\cos\phi\right]^n e^{-im\phi}\,d\phi.$$

Before we let $n \to \infty$, we note that for n sufficiently large, $\sin(x/n) = x/n$ and $\cos(x/n)$ is approximately equal to 1. Now we consider

$$\lim_{n\to\infty}\left[1 + i\frac{x}{n}\cos\phi\right]^n = e^{ix\cos\phi},$$

so that

$$\lim_{n\to\infty}\frac{n!P_n^m(x)}{(n+m)!} = \frac{1}{2\pi i^m}\int_{-\pi}^{\pi} e^{i(x\cos\phi - m\phi)}\,d\phi.$$

This solution of Bessel's differential equation is called the **Bessel function of the first kind of order m.** It is denoted by $J_m(x)$. (We have actually arrived at this solution of Bessel's differential equation by interchanging the operations of taking a limit and differentiation that requires justification; however, it is easier to verify that Bessel's function is indeed a solution of Bessel's differential equation.) This definition requires that m be a nonnegative integer, since we have used an integral representation of $P_n^m(x)$, which is valid only for these values. However, we can define for m a positive integer

$$J_{-m}(x) = \frac{1}{2\pi i^{-m}}\int_{-\pi}^{\pi} e^{i(x\cos\phi + m\phi)}\,d\phi.$$

Replacing ϕ by $-\phi$ in the integral yields

$$J_{-m}(x) = \frac{1}{2\pi i^{-m}}\int_{-\pi}^{\pi} e^{i(x\cos\phi - m\phi)}\,d\phi = (-1)^m J_m(x).$$

Hence $J_m(x)$ is now defined for m any integer.

2. Bessel functions of the first kind. The Bessel functions of the first kind of integral order satisfy the following identities:

B₁: $J_m(x) = \lim_{n\to\infty}\dfrac{n!P_n^m(x)}{(n+m)!}.$

B₂: $J_m(x) = \dfrac{1}{2\pi i^m}\displaystyle\int_{-\pi}^{\pi} e^{i(x\cos\phi - m\phi)}\,d\phi.$

B₃: $J_{-m}(x) = (-1)^m J_m(x).$

B₄: $x^2J_m''(x) + xJ_m'(x) + (x^2 - m^2)J_m(x) = 0.$
(Differential equation.)

B₅: $J_m(x) = \dfrac{1}{\pi}\displaystyle\int_0^{\pi}\cos(x\sin\phi - m\phi)\,d\phi.$

B₆: $e^{x[t-(1/t)]/2} = \displaystyle\sum_{m=-\infty}^{\infty} J_m(x)t^m.$

(Generating function.)

B₇: $J_m(x) = \sum_{k=0}^{\infty} \frac{(-1)^k (x/2)^{2k+m}}{k!(k+m)!}, \qquad m = 0, 1, 2, \cdots.$

$J_{-m}(x) = \sum_{k=m}^{\infty} \frac{(-1)^k (x/2)^{2k-m}}{k!(k-m)!}, \qquad m = 1, 2, \cdots.$

B₈: $J_m(-x) = (-1)^m J_m(x).$

B₉: $\frac{d}{dx}[x^m J_m(x)] = x^m J_{m-1}(x).$

B₁₀: $\frac{d}{dx}[x^{-m} J_m(x)] = -x^{-m} J_{m+1}(x).$

B₁₁: $xJ'_m(x) + mJ_m(x) = xJ_{m-1}(x).$
B₁₂: $xJ'_m(x) - mJ_m(x) = -xJ_{m+1}(x).$
B₁₃: $xJ_{m+1}(x) = 2mJ_m(x) - xJ_{m-1}(x).$
(Recurrence formula.)
B₁₄: $2J'_m(x) = J_{m-1}(x) - J_{m+1}(x).$

Proofs. B_1 is the definition of $J_m(x)$ for m a nonnegative integer, and B_2 is the definition of $J_m(x)$ for m a negative integer. We have already established B_2 for m a nonnegative integer. As we have seen, B_3 follows immediately from B_2. For m a negative integer, B_1 follows from

$$P_n^{-m}(x) = \frac{(-1)^m (n-m)!}{(n+m)!} P_n^m(x),$$

B_3, and B_1 for nonnegative integers. We have established B_4 for m a nonnegative integer, and by B_3, it follows for m a negative integer.

B_5: Let $\phi = \theta - \pi/2$ in B_2, simplify, and take the real part of both sides.

B_6: Expand the left-hand side in a Laurent series (see p. 324, Exercise 9). Alternatively, let $\phi = \theta - (\pi/2)$ in B_2 to obtain

$$J_m(x) = \frac{1}{2\pi} \int_{-\pi}^{\pi} e^{ix \sin \theta} e^{-im\theta} \, d\theta,$$

which indicates that $J_m(x)$ is the Fourier coefficient of $e^{ix \sin \theta}$. Hence, $e^{ix \sin \theta} = \sum_{m=-\infty}^{\infty} J_m(x) e^{im\theta}$. Letting $t = e^{i\theta}$ yields the result.

B_7: With B_6,

$$\sum_{m=-\infty}^{\infty} J_m(x) t^m = e^{xt/2} e^{-x/2t} = \sum_{n=0}^{\infty} \frac{x^n t^n}{2^n n!} \sum_{k=0}^{\infty} \frac{(-1)^k x^k}{2^k t^k k!}$$

$$= \sum_{m=0}^{\infty} t^m \left[\left(\frac{x}{2}\right)^m \sum_{k=0}^{\infty} \frac{-(x/2)^{2k}}{k!(k+m)!} \right]$$

$$+ \sum_{m=1}^{\infty} t^{-m} \left(-\frac{x}{2}\right)^m \sum_{k=0}^{\infty} \frac{(x/2)^{2k}}{k!(k+m)!},$$

and equating coefficients of t^m yields the first result. The second result is obtained by the use of B_3, and the first result by making the appropriate change of index in the summation.

B_8 follows immediately from B_7.

B_9 and B_{10} can be established with the use of B_7.

B_{11} and B_{12} follow with the use of B_9 and B_{10}.

B_{13} and B_{14} follow from B_{11} and B_{12}.

B_7 suggests the generalization that gives rise to the definition of Bessel functions of order more general than integral order. We need but generalize $(k + m)!$ to $\Gamma(k + \nu + 1)$, where ν is any real number, $\nu \neq -1, -2, \cdots$, and show that the series is convergent for all x and these values of ν. Hence, we define the **Bessel function of the first kind of order** ν as

$$\mathbf{B_7'}: \quad J_\nu(x) = \sum_{k=0}^{\infty} \frac{(-1)^k (x/2)^{2k+\nu}}{k!\Gamma(k + \nu + 1)}, \qquad \nu \neq -1, -2, \cdots.$$

$$J_\nu(x) = \sum_{k=\nu}^{\infty} \frac{(-1)^k (x/2)^{2k-\nu}}{k!(k - \nu)!}, \qquad \nu = -1, -2, \cdots.$$

The Bessel functions of order ν, where ν is any real number, satisfy the following identities:

$$\mathbf{B_4'}: \quad x^2 J_\nu''(x) + xJ_\nu'(x) + (x^2 - \nu^2)J_\nu(x) = 0.$$

(Differential equation.)

$$\mathbf{B_8'}: \quad J_\nu(-x) = (-1)^\nu J_\nu(x).$$

$$\mathbf{B_9'}: \quad \frac{d}{dx}[x^\nu J_\nu(x)] = x^\nu J_{\nu-1}(x).$$

$$\mathbf{B_{10}'}: \quad \frac{d}{dx}[x^{-\nu} J_\nu(x)] = -x^{-\nu} J_{\nu+1}(x).$$

$$\mathbf{B_{11}'}: \quad xJ_\nu'(x) + \nu J_\nu(x) = xJ_{\nu-1}(x).$$

$$\mathbf{B_{12}'}: \quad xJ_\nu'(x) - \nu J_\nu(x) = -xJ_{\nu+1}(x).$$

$$\mathbf{B_{13}'}: \quad xJ_{\nu+1}(x) = 2\nu J_\nu(x) - xJ_{\nu-1}(x).$$

(Recurrence formula.)

$$\mathbf{B_{14}'}: \quad 2J_\nu'(x) = J_{\nu-1}(x) - J_{\nu+1}(x).$$

Proofs. B_4' follows from the definition. The remaining identities are valid, since they correspond to B_8 to B_{14}, which were established from B_7 in such a manner that the proofs did not require that m be an integer. However, B_1, B_2, B_3, B_5, and B_6 are valid only for m an integer. In view of B_6, the Bessel functions of integral order are often called **Bessel coefficients.**

Since $\Gamma(k + \nu + 1)$ is defined for complex ν (see p. 460), $\text{Re}\,\nu \neq -1, -2, \cdots$, we can define Bessel functions of the first kind of complex order by means of B_7', where ν is now complex. To complete the generalization, we can replace x in the definition by the complex variable z. It can be shown readily that the resulting series is convergent for all z.

3. Zeros and orthogonality. Let us consider the function $J_\nu(\lambda x)$, where λ is a parameter. If in Bessel's differential equation B_4' we replace x by λx, we obtain

$$\frac{d}{dx}\left[x\frac{d}{dx}J_\nu(\lambda x)\right] + \left(\lambda^2 x - \frac{\lambda^2}{x}\right)J_\nu(\lambda x) = 0.$$

Let $u = J_\nu(\lambda_n x)$ and $v = J(\lambda_m x)$, where λ_n and λ_m are two different values of λ. Then

$$\text{(a)}\quad \frac{d}{dx}(xu') + \left(\lambda_n^2 x - \frac{\lambda^2}{x}\right)u = 0.$$

$$\text{(b)}\quad \frac{d}{dx}(xv') + \left(\lambda_m^2 x - \frac{\lambda^2}{x}\right)v = 0.$$

Multiplying (a) by v and (b) by u, and subtracting, we obtain

$$\frac{d}{dx}[x(u'v - v'u)] = (\lambda_n^2 - \lambda_m^2)xuv.$$

Now we wish to integrate both sides from 0 to c, where $c > 0$ is a constant. From B_7', it follows that $J_\nu(x)/x^\nu$ is continuous for all x, if $\nu > -1$. Hence, xuv can be written in the form $x^{2\nu+1}g(x)$, where g is continuous for all x if $\nu > -1$; hence, xuv is continuous for all x if $\nu > -1$. Integrating, we have

$$\text{(A)}\quad \int_0^c xJ_\nu(\lambda_n x)J_\nu(\lambda_m x)\,dx = \frac{c}{\lambda_n^2 - \lambda_m^2}[J_\nu'(\lambda_n c)J_\nu(\lambda_m c) - J_\nu(\lambda_n c)J_\nu'(\lambda_m c)], \qquad \nu > -1.$$

First, this result will be used in the proof of the

THEOREM. The zeros of $J_\nu(x)$, $\nu > -1$, are real, simple if they are nonzero, and form an infinite sequence.

Proof. Assume that α is a complex zero of $J_\nu(x)$. If α were pure imaginary, then when substituted for x in B_7', we would obtain a series of positive terms, contradicting the fact that α is a zero. Hence, $\alpha^2 - \bar{\alpha}^2 \neq 0$. Let $\lambda_n = \alpha$ and $\lambda_m = \bar{\alpha}$ and $c = 1$ in (A). Since $J_\nu(\alpha) = 0$ and, as is readily seen, $J_\nu(\bar{\alpha}) = 0$, we have

$$\int_0^1 xJ_\nu(\alpha x)J_\nu(\bar{\alpha}x)\,dx = 0,$$

or

$$\int_0^1 xJ_\nu(\alpha x)\overline{J_\nu(\alpha x)}\,dx = \int_0^1 x|J_\nu(\alpha x)|^2\,dx = 0,$$

which is impossible because the integrand is positive in $0 < x < 1$.

Bessel's differential equation B'_4 has only zero as a singular point. This is a multiple zero of $J_\nu(x)$, as B'_7 indicates. Let x_0 be any nonzero zero of $J_\nu(x)$. Then x_0 is a simple zero; for if this were not the case, both $J_\nu(x_0) = 0$ and $J'_\nu(x_0) = 0$ so that, by B'_7, $J''_\nu(x_0) = 0$, and by repeated differentiation of B'_7, we should have $J_\nu^{(p)}(x_0) = 0$, $p = 0, 1, \cdots$; hence, by Taylor's theorem, $J_\nu(x) = 0$.

The proof that the zeros of $J_\nu(x)$ form an infinite sequence will be omitted. It can be found in Watson, *A Treatise on the Theory of Bessel Functions*; which, incidentally, is the standard work on Bessel functions. The positive zeros of $J_\nu(x)$ are denoted as

$$j_{\nu,1} < j_{\nu,2} < \cdots < j_{\nu,n} < \cdots.$$

Given $J_\nu(x)$, $\nu > -1$; let ν be fixed. Let $\lambda_n = j_{\nu,n}/c$, $n = 1, 2, \cdots$, so that $J_\nu(\lambda_n c) = 0$. We prove that the sequence of functions $\{J_\nu(\nu_n x)\}$ is orthogonal with respect to the weight function x in $0 \le x \le c$; i.e., we have

$$\mathbf{B'_{15}}: \quad \int_0^c xJ_\nu(\lambda_n x)J_\nu(\lambda_m x)\,dx = 0, \qquad m \ne n, \quad m, n = 1, 2, \cdots,$$

which follows immediately from (A).

4. Bessel series. Given a function f defined in $0 \le x \le c$, $c > 0$. Assume that we can represent this function in the series

$$f(x) = \sum_{n=1}^{\infty} c_n J_\nu(\lambda_n x).$$

If we multiply both sides of this equation by $xJ_\nu(\lambda_m x)$, integrate term by term from 0 to c, and use the orthogonality property, we find that

$$c_n = \frac{\int_0^c xf(x)J_\nu(\lambda_n x)\,dx}{h_n},$$

where

$$h_n = \int_0^c xJ_\nu^2(\lambda_n x)\,dx.$$

Let us determine h_n. We multiply both sides of

$$\frac{d}{dx}\left[x\frac{d}{dx}J_\nu(\lambda x)\right] + \left(\lambda^2 x - \frac{\nu^2}{x}\right)J_\nu(\lambda x) = 0$$

by $2x(d/dx)J_\nu(\lambda x)$ and write the resulting equation in the form

$$\frac{d}{dx}\left[x\frac{d}{dx}J_\nu(\lambda x)\right]^2 + (\lambda^2x^2 - \nu^2)\frac{d}{dx}[J_\nu(\lambda x)]^2 = 0.$$

Integrating (the second term by parts) from 0 to c, we obtain

$$[cJ'_\nu(\lambda c)]^2 + (\lambda^2c^2 - \nu^2)J_\nu^2(\lambda c) - 2\lambda^2\int_0^c xJ_\nu^2(\lambda x)\,dx = 0.$$

Using B'_{12},

$$2\lambda^2\int_0^c xJ_\nu^2(\lambda x)\,dx = [\nu J_\nu(\lambda c) - \lambda cJ_{\nu+1}(\lambda c)]^2 + (\lambda^2c^2 - \nu^2)J_\nu^2(\lambda c).$$

If λ_n, $n = 1, 2, \cdots$, are the positive roots of $J_\nu(\lambda c) = 0$, we obtain

$$\mathbf{B}'_{16}: \quad \int_0^c x J_\nu^2(\lambda_n x)\, dx = \frac{c^2}{2} J_{\nu+1}^2(\lambda_n c).$$

The series $\sum_{n=1}^{\infty} c_n J_\nu(\lambda_n x)$, where

$$c_n = \frac{\int_0^c x f(x) J_\nu(\lambda_n x)\, dx}{h_n},$$

is called the **Bessel series** of f. The next theorem indicates sufficient conditions under which the Bessel series of a function converges to certain values of that function.

BESSEL EXPANSION THEOREM. If f is defined in $0 \le x \le c$, $c > 0$, and $\int_0^c \sqrt{x}\, f(x)\, dx$ exists (or is absolutely convergent if it is an improper integral), then

$$\frac{f(x+) + f(x-)}{2} = \sum_{n=1}^{\infty} c_n J_\nu(\lambda_n x),$$

where

$$c_n = \frac{2}{c^2 J_{\nu+1}^2(\lambda_n c)} \int_0^c x f(x) J_\nu(\lambda_n x)\, dx,$$

and λ_n, $n = 1, 2, \cdots$, are the positive roots of $J_\nu(\lambda c) = 0$.

The proof of this theorem can be found in Watson. The integral condition ensures convergence at the end points of the interval.

EXAMPLE. Expand in a series of the functions $J_0(\lambda_n x)$, where λ_n are the positive roots of $J_0(2\lambda) = 0$:

$$f(x) = \begin{cases} 1, & 0 < x < 1 \\ \frac{1}{2}, & x = 1 \\ 0, & 1 < x < 2 \end{cases}$$

Solution

$$c_n = \frac{1}{2J_1^2(2\lambda_n)} \int_0^2 x f(x) J_0(\lambda_n x)\, dx$$

$$= \frac{1}{2\lambda_n J_1^2(2\lambda_n)} \int_0^1 \lambda_n x J_0(\lambda_n x)\, dx$$

$$= \frac{1}{2\lambda_n^2 J_1^2(2\lambda_n)} \int_0^{\lambda_n} u J_0(u)\, du$$

$$= \frac{1}{2\lambda_n^2 J_1^2(2\lambda_n)} \int_0^{\lambda_n} d[u J_1(u)]$$

(since by B_{11}, $u J_0(u) = u J_1'(u) + J_1(u) = [u J_1(u)]'$)

$$= \frac{J_1(\lambda_n)}{2\lambda_n J_1^2(2\lambda_n)}.$$

Hence,

$$f(x) = \frac{1}{2} \sum_{n=1}^{\infty} \frac{J_1(\lambda_n)}{\lambda_n J_1^2(2\lambda_n)} J_0(\lambda_n x)$$

is the required expansion.

EXERCISES

1. Determine these approximate values:
(a) $J_0(0.1) = 0.9975$; (b) $J_0(1) = 0.7652$; (c) $J_0(2) = 0.2239$;
(d) $J_1(1) = 0.4401$; (e) $J_1(2) = 0.5767$.

2. Graph $J_0(x)$ and $J_1(x)$ on the same set of coordinate axes. What is the behavior of the functional values as x increases? What can you say of the zeros of $J_1(x)$ relative to those of $J_0(x)$? What well-known curves do these curves bring to mind?

3. Show that

(a) $J_m(x) = (-1)^m \left(\frac{d}{x\,dx}\right)^m J_0(x).$

[*Hint:* Use the definition of $P_n^m(x)$ and B_1.]

(b) $\left(\frac{d}{x\,dx}\right)^m [x^\nu J_\nu(x)] = x^{\nu-m} J_{\nu-m}(x).$

(c) $\left(\frac{d}{x\,dx}\right)^m [x^{-\nu} J_\nu(x)] = (-1)^m x^{-\nu-m} J_{\nu+m}(x).$

4. Show that

(a) $J_{-1/2}(x) = \sqrt{\frac{2}{\pi x}} \cos x.$

(b) $J_{1/2}(x) = \sqrt{\frac{2}{\pi x}} \sin x.$

(c) $J_{3/2}(x) = \sqrt{\frac{2}{\pi x}} \left(\frac{\sin x}{x} - \cos x\right).$

(d) $J_{-3/2}(x) = -\sqrt{\frac{2}{\pi x}} \left(\sin x + \frac{\cos x}{x}\right).$

(e) $J_{5/2}(x) = \sqrt{\frac{2}{\pi x}} \left(\frac{3 - x^2}{x^2} \sin x - \frac{3 \cos x}{x}\right).$

(f) $J_{-5/2}(x) = \sqrt{\frac{2}{\pi x}} \left(\frac{3}{x} \sin x + \frac{3 - x^2}{x^2} \cos x\right).$

(g) $J_{m+1/2}(x) = (-1)^m \sqrt{\frac{2}{\pi}}\, x^{m+1/2} \left(\frac{d}{x\,dx}\right)^m \left[\frac{\sin x}{x}\right].$

These functions are often called the **half-order Bessel functions,** or **spherical Bessel functions.** They are elementary functions.

5. Prove:

(a) $x^2 J_\nu''(x) = [\nu(\nu - 1) - x^2]J_\nu(x) + xJ_{\nu+1}(x)$.
(b) $4J_\nu''(x) = J_{\nu-2}(x) - 2J_\nu(x) + J_{\nu+2}(x)$.
(c) $8J_\nu'''(x) = J_{\nu-3}(x) - 3J_{\nu-1}(x) + 3J_{\nu+1}(x) - J_{\nu-3}(x)$.
(d) $4\nu J_\nu(x)J_\nu'(x) = x[J_{\nu-1}^2(x) - J_{\nu+1}^2(x)]$.

(e) $\dfrac{d}{dx}[J_\nu^2(x) + J_{\nu+1}^2(x)] = 2\left[\dfrac{\nu}{x} J_\nu^2(x) - \dfrac{\nu+1}{x}\right] J_{\nu+1}^2(x)$.

(f) $\dfrac{d}{dx}[xJ_\nu(x)J_{\nu+1}(x)] = x[J_\nu^2(x) - J_{\nu+1}^2(x)]$.

(g) $\dfrac{d}{dx}[x^2 J_{\nu-1}(x)J_{\nu+1}(x)] = 2x^2 J_\nu(x)J_\nu'(x)$.

(h) $J_{\nu-1}(x) = \dfrac{2}{x}[\nu J_\nu(x) - (\nu + 2)J_{\nu+2}(x) + (\nu + 4)J_{\nu+4}(x) + \cdots]$.

(i) $J_\nu'(x) = \dfrac{2}{x}\left[\dfrac{\nu}{2} J_\nu(x) - (\nu + 2)J_{\nu+2}(x) + (\nu + 4)J_{\nu+4}(x) + \cdots\right]$.

(j) $\displaystyle\int_0^x tJ_\nu^2(t)\,dt = \frac{x^2}{2}[J_\nu^2(x) - J_{\nu-1}(x)J_{\nu+1}(x)]$.

6. Show that between two zeros of $J_\nu(x)$ there is at least one zero of $J_{\nu-1}(x)$ and at least one zero of $J_{\nu+1}(x)$. (*Hint:* Use B_9', B_{10}', and Rolle's theorem.)

7. Show that

(a) $\displaystyle\int_0^{\pi/2} J_0(x\cos\theta)\cos\theta\,d\theta = \frac{\sin x}{x}$.

(b) $\displaystyle\int_0^{\pi/2} J_1(x\cos\theta)\,d\theta = \frac{1 - \cos x}{x}$.

(c) $\displaystyle\int_0^a \frac{x}{\sqrt{a^2 - x^2}} J_0(kx\sin\theta)\,dx = \frac{\sin(ka\sin\theta)}{k\sin\theta}$.

(*Hint:* Let $x = a\sin\phi$.)

8. Show that

(a) $\displaystyle 2^n \frac{d^n}{dx^n} J_\nu(x) = \sum_{k=0}^{n} (-1)^{n-k}\binom{n}{k} J_{\nu+n-2k}(x)$.

(b) $\displaystyle\int_0^x \frac{J_\nu(t)}{t}\,dt = \frac{1}{\nu}\left[J_\nu(x) + 2\sum_{k=0}^{\infty} J_{2k+\nu+2}(x)\right], \qquad n > 0.$

9. Show that

(a) $\displaystyle\cos(x\sin\theta) = J_0(x) + 2\sum_{m=1}^{\infty} J_{2m}(x)\cos 2m\theta$.

(b) $\displaystyle\sin(x\sin\theta) = 2\sum_{m=0}^{\infty} J_{2m+1}(x)\sin(2m + 1)\theta$.

(c) $\displaystyle\cos(x\cosh\theta) = J_0(x) + 2\sum_{m=1}^{\infty} (-1)^m J_{2m}(x)\cosh 2m\theta$.

(d) $\sin(x \cosh \theta) = 2 \sum_{m=1}^{\infty} (-1)^{m+1} J_{2m+1}(x) \cosh(2m+1)\theta.$

(e) $\cos(x \cos \theta) = J_0(x) + 2 \sum_{m=1}^{\infty} (-1)^m J_{2m}(x) \cos 2m\theta.$

(f) $\sin(x \cos \theta) = 2 \sum_{m=1}^{\infty} (-1)^{m+1} J_{2m+1}(x) \cos(2m+1)\theta.$

(g) $\cos x = J_0(x) + 2 \sum_{m=1}^{\infty} (-1)^m J_{2m}(x).$

(h) $\sin x = 2 \sum_{m=1}^{\infty} (-1)^{m+1} J_{2m+1}(x).$

(i) $x = 2 \sum_{m=0}^{\infty} (2m+1) J_{2m+1}(x).$

(*Hint:* Differentiate (b) and let $\theta = 0$.)

(j) $x \sin x = 2 \sum_{m=1}^{\infty} (2m)^2 J_{2m}(x).$

(k) $\int_0^{\pi/2} \cos(x \sin \theta)\, d\theta = \int_0^{\pi/2} \cos(x \cos \theta)\, d\theta = \frac{\pi}{2} J_0(x).$

(l) $\int_0^{\pi/2} \sin(x \sin \theta)\, d\theta = \int_0^{\pi/2} \sin(x \cos \theta)\, d\theta = 2 \sum_{m=0}^{\infty} \frac{J_{2m+1}(x)}{2m+1}.$

(m) $\int_0^{\pi/2} \cos(x \cos \theta) \cos 2m\theta\, d\theta = (-1)^m \frac{\pi}{2} J_{2m}(x).$

(n) $\int_0^{\pi/2} \sin(x \cos \theta) \cos(2m+1)\theta\, d\theta = (-1)^m \frac{\pi}{2} J_{2m+1}(x).$

(o) $\int_0^{\pi} \sin(x \cos \theta) \sin^{2n} \theta\, d\theta = 0.$

(p) $\sin(\theta - x \sin \phi) = \sum_{m=-\infty}^{\infty} J_m(x) \sin(\theta + m\phi).$

10. Show that

(a) $J_0^2(x) + 2 \sum_{m=1}^{\infty} J_m^2(x) = 1.$ (b) $|J_0(x)| \le 1.$

(c) $|J_m(x)| \le \frac{1}{\sqrt{2}}, \quad m \ge 1.$

11. Show that

(a) $\sum_{n=0}^{\infty} \frac{P_n(\cos \theta)}{n!} t^n = e^{t \cos \theta} J_0(t \sin \theta)$, $P_n(x)$ is the Legendre polynomial.

(b) $\sum_{n=0}^{\infty} \frac{J_n(x) t^n}{n!} = J_0(\sqrt{x^2 - 2xt}).$

(c) $\sum_{n=0}^{\infty} \frac{J_{\nu+n}(x)t^n}{n!} = \left(\frac{x-2t}{x}\right)^{-\nu/2} J_\nu(\sqrt{x^2-2xt}).$

(d) $\left[\sum_{n=0}^{\infty} \frac{P_{2n}(\cos\theta)}{(2n)!}\right]^2 - \left[\sum_{n=0}^{\infty} \frac{P_{2n+1}(\cos\theta)}{(2n+1)!}\right]^2 = [J_0(\sin\theta)]^2,$

$P_n(x)$ is the Legendre polynomial.

12. (a) Show that if x_0 is any zero of $J_\nu(x)$, then
(1) $J_{\nu-1}(x_0) = -J_{\nu+1}(x_0)$. (2) $J_\nu'(x_0) = J_{\nu-1}(x_0)$.
(3) $4J_\nu''(x_0) = J_{\nu-2}(x_0) + J_{\nu+2}(x_0)$.
(b) Show that $J_\nu(x)$ has a relative maximum or relative minimum at x_0 if

(1) $x_0 = \frac{\nu J_\nu(x_0)}{J_{\nu+1}(x_0)}$, (2) $x_0 = \frac{\nu J_\nu(x_0)}{J_{\nu-1}(x_0)}$, (3) $J_{\nu-1}(x_0) = J_{\nu+1}(x_0)$.

13. Show that

(a) $\lim_{x\to 0} \frac{J_\nu(x)}{x^\nu} = \frac{1}{2^\nu \Gamma(\nu+1)}$. (b) $\lim_{\nu\to\infty} J_\nu(x) = 0$ for x finite.

14. Show that

$$J_\nu(x) = \left(\frac{x}{2}\right)^\nu \frac{{}_0F_1\left(\nu+1; \frac{-x^2}{4}\right)}{\Gamma(\nu+1)} = \left(\frac{x}{2}\right)^\nu e^{-ix} \frac{{}_1F_1(\nu+\frac{1}{2}; 2\nu+1; 2ix)}{\Gamma(\nu+1)}.$$

(See p. 513, Exercise 14.)

15. Show that each of the following is an integral representation of $J_\nu(x)$, $\nu > -\frac{1}{2}$:

(a) $\frac{2(\frac{1}{2}x)^\nu}{\Gamma(\nu+\frac{1}{2})\sqrt{\pi}} \int_0^{\pi/2} \cos(x\sin\theta)(\cos\theta)^{2\nu}\, d\theta.$

(b) $\frac{(\frac{1}{2}x)^\nu}{\Gamma(\nu+\frac{1}{2})\sqrt{\pi}} \int_{-(\pi/2)}^{\pi/2} e^{ix\sin\theta}(\cos\theta)^{2\nu}\, d\theta.$

(c) $\frac{(\frac{1}{2}x)^\nu}{\Gamma(\nu+\frac{1}{2})\sqrt{\pi}} \int_{-1}^{1} e^{ixt}(1-t^2)^{\nu-1/2}\, dt.$

(d) $\frac{2(\frac{1}{2}x)^\nu}{\Gamma(\nu+\frac{1}{2})\sqrt{\pi}} \int_0^{1} (1-t^2)^{\nu-1/2}\cos(xt)\, dt.$

(e) $\frac{(\frac{1}{2}x)^\nu}{\Gamma(\nu+\frac{1}{2})\sqrt{\pi}} \int_0^{\pi} e^{ix\cos\theta}(\sin\theta)^{2\nu}\, d\theta.$

16. Establish each of the following:

(a) $\int_0^x t^3 J_0(t)\, dt = x^3 J_1(x) - 2x^2 J_2(x).$

(b) $\int_0^\pi e^{t-i\alpha x\cos\theta}\, d\theta = \pi e^t J_0(\alpha x).$

(c) $\frac{2}{\pi}\int_0^{\pi/2} \frac{\sin(x\sin\theta)}{\sin\theta}\cos 2m\theta\, d\theta = \int_0^x J_{2m}(t)\, dt.$

(*Hint:* Use B_5 and an interchange of order of integration.)

(d) $\int_0^\infty e^{-st}t^{\nu+1}J_\nu(\alpha t)\,dt = \dfrac{2^\nu\Gamma(\nu+\frac{1}{2})\alpha^\nu}{\sqrt{\pi}(s^2+\alpha^2)^{\nu+(1/2)}}.$

(Laplace integral.)

(e) $\int_0^\infty x^{-\nu}J_\nu(\alpha x)\cos(xy)\,dx = \dfrac{\sqrt{\pi}(\alpha^2-y^2)^{\nu-(1/2)}}{(2\alpha)^\nu\Gamma(\nu+\frac{1}{2})}.$

(Fourier cosine transform.)

17. Show that

(a) $\lim\limits_{n\to\infty}\left[n^{-\alpha}L_n^{(\alpha)}\left(\dfrac{x}{n}\right)\right] = x^{-1/2\alpha}J_\alpha(2\sqrt{x}),$

where $L_n^{(\alpha)}(t)$ is the Laguerre polynomial.

(b) $\lim\limits_{n\to\infty}\left[n^{-\alpha}P_n^{(\alpha,\beta)}\left(1-\dfrac{x^2}{2n^2}\right)\right] = \left(\dfrac{x}{2}\right)^{-\alpha}J_\alpha(x),$

where $P_n^{(\alpha,\beta)}(t)$ is the Jacobi polynomial.

18. Prove:

(a) $J_m(x+y) = \sum\limits_{k=-\infty}^{\infty} J_k(x)J_{m-k}(y),\qquad m$ an integer.

(Addition formula.)

(b) $J_\nu(\lambda x) = \lambda^\nu\sum\limits_{k=0}^{\infty}\dfrac{1}{k!}J_{\nu+k}(x)\left[\dfrac{1-\lambda^2}{2}x\right]^k,\qquad \lambda$ arbitrary.

(Multiplication formula.)

◇ **19.** (a) The function

$$Y_\nu(x) = \frac{J_\nu(x)\cos\nu\pi - J_{-\nu}(x)}{\sin\nu\pi}$$

is called the **Bessel function of the second kind** (or Neumann's function). If ν is an integer, the expression on the right-hand side is indeterminate, and we define $Y_m(x) = \lim\limits_{\nu\to m} Y_\nu(x)$. Show that if $J_\nu(x)$ is replaced by $Y_\nu(x)$ in B_4' to B_{14}', the identities remain valid.

(b) The functions

$$H_\nu^{(1)}(x) = J_\nu(x) + iY_\nu(x);$$
$$H_\nu^{(2)}(x) = J_\nu(x) - iY_\nu(x)$$

are called the **Bessel functions of the third kind** (or Hankel functions of the first and second kind). Show that if $J_\nu(x)$ is replaced by $H_\nu^{(1)}(x)$ or $H_\nu^{(2)}(x)$ in B_4' to B_{14}', the identities remain valid.

(c) The Bessel functions of the first, second, and third kinds are special cases of a class of functions known as **cylinder functions,** denoted by $\mathcal{C}_\nu(x)$. These are functions satisfying the identities

$$\mathcal{C}_{\nu-1}(x) + \mathcal{C}_{\nu+1}(x) = \frac{2\nu}{x}\mathcal{C}_\nu(x),$$

$$\mathcal{C}_{\nu-1}(x) - \mathcal{C}_{\nu+1}(x) = 2\mathcal{C}_\nu'(x),$$

which are B'_{13} and B'_{14} with $J_\nu(x)$ replaced by $\mathcal{C}_\nu(x)$. Are the remaining identities B'_4 to B'_{14} valid for $\mathcal{C}_\nu(x)$? Show that

$$e^{\pm kz}\mathcal{C}_\nu(kr)\begin{cases}\cos \nu\theta \\ \sin \nu\theta\end{cases}$$

are harmonic functions, where (r, θ, z) are cylindrical coordinates. This accounts for the name cylinder functions. [*Hint:* Use Problem 18(c), p. 165.]

20. (a) Establish the following Wronskians:

(1) $W[J_\nu(x), J_{-\nu}(x)] = \dfrac{-2}{\pi x} \sin \nu\pi.$

(2) $W[J_\nu(x), Y_\nu(x)] = \dfrac{2}{\pi x}.$

(3) $W[H_\nu^{(1)}(x), H_\nu^{(2)}(x)] = \dfrac{-4i}{\pi x}.$

(b) Show that the pairs of functions $J_\nu(x)$, $J_{-\nu}(x)$, ν not an integer; $J_\nu(x)$, $Y_\nu(x)$; $H_\nu^{(1)}(x)$, $H_\nu^{(2)}(x)$ are linearly independent. How can you establish the linear dependence of $J_m(x)$, $J_{-m}(x)$, m an integer, immediately?

(c) Show that the general solution of Bessel's differential equation can be written in any one of the following forms, A and B arbitrary constants:

(1) $AJ_\nu(x) + BJ_{-\nu}(x)$, ν nonintegral. (2) $AJ_\nu(x) + BY_\nu(x)$.

(3) $AH_\nu^{(1)}(x) + BH_\nu^{(2)}(x)$.

(4) $AJ_\nu(x) + BJ_\nu(x) \displaystyle\int \frac{dx}{xJ_\nu^2(x)}.$

21. Show that the indicated function is the general solution of the given differential equation:

(a) $y'' + \dfrac{1}{x} y' + 4\left(1 - \dfrac{1}{x^2}\right) y = 0; \qquad y = AJ_2(2x) + BY_2(2x).$

(b) $y'' + \dfrac{1}{x} y' + \left(3 - \dfrac{1}{4x^2}\right) y = 0; \qquad y = AJ_{1/2}(\sqrt{3}x) + BJ_{-1/2}(\sqrt{3}x).$

(c) $\dfrac{d}{dx}(xy') + \left(k^2x - \dfrac{\nu^2}{x}\right) y = 0;$

$y = AJ_m(kx) + BY_m(kx), \qquad \nu = m$, an integer;

$y = AJ_\nu(kx) + BJ_{-\nu}(kx), \qquad \nu$ nonintegral.

(d) $x^2y'' + (1 - 2a)xy' + [a^2 - b^2\nu^2 + b^2c^2x^{2b}]y = 0;$

$y = x^a[AJ_\nu(cx^b) + BY_\nu(cx^b)].$

22. The differential equation

$$x^2y'' + xy' - (x^2 + \nu^2)y = 0$$

is called the **modified** Bessel differential equation. Show that $I_\nu(x) = e^{-(1/2)\nu\pi i}J_\nu(ix)$ is a solution of this equation. $I_\nu(x)$ is called the **modified Bessel function of the first kind** of order ν. Show that $K_\nu(x) = \dfrac{\frac{1}{2}\pi[I_{-\nu}(x) - I_\nu(x)]}{\sin \nu\pi}$, where $K_m(x) = \lim_{\nu \to m} K_\nu(x)$, m an integer, is also a solution of this differential equation. $K_\nu(x)$ is called the **modified Bessel function of the second kind** of order ν. Establish the following:

(a) $I_{\nu-1}(x) - I_{\nu+1}(x) = \frac{2\nu}{x} I_\nu(x);\quad K_{\nu-1}(x) - K_{\nu+1}(x) = -\frac{2\nu}{x} K_\nu(x).$

(b) $I_{\nu-1}(x) + I_{\nu+1}(x) = 2I'_\nu(x);\quad K_{\nu-1}(x) + K_{\nu+1}(x) = -2K'_\nu(x).$

(c) $xI'_\nu(x) + \nu I_\nu(x) = xI_{\nu-1}(x);\quad xK'_\nu(x) + \nu K_\nu(x) = -xK_{\nu-1}(x).$

(d) $xI'_\nu(x) - \nu I_\nu(x) = xI_{\nu+1}(x);\quad xK'_\nu(x) - \nu K_\nu(x) = -xK_{\nu+1}(x).$

(e) $\left(\frac{d}{x\,dx}\right)^m [x^{-\nu}I_\nu(x)] = x^{-\nu-m}I_{\nu+m}(x);$

$$\left(\frac{d}{x\,dx}\right)^m [x^{-\nu}K_\nu(x)] = (-1)^m x^{-\nu-m}K_{\nu+m}(x).$$

(f) $W[I_\nu(x), K_\nu(x)] = -\frac{1}{x};\quad W[I_\nu(x), I_{-\nu}(x)] = -\frac{2\sin\nu\pi}{\pi x}.$

(g) $I_\nu(xe^{m\pi i}) = e^{m\nu\pi i}I_\nu(x).$

(h) $I_\nu(x) = \frac{2(x/2)^\nu}{\sqrt{\pi}\Gamma(\nu+\frac{1}{2})}\int_0^{\pi/2}\sin^2\theta\cosh(x\cos\theta)\,d\theta,\qquad \nu > -\frac{1}{2}.$

(i) $e^{(1/2)x[t+(1/t)]} = \sum_{m=-\infty}^{\infty} I_m(x)t^m.$

(j) $I_\nu(x) = \sum_{k=0}^{\infty}\frac{(\frac{1}{2}x)^{\nu+2k}}{k!\Gamma(\nu+k+1)}.$

Note that $I_\nu(x)$ is real.

23. Kelvin's functions are defined as

$$\begin{aligned} ber_\nu(x) &= \text{Re}\,[J_\nu(xe^{(3/4)\pi i})], \\ bei_\nu(x) &= \text{Im}\,[J_\nu(xe^{(3/4)\pi i})], \\ ker_\nu(x) &= \text{Re}\,[K_\nu(xe^{(3/4)\pi i})], \\ kei_\nu(x) &= \text{Im}\,[K_\nu(xe^{(3/4)\pi i})]. \end{aligned}$$

(If $\nu = 0$, it is omitted in the notation; note the suggestiveness of the notation.)

(a) Show that $A(ber_1(kx) + ibei_1(kx)) + B(-kei_1(kx) + iker_1(kx))$, where A and B are arbitrary constants, is the general solution of

$$x^2y'' + xy' - (ix^2k^2 + 1)y = 0.$$

(b) Show that $\int_0^a xJ_0(kxi^{3/2})\,dx = \frac{a}{k}[bei'(ka) - iber'(ka)].$

(c) Show that $ber'_1(x) - bei'_1(x) = \frac{1}{\sqrt{2}}[ber_2(x) - ber(x)].$

(d) Show that $ber'(x) + bei'(x) = \frac{1}{2}[bei_1^2(x) - ber_1^2(x)].$

(e) Show that

$$ber_m(x) = \sum_{k=0}^{\infty}\frac{(-1)^k(\frac{1}{2}x)^{m+2r}\cos\frac{3}{4}(m+2k)\pi}{k!(m+k)!};$$

$$bei_m(x) = \sum_{k=0}^{\infty}\frac{(-1)^k(\frac{1}{2}x)^{m+2k}\sin\frac{3}{4}(m+2k)\pi}{k!(m+k)!}.$$

24. Show that

(a) $1 = \frac{2}{c}\sum_{n=1}^{\infty}\frac{J_0(\lambda_n x)}{\lambda_n J_1(\lambda_n x)}, \qquad 0 < x < c, \text{ if } J_0(\lambda_n c) = 0.$

(b) $x = 2\sum_{n=1}^{\infty}\frac{J_1(\lambda_n x)}{\lambda_n J_2(\lambda_n)}, \qquad -1 < x < 1, \text{ if } J_1(\lambda) = 0.$

(c) $f(x) = \sum_{n=1}^{\infty}\frac{J_1(\lambda_n/2)J_0(\lambda_n x)}{\lambda_n J_1^2(\lambda_n)}; \quad f(x) = \begin{cases}1, & 0 < x < \frac{1}{2}\\ 0, & \frac{1}{2} < x < 1\end{cases}.$

25. (a) Show that for any fixed $\nu \geq 0$, $\{J_\nu(\lambda_n x)\}$ is an orthogonal sequence of functions with respect to the weight function x, where λ_n are the roots of $\lambda c J'(\lambda c) = -hJ(\lambda c)$, h any constant.

(b) Show that

$$\int_0^c xJ_\nu^2(\lambda_n x)\,dx = \frac{\lambda_n^2 c^2 - h^2 - n^2}{2\lambda_n^2}J_\nu^2(\lambda_n c).$$

26. Show that

(a) $J_\nu(x)J_\mu(x) = \sum_{n=0}^{\infty}\frac{\Gamma(\nu+\mu+2n+1)[-(x^2/4)]^n}{n!\Gamma(\nu+\mu+n+1)\Gamma(\nu+n+1)\Gamma(\mu+n+1)}.$

(b) $\int_0^\pi J_0(2x\sin\theta)\cos 2n\theta\,d\theta = \pi J_n^2(x).$

(c) $\int_0^\pi J_{2n}(2x\sin\theta)\,d\theta = \pi J_n^2(x).$

27. Define **Airy's function:**

$$A(x) = \frac{\pi}{3}\left(\frac{x}{3}\right)^{1/3}\left\{J_{-1/3}\left[2\left(\frac{x}{3}\right)^{3/2}\right] + J_{1/3}\left[2\left(\frac{x}{3}\right)^{3/2}\right]\right\}.$$

(a) Show that $A(x)$ satisfies the differential equation

$$y'' + \tfrac{1}{3}xy = 0.$$

(b) Show that

$$A(x) = \operatorname{Im}\left[e^{2\pi i/3}\int_0^\infty e^{-t^3 - te^{2\pi i/3}x}\,dx\right].$$

(c) Show that $9a^2A(\frac{1}{3}x - b)$ is a solution of $y'' + (ax+b)y = 0$.

28. We define the **Hankel transform** of order ν of $f(x)$ as

$$\mathcal{H}_\nu[f(x)] = \int_0^\infty f(x)J_\nu(xy)(xy)^{1/2}\,dx = g(y;\nu), \qquad y > 0.$$

Show that

(a) The Fourier sine and cosine transforms of $f(x)$ are special cases of the Hankel transform.

(b) $\mathcal{H}_\nu[f'(x)] = \frac{1}{2\nu}\left[\left(\nu - \frac{1}{2}\right)yg(y;\nu+1) - \left(\nu + \frac{1}{2}\right)yg(y;\nu-1)\right].$

(c) $\mathcal{H}_\nu\left\{x^{1/2-\nu}\left(\frac{d}{x\,dx}\right)^m[x^{\nu+m-1/2}f(x)]\right\} = y^m g(y;\nu+m).$

(d) $\mathcal{H}_\nu[f(ax)] = a^{-1}g(a^{-1}y;\nu), \qquad a > 0.$

(e) $\mathcal{H}_\nu[2\nu x^{-1}f(x)] = y[g(y;\nu-1) + yg(y;\nu+1)]$.
(f) $\mathcal{H}_\nu[x^{-1/2}] = y^{-1/2}$.
(g) $\mathcal{H}_0[x^{1/2}(a^2+x^2)^{-1/2}] = y^{-1/2}e^{-ay}, \quad a > 0$.

(h) $\mathcal{H}_\nu[f(x)] = y^{-1/2}J_{\nu+1}(y); f(x) = \begin{cases} x^{\nu+1/2}, & 0 < x < 1, \\ 0, & x > 1 \end{cases} \quad \nu > -1.$

29. (a) Show that $y_n(x) = {}_2F_0\left(-n, 1+n; -1; -\frac{x}{2}\right)$ is a polynomial of degree n. It is called **Bessel's polynomial** of degree n.

(b) Show that

(1) $y_n\left(\frac{1}{ix}\right) = \left(\frac{\pi x}{2}\right)^{1/2} e^{ix}\left[i^{-n-1} J_{n+1/2}(x) + i^n J_{-n-1/2}(x)\right]$.

(2) $J_{n+1/2}(x) = (2\pi x)^{-1/2}\left[i^{-n-1}e^{ix}y_n\left(\frac{-1}{ix}\right) + i^{n+1}e^{-ix}y_n\left(\frac{1}{ix}\right)\right]$.

(3) $J_{-n-1/2}(x) = (2\pi x)^{-1/2}\left[i^n e^{ix}y_n\left(-\frac{1}{ix}\right) + i^{-n}e^{-ix}y_n\left(\frac{1}{ix}\right)\right]$.

(c) Show that

(1) $y_n(x) = (2n-1)xy_{n-1}(x) + y_{n-2}(x)$.
(2) $x^2y_n'(x) = 2(1 - +nx)y_n(x) - 2y_{n-1}(x)$.
(3) $x^2y_n''(x) + 2(x+1)y_n'(x) = n(n+1)y_n(x)$.

(4) $\oint_{|z|=1} e^{-2/x}y_m(x)y_n(x)\,dx = 0, \qquad m \neq n$.

(5) $y_n(x) = 2^{-n}e^{2/x}\dfrac{d^n}{dx^n}(x^{2n}e^{-2/x})$.

30. Many of the special functions that we have studied have many common properties; this would lead us to suspect that there exist very general properties of functions for which these are special cases. Truesdell, in *A Unified Theory of Special Functions*, considers all functions that satisfy the functional equation

$$\text{(A)} \qquad \frac{\partial F(x,\alpha)}{\partial x} = F(x, \alpha+1).$$

(a) Show that the following functions satisfy (A):

(1) e^x; (2) $\sin\left(x - \frac{\alpha\pi}{2}\right)$; (3) $e^{i\alpha\pi}x^{-\alpha}\gamma(\alpha, x)$, γ is the incomplete gamma function;

(4) $e^{i\alpha\pi}\Gamma(\alpha)x^{-\alpha-(n/2)}P_n^{(\alpha)}\left(\frac{1}{\sqrt{x}}\right)$, $P_n^{(\alpha)}$ is the ultraspherical polynomial;

(5) $(1-x^2)^{-\alpha/2}P_n^\alpha(x)$, P_n^α is the associated Legendre function;
(6) $e^{i\alpha\pi}\Gamma(\alpha+1)x^{-\alpha-1}F(b, c; -\alpha; x)$, F is the hypergeometric function;
(7) $e^{i\alpha\pi}e^{-x}L_n^{(\alpha)}(x)$, $L_n^{(\alpha)}$ is the Laguerre polynomial;
(8) $e^{-x^2}H_\alpha(-x)$, H_α is the Hermite polynomial.

(b) Show that

$$F(x+y, \alpha) = \sum_{n=0}^{\infty} \frac{y^n}{n!} F(x, \alpha+n),$$

and obtain as a special case the generating function for Bessel functions in Exercise 11(c), p. 533.

(c) Show that

$$F(x, \alpha + n) = \frac{\partial^n}{\partial x^n} F(x, \alpha)$$

and derive for Laguerre polynomials:

$$\mathrm{L}_n^{(m)}(x) = (-1)^m e^x \frac{d^m}{dx^m} e^{-x}\mathrm{L}_n(x),$$

m a positive integer.

Chapter 17

The Sturm-Liouville Theory

1. Sturm-Liouville systems. The classical orthogonal polynomials, the associated Legendre functions, and the Bessel functions all satisfy second-order linear homogeneous differential equations. In the case of the associated Legendre functions and the Bessel functions, we established the orthogonality property of these functions with the use of the differential equations (see p. 509 and p. 529). Actually, if we had defined the classical orthogonal polynomials as certain normalized solutions of their differential equations, we could have established the orthogonality property of these polynomials in the same manner. Let us recall these differential equations, writing them in the form that enables us to establish the orthogonality property readily.

(1) **Jacobi:**

$$\frac{d}{dx}[(1-x)^{\alpha+1}(1+x)^{\beta+1}y'] + n(n+\alpha+\beta+1)(1-x)^{\alpha}(1+x)^{\beta}y = 0,$$
$$y = \mathrm{P}_n^{(\alpha,\beta)}(x), \qquad \alpha > -1, \quad \beta > -1.$$

(2) **Laguerre:**

$$\frac{d}{dx}[xy'] + \left[n + \left(\frac{\alpha+1}{2} - \frac{x}{4} - \frac{\alpha^2}{4x}\right)\right]y = 0,$$
$$y = e^{-(1/2)x}x^{(1/2)\alpha}\mathrm{L}_n^{(\alpha)}(x), \qquad \alpha > -1.$$

(3) **Hermite:**

$$y'' + (2n+1-x^2)y = 0, \qquad y = e^{-(1/2)x^2}\mathrm{H}_n(x).$$

(4) **Associated Legendre:**

$$\frac{d}{dx}[(1 - x^2)^{m+1}y'] + (n - m)(n + m + 1)(1 - x^2)^m y = 0,$$

$$y = P_n^m(x), \qquad m > 0.$$

(5) **Bessel:**

$$\frac{d}{dx}(xy') + \left(\lambda_n^2 x - \frac{\nu^2}{x}\right)y = 0, \qquad y = J_\nu(\lambda_n x), \qquad \nu > -1.$$

(6) **Trigonometric system:**

$$y'' + n^2 y = 0, \qquad y = \sin nx \quad \text{and} \quad y = \cos nx.$$

A careful study of the form of these differential equations reveals that they are all special cases of a more general differential equation. This differential equation, known as the **Sturm-Liouville differential equation** (after the two mathematicians who studied it extensively), is

$$\frac{d}{dx}[p(x)y'] + [\lambda q(x) - r(x)]y = 0.$$

In this equation λ is a parameter, independent of x (possibly complex), p, q, r are real functions, dp/dx, $q \not\equiv 0$, r continuous in some interval E (finite or infinite). These restrictions are imposed on p, q, r to ensure that the differential equation has solutions. Actually, this equation represents a set of differential equations, a specific equation of the set being determined by the particular value assigned to λ. Since in (1) to (6) the parameter is a function of the positive integer n, each of these equations is the nth term of a sequence of differential equations.

If in the Sturm-Liouville differential equation $p(x) > 0$, $q(x) \geq 0$ in the closed finite interval $a \leq x \leq b$, then we shall call it a **regular Sturm-Liouville differential equation.** If any of these properties do not hold, we shall call it a **singular Sturm-Liouville differential equation.** Equations (5) (only if the interval of orthogonality is $0 < a \leq x \leq b$) and (6) are examples of regular Sturm-Liouville differential equations, while (1) to (3) are examples of singular Sturm-Liouville differential equations. (Why?)

In establishing the orthogonality property for the solutions of each sequence of differential equations in (1) to (6), it is necessary that these solutions have certain properties at the end points of the interval of orthogonality. These properties are called **boundary conditions.** For example, the associated Legendre functions are bounded at $x = -1$ and $x = 1$, whereas for the Bessel functions, we have $J_\nu(\lambda c) = 0$—these are instances of boundary conditions. In generalizing from (1) to (6) to the Sturm-Liouville differential equation, our aim is to preserve the orthogonality property of certain solutions. This means that we shall have to impose certain boundary conditions on these solutions. The Sturm-Liouville differential equation together with any set of boundary conditions in the interval E is called a **Sturm-Liouville system.** We shall consider the following:

SL-R: A **regular Sturm-Liouville system,** which consists of a regular Sturm-Liouville differential equation and the following boundary conditions, called **separated end conditions:**

$$a_1 y(a) + a_2 y'(a) = 0, \qquad a_1^2 + a_2^2 \neq 0;$$
$$b_1 y(b) + b_2 y'(b) = 0, \qquad b_1^2 + b_2^2 = 0.$$

SL-S: A **singular Sturm-Liouville system,** which consists of a singular Sturm-Liouville differential equation and any set of boundary conditions.

SL-P: A **periodic Sturm-Liouville system,** which consists of a regular Sturm-Liouville differential equation whose coefficients are periodic functions with period $b - a$ and satisfying the periodic end-point conditions

$$y(a) = y(b) \quad \text{and} \quad y'(a) = y'(b).$$

Examples of SL-P are (1) $y'' + n^2 y = 0$, $y(-\pi) = y(\pi)$, $y'(-\pi) = y'(\pi)$; (2) $y'' + (\lambda + 16d \cos 2x)y$, $0 \le x \le \pi$ (Mathieu's differential equation), $y(0) = y(\pi)$, $y'(0) = y'(\pi)$.

A value of λ that yields nontrivial solutions (i.e., not identically zero solutions) of a Sturm-Liouville system is called an **eigenvalue** (or characteristic value), and these solutions are called **eigenfunctions** (characteristic functions). We say that the eigenfunctions belong to the eigenvalue that determines them. The set of eigenvalues of a Sturm-Liouville system is called its **spectrum.** We have a **discrete spectrum** if these values form a sequence (finite or infinite), and a **continuous spectrum** if these values are points in a region.

EXAMPLE 1
$$\begin{cases} y'' + \lambda y = 0 \\ y(0) = 0,\ y(\pi) = 0 \end{cases}$$

is SL-R in $0 \le x \le \pi$. If $\lambda = 0$, the solution of the equation is $y = Ax + B$, where A and B are constants, both of which must be zero in order that the boundary conditions be satisfied; hence, $\lambda = 0$ yields a trivial solution that is not an eigenvalue. If $\lambda < 0$, the solution to the equation is $y = Ae^{\sqrt{\lambda}x} + Be^{-\sqrt{\lambda}x}$, so that $x = 0$, $y = 0$ yields $B = -A$; we have, then, that $y = 2A \sinh \sqrt{\lambda}x$ and $2A \sinh \sqrt{\lambda}\pi = 0$ only if $A = 0$—again we obtain a trivial solution. If $\lambda > 0$, the solution to the equation is $y = A \cos \sqrt{\lambda}x + B \sin \sqrt{\lambda}x$; $x = 0$, $y = 0$ yields $A = 0$. In $y = B \sin \sqrt{\lambda}x$, $x = \pi$, $y = 0$ yields a nontrivial solution only if $\lambda = n^2$, $n = 1, 2, \cdots$. Hence, the eigenvalues of the system are n^2, $n = 1, 2, \cdots$ (a discrete spectrum) and the eigenfunctions are $\sin nx$, $n = 1, 2, \cdots$, determined uniquely up to a multiplicative constant.

EXAMPLE 2
$$\begin{cases} y'' + \lambda y = 0 \\ y(0) = y'(0),\ y(\pi) = y'(\pi) \end{cases}$$

is SL-R in $0 \le x \le \pi$. The general solution of the equation is $y = A \cos \sqrt{\lambda}x +$

$B \sin \sqrt{\lambda}x$, $\lambda > 0$ (it is readily seen that if $\lambda \le 0$, the solutions of the equation do not satisfy the boundary conditions). Applying the boundary conditions, we have $A = \sqrt{\lambda}B$ and $(\lambda + 1) \sin \sqrt{\lambda}\pi = 0$, so that the eigenvalues are $\lambda_n = n^2$, $n = 1, 2, \cdots$, with corresponding eigenfunctions $n \cos nx + \sin nx$, $n = 1, 2, \cdots$.

EXAMPLE 3
$$\begin{cases} y'' + \lambda y = 0 \\ y(0) = 0,\ y(\pi) = y'(\pi) \end{cases}$$

is SL-R in $0 \le x \le \pi$. We readily find that the eigenvalues are the zeros of $\tan \lambda\pi - \lambda = 0$. These zeros are real and form a sequence (see p. 290, Exercise 10), $\lambda_1, \lambda_2, \cdots$. These eigenvalues can be approximated by drawing the graphs of $u = \tan \lambda\pi$ and $u = \lambda$, and determining the points of intersection. The spectrum is discrete. The eigenfunctions are $\sin \lambda_n x$, $n = 1, 2, \cdots$.

EXAMPLE 4
$$\begin{cases} \dfrac{d}{dx}[(1 - x^2)y'] + \lambda y = 0 \\ |y(x)| < M \text{ in } |x| \le 1 \end{cases}$$

is SL-S in $|x| \le 1$. The general solution of the differential equation found by the method of series is

$$c_0 \sum_{k=0}^{\infty} \frac{(0\cdot1 - \lambda)(2\cdot3 - \lambda)\cdots[2k(2k+1) - \lambda]}{(2k)!} x^{2k} + c_1 \sum_{k=0}^{\infty} \frac{(1\cdot2 - \lambda)(3\cdot4 - \lambda)\cdots[(2k+1)(2k+2) - \lambda]}{(2k+1)!} x^{2k+1},$$

where c_0 and c_1 are arbitrary constants. Now if $\lambda = n(n + 1)$, where n is an even positive integer, then the first series is a polynomial of degree n, while the second series does not terminate. The polynomial is the Legendre polynomial $P_n(x)$, since with $\lambda = n(n + 1)$, the differential equation is Legendre's differential equation. Since polynomials are continuous everywhere, they are bounded in closed intervals. On the other hand, the nonterminating series represents an unbounded function in $|x| \le 1$. (See p. 494, Exercise 6.) Similarly, if $\lambda = n(n + 1)$ and n is an odd positive integer, the first series represents an unbounded function in $|x| \le 1$, and the second series is the Legendre polynomial of odd degree n. Consequently, the Legendre polynomials $P_n(x)$ are the eigenfunctions belonging to the eigenvalues $\lambda_n = n(n + 1)$. Are these the only eigenvalues? If $\lambda \ne n(n + 1)$, n a nonnegative integer, both series are nonterminating, and it can be shown that they represent functions that are unbounded in $|x| \le 1$.

EXAMPLE 5
$$\begin{cases} y'' + \lambda y = 0 \\ |y(x)| < M \text{ in } -\infty < x < \infty \end{cases}$$

is SL-S in $-\infty < x < \infty$. If $\lambda > 0$, $\sin \sqrt{\lambda}x$ and $\cos \sqrt{\lambda}x$ are linearly independent solutions of the differential equation that are bounded; if $\lambda = 0$, the only bounded solution is a constant; if $\lambda < 0$, $\sinh \sqrt{\lambda}x$ and $\cosh \sqrt{\lambda}x$ are the linearly independent solutions of the equation, and these are unbounded. Hence, the eigenvalues are all $\lambda \ge 0$, with the two eigenfunctions $\sin \sqrt{\lambda}x$ and $\cos \sqrt{\lambda}x$ belonging to each λ. The spectrum is continuous.

For SL-R, we have the following significant

THEOREM. The eigenvalues of a regular Sturm-Liouville system in $a \leq x \leq b$ are real and form an infinite sequence $\lambda_1 < \lambda_2 < \cdots$ such that $\lim_{n\to\infty} \lambda_n = \infty$.

The corresponding eigenfunctions $\{y_n\}$ are real (except for a possible multiplicative complex constant), uniquely determined up to a multiplicative constant, and $y_n(x)$ has exactly n zeros in $a < x < b$.

The proof of this theorem would take us too far afield. Proofs can be found in Ince, *Ordinary Differential Equations,* and Birkhoff and Rota, *Ordinary Differential Equations;* an elegant treatment occurs in the latter.

The situation is far more complex for singular Sturm-Liouville systems, as might be expected. Such a system may have a discrete spectrum (as in Example 4), or a continuous spectrum (as in Example 5), or a mixed spectrum; i.e., it is discrete in some intervals and continuous in others. Criteria for the nature of the spectrum can be found in Titchmarsh, *Eigenfunction Expansions* and in Birkhoff and Rota, *Ordinary Differential Equations.*

2. Orthogonality of eigenfunctions. Let λ and μ be two distinct values of the parameter in the Sturm-Liouville differential equation, which yield the solutions u and v so that

$$\text{(1)} \quad \frac{d}{dx}[p(x)u'] + [\lambda q(x) - r(x)]u = 0,$$

$$\text{(2)} \quad \frac{d}{dx}[p(x)v'] + [\mu q(x) - r(x)]v = 0.$$

Multiplying (1) by v and (2) by u, and subtracting the resulting equations, yields

$$(\lambda - \mu)q(x)u(x)v(x) = v(x)\frac{d}{dx}[p(x)u'(x)] - u(x)\frac{d}{dx}[p(x)v'(x)].$$

Assuming that both sides are integrable in $a \leq x \leq b$, we have, integrating each term on the right by parts,

$$(\lambda - \mu)\int_a^b q(x)u(x)v(x)\,dx = p(x)[v(x)u'(x) - u(x)v'(x)]\Big|_a^b.$$

Hence, we have the following

Lemma. If the set E of eigenfunctions of a Sturm-Liouville system is square-integrable in $a \leq x \leq b$ and if

$$p(x)[v(x)u'(x) - u(x)v'(x)]|_a^b = 0$$

for every pair of distinct functions u and v in E, then E is an orthogonal set of functions with respect to the weight function q in $a \leq x \leq b$.

The term on the left-hand side is called the **boundary term** of the Sturm-Liouville system. The preceding lemma enables us to establish readily the orthogonality of the eigenfunctions of various Sturm-Liouville systems. We have the following

THEOREM. The eigenfunctions of a regular Sturm-Liouville system in $a \le x \le b$ are orthogonal with respect to the weight function q in $a \le x \le b$.

Proof. The solutions of a regular Sturm-Liouville differential equation are continuously differentiable (see Birkhoff and Rota, *Ordinary Differential Equations*, chapter v); hence, they are integrable and therefore square-integrable in the finite interval $a \le x \le b$.

The boundary conditions for SL-R at b for the eigenfunctions u and v are

$$(1) \quad b_1 u(b) + b_2 u'(b) = 0,$$

$$(2) \quad b_1 v(b) + b_2 v'(b) = 0.$$

If $b_2 \neq 0$, we multiply (1) by $v(b)$ and (2) by $u(b)$ and subtract to obtain

$$b_2[u'(b)v(b) - u(b)v'(b)] = 0,$$

or

$$u'(b)v(b) - u(b)v'(b) = 0.$$

If $b_2 = 0$, then necessarily $b_1 \neq 0$, and we obtain the same result. Similarly, the boundary conditions at a yield

$$u'(a)v(a) - u(a)v'(a) = 0.$$

The result now follows from the lemma.

THEOREM. The eigenfunctions of a periodic Sturm-Liouville system in $a \le x \le b$ are orthogonal with respect to the weight function q in $a \le x \le b$.

Proof. The square-integrability of the eigenfunctions follows as in the preceding theorem.

The boundary conditions for SL-P for the eigenfunctions u and v are

$$u(a) = u(b), \qquad u'(a) = u'(b),$$
$$v(a) = v(b), \qquad v'(a) = v'(b),$$

so that the boundary term in the lemma becomes

$$[p(b) - p(a)][v(a)u'(a) - u(a)v'(a)],$$

which is zero, since p is periodic with period $b - a$ yielding $p(b) = p(a)$.

The orthogonality of the eigenfunctions of singular Sturm-Liouville systems is best established with the use of the lemma in any particular instance. As a matter of fact, we shall merely reword the lemma to obtain

THEOREM. The eigenfunctions of a singular Sturm-Liouville system in $a \le x \le b$ are orthogonal with respect to q in $a \le x \le b$ if they are square-integrable there and if

$$p(x)[v(x)u'(x) - u(x)v'(x)]\Big|_a^b = 0$$

for every distinct pair u and v.

3. Sturm-Liouville series. Given a Sturm-Liouville system with a discrete spectrum, having the eigenfunctions $\{\phi_n\}$, orthogonal with respect to the weight function q in $a \le x \le b$, let us assume that the square-integrable function f can be expanded in a series of these functions; i.e.,

$$f(x) = \sum_{n=0}^{\infty} c_n\phi_n(x).$$

Multiplying both sides by $q(x)\phi_m(x)$, integrating term by term from a to b, the orthogonality property yields, after interchanging m with n,

$$c_n = \frac{\int_a^b q(x)f(x)\phi_n(x)\,dx}{\int_a^b q(x)\phi_n^2(x)\,dx}, \qquad n = 0, 1, 2, \cdots.$$

We shall call these c_n, $n = 0, 1, 2, \cdots$, the **Sturm-Liouville coefficients** of the function f and the series

$$\sum_{n=0}^{\infty} c_n\phi_n(x),$$

where the c_n are the Sturm-Liouville coefficients of f, the **Sturm-Liouville series** of f. We indicate this by writing

$$f(x) \sim \sum_{n=0}^{\infty} c_n\phi_n(x),$$

the $\sim$ sign, as usual, indicating that the series corresponds to f only by virtue of the fact that the coefficients c_n are determined by f. The Sturm-Liouville series with eigenfunctions of a SL-R will be called a **regular Sturm-Liouville series,** whereas that with eigenfunctions of a SL-S will be called a **singular Sturm-Liouville series.** Of course we are interested in the conditions on f under which $\sim$ can be replaced by $=$, so that the Sturm-Liouville series of f is a representation of f. We have the following highly significant

EQUICONVERGENCE THEOREM. If f is any function that is integrable in $0 \le x \le \pi$, then the Sturm-Liouville series of f for the regular Sturm-Liouville system,

$$y'' + [\lambda - q(x)]y = 0,$$
$$a_1y(0) + a_2y'(0) = 0; \quad b_1y(\pi) + b_2y'(\pi) = 0,$$

converges or diverges at x_0, $0 \le x_0 \le \pi$, according as the Fourier sine series of f converges or diverges at x_0 and both series converge to the same value at points of convergence. Furthermore, any limit operations that are valid for the Fourier sine series are valid for the Sturm-Liouville series.

A proof of this theorem can be adapted from the one that appears in Indritz, *Methods of Analysis*, p. 420, or Ince, *Ordinary Differential Equations*, p. 276.

Any regular Sturm-Liouville system can be transformed into the special one (known as the **Liouville normal form**) indicated in the preceding equiconvergence theorem (see p. 551, Exercise 9). In view of this, we have as an immediate consequence of this theorem and the Fourier expansion theorem the

REGULAR STURM-LIOUVILLE EXPANSION THEOREM. If f is piecewise continuous and almost differentiable in $a \leq x \leq b$, then

$$\frac{f(x+) + f(x-)}{2} = \sum_{n=0}^{\infty} c_n \phi_n(x),$$

in $a \leq x \leq b$, where the series is the regular Sturm-Liouville series of f.

Singular Sturm-Liouville expansions present problems that we cannot treat here. Generally speaking, these have to be treated according to the nature of the singularity. This is done in Titchmarsh, *Eigenfunction Expansions*. We have already considered the expansions in some particular cases of interest, such as the Legendre series, which is a singular Sturm-Liouville series.

We have devoted considerable attention to the problem of representing a given function as a series of functions. We have restricted ourselves to those series whose functions have the orthogonality property, thus yielding the concept of the orthogonal series of a function. Special cases of orthogonal series that we have treated in detail are Fourier series, series of orthogonal polynomials, such as Jacobi series, Hermite series, Laguerre series, and Bessel series. The Fourier series, Jacobi series, and Bessel series are special cases of Sturm-Liouville series. The Hermite series and Laguerre series are not special cases of Sturm-Liouville series, since the Hermite and Laguerre differential equations as they stand cannot be expressed as Sturm-Liouville differential equations; however, series of the Hermite functions

$$e^{-x^2/2}\mathrm{H}_n(x)$$

and the Laguerre functions

$$e^{(-x/2)(\alpha/2)x}\mathrm{L}_n^{(\alpha)}(x)$$

are Sturm-Liouville series. The scheme of classification of orthogonal series is given in the accompanying table, which divides them into two classes, depending on whether the functions in the series satisfy a certain second-order linear differential equation system.

Orthogonal Series

Sturm-Liouville	Non-Sturm–Liouville
Fourier	Hermite (polynomials)
Jacobi	Laguerre (polynomials)
Hermite (functions)	Nonclassical orthogonal polynomials
Laguerre (functions)	
Associated Legendre	
Bessel	

Our theory of Sturm-Liouville series necessarily requires a discrete spectrum for the Sturm-Liouville system. As we might expect, a continuous spectrum would lead to the concept of the Sturm-Liouville integral, the special example of the Fourier integral having been treated. We cannot, however, pursue this fascinating subject any further, but hope that the student may be sufficiently aroused to contemplate exploration at a future date.

EXERCISES

1. Indicate whether the following Sturm-Liouville systems are regular, periodic, or singular. Determine the eigenvalues and eigenfunctions of each system.

(a) $y'' + \lambda y = 0;\ y(0) = y(\pi),\ y'(0) = 2y'(\pi).$

(b) $y'' + \lambda y = 0;\ y(0) = y'(c) = 0.$

(c) $y'' + \lambda y = 0;\ y(0) = 0;\ y(1) + ky'(1) = 0, \qquad k > 0.$

(d) $y'' + \lambda y = 0;\ y'(0) = y'(c) = 0.$

(e) $y'' - (k + \lambda)y = 0;\ y(0) = y(1) = 0, \qquad k$ constant.

(f) $\dfrac{d}{dx}[xy'] + \left[\lambda^2 x - \dfrac{n^2}{x}\right] y = 0, \qquad n$ fixed, $y(1) = y(2) = 0.$

(g) $\dfrac{d}{dx}[xy'] + \left[\nu^2 x - \dfrac{\lambda^2}{x}\right] y = 0, \qquad \nu$ fixed, $|y(x)| < M$ in $0 \le x \le c.$

(h) $\dfrac{d}{dx}[(x - a)(b - x)y'] + \lambda y = 0, \qquad a < b,\ |y(x)| < M$ on $a < x < b.$

(i) $\dfrac{d}{dx}[(1 - x^2)^{\alpha+1}y'] + \lambda(1 - x^2)^{\alpha} y = 0,$

$\alpha > -1,\ |y(x)| < M$ on $-1 < x < 1.$

(j) $\dfrac{d}{dx}(xe^{-x}y') + \lambda e^{-x} y = 0$ on $0 < x < \infty, \qquad |y(0)| < M,\ \lim_{x\to\infty} e^{-x}y(x) = 0.$

(k) $y'' + (\lambda - x^2)y = 0$ on $-\infty < x < \infty, \qquad |y(x)| < M$ as $x \to \pm\infty.$

(l) $\dfrac{d}{dx}[(1 + x)^{\beta+1}(1 - x)^{\alpha+1}y'] + \lambda(1 + x)^{\beta}(1 - x)^{\alpha} y = 0.$

$-1 < x < 1,\ |y(\pm 1)| < M.$

(m) $x^2y'' + xy' + \lambda y = 0; \quad y(1) = 0, y(e) = 0.$
(n) $(2x + 1)^2y'' + (2x + 1)y' + (\lambda + 1)y = 0; y(0) = 0, y(\pi) = 0.$
(o) $x^2y'' - y' + 2x\lambda y = 0; y(1) = 0, y'(\pi) = 0.$

2. Show that if the general second-order linear homogeneous differential equation

$$p_0(x)y'' + p_1(x)y' + [\lambda p_2(x) - p_3(x)]y = 0, \qquad p_0(x) \neq 0$$

is multiplied by

$$\frac{1}{p_0(x)} e^{\int p_1(x)/p_0(x)\, dx},$$

the resulting equation can be written as a Sturm-Liouville differential equation.

3. Show that the following are singular Sturm-Liouville systems and that their eigenfunctions are orthogonal in the given interval.

(a) $y'' + \lambda y = 0, \quad 0 \leq x < \infty; a_1y(0) + a_2y'(0) = 0, \quad |y(x)| < M$ as $x \to \infty$.

(b) $y'' + [\lambda - r(x)]y = 0; r(x) = \begin{cases} 0, & |x| > a \\ -k^2, & |x| < a \end{cases},$

$-\infty < x < \infty, |y(x)| < M$ as $x \to \pm\infty$.

(c) $x^2y'' + xy' + \lambda y = 0; y(0) = 0, y(1) = 1.$
(d) $2x^2y'' + xy' + (\lambda - x^2)y = 0; y(0) = 1, y'(1) = 0.$
(e) $(1 - x^2)y'' - 2xy' + \lambda y = 0, \quad |y(-1)| < M, y(1) = 1.$

4. Show that the solutions of the fourth-order Sturm-Liouville system:

$$\frac{d^2}{dx^2}[p(x)y''] + [\lambda q(x) - r(x)]y = 0,$$

$$a_1y(a) + a_2\frac{d}{dx}[p(x)y''(x)]\Big]_{x=a} = 0,$$

$$\alpha_1y'(a) + \alpha_2[p(x)y''(x)]\Big]_{x=a} = 0,$$

$$b_1y(b) + b_2\frac{d}{dx}[p(x)y''(x)]\Big]_{x=b} = 0,$$

$$\beta_1y'(b) + \beta_2[p(x)y''(x)]\Big]_{x=b} = 0,$$

$$a_1^2 + a_2^2 \neq 0, \quad \alpha_1^2 + \alpha_2^2 \neq 0, \qquad b_1^2 + b_2^2 \neq 0, \quad \beta_1^2 + \beta_2^2 \neq 0,$$

p and q continuous in $a \leq x \leq b$ and r continuous in $a < x < b$, are orthogonal with respect to q in $a \leq x \leq b$.

5. Determine the Sturm-Liouville series of each of the following functions for the given Sturm-Liouville system:

(a) $f(x) = |x|, \quad -1 < x < 1, \qquad \begin{cases} y'' + \lambda y = 0 \\ y(0) = 0, y(\pi) = y'(\pi) \end{cases}.$

(b) $f(x) = \begin{cases} 0, & 0 < x < \dfrac{c}{2} \\ 1, & \dfrac{c}{2} \leq x < c \end{cases}, \begin{cases} y'' + \lambda y = 0 \\ y(0) = y'(c) = 0 \end{cases}.$

(c) $f(x) = |\sin x|, \quad -\pi < x \leq \pi, \qquad \begin{cases} y'' + \lambda y = 0 \\ y(-\pi) = 0,\ y(\pi) + y'(\pi) = 0 \end{cases}$

(d) $f(x) = \begin{cases} x + 1, & 1 < x < 2 \\ x - 1, & 2 \leq x < 3 \end{cases}, \qquad \begin{cases} \dfrac{d}{dx}[xy'] + [\lambda^2 x]y = 0 \\ y(1) = y(3) = 0 \end{cases}$

6. If $(d/dx)[p(x)y'] + [\lambda q(x) - r(x)]y$, $y(-a) = y(a) = 0$ is a regular Sturm-Liouville system and p, q, r are even functions, show that the eigenfunctions are either even or odd. Show that the eigenfunction y_n corresponding to the eigenvalue λ_n is even if and only if n is odd.

7. Assume that in a regular Sturm-Liouville system, p, q, r are real functions and λ is a complex eigenvalue, $\lambda = \alpha + i\beta$, with complex eigenfunction $u(x) + iv(x)$.

(a) Show that $\alpha - i\beta$ is an eigenvalue with eigenfunction $u(x) - iv(x)$.

(b) Show that an eigenvalue of the form $\alpha - i\beta$, $\beta \neq 0$, cannot exist, and hence that the eigenvalues must all be real.

(c) Show that if $u(x) + iv(x)$ is an eigenfunction belonging to the eigenvalue λ, then $u(x)$ and $v(x)$ belong to λ.

8. Show that a regular Sturm-Liouville differential equation, together with the boundary conditions

$$\begin{aligned} a_1y(a) + a_2y(b) + a_3y'(a) + a_4y'(b) &= 0, \\ b_1y(a) + b_2y(b) + b_3y'(a) + b_4y'(b) &= 0, \end{aligned}$$

is a generalization of the regular Sturm-Liouville system. Show that if u and v are solutions of this generalized system, $u \neq cv$, c constant, then u and v are orthogonal with respect to $q(x)$ in $a \leq x \leq b$. (The student who is familiar with matrix theory will find an elegant solution in Indritz, *Methods in Analysis*, p. 374, Ex. 3.)

◇ **9.** (a) Show that the Sturm-Liouville differential equation can be written in the form

$$\frac{d^2w}{dt^2} + [\lambda - Q(t)]w = 0,$$

where

$$Q(t) = \frac{r(t)}{q(t)} + [p(t)q(t)]^{-1/4} \frac{d^2}{dt^2} [p(t)q(t)]^{1/4},$$

by the substitutions

$$y = \frac{w}{\sqrt[4]{p(x)q(x)}}, \qquad t = \int \sqrt{\frac{q(x)}{p(x)}}\, dx.$$

This is called the **Liouville normal form** of the given Sturm-Liouville differential equation and the preceding substitutions are called **Liouville's reduction.**

(b) Show that Liouville's reduction transforms regular Sturm-Liouville systems with separated (periodic) boundary conditions into Sturm-Liouville systems with separated (periodic) boundary conditions.

(c) Show that the eigenvalues of a Sturm-Liouville system are invariant under Liouville's reduction.

(d) Show that Liouville's reduction transforms functions orthogonal with respect to the weight function q into orthogonal functions with respect to the unit weight.

(e) Reduce the differential equations of Hermite, Laguerre, and Jacobi to Liouville normal form.

10. (a) Given

$$(1) \quad \frac{d}{dx}[p_1(x)u'(x)] + q_1(x)u = 0,$$

$$(2) \quad \frac{d}{dx}[p_2(x)v'(x)] + q_2(x)v = 0,$$

$p_2(x) > 0$ and $q_2(x)$ continuous in $a \leq x \leq b$, $u(a) = u(b) = 0$, $v(x) \neq 0$ in $a \leq x \leq b$, establish **Picone's identity:**

$$\int_a^b [q_2(x) - q_1(x)]u(x)\,dx + \int_a^b [p_1(x) - p_2(x)][u'(x)]^2\,dx$$
$$+ \int_a^b p_1(x)\left[u'(x) - \frac{u(x)v'(x)}{v(x)}\right]^2 dx = 0.$$

(b) Prove the **Sturm comparison theorem:** If in (1), (2) in (a), $p_1(x) \geq p_2(x) > 0$ and $q_1(x) \geq q_2(x)$, then between any two zeros of a nontrivial solution of (1), there exists at least one zero of every solution of (2) except when $u(x) \equiv cv(x)$, $p_1(x) \equiv p_2(x)$, $q_1(x) \equiv q_2(x)$.

(c) Prove the **Sturm separation theorem:** If u_1 and u_2 are linearly independent solutions of (1) in (a), then $u_1(x) = 0$ for some x between two successive zeros of u_2, and conversely.

SUPPLEMENTARY PROBLEMS

MECHANICS

1. Let l be the length of a simple pendulum and θ its angular displacement from its equilibrium position. Let the mass of the bob on the pendulum be m and that of the rod be negligible. The potential energy of the bob is $-mgl\cos\theta$ and its kinetic energy is $\frac{1}{2}ml^2(d\theta/dt)^2$. If θ_0 is the maximum value of θ, then the total energy is the potential energy; i.e., $-mgl\cos\theta_0$. By the law of conservation of energy

$$-mgl\cos\theta + \tfrac{1}{2}ml^2\left(\frac{d\theta}{dt}\right)^2 = -mgl\cos\theta_0$$

or

$$\frac{d\theta}{dt} = \pm\sqrt{\frac{2g}{l}}\sqrt{\cos\theta - \cos\theta_0}.$$

Since θ is increasing and equals 0 at $t = 0$,

$$\int_0^\theta \frac{d\theta}{\sqrt{\cos\theta - \cos\theta_0}} = \int_0^t \sqrt{\frac{2g}{l}}\,dt.$$

(a) Show that the transformation $\sin\theta/2 = k\sin\phi$, $k = \sin\theta_0/2$ yields

$$\sqrt{2}\int_0^\phi \frac{d\phi}{\sqrt{1 - k^2\sin^2\phi}} = \sqrt{2g/l}\,t$$

and hence $t = \sqrt{l/g}\,F(k, \phi)$. Then $\phi = am\sqrt{g/l}\,t$, $\sin\phi = \sin\sqrt{g/l}\,t$, (see p. 469, Exercise 23). Show that the period of motion of the pendulum is $T = 4\sqrt{l/g}\,K(k)$.

(b) Show that the period of a pendulum whose total energy is sufficient to cause it to make complete revolutions is $(4/\omega_0)K(2\sqrt{g/l}\,\omega_0)$, where $\omega_0 = d\theta/dt]_{\theta=0}$. $\left(\textit{Hint:}\text{ The energy equation is } -mgl\cos\theta + \frac{1}{2}ml^2\left(\frac{d\theta}{dt}\right)^2 = -mgl + \frac{1}{2}ml^2\omega_0^2.\right)$

2. The midpoint of a rod AB of length l is constrained to move along the y-axis while the point A moves along the x-axis. Show that the length of the curve traced by B as A moves from $(0, 0)$ to $(-l/4, 0)$ is $lE(\pi/3, \sqrt{3}/2)$. (*Hint:* Express the coordinates of B in terms of θ, the angle between the rod and the x-axis.)

3. A sphere of radius r, density $\rho/2$, is bobbing in a liquid of density ρ. The center of the sphere is depressed vertically through a distance h and released from rest. Show that the period of motion is $(8rk/h)\sqrt{r/g}\,K(k)$, where

$$k = h/\sqrt{6a^2 - h^2}.$$

4. The ends of a uniform flexible rope, of length $2l$ and mass m per unit length, are fixed to two points at a distance $2b$ apart, and the rope revolves in relative equilibrium with constant angular velocity ω about the line joining its ends. Find the shape of the rope, neglecting the force of gravity. [Solution in outline: Let the ends of the rope be at $(0, 0)$ and $(2b, 0)$ in the xy-plane. Let P be any point of the rope, θ the angle between the tangent at P and the x-axis, and T the tension at P. Let an element of rope at P have length ds, where s is the length of the rope from the origin to P. The equations of motion are $d(T\cos\theta)/ds = 0$, $d(T\sin\theta)/ds = -my\omega^2$. Hence $T\cos\theta = H = $ constant and

$$\frac{d}{dx}(H\tan\theta) = \frac{d}{dx}\left(H\frac{dy}{dx}\right) = H\frac{d^2y}{dx^2} = -m\omega^2 y\frac{ds}{dx}.$$

Let $p = \dfrac{dy}{dx}$ and $h^2 = 4H/m\omega^2$. Then $pdp/dy = -(4y/h^2)\sqrt{1+p^2}$. Integrating with $y = b$, $p = 0$, and simplifying

$$p^2 = \frac{4b^2(h^2+b^2)}{h^4}\left(1 - \frac{y^2}{b^2}\right)\left(1 - \frac{y^2}{h^2+b^2}\right).$$

Let $y/b = u$, $h^2/2\sqrt{h^2+b^2} = a$, $k = b/\sqrt{h^2+b^2}$,

$$\frac{du}{\sqrt{1-u^2}\sqrt{1-k^2u^2}} = \frac{dx}{a}.$$

Now show that $y = b\sin(x/a)$. (See p. 468, Exercise 20(c)). Draw the graph of this function.]

5. A heavy bead is projected from the lowest point of a smooth circular wire, fixed in a vertical plane, so that it describes one-third of the circumference before coming to rest. Show that during the first half of the time it describes one-fourth of the circumference.

6. Show that the radiation density integral $\dfrac{8\pi h}{c^2}\displaystyle\int_0^\infty \frac{\omega^3\,d\omega}{e^{h\omega/kT} - 1}$, where c is the speed of light, h is Planck's constant, k is Boltzmann's constant, and T is temperature, is $8\pi^5k^4T^4/15c^3h^3$. (*Hint:* Let $x = e^{-h\omega/kT}$, expand $1/(1-x)$ in the resulting integrand, and integrate term by term.)

7. A particle P of variable mass m starting at rest at a distance b from the origin O is attracted to O by a force always directed toward O and whose magnitude is kmy, y the distance from P to O, k constant. If $m = 1/(c + dt)$, c and d constants, t time, determine the time required for P to reach O. (*Hint:* The equation of motion is $\frac{d}{dt}\left(m \frac{dy}{dt}\right) = -k^2my$ which becomes $x^2y'' - xy' + k^2x^2y = 0$ under the change of variable $c + dt = dx$. The general solution of this equation is $y = C_1xJ_1(kx) + C_2xY_1(kx)$. C_1 and C_2 can be determined from the conditions: $y = l$, $dy/dt = dy/dx = 0$, at $x = c/d$. Now approximate x for $y = 0$ and hence determine t for that value of x.)

8. A simple pendulum has a bob of constant mass m and rod of negligible weight whose length r is variable according to $r = a + bt$, a and b constants, t time. Let θ be the angle the rod makes with the vertical; $\theta = \theta_0$ at $t = 0$. If the oscillations are small, show that

$$\theta = \frac{\pi\theta_0 a}{b}\sqrt{\frac{g}{a + bt}}\left[J_2\left(\frac{2\sqrt{ag}}{b}\right) Y_1\left(\frac{2}{b}\sqrt{g(a + bt)}\right) - J_1\left(\frac{2}{b}\sqrt{g(a + bt)}\right) Y_2\left(\frac{2\sqrt{ag}}{b}\right)\right].$$

(*Hint:* The equation of motion is $\theta'' + [2b/(a + bt)]\theta' + [g/(a + bt)]\theta = 0$, where $\sin\theta$ has been replaced by θ. Let $a + bt = bx$ to obtain

$$x^2\theta'' + 2x\theta' + gx\theta/b = 0.)$$

9. A circular membrane of radius a is fixed along the circumference. It has normal modes of vibration; i.e., all points in the membrane vibrate with the same period and pass through their mean positions simultaneously. The motion is symmetric about the center. It can be shown that the vertical displacement u of any point in the membrane at a distance r from the center at any time t satisfies $u_{tt} = c^2(u_{rr} + (1/r)u_r)$, c constant. For the normal modes of vibration, $u = R\cos(\omega t - \theta)$, R a function of r only. Hence we have the equation

$$R'' + \frac{1}{r}R' + \frac{\omega^2}{c^2}R = 0$$

whose general solution is $C_1J_0(\omega r/c) + C_2Y_0(\omega r/c)$. Since u is small at $r = 0$, C_2 must be zero, for $Y_0(\omega r/c) \to \infty$ as $r \to 0$. Hence $u = C_1J_0(\omega r/c)\cos(\omega t - \theta)$. But $u = 0$ when $r = 0$ so that $J_0(\omega a/c) = 0$. There are an infinite number of normal modes of vibration with frequencies u_ic/a, $i = 1, 2, \cdots$, where u_i is the ith zero of $J_0(x) = 0$.

10. A planet P moves in an ellipse under the gravitational attraction of a sun S situated at one of the foci; the area swept out by the radius vector SP during any interval of time is proportional to that interval. Let $A'A$ be the major axis of the ellipse, and let a line drawn through P perpendicular to $A'A$ meet the circle described on $A'A$ as diameter in the point Q. (See figure.) Draw CP, CQ, SQ. Let $2a$ be the length of the major axis, $2b$ that of the minor axis, and e the eccentricity. Let a point M describe the circle AQA' at such a constant speed that it coincides with P at A and A'. Let the time t be measured from an instant when P is passing through A, and let $r = SP$, $\theta = \angle ASP$, $\phi = \angle ACQ$, $\psi = \angle ACM$, all measured at time t. (θ is called the true anomaly, ϕ the eccentric anomaly, and ψ, which is proportional to t, the mean anomaly.) We wish to express r, θ, ϕ as functions of t, or equivalently as functions of ψ.

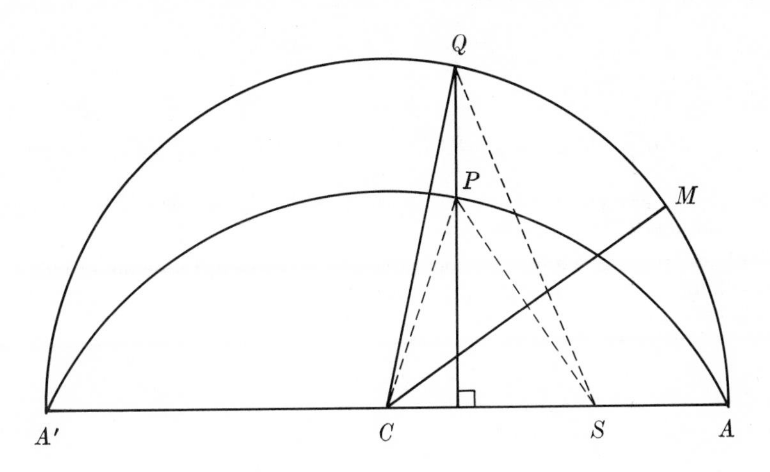

Supplementary Problem 10

If T is the period in which P describes the complete ellipse,

$$\frac{t}{T} = \frac{\psi}{2\pi} = \frac{\text{area } ASP}{\pi ab} = \frac{\text{area } ASQ}{\pi a^2}$$

But area ASQ = area ACQ − area $SCQ = \frac{1}{2}a^2\phi - \frac{1}{2}a^2 e \sin\phi$ so that $\psi = \phi - e\sin\phi$. We solve this equation for ϕ. Since $\phi - \psi$ is an odd function of ψ of period 2π (why?), we can expand it in a Fourier sine series:

$$\phi - \psi = \sum_{n=1}^{\infty} b_n \sin n\psi,$$

where

$$b_n = \frac{2}{\pi}\int_0^{\pi} (\phi - \psi)\sin n\psi\, d\psi = \frac{2}{\pi n}\int_0^{\pi} \cos n\psi\, d\phi$$

$$= \frac{2}{\pi n}\int_0^{\pi} \cos(n\phi - ne\sin\phi)\, d\phi = \frac{2}{n} J_n(ne).$$

Now r is an even function of ψ with period 2π. Show that

$$r = a\left(1 + \tfrac{1}{2}e^2 - 2e\sum_{n=1}^{\infty} J_n'(e)(\cos n\psi)/n\right).$$

Express θ as a function of ψ.

ELECTRICAL ENGINEERING

11. The general equation for the instantaneous value I_t of an unmodulated sinusoidal carrier current is $I_t = I_m \sin(\Omega t + \theta)$, where I_m is the amplitude, $\Omega = 2\pi F$, F is the frequency and θ is the phase. If I_m and θ are kept constant and F is varied, we then have a frequency modulated wave. If we vary F by means of $i_t = i_m \cos \omega t$, $\omega = 2\pi f$, with maximum frequency swings of $\pm\Delta F$, the modulated wave can be written in the form

$$I_t = I_m \sin(\Omega t + \beta \sin \omega t),$$

where $\beta = \Delta F/f$. Show that

$$I_t = I_m \left\{ J_0(\beta) \sin \Omega t + \sum_{n=1}^{\infty} J_n(\beta) [\sin(\Omega + n\omega)t + (-1)^n \sin(\Omega - n\omega)t] \right\}$$

(*Hint:* p. 532, Exercise 9). I_t can be approximated to a high degree of accuracy by a finite number of terms in the series. (Why?)

12. A straight wire of circular cross section of radius a, conductivity σ and permeability μ, carries an alternating current of angular frequency ω. In cylindrical coordinates with the z-axis along the axis of the wire, the current density i satisfies

$$i_{rr} + \frac{1}{r} i_r = \mu\sigma i_t,$$

i being independent of θ from the symmetry. Now $i = \text{Re}\, \phi$, where

$$\phi_{rr} + \frac{1}{r} \phi_r = \mu\sigma\phi_t.$$

Substituting $\phi = f(r)e^{i\omega t}$ in this equation, we obtain

$$f'' + \frac{1}{r} f' - k^2 f = 0, \quad k^2 = \mu\sigma\omega i.$$

The solution of this equation is

$$f(r) = AI_0(kr) + BK_0(kr)$$

(see p. 536, Exercise 22). Since i and hence $f(r)$ is finite at $r = 0$, $B = 0$, for $K_0(0)$ is infinite. Hence $i = \text{Re}\, AI_0(kr)e^{i\omega t}$. The total complex current is

$$Te^{i\omega t} = \int_0^a 2\pi r\phi\, dr = 2\pi A e^{i\omega t} \int_0^a I_0(kr) r\, dr = (2\pi Aa/k) I_0'(ka),$$

from which we obtain the constant A. Then

$$i = \text{Re}\left[\frac{kI_0(kr)e^{i\omega t}}{2\pi a I_0'(ka)}\right].$$

SUGGESTED REFERENCES

Books on Special Functions

ERDÉLYI, A., et al. *Higher Transcendental Functions*, Vols. 1, 2, 3. New York: The McGraw-Hill Book Co., Inc., 1953. Every student of special functions should have these volumes on his desk. This is the most extensive compendium on special functions in existence. Although the main feature is a catalog of the properties of these functions, in most instances outlines of proofs are indicated.

FARRELL, O. J., and ROSS, B. *Solved Problems: Gamma and Beta Functions, Legendre Polynomials, Bessel Functions.* New York: The Macmillan Company, 1963. Many of the properties of the indicated functions are established with meticulous detail.

HOCHSTADT, H. *Special Functions of Mathematical Physics.* New York: Holt, Rinehart, and Winston, Inc., 1961. It is a courageous man who undertakes an exposition of special functions in 75 pages. This book, nevertheless, packs a great deal of material in these few pages and is strongly recommended as a first reading.

JAHNKE, F., and EMDE, F. *Tables of Functions with Formulae and Curves.* New York: Dover Publications, 1945. In addition to listing the properties of the principal special functions, many excellent graphs of these functions are included.

MACROBERT, T. M. *Spherical Harmonics.* New York: Dover Publications, 1948. A good exposition of Legendre and Bessel functions and functions related to these functions.

MAGNUS, W., and OBERHETTINGER, F. *Formulas and Theorems for the Special Functions of Mathematical Physics.* New York: Chelsea Publishing Company, 1949. A handy small volume of the main properties of the principal special functions.

MCLACHLAN, N. W. *Bessel Functions for Engineers.* New York: Oxford University Press, 1946. The theory of Bessel functions is developed with an eye on applications, which then take up a considerable part of the book. A wide variety of exercises is a good feature of this book.

RAINVILLE, E. D. *Special Functions.* New York: The Macmillan Company, 1960. The theory of the principal special functions is developed, including some of the results of recent years. The exercises are a noteworthy feature.

SZEGÖ, G. *Orthogonal Polynomials.* American Mathematical Society, Colloquium Publications, Vol. 23, rev. ed., 1959. This is the standard work on orthogonal polynomials. It treats the general theory as well as that of the classical orthogonal polynomials.

TITCHMARSH, E. C. *Eigenfunction Expansions.* New York: Oxford University Press, 1946. An exposition of the Sturm-Liouville theory. This is not easy reading for the beginner; however, it considers topics that are not accessible elsewhere.

TRUESDELL, C. A. *An Essay Toward a Unified Theory of Special Functions.* Princeton University Press, 1948. Many of the principal special functions are solutions of $\left(\frac{\partial}{\partial z}\right) F(z, \alpha) = F(a, \alpha + 1)$, and this is made the basis of a general theory.

WATSON, G. N. *A Treatise on the Theory of Bessel Functions.* Cambridge University Press, 1948. This is the standard work on Bessel functions, exploring in detail every aspect of the subject.

Other Books of Interest

BIRKHOFF, G., and ROTA, G. *Ordinary Differential Equations.* Boston: Ginn & Company, 1962. A good chapter on Sturm-Liouville systems. The classical orthogonal polynomials emerge as solutions of these systems.

INCE, E. L. *Ordinary Differential Equations.* New York: Dover Publications, 1959. A good chapter on the Sturm-Liouville theory.

INDRITZ, JACK. *Methods in Analysis.* New York: The Macmillan Company, 1963. An elegant proof of the equiconvergence theorem leading to the Sturm-Liouville expansion theorem, using asymptotic methods, is included.

Other books that contain material on special functions have been listed at the end of Part III.

VALUES OF THE GAMMA FUNCTION

x	$\Gamma(x)$	x	$\Gamma(x)$	x	$\Gamma(x)$	x	$\Gamma(x)$
1.01	.99 433	**1.26**	.90 440	**1.51**	.88 659	**1.76**	.92 137
1.02	.98 884	1.27	.90 250	1.52	.88 704	1.77	.92 376
1.03	.98 355	1.28	.90 072	1.53	.88 757	1.78	.92 623
1.04	.97 844	1.29	.89 904	1.54	.88 818	1.79	.92 877
1.05	.97 350	1.30	.89 747	1.55	.88 887	1.80	.93 138
1.06	.96 874	**1.31**	.89 600	**1.56**	.88 964	**1.81**	.93 408
1.07	.96 415	1.32	.89 464	1.57	.89 049	1.82	.93 685
1.08	.95 973	1.33	.89 338	1.58	.89 142	1.83	.93 969
1.09	.95 546	1.34	.89 222	1.59	.89 243	1.84	.94 261
1.10	.95 135	1.35	.89 115	1.60	.89 352	1.85	.94 561
1.11	.94 740	**1.36**	.89 018	**1.61**	.89 468	**1.86**	.94 869
1.12	.94 359	1.37	.88 931	1.62	.89 592	1.87	.95 184
1.13	.93 993	1.38	.88 854	1.63	.89 724	1.88	.95 507
1.14	.93 642	1.39	.88 785	1.64	.89 864	1.89	.95 838
1.15	.93 304	1.40	.88 726	1.65	.90 012	1.90	.96 177
1.16	.92 980	**1.41**	.88 676	**1.66**	.90 167	**1.91**	.96 523
1.17	.92 670	1.42	.88 636	1.67	.90 330	1.92	.96 877
1.18	.92 373	1.43	.88 604	1.68	.90 500	1.93	.97 240
1.19	.92 089	1.44	.88 581	1.69	.90 678	1.94	.97 610
1.20	.91 817	1.45	.88 566	1.70	.90 864	1.95	.97 988
1.21	.91 558	**1.46**	.88 560	**1.71**	.91 057	**1.96**	.98 374
1.22	.91 311	1.47	.88 563	1.72	.91 258	1.97	.98 768
1.23	.91 075	1.48	.88 575	1.73	.91 467	1.98	.99 171
1.24	.90 852	1.49	.88 595	1.74	.91 683	1.99	.99 581
1.25	.90 640	1.50	.88 623	1.75	.91 906	2.00	1.00 000

Index

Numbers in parentheses refer to exercises or problems. Letters in brackets refer to the Summary of Elementary Mathematics.